Factoring and Special Case Products

$a^2 + 2ab + b^2 = (a + b)^2$

$a^2 - 2ab + b^2 = (a - b)^2$

$a^2 - b^2 = (a + b)(a - b)$

$a^3 + b^3 = (a + b)(a^2 - ab + b^2)$

$a^3 - b^3 = (a - b)(a^2 + ab + b^2)$

Complex Numbers

$i = \sqrt{-1}$ and $i^2 = -1$

For a real number $b > 0$, $\sqrt{-b} = i\sqrt{b}$

The complex numbers $a + bi$ and $a - bi$ are conjugates, and $(a + bi)(a - bi) = a^2 + b^2$.

Quadratic Formula

Given $ax^2 + bx + c = 0$, $a \neq 0$, the solutions are

$$x = \frac{-b \pm \sqrt{b^2 - 4ac}}{2a}$$

Absolute Value Equations/Inequalities

If $k \geq 0$, then

$|u| = k$ is equivalent to $u = k$ or $u = -k$.

$|u| = |w|$ is equivalent to $u = w$ or $u = -w$.

$|u| < k$ is equivalent to $-k < u < k$.

$|u| > k$ is equivalent to $u < -k$ or $u > k$.

Distance Formulas

The distance between two points a and b on a number line is given by $|a - b|$ or $|b - a|$.

The distance between (x_1, y_1) and (x_2, y_2) is

$$d = \sqrt{(x_2 - x_1)^2 + (y_2 - y_1)^2}$$

Midpoint Formula

The midpoint of the line segment between (x_1, y_1) and (x_2, y_2) is

$$M = \left(\frac{x_1 + x_2}{2}, \frac{y_1 + y_2}{2} \right)$$

Linear and Quadratic Functions

$f(x) = b$ constant function: slope 0 and y-intercept $(0, b)$

$f(x) = mx + b$ linear function: slope m and y-intercept $(0, b)$

$f(x) = ax^2 + bx + c$ $(a \neq 0)$ quadratic function: vertex $\left[\frac{-b}{2a}, f\left(\frac{-b}{2a}\right) \right]$

Slope and Average Rate of Change

Slope of a line through (x_1, y_1) and (x_2, y_2):

$$m = \frac{\Delta y}{\Delta x} = \frac{y_2 - y_1}{x_2 - x_1}$$

Average rate of change of $f(x)$ between (x_1, y_1) and (x_2, y_2): $\dfrac{f(x_2) - f(x_1)}{x_2 - x_1}$

Difference quotient: $\dfrac{f(x + h) - f(x)}{h}$

Circle

$(x - h)^2 + (y - k)^2 = r^2$ where $r > 0$

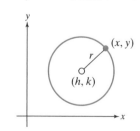

Parabola

Vertical Axis of Symmetry
$(x - h)^2 = 4p(y - k)$

Horizontal Axis of Symmetry
$(y - k)^2 = 4p(x - h)$

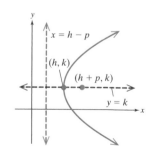

Graphs of Basic Functions

Constant Function

$f(x) = b$

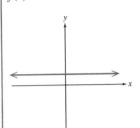

Linear Function

$f(x) = mx + b$

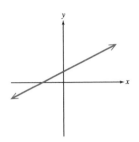

Identity Function

$f(x) = x$

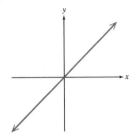

Quadratic Function

$f(x) = x^2$

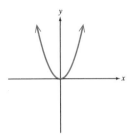

Cubic Function

$f(x) = x^3$

Absolute Value Function

$f(x) = |x|$

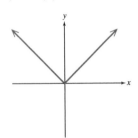

Square Root Function

$f(x) = \sqrt{x}$

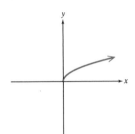

Cube Root Function

$f(x) = \sqrt[3]{x}$

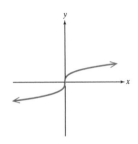

Reciprocal Function

$f(x) = \dfrac{1}{x}$

Greatest Integer Function

$f(x) = \lfloor x \rfloor$

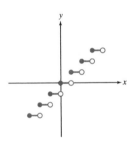

Exponential Function

$f(x) = b^x$, where $b > 0$ and $b \neq 1$

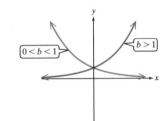

Logarithmic Function

$f(x) = \log_b x$, where $b > 0$ and $b \neq 1$

$y = \log_b x \Leftrightarrow b^y = x$

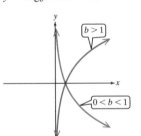

Ellipse

Major Axis Horizontal

$$\frac{(x - h)^2}{a^2} + \frac{(y - k)^2}{b^2} = 1$$

Major Axis Vertical

$$\frac{(x - h)^2}{b^2} + \frac{(y - k)^2}{a^2} = 1$$

$a > b$, and $c^2 = a^2 - b^2$, where $c > 0$.

Foci are c units from the center on the major axis.

Hyperbola

Transverse Axis Horizontal

$$\frac{(x - h)^2}{a^2} - \frac{(y - k)^2}{b^2} = 1$$

Transverse Axis Vertical

$$\frac{(y - k)^2}{a^2} - \frac{(x - h)^2}{b^2} = 1$$

$c^2 = a^2 + b^2$, where $c > 0$.

Foci are c units from the center on the transverse axis.

College Algebra

Julie Miller
Daytona State College

Digital Author
Donna Gerken
Miami Dade College

Connect Learn Succeed™

COLLEGE ALGEBRA

Published by McGraw-Hill, a business unit of The McGraw-Hill Companies, Inc., 1221 Avenue of the Americas, New York, NY 10020. Copyright © 2014 by The McGraw-Hill Companies, Inc. All rights reserved. Printed in the United States of America. No part of this publication may be reproduced or distributed in any form or by any means, or stored in a database or retrieval system, without the prior written consent of The McGraw-Hill Companies, Inc., including, but not limited to, in any network or other electronic storage or transmission, or broadcast for distance learning.

Some ancillaries, including electronic and print components, may not be available to customers outside the United States.

This book is printed on acid-free paper.

8 9 0 DOW/DOW 1 0 9 8 7 6 5

ISBN 978–0–07–803563–0
MHID 0–07–803563–5

ISBN 978–0–07–753861–3 (Annotated Instructor's Edition)
MHID 0–07–753861–7

Senior Vice President, Products & Markets: *Kurt L. Strand*
Vice President, General Manager, Products & Markets: *Marty Lange*
Vice President, Content Production & Technology Services: *Kimberly Meriwether David*
Director of Development: *Rose Koos*
Managing Director: *Ryan Blankenship*
Brand Manager: *Caroline Celano*
Director of Digital Content Development: *Emilie J. Berglund*
Development Editor: *Emily Williams*
Market Development Manager: *Kim M. Leistner*
Marketing Manager: *Kevin M. Ernzen*
Lead Project Manager: *Peggy J. Selle*
Buyer: *Nicole Baumgartner*
Senior Media Project Manager: *Sandra M. Schnee*
Senior Designer: *Laurie B. Janssen*
Cover Designer: *Ron Bissell*
Cover Image: © *Thom Gourley/Flatbread Images, LLC/Spaces Images/Corbis*
Lead Content Licensing Specialist: *Carrie K. Burger*
Compositor: *Aptara®, Inc.*
Typeface: *10.5/12 Times Lt Std*
Printer: *R. R. Donnelley*

All credits appearing on page or at the end of the book are considered to be an extension of the copyright page.

Library of Congress Cataloging-in-Publication Data

Miller, Julie, 1962-
  College algebra / Julie Miller. – 1st ed.
    p. cm.
  Includes index.
  ISBN 978–0–07–803563–0 — ISBN 0–07–803563–5 (hbk. : alk. paper) 1. Algebra. I. Title.
  QA154.3.M54 2014
  512–dc23
                    2012019638

About the Authors

Julie Miller is from Daytona State College where she has taught developmental and upper-level mathematics courses for 20 years. Prior to her work at DSC, she worked as a software engineer for General Electric in the area of flight and radar simulation. Julie earned a bachelor of science in applied mathematics from Union College in Schenectady, New York, and a master of science in mathematics from the University of Florida. In addition to this textbook, she has authored eight textbooks in developmental mathematics, several course supplements for trigonometry and precalculus, as well as several short works of fiction and nonfiction for young readers.

"My father is a medical researcher, and I got hooked on math and science when I was young and would visit his laboratory. I remember doing simple calculations with him and using graph paper to plot data points for his experiments. He would then tell me what the peaks and features in the graph meant in the context of his experiment. I think that applications and hands-on experience made math come alive for me, and I'd like to see math come alive for my students."

Donna Gerken is currently a professor at Miami Dade College where she has taught developmental courses, honors classes, and upper-level mathematics classes for 30 years. Throughout the years, she has been involved with many projects at Miami Dade on curriculum redesign and the use of technology in the classroom. Donna's bachelor of science in mathematics and master of science in mathematics are both from the University of Miami. Before finishing her undergraduate and graduate degrees at the University of Miami, she also attended Miami Dade College as a student where she discovered an amazing group of faculty who inspired her to continue on with a career in mathematics.

Donna has kept a quote passed along from one of her undergraduate professors for many years:

Pure mathematics is, in its way, the poetry of logical ideas.

—Albert Einstein, in a letter to the editor of the New York Times upon the death of Emmy Noether.

If Donna is not in the classroom or peering into her computer screen, she can be found reading, in her kitchen cooking for crowds, or working out with friends at the gym.

Letter from the Authors

For many students, college algebra is a daunting course that serves as a gateway between developmental math and the realm of higher level mathematics taken by engineers and scientists. For this reason many years ago, we began writing a series of textbooks to bridge the gap between preparatory courses and the more abstract world of college algebra. For thousands of students, the Miller/O'Neill/Hyde textbook series has provided a solid foundation in intermediate algebra. Now, we want to address student needs on the other side of the bridge. Our goal is to carry the clear, concise writing style and popular pedagogical features of our textbooks to college algebra students.

The main objectives of this college algebra textbook are threefold:

- To provide students with a clear and logical presentation of the basic concepts that will prepare them for continued study in mathematics.
- To help students develop logical thinking and problem-solving skills that will benefit them in all aspects of life.
- To motivate students by demonstrating the significance of mathematics in their lives through practical applications.

-Julie Miller   julie.miller.math@gmail.com
Donna Gerken   dgerken@mdc.edu

Table of Contents

CHAPTER **3**   **Polynomial and Rational Functions   319**

CHAPTER **4**   **Exponential and Logarithmic Functions   431**

CHAPTER **5**   **Systems of Equations and Inequalities   521**

Key Features

Clear, Precise Writing

Because a diverse group of students take this course, Julie Miller has written this manuscript to use simple and accessible language. Through her friendly and engaging writing style, students are able to understand the material easily.

Exercise Sets

The exercises at the end of each section are graded, varied, and carefully organized to maximize student learning:

- **Review Exercises** begin the section-level exercises and ensure that students have the prerequisite skills to complete the homework sets successfully.
- **Concept Connections** exercises prompt students to review the vocabulary and key concepts presented in the section.
- The core exercises are presented next and are grouped by objective. These exercises are linked to examples in the text and direct students to similar problems whose solutions have been stepped-out in detail.
- **Mixed Exercises** do *not* refer to specific examples so that students can dip into their mathematical toolkit and decide on the best technique to use.
- **Write About It** exercises are designed to emphasize mathematical language by asking students to explain important concepts.
- **Technology Connections** exercises require the use of a graphing utility and are found at the end of exercise sets. They can be easily skipped for those who do not encourage the use of calculators.

Problem Recognition Exercises

Problem Recognition Exercises appear in strategic locations in each chapter of the text. These exercises help students compare and contrast a variety of problem types and determine which mathematical tool to apply to a given problem.

Examples

- The examples in the textbook are stepped-out in detail with thorough annotations at the right explaining each step.
- Following each example is a similar **Skill Practice** exercise to engage students by practicing what they have just learned.
- For the instructor, references to an even-numbered exercise are provided next to each example. These exercises are highlighted in the exercise sets and mirror the related examples. With increased demands on faculty time, this has been a popular feature to help faculty write their lectures and develop their presentation of material. If an instructor presents all of the highlighted exercises, then each objective of that section of text will be covered.

Modeling and Applications

One of the most important tools to motivate our students is to make the mathematics they learn meaningful in their lives. The textbook is filled with robust applications and numerous opportunities for mathematical modeling for those instructors looking to incorporate these features into their course.

Callouts

Throughout the text, popular tools are included to highlight important ideas. These consist of

- **Tip** boxes that offer additional insight to a concept or procedure.
- **Avoiding Mistakes** boxes that fend off common mistakes.
- **Points of Interest** boxes that offer interesting and historical mathematical facts.
- **Instructor Notes** to assist with lecture preparation.

Section 4.6 Modeling with Exponential and Logarithmic Functions   503

EXAMPLE 6   Using Logistic Growth to Model Population

The population of California $P(t)$ (in millions) can be approximated by the logistic growth function

$$P(t) = \frac{95.2}{1 + 1.8e^{-0.018t}},$$ where t is the number of years since the year 2000.

a. Determine the population in the year 2000.
b. Use this function to determine the time required for the population of California to double from its value in 2000. Compare this with the result from Example 3(c).
c. What is the limiting value of the population of California under this model?

Solution:

a. $P(t) = \dfrac{95.2}{1 + 1.8e^{-0.018t}}$

$P(0) = \dfrac{95.2}{1 + 1.8e^{-0.018(0)}} = \dfrac{95.2}{1 + 1.8(1)} = 34$ Substitute 0 for t. Recall that $e^0 = 1$.

The population was approximately 34 million in the year 2000.

b. $68 = \dfrac{95.2}{1 + 1.8e^{-0.018t}}$ Substitute 68 for $P(t)$.

$68(1 + 1.8e^{-0.018t}) = 95.2$ Multiply both sides by $(1 + 1.8e^{-0.018t})$.

$1 + 1.8e^{-0.018t} = 1.4$ Divide by 68 on both sides.

$1.8e^{-0.018t} = 1.4 - 1$ Subtract 1 from both sides.

$e^{-0.018t} = \dfrac{0.4}{1.8}$ Divide by 1.8 on both sides.

$-0.018t = \ln\left(\dfrac{0.4}{1.8}\right)$ Take the natural logarithm of both sides.

$t = \dfrac{\ln\left(\dfrac{0.4}{1.8}\right)}{-0.018} \approx 83.6$ Divide by -0.018 on both sides.

The population will double in approximately 83.6 yr. This is 9 yr later than the predicted value from Example 3(c).

The graphs of $P(t) = \dfrac{95.2}{1 + 1.8e^{-0.018t}}$ and $P(t) = 34e^{0.0092t}$ are shown in Figure 4-17. Notice that the two models agree relatively closely for short-term population growth (out to about 2060). However, in the long term, the unbounded exponential model breaks down. The logistic growth model approaches a limiting population, which is reasonable due to the limited resources to sustain a large human population.

$P(t)$
200
160   $P(t) = 34e^{0.0092t}$
120
80
40   $P(t) = \frac{95.2}{1 + 1.8e^{-0.018t}}$
0   40   80   120   160   200 t
Figure 4-17

c. $P(t) = \dfrac{95.2}{1 + 1.8e^{-0.018t}} = \dfrac{95.2}{1 + \dfrac{1.8}{e^{0.018t}}}$ As $t \to \infty$, the term $\dfrac{1.8}{e^{0.018t}} \to 0$.

As t becomes large, the denominator of $\dfrac{1.8}{e^{0.018t}}$ also becomes large. This causes the quotient to approach zero. Therefore, as t approaches infinity, $P(t)$ approaches 95.2. Under this model, the limiting value for the population of California is 95.2 million.

---

340   Chapter 3 Polynomial and Rational Functions

The intermediate value theorem can be used repeatedly in a technique called the bisection method to approximate the value of a zero. See the online group activity "Investigating the Bisection Method for Finding Zeros."

Point of Interest

The modern definition of a computer is a programmable device designed to carry out a sequence of arithmetic or logical operations. However, the word "computer" originally referred to a person who did such calculations using paper and pencil. "Human computers" were notably used in the eighteenth century to predict the path of Halley's comet and to produce astronomical tables critical to surveying and navigation. Later, during World Wars I and II, human computers developed ballistic firing tables that would describe the trajectory of a shell.

Computing tables of values was very time consuming, and the "computers" would often interpolate to find intermediate values within a table. Interpolation is a method by which intermediate values between two numbers are estimated. Often the interpolated values were based on a polynomial function.

4. Sketch a Polynomial Function

The graph of a polynomial function may also have "turning points." For example, consider $f(x) = x(x + 2)(x - 2)^2$. See Figure 3-11.

Multiplying the leading terms within the factors, we have a leading term of $(x)(x)(x)^2 = x^4$. Therefore, the end behavior of the graph is up to the left and up to the right.

TIP Even with advanced techniques from calculus or the use of a graphing utility, it is often difficult or impossible to find the exact location of the turning points of a polynomial function.

$f(x)$ $f(x) = x(x + 2)(x - 2)^2$
Turning point
Turning point
Turning point
Figure 3-11

Avoiding Mistakes

A polynomial of degree n may have fewer than $n - 1$ turning points. For example, $f(x) = x^3$ is a degree 3 polynomial function (indicating that it could have a maximum of two turning points), yet the graph has no turning points.

$f(x)$
$f(x) = x^3$

Starting from the far left, the graph of f decreases to the x-intercept of -2. Since -2 is a zero with an odd multiplicity, the graph must cross the x-axis at -2. For the same reason, the graph must cross the x-axis again at the origin. Therefore, somewhere between $x = -2$ and $x = 0$, the graph must "turn around." This point is called a "turning point."

The turning points of a polynomial function are the points where the function changes from increasing to decreasing or vice versa.

Number of Turning Points of a Polynomial Function

Let f represent a polynomial function of degree n. Then the graph of f has at most $n - 1$ turning points.

At this point we are ready to outline a strategy for sketching a polynomial function.

Graphing Calculator Coverage

Material is presented throughout the book illustrating how a graphing utility can be used to view a concept in a graphical manner. The goal of the calculator material is not to replace algebraic analysis, but rather to enhance understanding with a visual approach. Graphing calculator examples are placed in self-contained boxes and may be skipped by instructors who choose not to implement the calculator. Similarly, the graphing calculator exercises are found at the end of the exercise sets and may also be easily skipped.

End-of-Chapter Materials

The textbook has the following end-of-chapter materials for students to review before test time.

- Brief summary with references to key concepts. A detailed summary is located at www.mhhe.com/millerca.
- Chapter review exercises.
- Chapter test.
- Cumulative review exercises. These exercises cover concepts in the current chapter as well as all preceding chapters.

Digital Media

Digital assets were created exclusively by the author team to ensure that the author voice is present and consistent throughout the supplement package.

- The **digital coauthor**, Donna Gerken, ensures that each algorithm in the online homework has a stepped-out solution unique to the Miller style.
- Julie Miller created **video content** (lecture videos, exercise videos, graphing calculator videos, and Excel videos) to give students access to classroom-type instruction by the author.
- Julie Miller constructed over 50 **dynamic math animations** to accompany the college algebra text. The animations are diverse in scope and give students an interactive approach to conceptual learning. The animated content illustrates difficult concepts by leveraging the use of on-screen movement where static images in the text may fall short. They are organized in Connect hosted by ALEKS by chapter and section, as well as grouped by various categories including a Functions Library, Applications/Modeling, and Graphing.
- The authors developed lecture notes in both ready-made PDF format and in Word format so that instructors can tailor the material to their course.
- The authors created a library of activities in the Student Resource Manual that include group activities and Wolfram Alpha activities.

Supplement Package

The Miller *College Algebra* series has brought on a digital coauthor, Donna Gerken, to oversee the incorporation of online materials. One of the digital coauthor's primary roles is to see that the author's voice is consistent in every supplement that accompanies the text as well as to ensure that each algorithm in Connect Hosted by ALEKS has a stepped-out solution unique to the author's style.

Supplements for the Instructor

Lecture Videos, Exercise Videos, Graphing Calculator Videos, and Excel Videos give students access to classroom-type instruction by the author.

Dynamic Math Animations give students an interactive approach to conceptual learning. The animated content illustrates difficult concepts by leveraging the use of on-screen movement where static images in the text may fall short.

The *Instructor's Resource Manual* **(IRM)** is a printable electronic supplement put together by the author team. The IRM includes Guided Lecture Notes, Classroom Activities using Wolfram Alpha, and Group Activities.

- The Guided Lecture Notes are keyed to the objectives in each section of the text. The notes step through the material with a series of questions and exercises that can be used in conjunction with lecture. With increasing demands on faculty schedules, these ready-made lessons offer a convenient means for both full-time and adjunct faculty to provide a note-taking structure for their students in order to enforce study skills as well as allow students to spend less time writing and more time listening to the lecture. The material in the IRM is available in both pdf and Word format so that instructors can also customize the material to suit their individual needs.

- The Classroom Activities using Wolfram Alpha can be assigned to individual students, or to pairs or groups of students. The idea is to keep students active and engaged during the presentation of material and to foster accountability and classroom participation. These activities promote active learning in the classroom by using a powerful online resource.

- A Group Activity is available for each chapter of the book to promote classroom discussion and collaboration. The activities help students not only to solve problems but to explain their solutions for better mathematical mastery. Group Activities are great for instructors and adjuncts, bringing a more interactive approach to teaching mathematics. Estimated time and suggested group sizes are provided in the directions of the activity.

The *Instructor's Solution Manual* provides comprehensive, worked-out solutions to all exercises in the section exercises, review exercises, problem recognition exercises, chapter tests, and cumulative reviews. The steps shown in the solutions match the style and methodology of solved examples in the textbook.

Instructor's Testing and Resource Online. Among the supplements is a computerized test bank utilizing Brownstone Diploma algorithm-based testing software to create customized exams quickly. This user-friendly program enables instructors to search for questions by topic, format, or difficulty level; to edit existing questions, or to add new ones; and to scramble questions and answer keys for multiple versions of a single test. Hundreds of text-specific, open-ended, and multiple-choice questions are included in the question bank. Sample chapter tests are also provided. CDs are available upon request.

Annotated Instructor's Edition

- Answers to exercises appear adjacent to each exercise set, in a color used only for annotations.
- Instructors will find helpful notes within the margins to consider while teaching.
- References to even-numbered exercises appear in the margin next to each example for the instructor to use as Classroom Examples.

Powerpoints present key concepts and definitions with fully editable slides that follow the textbook. An instructor may project the slides in class or post to a website in an online course.

Supplements for the Student

Detailed Chapter Summaries are available at www.mhhe.com/millerca.

The *Student's Solution Manual* provides comprehensive, worked-out solutions to the odd-numbered exercises in the Practice Exercise sets, the Problem Recognition Exercises, the end-of-chapter Review Exercises, the Chapter Tests, and the Cumulative Review Exercises.

ALEKS® Prep for College Algebra

ALEKS Prep for College Algebra focuses on prerequisites and introductory material for College Algebra. These prep products can be used during the first 3 weeks of a course to prepare students for future success in the course and to increase retention and pass rates.

Connect Math® Hosted by ALEKS

Connect Math Hosted by ALEKS Corp. is an exciting, new assignment and assessment ehomework platform. Starting with an easily viewable, intuitive interface, students will be able to access key information, complete homework assignments, and utilize an integrated, media-rich eBook.

ALEKS is a unique, online program that significantly raises student proficiency and success rates in mathematics, while reducing faculty workload and office-hour lines. ALEKS uses artificial intelligence and adaptive questioning to assess precisely a student's knowledge, and deliver individualized learning tailored to the student's needs. With a comprehensive library of math courses, ALEKS delivers an unparalleled adaptive learning system that has helped millions of students achieve math success.

ALEKS Delivers a Unique Math Experience:

- **Research-Based, Artificial Intelligence** precisely measures each student's knowledge
- **Individualized Learning** presents the exact topics each student is most **ready to learn**
- **Adaptive, Open-Response Environment** includes comprehensive tutorials and resources
- **Detailed, Automated Reports** track student and class progress toward course mastery
- **Course Management Tools** include textbook integration, custom features, and more

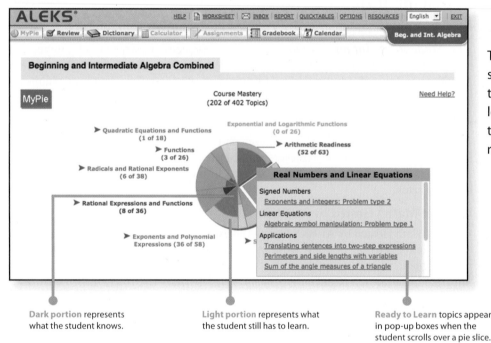

The ALEKS Pie summarizes a student's current knowledge, then delivers an individualized learning path with the exact topics the student is most ready to learn.

Dark portion represents what the student knows.

Light portion represents what the student still has to learn.

Ready to Learn topics appear in pop-up boxes when the student scrolls over a pie slice.

> "My experience with ALEKS has been effective, efficient, and eloquent. **Our students' pass rates improved from 49 percent to 82 percent with ALEKS.** We also saw student retention rates increase by 12% in the next course. Students feel empowered as they guide their own learning through ALEKS."
>
> —Professor Eden Donahou, *Seminole State College of Florida*

To learn more about ALEKS, please visit: **www.aleks.com/highered/math**

ALEKS® Prep Products

ALEKS Prep products focus on prerequisite and introductory material, and can be used during the first six weeks of the term to ensure student success in math courses ranging from Beginning Algebra through Calculus. ALEKS Prep quickly fills gaps in prerequisite knowledge by assessing precisely each student's preparedness and delivering individualized instruction on the exact topics students are most ready to learn. As a result, instructors can focus on core course concepts and see improved student performance with fewer drops.

> "ALEKS is wonderful. It is a professional product that takes very little time as an instructor to administer. Many of our students have taken Calculus in high school, but they have forgotten important algebra skills. ALEKS gives our students an opportunity to review these important skills."
>
> —Professor Edward E. Allen, *Wake Forest University*

ALEKS®360
With *eBook* Integration

A Total Course Solution

A cost-effective total course solution: fully integrated, interactive eBook combined with the power of ALEKS adaptive learning and assessment.

Students can easily access the full eBook content, multimedia resources, and their notes from within their ALEKS Student Accounts.

To learn more about ALEKS, please visit: **www.aleks.com/highered/math**

Connect Math Hosted by ALEKS Corp.

Built By Today's Educators, For Today's Students

Fewer clicks means more time for you...

Change assignment dates right from the home page.

Teaching multiple sections? Easily move from one to another.

Edit, print, and view assignments in just one click.

...and your students.

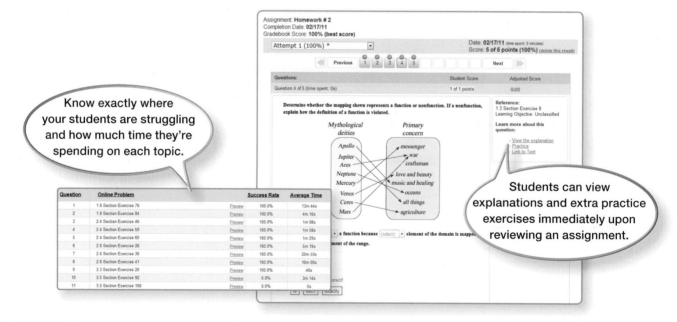

Know exactly where your students are struggling and how much time they're spending on each topic.

Students can view explanations and extra practice exercises immediately upon reviewing an assignment.

Quality Content For Today's Online Learners

Online Exercises were carefully selected and developed to provide a seamless transition from textbook to technology.

For consistency, the guided solutions match the style and voice of the original text as though the author is guiding the students through the problems.

Multimedia eBook includes access to a variety of media assets and a place to highlight and keep track of class notes

ALEKS Corporation's experience with algorithm development ensures a commitment to accuracy and a meaningful experience for students to demonstrate their understanding with a focus towards online learning.

The ALEKS® Initial Assessment is an artificially intelligent (AI), diagnostic assessment that identifies precisely what a student knows. Instructors can then use this information to make more informed decisions on what topics to cover in more detail with the class.

Our Commitment to Market Development and Accuracy

McGraw-Hill's Development Process is an ongoing, never-ending, market-oriented approach to building accurate and innovative print and digital products. We begin developing a series by partnering with authors who desire to make an impact within their discipline to help students succeed. Next, we share these ideas and manuscript with instructors for review for feedback and to ensure that the authors' ideas represent the needs within that discipline. Throughout multiple drafts, we help our authors adapt to incorporate ideas and suggestions from reviewers to ensure that the series carries the same pulse as today's classrooms. With any new series, we commit to accuracy across the series and its supplements. In addition to involving instructors as we develop our content, we also utilize accuracy checks through our various stages of development and production. The following is a summary of our commitment to market development and accuracy:

1. 3 drafts of author manuscript
2. 3 rounds of manuscript review
3. 3 focus groups
4. 2 accuracy checks
5. 3 rounds of proofreading and copyediting
6. Toward the final stages of production, we incorporate additional rounds of quality assurance from instructors as they help contribute toward our digital content and print supplements

This process then will start again immediately upon publication in anticipation of the next edition. With our commitment to this process, we are confident that our series has the most developed content the industry has to offer, thus pushing our desire for quality and accurate content that meets the needs of today's students and instructors.

Acknowledgments:

Paramount to the development of *College Algebra* was the invaluable feedback provided by the instructors from around the country who reviewed the manuscript or attended a market development event over the course of the several years the text was in development.

A Special Thanks to All of the Event Attendees Who Helped Shape College Algebra.

Focus groups and symposia were conducted with instructors from around the country to provide feedback to editors and the authors and ensure the direction of the text was meeting the needs of students and instructors.

Marwan Abusawwa, *Florida State College*

Phil Anderson, *South Plains College*

Sofya Antonova, *Collin County Community College–Plano*

Shatila Bariaa, *Flagler College*

Donna Beatty, *Ventura College*

Denise Brown, *Collin County Community College–Plano*

Bill Burgin, *Gaston College*

Martha Chalhoub, *Collin County Community College–Plano*

Tim Chappell, *Metropolitan Community College–Penn Valley*

John Church, *Metropolitan Community College–Longview*

Nelson De La Rosa, *Miami Dade College–Kendall*

Ginger Eaves, *Bossier Parish Community College*

Nancy Eschen, *Florida State College*

Mahshid Hassani, *Hillsborough Community College–Brandon*

Mary Beth Headlee, *State College of Florida–Manatee*

Esmarie Kennedy, *San Antonio College*

Lynette Kenyon, *Collin County Community College–Plano*

Reza Khademakbari, *San Jacinto College*

Raja Khoury, *Collin County Community College–Plano*

Stephanie Krehl, *Mid-South Community College*

Lorraine Lopez, *San Antonio College*

Beverly, Meyers, *Jefferson College*

Altay Ozgener, *State College of Florida–Manatee*

Mari Peddycoart, *Lone Star College*

Davidson Pierre, *State College of Florida–Manatee*
Joni Pirnot, *State College of Florida–Manatee*
Di Di Quesada, *Miami Dade College–Kendall*
Paul Seeburger, *Monroe Community College*

Julia Simms, *Southern Illinois University*
Michelle Whitmer, *Lansing Community College*
Nathan Wilson, *Saint Louis Community College–Meramac–Kirkwood*

Manuscript Reviewers

Over 80 instructors reviewed the various drafts of the manuscript to give feedback on content, design, pedagogy, and organization. Their reviews were used to guide the direction of the text.

Drew Aberle, *Ozarks Technical Community College*
Marwan Abusawwa, *Florida State College*
Jeff Aldridge, *Northeast Oklahoma A&M College*
Phil Anderson, *South Plains College*
Sofya Antonova, *Collin County Community College–Plano*
Shatila Bariaa, *Flagler College*
Disa Beaty, *Rose State College*
Denise Brown, *Collin County Community College–Plano*
Bill Burgin, *Gaston College*
Sylvia Carr, *Missouri State University*
Martha Chalhoub, *Collin County Community College–Plano*
Tim Chappell, *Metropolitan Community College–Penn Valley*
John Church, *Metropolitan Community College Longview*
Cindy Cummings, *Ozarks Technical Community College*
Nelson De La Rosa, *Miami Dade College–Kendall*
Letitia Downen, *Southern Illinois University–Edwardsville*
Ginger Eaves, *Bossier Parish Community College*
Gay Ellis, *Missouri State*
Nancy Eschen, *Florida State College*
Karen Estes, *Saint Petersburg College*
Jane Golden, *Hillsborough Community College–Brandon*
Melissa Hardeman, *University of Arkansas–Little Rock*
Matt Harris, *Ozarks Technical Community College*
Mahshid Hassani, *Hillsborough Community College–Brandon*
Tom Hayes, *Montana State University*
David Hays, *Cowley County Community College*
Mary Beth Headlee, *State College of Florida–Manatee*
Bill Hemme, *Saint Petersburg College*
Paul Hernandez, *Palo Alto College*
Ken Hirschel, *Orange County Community College*
David Hope, *Palo Alto College*
Linda Hoppe, *Jefferson College*
Steve Howard, *Rose State College*
Krzysztof Jarosz, *Southern Illinois University–Edwardsville*
Esmarie Kennedy, *San Antonio College*

Lynette Kenyon, *Collin County Community College–Plano*
Reza Khademakbari, *San Jacinto College–Padadena*
Raja Khoury, *Collin County Community College–Plano*
Roseanne Killion, *Ozarks Technical Community College*
Gary King, *Ozarks Technical Community College*
Stephanie Krehl, *Mid-South Community College*
Ramesh Krishnan, *South Plains College*
Krishna Kulkarni, *Elizabeth City State University*
Nic Lahue, *Metropolitan Community College Penn Valley*
Lorraine Lopez, *San Antonio College*
Vinod Manglik, *Elizabeth City State University*
Linda Mayhew, *KCTCS Elizabethtown Community College*
Jerry Mccormack, *Tyler Junior College*
Beverly Meyers, *Jefferson College*
Mary Ann Moore, *Florida Gulf Coast University*
Altay Ozgener, *State College of Florida–Manatee*
Jason Pallett, *Metropolitan Community College–Longview*
Alan Papen, *Ozarks Technical Community College*
Priti Patel, *Tarrant County College*
Mari Peddycoart, *Lonestar College–Kingwood*
Davidson Pierre, *State College of Florida–Manatee*
Joni Pirnot, *State College of Florida–Manatee*
David Platt, *Front Range Community College–Fort Collins*
Cary Powell, *Wayne County Community College*
Hadley Pridgen, *Gulf Coast Community College*
Di Di Quesada, *Miami Dade College–Kendall*
Brooke Quinlan, *Hillsborough Community College–Dale Mabry*
Ronda Sanders, *University of Southern Carolina*
Rebecca Schantz, *East Central College*
Linda Schott, *Ozarks Technical Community College*
Paul Seeburger, *Monroe Community College*
Pavel Sikorskii, *Michigan State University–East Lansing*
Joe Siler, *Ozarks Technical Community College*
Bert Simmons, *Ozarks Technical Community College*
Julia Simms, *Southern Illinois University–Edwardsville*
Jed Soifer, *Atlantic Cape Community College*
Gary Stafford, *Missouri State University*

Pam Stogsdill, *Bossier Parish Community College*

Mohammed Talukder, *Elizabeth City State University*

Joan Van Glabek, *Edison College–Fort Myers*

Clare Wagner, *University of South Dakota*

Tracy Watson, *University of Arkansas–Little Rock*

Pamela Webster, *Texas A&M University–Commerce*

Michelle Whitmer, *Lansing Community College*

Nathan Wilson, *Saint Louis Community College–Meramac–Kirkwood*

Janet Wyatt, *Metropolitan Community College–Longview*

Fan Zhou, *Ozarks Technical Community College*

Author Acknowledgments:

An editor once told me that publishing a book is like making a movie because there are so many people behind the scenes that make the final product a success. I don't think that words can begin to express my heartfelt thanks to all of you, but I'll do my best. First and foremost, I want to thank my editor Emily Williams who started with me on this project when it was just idea, and then lent her unwavering, day-to-day support through final publication. Without you, I'd still be on page 1. To Marty Lange and Kurt Strand, I love my job and am forever grateful for the amazing opportunities you and McGraw-Hill have given me.

To my sponsoring editor and fellow tennis player, Caroline Celano, I'm so happy that you joined the team with your new and creative ideas at the most critical time. To Dawn Bercier, you've worn many hats within the math team, and with each role, you've always offered genuine and consistent support. To Ryan Blankenship, the managing director for mathematics, I can't thank you enough for sharing your big-picture view of the publishing world and for your vision for this project. To Kim Leistner, Kevin Ernzen, and the marketing team, what would we do without your imagination to make the project come to life. To the dedicated people in the McGraw-Hill sales force, thank you so much for your continued confidence, encouragement, and support.

To Patricia Steele, the best copy editor ever, thank you for mentoring me through the process of working with electronic manuscript, and for ensuring consistency throughout the work. I'm also grateful for your lessons on grammar :-) and for our great talks. To Hal Whipple and Peggy Irish, many thanks for doing multiple levels of accuracy checking. Your talents are absolutely amazing. Additional thanks to Julie Kennedy, Carey Lange, and Marilee Aschenbrenner for their tireless attention to detail proofreading pages.

Special thanks go to digital coauthor Donna Gerken for overseeing the enormous job of authoring and editing digital content and for ensuring consistency of the author voice to the supplements package—a Herculean task. I also want to express my gratitude to Alina Coronel, Esmarie Kennedy, Tim Chappell, Stephen Toner, Michael Larkin, and Lizette Foley for their diligence writing digital content, and to Emilie Berglund at McGraw-Hill who had to keep the digital train on the tracks. All of you are amazing. To my colleague and friend Kimberly Alacan, many thanks for your creativity in preparing the chapter openers and the group activities. To Hal Whipple and Peggy Irish, thank you for preparing the Instructor's Solutions Manual and Student's Solutions Manual. No doubt, many instructors and students thank you as well.

My deepest gratitude goes to the production manager Peggy Selle for steering the ship and keeping us all on task. To Laurie Janssen, many thanks for a beautiful design. The book is gorgeous.

Most importantly, I want to give special thanks to all the students and instructors who use *College Algebra* in their classes.

—Julie Miller

Dedications

To my parents Kent and Joanne Miller who have always taught me the value of education.   —Julie Miller

To all my friends and colleagues who have given me so many pushes and so many pats.   —Donna Gerken

Applications Index

Sports

Statistics/Demographics

R

Review of Prerequisites

Chapter Outline

Athletes know that in order to optimize their performance they need to pace themselves and be mindful of their target heart rate. For example, a 25-year-old with a maximum heart rate of 195 beats per minute should strive for a target heart rate zone of between 98 and 166 beats per minute. This correlates to between 50% and 85% of the individual's maximum heart rate (Source: American Heart Association, www.americanheart.org). The mathematics involved with finding maximum heart rate and an individual's target heart rate zone use a linear model relating age and resting heart rate. An introduction to modeling is presented here in Chapter R along with the standard order of operations used to carry out these calculations.

   Chapter R reviews skills and concepts required for success in college algebra. Just as an athlete must first learn the basics of a sport and build endurance and speed, a student studying mathematics must focus on necessary basic skills to prepare for the challenge ahead. Preparation for algebra is comparable to an athlete preparing for a sporting event. Putting the time and effort into the basics here in Chapter R will be your foundation for success in later chapters.

Sets and the Real Number Line

Weight is the force generated by the gravitational attraction of the Earth on an object. At a high altitude, the gravitational attraction of the Earth is slightly decreased and objects weigh less. So how would this affect the weight of a 150-lb passenger in an airplane flying at 37,000 ft?

Scientists know that the weight of an object at an altitude of h miles above sea level is given by the formula

$$W_h = W_s \left(\frac{4000}{4000 + h} \right)^2$$

W_s is weight (in lb) at sea level.
W_h is weight (in lb) at a height of h miles.

In this formula, h, W_h, and W_s are called **variables.** Variables represent values that are subject to change. The number 4000 is a **constant** because its value does not change in the formula. (In fact, the value 4000 represents the radius of the Earth in miles, and this value does not change.)

A height of 37,000 ft is approximately 7 mi. Therefore, the weight of a 150-lb person at an elevation of 7 mi is given by

$$W_h = (150) \left(\frac{4000}{4000 + 7} \right)^2 \text{ lb}$$
Substitute 7 for h and 150 for W_s.

$$W_h \approx 149.5 \text{ lb}$$
A person weighing 150 lb at sea level would weigh approximately 149.5 lb at an altitude of 7 mi.

1. Identify Subsets of the Set of Real Numbers

In this example, we used numbers and variables to model the weight of a person at a given height above sea level. Numbers used in day-to-day life to quantify observed physical phenomena come from the set of real numbers. All real numbers can be represented with a point on the real number line (Figure R-1). A point of reference called the **origin** is labeled as zero on the number line. Positive numbers lie to the right of zero, and negative numbers lie to the left of zero.

Figure R-1

Every real number, x, has an **opposite**, denoted by $-x$. On the number line, the opposite of x is located on the opposite side of zero from x, but the same distance from zero. For example, the numbers 4 and -4 are opposites.

A **set** is a collection of items called **elements. Braces** { and } are used to enclose the elements of a set. For example, {gold, silver, bronze} represents the set of medals awarded to the first, second, and third place finishers for an Olympic event. A set that contains no elements is called the **empty set** (or **null set**) and is denoted by { } or by ∅.

In mathematics, there are several important sets of numbers. The numbers used for counting are called the natural numbers. The set of natural numbers is often given the symbol, $\mathbb{N}$. The set of whole numbers, $\mathbb{W}$, includes the natural numbers along with the element 0. The set of integers, $\mathbb{Z}$, consists of the whole numbers along with their opposites.

$$\mathbb{N} = \{1, 2, 3, \dots\}$$ the **set of natural numbers**

$$\mathbb{W} = \{0, 1, 2, 3, \dots\}$$ the **set of whole numbers**

$$\mathbb{Z} = \{\dots, -3, -2, -1, 0, 1, 2, 3, \dots\}$$ the **set of integers**

Notice from the definitions, that the set of natural numbers is a part of, or a **subset** of, the set of whole numbers. The symbol $\subset$ is used to indicate that one set is a *proper subset* of another. Therefore,

$$\mathbb{N} \subset \mathbb{W}$$ The set of natural numbers is a proper subset of the set of whole numbers.

> **TIP** The statement $\mathbb{N} \subset \mathbb{W}$ means that all elements of $\mathbb{N}$ are contained in $\mathbb{W}$, but that $\mathbb{N} \neq \mathbb{W}$. The definition of a proper subset does not allow for two sets to be equal.

When referring to individual elements of a set, the symbol $\in$ means "is an element of," and the symbol $\notin$ means "is *not* an element of." For example,

$$5 \in \{1, 3, 5, 7\}$$ is read as "5 is an element of $\{1, 3, 5, 7\}$."

$$4 \notin \{1, 3, 5, 7\}$$ is read as "4 is *not* an element of $\{1, 3, 5, 7\}$."

A set can be defined in several ways. Listing the elements in a set within braces is called the **roster method.** The roster method representing the set of the first five whole numbers is $\{0, 1, 2, 3, 4\}$. Another way to define this set is by using **set-builder notation.** This uses a description of the elements of the set. For example:

$$\{x \mid x \text{ is a whole number less than } 5\}$$

The set of   all x such that x is a whole number less than 5

EXAMPLE 1   Identifying Elements and Subsets of Sets

Answer true or false.

Solution:

a. $-18 \in \mathbb{Z}$ True $\mathbb{Z} = \{\dots, -2, -1, 0, 1, 2, \dots\}$. This includes -18.

b. $0 \in \mathbb{N}$ False $\mathbb{N} = \{1, 2, 3, \dots\}$ does not include the element 0.

c. $20 \in \{x \mid x \text{ is an integer and is a multiple of } 10\}$ True   The set given can be written in roster form as $\{\dots, -20, -10, 0, 10, 20, \dots\}$. The number 20 is an element of this set.

d. $\{a, e, i, o, u\} \subset \{a, b, c, d, e, f, g\}$ False   The first set is not a subset of the second, because the elements i, o, and u do not belong to the second set. That is: $i, o, u \notin \{a, b, c, d, e, f, g\}$

e. $\mathbb{W} \subset \mathbb{Z}$ True $\mathbb{W} = \{0, 1, 2, 3, \dots\}$ and $\mathbb{Z} = \{\dots, -3, -2, -1, 0, 1, 2, 3, \dots\}$. All elements in $\mathbb{W}$ are contained in $\mathbb{Z}$ but $\mathbb{W} \neq \mathbb{Z}$.

Skill Practice 1   Answer true or false.

a. $-5 \in \mathbb{N}$

b. $0 \in \mathbb{W}$

c. $-3 \in \{x \mid x \text{ is a whole number less than } 8\}$

d. {Chicago, New York, Miami} $\subset$ {Sacramento, Albany, Chicago, Miami}

e. $\mathbb{N} \subset \mathbb{Z}$

Answers

1. a. False **b.** True **c.** False

d. False **e.** True

You may have noticed that fractions and decimals such as $\frac{3}{7}$, 0.142, and $0.\overline{93}$ are not elements of the set of natural numbers, whole numbers, or integers. These fractions and decimals belong to the set of rational numbers. Rational numbers can be expressed as a ratio of two integers where the divisor is not zero.

TIP Notice that the first five letters of the word *rational* spell *ratio*. This will help you remember that a rational number is a *ratio* of integers.

The Set of Rational Numbers, $\mathbb{Q}$

The **set of rational numbers,** $\mathbb{Q}$, is defined as $\left\{\dfrac{p}{q} \,\middle|\, p, q \in \mathbb{Z}, \text{ and } q \neq 0\right\}$.

Verbal Interpretation	Numerical Example
Rational numbers can be expressed as a ratio of two integers where the divisor is not zero.	• $-\frac{5}{17}$ can be written as $\frac{-5}{17}$ which is the ratio of -5 and 17. • 9 can be written as $\frac{9}{1}$ which is the ratio of 9 and 1.
All terminating and repeating decimals are rational numbers.	• 0.71 can be written as $\frac{71}{100}$. • $0.\overline{6} = 0.666\ldots$ can be written as $\frac{2}{3}$.

Point of Interest

Computers have approximated π to over 1 trillion digits, but for most applications, the approximation 3.14159 is sufficient. Some mathematics enthusiasts have named March 14 (that is, the date 3.14) to be World Pi Day.

Real numbers that cannot be represented as a ratio of integers are called **irrational numbers.** We will denote the set of irrational numbers by $\mathbb{H}$. In decimal form, an irrational number cannot be represented by a terminating decimal or by a repeating decimal. One such example is the number π. The number π represents the ratio of the circumference of a circle to the diameter of a circle. In decimal form, π is approximately 3.14159 ($\pi \approx 3.14159$). However, the decimal digits go on indefinitely with no repeated pattern. Other examples of irrational numbers include the square roots of nonperfect squares, such as $\sqrt{7}$. A decimal approximation for $\sqrt{7}$ is 2.645751311, but once again, this is not the exact value. The decimal digits go on indefinitely with no repeated pattern.

TECHNOLOGY CONNECTIONS

Approximating Rational and Irrational Numbers

The number $-\frac{6}{11}$ is a rational number, and the number π is an irrational number. It is important to realize that for nonterminating decimals, a calculator or spreadsheet will only give approximate values, not exact values.

```
-(6/11)
        -.5454545455
π
        3.141592654
```

	A	B
1	**Number**	**Decimal Approximation**
2	-(6/11)	-0.545454545
3	Pi()	3.141592654

Together the elements of the set of rational numbers and the set of irrational numbers make up the set of **real numbers,** denoted by $\mathbb{R}$. See Figure R-2.

Real Numbers ($\mathbb{R}$) (Includes the rational numbers and the irrational numbers)

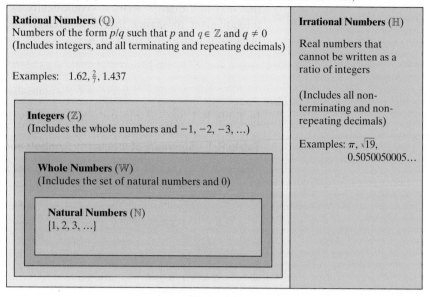

Figure R-2

EXAMPLE 2   **Identifying Elements of a Set**

Given $A = \left\{ \sqrt{3}, 0.\overline{83}, -\frac{19}{7}, 0.39, -16, 0, 11, 0.2020020002..., 0.444 \right\}$, determine which elements belong to the following sets.

Solution:

a. $\mathbb{N}$ $11 \in \mathbb{N}$

b. $\mathbb{W}$ $0, 11 \in \mathbb{W}$

c. $\mathbb{Z}$ $-16, 0, 11 \in \mathbb{Z}$

d. $\mathbb{Q}$ $0.\overline{83}, -\frac{19}{7}, 0.39, -16, 0, 11, 0.444 \in \mathbb{Q}$

e. $\mathbb{H}$ $\sqrt{3}, 0.2020020002... \in \mathbb{H}$

f. $\mathbb{R}$ $\sqrt{3}, 0.\overline{83}, -\frac{19}{7}, 0.39, -16, 0, 11, 0.2020020002..., 0.444 \in \mathbb{R}$

Skill Practice 2   Given set B, determine which elements belong to the following sets. $B = \left\{ -\frac{11}{7}, \sqrt{59}, 4.3, 0, 23, -13, \pi, 4.\overline{9} \right\}$

a. $\mathbb{N}$ **b.** $\mathbb{W}$ **c.** $\mathbb{Z}$ **d.** $\mathbb{Q}$ **e.** $\mathbb{H}$ **f.** $\mathbb{R}$

---

2. Use Inequality Symbols and Interval Notation

All real numbers can be located (or graphed) on the real number line. For example, the numbers $-1, -\sqrt{19}, \frac{\pi}{2}, 0.\overline{26}$, and $\frac{39}{10}$ are graphed here.

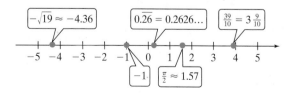

Answers

2. a. $23 \in \mathbb{N}$ **b.** $0, 23 \in \mathbb{W}$

c. $0, 23, -13 \in \mathbb{Z}$

d. $-\frac{11}{7}, 4.3, 0, 23, -13, 4.\overline{9} \in \mathbb{Q}$

e. $\sqrt{59}, \pi \in \mathbb{H}$

f. $-\frac{11}{7}, \sqrt{59}, 4.3, 0, 23, -13,$
$\pi, 4.\overline{9} \in \mathbb{R}$

The values of two numbers can be compared by using the real number line. We say that a is less than b (written symbolically as $a < b$) if a lies to the *left* of b. This is equivalent to saying that b is greater than a (written symbolically as $b > a$) because b lies to the *right* of a.

$a < b$ is equivalent to $b > a$

In Table R-1, we summarize other symbols used to compare two real numbers.

Table R-1   Summary of Inequality Symbols and Their Meanings

Inequality	Verbal Interpretation	Other Implied Meanings	Numerical Examples
$a < b$	a is less than b	b exceeds a b is greater than a	$5 < 7$
$a > b$	a is greater than b	a exceeds b b is less than a	$-3 > -6$
$a \le b$	a is less than or equal to b	a is at most b a is no more than b	$4 \le 5$ $5 \le 5$
$a \ge b$	a is greater than or equal to b	a is no less than b a is at least b	$9 \ge 8$ $9 \ge 9$
$a = b$	a is equal to b		$-4.3 = -4.3$
$a \ne b$	a is not equal to b		$-6 \ne -7$
$a \approx b$	a is approximately equal to b		$-12.99 \approx -13$

Point of Interest

The infinity symbol ∞ is called a lemniscate from the Latin *lemniscus* meaning "ribbon." English mathematician John Wallis is credited with introducing the symbol in the seventeenth century. The symbols $-\infty$ and ∞ are not themselves real numbers, but instead refer to quantities without bound or end.

An interval on the real number line can be represented in set-builder notation or in interval notation. In Table R-2, note that a parenthesis) or (indicates that an endpoint is not included in an interval. A bracket] or [indicates that an endpoint *is* included in the interval. The real number line extends infinitely far to the left and right. We use the symbols $-\infty$ and ∞ to denote the unbounded behavior to the left and right, respectively.

Table R-2   Summary of Interval Notation and Set-Builder Notation

Let a, b, and x represent real numbers.

Set-Builder Notation	Verbal Interpretation	Graph	Interval Notation
$\{x \mid x > a\}$	the set of real numbers greater than a		(a, ∞)
$\{x \mid x \ge a\}$	the set of real numbers greater than or equal to a		$[a, \infty)$
$\{x \mid x < b\}$	the set of real numbers less than b		$(-\infty, b)$
$\{x \mid x \le b\}$	the set of real numbers less than or equal to b		$(-\infty, b]$
$\{x \mid a < x < b\}$	the set of real numbers between a and b		(a, b)
$\{x \mid a \le x < b\}$	the set of real numbers greater than or equal to a and less than b		$[a, b)$
$\{x \mid a < x \le b\}$	the set of real numbers greater than a and less than or equal to b		$(a, b]$
$\{x \mid a \le x \le b\}$	the set of real numbers between a and b, inclusive		$[a, b]$
$\{x \mid x \text{ is a real number}\}$ $\mathbb{R}$	the set of all real numbers		$(-\infty, \infty)$

TIP As an alternative to using parentheses and brackets to represent the endpoints of an interval, an open dot or closed dot may be used. For example, $\{x \mid a \le x < b\}$ would be represented as follows.

EXAMPLE 3	Expressing Sets in Interval Notation and Set-Builder Notation

Complete the table.

Graph	Interval Notation	Set-Builder Notation
(number line from -5 to 5 with bracket at 2 extending left)		
	$\left(\frac{7}{2}, \infty\right)$	
		$\{y \mid -4 \leq y < 2.3\}$

Solution:

Graph	Interval Notation	Set-Builder Notation	Comments
(number line -5 to 5, bracket at 2 extending left)	$(-\infty, 2]$	$\{x \mid x \leq 2\}$	The bracket at 2 indicates that 2 is included in the set.
(number line -5 to 5, parenthesis at $\frac{7}{2}$ extending right)	$\left(\frac{7}{2}, \infty\right)$	$\left\{x \mid x > \frac{7}{2}\right\}$	The parenthesis at $\frac{7}{2} = 3.5$ indicates that $\frac{7}{2}$ is not included in the set.
(number line -5 to 5, bracket at -4 to parenthesis at 2.3)	$[-4, 2.3)$	$\{y \mid -4 \leq y < 2.3\}$	The set includes the real numbers between -4 and 2.3, including the endpoint -4.

Skill Practice 3

a. Write the set represented by the graph in interval notation and set-builder notation.

b. Given the interval, $\left(-\infty, -\frac{4}{3}\right]$, graph the set and write the set-builder notation.

c. Given the set, $\{x \mid 1.6 < x \leq 5\}$, graph the set and write the interval notation.

3. Evaluate Absolute Value Expressions

The number line can be used to visualize the absolute value of a real number. The absolute value of a real number x, denoted by $|x|$, is the distance between x and zero on the number line. For example:

$$|-5| = 5 \quad \text{because } -5 \text{ is 5 units from zero on the number line.}$$
$$|5| = 5 \quad \text{because } 5 \text{ is 5 units from zero on the number line.}$$

(number line from -6 to 6 showing $|-5| = 5$, 5 units, and $|5| = 5$, 5 units)

We now give the formal definition of absolute value.

Answers

3. a. Interval notation: $(-4, \infty)$;
   Set-builder notation: $\{x \mid x > -4\}$
   b.

   Set-builder notation: $\left\{x \mid x \leq -\frac{4}{3}\right\}$
   c.

(number line -5 to 5 with parenthesis at 1.6 and bracket at 5)

   Interval notation: $(1.6, 5]$

Absolute Value

Let x be a real number. Then $|x| = \begin{cases} x \text{ if } x \geq 0 \\ -x \text{ if } x < 0 \end{cases}$

Verbal Interpretation	Numerical Example
• If x is positive or zero, then $|x|$ is just x itself.	• $|4| = 4$
	• $|0| = 0$
• If x is negative, then $|x|$ is the opposite of x.	• $|-4| = -(-4) = 4$

EXAMPLE 4   Removing Absolute Value Symbols

Use the definition of absolute value to rewrite each expression without absolute value bars.

a. $|\sqrt{3} - 3|$ **b.** $|3 - \sqrt{3}|$

Solution:

a. $|\sqrt{3} - 3| = -(\sqrt{3} - 3)$
$$= -\sqrt{3} + 3 \quad \text{or} \quad 3 - \sqrt{3}$$

The value $\sqrt{3} \approx 1.73 < 3$, which implies that $\sqrt{3} - 3 < 0$. Since the expression inside the absolute value bars is negative, take the opposite.

b. $|3 - \sqrt{3}| = 3 - \sqrt{3}$

The value $\sqrt{3} \approx 1.73 < 3$, which implies that $3 - \sqrt{3} > 0$. Since the expression inside the absolute value bars is positive, the simplified form is the expression itself.

Skill Practice 4   Use the definition of absolute value to rewrite each expression without absolute value bars.

a. $|5 - \sqrt{7}|$ **b.** $|\sqrt{7} - 5|$

EXAMPLE 5   Removing Absolute Value Symbols

Use the definition of absolute value to rewrite each expression without absolute value bars.

a. $\dfrac{|x - 4|}{x - 4}$ for $x > 4$ **b.** $\dfrac{|x - 4|}{x - 4}$ for $x < 4$

Solution:

a. $\dfrac{|x - 4|}{x - 4}$ for $x > 4$

$$= \dfrac{x - 4}{x - 4}$$

Because $x > 4$, it follows that $x - 4 > 0$. Since $x - 4$ is positive, $|x - 4|$ simplifies as $x - 4$.

$$= 1$$

Simplify.

b. $\dfrac{|x - 4|}{x - 4}$ for $x < 4$

$$= \dfrac{-(x - 4)}{x - 4}$$

The condition $x < 4$, implies that $x - 4 < 0$. Since the expression inside the absolute value bars is negative, take the opposite.

$$= -1 \cdot \dfrac{x - 4}{x - 4}$$

Simplify.

$$= -1$$

> **TIP** The ratio of any real-valued expression and itself is 1. For example:
>
> $$\dfrac{5}{5} = 1$$
>
> $$\dfrac{-3.1}{-3.1} = 1$$
>
> $$\dfrac{x - 4}{x - 4} = 1$$

Skill Practice 5   Use the definition of absolute value to rewrite each expression without absolute value bars.

a. $\dfrac{x + 6}{|x + 6|}$ for $x < -6$ **b.** $\dfrac{x + 6}{|x + 6|}$ for $x > -6$

Answers

4. a. $5 - \sqrt{7}$ **b.** $5 - \sqrt{7}$
5. a. -1 **b.** 1

4. Use Absolute Value to Represent Distance

Absolute value is also used to denote distance between two points on a number line.

Distance Between Two Points on a Number Line		
The distance between two points a and b on a number line is given by $$\lvert a - b \rvert \quad \text{or} \quad \lvert b - a \rvert$$		
Verbal Interpretation	**Numerical Example**	**Graphical Example**
The distance between two points on a number line is the absolute value of their difference.	The distance between 3 and 5 is $\lvert 5 - 3 \rvert = 2$ or $\lvert 3 - 5 \rvert = 2$	2 units $$0 \quad 1 \quad 2 \quad 3 \quad 4 \quad 5 \quad 6$$

EXAMPLE 6   **Determining the Distance Between Two Points**

Write an absolute value expression that represents the distance between the two points on the number line. Then simplify.

a. The distance between 4 and -1 **b.** The distance between 3 and $\sqrt{3}$

Solution:

a. $\lvert 4 - (-1) \rvert = \lvert 5 \rvert = 5$

   $\lvert -1 - 4 \rvert = \lvert -5 \rvert = 5$

The distance between 4 and -1 is represented by $\lvert 4 - (-1) \rvert$ or by $\lvert -1 - 4 \rvert$.

5 units
$$-2 \quad -1 \quad 0 \quad 1 \quad 2 \quad 3 \quad 4 \quad 5$$

b. $\lvert 3 - \sqrt{3} \rvert = 3 - \sqrt{3} \approx 1.268$

   $\lvert \sqrt{3} - 3 \rvert = 3 - \sqrt{3} \approx 1.268$

The distance between 3 and $\sqrt{3}$ is represented by $\lvert 3 - \sqrt{3} \rvert$ or by $\lvert \sqrt{3} - 3 \rvert$.

From Example 4, both expressions simplify to $3 - \sqrt{3}$.

Skill Practice 6   Write an absolute value expression that represents the distance between the two points on the number line. Then simplify.

a. The distance between -9 and 2   **b.** The distance between 2π and 5

5. Evaluate Exponential Expressions, Square Roots, and Cube Roots

Repeated multiplication can be written by using exponential notation. For example, the product $5 \cdot 5 \cdot 5$ can be written as 5^3. In this case, 5 is called the base of the expression and 3 is the exponent (or power). The exponent indicates how many times the base is used as a factor.

Definition of b^n
Let b be a real number and let n represent a natural number. Then $$b^n = \underbrace{b \cdot b \cdot b \cdot \ \ldots \ \cdot b}_{b \text{ is used as a factor } n \text{ times}}$$ b^n is read as "b to the nth-power." b is the **base** and n is the **exponent** or **power.**

Answers

6. a. $\lvert -9 - 2 \rvert$ or $\lvert 2 - (-9) \rvert$;
       The distance is 11 units.
   b. $\lvert 2\pi - 5 \rvert$ or $\lvert 5 - 2\pi \rvert$;
       The distance is $2\pi - 5 \approx 1.283$ units.

EXAMPLE 7 **Simplifying Expressions with Exponents**

Simplify.

a. 4^2 **b.** $\left(\dfrac{3}{4}\right)^3$ **c.** $(-5)^2$ **d.** -5^2

Solution:

a. $4^2 = 4 \cdot 4 = 16$ The base 4 is used as a factor twice.

b. $\left(\dfrac{3}{4}\right)^3 = \dfrac{3}{4} \cdot \dfrac{3}{4} \cdot \dfrac{3}{4} = \dfrac{27}{64}$ The base $\frac{3}{4}$ is used as a factor three times.

c. $(-5)^2 = (-5)(-5) = 25$ The base is -5.

d. $-5^2 = -(5 \cdot 5) = -25$ The base in this expression is 5 (not -5). Therefore, this expression is interpreted as the opposite of 5^2.

Skill Practice 7 Simplify.

a. 8^2 **b.** $\left(-\dfrac{5}{6}\right)^3$ **c.** $(-1)^4$ **d.** -1^4

To find a square root of a nonnegative real number, we reverse the process to square a number. For example, a square root of 25 is a number that when squared equals 25. Both 5 and -5 are square roots of 25, because $5^2 = 25$ and $(-5)^2 = 25$. A radical sign $\sqrt{}$ is used to denote the principal square root of a number. The **principal square root** of a nonnegative real number is the square root that is greater than or equal to zero. Therefore, the principal square root of 25, denoted by $\sqrt{25}$, equals 5.

$$\sqrt{25} = 5 \text{ because } 5 \geq 0 \text{ and } 5^2 = 25$$

TIP Note that the square of any real number is nonnegative. Therefore, there is no real-valued square root of a negative number. For example:

$\sqrt{-25}$ is not a real number because no real number when squared equals -25.

Note: The value $\sqrt{-25}$ is an imaginary number and will be discussed in Section 1.3.

The symbol $\sqrt[3]{}$ represents the cube root of a number. For example:

$$\sqrt[3]{64} = 4 \text{ because } 4^3 = 64$$

EXAMPLE 8 **Simplifying Expressions with Radicals**

Simplify.

a. $\sqrt{4}$ **b.** $\sqrt[3]{-125}$ **c.** $\sqrt{\dfrac{49}{81}}$ **d.** $\sqrt{-9}$

Solution:

a. $\sqrt{4} = 2$ The principal square root of 4 is 2, because $2 \geq 0$ and $(2)^2 = 4$.

b. $\sqrt[3]{-125} = -5$ $\sqrt[3]{-125} = -5$ because $(-5)^3 = -125$.

c. $\sqrt{\dfrac{49}{81}} = \dfrac{7}{9}$ $\sqrt{\dfrac{49}{81}} = \dfrac{7}{9}$ because $\dfrac{7}{9} > 0$ and $\left(\dfrac{7}{9}\right)^2 = \dfrac{49}{81}$.

d. $\sqrt{-9}$ is not a real number.   No real number when squared equals -9.

Answers

7. a. 64 **b.** $-\dfrac{125}{216}$

    c. 1 **d.** -1

| Skill Practice 8 | Simplify. |

a. $\sqrt{100}$ **b.** $\sqrt[3]{-8}$ **c.** $\sqrt{\dfrac{9}{121}}$ **d.** $\sqrt{-16}$

6. Apply the Order of Operations

Many expressions involve multiple operations. In such a case, it is important to follow the order of operations.

Order of Operations

Step 1 Simplify expressions within parentheses and other grouping symbols. These include absolute value bars, fraction bars, and radicals. If nested grouping symbols are present, start with the innermost symbols.

Step 2 Evaluate expressions involving exponents.

Step 3 Perform multiplication or division in the order in which they occur from left to right.

Step 4 Perform addition or subtraction in the order in which they occur from left to right.

EXAMPLE 9   **Simplifying an Expression Involving Nested Grouping Symbols**

Simplify. $7 - \{8 + 4[2 - (5 - 8)^2]\}$

Solution:

$$7 - \{8 + 4[2 - (5 - 8)^2]\}$$
$$= 7 - \{8 + 4[2 - (-3)^2]\} \qquad \text{Simplify within the inner parentheses.}$$
$$= 7 - [8 + 4(2 - 9)] \qquad \text{Continue simplifying within the inner parentheses. Simplify } (-3)^2 \text{ to get 9.}$$
$$= 7 - [8 + 4(-7)] \qquad \text{Simplify } (2 - 9) \text{ to get } (-7).$$
$$= 7 - (8 - 28) \qquad \text{Multiply before adding or subtracting.}$$
$$= 7 - (-20) \qquad \text{Simplify within parentheses.}$$
$$= 27 \qquad \text{Subtract.}$$

Skill Practice 9   Simplify. $50 - \{2 - [11 + 3(-1 - 3)^2]\}$

TECHNOLOGY CONNECTIONS

Nested Parentheses on a Calculator or Spreadsheet

For expressions containing nested parentheses, calculators and spreadsheets do not recognize brackets and braces as grouping symbols. For example, the expression $7 - \{8 + 4[2 - (5 - 8)^2]\}$ would be entered on a calculator or spreadsheet as

$$7 - (8 + 4*(2 - (5 - 8)\wedge2)).$$

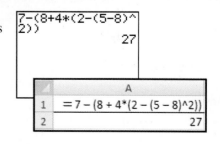

Answers

8. a. 10   **b.** -2

   c. $\dfrac{3}{11}$ **d.** Not a real number

9. 107

EXAMPLE 10   **Simplifying Expressions Involving Fractions**

Simplify. $\left(\dfrac{5}{3} - \dfrac{1}{2}\right)^2 \cdot 8$

Solution:

$\left(\dfrac{5}{3} - \dfrac{1}{2}\right)^2 \cdot 8 = \left(\dfrac{2}{2} \cdot \dfrac{5}{3} - \dfrac{3}{3} \cdot \dfrac{1}{2}\right)^2 \cdot 8$ Subtract the fractions within parentheses. The least common denominator is 6.

$= \left(\dfrac{10}{6} - \dfrac{3}{6}\right)^2 \cdot 8$ Simplify within parentheses.

$= \left(\dfrac{7}{6}\right)^2 \cdot 8$ Subtract fractions within parentheses.

$= \dfrac{49}{36} \cdot \dfrac{8}{1}$ Simplify the exponential expression. Write the whole number as a fraction.

$= \dfrac{49}{36} \cdot \dfrac{\overset{2}{8}}{1}$ Multiply the fractions.
$\phantom{= \dfrac{49}{36}}{\scriptstyle 9}$

$= \dfrac{98}{9}$ Simplify.

Skill Practice 10   Simplify. $\left(\dfrac{3}{4} - \dfrac{1}{2}\right)^3 \cdot 6$

EXAMPLE 11   **Simplifying an Expression with Implied Grouping Symbols**

Simplify. $\dfrac{\sqrt{6^2 + 8^2} - 5}{-3 \cdot 2 + |3 - 9|}$

Solution:

$\dfrac{\sqrt{6^2 + 8^2} - 5}{-3 \cdot 2 + |3 - 9|} = \dfrac{\sqrt{36 + 64} - 5}{-3 \cdot 2 + |-6|}$ Simplify within the radical. Subtract within the absolute value bars.

$= \dfrac{\sqrt{100} - 5}{-3 \cdot 2 + 6}$ Simplify further under the radical sign. Simplify the absolute value. $|-6| = 6$.

$= \dfrac{10 - 5}{-6 + 6}$ Simplify the radical $\sqrt{100} = 10$. Multiply $-3 \cdot 2 = -6$.

$= \dfrac{5}{0}$ (Undefined)   The quotient of 5 and 0 is undefined because there is no number that when multiplied by 0 equals 5.

Skill Practice 11   Simplify. $\dfrac{5 - \sqrt{5^2 - 4^2}}{|2 - 3 \cdot 4| - 10}$

In Example 11, we identified $\dfrac{5}{0}$ as undefined. Expressions involving division and the number zero can often present difficulty for students. Take a minute to review the summary given here of three cases involving division with zero.

Answers

10. $\dfrac{3}{32}$ **11.** Undefined

> ### Division Involving Zero
>
> To investigate division involving zero, consider the expressions $\frac{5}{0}$, $\frac{0}{5}$, and $\frac{0}{0}$ and their related multiplicative forms.
>
> 1. Division by zero is undefined.
>   <u>Example:</u> $\frac{5}{0} = n$ implies that $n \cdot 0 = 5$. No number, n, satisfies this requirement.
> 2. Zero divided by any nonzero number is zero.
>   <u>Example:</u> $\frac{0}{5} = 0$ implies that $0 \cdot 5 = 0$ which is a true statement.
> 3. We say that $\frac{0}{0}$ is **indeterminant** (cannot be determined). This concept is investigated in detail in a first course in calculus.
>   <u>Example:</u> $\frac{0}{0} = n$ implies that $n \cdot 0 = 0$. This is true for any number n. Therefore, the quotient cannot be determined.

SECTION R.1   Practice Exercises

Concept Connections

1. A _____ is a collection of items called elements.

2. $\mathbb{W} = \{0, 1, 2, 3, \dots\}$ is called the set of _____ numbers.

3. $\mathbb{N} = \{1, 2, 3, \dots\}$ is called the set of _____ numbers.

4. $\mathbb{Z} = \{\dots, -3, -2, -1, 0, 1, 2, 3, \dots\}$ is called the set of _____.

5. A set can be defined using _____ - _____ notation by using a description of the set.

6. Listing elements in a set within set braces is called the _____ method to define a set.

7. Real numbers that can be expressed as a ratio of two integers are called _____ numbers.

8. An _____ number is a real number that cannot be expressed as a ratio of two integers.

9. The statement $x < y$ means that x lies to the _____ of y on the number line.

10. The _____ _____ of x is denoted by $|x|$.

11. Write an absolute value expression to represent the distance between a and b on the number line: _____.

12. Given the expression b^n, the value of b is called the _____ and n is called the _____.

13. The symbol $\sqrt{x}$ represents the principal _____ root of x.

14. The expression $\frac{0}{5}$ equals _____, whereas $\frac{5}{0}$ is _____.

Objective 1: Identify Subsets of the Set of Real Numbers

For Exercises 15–20, write an English sentence to represent the algebraic statement.

15. $3 \in \mathbb{N}$

16. $\dfrac{2}{5} \in \mathbb{Q}$

17. $-3.1 \notin \mathbb{Z}$

18. $\pi \notin \mathbb{Q}$

19. $\mathbb{Z} \subset \mathbb{R}$

20. $\mathbb{Q} \subset \mathbb{R}$

For Exercises 21–38, determine whether the statement is true or false. (See Example 1)

21. a. $-5 \in \mathbb{N}$ b. $-5 \in \mathbb{W}$

    c. $-5 \in \mathbb{Z}$ d. $-5 \in \mathbb{Q}$

22. a. $\dfrac{1}{3} \in \mathbb{N}$ b. $\dfrac{1}{3} \in \mathbb{W}$

    c. $\dfrac{1}{3} \in \mathbb{Z}$ d. $\dfrac{1}{3} \in \mathbb{Q}$

23. a. $0.\overline{25} \in \mathbb{N}$ b. $0.\overline{25} \in \mathbb{W}$

    c. $0.\overline{25} \in \mathbb{Z}$ d. $0.\overline{25} \in \mathbb{Q}$

24. a. $\pi \in \mathbb{Z}$ b. $\pi \in \mathbb{Q}$

    c. $\pi \in \mathbb{H}$ d. $\pi \in \mathbb{R}$

25. $25 \in \{x \mid x$ is an integer and a multiple of 5$\}$

26. $-7 \in \{x \mid x$ is a natural number less than 10$\}$

27. $-0.\overline{8} \in \{x \mid x$ is a rational number greater than $-0.8\}$

28. $0.45 \in \{x \mid x$ is a rational number less than $0.\overline{45}\}$

29. $22 \in \{x \mid x$ is an even whole number$\}$

30. $-24 \in \{x \mid x$ is an integer and a multiple of 4$\}$

31. A number can be both a rational number and an irrational number.

32. A number can be both an integer and a rational number.

33. a. $\{-2, -4, -6\} \subset \{-6, -4, -2, 0\}$
b. $\{-6, -4, -2, 0\} \subset \{-2, -4, -6\}$

34. a. $\{FL, GA\} \subset \{FL, NM, GA, TX\}$
b. $\{FL, NM, GA, TX\} \subset \{FL, GA\}$

35. a. $\mathbb{Z} \subset \mathbb{W}$ **b.** $\mathbb{W} \subset \mathbb{Z}$

36. a. $\mathbb{Z} \subset \mathbb{Q}$ **b.** $\mathbb{Q} \subset \mathbb{Z}$

37. a. $\mathbb{Q} \subset \mathbb{H}$ **b.** $\mathbb{H} \subset \mathbb{Q}$

38. a. $\mathbb{H} \subset \mathbb{R}$ **b.** $\mathbb{Q} \subset \mathbb{R}$

39. Refer to $A = \left\{\sqrt{5}, 0.\overline{3}, 0.33, -0.9, -12, \frac{11}{4}, 6, \frac{\pi}{6}\right\}$. Determine which elements belong to the given set. **(See Example 2)**
a. $\mathbb{N}$ **b.** $\mathbb{W}$
c. $\mathbb{Z}$ **d.** $\mathbb{Q}$
e. $\mathbb{H}$ **f.** $\mathbb{R}$

40. Refer to $B = \left\{\frac{\pi}{2}, 0, -4, 0.\overline{48}, 1, -\sqrt{13}, 9.4\right\}$. Determine which elements belong to the given set.
a. $\mathbb{N}$ **b.** $\mathbb{W}$
c. $\mathbb{Z}$ **d.** $\mathbb{Q}$
e. $\mathbb{H}$ **f.** $\mathbb{R}$

Objective 2: Use Inequality Symbols and Interval Notation

For Exercises 41–46, write each statement as an inequality.

41. a is at least 5.

42. b is at most -6.

43. $3c$ is no more than 9.

44. $8d$ is no less than 16.

45. The quantity $(m + 4)$ exceeds 70.

46. The quantity $(n - 7)$ is approximately equal to 4.

For Exercises 47–54, determine whether the statement is true or false.

47. $3.14 < \pi$

48. $-7 < -\sqrt{7}$

49. $6.7 \geq 6.7$

50. $-2.1 \leq -2.1$

51. $6.\overline{15} > 6.1\overline{5}$

52. $2.9\overline{3} > 2.\overline{93}$

53. $-\dfrac{9}{7} < -\dfrac{11}{8}$

54. $-\dfrac{5}{3} < -\dfrac{9}{5}$

For Exercises 55–60, write the interval notation and set-builder notation for each given graph. **(See Example 3)**

55.
-7

56.
2

57.
4.1

58.
-2.93

59.
$-6 \qquad 0$

60.
$2 \qquad 8$

For Exercises 61–66, graph the given set and write the corresponding interval notation. **(See Example 3)**

61. $\{x \mid x \leq 6\}$

62. $\{x \mid x < -4\}$

63. $\left\{x \mid -\dfrac{7}{6} < x \leq \dfrac{1}{3}\right\}$

64. $\left\{x \mid -\dfrac{4}{3} \leq x < \dfrac{7}{4}\right\}$

65. $\{x \mid 4 < x\}$

66. $\{x \mid -3 \leq x\}$

For Exercises 67–72, interval notation is given for several sets of real numbers. Graph the set and write the corresponding set-builder notation. **(See Example 3)**

67. $(-3, 7]$

68. $[-4, -1)$

69. $(-\infty, 6.7]$

70. $(-\infty, -3.2)$

71. $\left[-\dfrac{3}{5}, \infty\right)$

72. $\left(\dfrac{7}{8}, \infty\right)$

Objective 3: Evaluate Absolute Value Expressions

For Exercises 73–84, simplify each expression by writing the expression without absolute value bars. (See Examples 4–5)

73. $|-6|$

74. $|-4|$

75. $|0|$

76. $|1|$

77. $|\sqrt{2} - 2|$

78. $|\sqrt{6} - 6|$

79. a. $|\pi - 3|$

    b. $|3 - \pi|$

80. a. $|m - 11|$ for $m \geq 11$

    b. $|m - 11|$ for $m < 11$

81. a. $|x + 2|$ for $x \geq -2$

    b. $|x + 2|$ for $x < -2$

82. a. $|t + 6|$ for $t < -6$

    b. $|t + 6|$ for $t \geq -6$

83. a. $\dfrac{|z - 5|}{z - 5}$ for $z > 5$

    b. $\dfrac{|z - 5|}{z - 5}$ for $z < 5$

84. a. $\dfrac{7 - x}{|7 - x|}$ for $x < 7$

    b. $\dfrac{7 - x}{|7 - x|}$ for $x > 7$

Objective 4: Use Absolute Value to Represent Distance

For Exercises 85–92, write an absolute value expression to represent the distance between the two points on the number line. Then simplify without absolute value bars. (See Example 6)

85. 1 and 6

86. 2 and 9

87. 3 and -4

88. -8 and 2

89. 8 and $\sqrt{3}$

90. 11 and $\sqrt{5}$

91. 6 and 2π

92. 3 and π

Objective 5: Evaluate Exponential Expressions, Square Roots, and Cube Roots

For Exercises 93–102, simplify the expression. (See Examples 7–8)

93. a. 4^2 **b.** $(-4)^2$ **c.** -4^2 **d.** $\sqrt{4}$ **e.** $-\sqrt{4}$ **f.** $\sqrt{-4}$

94. a. 9^2 **b.** $(-9)^2$ **c.** -9^2 **d.** $\sqrt{9}$ **e.** $-\sqrt{9}$ **f.** $\sqrt{-9}$

95. a. $\sqrt[3]{8}$ **b.** $\sqrt[3]{-8}$ **c.** $-\sqrt[3]{8}$ **d.** $\sqrt{100}$ **e.** $\sqrt{-100}$ **f.** $-\sqrt{100}$

96. a. $\sqrt[3]{27}$ **b.** $\sqrt[3]{-27}$ **c.** $-\sqrt[3]{27}$ **d.** $\sqrt{49}$ **e.** $\sqrt{-49}$ **f.** $-\sqrt{49}$

97. $\left(\dfrac{2}{3}\right)^3$

98. $\left(\dfrac{4}{5}\right)^3$

99. $(-0.2)^4$

100. $(-0.1)^4$

101. $\sqrt{\dfrac{169}{25}}$

102. $\sqrt{\dfrac{121}{36}}$

Objective 6: Apply the Order of Operations

For Exercises 103–116, simplify the expression. (See Examples 9–11)

103. $20 - 12(36 \div 3^2 \div 2)$

104. $200 - 2^2(6 \div \dfrac{1}{2} \cdot 4)$

105. $6 - \{-12 + 3[(1 - 6)^2 - 18]\}$

106. $-5 - \{4 - 6[(2 - 8)^2 - 31]\}$

107. $\sqrt{5^2 - 3^2}$

108. $\sqrt{6^2 + 8^2}$

109. $\left(\sqrt{9} + \sqrt{16}\right)^2$

110. $\left(\sqrt[3]{8} + \sqrt[3]{125}\right)^3$

111. $-4 \cdot \left(\dfrac{2}{5} - \dfrac{7}{10}\right)^2$

112. $6 \cdot \left[\left(\dfrac{1}{3}\right)^2 - \left(\dfrac{1}{2}\right)^2\right]$

113. $9 - (6 + ||3 - 7| - 8|) \div \sqrt{25}$

114. $8 - 2(4 + ||2 - 5|-5|) \div \sqrt{9}$

115. $\dfrac{|11 - 13| - 4 \cdot 2}{\sqrt{12^2 + 5^2} - 3 - 10}$

116. $\dfrac{(4 - 9)^2 + 2^2 - 3^2}{|-7 + 4| + (-12) \div 4}$

For Exercises 117–118, use the formula $W_h = W_s\left(\dfrac{4000}{4000 + h}\right)^2$ to compute the weight of an object W_h (in lb) at a height of h mi above sea level. The value of W_s is the weight of the object (in lb) at sea level.

117. If a man weighs 200 lb at sea level, evaluate $W_h = (200)\left(\dfrac{4000}{4000 + 5.5}\right)^2$ to determine his weight at the top of Mt. Everest. (Mt. Everest is 29,029 ft above sea level, or approximately 5.5 mi.) Round to 1 decimal place.

118. In 1976, an SR-71 Blackbird aircraft broke the world record for altitude by an airplane (not a rocket) by reaching an altitude of 85,135 ft (approximately 16.1 mi). (*Source*: Lockheed Martin, www.lockheedmartin.com) If the pilot weighs 175 lb at sea level, use the formula $W_h = (175)\left(\dfrac{4000}{4000 + 16.1}\right)^2$ to determine his weight at an altitude of 16.1 mi. Round to 1 decimal place.

119. Cone-shaped paper cups are used at the water cooler in many exercise facilities. Using the formula for the volume of a cone, the volume in cubic centimeters (cc) of this cup is $V = \dfrac{\pi(3.8)^2 \cdot 8}{3}$. Approximate the volume to the nearest cubic centimeter.

120. An inflated balloon has a volume of 6.0 L (liters) at sea level, where the pressure is 1.0 atm (atmosphere). The balloon is allowed to ascend until the pressure is 0.5 atm. During the ascent, the temperature of the gas in the balloon falls from 20°C to −23°C. Using the ideal-gas equation from chemistry, the new volume (in liters) of the gas in the balloon is $V = 6.0\left(\dfrac{1.0}{0.5}\right)\left(\dfrac{250}{293}\right)$. Approximate this volume to the nearest tenth of a liter.

Write About It

121. Explain why all terminating decimal numbers are rational numbers.

122. Explain why all integers are rational numbers.

123. When is a parenthesis used when writing interval notation?

124. When is a bracket used when writing interval notation?

125. Explain why $\mathbb{Z} \subset \mathbb{Q}$ but $\mathbb{Q} \not\subset \mathbb{Z}$.

126. Explain why the statement $\{1\} \subset \mathbb{Z}$ is a valid statement, but $1 \subset \mathbb{Z}$ does not make sense.

Expanding Your Skills

127. If $n > 0$, then $n - |n| =$ _____.

128. If $n < 0$, then $n - |n| =$ _____.

129. If $n > 0$, then $n + |n| =$ _____.

130. If $n < 0$, then $n + |n| =$ _____.

131. If $n > 0$, then $-|n| =$ _____.

132. If $n < 0$, then $-|n| =$ _____.

For Exercises 133–136, write an inequality representing the given statement.

133. b is positive.

134. a is negative.

135. b is nonnegative.

136. a is not positive.

For Exercises 137–140, determine the sign of the expression. Assume that a, b, and c are real numbers and $a < 0$, $b > 0$, and $c < 0$.

137. $\dfrac{ab^2}{c^3}$

138. $\dfrac{a^2c}{b^4}$

139. $\dfrac{b(a + c)^3}{a^2}$

140. $\dfrac{(a + b)^2(b + c)^4}{b}$

Technology Connections

For Exercises 141–144, use a calculator to approximate the expression to 2 decimal places.

141. $5000\left(1 + \dfrac{0.06}{12}\right)^{(12)(5)}$

142. $8500\left(1 + \dfrac{0.05}{4}\right)^{(4)(30)}$

143. $\dfrac{-3 + 5\sqrt{2}}{7}$

144. $\dfrac{6 - 3\sqrt{5}}{4}$

145. To evaluate the expression $\dfrac{-3 + \sqrt{3^2 - 4(-5)(2)}}{2(-5)}$ a student entered this expression on a calculator as shown. Find the error made by the student, and correct the mistake.

SECTION R.2   Models, Algebraic Expressions, and Properties of Real Numbers

OBJECTIVES

1. **Use Algebraic Models**
2. **Identify Terms and Coefficients**
3. **Apply Properties of Real Numbers**
4. **Simplify Algebraic Expressions**

1. Use Algebraic Models

In 1973, the Motorola Corporation unveiled its first mobile phone prototype intended for commercial use. The phone was $9 \times 5 \times 1.75$ in., weighed 2.5 lb, and had a 35-min talk time. By today's standards, the phone would be considered clunky and cumbersome, but this technology opened a new age of communication and a new commercial market. So who spends the most on cellular service? Figure R-3 shows

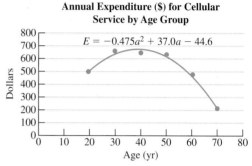

Figure R-3

the annual expenditure, E (in dollars), for individuals according to age, a. (*Source*: U.S. Bureau of Labor Statistics, www.bls.gov)

From the figure, the annual expenditure for cellular services can be approximated by the formula (or algebraic model):

$$E = -0.475a^2 + 37.0a - 44.6 \qquad \text{where } E \text{ is the annual expenditure in dollars and } a \text{ is an individual's age.}$$

One type of **mathematical model** is a formula that approximates the value of one variable (called the **dependent variable**) based on one or more **independent variables.** In this case, the independent variable is age, a. The dependent variable, E, depends on the values of a substituted into the model.

EXAMPLE 1   Interpreting an Algebraic Model

Use the model $E = -0.475a^2 + 37.0a - 44.6$ to approximate the annual expenditure E for cellular service for individuals of the following ages. Round to the nearest dollar.

a. 24 yr   **b.** 80 yr

Solution:

a. $E = -0.475a^2 + 37.0a - 44.6$

$E = -0.475(24)^2 + 37.0(24) - 44.6$ For a 24-yr-old, substitute $a = 24$.

$E \approx 570$ 24-yr-olds spend approximately \$570 per year on cellular service.

b. $E = -0.475a^2 + 37.0a - 44.6$

$E = -0.475(80)^2 + 37.0(80) - 44.6$ For an 80-yr-old, substitute $a = 80$.

$E \approx -124.6$ (model breakdown)   It is impossible to spend a negative amount.

If a mathematical model gives a poor or unreasonable estimate for the dependent variable, we say that **model breakdown** has occurred. This often happens when a value for the independent variable is substituted outside the observed range of data.

Skill Practice 1   Use the model $E = -0.475a^2 + 37.0a - 44.6$ to approximate the annual expenditure E for cellular service for individuals of the following ages. Round to the nearest dollar.

   a. 52 yr   **b.** 78 yr

An important skill in mathematics and science is to develop mathematical models. Examples 2 and 3 offer practice writing models based on verbal statements.

EXAMPLE 2   **Writing an Algebraic Model**

   a. The maximum recommended heart rate M for adults is the difference of 220 and the person's age a. Write a model to represent an adult's maximum recommended heart rate in terms of age.
   b. After eating at a restaurant, it is customary to leave a tip t for the server for at least 15% of the cost of the meal c. Write a model to represent the amount of the tip based on the cost of the meal.
   c. Kinetic energy is the energy of an object resulting from motion. Write a model for kinetic energy if kinetic energy E is equal to one-half the product of the mass of the object m times the square of the object's velocity v.

Solution:

   a. $M = 220 - a$ The word "difference" implies subtraction in the order given.
   b. $t \geq 0.15c$ 15% of c implies multiplication.
   c. $E = \dfrac{1}{2}mv^2$ The word "product" implies multiplication. The square of the velocity is v^2.

Skill Practice 2

   a. The sale price S on a lawn mower is the difference of the original price P and the amount of discount D. Write a model to represent the sale price.
   b. The amount of simple interest I earned on a certain certificate of deposit is 4.65% of the amount of principal invested P. Write a model for the amount of interest.
   c. The distance d traveled by an object dropped from rest is the product of $\frac{1}{2}$ times the Earth's acceleration due to gravity g times the square of the time of travel t. Write a model for the distance under these conditions.

EXAMPLE 3   **Writing and Evaluating an Algebraic Model**

A wireless phone bill is computed as follows. There is a monthly service charge of $59.98, various monthly taxes that total $14.07, a $0.30 charge per text message, a $2.50 charge per megabyte of data transfer, and $3.99 for each call to directory assistance.

   Let t represent the number of text messages.
   Let m represent the number of megabytes of data transfer.
   Let d represent the number of directory assistance calls made.

   a. Write a formula for the total amount of the bill A (in dollars) in terms of the variables t, m, and d.
   b. Determine the monthly cost if 14 text messages and 2 calls to directory assistance are made, and 4 megabytes of data transfer is used.

Answers
1. **a.** $595
   b. −$48.50; model breakdown
2. **a.** $S = P - D$
   b. $I = 0.0465P$
   c. $d = \dfrac{1}{2}gt^2$

Solution:

a. Amount = (Fixed costs) + (Variable costs)

The total bill consists of fixed costs (those not subject to change) plus variable costs.

| service charge | taxes | texting | data transfer | directory assistance |

$A = (59.98 + 14.07) + (0.30t + 2.50m + 3.99d)$

$A = 74.05 + 0.30t + 2.50m + 3.99d$

Monthly service charge and taxes are *fixed* each month.

The number of text messages, amount of data transfer, and calls to directory assistance can change (*vary*) from month to month.

b. $A = 74.05 + 0.30(14) + 2.5(4) + 3.99(2)$

$A = 96.23$ The total bill is $96.23.

Replace each variable with empty parentheses. Substitute 14 for t, 4 for m, and 2 for d.

Skill Practice 3

a. To rent a car, there is a daily charge of $24.99, a charge of $18.99 for each additional driver, $16.00 for each child safety seat, and $42.70 in taxes. Write a model for the cost C to rent a car for t days, d additional drivers, and n child safety seats.

b. Use this model to compute the cost to rent a car for 5 days, with one additional driver, and two safety seats.

---

2. Identify Terms and Coefficients

An algebraic **term** is a product of factors that may include constants and variables. For example:

$$-3xz^2 \qquad x \qquad 9 \qquad \frac{4}{b} \qquad z\sqrt{x-y}$$

An algebraic **expression** is a single term or the sum of two or more terms. From Example 1, the expression $-0.475a^2 + 37.0a - 44.6$ has three terms. Note that this can be written as a sum:

$$-0.475a^2 + 37.0a + (-44.6)$$

The terms $-0.475a^2$ and $37.0a$ are called **variable terms** because they contain a variable. The last term -44.6 has no variable, and therefore is not subject to change. It is called a **constant term.** The constant factor within each term is called the **numerical coefficient,** or simply **coefficient.** The coefficients of this expression are -0.475, 37.0, and -44.6, respectively.

EXAMPLE 4   **Identifying the Number of Terms and Coefficients of Each Term**

List the terms of each expression and identify the coefficients.

a. $5a^2b - 7ab^2 + a - 9.1$ **b.** $z\sqrt{x-y}$

Solution:

a. $5a^2b - 7ab^2 + a - 9.1$

$= 5a^2b + (-7ab^2) + a + (-9.1)$

This has four terms: $5a^2b$, $-7ab^2$, a, and -9.1

The coefficients are: 5, -7, 1, and -9.1

Rewrite as a sum of terms.

The term a can be written as $1a$. It has an implied coefficient of 1.

b. $z\sqrt{x - y} = 1z\sqrt{x - y}$

This expression has one term: $z\sqrt{x - y}$
The coefficient is 1.

This is a single term because the expression is a product of z and the quantity $\sqrt{x - y}$.

> **Skill Practice 4**   List the terms of each expression and identify the coefficients.
>
> **a.** $3x^5 + x^3y^2 - 8$ **b.** $8|x - y|$

3. Apply Properties of Real Numbers

Table R-3 summarizes important properties of real numbers.

Table R-3   Properties of Real Numbers

Let a, b, and c represent real numbers or real-valued expressions.

Property	In Symbols and Words	Examples
Commutative property of addition	$a + b = b + a$ The order in which real numbers are added does not affect the sum.	ex: $4 + (-7) = -7 + 4$ ex: $6 + w = w + 6$
Commutative property of multiplication	$a \cdot b = b \cdot a$ The order in which real numbers are multiplied does not affect the product.	ex: $5 \cdot (-4) = -4 \cdot 5$ ex: $x \cdot 12 = 12x$
Associative property of addition	$(a + b) + c = a + (b + c)$ The order in which real numbers are grouped under addition does not affect the sum.	ex: $(3 + 5) + 2 = 3 + (5 + 2)$ ex: $-9 + (2 + t) = (-9 + 2) + t$ $= -7 + t$
Associative property of multiplication	$(a \cdot b) \cdot c = a \cdot (b \cdot c)$ The order in which real numbers are grouped under multiplication does not affect the product.	ex: $(6 \cdot 7) \cdot 3 = 6 \cdot (7 \cdot 3)$ ex: $8 \cdot \left(\frac{1}{8} \cdot y\right) = \left(8 \cdot \frac{1}{8}\right) \cdot y$ $= 1y$
Identity property of addition	$a + 0 = a$ and $0 + a = a$ The number 0 is called the **identity element of addition** because any number plus 0 is the number itself.	ex: $-5 + 0 = -5$ ex: $0 + \sqrt{z} = \sqrt{z}$
Identity property of multiplication	$a \cdot 1 = a$ and $1 \cdot a = a$ The number 1 is called the **identity element of multiplication** because any number times 1 is the number itself.	ex: $\sqrt{2} \cdot 1 = \sqrt{2}$ ex: $1 \cdot (2w + 3) = 2w + 3$
Inverse property of addition	$a + (-a) = 0$ and $(-a) + a = 0$ For any real number a, the value $-a$ is called the **additive inverse of a** (also called the **opposite of a**). The sum of any number and its additive inverse is the identity element for addition, 0.	ex: $4\pi + (-4\pi) = 0$ ex: $-e + e = 0$
Inverse property of multiplication	$a \cdot \frac{1}{a} = 1$ and $\frac{1}{a} \cdot a = 1$ where $a \neq 0$ For any nonzero real number a, the value $\frac{1}{a}$ is called the **multiplicative inverse of a** (also called the **reciprocal of a**). The product of any nonzero number and its multiplicative inverse is the identity element, 1.	ex: $-5 \cdot \left(-\frac{1}{5}\right) = 1$ ex: $\frac{1}{x^2} \cdot x^2 = 1$ for $x \neq 0$ *Note*: The number zero does not have a multiplicative inverse (reciprocal).
Distributive property of multiplication over addition	$a \cdot (b + c) = a \cdot b + a \cdot c$ The product of a number and a sum equals the sum of the products of the number and each term in the sum.	ex: $4 \cdot (5 + x) = 4 \cdot 5 + 4 \cdot x$ $= 20 + 4x$ ex: $2 \cdot (x + \sqrt{3}) = 2x + 2\sqrt{3}$

Answers

4. a. Terms: $3x^5, x^3y^2, -8$;
    Coefficients: 3, 1, −8
  b. Term: $8|x - y|$; Coefficient: 8

It is important to note that the commutative and associative properties hold true only for addition and multiplication, not for subtraction and division. For example:

$$5x - 3 \neq 3 - 5x \qquad \text{Subtraction is not commutative.}$$

However, a difference of terms can be written as a related expression involving addition. Then the commutative property of addition can be applied.

$$5x - 3 = 5x + (-3) \qquad \text{Write the related statement using addition.}$$
$$= -3 + 5x \qquad \text{Apply the commutative property of addition.}$$

4. Simplify Algebraic Expressions

The distributive property is particularly useful because it is used to combine like terms and to simplify expressions. Like terms have the same variables and the corresponding variables are raised to the same power. For example:

Like Terms	Unlike Terms
$-7w$ and $\dfrac{1}{2}w$	$-7w$ and $\dfrac{1}{2}x$
$2.8ac$ and $-ac$	$2.8ac$ and $-a$
$\pi x^2 y^5$ and $\sqrt{5}x^2 y^5$	$\pi x^2 y^5$ and $\sqrt{5}x^2 y^4$
-3 and 7	$-3c$ and 7

EXAMPLE 5   **Combining Like Terms**

Simplify.

    a. $8x^2 + 6x^2 - x^2$ **b.** $1.2ab^3 - 6.8a^2 b - 5.4ab^3 + 2.3a^2 b$

Solution:

    a. $8x^2 + 6x^2 - x^2 = (8 + 6 - 1)x^2$ Apply the distributive property.

                               $= 13x^2$ Simplify.

> **TIP** Although the distributive property is used to add and subtract like terms, it is tedious to write each step. Adding or subtracting like terms can also be done by combining the coefficients and leaving the variable factor unchanged.
>
> $$8x^2 + 6x^2 - 1x^2 = 13x^2 \qquad \text{This method will be used throughout the text.}$$

    b. $1.2ab^3 - 6.8a^2 b - 5.4ab^3 + 2.3a^2 b$

        $= 1.2ab^3 - 5.4ab^3 - 6.8a^2 b + 2.3a^2 b$ Group like terms.

        $= -4.2ab^3 - 4.5a^2 b$ Combine like terms.

Skill Practice 5   Combine like terms.

    a. $-4p^5 - p^5 + 10p^5$ **b.** $3.1c^4 d + 7.8cd - 4.4c^4 d - 1.1cd$

The distributive property is also used to simplify algebraic expressions.

EXAMPLE 6   **Applying the Distributive Property**

Apply the distributive property.

a. $4(2x^2 - 5.1x + 3)$ **b.** $-(9y - \sqrt{2})$

Solution:

a. $4(2x^2 - 5.1x + 3)$

$= 4[2x^2 + (-5.1x) + 3]$ Write subtraction in terms of addition.

$= 4 \cdot (2x^2) + 4 \cdot (-5.1x) + 4 \cdot (3)$ Apply the distributive property.

$= 8x^2 - 20.4x + 12$ Simplify.

b. $-(9y - \sqrt{2})$

$= -1[(9y + (-\sqrt{2})]$ The negative sign in front of parentheses
                                     can be interpreted as -1 times the
                                     expression in parentheses.

$= -9y + \sqrt{2}$ Apply the distributive property.

> **TIP** A negative factor preceding the parentheses will change the signs of the terms within parentheses.
>
> $-(+9y - \sqrt{2})$
> $= -9y + \sqrt{2}$

Skill Practice 6   Apply the distributive property.

a. $5(6y^3 - 4y^2 + 7)$ **b.** $-2(5t - \pi)$

EXAMPLE 7   **Clearing Parentheses and Combining Like Terms**

Simplify.

a. $5 - 2(4c - 8d) + 3(1 - d) + c$

b. $-3x^2 - \left[8 + \dfrac{1}{2}(2x^2 - 6) - 4x^2\right]$

Solution:

a. $5 - 2(4c - 8d) + 3(1 - d) + c$ Apply the distributive property to clear
                                       parentheses.

$= 5 - 8c + 16d + 3 - 3d + c$ Combine like terms.

$= 8 - 7c + 13d$

b. $-3x^2 - \left[8 + \dfrac{1}{2}(2x^2 - 6) - 4x^2\right]$ Apply the distributive property.

$= -3x^2 - [8 + x^2 - 3 - 4x^2]$ Combine like terms inside brackets.

$= -3x^2 - [-3x^2 + 5]$ Apply the distributive property.

$= -3x^2 + 3x^2 - 5$ Combine like terms.

$= -5$

> **TIP** After applying the distributive property, the original parentheses are removed. For this reason, we often call this process "clearing parentheses."

Skill Practice 7   Clear parentheses and combine like terms.

a. $12 - 3(5x - 2y) + 5(3 - x) - y$

b. $4w^3 - \left[3 - \dfrac{1}{4}(4 + 8w^3) - w^3\right] + 2$

Answers

6. a. $30y^3 - 20y^2 + 35$
  b. $-10t + 2\pi$
7. a. $-20x + 5y + 27$ **b.** $7w^3$

Review Exercises

For Exercises 1–2, write the interval notation and set-builder notation for the set defined by the graph.

1. [number line with bracket at -5 and parenthesis at 2]

2. [number line with parenthesis at -1]

For Exercises 3–4, write an absolute value expression to represent the distance between the two points on the number line. Then simplify the expression without absolute value bars.

3. $\sqrt{2}$ and 9

4. π and 6

For Exercises 5–8, determine whether the statement is true or false.

5. $0.\overline{34} \in \mathbb{Q}$

6. $\pi \in \mathbb{Q}$

7. $\mathbb{Z} \subset \mathbb{N}$

8. $\{1\} \subset \{1, 2\}$

For Exercises 9–10, simplify.

9. $\dfrac{12 - (9 - \sqrt{9})^2 \div (-2) \cdot 3}{|-7 + 1|}$

10. $\dfrac{\sqrt{10^2 - 8^2}}{(\sqrt{16} - \sqrt{4})^2}$

Concept Connections

11. One type of mathematical model is a formula that approximates the value of the _____ variable in terms of one or more independent variables.

12. Model _____ is a term used to describe a situation in which a formula or model gives a poor or unreasonable estimate for the dependent variable.

13. A _____ is a product of factors that may include constants and variables.

14. The numerical _____ of a term is the constant factor within the term.

15. The _____ properties of addition and multiplication indicate that the order in which two real numbers are added or multiplied does not affect the sum or product.

16. The sum of a number and its additive inverse is _____.

17. The number _____ is the identity element of multiplication.

18. Zero is the _____ element of addition.

19. The additive inverse of a real number x is _____.

20. The statement $a(b + c) = ab + ac$ represents the _____ property of multiplication over addition.

21. The multiplicative inverse of a nonzero real number is also called the _____ of the number.

22. The _____ property of addition indicates that $a + (b + c) = (a + b) + c$.

23. The associative property of multiplication indicates that $a \cdot (b \cdot c) = $ _____.

24. The number _____ is the only real number that does not have a multiplicative inverse.

Objective 1: Use Algebraic Models

25. Gas mileage depends in part on the speed of the vehicle. The gas mileage m (in mpg) of a certain subcompact car is given by $m = -0.04x^2 + 3.6x - 49$, where x is the speed of the car (in mph). (**See Example 1**)

    a. Use the model to approximate the gas mileage for a car traveling 35 mph.

    b. Use the model to approximate the gas mileage for a car traveling 50 mph.

    c. Use the model to approximate the gas mileage for a car traveling 75 mph.

Gas Mileage Based on Speed of Car

$m = -0.04x^2 + 3.6x - 49$

26. The bacterium *Pseudomonas aeruginosa* is cultured with an initial population of approximately 10,000 active organisms. The population of active bacteria increases up to a point. Then, due to a limited food supply and an increase of waste products, the population decreases. The population P can be approximated by

$$P = -1718t^2 + 82,000t + 10,000$$

where t is the number of hours since the culture was started.

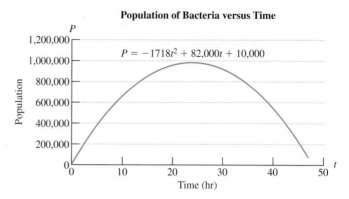

Population of Bacteria versus Time

$P = -1718t^2 + 82,000t + 10,000$

a. Use the model to approximate the population after 22 hr. Round to the nearest thousand.

b. Use the model to approximate the population after 1.5 days. Round to the nearest thousand.

c. Use the model to approximate the population after 48 hr. Round to the nearest thousand.

27. Data from the Bureau of Labor Statistics *Consumer Expenditure Survey* show a decrease in spending on residential landline phone services. (*Source*: www.bls.gov)

The average yearly expenditure for landline service E (in \$) can be modeled by $E = -27.45t + 704.6$, where t is the number of years since the year 2000.

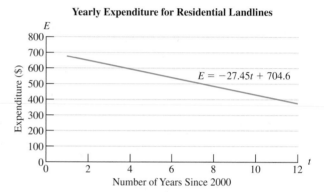

Yearly Expenditure for Residential Landlines

$E = -27.45t + 704.6$

a. Use the model to approximate the expenditure for the year 2003.

b. If this trend continues, predict the expenditure for the year 2015.

c. Can this model extend indefinitely? Explain why or why not.

28. Selena started a new diet and exercise program, and lost 1.2 lb per week. If her starting weight was 150 lb, then her weight W (in lb) can be modeled by

$$W = 150 - 1.2t$$

where t is the number of weeks after starting the diet.

Weight versus Time

$W = 150 - 1.2t$

a. Use the model to determine Selena's weight after 6 weeks.

b. If Selena continues her diet and exercise program, determine her weight after 12 weeks.

c. Is it reasonable to expect that this model will extend indefinitely? Explain why or why not.

For Exercises 29–38, write an appropriate mathematical model. (See Example 2)

29. The temperature at noon in Orlando, Florida, in July is typically 16°F warmer than the temperature at 6:00 A.M. Write a model for the noon temperature T_n in terms of the 6:00 A.M. temperature T_s.

30. Scientists often use the Kelvin scale to measure temperature. The temperature in Kelvin K is 273.15 more than the corresponding temperature in Celsius C. Write a model for the temperature in Kelvin in terms of the Celsius temperature.

31. The retail price P for a sofa is the sum of the wholesale price W and the markup M. Write a model to represent the retail price.

32. The sale price S for a tractor is the difference of the original price P and the discount D. Write a model to represent the sale price.

33. Jake is 1 yr younger than Charlotte.

   a. Write a model for Jake's age J in terms of Charlotte's age C.

   b. Write a model for Charlotte's age C in terms of Jake's age J.

34. For a recent NFL season, Aaron Rogers had 9 more touchdown passes than Joe Flacco.

   a. Write a model for the number of touchdown passes R thrown by Rogers in terms of the number thrown by Flacco F.

   b. Write a model for the number of touchdown passes F thrown by Flacco in terms of the number thrown by Rogers R.

35. At the end of the summer, a home store discounts an outdoor grill for at least 25% of the original price. If the original price is P, write a model for the amount of the discount D.

36. When Ms. Tibbets has excellent service at a restaurant, the amount she leaves for a tip t is at least 20% of the cost of the meal c. Write a model representing the amount of the tip.

37. Suppose that an object is dropped from a height h. Its velocity v at impact with the ground is given by the square root of twice the product of the acceleration due to gravity g and the height h. Write a model to represent the velocity of the object at impact.

38. The height of a sunflower plant can be determined by the time t in weeks after the seed has germinated. Write a model to represent the height h if the height is given by the product of 8 and the square root of t.

39. A power company charges one household $0.12 per kilowatt-hour (kWh) and $14.89 in monthly taxes. (**See Example 3**)

   a. Write a formula for the monthly charge C for this household if it uses k kilowatt-hour.

   b. Compute the monthly charge if the household uses 1200 kWh.

40. A utility company charges a base rate for water usage of $13.50 per month, plus $3.58 for every additional 1000 gal of water used over a 2000-gal base.

   a. Write a formula for the monthly charge C for a household that uses n thousand gallons over the 2000-gal base.

   b. Compute the cost for a family that uses a total of 5000 gal of water for a given month.

41. The cost C (in $) to rent an apartment is $640 per month, plus a $500 nonrefundable security deposit, plus a $200 deposit for each dog or cat.

   a. Write a formula for the total cost to rent an apartment for m months with n cats/dogs.

   b. Determine the cost to rent the apartment for 12 months, with 2 cats and 1 dog.

42. For a certain college, the cost C (in $) for taking classes the first semester is $105 per credit-hour, $35 for each lab, plus a one-time admissions fee of $40.

   a. Write a formula for the total cost to take n credit-hours and L labs the first semester.

   b. Determine the cost for the first semester if a student takes 12 credit-hours with 2 labs.

43. A hotel charges $159 per night plus an 11% nightly room tax.

   a. Write a formula to represent the total cost C for n nights in the hotel. (*Hint*: The total cost is the cost for n nights, plus the tax on the cost for n nights.)

   b. Determine the cost to stay in the hotel for four nights.

44. A hotel charges $149 per night plus a 16% nightly room tax. In addition, there is a one-time parking fee of $40.

   a. Write a formula to represent the total cost C for n nights in the hotel.

   b. Determine the cost to stay in the hotel for two nights.

Objective 2: Identify Terms and Coefficients

For Exercises 45–50, list the terms and coefficients of each term. (See Example 4)

45. $12x^2y^5 - xy^4 + 9.2xy^3$

46. $6c^2d - 6.4cd^5 + d^6$

47. $\dfrac{5}{m}$

48. $-\dfrac{2}{n}$

49. $x|y + z|$

50. $m\sqrt{3 + n}$

Objective 3: Apply Properties of Real Numbers

For Exercises 51–56, apply the commutative property of addition or multiplication.

51. $7 + x$

52. $9 + z$

53. $-3 + w$

54. $-11 + p$

55. $y \cdot \dfrac{1}{3}$

56. $z \cdot \dfrac{5}{2}$

For Exercises 57–60, apply the associative property of addition or multiplication. Then simplify if possible.

57. $(t + 3) + 9$

58. $(c + 4) + 5$

59. $\dfrac{1}{5}(5w)$

60. $-\dfrac{4}{9}\left(-\dfrac{9}{4}p\right)$

For Exercises 61–68, (a) identify the additive inverse and (b) identify the multiplicative inverse, if possible.

61. -8 **62.** 9 **63.** $\dfrac{5}{4}$ **64.** $-\dfrac{7}{9}$

65. 0 **66.** 1 **67.** 2.1 **68.** 4.5

Objective 4: Simplify Algebraic Expressions

For Exercises 69–74, combine like terms. (See Example 5)

69. $-14w^3 - 3w^3 + w^3$

70. $12t^5 - t^5 - 6t^5$

71. $3.9x^3y - 2.2xy^3 + 5.1x^3y - 4.7xy^3$

72. $0.004m^4n - 0.005m^3n^2 - 0.01m^4n + 0.007m^3n^2$

73. $\dfrac{1}{3}c^7d + \dfrac{1}{2}cd^7 - \dfrac{2}{5}c^7d - 2cd^7$

74. $\dfrac{1}{10}yz^4 - \dfrac{3}{4}y^4z + yz^4 + \dfrac{3}{2}y^4z$

For Exercises 75–82, apply the distributive property. (See Example 6)

75. $3(4p^3 - 6.1p^2 - 8p + 2.2)$

76. $2(-5a^4 - a^3 + 0.4a - 0.8)$

77. $-(4x - \pi)$

78. $-\left(\dfrac{1}{2}k - \sqrt{7}\right)$

79. $-8(3x^2 + 2x - 1)$

80. $-6(-5y^2 - 3y + 4)$

81. $\dfrac{2}{3}(-6x^2y - 18yz^2 + 2z^3)$

82. $\dfrac{3}{4}(12p^5q - 8p^4q^2 - 6p^3q)$

For Exercises 83–90, simplify each expression. (See Example 7)

83. $2(4w + 8) + 7(2w - 4) + 12$

84. $3(2z - 4) + 8(z - 9) + 84$

85. $-(4u - 8v) - 3(7u - 2v) + 2v$

86. $-(10x - z) - 2(8x - 4z) - 3x$

87. $12 - 4[(8 - 2v) + 5(-3w - 4v)] - w$

88. $6 - 2[(9z + 6y) - 8(y - z)] - 11$

89. $2y^2 - \left[13 - \dfrac{2}{3}(6y^2 - 9) - 10\right] + 9$

90. $6 - \left[5t^2 - \dfrac{3}{4}(12 - 8t^2) + 5\right] + 11t^2$

Mixed Exercises

For Exercises 91–96, evaluate each expression for the given values of the variables.

91. $\dfrac{-b}{2a}$ for $a = -1$, $b = -6$

92. $\sqrt{b^2 - 4ac}$ for $a = 2$, $b = -6$, $c = 4$

93. $\sqrt{(x_2 - x_1)^2 + (y_2 - y_1)^2}$ for $x_1 = 2$, $x_2 = -1$, $y_1 = -4$, $y_2 = 1$

94. $\dfrac{y_2 - y_1}{x_2 - x_1}$ for $x_1 = -1.4$, $x_2 = 2$, $y_1 = 3.1$, $y_2 = -3.7$

95. $\dfrac{1}{3}\pi r^2 h$ for $\pi \approx \dfrac{22}{7}$, $r = 7$, $h = 6$

96. $\dfrac{4}{3}\pi r^3$ for $\pi \approx \dfrac{22}{7}$, $r = 3$

97. The width of a rectangle is 3 ft less than twice the length. Write a model for the width W in terms of the length L.

98. The longest side of a triangle is 5 ft less than three times the shortest side. Write a model for the length of the longest side L in terms of the length of the shortest side S.

99. Total college enrollment in the United States increased by 489,000 students between the years 2008 and 2009. (*Source*: National Center for Educational Statistics, www.nces.ed.gov) Let E_{2008} represent the college enrollment in 2008, and let E_{2009} represent enrollment for 2009. Write a model for the college enrollment in 2009 in terms of the enrollment in 2008.

100. The average cost per kilowatt-hour for residential electricity increased by 0.25¢ between 2010 and 2011. (*Source*: U.S. Energy Information Administration, www.eia.gov) Write a model for the cost per kilowatt-hour (in ¢) in 2011 (C_{2011}) in terms of the cost in 2010 (C_{2010}).

101. Under selected conditions, a sports car gets 15 mpg in city driving and 25 mpg for highway driving. The model $G = \frac{1}{15}c + \frac{1}{25}h$ represents the amount of gasoline used (in gal) for c miles driven in the city and h miles driven on the highway. Determine the amount of gas required to drive 240 mi in the city and 500 mi on the highway.

102. Under selected conditions, a sedan gets 22 mpg in city driving and 32 mpg for highway driving. The model $G = \frac{1}{22}c + \frac{1}{32}h$ represents the amount of gasoline used (in gal) for c miles driven in the city and h miles driven on the highway. Determine the amount of gas required to drive 220 mi in the city and 512 mi on the highway.

Write About It

103. Explain the difference between the commutative property of addition and the associative property of addition.

104. Explain why 0 has no multiplicative inverse.

Technology Connections

For Exercises 105–106, use a calculator to evaluate each expression for the given values of the variables.

105. $\dfrac{(x+h)^2 - x^2}{h}$ for $x = 3$, $h = 0.01$

106. $\dfrac{(x+h)^3 - x^3}{h}$ for $x = 2$, $h = 0.1$

SECTION R.3	Integer Exponents and Scientific Notation

OBJECTIVES

1. Simplify Expressions with Zero and Negative Exponents
2. Apply Properties of Exponents
3. Apply Scientific Notation

1. Simplify Expressions with Zero and Negative Exponents

In Section R.1, we learned that exponents are used to represent repeated multiplication. Applications of exponents appear in many fields of study, including computer science. Computer engineers define a *bit* as a fundamental unit of information having just two possible values. These values are represented by either 0 or 1. A *byte* is usually taken as 8 bits. Computer programmers know that there are 2^n possible values for an n-bit variable. So 1 byte has $2^8 = 256$ possible values.

Three bytes are often used to represent color on a computer screen. The intensity of each of the colors red, green, and blue ranges from 0 to 255 (a total of 256 possible values each). So the number of colors that can be represented by this system is

$$2^8 \cdot 2^8 \cdot 2^8 = (256)(256)(256) = 16{,}777{,}216$$

There are over 16 million possible colors available using this system. For example, the color given by red 137, green 21, blue 131, is a deep pink. See Figure R-4.

Figure R-4

The product $2^8 \cdot 2^8 \cdot 2^8$ can be visualized by expanding factors.

$$= \overbrace{(2 \cdot 2 \cdot 2 \cdot 2 \cdot 2 \cdot 2 \cdot 2 \cdot 2)}^{8 \text{ factors}}\overbrace{(2 \cdot 2 \cdot 2 \cdot 2 \cdot 2 \cdot 2 \cdot 2 \cdot 2)}^{8 \text{ factors}}\overbrace{(2 \cdot 2 \cdot 2 \cdot 2 \cdot 2 \cdot 2 \cdot 2 \cdot 2)}^{8 \text{ factors}}$$
$$= 2^{24} = 16{,}777{,}216$$

The same result can be obtained by adding exponents.

$$2^8 \cdot 2^8 \cdot 2^8 = 2^{8+8+8} = 2^{24} = 16{,}777{,}216$$

This idea can be expanded to an expression of the form $b^m \cdot b^n$, where b is a real number and m and n are natural numbers.

$$b^m \cdot b^n = \underbrace{\overbrace{(b \cdot b \cdot b \cdot \ldots \cdot b)}^{m \text{ factors of } b}\overbrace{(b \cdot b \cdot b \cdot \ldots \cdot b)}^{n \text{ factors of } b}}_{m+n \text{ factors of } b} = b^{m+n}$$

This result is called the **product rule for exponents.**

We would like to extend the product rule to expressions where m and n are negative integers or zero. For example,

$$\begin{array}{l} b^0 \cdot b^4 = b^{0+4} = b^4 \\ \underline{} \\ 1 \cdot b^4 = b^4 \end{array}$$ For this to be true, the value b^0 must be 1.

Consider another example involving a negative exponent.

$$\begin{array}{l} b^{-4} \cdot b^4 = b^{-4+4} = b^0 = 1 \\ \underline{} \\ \dfrac{1}{b^4} \cdot b^4 = 1 \end{array}$$ For the product $b^{-4} \cdot b^4$ to be equal to 1, it follows that b^{-4} must be the reciprocal of b^4. That is, $b^{-4} = \dfrac{1}{b^4}$.

These observations lead to the following definitions.

Definition of b^0 and b^{-n}

If b is a nonzero real number and n is a positive integer, then

$$b^0 = 1 \quad \text{and} \quad b^{-n} = \frac{1}{b^n}$$

Verbal Interpretation	Algebraic Example
A nonzero real number raised to the zero power is 1.	• $(1000)^0 = 1$ • $y^0 = 1$ • $(-5x)^0 = 1$ for $x \neq 0$
A nonzero real number raised to a negative exponent can be rewritten by using the reciprocal of the base and the corresponding positive exponent.	• $4^{-1} = \dfrac{1}{4^1}$ or $\dfrac{1}{4}$ • $x^{-3} = \dfrac{1}{x^3}$ for $x \neq 0$

The definitions given here have two important restrictions.

By definition, $b^0 = 1$ provided that $b \neq 0$. Therefore,

- The value of 0^0 is not defined here. The value of 0^0 is said to be indeterminant and is examined in calculus.

For a positive integer, n, by definition, $b^{-n} = \dfrac{1}{b^n}$ provided that $b \neq 0$. Therefore,

- The value of 0^{-n} is not defined here.

All examples and exercises in the text will be given under the assumption that the variable expressions avoid these restrictions. For example, the expression x^0 will be stated with the implied restriction that $x \neq 0$.

EXAMPLE 1 **Simplifying Expressions with a Zero Exponent**

Simplify.

a. $\left(-\dfrac{2}{3}\right)^0$ **b.** $6y^0$ **c.** $(6y)^0$ **d.** -5^0 **e.** 0^0

Solution:

a. $\left(-\dfrac{2}{3}\right)^0 = 1$ By definition any nonzero base raised to the zero power is 1.

b. $6y^0 = 6 \cdot y^0 = 6 \cdot 1 = 6$ The base for the exponent of 0 is y, not $6y$. The product of 6 and y^0 is $6 \cdot 1 = 6$.

c. $(6y)^0 = 1$ The base for the exponent of 0 is $6y$.

d. $-5^0 = -1 \cdot 5^0 = -1 \cdot 1 = -1$ This is interpreted as the opposite of 5^0 or $-1 \cdot 5^0$.

e. 0^0 is undefined   An expression with an exponent of zero is defined only if the base is not zero.

Skill Practice 1 Simplify.

a. $(1.27)^0$ **b.** $4z^0$ **c.** $(4z)^0$ **d.** $-4z^0$ **e.** 1^0

In Example 2, we simplify expressions with negative exponents.

EXAMPLE 2 **Simplifying Expressions with Negative Exponents**

Simplify.

a. 5^{-2} **b.** $\dfrac{1}{p^{-4}}$ **c.** $5x^{-8}y^2$

Solution:

a. $5^{-2} = \dfrac{1}{5^2}$ or $\dfrac{1}{25}$ Rewrite the expression using the reciprocal of 5 and change the exponent to positive 2.

b. $\dfrac{1}{p^{-4}} = \dfrac{1}{\dfrac{1}{p^4}} = 1 \cdot \dfrac{p^4}{1} = p^4$ Rewrite p^{-4} as $\dfrac{1}{p^4}$. Then divide fractions.

c. $5x^{-8}y^2 = 5 \cdot x^{-8} \cdot y^2$ The exponent of -8 applies to x only, not to the factors of 5 or y.

$= 5 \cdot \dfrac{1}{x^8} \cdot y^2 = \dfrac{5y^2}{x^8}$

Skill Practice 2 Simplify.

a. 2^{-3} **b.** $\dfrac{1}{n^{-5}}$ **c.** $-3a^4b^{-9}$

Answers

1. a. 1   **b.** 4   **c.** 1
   d. -4 **e.** 1

2. a. $\dfrac{1}{2^3}$ or $\dfrac{1}{8}$ **b.** n^5 **c.** $\dfrac{-3a^4}{b^9}$

From Examples 2(a) and 2(b), notice that $5^{-2} = \dfrac{1}{5^2}$ and $\dfrac{1}{p^{-4}} = p^4$. From this observation and from the definition of a nonzero base raised to a negative power, we have

$$b^{-n} = \frac{1}{b^n} \quad \text{and} \quad \frac{1}{b^{-n}} = b^n \quad \text{for } b \neq 0$$

2. Apply Properties of Exponents

The properties of exponents in Table R-4 are often used to simplify algebraic expressions.

Table R-4 Properties of Exponents

Let a and b be real numbers and m and n be integers.*

Name	Property	Example	Expanded Form
Product rule for exponents	$b^m \cdot b^n = b^{m+n}$	$x^4 \cdot x^3 = x^{4+3} = x^7$	$x^4 \cdot x^3 = (x \cdot x \cdot x \cdot x)(x \cdot x \cdot x) = x^7$
Quotient rule for exponents	$\dfrac{b^m}{b^n} = b^{m-n}$	$\dfrac{t^6}{t^2} = t^{6-2} = t^4$	$\dfrac{t^6}{t^2} = \dfrac{t \cdot t \cdot t \cdot t \cdot t \cdot t}{t \cdot t} = t^4$
Power rule for exponents	$(b^m)^n = b^{m \cdot n}$	$(x^2)^3 = x^{2 \cdot 3} = x^6$	$(x^2)^3 = (x^2)(x^2)(x^2) = x^6$
Power of a product	$(ab)^m = a^m b^m$	$(4x)^3 = 4^3 x^3$	$(4x)^3 = (4x)(4x)(4x)$ $= (4 \cdot 4 \cdot 4)(x \cdot x \cdot x)$ $= 4^3 x^3$
Power of a quotient	$\left(\dfrac{a}{b}\right)^m = \dfrac{a^m}{b^m}$	$\left(\dfrac{2}{y}\right)^2 = \dfrac{2^2}{y^2}$	$\left(\dfrac{2}{y}\right)^2 = \left(\dfrac{2}{y}\right) \cdot \left(\dfrac{2}{y}\right) = \dfrac{2^2}{y^2}$

*The properties are stated under the assumption that the variables are restricted to avoid the expressions 0^0 and $\frac{1}{0}$.

Examples 3 and 4 give practice simplifying expressions using the product and quotient rules for exponents.

EXAMPLE 3   Simplifying Expressions Using the Product Rule

Simplify. Write the answers with positive exponents only.

    a. $5^3 \cdot 5^{10}$ **b.** $(-6a^7b^2)(2a^{-4}b)$

Solution:

a. $5^3 \cdot 5^{10} = 5^{3+10} = 5^{13}$ To multiply expressions with the same base, keep the base the same and add the exponents.

> **TIP** In Example 3(a), the answer can be written as either 5^{13} or as 1,220,703,125. We did not expand 5^{13} because the calculation is tedious without the use of a calculator.

b. $(-6a^7b^2)(2a^{-4}b)$

    $= -6 \cdot 2 \cdot a^7 \cdot a^{-4} \cdot b^2 \cdot b$ Use the associative and commutative properties of multiplication to regroup factors.

    $= -12 \cdot a^{7+(-4)} \cdot b^{2+1}$ Add the exponents on the common bases.

    $= -12a^3b^3$ Simplify.

Skill Practice 3   Simplify. Write the answers with positive exponents only.

    a. $8^2 \cdot 8^8$ **b.** $(-7m^{15}n)(-3m^{-4}n^3)$

Answers

3. a. 8^{10} **b.** $21m^{11}n^4$

EXAMPLE 4   **Simplifying Expressions Using the Quotient Rule**

Simplify. Write the answers with positive exponents only.

a. $\dfrac{x^4 \cdot x^6}{x^2}$ **b.** $\dfrac{16m^{18}n^5}{24m^6n^7}$

Solution:

a. $\dfrac{x^4 \cdot x^6}{x^2} = \dfrac{x^{4+6}}{x^2} = \dfrac{x^{10}}{x^2}$ Simplify the expression in the numerator by adding the exponents on the common base.

$= x^{10-2}$ To divide expressions with the same base, keep the base the same and subtract the exponents.

$= x^8$

b. $\dfrac{16m^{18}n^5}{24m^6n^7} = \dfrac{16}{24} \cdot \dfrac{m^{18}}{m^6} \cdot \dfrac{n^5}{n^7}$ Group the coefficients and like factors.

$= \dfrac{2}{3} \cdot m^{18-6} \cdot n^{5-7}$ Simplify the ratio of coefficients. For the division of like bases, subtract exponents.

$= \dfrac{2}{3} \cdot m^{12} \cdot n^{-2}$

$= \dfrac{2}{3} \cdot m^{12} \cdot \dfrac{1}{n^2}$ Simplify the factor with the negative exponent.

$= \dfrac{2m^{12}}{3n^2}$ Multiply.

Skill Practice 4   Simplify. Write the answers with positive exponents only.

a. $\dfrac{t^9 \cdot t^7}{t^5}$ **b.** $\dfrac{15c^{13}d^4}{20c^{19}d}$

Example 5 demonstrates the use of the power rules to simplify expressions that contain a product or quotient raised to a power.

EXAMPLE 5   **Simplifying Expressions Using the Power Rules**

Simplify. Write the answers with positive exponents only.

a. $(2^3)^4$ **b.** $(w^{-3})^6$ **c.** $(-5ab)^3$ **d.** $\left(\dfrac{4y}{x}\right)^5$

Solution:

a. $(2^3)^4 = 2^{3 \cdot 4} = 2^{12}$ For a base raised to a power raised to a subsequent power, multiply the exponents.

b. $(w^{-3})^6 = w^{-3 \cdot 6}$ Multiply the exponents.

$= w^{-18}$

$= \dfrac{1}{w^{18}}$ Simplify the factor with the negative exponent.

c. $(-5ab)^3 = (-5)^3(a)^3(b)^3$ To simplify a product raised to a power, raise each factor in parentheses to the power.

$= -125a^3b^3$ Simplify.

Answers

4. a. t^{11} **b.** $\dfrac{3d^3}{4c^6}$

d. $\left(\dfrac{4y}{x}\right)^5 = \dfrac{(4y)^5}{(x)^5}$

To simplify a quotient raised to a power, raise the numerator and denominator to the power.

$= \dfrac{(4)^5(y)^5}{x^5}$

Raise each factor in the numerator to the fifth power.

$= \dfrac{4^5y^5}{x^5}$ or $\dfrac{1024y^5}{x^5}$

Simplify.

Skill Practice 5   Simplify. Write the answers with positive exponents only.

a. $(5^6)^2$ **b.** $(z^4)^{-6}$ **c.** $(-2pq)^6$ **d.** $\left(\dfrac{y}{5z}\right)^8$

In Example 6, we apply all of the properties of exponents learned thus far.

EXAMPLE 6   **Simplifying Expressions Containing Exponents**

Simplify. Write the answers with positive exponents only.

a. $13^0 + \left(\dfrac{1}{3}\right)^{-2} + \left(\dfrac{1}{9}\right)^{-1}$ **b.** $\left(\dfrac{14a^2b^7}{2a^5b}\right)^{-2}$ **c.** $(-3x)^{-4}(4x^{-2}y^3)^3$

Solution:

a. $13^0 + \left(\dfrac{1}{3}\right)^{-2} + \left(\dfrac{1}{9}\right)^{-1}$

$= 1 + 3^2 + 9^1$

By definition, $13^0 = 1$. Also simplify expressions with negative exponents.

$= 1 + 9 + 9$

$= 19$

Add.

b. $\left(\dfrac{14a^2b^7}{2a^5b}\right)^{-2} = (7a^{2-5}b^{7-1})^{-2}$

Simplify within parentheses first.
To divide common bases, subtract the exponents.

$= (7a^{-3}b^6)^{-2}$

$= (7)^{-2}(a^{-3})^{-2}(b^6)^{-2}$

Apply the power rule. Raise each factor within parentheses to the -2 power.

$= 7^{-2}a^6b^{-12}$

$= \dfrac{1}{7^2} \cdot a^6 \cdot \dfrac{1}{b^{12}}$

Simplify factors with negative exponents.

$= \dfrac{a^6}{49b^{12}}$

Simplify.

c. $(-3x)^{-4}(4x^{-2}y^3)^3$

$= (-3)^{-4}x^{-4} \cdot 4^3(x^{-2})^3(y^3)^3$

Apply the power rule. Raise each factor inside parentheses to the power outside parentheses.

$= (-3)^{-4} \cdot 4^3 \cdot x^{-4} \cdot x^{-6} \cdot y^9$

Regroup factors, and apply the power rule again.

$= (-3)^{-4} \cdot 4^3 \cdot x^{-10} \cdot y^9$

To multiply the factors of x, add the exponents.

$= \dfrac{4^3y^9}{(-3)^4x^{10}}$

Simplify factors with negative exponents.

$= \dfrac{64y^9}{81x^{10}}$

Simplify.

Answers

5. a. 5^{12} **b.** $\dfrac{1}{z^{24}}$

c. $64p^6q^6$ **d.** $\dfrac{y^8}{5^8z^8}$

> **Skill Practice 6** Simplify. Write the answers with positive exponents only.
>
> **a.** $\left(\dfrac{2}{3}\right)^{-2} - 4^{-1} + 9^0$ **b.** $(3w)^{-3}(5wt^5)^2$ **c.** $\left(\dfrac{26c^5d^{-2}}{13cd^8}\right)^{-3}$

3. Apply Scientific Notation

In many applications of science, technology, and business we encounter very large or very small numbers. For example:

- eBay Inc. purchased the Internet communications company, Skype Technologies, for approximately $2,600,000,000. (*Source*: www.ebay.com)
- The diameter of a capillary is measured as 0.000 005 m.
- The mean surface temperature of the planet Saturn is −300°F.

Very large and very small numbers are sometimes cumbersome to write because they contain numerous zeros. Furthermore, it is difficult to determine the location of the decimal point when performing calculations with such numbers. For these reasons, scientists will often write numbers using scientific notation.

Scientific Notation

A number expressed in the form $a \times 10^n$, where $1 \le |a| < 10$ and n is an integer, is said to be in **scientific notation.**

Verbal Interpretation	Numerical Example		
A number written in scientific notation is the product of two numbers: a number whose absolute value is greater than or equal to 1 and less than 10, and an appropriate power of 10.	Skype Purchase $2,600,000,000 = $2.6 \times 1,000,000,000 = 2.6×10^9	Capillary Size 0.000 005 m $= 5.0 \times 0.000001$ m $= 5.0 \times 10^{-6}$ m	Saturn Temp. −300°F $= -3 \times 100°$F $= -3 \times 10^2$ °F

For a number written in scientific notation, the power of 10 is sometimes called the **order of magnitude.** If two numbers differ by one order of magnitude, one number is on the order of 10 times larger than the other. If they differ by two orders of magnitude, then one number is 100 times larger than the other. For example, suppose that a television celebrity earns a yearly income of $40 million ($4.0 \times 10^7$), whereas the income for a general surgeon is $400 thousand ($4.0 \times 10^5$). This is an order of magnitude difference of 2. This means that the celebrity earns 100 times more money than the general surgeon.

To write a number in scientific notation, the number of positions that the decimal point must be moved determines the power of 10. Numbers 10 or greater require a positive exponent on 10. Numbers between 0 and 1 require a negative exponent on 10.

> **EXAMPLE 7**   **Writing Numbers in Scientific Notation**
>
> Write the numerical values in scientific notation.
>
> **a.** The size of the smallest visible object in an optical microscope is 0.0000002 m.
>
> **b.** One estimate for the number of stars in the Milky Way is 230 billion.
>
> **c.** The recommended daily intake of calcium is 1.2 g.

Answers

6. a. 3   **b.** $\dfrac{25t^{10}}{27w}$ **c.** $\dfrac{d^{30}}{8c^{12}}$

Solution:

a. $0.0000002 \text{ m} = 2 \times 10^{-7} \text{ m}$

7 place positions

The number 0.0000002 is between 0 and 1. Use a negative power of 10.

b. 230 billion = 230,000,000,000

First write 230 billion in standard form.

230,000,000,000 stars = 2.3×10^{11} stars

The number 230 billion is greater than 10. Use a positive power of 10.

11 place positions

c. $1.2 \text{ g} = 1.2 \times 10^{0} \text{ g}$

The decimal point is moved zero units, so the exponent on 10 is 0.

Skill Practice 7   Write the numerical values in scientific notation.

a. Salmonella bacteria are elongated bacteria and average 0.0000035 m in length.

b. The distance from Earth to Barnard's Star is 32,000,000,000,000 mi.

c. The average weight of a newborn baby is 7.5 lb.

EXAMPLE 8   Writing Numbers in Standard Decimal Notation

Write the numerical values in standard decimal notation.

a. The temperature at the core of the Sun is estimated to be 1.36×10^{7} °C.

b. The thickness of a dollar bill is approximately 3.9×10^{-3} in.

Solution:

a. 1.36×10^{7} °C = 13,600,000 °C

7 place positions

10^{7} is greater than 10. Move the decimal point 7 places to the right. Insert zeros to the right as needed.

b. 3.9×10^{-3} in. = 0.0039 in.

3 place positions

10^{-3} is between 0 and 1. Move the decimal point 3 places to the left. Insert zeros to the left as needed.

Skill Practice 8   Write the numerical values in standard decimal notation.

a. Alaska is the largest state geographically with a land area of 5.86×10^{5} mi².

b. A doctor orders 2.0×10^{-2} g of the drug atropine given by injection.

Example 9 demonstrates the process to multiply and divide numbers written in scientific notation.

EXAMPLE 9   Performing Calculations with Scientific Notation

a. A light-year is the distance that light travels in 1 yr. If light travels at a speed of 6.7×10^{8} mph, how far will it travel in 1 yr (8.76×10^{3} hr)?

b. California has a land area of 1.56×10^{5} mi². If the population of California for a recent year was 3.9×10^{7}, determine the population density (number of people per square mile).

Answers

7. a. 3.5×10^{-6} m
  b. 3.2×10^{13} mi
  c. 7.5×10^{0} lb
8. a. 586,000 mi²
  b. 0.02 g

Solution:

a. Distance = (Rate)(Time)

$= (6.7 \times 10^8 \text{ mph})(8.76 \times 10^3 \text{ hr})$

$= (6.7)(8.76) \times (10^8)(10^3) \text{ mi}$

Regroup factors. Multiply and add the powers of 10.

$= 58.692 \times 10^{11} \text{ mi}$

The number 58.692 is not between 1 and 10. Rewrite this as 5.8692×10^1.

$= (5.8692 \times 10^1) \times 10^{11} \text{ mi}$

$= 5.8692 \times 10^{12} \text{ mi}$

One light-year is approximately 5.87 trillion miles.

b. $\dfrac{3.9 \times 10^7 \text{ people}}{1.56 \times 10^5 \text{ mi}^2} = \left(\dfrac{3.9}{1.56}\right) \times \left(\dfrac{10^7}{10^5}\right) \text{ people/mi}^2$

Population density is the number of people per square mile.

$= 2.5 \times 10^2 \text{ people/mi}^2$

At that time, California had a population density of 2.5×10^2 people/mi² or 250 people/mi².

Skill Practice 9

a. A satellite travels 1.72×10^4 mph. How far does it travel in 24 hr (2.4×10^1 hr)?

b. The land area of Texas is 2.6×10^5 mi². If the population of Texas for a recent year was 2.5×10^7, determine the population density.

The calculations for Example 9 can also be performed on a calculator.

TECHNOLOGY CONNECTIONS

Using Scientific Notation on a Calculator

On many calculators, the EE key is used to enter the exponent for a number in scientific notation. The result on the screen shows the symbol E to indicate the exponent for the power of 10. For example, the number 5.8692E12 is read as 5.8692×10^{12}.

```
(6.7E8)*(8.76E3)
        5.8692E12
(3.9E7)/(1.56E5)
              250
```

Answers

9. a. 4.128×10^5 mi
   b. Approximately 9.6×10^1 people/mi² or 96 people/mi²

SECTION R.3   Practice Exercises

Review Exercises

For Exercises 1–2, simplify the expressions.

1. $-\dfrac{1}{5}(5x + 2y - 15) - \dfrac{1}{10}(2y + 20)$

2. $\dfrac{1}{3}(3a + 2b - 6) - \dfrac{5}{6}(12a - 2b)$

For Exercises 3–4, simplify by writing the expression without absolute value bars.

3. $|a - 6|$ for $a < 6$

4. $|2 - t|$ for $t > 2$

5. At the end of a day's trading, the stock price for Target closed $1.93 higher than the stock price for Walmart. (*Source*: www.nytimes.com) Write a model that represents the Target stock price t in terms of the Walmart stock price w.

6. For a recent year, Jay Leno earned $3 million less than Ellen DeGeneres. Write a model that represents Jay Leno's earnings L in terms of Ellen DeGeneres's earnings D (in $ millions).

Concept Connections

7. For a nonzero real number b, the value of $b^0 =$ _____.

8. For a nonzero real number b, the value $b^{\boxed{}} = \dfrac{1}{b^n}$.

9. A number expressed in the form $a \times 10^n$, where $1 \le |a| < 10$ and n is an integer is said to be written in _____ notation.

10. For a number written in scientific notation the power of 10 is sometimes called the order of _____.

11. The product rule for exponents indicates that $b^m b^n = b^{\boxed{}}$.

12. The _____ rule for exponents indicates that $\dfrac{b^m}{b^n} = b^{m-n}$ for $b \ne 0$.

Objective 1: Simplify Expressions with Zero and Negative Exponents

For Exercises 13–20, simplify each expression. (See Examples 1–2)

13. a. 8^0 **b.** -8^0 **c.** $8x^0$ **d.** $(8x)^0$

14. a. 7^0 **b.** -7^0 **c.** $7y^0$ **d.** $(7y)^0$

15. a. $\left(-\dfrac{2}{3}\right)^0$ **b.** $-\dfrac{2^0}{3}$ **c.** $-\dfrac{2}{3}p^0$ **d.** $\left(-\dfrac{2}{3}p\right)^0$

16. a. $\left(-\dfrac{3}{7}\right)^0$ **b.** $-\dfrac{3^0}{7}$ **c.** $-\dfrac{3}{7}w^0$ **d.** $\left(-\dfrac{3}{7}w\right)^0$

17. a. 8^{-2} **b.** $8x^{-2}$ **c.** $(8x)^{-2}$ **d.** -8^{-2}

18. a. 7^{-2} **b.** $7y^{-2}$ **c.** $(7y)^{-2}$ **d.** -7^{-2}

19. a. $\dfrac{1}{q^{-2}}$ **b.** q^{-2} **c.** $5p^3 q^{-2}$ **d.** $5p^{-3}q^2$

20. a. $\dfrac{1}{t^{-4}}$ **b.** t^{-4} **c.** $11t^{-4}u^2$ **d.** $11t^4 u^{-2}$

Objective 2: Apply Properties of Exponents

For Exercises 21–70, use the properties of exponents to simplify each expression. (See Examples 3–6)

21. $2^5 \cdot 2^7$

22. $4^3 \cdot 4^8$

23. $x^7 \cdot x^6 \cdot x^{-2}$

24. $y^{-3} \cdot y^7 \cdot y^4$

25. $(-3c^2 d^7)(4c^{-5}d)$

26. $(-7m^{-3}n^{-8})(3m^{-5}n)$

27. $\dfrac{y^{-3}y^6}{y^2}$

28. $\dfrac{z^{-8}z^{12}}{z^3}$

29. $\dfrac{6^5}{6^8}$

30. $\dfrac{7^2}{7^4}$

31. $\dfrac{18k^2 p^9}{27k^5 p^2}$

32. $\dfrac{10a^3 b^{11}}{25a^7 b^3}$

33. $\dfrac{2m^{-6}n^4}{6m^{-2}n^{-1}}$

34. $\dfrac{4p^{-7}q^5}{2p^{-2}q^{-2}}$

35. $(4^2)^3$

36. $(2^3)^5$

37. $(p^{-2})^7$

38. $(q^{-4})^2$

39. $(-2cd)^3$

40. $(-8mn)^2$

41. $\left(\dfrac{7a}{b}\right)^2$

42. $\left(\dfrac{pq}{4}\right)^4$

43. $(4x^2 y^{-3})^2$

44. $(-3w^{-3}z^5)^2$

45. $\left(\dfrac{7k}{n^2}\right)^{-2}$

46. $\left(\dfrac{5w^5}{v}\right)^{-3}$

47. $\left(\dfrac{1}{8}\right)^{-2} - \left(\dfrac{1}{4}\right)^{-3} - \left(\dfrac{1}{2}\right)^0$

48. $\left(\dfrac{1}{9}\right)^{-2} - \left(\dfrac{1}{3}\right)^{-4} + \left(\dfrac{1}{27}\right)^0$

49. $\left(\dfrac{-16m^2 n^7}{8m^5 n^{-2}}\right)^{-2}$

50. $\left(\dfrac{-36a^6 b^9}{9a^2 b^{-4}}\right)^{-2}$

51. $\left(\dfrac{4x^3z^{-5}}{12y^{-2}}\right)^{-3}$

52. $\left(\dfrac{3z^2w^{-1}}{15p^{-4}}\right)^{-3}$

53. $(-2y)^{-3}(6y^{-2}z^8)^2$

54. $(-15z)^{-2}(5z^4w^{-6})^3$

55. $\left(\dfrac{1}{2} - \dfrac{1}{3} + \dfrac{1}{6}\right)^{-3}$

56. $\left(-\dfrac{1}{3} - \dfrac{1}{4} + \dfrac{1}{2}\right)^{-2}$

57. $\left(\dfrac{1}{2}\right)^{-3} - \left(\dfrac{1}{3}\right)^{-3} + \left(\dfrac{1}{6}\right)^{-3}$

58. $\left(-\dfrac{1}{3}\right)^{-2} - \left(\dfrac{1}{4}\right)^{-2} + \left(\dfrac{1}{2}\right)^{-2}$

59. $\left(\dfrac{1}{4x^3y^{-5}}\right)^{-2}\left(\dfrac{8}{x^{-13}y^{14}}\right)^{-1}$

60. $\left(\dfrac{1}{3a^2b^{-4}}\right)^{-3}\left(\dfrac{3}{a^{-5}b^4}\right)^{-1}$

61. $\left(\dfrac{(x^{-3})^{-4}x^{-2}}{x^{-6}}\right)^{-1}$

62. $\left(\dfrac{(y^2)^{-6}y^{-3}}{y^{-4}}\right)^{-1}$

63. $\dfrac{(4vw^{-3}x^2)^2}{(2v^2w^3x^{-2})^4} \cdot (-v^3w^2x^{-4})^{-5}$

64. $\dfrac{(14v^2w^{-3}x^2)^3}{(21v^{-5}w^3x^{-2})^{-1}} \cdot (-7v^4w^{-1}x^{-4})^{-4}$

65. $(3x + 5)^{14}(3x + 5)^{-2}$

66. $(2y - 7z)^{-4}(2y - 7z)^{13}$

67. $\left[(6v - 7)^{10}\right]^9$

68. $\left[(4x - 9)^5\right]^{11}$

69. $2^{-2} + 2^{-1} + 2^0 + 2^1 + 2^2$

70. $3^{-2} + 3^{-1} + 3^0 + 3^1 + 3^2$

Objective 3: Apply Scientific Notation

For Exercises 71–74, write the numbers in scientific notation. (See Example 7)

71. a. 350,000

b. 0.000035

c. 3.5

72. a. 2710

b. 0.00271

c. 2.71

73. a. 0.86

b. 8.6

c. 86

74. a. 0.792

b. 7.92

c. 79.2

For Exercises 75–80, write the numbers in scientific notation. (See Example 7)

75. The speed of light is approximately 29,980,000,000 cm/sec.

76. The mean distance between the Earth and the Sun is approximately 149,000,000 km.

77. The size of an HIV particle is approximately 0.00001 cm.

78. One picosecond is 0.000 000 000 001 sec.

79. For a test group of adult females between 18 and 20 yr old, the mean blood volume was 4.2 L.

80. The longest table tennis rally ever played lasted 8.25 hr.

For Exercises 81–84, write the number in standard decimal notation. (See Example 8)

81. a. 2.61×10^{-6}

b. 2.61×10^6

c. 2.61×10^0

82. a. 3.52×10^{-2}

b. 3.52×10^2

c. 3.52×10^0

83. a. 6.718×10^{-1}

b. 6.718×10^0

c. 6.718×10^1

84. a. 1.87×10^{-1}

b. 1.87×10^0

c. 1.87×10^1

For Exercises 85–88, write the numbers in standard decimal notation. (See Example 8)

85. A drop of water has approximately 1.67×10^{21} molecules of H_2O.

86. A computer with a 3-terabyte hard drive can store approximately 3.0×10^{12} bytes.

87. A typical red blood cell is 7.0×10^{-6} m.

88. The blue light used to read a laser disc has a wavelength of 4.7×10^{-7} m.

For Exercises 89–98, perform the indicated operation. Write the answer in scientific notation. (See Example 9)

89. $(2 \times 10^{-3})(4 \times 10^8)$

90. $(3 \times 10^4)(2 \times 10^{-1})$

91. $\dfrac{8.4 \times 10^{-6}}{2.1 \times 10^{-2}}$

92. $\dfrac{6.8 \times 10^{11}}{3.4 \times 10^3}$

93. $(6.2 \times 10^{11})(3 \times 10^4)$

94. $(8.1 \times 10^6)(2 \times 10^5)$

95. $\dfrac{3.6 \times 10^{-14}}{5 \times 10^5}$

96. $\dfrac{3.68 \times 10^{-8}}{4 \times 10^2}$

97. $\dfrac{(6.2 \times 10^5)(4.4 \times 10^{22})}{2.2 \times 10^{17}}$

98. $\dfrac{(3.8 \times 10^4)(4.8 \times 10^{-2})}{2.5 \times 10^{-5}}$

99. For a recent year, the United States consumed about 1.0×10^4 gal of petroleum per second. (*Source:* U.S. Energy Information Administration, www.eia.gov)

    a. How many seconds are in a year?

    b. How many gallons of petroleum did the United States use that year?

100. Geoff's average heart rate is 65 beats/min.

    a. How many minutes are in one day?

    b. How many times will Geoff's heart beat per day?

101. Jonas has a personal music player with 80 gigabytes of memory (80 gigabytes is approximately 8×10^{10} bytes). If each song requires an average of 4 megabytes of memory (approximately 4×10^6 bytes), how many songs can Jonas store on the device?

102. Joelle has a personal web page with 60 gigabytes of memory (approximately 6×10^{10} bytes). She stores math videos on the site for her students to watch outside of class. If each video requires an average of 5 megabytes of memory (approximately 5×10^6 bytes), how many videos can she store on her website?

103. A typical adult human has 5 L of blood in the body. If 1 μL (1 microliter) contains 5×10^6 red blood cells, how many red blood cells does a typical adult have? (*Hint:* $1 \text{ L} = 10^6 \ \mu$L.)

104. The star Proxima Centauri is the closest star (other than the Sun) to the Earth. It is approximately 4.3 light-years away. If 1 light-year is approximately 5.9×10^{12} mi, how many miles is Proxima Centauri from the Earth?

Write About It

105. Explain the difference between the expressions $6x^0$ versus $(6x)^0$.

106. Explain why scientific notation is used.

Expanding Your Skills

107. If $x < 0$ and $m \in \mathbb{Z}$, can x^m be positive? If so, give an example.

108. If $x < 0$ and $m \in \mathbb{Z}$, can x^m be negative? If so, give an example.

109. If x is a real number, can x^{-2} be negative? If so, give an example.

110. If $x > 10$ and $m \in \mathbb{Z}$, can x^m be less than 1? If so, given an example.

For Exercises 111–112, refer to the formula $F = \dfrac{Gm_1 m_2}{d^2}$. This gives the gravitational force F (in Newtons, N) between two masses m_1 and m_2 (each measured in kg) that are a distance of d meters apart. In the formula, $G = 6.6726 \times 10^{-11}\,\text{N-m}^2/\text{kg}^2$.

111. Determine the gravitational force between the Earth (mass = 5.98×10^{24} kg) and Jupiter (mass = 1.901×10^{27} kg) if at one point in their orbits, the distance between them is 7.0×10^{11} m.

112. Determine the gravitational force between the Earth (mass = 5.98×10^{24} kg) and an 80-kg human standing at sea level. The mean radius of the Earth is approximately 6.371×10^6 m.

For Exercises 113–116, without the assistance of a calculator, fill in the blank with the appropriate symbol $<$, $>$, or $=$.

113. a. 5^{15} ____ 5^{17} **b.** 5^{-15} ____ 5^{-17}

114. a. $\left(\dfrac{1}{5}\right)^{15}$ ____ $\left(\dfrac{1}{5}\right)^{17}$ **b.** $\left(\dfrac{1}{5}\right)^{-15}$ ____ $\left(\dfrac{1}{5}\right)^{-17}$

115. a. $(-1)^{86}$ ____ $(-1)^{87}$ **b.** $(1)^{86}$ ____ $(1)^{87}$

116. a. $(-1)^0$ ____ -1^{41} **b.** $(-1)^{42}$ ____ $(-1)^0$

For Exercises 117–128, simplify each expression. Assume that m and n are integers and that x and y are nonzero real numbers.

117. $x^m x^4$

118. $y^n y^7$

119. $x^{m+9} x^{m-2}$

120. $y^{n+9} y^{n-1}$

121. $\dfrac{x^m}{x^8}$

122. $\dfrac{y^n}{y^3}$

123. $\dfrac{x^{2m+7}}{x^{m+5}}$

124. $\dfrac{y^{3n+5}}{y^{2n-4}}$

125. $(x^{4m})^{3n}$

126. $(y^{5m})^{2n}$

127. $\dfrac{x^{4m-3} y^{5n+7}}{x^{m-7} y^{3n+2}}$

128. $\dfrac{x^{2n-4} y^{5n}}{x^{n+1} y^{3n-7}}$

Technology Connections

For Exercises 129–132, write the standard decimal notation for the number given in the calculator display or spreadsheet.

129. $\boxed{6.284\text{E}6}$

130. $\boxed{9.128\text{E}-4}$

131.

	A	B
1	2.45E-07	
2		

132.

	A	B
1	1.78E+10	
2		

SECTION R.4 — Rational Exponents and Radicals

OBJECTIVES

1. Evaluate *n*th-Roots
2. Simplify Expressions of the Forms $a^{1/n}$ and $a^{m/n}$
3. Simplify Expressions with Rational Exponents
4. Simplify Radicals

As scientists search for life beyond our solar system, they look for planets on which liquid water can exist. This means that for a planet with atmospheric pressure similar to Earth, the temperature of the planet must be greater than 0°C (the temperature at which water turns to ice) but less than 100°C (the temperature at which water turns to steam).

The following model approximates the surface temperature T_p (in °C) of an Earth-like planet based on its distance d (in km) from its primary star, the radius r (in km) of the star, and the temperature T_s (in °C) of the star.

$$T_p = 0.7(T_s + 273)\left(\frac{r}{d}\right)^{1/2} - 273$$

The expression on the right contains an exponent that is a rational number. In this section, we learn how to evaluate and simplify such expressions.

1. Evaluate *n*th-Roots

In Section R.3 we defined b^n, where b is a real number and n is an integer. In this section, we want to extend this definition to expressions in which the exponent, n, is a rational number.

First we need to understand the relationship between *n*th-powers and *n*th-roots. For an integer $n > 1$,

- b is an **nth-root** of a if $b^n = a$.
- b is a **square root** (second root) of a if $b^2 = a$.
- b is a **cube root** (third root) of a if $b^3 = a$.

Every positive number has two square roots. For example:

5 is a square root of 25 because $(5)^2 = 25$.

-5 is a square root of 25 because $(-5)^2 = 25$.

The nonnegative square root is called the principal square root. So the principal square root of 25, denoted by $\sqrt{25}$ is 5 (not -5). The **principal *n*th-root** of a real number a is denoted by $\sqrt[n]{a}$.

Principal *n*th-Root

Let $n > 1$ be an integer and a be a real number. Then,

index $\longrightarrow \sqrt[n]{a}$ is called the **principal *n*th-root** of a.
$\uparrow$
radicand

The expression a is called the **radicand,** and n is called the **index.**
For a square root, the index is understood to be 2. That is, $\sqrt{a} = \sqrt[2]{a}$.

If n is *even*, and

- $a \geq 0$, then $\sqrt[n]{a}$ is the nonnegative real
  number b such that $b^n = a$.
- $a < 0$, then $\sqrt[n]{a}$ is not a real number.
  ($\sqrt[n]{a}$ is an imaginary number—Section 1.3.)

If n is *odd*, then

- $\sqrt[n]{a}$ is the real number b such that $b^n = a$.

Examples:

- $\sqrt{25} = 5$

- $\sqrt[4]{-16}$ is not a real number

- $\sqrt[3]{8} = 2$
- $\sqrt[3]{-8} = -2$

EXAMPLE 1   Simplifying *n*th-Roots

Simplify.

a. $\sqrt[5]{32}$ **b.** $\sqrt{\dfrac{49}{64}}$ **c.** $\sqrt[3]{-0.008}$ **d.** $\sqrt[4]{-1}$ **e.** $-\sqrt[4]{1}$

Solution:

a. $\sqrt[5]{32} = 2$ $\sqrt[5]{32} = 2$ because $2^5 = 32$.

b. $\sqrt{\dfrac{49}{64}} = \dfrac{7}{8}$ $\sqrt{\dfrac{49}{64}} = \dfrac{7}{8}$ because $\dfrac{7}{8}$ is nonnegative and $\left(\dfrac{7}{8}\right)^2 = \dfrac{49}{64}$.

c. $\sqrt[3]{-0.008} = -0.2$ $\sqrt[3]{-0.008} = -0.2$ because $(-0.2)^3 = -0.008$.

d. $\sqrt[4]{-1}$ is not a real number $\sqrt[4]{-1}$ is not a real number because no real number
                                                        when raised to the fourth power equals -1.

e. $-\sqrt[4]{1} = -1 \cdot \sqrt[4]{1}$ $-\sqrt[4]{1}$ is interpreted as $-1\sqrt[4]{1}$. The factor of -1 is
$\phantom{-\sqrt[4]{1}} = -1 \cdot 1$ outside the radical.
$\phantom{-\sqrt[4]{1}} = -1$

Skill Practice 1   Simplify.

a. $\sqrt[3]{-125}$ **b.** $\sqrt{\dfrac{144}{121}}$ **c.** $\sqrt[5]{0.00001}$ **d.** $\sqrt[6]{-64}$ **e.** $-\sqrt[6]{64}$

---

2. Simplify Expressions of the Forms $a^{1/n}$ and $a^{m/n}$

Next, we want to define an expression of the form a^n, where n is a rational number. Furthermore, we want a definition for which the properties of integer exponents can be extended to rational exponents. For example, we want

$$(25^{1/2})^2 = 25^{(1/2)\cdot 2} = 25^1 = 25$$
$\uparrow$

$25^{1/2}$ must be a square root of 25, because when squared, it equals 25.

Answers

1. a. -5 **b.** $\dfrac{12}{11}$ **c.** 0.1

d. Not a real number   **e.** -2

Definition of $a^{1/n}$

Let $n > 1$ be an integer. Then $a^{1/n} = \sqrt[n]{a}$ provided that $\sqrt[n]{a}$ is a real number.

Verbal Interpretation	Algebraic Example
$a^{1/n}$ equals the nth-root of a, provided that the nth-root of a is a real number.	• $8^{1/3} = \sqrt[3]{8}$ • $(-25)^{1/2}$ is not defined by this definition because $\sqrt{-25}$ is not a real number.

EXAMPLE 2   **Simplifying Expressions of the Form $a^{1/n}$**

Write the expressions using radical notation and simplify if possible.

a. $(-1000)^{1/3}$ **b.** $\left(\dfrac{64}{121}\right)^{1/2}$ **c.** $(-81)^{1/4}$ **d.** $-81^{1/4}$

Solution:

a. $(-1000)^{1/3} = \sqrt[3]{-1000} = -10$

b. $\left(\dfrac{64}{121}\right)^{1/2} = \sqrt{\dfrac{64}{121}} = \dfrac{8}{11}$

c. $(-81)^{1/4}$ is undefined $(-81)^{1/4}$ is undefined because $\sqrt[4]{-81}$ is not a real number.

d. $-81^{1/4} = -\sqrt[4]{81} = -(3) = -3$ This expression is interpreted as the opposite of $81^{1/4}$ which can be expressed as $-\sqrt[4]{81}$.

Skill Practice 2   Simplify if possible.

a. $(-32)^{1/5}$ **b.** $\left(\dfrac{100}{81}\right)^{1/2}$ **c.** $(-9)^{1/2}$ **d.** $-9^{1/2}$

Next we want to define expressions of the form $a^{m/n}$ so that the properties of integer exponents can be extended to rational exponents.

$$a^{m/n} = (a^{1/n})^m \quad \text{and} \quad a^{m/n} = (a^m)^{1/n}$$

Definition of $a^{m/n}$

Let m and n be positive integers such that m/n is in lowest terms and $n > 1$. Then if $\sqrt[n]{a}$ is a real number,

$$a^{m/n} = (a^{1/n})^m = \left(\sqrt[n]{a}\right)^m \quad \text{and} \quad a^{m/n} = (a^m)^{1/n} = \sqrt[n]{a^m}$$

The definition of $a^{m/n}$ indicates that $a^{m/n}$ can be written as a radical whose index is the denominator of the rational exponent. The order in which the nth-root and exponent m are performed within the radical does not affect the outcome. For example:

Take the 4th root first:
$$16^{3/4} = \left(\sqrt[4]{16}\right)^3$$
$$= (2)^3$$
$$= 8$$

or   Cube 16 first:
$$16^{3/4} = \sqrt[4]{16^3}$$
$$= \sqrt[4]{4096}$$
$$= 8$$

Answers

2. a. -2 **b.** $\dfrac{10}{9}$

c. Undefined   **d.** -3

EXAMPLE 3   Writing Expressions with Rational Exponents as Radicals

Write the expressions using radical notation and simplify if possible.

a. $32^{3/5}$ **b.** $(-27)^{2/3}$ **c.** $(-1)^{5/6}$ **d.** $x^{3/7}$ **e.** $5a^{2/3}$

Solution:

a. $32^{3/5} = \left(\sqrt[5]{32}\right)^3 = (2)^3 = 8$

b. $(-27)^{2/3} = \left(\sqrt[3]{-27}\right)^2 = (-3)^2 = 9$

c. $(-1)^{5/6}$ is undefined because $\sqrt[6]{-1}$ is not a real number.

d. $x^{3/7} = \sqrt[7]{x^3}$ or $\left(\sqrt[7]{x}\right)^3$

e. $5a^{2/3} = 5\sqrt[3]{a^2}$ or $5\left(\sqrt[3]{a}\right)^2$

Skill Practice 3   Simplify if possible.

a. $81^{3/4}$ **b.** $(-125)^{2/3}$ **c.** $(-81)^{3/4}$

d. $y^{5/7}$ **e.** $4t^{3/11}$

TECHNOLOGY CONNECTIONS

Evaluating Rational Exponents

Try using a calculator to evaluate the expressions from Example 3. Most calculators have a cube root function and an *n*th-root function. The values from Examples 3(b) and 3(c) are shown here.

```
(-27)^(2/3)
                 9
(³√(-27))²
                 9
```

```
(-1)^(5/6)
             Error
(6ˣ√(-1))^5
ERR:NONREAL ANS
1⯠Quit
2:Goto
```

EXAMPLE 4   Writing Radicals as Expressions with Rational Exponents

Write the expression using rational exponents. Assume that the variables represent positive real numbers.

a. $\sqrt[4]{x^3}$ **b.** $\sqrt{14z}$ **c.** $14\sqrt{z}$ **d.** $\sqrt[3]{c^3 + d^3}$

Solution:

a. $\sqrt[4]{x^3} = x^{3/4}$ **b.** $\sqrt{14z} = (14z)^{1/2}$

c. $14\sqrt{z} = 14z^{1/2}$ **d.** $\sqrt[3]{c^3 + d^3} = (c^3 + d^3)^{1/3}$

Answers

3. a. 27   **b.** 25   **c.** Undefined

d. $\sqrt[7]{y^5}$ or $\left(\sqrt[7]{y}\right)^5$

e. $4\sqrt[11]{t^3}$ or $4\left(\sqrt[11]{t}\right)^3$

4. a. $y^{5/6}$ **b.** $(8p)^{1/2}$

c. $8p^{1/2}$ **d.** $(a^4 + b^4)^{1/4}$

Skill Practice 4   Write the expression using rational exponents.

a. $\sqrt[6]{y^5}$ **b.** $\sqrt{8p}$ **c.** $8\sqrt{p}$ **d.** $\sqrt[4]{a^4 + b^4}$

3. Simplify Expressions with Rational Exponents

The properties of integer exponents learned in Section R.3 can be extended to expressions with rational exponents.

EXAMPLE 5   **Simplifying Expressions with Rational Exponents**

Simplify. Assume that all variables represent positive real numbers.

a. $\dfrac{x^{4/7}x^{2/7}}{x^{1/7}}$ **b.** $(8x^{-2}y^{3/4})^{2/3}$ **c.** $\left(\dfrac{5c^{3/4}}{d^{1/2}}\right)^2\left(\dfrac{d^{5/3}}{2c^{1/2}}\right)^3$ **d.** $81^{-3/4}$

Solution:

a. $\dfrac{x^{4/7}x^{2/7}}{x^{1/7}} = \dfrac{x^{4/7+2/7}}{x^{1/7}} = \dfrac{x^{6/7}}{x^{1/7}}$ Add the exponents in the numerator.

$\qquad = x^{6/7-1/7} = x^{5/7}$ Subtract exponents.

b. $(8x^{-2}y^{3/4})^{2/3} = (8)^{2/3}(x^{-2})^{2/3}(y^{3/4})^{2/3}$ Apply the power rule for exponents.

$\qquad = (\sqrt[3]{8})^2 x^{-2\cdot(2/3)}y^{(3/4)(2/3)}$ Rewrite $8^{2/3}$ in radical form.
Multiply the exponents.

$\qquad = (2)^2 x^{-4/3}y^{6/12}$

$\qquad = \dfrac{4y^{1/2}}{x^{4/3}}$

c. $\left(\dfrac{5c^{3/4}}{d^{1/2}}\right)^2\left(\dfrac{d^{5/3}}{2c^{1/2}}\right)^3 = \dfrac{5^2 c^{(3/4)\cdot2}}{d^{(1/2)\cdot2}}\cdot\dfrac{d^{(5/3)\cdot3}}{2^3 c^{(1/2)\cdot3}}$ Apply the power rule.

$\qquad = \dfrac{25c^{3/2}}{d}\cdot\dfrac{d^5}{8c^{3/2}}$ Multiply exponents.

$\qquad = \dfrac{25d^4}{8}$ Simplify.

d. $81^{-3/4} = \dfrac{1}{81^{3/4}}$ Rewrite the expression to remove the negative exponent.

$\qquad = \dfrac{1}{(\sqrt[4]{81})^3} = \dfrac{1}{(3)^3} = \dfrac{1}{27}$ Rewrite $81^{3/4}$ using radical notation.

Skill Practice 5   Simplify. Assume that all variables represent positive real numbers.

a. $\dfrac{c^{3/4}c^{7/4}}{c^{1/4}}$ **b.** $(16x^{-12}y^{1/8})^{3/4}$ **c.** $\left(\dfrac{4a^{2/3}}{b^{1/6}}\right)^3\left(\dfrac{b^{1/4}}{3a^{3/4}}\right)^2$ **d.** $(-125)^{-2/3}$

4. Simplify Radicals

In Example 5, we simplified several expressions with rational exponents. Next, we want to simplify radical expressions. First consider expressions of the form $\sqrt[n]{a^n}$. The value of $\sqrt[n]{a^n}$ is not necessarily a. Since $\sqrt[n]{a}$ represents the principal nth-root of a, then $\sqrt[n]{a}$ must be nonnegative for even values of n. For example:

$$\sqrt{(5)^2} = 5 \quad \text{and} \quad \sqrt{(-5)^2} = |-5| = 5$$

The absolute value is needed here to guarantee a nonnegative result.

$$\sqrt[4]{(2)^4} = 2 \quad \text{and} \quad \sqrt[4]{(-2)^4} = |-2| = 2$$

Answers

5. a. $c^{9/4}$ **b.** $\dfrac{8y^{3/32}}{x^9}$

$\quad$ **c.** $\dfrac{64a^{1/2}}{9}$ **d.** $\dfrac{1}{25}$

Simplifying $\sqrt[n]{a^n}$

Let $n > 1$ be an integer and let a be a real number.

- If n is *even* then $\sqrt[n]{a^n} = |a|$.
- If n is *odd* then $\sqrt[n]{a^n} = a$.

EXAMPLE 6 **Simplifying Expressions of the Form $\sqrt[n]{a^m}$**

Simplify each expression.

a. $\sqrt{x^2}$ **b.** $\sqrt[3]{x^3}$ **c.** $\sqrt[4]{(3c+5)^4}$ **d.** $\sqrt[4]{y^8}$

Solution:

a. $\sqrt{x^2} = |x|$ The index is *even*. Absolute value bars are needed to guarantee a nonnegative result.

b. $\sqrt[3]{x^3} = x$ The index is *odd*. No absolute value bars are needed.

c. $\sqrt[4]{(3c+5)^4} = |3c+5|$ The index is *even*. Absolute value bars are needed to guarantee a nonnegative result.

d. $\sqrt[4]{y^8} = |y^2| = y^2$ The index is even. However, absolute value bars are dropped in the final answer because y^2 is nonnegative for all real numbers y.

Skill Practice 6   Simplify each expression.

a. $\sqrt[4]{x^4}$ **b.** $\sqrt[5]{x^5}$ **c.** $\sqrt[6]{(7a+3)^6}$ **d.** $\sqrt[6]{z^{24}}$

In Examples 6(a), 6(c), and 6(d), the indices are even numbers. Therefore, we used absolute value bars around the variable factors to guarantee nonnegative answers. If we had made an assumption that the variables all represent nonnegative real numbers, then the absolute value bars would not be necessary. This assumption will be made for Examples 7–11.

Next, we summarize three important properties that are used to simplify radical expressions. These properties follow from the definition of $a^{1/n}$ and the properties of rational exponents.

Properties of Radicals

For real numbers a and b, the following properties are true provided that the given roots represent real numbers.

Property Name	Algebraic Representation	Example
Product property of radicals	$\sqrt[n]{a} \cdot \sqrt[n]{b} = \sqrt[n]{ab}$	$\sqrt[3]{7} \cdot \sqrt[3]{x} = \sqrt[3]{7x}$
Quotient property of radicals	$\dfrac{\sqrt[n]{a}}{\sqrt[n]{b}} = \sqrt[n]{\dfrac{a}{b}}$	$\dfrac{\sqrt{125}}{\sqrt{5}} = \sqrt{\dfrac{125}{5}} = \sqrt{25} = 5$
Property of nested radicals	$\sqrt[m]{\sqrt[n]{a}} = \sqrt[m \cdot n]{a}$	$\sqrt[4]{\sqrt[3]{x}} = \sqrt[12]{x}$

Answers

6. a. $|x|$ **b.** x
c. $|7a+3|$ **d.** z^4

In Examples 7–9, we will use the properties of radicals to simplify and manipulate radical expressions. A radical is considered simplified if all the following conditions are met.

Simplified Form of a Radical

Suppose that the radicand of a radical is written as a product of prime factors. Then the radical is simplified if all of the following conditions are met.

1. The radicand has no factor other than 1 that is a perfect nth-power. This means that all exponents in the radicand must be less than the index.
2. No fractions may appear in the radicand.
3. No denominator of a fraction may contain a radical.
4. The exponents in the radicand may not all share a common factor with the index.

In Example 7, the product property of radicals is used to simplify expressions that fail condition 1.

EXAMPLE 7   Simplifying Radicals Using the Product Property

Simplify each expression. Assume that all variables represent positive real numbers.

a. $\sqrt[3]{c^5}$ b. $\sqrt{50}$ c. $\sqrt[4]{32x^9y^6}$

Solution:

a. $\sqrt[3]{c^5} = \sqrt[3]{c^3 \cdot c^2}$ Write the radicand as a product of a perfect cube and another factor.

$\phantom{\sqrt[3]{c^5}} = \sqrt[3]{c^3} \cdot \sqrt[3]{c^2}$ Apply the product property of radicals.

$\phantom{\sqrt[3]{c^5}} = c\sqrt[3]{c^2}$ Simplify $\sqrt[3]{c^3}$ as c.

b. $\sqrt{50} = \sqrt{5^2 \cdot 2}$ Factor the radicand. The radical is not simplified because the radicand has a perfect square.

$\phantom{\sqrt{50}} = \sqrt{5^2} \cdot \sqrt{2}$ Apply the product property of radicals.

$\phantom{\sqrt{50}} = 5\sqrt{2}$ Simplify.

c. $\sqrt[4]{32x^9y^6}$

$ = \sqrt[4]{2^5x^9y^6}$ Factor the radicand.

$ = \sqrt[4]{(2^4x^8y^4)(2xy^2)}$ Write the radicand as the product of a perfect 4th power and another factor.

$ = \sqrt[4]{2^4x^8y^4} \cdot \sqrt[4]{2xy^2}$ Apply the product property of radicals.

$ = 2x^2y\,\sqrt[4]{2xy^2}$ Simplify the first radical.

Skill Practice 7   Simplify each expression. Assume that all variables represent positive real numbers.

a. $\sqrt[4]{d^7}$ b. $\sqrt{45}$ c. $\sqrt[3]{54x^{13}y^8}$

Answers

7. a. $d\sqrt[4]{d^3}$ **b.** $3\sqrt{5}$
    c. $3x^4y^2\,\sqrt[3]{2xy^2}$

TECHNOLOGY CONNECTIONS

Approximating a Radical on a Calculator

We can check the result of Example 7(b) on a calculator. The original radical and simplified radical have the same decimal approximation on the calculator. This in itself does not guarantee that the expressions are equal (remember, the calculator returns decimal approximations only). It is the product property of radicals that guarantees that the expressions $\sqrt{50}$ and $5\sqrt{2}$ are equal.

```
√(50)
          7.071067812
5*√(2)
          7.071067812
```

In Example 7, the product property of radicals was used to simplify radical expressions. In Example 8, we will use the quotient property of radicals to simplify expressions that fail conditions 2 and 3 for a simplified radical. Removing a radical from the denominator of a fraction is called **rationalizing the denominator.**

EXAMPLE 8   **Applying the Quotient Property of Radicals**

Simplify the expressions. Assume that x and y are nonzero real numbers.

$$\textbf{a. } \sqrt{\dfrac{x^3}{9}} \qquad \textbf{b. } \dfrac{\sqrt[3]{3x^7y}}{\sqrt[3]{81xy^4}}$$

Solution:

a. $\sqrt{\dfrac{x^3}{9}} = \dfrac{\sqrt{x^3}}{\sqrt{9}}$ Apply the quotient property of radicals.

$\phantom{\sqrt{\dfrac{x^3}{9}}} = \dfrac{\sqrt{x^2 \cdot x}}{3}$ Write the radicand as a product of a perfect square and another factor.

$\phantom{\sqrt{\dfrac{x^3}{9}}} = \dfrac{\sqrt{x^2} \cdot \sqrt{x}}{3}$ Apply the product property of radicals.

$\phantom{\sqrt{\dfrac{x^3}{9}}} = \dfrac{x\sqrt{x}}{3}$ Simplify.

b. $\dfrac{\sqrt[3]{3x^7y}}{\sqrt[3]{81xy^4}} = \sqrt[3]{\dfrac{3x^7y}{81xy^4}}$ Apply the quotient property of radicals to write the expression as a single radical.

$\phantom{\dfrac{\sqrt[3]{3x^7y}}{\sqrt[3]{81xy^4}}} = \sqrt[3]{\dfrac{x^6}{27y^3}}$ The numerator and denominator share common factors. Simplify the fraction.

$\phantom{\dfrac{\sqrt[3]{3x^7y}}{\sqrt[3]{81xy^4}}} = \dfrac{x^2}{3y}$ Simplify.

> **TIP** In Example 8(b), the purpose of writing the quotient of two radicals as a single radical is to simplify the resulting fraction in the radicand.

Skill Practice 8   Simplify the expressions. Assume that x and y are nonzero real numbers.

$$\textbf{a. } \sqrt{\dfrac{y^5}{49}} \qquad \textbf{b. } \dfrac{\sqrt[3]{625c^2d^{10}}}{\sqrt[3]{5c^5d}}$$

Answers

8. a. $\dfrac{y^2\sqrt{y}}{7}$ **b.** $\dfrac{5d^3}{c}$

In Example 9, we use the product property of radicals to multiply two radical expressions.

EXAMPLE 9 **Multiplying Radicals**

Multiply. Assume that x represents a positive real number.

a. $\sqrt{6} \cdot \sqrt{10}$ **b.** $\left(2\sqrt[4]{x^3}\right)\left(5\sqrt[4]{x^7}\right)$

Solution:

a. $\sqrt{6} \cdot \sqrt{10} = \sqrt{60}$ | The radicals have the same index. Apply the product property of radicals.

$= \sqrt{2^2 \cdot 3 \cdot 5}$ | Factor the radicand.

$= \sqrt{(2^2) \cdot (3 \cdot 5)}$ | Write the radicand as the product of a perfect square and another factor.

$= \sqrt{2^2} \cdot \sqrt{3 \cdot 5}$ | Apply the product property of radicals.

$= 2\sqrt{15}$ | Simplify.

b. $\left(2\sqrt[4]{x^3}\right)\left(5\sqrt[4]{x^7}\right) = 2 \cdot 5 \sqrt[4]{x^3 \cdot x^7}$ | Regroup factors, and apply the product property of radicals.

$= 10\sqrt[4]{x^{10}}$ | Simplify the radicand.

$= 10\sqrt[4]{x^8 \cdot x^2}$ | Write the radicand as the product of a perfect 4th power and another factor.

$= 10\sqrt[4]{x^8} \cdot \sqrt[4]{x^2}$ | Apply the product property of radicals.

$\left.\begin{array}{l} = 10x^2\sqrt[4]{x^2} \\ = 10x^2\sqrt[2]{x^1} \\ = 10x^2\sqrt{x} \end{array}\right\}$ | The expression $\sqrt[4]{x^2}$ fails condition 4 for a simplified radical. (The exponents in the radicand cannot all share a common factor with the index.)
So, $\sqrt[4]{x^2} = x^{2/4} = x^{1/2} = \sqrt{x}$.

Skill Practice 9 Multiply. Assume that y represents a positive real number.

a. $\sqrt{15} \cdot \sqrt{21}$ **b.** $\left(3\sqrt[6]{y^5}\right)\left(4\sqrt[6]{y^{11}}\right)$

We can use the distributive property to add or subtract radical expressions. However, the radicals must be like radicals. This means that the radicands must be the same and the indices must be the same. For example:

$3\sqrt{2x}$ and $-5\sqrt{2x}$ are like radicals.

$3\sqrt{2x}$ and $-5\sqrt[3]{2x}$ are not like radicals because the indices are different.

$3\sqrt{2x}$ and $-5\sqrt{2y}$ are not like radicals because the radicands are different.

EXAMPLE 10 **Adding and Subtracting Radicals**

Add or subtract as indicated. Assume that all variables represent positive real numbers.

a. $5\sqrt[3]{7t^2} - 2\sqrt[3]{7t^2} + \sqrt[3]{7t^2}$

b. $x\sqrt{98x^3y} + 5\sqrt{18x^5y}$

c. $3\sqrt{5x} + 2x\sqrt{5x}$

Solution:

a. $5\sqrt[3]{7t^2} - 2\sqrt[3]{7t^2} + 1\sqrt[3]{7t^2}$ — The radicals are like radicals. They have the same radicand and same index.

$= (5 - 2 + 1)\sqrt[3]{7t^2}$ — Apply the distributive property.

$= 4\sqrt[3]{7t^2}$ — Simplify.

b. $x\sqrt{98x^3y} + 5\sqrt{18x^5y}$ — Each radical can be simplified.

$x\sqrt{98x^3y} = x\sqrt{(7^2x^2) \cdot (2xy)} = 7x^2\sqrt{2xy}$
$5\sqrt{18x^5y} = 5\sqrt{(3^2x^4)(2xy)} = 15x^2\sqrt{2xy}$

$= 7x^2\sqrt{2xy} + 15x^2\sqrt{2xy}$ — The terms are like terms.

$= (7 + 15)x^2\sqrt{2xy}$ — Apply the distributive property.

$= 22x^2\sqrt{2xy}$ — Simplify.

c. $3\sqrt{5x} + 2x\sqrt{5x}$ — The radicals are like radicals.

$= (3 + 2x)\sqrt{5x}$ — Apply the distributive property. The expression cannot be further simplified because the terms within parentheses are not like terms.

Skill Practice 10   Add or subtract as indicated. Assume that all variables represent positive real numbers.

a. $-4\sqrt[3]{5w} + 9\sqrt[3]{5w} - 11\sqrt[3]{5w}$ **b.** $\sqrt{75cd^4} + 6d\sqrt{27cd^2}$
c. $8\sqrt{7z} + 3z\sqrt{7z}$

In Example 11, we investigate operations on radicals with different indices.

EXAMPLE 11   **Performing Operations on Radicals with Different Indices**

Perform the indicated operations and write the answer in radical notation. Assume that all variables represent positive real numbers.

a. $\sqrt[3]{x^2y} \cdot \sqrt[4]{x}$ **b.** $\sqrt[7]{x} \cdot \sqrt[3]{x^2}$ **c.** $\sqrt[3]{c} + \sqrt[4]{c} + \sqrt[3]{d}$

Solution:

a. $\sqrt[3]{x^2y} \cdot \sqrt[4]{x}$ — Since the radicals have different indices, we cannot apply the product property of radicals directly. Instead, rewrite the expression with rational exponents and simplify.

$= (x^2y)^{1/3} \cdot x^{1/4}$

$= x^{2/3}y^{1/3}x^{1/4}$ — Apply the power rule for exponents.

$= x^{2/3 + 1/4}y^{1/3}$ — Add exponents on like bases.

$= x^{8/12 + 3/12}y^{1/3}$

$= x^{11/12}y^{4/12}$ — Write each exponent with the same denominator, so that in radical notation, the factors will have the same index.

$= (x^{11}y^4)^{1/12}$

$= \sqrt[12]{x^{11}y^4}$ — Convert to radical notation.

b. $\sqrt[7]{x} \cdot \sqrt[3]{x^2} = (x \cdot x^{2/3})^{1/7}$ — Write the expression with rational exponents.

$= (x^{1 + 2/3})^{1/7}$ — Multiply like bases by adding the exponents.

$= (x^{5/3})^{1/7}$

$= x^{5/21}$ — Multiply the exponents.

$= \sqrt[21]{x^5}$ — Convert to radical notation.

Answers
10. **a.** $-6\sqrt[3]{5w}$ **b.** $23d^2\sqrt{3c}$
    c. $(8 + 3z)\sqrt{7z}$

c. $\sqrt[3]{c} + \sqrt[4]{c} + \sqrt[3]{d}$

This expression cannot be simplified further because the terms are not like radicals. The first two terms have different indices. The first and third terms have different radicands.

Skill Practice 11   Perform the indicated operations. Assume that all variables represent positive real numbers.

a. $\sqrt[4]{cd} \cdot \sqrt[5]{c^2}$ **b.** $\sqrt[4]{y} \cdot \sqrt[3]{y}$ **c.** $\sqrt[5]{x} + \sqrt[5]{y} + \sqrt[4]{x}$

Answers
11. a. $\sqrt[20]{c^{13}d^5}$ **b.** $\sqrt[12]{y^7}$
    c. Cannot be simplified further

SECTION R.4   Practice Exercises

Review Exercises

1. Determine which elements from A belong to the given set.

$$A = \left\{ \sqrt{37}, \sqrt{36}, \sqrt{\frac{9}{49}}, \sqrt{-4}, -\sqrt{4}, \sqrt{0} \right\}$$

   a. $\mathbb{N}$ **b.** $\mathbb{W}$ **c.** $\mathbb{Z}$

   d. $\mathbb{Q}$ **e.** $\mathbb{H}$ **f.** $\mathbb{R}$

For Exercises 2–6, simplify the expression.

2. $\dfrac{t^{-3}t^7}{t^2}$ **3.** $\dfrac{w^{-4}}{v^{-2}}$ **4.** $(8x^5y^{-2})^{-1}$

5. $(-3x^5y^2)(2x^{-3}y)$ **6.** $\left(\dfrac{3x^2}{y^{-3}}\right)^{-2}$

Concept Connections

7. b is an nth-root of a if $b^{\square} = a$.

8. Given the expression $\sqrt[n]{a}$, the value a is called the _____ and n is called the _____.

9. The expression $a^{m/n}$ can be written in radical notation as _____, provided that $\sqrt[n]{a}$ is a real number.

10. The expression $a^{1/n}$ can be written in radical notation as _____, provided that $\sqrt[n]{a}$ is a real number.

11. If x represents any real number, then $\sqrt{x^2} = $ _____.

12. If x represents any real number, then $\sqrt[3]{x^3} = $ _____.

13. The product property of radicals indicates that $\sqrt[n]{a} \cdot \sqrt[n]{b} = $ _____ provided that $\sqrt[n]{a}$ and $\sqrt[n]{b}$ represent real numbers.

14. Removing a radical from the denominator of a fraction is called _____ the denominator.

Objective 1: Evaluate nth-Roots

For Exercises 15–26, simplify the expression. (See Example 1)

15. $\sqrt[4]{81}$ **16.** $\sqrt[3]{125}$ **17.** $\sqrt{\dfrac{4}{49}}$ **18.** $\sqrt{\dfrac{9}{121}}$

19. $\sqrt{0.09}$ **20.** $\sqrt{0.16}$ **21.** $\sqrt[4]{-81}$ **22.** $\sqrt[4]{-625}$

23. $-\sqrt[4]{81}$ **24.** $-\sqrt[4]{625}$ **25.** $\sqrt[3]{-\dfrac{1}{8}}$ **26.** $\sqrt[3]{-\dfrac{64}{125}}$

Objective 2: Simplify Expressions of the Forms $a^{1/n}$ and $a^{m/n}$

For Exercises 27–36, simplify each expression. (See Examples 2–3)

27. **a.** $25^{1/2}$ **b.** $(-25)^{1/2}$ **c.** $-25^{1/2}$

28. **a.** $36^{1/2}$ **b.** $(-36)^{1/2}$ **c.** $-36^{1/2}$

29. **a.** $27^{1/3}$ **b.** $(-27)^{1/3}$ **c.** $-27^{1/3}$

30. **a.** $125^{1/3}$ **b.** $(-125)^{1/3}$ **c.** $-125^{1/3}$

31. **a.** $\left(\dfrac{121}{169}\right)^{1/2}$ **b.** $\left(\dfrac{121}{169}\right)^{-1/2}$

32. **a.** $\left(\dfrac{49}{144}\right)^{1/2}$ **b.** $\left(\dfrac{49}{144}\right)^{-1/2}$

33. **a.** $16^{3/4}$ **b.** $16^{-3/4}$ **c.** $-16^{3/4}$
     d. $-16^{-3/4}$ **e.** $(-16)^{3/4}$ **f.** $(-16)^{-3/4}$

34. **a.** $81^{3/4}$ **b.** $81^{-3/4}$ **c.** $-81^{3/4}$
     d. $-81^{-3/4}$ **e.** $(-81)^{3/4}$ **f.** $(-81)^{-3/4}$

35. **a.** $64^{2/3}$ **b.** $64^{-2/3}$ **c.** $-64^{2/3}$
     d. $-64^{-2/3}$ **e.** $(-64)^{2/3}$ **f.** $(-64)^{-2/3}$

36. **a.** $8^{2/3}$ **b.** $8^{-2/3}$ **c.** $-8^{2/3}$
     d. $-8^{-2/3}$ **e.** $(-8)^{2/3}$ **f.** $(-8)^{-2/3}$

For Exercises 37–38, write the expression using radical notation. Assume that all variables represent positive real numbers.

37. **a.** $y^{4/11}$ **b.** $6y^{4/11}$ **c.** $(6y)^{4/11}$

38. **a.** $z^{3/10}$ **b.** $8z^{3/10}$ **c.** $(8z)^{3/10}$

For Exercises 39–46, write the expression using rational exponents. Assume that all variables represent positive real numbers. (See Example 4)

39. $\sqrt[5]{a^3}$ 40. $\sqrt[7]{z^4}$ 41. $\sqrt{6x}$

42. $\sqrt{11t}$ 43. $6\sqrt{x}$ 44. $11\sqrt{t}$

45. $\sqrt[5]{a^5 + b^5}$ 46. $\sqrt[3]{m^3 + n^3}$

Objective 3: Simplify Expressions with Rational Exponents

For Exercises 47–56, simplify each expression. Assume that all variable expressions represent positive real numbers. (See Example 5)

47. $\dfrac{a^{2/3}a^{5/3}}{a^{1/3}}$ 48. $\dfrac{y^{7/5}y^{4/5}}{y^{1/5}}$ 49. $\dfrac{3w^{-2/3}}{y^{-1/3}}$

50. $\dfrac{8d^{-5/7}}{c^{-3/4}}$ 51. $(16x^{-8}y^{1/5})^{3/4}$ 52. $(125a^6b^{-7/5})^{1/3}$

53. $\left(\dfrac{2m^{2/3}}{n^{3/4}}\right)^{12}\left(\dfrac{n^{1/5}}{2m^{1/2}}\right)^{10}$ 54. $\left(\dfrac{3x^{1/2}}{y^{3/8}}\right)^{4}\left(\dfrac{y^{1/2}}{3x^{4/3}}\right)^{3}$ 55. $\left(\dfrac{m^2}{m+n}\right)^{-1}\left(\dfrac{m^2}{m+n}\right)^{1/2}$

56. $\left(\dfrac{c^2}{c-d}\right)^{-2}\left(\dfrac{c^2}{c-d}\right)^{3/2}$

Objective 4: Simplify Radicals

57. **a.** For what values of t will the statement be true? $\sqrt{t^2} = t$
     b. For what value of t will the statement be true? $\sqrt{t^2} = |t|$

58. **a.** For what values of c will the statement be true? $\sqrt[4]{(c + 8)^4} = c + 8$
     b. For what value of c will the statement be true? $\sqrt[4]{(c + 8)^4} = |c + 8|$

For Exercises 59–66, simplify each expression. (See Example 6)

59. $\sqrt{y^2}$ **60.** $\sqrt[4]{y^4}$ **61.** $\sqrt[3]{y^3}$ **62.** $\sqrt[5]{y^5}$

63. $\sqrt[4]{(2x-5)^4}$ **64.** $\sqrt{(3z+2)^2}$ **65.** $\sqrt{w^{12}}$ **66.** $\sqrt[4]{c^{32}}$

For Exercises 67–82, simplify each expression. Assume that all variable expressions represent positive real numbers. (See Examples 7–8)

67. a. $\sqrt{c^7}$ **b.** $\sqrt[3]{c^7}$ **c.** $\sqrt[4]{c^7}$ **d.** $\sqrt[9]{c^7}$

68. a. $\sqrt{d^{11}}$ **b.** $\sqrt[3]{d^{11}}$ **c.** $\sqrt[4]{d^{11}}$ **d.** $\sqrt[12]{d^{11}}$

69. a. $\sqrt{24}$ **b.** $\sqrt[3]{24}$

70. a. $\sqrt{54}$ **b.** $\sqrt[3]{54}$

71. $\sqrt[3]{250x^2y^6z^{11}}$ **72.** $\sqrt[3]{40ab^{13}c^{17}}$ **73.** $\sqrt[4]{96p^{14}q^7}$ **74.** $\sqrt[4]{243m^{19}n^{10}}$

75. $\sqrt{84(y-2)^3}$ **76.** $\sqrt{18(w-6)^3}$ **77.** $\sqrt{\dfrac{p^7}{36}}$ **78.** $\sqrt{\dfrac{q^{11}}{4}}$

79. $4\sqrt[3]{\dfrac{w^3z^5}{8}}$ **80.** $8\sqrt[3]{\dfrac{c^6d^7}{64}}$ **81.** $\dfrac{\sqrt[3]{5x^5y}}{\sqrt[3]{625x^2y^4}}$ **82.** $\dfrac{\sqrt[3]{2m^2n^7}}{\sqrt[3]{16m^{14}n^4}}$

For Exercises 83–96, simplify each expression. Assume that all variables represent positive real numbers. (See Examples 9 and 11)

83. $\sqrt{10}\cdot\sqrt{14}$ **84.** $\sqrt{6}\cdot\sqrt{21}$ **85.** $\sqrt[3]{xy^2}\cdot\sqrt[3]{x^2y}$

86. $\sqrt[4]{a^3b}\cdot\sqrt[4]{ab^3}$ **87.** $(3\sqrt[4]{a^3})(-5\sqrt[4]{a^3})$ **88.** $(7\sqrt[6]{t^5})(-2\sqrt[6]{t^5})$

89. $\left(-\dfrac{1}{2}\sqrt[3]{6a^2b^2c}\right)\left(\dfrac{4}{3}\sqrt[3]{4a^2c^2}\right)$ **90.** $\left(-\dfrac{3}{4}\sqrt[3]{9m^2n^5p}\right)\left(\dfrac{1}{6}\sqrt[3]{6m^2np^4}\right)$ **91.** $\sqrt[5]{x^3y^2}\cdot\sqrt[4]{x}$

92. $\sqrt[4]{a^2b}\cdot\sqrt[3]{ab^2}$ **93.** $\sqrt[6]{m}\sqrt[3]{m^2}$ **94.** $\sqrt[5]{y}\sqrt[4]{y^3}$

95. $\sqrt{x\sqrt{x\sqrt{x}}}$ **96.** $\sqrt[3]{y\sqrt[3]{y\sqrt[3]{y}}}$

For Exercises 97–106, add or subtract as indicated. Assume that all variables represent positive real numbers. (See Example 10)

97. $3\sqrt[3]{2y^2}-9\sqrt[3]{2y^2}+\sqrt[3]{2y^2}$ **98.** $8\sqrt[4]{3z^3}-\sqrt[4]{3z^3}+2\sqrt[4]{3z^3}$

99. $\dfrac{1}{5}\sqrt{50}-\dfrac{7}{3}\sqrt{18}+\dfrac{5}{6}\sqrt{72}$ **100.** $\dfrac{2}{5}\sqrt{75}-\dfrac{2}{3}\sqrt{27}-\dfrac{1}{2}\sqrt{12}$

101. $-3x\sqrt[3]{16xy^4}+xy\sqrt[3]{54xy}-5\sqrt[3]{250x^4y^4}$ **102.** $8\sqrt[4]{32a^5b^6}-5b\sqrt[4]{2a^5b^2}-ab\sqrt[4]{162ab^2}$

103. $12\sqrt{2y}+5y\sqrt{2y}$ **104.** $-8\sqrt{3w}+3w\sqrt{3w}$

105. $-\dfrac{1}{2}\sqrt{8z^3}+\dfrac{3}{7}\sqrt{98z}$ **106.** $\dfrac{2}{3}\sqrt{45c}+\dfrac{1}{2}\sqrt{20c^3}$

Mixed Exercises

For Exercises 107–108, use Heron's formula to determine the area (A) of a triangle with sides of length a, b, and c. Write each answer as a simplified radical.

$$A=\sqrt{s(s-a)(s-b)(s-c)}\qquad\text{where }s=\dfrac{a+b+c}{2}$$

107.

6 in. 7 in. 9 in.

108.

5 cm 3 cm 6 cm

For Exercises 109–110, use the Pythagorean theorem to determine the length of the missing side. Write the answer as a simplified radical.

109.

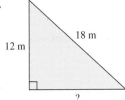

12 m

18 m

?

110.

8 m

?

16 m

111. The size of a television is identified by the length of the diagonal. If Lynn's television is 48 in. across and 32 in. high, what size television does she have? Give the exact value and a decimal approximation to the nearest inch.

48 in.

d

32 in.

112. If the span of a roof is 36 ft and the rise is 12 ft, determine the length of the rafter R. Give the exact value and a decimal approximation to the nearest tenth of a foot.

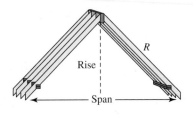

R

Rise

Span

113. The slant length L for a right circular cone is given by $L = \sqrt{r^2 + h^2}$ where r and h are the radius and height of the cone. Find the slant length of a cone with radius 4 in. and height 10 in. Determine the exact value and a decimal approximation to the nearest tenth of an inch.

$L = ?$

10 in.

4 in.

114. The lateral surface area A of a right circular cone is given by $A = \pi r \sqrt{r^2 + h^2}$ where r and h are the radius and height of the cone. Determine the exact value (in terms of π) of the lateral surface area of a cone with radius 6 m and height 4 m. Then give a decimal approximation to the nearest square meter.

4 m

6 m

For Exercises 115–116, determine the exact area for the given circle.

115.

$3\sqrt{5}$ in.

116.

$8\sqrt{7}$ cm

117. The depreciation rate for a car is given by $r = 1 - \left(\frac{S}{C}\right)^{1/n}$, where S is the value of the car after n years, and C is the initial cost. Determine the depreciation rate for a car that originally cost $22,990 and was valued at $11,500 after 4 yr. Round to the nearest tenth of a percent.

118. For a certain oven, the baking time t (in hr) for a turkey that weighs x pounds can be approximated by the model $t = 0.84x^{3/5}$. Determine the baking time for a 15-lb turkey. Round to 1 decimal place.

119. On a piano, the note A440 (located above Middle C) has a frequency of 440 Hz. Using the method of equal temperament, a piano tuner can determine the frequency (in Hz) of a note n keys above or below A440 by the formula $f = 440 \cdot 2^{n/12}$ where n is an integer.

   a. Use $n = 1, 2$, and 3 to determine the frequencies of the next three notes above A440. Round to 1 decimal place.

   b. Determine the frequency of Middle C if Middle C is located nine notes *below* A440.

120. For a certain airline, the cost C (in $ millions) for x thousand passengers to travel round trip from New York to Los Angeles is modeled by $C = 1.4(0.3x + 1)^{1/2}$.

   a. Determine the airline's cost for 10,000 passengers to travel from New York to Los Angeles.

   b. If the airline charges an average of $450 per ticket, determine the *profit* made by the airline for 10,000 passengers making this flight.

Write About It

121. Explain the similarity in simplifying the given expressions.

   a. $2x + 3x$

   b. $2\sqrt{x} + 3\sqrt{x}$

   c. $2\sqrt[3]{x} + 3\sqrt[3]{x}$

122. Explain why the given expressions cannot be simplified further.

   a. $2x + 3y$

   b. $2\sqrt{x} + 3\sqrt{y}$

   c. $2\sqrt[3]{x} + 3\sqrt{x}$

Expanding Your Skills

For Exercises 123–124, evaluate the expression without the use of a calculator.

123. $\sqrt{\dfrac{8.0 \times 10^{12}}{2.0 \times 10^{4}}}$

124. $\sqrt{\dfrac{1.44 \times 10^{16}}{9.0 \times 10^{10}}}$

For Exercises 125–126, simplify the expression.

125. $\sqrt{\sqrt[3]{6} + \sqrt[4]{16}} + \sqrt{\sqrt{25} + \sqrt{16}} + \sqrt{9}$

126. $\sqrt{\sqrt[4]{11} + \sqrt[3]{125}} + \sqrt{\sqrt{81} + \sqrt[3]{1000}} + \sqrt{36} + \sqrt{25}$

The mean surface temperature T_p (in °C) of an Earth-like planet can be approximated based on its distance from its primary star d (in km), the radius of the star r (in km), and the temperature of the star T_s (in °C) by the following formula.

$$T_p = 0.7(T_s + 273)\left(\frac{r}{d}\right)^{1/2} - 273 \qquad \text{For Exercises 127–128, use the model to find } T_p.$$

127. The star Altair is relatively close to the Earth (16.8 light-years) and has a mean surface temperature of approximately 7700°C. Although not completely spherical in shape, Altair has a mean radius of approximately 1.26×10^{6} km. If a planet with an atmosphere similar to that of the Earth is 4.3×10^{8} km away from Altair, will the temperature on the surface of the planet be suitable for liquid water to exist? (Recall that under pressure similar to that at sea level on Earth, water freezes at 0°C and turns to steam at 100°C.)

128. Suppose the Sun has a mean surface temperature of 5700°C and a radius of approximately 7.0×10^{5} km. If the Earth is a distance of 1.49×10^{8} km from the Sun, approximate the mean surface temperature for the Earth.

SECTION R.5 Polynomials and Multiplication of Radicals

OBJECTIVES

1. Identify Key Elements of a Polynomial
2. Add and Subtract Polynomials
3. Multiply Polynomials
4. Identify and Simplify Special Case Products
5. Multiply Radical Expressions Involving Multiple Terms

1. Identify Key Elements of a Polynomial

The Environmental Protection Agency (EPA) is responsible for providing fuel economy data (gas mileage information) that is posted on the window stickers of new vehicles. Many variables contribute to fuel consumption including the speed of the vehicle. For example, for one midsize sedan tested, the gas mileage G (in miles per gallon, mpg) can be approximated by

$$G = -0.008x^2 + 0.748x + 13.5, \qquad \text{where } x \text{ is the speed of the vehicle in mph and } 15 \leq x \leq 75 \text{ mph.}$$

The expression on the right side of this equation is called a polynomial. A **polynomial** in the variable x is a finite sum of terms of the form ax^n. In each term, the coefficient, a, is a real number, and the exponent, n, is a whole number. The degree of ax^n is n.

   The terms of the polynomial $-0.008x^2 + 0.748x + 13.5$ are written in **descending order** by degree. The term with highest degree is written first. This is called the **leading term,** and its coefficient is called the **leading coefficient.** The **degree of the polynomial** is the same as the degree of the leading term. Therefore, the polynomial $-0.008x^2 + 0.784x + 13.5$ is a degree 2 polynomial.

The preceding discussion is meant as an informal introduction to polynomials and associated key vocabulary. However, as your level of mathematical sophistication increases, you should strive to understand definitions written in a more concise mathematical language. Take a minute to read the formal definition of a polynomial.

Definition of a Polynomial in x

A **polynomial in the variable x** is an expression of the form:

$$a_n x^n + a_{n-1} x^{n-1} + a_{n-2} x^{n-2} + \cdots + a_1 x + a_0$$

The coefficients a_n, a_{n-1}, a_{n-2}, ... , a_0 are real numbers, where $a_n \neq 0$, and the exponents n, $n-1$, $n-2$, ... , 0 are whole numbers.

The term $a_n x^n$ is called the **leading term,** the coefficient a_n is the **leading coefficient,** and the exponent n is the **degree of the polynomial.**

In the preceding definition, subscript notation a_n (read as "a sub n"), a_{n-1} (read as "a sub $n-1$"), and so on, is used to denote the coefficients of the terms. Subscript notation is used rather than lettered variables such as a, b, c, and the like, when a large or undetermined number of terms is suggested.

A polynomial with one term is also called a **monomial.** A polynomial with two terms is called a **binomial,** and a polynomial with three terms is called a **trinomial.**

EXAMPLE 1 **Identifying Key Components of a Polynomial**

If the expression in the first column is a polynomial, write the polynomial in descending order. Then identify the leading coefficient and degree of the polynomial. Categorize the polynomial as a monomial, binomial, or trinomial.

Solution:

	Descending Order	Leading Coefficient	Degree	Category
a. $3.1x^2 - 4x^3 + 6$	$-4x^3 + 3.1x^2 + 6$	-4	3	trinomial
b. $\frac{1}{2}y^7$	$\frac{1}{2}y^7$	$\frac{1}{2}$	7	monomial
c. $\sqrt{2} + w$	$1w^1 + \sqrt{2}$	1	1	binomial
d. $2 + \sqrt{w}$	Not a polynomial because $2 + \sqrt{w} = 2 + w^{1/2}$. The exponent on the variable is not a whole number.			
e. $2 + \frac{1}{w}$	Not a polynomial because $2 + \dfrac{1}{w} = 2 + w^{-1}$. The exponent on the variable is not a whole number.			

Skill Practice 1 Write each polynomial in descending order, and identify the leading coefficient and degree of the polynomial. Categorize the polynomial as a monomial, binomial, or trinomial.

a. $-8x^3 + 7x - 3x^5$ **b.** $-5.72y^3$ **c.** $\frac{1}{2} - 8x$

d. $\frac{1}{x} - 8x$ **e.** $|x| - 8x$

Answers

1. a. $-3x^5 - 8x^3 + 7x$; leading coefficient: -3; degree 5; trinomial
b. $-5.72y^3$; leading coefficient: -5.72; degree 3; monomial
c. $-8x + \frac{1}{2}$; leading coefficient: -8; degree 1; binomial
d. Not a polynomial
e. Not a polynomial

Some polynomials have more than one variable:

$$-4x^4y^7 + x^2y^5 + 5xy^4$$

This polynomial has three terms. The degree of each term is the sum of the exponents on the variable factors.

$-4x^4y^7$	degree 11	(sum of $4 + 7$)
x^2y^5	degree 7	(sum of $2 + 5$)
$5xy^4$	degree 5	(sum of $1 + 4$)

2. Add and Subtract Polynomials

To add or subtract polynomials, combine like terms. This is demonstrated in Example 2.

EXAMPLE 2 **Adding and Subtracting Polynomials**

Add or subtract as indicated, and simplify.

a. $(-4w^3 - 5w^2 + 6w + 3) + (8w^2 - 4w + 2)$
b. $(6.1a^2b + 2.9ab - 4.5b^2) - (2.6a^2b - 4.1ab + 2.1b^2)$

Solution:

a. $(-4w^3 - 5w^2 + 6w + 3) + (8w^2 - 4w + 2)$
$= -4w^3 - 5w^2 + 8w^2 + 6w - 4w + 3 + 2$ Group like terms.
$= -4w^3 + 3w^2 + 2w + 5$ Combine like terms.

b. $(6.1a^2b + 2.9ab - 4.5b^2) - (2.6a^2b - 4.1ab + 2.1b^2)$
$= (6.1a^2b + 2.9ab - 4.5b^2) + (-2.6a^2b + 4.1ab - 2.1b^2)$
$= 6.1a^2b - 2.6a^2b + 2.9ab + 4.1ab - 4.5b^2 - 2.1b^2$ Group like terms.
$= 3.5a^2b + 7ab - 6.6b^2$ Combine like terms.

Skill Practice 2 Add or subtract as indicated, and simplify.

a. $(7t^5 - 3t^2 - 2t) + (2t^5 + 3t^2 - 5t - 4)$
b. $(0.08x^3y - 0.02x^2y - 0.1xy) - (0.05x^3y - 0.07x^2y + 0.02xy)$

Point of Interest

The sixteenth century brought the use of many modern symbols in algebra. Mathematicians Christoff Rudolff and Richard Stifel of Germany introduced the "+" and "−" signs, and Robert Record of England introduced the modern "=" sign.

TIP Addition and subtraction of polynomials can also be done by aligning like terms in columns. The difference of polynomials from Example 2(b) is shown here.

$$6.1a^2b + 2.9ab - 4.5b^2$$
$$-(2.6a^2b - 4.1ab + 2.1b^2)$$

$$6.1a^2b + 2.9ab - 4.5b^2$$
$$+ (-2.6a^2b + 4.1ab - 2.1b^2)$$
$$\overline{3.5a^2b + 7ab - 6.6b^2}$$

⟶ Add the opposite.

Answers
2. a. $9t^5 - 7t - 4$
   b. $0.03x^3y + 0.05x^2y - 0.12xy$

3. Multiply Polynomials

- To multiply two monomials, use the commutative and associative properties of multiplication to regroup like factors. Then apply the properties of exponents to simplify.

$$(-4x^2y^5)\left(\frac{1}{2}x^3y\right) = -4 \cdot \frac{1}{2}x^2x^3y^5y = -2x^5y^6$$

- To multiply a polynomial by a monomial, apply the distributive property.

$$-3x^3(4x^2 - 2x + 6) = -3x^3(4x^2) + (-3x^3)(-2x) + (-3x^3)(6)$$
$$= -12x^5 + 6x^4 - 18x^3$$

- To multiply two polynomials with two or more terms, we also use the distributive property. Ultimately, each term in the first polynomial must be multiplied by each term in the second. Then simplify and combine like terms.

$$(4w + 7)(2w - 3) = 4w(2w) + 4w(-3) + 7(2w) + 7(-3)$$
$$= 8w^2 - 12w + 14w - 21$$
$$= 8w^2 + 2w - 21$$

EXAMPLE 3 **Multiplying Polynomials**

Multiply and simplify.

a. $(5y^2 - 6x)(2y^2 + 3x)$ **b.** $(4x + 2)\left(x^2 - 6x + \frac{1}{2}\right)$

Solution:

a. $(5y^2 - 6x)(2y^2 + 3x)$

Multiply each term in the first polynomial by each term in the second.

$$= 5y^2(2y^2) + 5y^2(3x) + (-6x)(2y^2) + (-6x)(3x)$$

$$= 10y^4 + 15xy^2 - 12xy^2 - 18x^2$$ Simplify.

$$= 10y^4 + 3xy^2 - 18x^2$$ Combine like terms.

TIP Multiplication of polynomials can also be performed vertically.

$$
\begin{array}{r}
x^2 - 6x + \frac{1}{2} \\
\times \quad\quad 4x + 2 \\
\hline
2x^2 - 12x + 1 \\
4x^3 - 24x^2 + 2x \quad\quad \\
\hline
4x^3 - 22x^2 - 10x + 1
\end{array}
$$

b. $(4x + 2)\left(x^2 - 6x + \frac{1}{2}\right)$

Multiply each term in the first polynomial by each term in the second.

$$= 4x(x^2) + 4x(-6x) + 4x\left(\frac{1}{2}\right) + 2(x^2) + 2(-6x) + 2\left(\frac{1}{2}\right)$$

$$= 4x^3 - 24x^2 + 2x + 2x^2 - 12x + 1$$ Simplify.

$$= 4x^3 - 22x^2 - 10x + 1$$ Combine like terms.

Skill Practice 3 Multiply and simplify.

a. $(7a^3 + 2b)(3a^3 - b)$ **b.** $(3y - 6)\left(y^2 + 4y + \frac{2}{3}\right)$

Answers

3. a. $21a^6 - a^3b - 2b^2$
  b. $3y^3 + 6y^2 - 22y - 4$

TIP The product of conjugates equals the square of the first term from the binomials, minus the square of the second term from the binomials.

4. Identify and Simplify Special Case Products

Two expressions of the form $a - b$ and $a + b$ are called **conjugates.** The product of two conjugates results in a **difference of squares.**

$$(a - b)(a + b) = a^2 + ab - ab - b^2$$
$$= a^2 - b^2 \quad \text{(difference of squares)}$$

EXAMPLE 4   **Multiplying Conjugates**

Multiply and simplify.

a. $(2x + 5)(2x - 5)$ **b.** $\left(\dfrac{1}{3}c^2 - \dfrac{1}{2}d\right)\left(\dfrac{1}{3}c^2 + \dfrac{1}{2}d\right)$

Solution:

a. $(2x + 5)(2x - 5)$ This is a product of conjugates.

$\quad = (2x)^2 - (5)^2$ The product is a difference of squares.

$\quad = 4x^2 - 25$ Simplify.

b. $\left(\dfrac{1}{3}c^2 - \dfrac{1}{2}d\right)\left(\dfrac{1}{3}c^2 + \dfrac{1}{2}d\right)$ This is a product of conjugates.

$\quad = \left(\dfrac{1}{3}c^2\right)^2 - \left(\dfrac{1}{2}d\right)^2$ The product is a difference of squares.

$\quad = \dfrac{1}{9}c^4 - \dfrac{1}{4}d^2$ Simplify.

Skill Practice 4   Multiply and simplify.

a. $(3y - 7)(3y + 7)$ **b.** $\left(\dfrac{2}{5}t - \dfrac{1}{4}w^2\right)\left(\dfrac{2}{5}t + \dfrac{1}{4}w^2\right)$

TIP The square of a binomial results in the square of the first term in the binomial, plus twice the product of terms in the binomial, plus the square of the second term in the binomial.

An expression of the form $(a + b)^2$ or $(a - b)^2$ is called a **square of a binomial.** In expanded form, the product is a **perfect square trinomial.**

$$(a + b)^2 = (a + b)(a + b) = a^2 + ab + ab + b^2$$
$$= a^2 + 2ab + b^2 \quad \text{(perfect square trinomial)}$$

$$(a - b)^2 = (a - b)(a - b) = a^2 - ab - ab + b^2$$
$$= a^2 - 2ab + b^2 \quad \text{(perfect square trinomial)}$$

Answers

4. a. $9y^2 - 49$ **b.** $\dfrac{4}{25}t^2 - \dfrac{1}{16}w^4$

EXAMPLE 5 Squaring Binomials

Square the binomials.

  a. $(3x - 7)^2$ **b.** $(5t^2 + 2v^2)^2$

Solution:

a. $(3x - 7)^2$

| square of first term | twice the product of terms | square of second term |

$$= (3x)^2 - 2(3x)(7) + (7)^2$$
$$= 9x^2 - 42x + 49$$

This is the square of a binomial, $(a - b)^2$, where $a = 3x$ and $b = 7$.

The product is $a^2 - 2ab + b^2$.

Simplify.

b. $(5t^2 + 2v^2)^2$

$$= (5t^2)^2 + 2(5t^2)(2v^2) + (2v^2)^2$$
$$= 25t^4 + 20t^2v^2 + 4v^4$$

This is the square of a binomial, $(a + b)^2$, where $a = 5t^2$ and $b = 2v^2$.

The product is $a^2 + 2ab + b^2$.

Simplify.

Skill Practice 5 Square the binomials.

  a. $(8z - 2)^2$ **b.** $(3c^2 + 4d^3)^2$

The patterns associated with the product of conjugates and the square of a binomial are important to understand and memorize. These will be used again in many more applications of algebra, including factoring in the next section.

Special Case Products

Product of Conjugates: $(a + b)(a - b) = a^2 - b^2$ (difference of squares)

Square of a Binomial: $(a + b)^2 = a^2 + 2ab + b^2$ (perfect square trinomial)

  $(a - b)^2 = a^2 - 2ab + b^2$ (perfect square trinomial)

In Example 6, we apply operations on polynomials to geometric formulas.

EXAMPLE 6 Applying Operations on Polynomials to Geometry

a. Write a polynomial that represents the area of the rectangle.

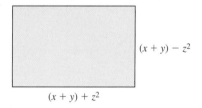

$(x + y) - z^2$

$(x + y) + z^2$

b. Write a polynomial that represents the volume of the cube.

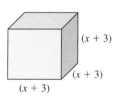

$(x + 3)$

$(x + 3)$

$(x + 3)$

Solution:

a. $A = lw$

$$A = \overbrace{[(x + y) + z^2]}^{l}\overbrace{[(x + y) - z^2]}^{w}$$

$$= (x + y)^2 - (z^2)^2$$

$$= x^2 + 2xy + y^2 - z^4$$

The area of a rectangle is length times width.

Substitute $[(x + y) + z^2]$ for l, and $[(x + y) - z^2]$ for w.

This is a product of conjugates. The result is a difference of squares.

Square the binomial $(x + y)^2$ as $x^2 + 2xy + y^2$.

Answers
5. a. $64z^2 - 32z + 4$
  b. $9c^4 + 24c^2d^3 + 16d^6$

b. $V = s^3$

The volume of a cube is the product of the lengths of the sides.

$V = (x + 3)^3$

Substitute $(x + 3)$ for s.

$\quad = (x + 3)^2(x + 3)$

This product can be written as $(x + 3)(x + 3)(x + 3)$ or as $(x + 3)^2(x + 3)$.

$\quad = (x^2 + 6x + 9)(x + 3)$

$\quad = x^2(x) + x^2(3) + 6x(x) + 6x(3) + 9(x) + 9(3)$

$\quad = x^3 + 3x^2 + 6x^2 + 18x + 9x + 27$ Simplify.

$\quad = x^3 + 9x^2 + 27x + 27$ Combine like terms.

Skill Practice 6

a. Write a polynomial that represents the area of the rectangle.

b. Write a polynomial that represents the volume of the cube.

$(x + 3) - y$

$(x + 3) + y$

$(x + 2)$

$(x + 2)$

$(x + 2)$

---

5. Multiply Radical Expressions Involving Multiple Terms

The process used to multiply polynomials can be extended to algebraic expressions that are not polynomials. In Example 7 we multiply expressions containing two or more radical terms.

EXAMPLE 7   **Multiplying Radical Expressions**

Multiply and simplify.

  a. $3\sqrt{5}(2\sqrt{5} + 4\sqrt{2} + 1)$ **b.** $(3\sqrt{x} + 5)(2\sqrt{x} - 7)$

Solution:

a. $3\sqrt{5}(2\sqrt{5} + 4\sqrt{2} + 1)$

Apply the distributive property.

$= (3\sqrt{5})(2\sqrt{5}) + (3\sqrt{5})(4\sqrt{2}) + (3\sqrt{5})(1)$

$= 6\sqrt{25} + 12\sqrt{10} + 3\sqrt{5}$

Apply the product property of radicals.

$= 6(5) + 12\sqrt{10} + 3\sqrt{5}$

$= 30 + 12\sqrt{10} + 3\sqrt{5}$

Simplify.

b. $(3\sqrt{x} + 5)(2\sqrt{x} - 7)$

Apply the distributive property.

$= (3\sqrt{x})(2\sqrt{x}) + (3\sqrt{x})(-7) + (5)(2\sqrt{x}) + (5)(-7)$

$= 6\sqrt{x^2} - 21\sqrt{x} + 10\sqrt{x} - 35$

$= 6x - 11\sqrt{x} - 35$

Combine like terms.

Skill Practice 7   Multiply and simplify.

  a. $2\sqrt{11}(2\sqrt{11} + 4\sqrt{2} - 3)$ **b.** $(4\sqrt{t} + 10)(3\sqrt{t} - 8)$

Answers

6. a. $x^2 + 6x + 9 - y^2$

  b. $x^3 + 6x^2 + 12x + 8$

7. a. $44 + 8\sqrt{22} - 6\sqrt{11}$

  b. $12t - 2\sqrt{t} - 80$

In Example 8, we evaluate special case products for expressions with radicals.

EXAMPLE 8   **Simplifying Special Case Products Involving Radicals**

Multiply and simplify.

    a. $(4\sqrt{5} + \sqrt{6})(4\sqrt{5} - \sqrt{6})$ **b.** $(3x + \sqrt{2})^2$

Solution:

   a. $(4\sqrt{5} + \sqrt{6})(4\sqrt{5} - \sqrt{6})$ This is a product of conjugates: $(a + b)(a - b)$.

       $= (4\sqrt{5})^2 - (\sqrt{6})^2$ The product is a difference of squares. Note that

       $= 16 \cdot 5 - 6$ $(\sqrt{5})^2 = 5$ and $(\sqrt{6})^2 = 6$.

       $= 80 - 6$

       $= 74$

   b. $(3x + \sqrt{2})^2$ This is the square of a binomial, $(a + b)^2$, where $a = 3x$ and $b = \sqrt{2}$.

       $= (3x)^2 + 2(3x)(\sqrt{2}) + (\sqrt{2})^2$ The product is $a^2 + 2ab + b^2$.

       $= 9x^2 + 6\sqrt{2}x + 2$ Simplify.

Skill Practice 8   Multiply and simplify.

    a. $(3\sqrt{7} - \sqrt{5})(3\sqrt{7} + \sqrt{5})$ **b.** $(4y - \sqrt{3})^2$

Answers

8. a. 58   **b.** $16y^2 - 8\sqrt{3}y + 3$

SECTION R.5   Practice Exercises

Review Exercises

For Exercises 1–6, simplify the expression.

   1. $-3(8 - 4x) - \dfrac{1}{3}(15x - 6z)$ **2.** $-11(y + 7x) - \dfrac{1}{2}(4x - 6y)$ **3.** $(\sqrt{5})^2$

   4. $(\sqrt[5]{x})^5$ **5.** $(3x^2 y^{-1})^4 \left(-\dfrac{1}{2}xy^3\right)^3$ **6.** $(4a^3 b^{-2})^3 \left(\dfrac{1}{3}ab^5\right)^2$

Concept Connections

   7. A _____ in the variable x is a finite sum of terms of the form ax^n where a is a real number and n is a whole number.

   8. The polynomial $5x^3 - 2x^2 + 4$ is written in _____ order by degree.

   9. The _____ term of a polynomial is the term of highest degree.

  10. The leading _____ of a polynomial is the numerical factor of the leading term.

  11. A _____ is a polynomial that has two terms, and a _____ is a polynomial with three terms.

  12. The expanded form of the square of a binomial is a trinomial called a _____ square trinomial.

  13. The product of conjugates $(a + b) \cdot$ _____ results in a difference of squares $a^2 - b^2$.

  14. The conjugate of $3 - \sqrt{x}$ is _____.

Objective 1: Identify Key Elements of a Polynomial

For Exercises 15–16, determine if the expression is a polynomial. (See Example 1)

15. a. $4a^2 + 7b - 3$ **b.** $\frac{3}{4}x^2y$ **c.** $6x + \frac{7}{x} + 5$ **d.** $\sqrt{p^2 + 2p - 5}$

16. a. $3x^5 - 9x^2 + \frac{2}{x^3}$ **b.** $\sqrt{2}ab^4$ **c.** $3|y| + 2$ **d.** $-7x^3 - 4x^2 + 2x - 5$

For Exercises 17–20, write the polynomial in descending order. Then identify the leading coefficient and degree of the polynomial. (See Example 1)

17. $7.2x^3 - 18x^7 - 4.1$

18. $9.1y^5 + 4.6y^2 - 1.7y^8$

19. $\frac{1}{3}y - y^2$

20. $\frac{4}{5}c^2 + c^5$

For Exercises 21–22, determine the degree of the polynomial.

21. $-8p^2qr^5 + 4pq^8r^2 + 5p^3q^3r$

22. $-4.7abc^4 - 5.2a^2bc^5 + 2.6a^3c$

Objective 2: Add and Subtract Polynomials

For Exercises 23–28, add or subtract as indicated and simplify. (See Example 2)

23. $(-8p^7 - 4p^4 + 2p - 5) + (2p^7 + 6p^4 + p^2)$

24. $(-7w^5 + 3w^3 - 6) + (9w^5 - 5w^3 + 4w - 3)$

25. $(0.05c^3b + 0.02c^2b^2 - 0.09cb^3) - (-0.03c^3b + 0.08c^2b^2 - 0.1cb^3)$

26. $(0.004mn^5 - 0.001mn^4 + 0.05mn^3) - (0.003mn^5 + 0.007mn^4 - 0.07mn^3)$

27. Subtract $\left(\frac{1}{2}x^2 - \frac{3}{4}x - \sqrt{2}\right)$ from $\left(\frac{1}{4}x^2 + \frac{5}{8}x + 5\sqrt{2}\right)$.

28. Subtract $\left(\frac{3}{10}y^3 + \frac{7}{5}y + 5\sqrt{7}\right)$ from $\left(\frac{2}{5}y^3 - \frac{1}{10}y + \sqrt{7}\right)$.

Objective 3: Multiply Polynomials

For Exercises 29–38, multiply and simplify. (See Example 3)

29. $(-6a^5b)\left(\frac{1}{3}a^2b^2\right)$

30. $(-10c^2d^5)\left(\frac{1}{2}cd^7\right)$

31. $7m^2(2m^4 - 3m + 4)$

32. $8p^5(-2p^2 - 5p - 1)$

33. $(2x - 5)(x + 4)$

34. $(w + 7)(6w - 3)$

35. $(4u^2 - 5v^2)(2u^2 + 3v^2)$

36. $(2z^3 + 5u^2)(7z^3 - u^2)$

37. $(3y + 6)\left(\frac{1}{3}y^2 - 5y - 4\right)$

38. $(10v - 5)\left(\frac{1}{5}v^2 - 3v + 1\right)$

Objective 4: Identify and Simplify Special Case Products

39. Write the expanded form for $(a + b)^2$.

40. Write the expanded form for $(a + b)(a - b)$.

For Exercises 41–54, perform the indicated operations and simplify. (See Examples 4–5)

41. $(4x - 5)(4x + 5)$

42. $(3p - 2)(3p + 2)$

43. $(3w^2 - 7z)(3w^2 + 7z)$

44. $(9v^3 + 2u)(9v^3 - 2u)$

45. $\left(\frac{1}{5}c - \frac{2}{3}d^3\right)\left(\frac{1}{5}c + \frac{2}{3}d^3\right)$

46. $\left(\frac{1}{6}n - \frac{4}{5}p^4\right)\left(\frac{1}{6}n + \frac{4}{5}p^4\right)$

47. $(5m - 3)^2$

48. $(7v - 2)^2$

49. $(4t^2 + 3p^3)^2$

50. $(2a^2 + 11b^3)^2$

51. $(w + 4)^3$

52. $(p - 2)^3$

53. $[(u + v) - w][(u + v) + w]$

54. $[(c + d) - a][(c + d) + a]$

Mixed Exercises

The total national expenditure for health care has been increasing since the year 2000. For privately insured individuals in the United States, the following models give the total amount spent for health insurance premiums I (in \$ billions) and the total amount spent on other out-of-pocket health-related expenses P (in \$ billions). (*Source*: U.S. Centers for Medicare & Medicaid Services, www.census.gov)

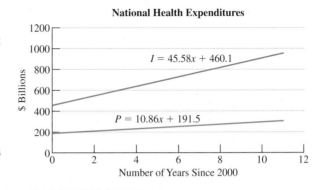

National Health Expenditures

$I = 45.58x + 460.1$ Total spent on health insurance premiums x years since 2000.

$P = 10.86x + 191.5$ Other out-of-pocket health-related expenses x years since 2000.

Use these models for Exercises 55–58.

55. Determine the total expenditure for private health insurance premiums for the year 2008.

56. Determine the total expenditure for other health-related out-of-pocket expenses for the year 2005.

57. a. Write and simplify the polynomial representing $I + P$.

    b. Interpret the meaning of the polynomial from part (a).

    c. Evaluate the polynomial $I + P$ for $x = 6$, and interpret the meaning of this value.

58. a. Determine the total expenditure for private health insurance premiums for the year 2010.

    b. Determine the total expenditure for other health-related out-of-pocket expenses for the year 2010.

    c. Evaluate the polynomial $I + P$ found in Exercise 57(a) for $x = 10$.

For Exercises 59–66, write an expression that represents the perimeter, area, or volume as indicated, and simplify. (See Example 6)

59. Perimeter

60. Perimeter

61. Area

62. Area

63. Volume

64. Volume

65. Area

66. Area

For Exercises 67–68, write an expression that represents the area of the shaded region and simplify the expression.

67.

68.

69. Suppose that x represents the smaller of two consecutive integers.

    a. Write a polynomial that represents the larger integer.

    b. Write a polynomial that represents the sum of the two integers. Then simplify.

    c. Write a polynomial that represents the product of the two integers. Then simplify.

    d. Write a polynomial that represents the sum of the squares of the two integers. Then simplify.

70. Suppose that x represents the larger of two consecutive odd integers.

    a. Write a polynomial that represents the smaller integer.

    b. Write a polynomial that represents the sum of the two integers. Then simplify.

    c. Write a polynomial that represents the product of the two integers. Then simplify.

    d. Write a polynomial that represents the difference of the squares of the two integers. Then simplify.

For Exercises 71–80, simplify each expression.

71. $(y + 7)^2 - 2(y - 3)^2$

72. $(x - 4)^2 - 6(x + 1)^2$

73. $(x^n + 3)(x^n - 7)$

74. $(y^n + 4)(y^n - 5)$

75. $(z^n + w^m)^2$

76. $(w^n - y^m)^2$

77. $(a^n - 5)(a^n + 5)$

78. $(b^n + 7)(b^n - 7)$

79. $(6x + 5)(6x - 5) - (6x + 5)^2$

80. $(2y - 7)(2y + 7) - (2y - 7)^2$

Objective 5: Multiply Radical Expressions Involving Multiple Terms

For Exercises 81–104, multiply and simplify. Assume that all variable expressions represent positive real numbers. (See Examples 7–8)

81. $5\sqrt{2}(2\sqrt{2} + 6\sqrt{3} - 4)$

82. $5\sqrt{7}(3\sqrt{7} - 2\sqrt{5} + 3)$

83. $3\sqrt{6}(5\sqrt{3} - 4\sqrt{2} - \sqrt{6})$

84. $4\sqrt{10}(7\sqrt{2} - 3\sqrt{5} + \sqrt{10})$

85. $(2\sqrt{y} - 3)(4\sqrt{y} + 5)$

86. $(5\sqrt{z} - 4)(3\sqrt{z} + 6)$

87. $(4\sqrt{3} - 2\sqrt{5})(6\sqrt{3} + 5\sqrt{5})$

88. $(3\sqrt{11} - 7\sqrt{2})(2\sqrt{11} + 9\sqrt{2})$

89. $(2\sqrt{3} + \sqrt{7})(2\sqrt{3} - \sqrt{7})$

90. $(5\sqrt{2} - \sqrt{11})(5\sqrt{2} + \sqrt{11})$

91. $(4x\sqrt{y} - 2y\sqrt{x})(4x\sqrt{y} + 2y\sqrt{x})$

92. $(5u\sqrt{v} - 6v\sqrt{u})(5u\sqrt{v} + 6v\sqrt{u})$

93. $(6z - \sqrt{5})^2$

94. $(2v - \sqrt{17})^2$

95. $(5a^2\sqrt{b} + 7b^2\sqrt{a})^2$

96. $(2c^3\sqrt{d} + 3d^3\sqrt{c})^2$

97. $(\sqrt{x + 1} - 5)(\sqrt{x + 1} + 5)$

98. $(\sqrt{y + 2} - 4)(\sqrt{y + 2} + 4)$

99. $(\sqrt{x + 1} - 5)^2$

100. $(\sqrt{y + 2} - 4)^2$

101. $(\sqrt{5} + 2\sqrt{x})(\sqrt{5} - 2\sqrt{x})$

102. $(\sqrt{7} + 3\sqrt{z})(\sqrt{7} - 3\sqrt{z})$

103. $(\sqrt{x + y} - \sqrt{x - y})^2$

104. $(\sqrt{a + 2} - \sqrt{a - 2})^2$

For Exercises 105–106, find the area of each triangle.

105.

106.

Write About It

107. A polynomial in the variable x is defined as an expression of the form
$a_n x^n + a_{n-1} x^{n-1} + a_{n-2} x^{n-2} + \cdots + a_1 x + a_0$.
Explain what this means.

108. Explain why $x + \sqrt{7}$ is a polynomial, but $\sqrt{x} + 7$ is not a polynomial.

109. Explain the similarity in simplifying the given expressions.
   a. $(3x + 2)(4x - 7)$
   b. $\left(3\sqrt{x} + \sqrt{2}\right)\left(4\sqrt{x} - \sqrt{7}\right)$

110. Explain the similarity in simplifying the given expressions.
   a. $(x + 3)(x - 3)$
   b. $\left(\sqrt{x} + \sqrt{3}\right)\left(\sqrt{x} - \sqrt{3}\right)$

Expanding Your Skills

For Exercises 111–114, determine if the statement is true or false.

111. The sum of two polynomials each of degree 5 will be degree 5.

112. The sum of two polynomials each of degree 5 will be less than or equal to degree 5.

113. The product of two polynomials each of degree 4 will be degree 8.

114. The product of two polynomials each of degree 4 will be less than degree 8.

115. We know that $(a + b)^2 = a^2 + 2ab + b^2$. Derive a special product formula for $(a + b)^3$.

116. We know that $(a - b)^2 = a^2 - 2ab + b^2$. Derive a special product formula for $(a - b)^3$.

PROBLEM RECOGNITION EXERCISES

Simplifying Algebraic Expressions

Many expressions in algebra look similar but the methods used to simplify the expressions may be different. For Exercises 1–14, simplify each expression. Assume that the variables are restricted so that each expression is well defined.

1. a. $64^{1/2}$
   b. $64^{1/3}$
   c. $64^{2/3}$
   d. 64^{-1}
   e. $-64^{1/2}$
   f. $(-64)^{1/2}$
   g. $(-64)^{2/3}$
   h. $(-64)^{-2/3}$

2. a. $(5ab^3)^2$
   b. $(5a + b^3)^2$
   c. $(5ab^3)^{-2}$
   d. $(5a + b^3)^{-2}$

3. a. $(2x^4 y)^2$
   b. $(2x^4 - y)^2$
   c. $(2x^4 y)^{-2}$
   d. $(2x^4 - y)^{-2}$

4. a. $x^5 x^3$
   b. $\dfrac{x^5}{x^3}$
   c. $x^{-5} x^3$
   d. $(x^5)^{-3}$

5. a. $\sqrt{x^8}$
   b. $\sqrt[3]{x^8}$
   c. $\sqrt[5]{x^8}$
   d. $\sqrt[9]{x^8}$

6. a. $(3a + 4b^2) - (2a - b^2)$
   b. $(3a + 4b^2)(2a - b^2)$

7. a. $(a^2 - b^2) + (a^2 + b^2)$
   b. $(a^2 - b^2)(a^2 + b^2)$
   c. $(a - b)^2 - (a + b)^2$
   d. $(a - b)^2(a + b)^2$

8. a. $|a - b|$ for $a < b$
   b. $|a - b|$ for $a > b$

9. a. $|x + 2|$ for $x > -2$
   b. $|x + 2|$ for $x < -2$

10. a. $\left(\sqrt{x}\right)^2 + \left(\sqrt{y}\right)^2$
   b. $\sqrt{x^2 + y^2}$
   c. $\left(\sqrt{x} + \sqrt{y}\right)^2$
   d. $\left(\sqrt{x} + \sqrt{y}\right)\left(\sqrt{x} - \sqrt{y}\right)$

11. a. $\sqrt[3]{2x} \cdot \sqrt[3]{2x}$
   b. $\sqrt[3]{2x} + \sqrt[3]{2x}$

12. a. $\sqrt[4]{y} \cdot \sqrt[3]{y}$
   b. $\sqrt[4]{y} + \sqrt[3]{y}$

13. a. $36 \div 12 \div 6 \div 2$
   b. $36 \div (12 \div 6) \div 2$
   c. $36 \div 12 \div (6 \div 2)$
   d. $(36 \div 12) \div (6 \div 2)$

14. a. $\sqrt{6^2 + 8^2}$
   b. $\sqrt{6^2} + \sqrt{8^2}$

SECTION R.6 **Factoring**

In Section R.5 we learned how to multiply polynomials. In this section, we reverse this process. The goal is to decompose a polynomial into a product of factors. This process is called factoring. Factoring is important in a variety of applications. In particular, factoring is often used to solve equations. For example, the two equations that follow are equivalent (that is, they have the same solution set).

$$x^2 - 19x + 88 = 0 \qquad (x - 8)(x - 11) = 0$$

Both equations ask, for what values of x will the left side equal zero? In the first equation it is difficult to determine the correct values of x. However, in the second equation with the left side factored, we can see by inspection that $x = 8$ and $x = 11$.

1. Factor Out the Greatest Common Factor

There are many techniques used to factor a polynomial, but the first step is always to factor out the greatest common factor.

The **greatest common factor (GCF)** of a polynomial is the expression of highest degree that divides evenly into each term of the polynomial. For example, the GCF of the following polynomial is $6x^3$.

x^3 is the greatest power of x common to all three terms.

$$12x^5 + 18x^4 - 24x^3 \qquad \text{The GCF is } 6x^3.$$

6 is the greatest integer that divides evenly into 12, 18, and -24.

To factor out the greatest common factor, we use the distributive property as shown in Example 1.

EXAMPLE 1   **Factoring Out the Greatest Common Factor**

Factor out the greatest common factor.

a. $12x^5 + 18x^4 - 24x^3$ **b.** $3y(2y - 5) + (2y - 5)$

Solution:

a. $12x^5 + 18x^4 - 24x^3$ The GCF is $6x^3$.

$\quad = 6x^3(2x^2) + 6x^3(3x) + 6x^3(-4)$ Write each term as a product of the GCF and another factor.

$\quad = 6x^3(2x^2 + 3x - 4)$ Apply the distributive property.

Check: $6x^3(2x^2 + 3x - 4)$
$\qquad = 12x^5 + 18x^4 - 24x^3$ ✓

b. $3y(2y - 5) + (2y - 5)$ The GCF is the binomial $(2y - 5)$.

$\quad = 3y(2y - 5) + 1(2y - 5)$ Write each term as a product of the GCF and another factor.

$\quad = (2y - 5)(3y + 1)$ Apply the distributive property.

Avoiding Mistakes

In Example 1(b), there is an understood factor of 1 in the second term: $1(2y - 5)$.
   Do not forget to include this in the factored form.

Skill Practice 1   Factor out the greatest common factor.
   a. $9z^6 - 27z^4 + 12z^2$ **b.** $5w(w - 3) - (w - 3)$

Answers

1. a. $3z^2(3z^4 - 9z^2 + 4)$
   b. $(w - 3)(5w - 1)$

Sometimes it is preferable to factor out a negative factor from a polynomial. For example, consider the polynomial, $-4x^2 - 8x + 12$. If we factor out -4, then the leading coefficient of the remaining polynomial will be positive.

EXAMPLE 2   **Factoring Out a Negative Factor**

Factor out -4 from the polynomial. $-4x^2 - 8x + 12$

Solution:

$-4x^2 - 8x + 12$	
$= (-4)(x^2) + (-4)(2x) + (-4)(-3)$	Write each term as a product of -4 and another factor.
$= -4(x^2 + 2x - 3)$	Apply the distributive property.

> **TIP** When a negative factor is factored out of a polynomial, the remaining terms in parentheses will have signs opposite to those in the original polynomial.

Skill Practice 2   Factor out -6 from the polynomial. $-6y^4 + 24y^2 + 6$

---

2. Factor by Grouping

To factor a polynomial containing four terms, we often try factoring by grouping. This is demonstrated in Example 3.

EXAMPLE 3   **Factoring by Grouping**

Factor by grouping.

a. $2ax - 6ay + 5x - 15y$ **b.** $m^2 - 3n + 3m - mn$

Solution:

a. $2ax - 6ay \mid + 5x - 15y$ Consider the first pair of terms and second pair of terms separately.

$= 2a(x - 3y) + 5(x - 3y)$ Factor out the GCF from the first two terms and from the second two terms.

$= (x - 3y)(2a + 5)$ Factor out the common binomial factor $(x - 3y)$ from each term.

Check: $(x - 3y)(2a + 5)$

$= 2ax + 5x - 6ay - 15y$ ✓

> **Avoiding Mistakes**
> After factoring out the GCF from each pair of terms, the binomial factors must match to be able to complete the process of factoring by grouping.

b. $m^2 - 3n \mid + 3m - mn$

$= 1(m^2 - 3n) + m(3 - n)$ After factoring out the GCF from each pair of terms, the resulting binomial factors do not match. Therefore, try rearranging terms.

These do not match.

$m^2 + 3m \mid - mn - 3n \xleftarrow{\text{rearrange}}$ In this case, we rearranged terms so that there is a common ratio between the coefficients of each pair of terms. We have 1:3 and -1:(-3). These have the same ratio, resulting in a greater likelihood that the binomial factors will match.

$= m(m + 3) - n(m + 3)$ Factor out the GCF from each pair of terms.

$= (m + 3)(m - n)$ Factor out the common binomial factor.

> **TIP** Sometimes a polynomial has more than one factored form. For example, the polynomial $m^2 - 3n + 3m - mn$, can be written as $(m + 3)(m - n)$ or as $(-m - 3)(n - m)$ or as $-1(m + 3)(n - m)$. You can verify by multiplying factors.

Skill Practice 3   Factor by grouping.

a. $7cd - c^2 + 14d - 2c$ **b.** $xy + 8x - 2x^2 - 4y$

Answers

2. $-6(y^4 - 4y^2 - 1)$
3. a. $(7d - c)(c + 2)$
   b. $(y - 2x)(x - 4)$

3. Factor Quadratic Trinomials

Next we want to factor quadratic trinomials. These are trinomials of the form $ax^2 + bx + c$, where the coefficients a, b, and c are integers and $a \neq 0$. To understand the basis to factor a trinomial, first consider the product of two binomials.

Product of $2x$ and x Product of 3 and 2

$$(2x + 3)(x + 2) = 2x^2 + 4x + 3x + 6$$

Sum of products of inner
terms and outer terms

To factor a trinomial, this process is reversed.

EXAMPLE 4   **Factoring a Quadratic Trinomial with Leading Coefficient 1**

Factor. $x^2 - 8x + 12$

Solution:

factors of x^2

$x^2 - 8x + 12 = (\Box x + \Box)(\Box x + \Box)$ First fill in the blanks so that the product of first terms in the binomials is x^2. In this case, we have $1x$ and $1x$.

factors of 12

$x^2 - 8x + 12 = (1x + \Box)(1x + \Box)$ Fill in the remaining blanks with numbers whose product is 12 and whose sum is the middle term coefficient, -8. The numbers are -2 and -6.

$= (x - 2)(x - 6)$ Check: $(x - 2)(x - 6) = x^2 - 6x - 2x + 12$
$= x^2 - 8x + 12$ ✓

Skill Practice 4   Factor. $y^2 - 9y + 14$

The trinomial in Example 4 has a leading coefficient of 1. This simplified the factorization process. For any trinomial with a leading coefficient of 1 ($x^2 + bx + c$), the constant terms in the binomial factors have a product of c and a sum equal to the middle term coefficient, b.

To factor a trinomial of the form $ax^2 + bx + c$, where $a \neq 1$, all possible factors of ax^2 must be tested with all factors of c until the correct middle term is found. This is demonstrated in Example 5.

EXAMPLE 5   **Factoring a Quadratic Trinomial with Leading Coefficient $\neq 1$**

Factor. $27y + 10y^2 + 5$

Solution:

$10y^2 + 27y + 5$ First write the polynomial in the form $ax^2 + bx + c$.

factors of $10y^2$

$10y^2 + 27y + 5 = (\Box y + \Box)(\Box y + \Box)$ Fill in the blanks so that the product of first terms in the binomials is $10y^2$. We have $1y$ and $10y$ or $2y$ and $5y$.

factors of 5

$(1y + \Box)(10y + \Box)$ or $(2y + \Box)(5y + \Box)$ Fill in the remaining blanks with factors of 5. Since the middle term of the trinomial is positive, consider only positive factors of 5: (1)(5) and (5)(1).

Answer

4. $(y - 7)(y - 2)$

$(y + 1)(10y + 5) = 10y^2 + 5y + 10y + 5 = 10y^2 + 15y + 5$ Incorrect. Wrong middle term.

$(y + 5)(10y + 1) = 10y^2 + y + 50y + 5 = 10y^2 + 51y + 5$ Incorrect. Wrong middle term.

$(2y + 1)(5y + 5) = 10y^2 + 10y + 5y + 5 = 10y^2 + 15y + 5$ Incorrect. Wrong middle term.

$(2y + 5)(5y + 1) = 10y^2 + 2y + 25y + 5 = 10y^2 + 27y + 5$ Correct! ✓

The trinomial $10y^2 + 27y + 5$ factors as $(2y + 5)(5y + 1)$.

Skill Practice 5   Factor. $6x^2 + 23x + 7$

The technique shown in Examples 4 and 5 is called the trial-and-error method to factor a trinomial. The process is somewhat tedious, but we can often eliminate some of the possible binomials to test. For instance, the trinomial $10y^2 + 27y + 5$ has no common factor other than 1. Therefore, the terms within the binomials in the factored form must not have a common factor other than 1. From Example 5,

$(y + 1)(10y + 5)$ is not correct because $10y$ and 5 share a common factor of 5.

$(2y + 1)(5y + 5)$ is not correct because $5y$ and 5 share a common factor of 5.

Eliminating these possibilities leaves us with only two pairs of binomials to test.

EXAMPLE 6   **Factoring a Quadratic Trinomial**

Factor. $10x^3 + 105x^2y - 55xy^2$

Solution:

$10x^3 + 105x^2y - 55xy^2$

$= 5x(2x^2 + 21xy - 11y^2)$ Factor out the GCF, $5x$.

factors of $2x^2$

$= 5x(2x^2 + 21xy - 11y^2) = 5x(\square x + \square y)(\square x + \square y)$ Fill in the blanks so that the product of first terms in the binomials is $2x^2$. We have $2x$ and x.

factors of $-11y^2$

$= 5x(2x^2 + 21xy - 11y^2) = 5x(2x + \square)(x + \square)$ Fill in the remaining blanks with factors of $-11y^2$.

> **TIP** The order in which the product of factors is written does not affect the product. Therefore, $5x(2x - y)(x + 11y)$ equals $5x(x + 11y)(2x - y)$. This is guaranteed by the commutative property of multiplication.

$(2x + 11y)(x - 1y) = 2x^2 - 2xy + 11xy - 11y^2 = 2x^2 + 9xy - 11y^2$ Incorrect.

$(2x + y)(x - 11y) = 2x^2 - 22xy + xy - 11y^2 = 2x^2 - 21xy - 11y^2$ Incorrect.

$(2x - 11y)(x + y) = 2x^2 + 2xy - 11xy - 11y^2 = 2x^2 - 9xy - 11y^2$ Incorrect.

$(2x - y)(x + 11y) = 2x^2 + 22xy - xy - 11y^2 = 2x^2 + 21xy - 11y^2$ Correct! ✓

The trinomial $10x^3 + 105x^2y - 55xy^2$ factors as $5x(2x - y)(x + 11y)$.

Do not forget to write the GCF.

Skill Practice 6   Factor. $30m^3 - 200m^2n - 70mn^2$

Answers

5. $(2x + 7)(3x + 1)$

6. $10m(3m + n)(m - 7n)$

The process to factor a trinomial can be challenging if the coefficients are large. In fact, we will learn other techniques that will come in handy in such cases. One technique we show here is to recognize a perfect square trinomial and factor it as the square of a binomial. From Section R.5, we have the following formulas.

Factored Form of a Perfect Square Trinomial

$a^2 + 2ab + b^2 = (a + b)^2$ $a^2 - 2ab + b^2 = (a - b)^2$	A perfect square trinomial factors as the square of a binomial.

To identify a perfect square trinomial:	$4x^2 + 12x + 9 = (2x + 3)^2$
• First check whether the first and third terms are perfect squares.	perfect squares
• If so, label their principal square roots as a and b.	$a = 2x$ and $b = 3$
• Then determine if the absolute value of the middle term is $2ab$.	$12x \stackrel{?}{=} 2(2x)(3)$ ✓

EXAMPLE 7   **Factoring a Perfect Square Trinomial**

Factor.

    a. $4x^2 - 28x + 49$ **b.** $81c^4 + 90c^2d + 25d^2$

Solution:

    a. $4x^2 - 28x + 49$

         $= (2x)^2 - 2(2x)(7) + (7)^2$ The trinomial fits the pattern $a^2 - 2ab + b^2$, where $a = 2x$ and $b = 7$.

         $= (2x - 7)^2$ Factor as $a^2 - 2ab + b^2 = (a - b)^2$.

    b. $81c^4 + 90c^2d + 25d^2$

         $= (9c^2)^2 + 2(9c^2)(5d) + (5d)^2$ The trinomial fits the pattern $a^2 + 2ab + b^2$, where $a = 9c^2$ and $b = 5d$.

         $= (9c^2 + 5d)^2$ Factor as $a^2 + 2ab + b^2 = (a + b)^2$.

Skill Practice 7   Factor.

    a. $64y^2 + 16y + 1$ **b.** $9m^4 - 30m^2n + 25n^2$

---

4. Factor Binomials

Recall that the product of conjugates results in a difference of squares. Therefore, the factored form of a difference of squares is a product of conjugates.

Factored Form of a Difference of Squares

$$a^2 - b^2 = (a + b)(a - b)$$

Note: If a and b share no common factors other than 1, then a sum of squares $a^2 + b^2$ is not factorable over the set of real numbers.

Answers

7. a. $(8y + 1)^2$ **b.** $(3m^2 - 5n)^2$

EXAMPLE 8 **Factoring a Difference of Squares**

Factor completely.

a. $p^2 - 100$ **b.** $32y^4 - 162$

Solution:

a. $p^2 - 100$

$= (p)^2 - (10)^2$ | The binomial fits the pattern $a^2 - b^2$, where $a = p$ and $b = 10$.

$= (p + 10)(p - 10)$ | Factor as $a^2 - b^2 = (a + b)(a - b)$.

b. $32y^4 - 162$

$= 2(16y^4 - 81)$ | Factor out the GCF, 2.

$= 2[(4y^2)^2 - (9)^2]$ | The binomial fits the pattern $a^2 - b^2$, where $a = 4y^2$ and $b = 9$.

$= 2(4y^2 + 9)(4y^2 - 9)$ | Factor as $a^2 - b^2 = (a + b)(a - b)$.

$= 2(4y^2 + 9)[(2y)^2 - (3)^2]$ | The factor $(4y^2 - 9)$ is also a difference of squares, with $a = 2y$ and $b = 3$.

$= 2(4y^2 + 9)(2y + 3)(2y - 3)$ | The polynomial is now factored completely.

Skill Practice 8 Factor completely.

a. $t^2 - 121$ **b.** $625z^5 - z$

A binomial can also be factored if it fits the pattern of a difference of cubes or a sum of cubes.

> **TIP** The factored form of a sum or difference of cubes is a binomial times a trinomial. To help remember the pattern for the signs, remember **SOAP: S**ame sign, **O**pposite signs, **A**lways **P**ositive.

Factored Form of a Sum and Difference of Cubes

Sum of cubes: $a^3 + b^3 = (a + b)(a^2 - ab + b^2)$

Difference of cubes: $a^3 - b^3 = (a - b)(a^2 + ab + b^2)$

Same sign ⎵ Always **P**ositive

Opposite signs

EXAMPLE 9 **Factoring a Sum and Difference of Cubes**

Factor completely.

a. $x^3 + 125$ **b.** $8m^6 - 27n^3$

Solution:

a. $x^3 + 125$

$= (x)^3 + (5)^3$ | The binomial fits the pattern of a sum of cubes $a^3 + b^3$, where $a = x$ and $b = 5$.

$= (x + 5)[(x)^2 - (x)(5) + (5)^2]$ | Factor as $a^3 + b^3 = (a + b)(a^2 - ab + b^2)$.

$= (x + 5)(x^2 - 5x + 25)$ | Simplify.

b. $8m^6 - 27n^3$

$= (2m^2)^3 - (3n)^3$ | The binomial fits the pattern of a difference of cubes $a^3 - b^3$, where $a = 2m^2$ and $b = 3n$.

$= (2m^2 - 3n)[(2m^2)^2 + (2m^2)(3n) + (3n)^2]$ | Factor as $a^3 - b^3$ $= (a - b)(a^2 + ab + b^2)$.

$= (2m^2 - 3n)(4m^4 + 6m^2n + 9n^2)$ | Simplify.

Answers

8. a. $(t + 11)(t - 11)$
  b. $z(25z^2 + 1)(5z + 1)(5z - 1)$

5. Apply a General Strategy to Factor Polynomials

Factoring polynomials is a strategy game. The process requires that we identify the technique or techniques that best apply to a given polynomial. To do this we can follow the guidelines given in Table R-5.

Table R-5   Factoring Strategy

First Step	Number of Terms	Technique
Factor out the GCF	4 or more terms	Try factoring by grouping.
	3 terms	If possible write the trinomial in the form $ax^2 + bx + c$. • If the trinomial is a perfect square trinomial, factor as $$a^2 + 2ab + b^2 = (a + b)^2$$ $$a^2 - 2ab + b^2 = (a - b)^2$$ • Otherwise try factoring by the trial-and-error method.
	2 terms	• If the binomial is a difference of squares, factor as $$a^2 - b^2 = (a + b)(a - b).$$ • If the binomial is a sum of cubes, factor as $$a^3 + b^3 = (a + b)(a^2 - ab + b^2)$$ • If the binomial is a difference of cubes, factor as $$a^3 - b^3 = (a - b)(a^2 + ab + b^2)$$ *Note*: A sum of squares, $a^2 + b^2$, cannot be factored over the real numbers.

EXAMPLE 10   **Factoring a 4-Term Polynomial**

Factor completely. $20xy^3 + 50xy^2 - 180xy - 450x$

Solution:

$$20xy^3 + 50xy^2 - 180xy - 450x$$
The GCF is $10x$.

$$= 10x(2y^3 + 5y^2 - 18y - 45)$$
This polynomial has 4 terms. Try factoring by grouping.

$$= 10x[y^2(2y + 5) - 9(2y + 5)]$$
The terms have a common binomial factor.

$$= 10x[(2y + 5)(y^2 - 9)]$$
The expression $y^2 - 9$ can be factored further as a difference of squares.

$$= 10x(2y + 5)(y + 3)(y - 3)$$
The polynomial is factored completely.

Avoiding Mistakes

Do not forget to write the greatest common factor as part of the final answer.

Skill Practice 10   Factor completely. $15x^3 + 10x^2 - 240x - 160$

EXAMPLE 11   Factoring by Grouping 1 Term with 3 Terms

Factor completely. $25 - x^2 - 4xy - 4y^2$

Solution:

This polynomial has 4 terms. However, the standard grouping method does not work even if we try rearranging terms.

$25 - x^2 - 4xy - 4y^2$ perfect square trinomial	We might try grouping 1 term with 3 terms. The reason is that after factoring out -1 from the last 3 terms we have a perfect square trinomial.
$= 25 - (x^2 + 4xy + 4y^2)$	
$= 25 - (x + 2y)^2$ ← difference of squares	The resulting expression is a difference of squares $a^2 - b^2$ where $a = 5$ and $b = (x + 2y)$.
$= (5)^2 - (x + 2y)^2$	
$= [5 + (x + 2y)][5 - (x + 2y)]$	Factor as $a^2 - b^2 = (a + b)(a - b)$.
$= (5 + x + 2y)(5 - x - 2y)$	Simplify.

Skill Practice 11   Factor completely. $36 - m^2 - 6mn - 9n^2$

In Example 11, it may be helpful to write the expression $25 - (x + 2y)^2$ by using a convenient substitution. If we let $u = x + 2y$, then the expression becomes $25 - u^2$. This is easier to recognize as a difference of squares.

$$25 - u^2 = (5 + u)(5 - u)$$
$$= [5 + (x + 2y)][5 - (x + 2y)] \quad \text{Back substitute.}$$
$$= (5 + x + 2y)(5 - x - 2y)$$

In Example 12, we practice making an appropriate substitution to convert a cumbersome expression into one that is more easily recognizable and factorable.

EXAMPLE 12   Factoring a Trinomial by Using Substitution

Factor completely. $(x^2 - 5)^2 + 2(x^2 - 5) - 24$

Solution:

$(x^2 - 5)^2 + 2(x^2 - 5) - 24$	Notice that the first two terms in the polynomial share a common factor of $(x^2 - 5)$. Suppose that we let u represent this expression. That is, $u = x^2 - 5$.
$= u^2 + 2u - 24$	The polynomial becomes $u^2 + 2u - 24$. This is more easily recognized as a polynomial that is in quadratic form.
$= (u + 6)(u - 4)$	Factor.
$= [(x^2 - 5) + 6][(x^2 - 5) - 4]$	Back substitute. Replace u by $(x^2 - 5)$.
$= (x^2 + 1)(x^2 - 9)$	Simplify.
$= (x^2 + 1)(x + 3)(x - 3)$	Factor $x^2 - 9$ as a difference of squares.

Skill Practice 12   Factor completely. $(x^2 - 2)^2 + 5(x^2 - 2) - 14$

Answers
11. $(6 + m + 3n)(6 - m - 3n)$
12. $(x^2 + 5)(x + 2)(x - 2)$

Some polynomials cannot be factored with the techniques learned thus far. For example, no combination of binomial factors with integer coefficients will produce the trinomial $3x^2 + 9x + 5$.

$$(3x + 5)(x + 1) = 3x^2 + 3x + 5x + 5 \qquad \text{Incorrect. Wrong middle term.}$$
$$= 3x^2 + 8x + 5$$
$$(3x + 1)(x + 5) = 3x^2 + 15x + x + 5 \qquad \text{Incorrect. Wrong middle term.}$$
$$= 3x^2 + 16x + 5$$

In such a case we say that the polynomial is a **prime polynomial.** Its only factors are 1 and itself.

6. Factor Expressions Containing Negative and Rational Exponents

We now revisit the process to factor out the greatest common factor. In some applications, it is necessary to factor out a variable factor with a negative integer exponent or a rational exponent. Before we demonstrate this in Example 13, take a minute to review a similar example with positive integer exponents.

$$2x^6 + 5x^5 + 7x^4 \qquad \text{The GCF is } x^4. \text{ This is } x \text{ raised to the } \textit{smallest}$$
$$\textit{exponent to which it appears in any term.}$$

$$\boxed{6-4}\ \boxed{5-4}\ \boxed{4-4}$$

$$= x^4(2x^2 + 5x^1 + 7x^0) \qquad \text{The powers on the factors of } x \text{ within parentheses are found by subtracting 4 from the original exponents.}$$

EXAMPLE 13   **Factoring Out Negative and Rational Exponents**

Factor.

a. $2x^{-6} + 5x^{-5} + 7x^{-4}$ **b.** $x(2x + 5)^{-1/2} + (2x + 5)^{1/2}$

Solution:

a. $2x^{-6} + 5x^{-5} + 7x^{-4}$ The smallest exponent on x is -6.
Factor out x^{-6}.

$$\boxed{-6 - (-6)}\ \boxed{-5 - (-6)}\ \boxed{-4 - (-6)}$$

$$= x^{-6}(2x^0 + 5x^1 + 7x^2) \qquad \text{The powers on the factors of } x \text{ within parentheses are found by subtracting } -6 \text{ from the original exponents.}$$

$$= x^{-6}(2 + 5x + 7x^2)$$

$$= \frac{7x^2 + 5x + 2}{x^6} \qquad \text{Simplify the negative exponent.}$$
$$b^{-n} = \frac{1}{b^n}$$

b. $x(2x + 5)^{-1/2} + (2x + 5)^{1/2}$ The smallest exponent on $(2x + 5)$ is $-\frac{1}{2}$.

$$\boxed{-1/2 - (-1/2)}\ \boxed{1/2 - (-1/2)} \quad \text{Factor out } (2x + 5)^{-1/2}.$$

$$= (2x + 5)^{-1/2}\,[x(2x + 5)^0 + (2x + 5)^1] \qquad \text{The powers on the factors of } (2x + 5) \text{ within parentheses are found by subtracting } -\frac{1}{2} \text{ from the original exponents.}$$

$$= (2x + 5)^{-1/2}\,[x + (2x + 5)] \qquad \text{The expression } (2x + 5)^0 = 1, \text{ for } 2x + 5 \neq 0.$$

$$= (2x + 5)^{-1/2}\,(3x + 5) \qquad \text{Simplify.}$$

$$= \frac{3x + 5}{(2x + 5)^{1/2}} \qquad \text{Simplify the negative exponent.}$$

Answers

13. a. $\dfrac{2a^2 - 3a + 11}{a^5}$

b. $\dfrac{5x + 3}{(4x + 3)^{3/4}}$

> **Skill Practice 13** Factor.
>
> **a.** $11a^{-5} - 3a^{-4} + 2a^{-3}$ **b.** $x(4x + 3)^{-3/4} + (4x + 3)^{1/4}$

SECTION R.6 Practice Exercises

Review Exercises

For Exercises 1–8, perform the indicated operations.

1. a. $(2x^4y^2)^2$
 b. $(2x^4 - y^2)^2$

2. a. $(5a^3b^2)^2$
 b. $(5a^3 + b^2)^2$

3. $(3x - 4y^2)(2x + 5y^2)$

4. $(6a^2 + 2k)(a^2 - 7k)$

5. $\left(\dfrac{1}{5}c^4 - \dfrac{3}{8}ab\right)\left(\dfrac{1}{5}c^4 + \dfrac{3}{8}ab\right)$

6. $\left(\dfrac{3}{2}m^5 + \dfrac{5}{7}np\right)\left(\dfrac{3}{2}m^5 - \dfrac{5}{7}np\right)$

7. $(2x + 3)(4x^2 - 6x + 9)$

8. $(3y - 5)(9y^2 + 15y + 25)$

Concept Connections

9. The binomial $a^3 + b^3$ is called a sum of _____ and factors as _____.

10. The binomial $a^3 - b^3$ is called a _____ of cubes and factors as _____.

11. The trinomial $a^2 + 2ab + b^2$ is a _____ square trinomial. Its factored form is _____.

12. The binomial $a^2 - b^2$ is called a difference of _____ and factors as _____.

Objective 1: Factor Out the Greatest Common Factor

For Exercises 13–20, factor out the greatest common factor. **(See Example 1)**

13. $15c^5 - 30c^4 + 5c^3$

14. $12m^4 + 15m^3 + 3m^2$

15. $21a^2b^5 - 14a^3b^4 + 35a^4b$

16. $36p^4q^7 + 18p^3q^5 - 27p^2q^6$

17. $5z(x - 6y) + 7(x - 6y)$

18. $4t(u + 8v) - 3(u + 8v)$

19. $10k^2(3k^2 + 7) - 5k(3k^2 + 7)$

20. $8j^3(4j + 9) + 4j^2(4j + 9)$

For Exercises 21–24, factor out the indicated common factor. **(See Example 2)**

21. a. Factor out 3. $-6x^2 + 12x + 9$
 b. Factor out -3. $-6x^2 + 12x + 9$

22. a. Factor out 5. $-15y^2 - 10y + 25$
 b. Factor out -5. $-15y^2 - 10y + 25$

23. Factor out $-4x^2y$. $-12x^3y^2 - 8x^4y^3 + 4x^2y$

24. Factor out $-7a^3b$. $-14a^4b^3 + 21a^3b^2 - 7a^3b$

Objective 2: Factor by Grouping

For Exercises 25–30, factor by grouping. **(See Example 3)**

25. $8ax + 18a + 20x + 45$

26. $6ty + 9y + 14t + 21$

27. $12x^3 - 9x^2 - 40x + 30$

28. $30z^3 - 35z^2 - 24z + 28$

29. $cd - 8d + 4c - 2d^2$

30. $7t - 6v^2 + tv - 42v$

Objective 3: Factor Quadratic Trinomials

For Exercises 31–44, factor the trinomials. **(See Examples 4–7)**

31. $p^2 + 2p - 63$

32. $w^2 + 5w - 66$

33. $2t^3 - 28t^2 + 80t$

34. $5u^4 - 40u^3 + 35u^2$

35. $25z + 6z^2 + 14$

36. $8 + 15m^2 + 26m$

37. $7y^3z - 40y^2z^2 - 12yz^3$

38. $11a^3b + 18a^2b^2 - 8ab^3$

39. $t^2 - 18t + 81$

40. $p^2 + 8p + 16$

41. $50x^3 + 160x^2y + 128xy^2$

42. $48y^3 - 72y^2z + 27yz^2$

43. $4c^4 - 20c^2d^3 + 25d^6$

44. $9m^4 + 42m^2n^4 + 49n^8$

Objective 4: Factor Binomials

For Exercises 45–56, factor the binomials. (See Examples 8–9)

45. $9w^2 - 64$

46. $16t^2 - 49$

47. $200u^4 - 18v^6$

48. $75m^6 - 27n^4$

49. $625p^4 - 16$

50. $81z^4 - 1$

51. $y^3 + 64$

52. $u^3 + 343$

53. $c^4 - 27c$

54. $d^4 - 8d$

55. $8a^6 - 125b^9$

56. $27m^{12} - 64n^9$

Objective 5:   Apply a General Strategy to Factor Polynomials

For Exercises 57–84, factor completely. (See Examples 10–12)

57. $30x^4 + 70x^3 - 120x^2 - 280x$

58. $4y^4 - 10y^3 - 36y^2 + 90y$

59. $a^2 - y^2 + 10y - 25$

60. $c^2 - z^2 + 8z - 16$

61. $30x^3y + 125x^2y + 120xy$

62. $60t^4v + 78t^3v - 180t^2v$

63. $(x^2 - 2)^2 - 3(x^2 - 2) - 28$

64. $(y^2 + 2)^2 + 5(y^2 + 2) - 24$

65. $(x^3 + 12)^2 - 16$

66. $(y^3 + 34)^2 - 49$

67. $(x + y)^2 - z^2$

68. $(a + 5)^2 - y^2$

69. $(x + y)^3 + z^3$

70. $(a + 5)^3 - b^3$

71. $9m^2 + 42m(3n + 1) + 49(3n + 1)^2$

72. $4x^2 + 36x(7y - 1) + 81(7y - 1)^2$

73. $(c - 3)^2 - (2c - 5)^2$

74. $(d + 6)^2 - (4d - 3)^2$

75. $p^{11} - 64p^8 - p^3 + 64$

76. $t^7 + 27t^4 - t^3 - 27$

77. $m^6 + 26m^3 - 27$

78. $n^6 - 7n^3 - 8$

79. $16x^6z + 38x^3z - 54z$

80. $24y^7 + 21y^4 - 3y$

81. $x^2 - y^2 - x + y$

82. $a^2 - b^2 - a - b$

83. $a^2 + ac - 2c^2 - c + a$

84. $x^2 + 2xy - 3y^2 - y + x$

Objective 6: Factor Expressions Containing Negative and Rational Exponents

For Exercises 85–94, factor completely. (See Example 13)

85. $2x^{-4} - 7x^{-3} + x^{-2}$

86. $5t^{-7} + 2t^{-6} - t^{-5}$

87. $y^{-2} - y^{-3} - 12y^{-4}$

88. $w^{-3} + 10w^{-4} + 9w^{-5}$

89. $2c^{7/4} + 4c^{3/4}$

90. $10y^{9/5} - 15y^{4/5}$

91. $5x(3x + 1)^{2/3} + (3x + 1)^{5/3}$

92. $7t(4t + 1)^{3/4} + (4t + 1)^{7/4}$

93. $x(3x + 2)^{-2/3} + (3x + 2)^{1/3}$

94. $x(5x - 8)^{-4/5} + (5x - 8)^{1/5}$

Mixed Exercises

For Exercises 95–96, write an expression for the shaded area, and factor the expression.

95.

96.

For Exercises 97–100, write the expression in factored form.

97. $2\pi r^2 + 2\pi rh$ Surface area of a right circular cylinder

98. $P + Prt$ Principal and simple interest

99. $\dfrac{4}{3}\pi R^3 - \dfrac{4}{3}\pi r^3$ Volume between two concentric spheres

100. $\pi R^2 - \pi r^2$ Area between two concentric circles

101. Simplify the expression $21^2 - 19^2$ by first factoring the expression. Do not use a calculator.

102. Simplify the expression $17^2 - 13^2$ by first factoring the expression. Do not use a calculator.

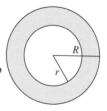

Write About It

103. Explain how to construct a perfect square trinomial.

104. Why is the sum of squares $a^2 + b^2$ not factorable over the real numbers?

105. Explain the similarity in the process to factor out the GCF in the following two expressions.

$5x^4 + 4x^3$ and $5x^{-4} + 4x^{-3}$

106. Explain the similarity in the process to factor out the GCF in the following two expressions.

$6x^5 + 5x^2$ and $6x^{5/3} + 5x^{2/3}$

Expanding Your Skills

We say that the expression $x^2 - 4$ is factorable over the integers as $(x + 2)(x - 2)$. Notice that the constant terms in the binomials are integers. The expression $x^2 - 3$ can be factored over the irrational numbers as $x^2 - 3 = (x + \sqrt{3})(x - \sqrt{3})$. For Exercises 107–112, factor each expression over the irrational numbers.

107. $x^2 - 5$

108. $y^2 - 11$

109. $z^4 - 36$

110. $w^4 - 49$

111. $x^2 - 2\sqrt{5}x + 5$

112. $c^2 - 2\sqrt{3}c + 3$

113. Consider the following binomials and their factored forms. (The factored forms can be verified by multiplying the expressions on the right.)

$x^2 - 1 = (x - 1)(x + 1)$

$x^3 - 1 = (x - 1)(x^2 + x + 1)$

$x^4 - 1 = (x - 1)(x^3 + x^2 + x + 1)$

a. Use the pattern to factor the expression $x^5 - 1$.

b. Use the pattern to write a generic formula for $x^n - 1$ where n is a positive integer.

114. For a positive integer n, the expression $a^n - b^n$ can be factored as

$a^n - b^n = (a - b)(a^{n-1} + a^{n-2}b + a^{n-3}b^2 + \cdots + ab^{n-2} + b^{n-1})$.

a. Use this formula to factor $a^5 - b^5$.

b. Check the result to part (a) by multiplication.

Consider the trinomial $ax^2 + bx + c$ with integer coefficients a, b, and c. The trinomial can be factored as the product of two binomials with integer coefficients if $b^2 - 4ac$ is a perfect square. For Exercises 115–120, determine whether the trinomial can be factored as a product of two binomials with integer coefficients.

115. $36p^2 - 33p - 12$

116. $24w^2 - 25w + 8$

117. $8x^2 + 2x - 15$

118. $6x^2 - 7x - 20$

119. $18y^2 + 45y - 48$

120. $54z^2 - 39z - 60$

SECTION R.7   Rational Expressions and More Operations on Radicals

OBJECTIVES

1. Determine Restricted Values for a Rational Expression
2. Simplify Rational Expressions
3. Multiply and Divide Rational Expressions
4. Add and Subtract Rational Expressions
5. Simplify Complex Fractions
6. Rationalize the Denominator of a Radical Expression

1. Determine Restricted Values for a Rational Expression

Suppose that an object that is originally 35°C is placed in a freezer. The temperature T (in °C) of the object t hours after being placed in the freezer can be approximated by the model

$$T = \frac{350}{t^2 + 3t + 10}$$

For example, 2 hr after being placed in the freezer the temperature of the object is

$$T = \frac{350}{(2)^2 + 3(2) + 10} = 17.5°C$$

The expression $\dfrac{350}{t^2 + 3t + 10}$ is called a rational expression. A **rational expression** is a ratio of two polynomials. Since a rational expression may have a variable in the denominator, we must be careful to exclude values of the variable that make the denominator zero.

EXAMPLE 1   **Determining Restricted Values for a Rational Expression**

Determine the restrictions on the variable for each rational expression.

a. $\dfrac{x-3}{x+2}$ b. $\dfrac{x}{x^2-49}$ c. $\dfrac{4}{5x^2y}$

Solution:

a. $\dfrac{x-3}{x+2}$

$\boxed{x \neq -2}$

Division by zero is undefined.
For this expression $x \neq -2$. If -2 were substituted for x, the denominator would be zero. $-2 + 2 = 0$

b. $\dfrac{x}{x^2-49} = \dfrac{x}{(x+7)(x-7)}$

$\boxed{x \neq -7}$ $\boxed{x \neq 7}$

For this expression, $x \neq -7$ and $x \neq 7$. If x were -7, then $-7 + 7 = 0$. If x were 7, then $7 - 7 = 0$. In either case, the denominator would be zero.

c. $\dfrac{4}{5x^2y}$

$\boxed{x \neq 0}$ $\boxed{y \neq 0}$

For this expression, $x \neq 0$ and $y \neq 0$. If either x or y were zero, then the product would be zero.

Skill Practice 1   Determine the restrictions on the variable.

a. $\dfrac{x+4}{x-3}$ b. $\dfrac{5}{c^2-16}$ c. $\dfrac{6}{7ab^3}$

2. Simplify Rational Expressions

A rational expression is simplified (in lowest terms) if the only factors shared by the numerator and denominator are 1 or -1. To simplify a rational expression, factor the numerator and denominator, then apply the property of equivalent algebraic fractions.

Equivalent Algebraic Fractions

If a, b, and c represent real-valued expressions, then

$$\frac{ac}{bc} = \frac{a}{b} \quad \text{for } b \neq 0 \text{ and } c \neq 0$$

Verbal Interpretation	Algebraic Example
A common factor in the numerator and denominator of an algebraic fraction can be divided out.	$\dfrac{10x}{15x} = \dfrac{2 \cdot 5 \cdot x}{3 \cdot 5 \cdot x} = \dfrac{2}{3}$

EXAMPLE 2   **Simplifying Rational Expressions**

Simplify.

a. $\dfrac{x^2-16}{x^2-x-12}$ b. $\dfrac{8+2\sqrt{7}}{4}$

Answers

1. a. $x \neq 3$ **b.** $c \neq -4$ and $c \neq 4$
   c. $a \neq 0$ and $b \neq 0$

Solution:

a. $\dfrac{x^2 - 16}{x^2 - x - 12} = \dfrac{(x+4)(x-4)}{(x+3)(x-4)}$ Factor the numerator and denominator. We have the restrictions that $x \neq -3$, $x \neq 4$.

$= \dfrac{(x+4)(x-4)^{\,1}}{(x+3)(x-4)_{\,1}}$ Divide out common factors that form a ratio of $\frac{1}{1}$.

$= \dfrac{x+4}{x+3}$ for $x \neq -3$, $x \neq 4$ The same restrictions for the original expression also apply to the simplified expression.

b. $\dfrac{8 + 2\sqrt{7}}{4} = \dfrac{2(4 + \sqrt{7})}{2 \cdot 2}$ Factor the numerator and denominator.

$= \dfrac{2^{\,1}(4 + \sqrt{7})}{2 \cdot 2_{\,1}}$ Divide out common factors.

$= \dfrac{4 + \sqrt{7}}{2}$ There are no variables in the denominator. Therefore, there are no restricted values for either expression.

Skill Practice 2   Simplify.

a. $\dfrac{x^2 - 8x}{x^2 - 7x - 8}$ **b.** $\dfrac{3 + 9\sqrt{5}}{6}$

It is important to understand that the restrictions on the variable for a rational expression also apply to a simplified form of the expression. In Example 2(a), the expressions $\dfrac{x^2 - 16}{x^2 - x - 12}$ and $\dfrac{x + 4}{x + 3}$ are equal for all values of x for which *both* expressions are defined. This excludes the values $x = -3$ and $x = 4$.

The property of equivalent algebraic fractions tells us that we can divide out common factors that form a ratio of 1. We can also divide out factors that form a ratio of -1. For example:

TIP The expressions $4 - x$ and $x - 4$ are opposite polynomials (the signs of their terms are opposites). The ratio of two opposite factors is -1.

$$\dfrac{4 - x}{x - 4} \xrightarrow{\text{Factor out } -1 \text{ from the numerator.}} \dfrac{-1(-4 + x)}{x - 4} = \dfrac{-1(x - 4)}{x - 4} = -1$$

Numerator and denominator are opposite polynomials. Their ratio is -1.

EXAMPLE 3   **Simplifying Rational Expressions**

Simplify. $\dfrac{14 - 2x}{x^2 - 7x}$

Solution:

$\dfrac{14 - 2x}{x^2 - 7x} = \dfrac{2(7 - x)}{x(x - 7)}$ Factor the numerator and denominator. We have the restrictions that $x \neq 0$, $x \neq 7$.

$= \dfrac{2(7 - x)^{\,(-1)}}{x(x - 7)}$ The factors $(7 - x)$ and $(x - 7)$ are opposites. Their ratio is -1.   Divide out opposite factors that form a ratio of -1.

$= -\dfrac{2}{x}$ for $x \neq 0$, $x \neq 7$ The same restrictions for the original expression also apply to the simplified expression.

Answers

2. a. $\dfrac{x}{x + 1}$; $x \neq 8$, $x \neq -1$

   b. $\dfrac{1 + 3\sqrt{5}}{2}$

In Example 3, the negative sign in the answer can be placed in the numerator, denominator, or out in front of the fraction.

$$\frac{-2}{x} = \frac{2}{-x} = -\frac{2}{x}$$

3. Multiply and Divide Rational Expressions

To multiply and divide rational expressions, use the following properties.

Multiplication and Division of Algebraic Fractions	
Let a, b, c, and d be real-valued expressions. $\dfrac{a}{b} \cdot \dfrac{c}{d} = \dfrac{ac}{bd}$ for $b \neq 0, d \neq 0$ $\dfrac{a}{b} \div \dfrac{c}{d} = \dfrac{a}{b} \cdot \dfrac{d}{c} = \dfrac{ad}{bc}$ for $b \neq 0, c \neq 0, d \neq 0$	**Examples:** • $\dfrac{2}{y} \cdot \dfrac{x}{7} = \dfrac{2x}{7y}$ for $y \neq 0$ • $\dfrac{x + 1}{6} \div \dfrac{3}{11} = \dfrac{x + 1}{6} \cdot \dfrac{11}{3} = \dfrac{11(x + 1)}{18}$

To multiply or divide rational expressions, factor the numerator and denominator of each fraction completely. Then apply the multiplication and division properties for algebraic fractions.

Restriction Agreement

Operations on rational expressions are valid for all values of the variable for which the rational expressions are defined. In Examples 4–11 and in the exercises, we will perform operations on rational expressions without explicitly stating the restrictions. Instead, the restrictions on the variables will be implied.

EXAMPLE 4   **Multiplying Rational Expressions**

Multiply. $\dfrac{2xy}{x^2y + 3xy} \cdot \dfrac{x^2 + 6x + 9}{4x + 12}$

Solution:

$$\frac{2xy}{x^2y + 3xy} \cdot \frac{x^2 + 6x + 9}{4x + 12}$$

$$= \frac{2xy}{xy(x + 3)} \cdot \frac{(x + 3)^2}{4(x + 3)} \qquad \text{Factor the numerator and denominator.}$$

$$= \frac{\overset{1}{2} \cdot \overset{1}{\cancel{xy}} \cdot \overset{1}{(\cancel{x + 3})}(\cancel{x + 3})}{\cancel{xy}(\cancel{x + 3}) \cdot 2 \cdot 2(\cancel{x + 3})} \qquad \begin{array}{l} \text{Apply the multiplication property of fractions.} \\ \text{Divide out common factors.} \end{array}$$

$$= \frac{1}{2}$$

Avoiding Mistakes

All factors from the numerator divided out, leaving a factor of 1. Do not forget to write 1 in the numerator.

Answers

3. $-\dfrac{10}{m + 3}; m \neq 3, m \neq -3$

4. $\dfrac{1}{3}$

EXAMPLE 5   **Dividing Rational Expressions**

Divide. $\dfrac{x^3 - 8}{4 - x^2} \div \dfrac{3x^2 + 6x + 12}{x^2 - x - 6}$

Solution:

$$\dfrac{x^3 - 8}{4 - x^2} \div \dfrac{3x^2 + 6x + 12}{x^2 - x - 6}$$

$$= \dfrac{x^3 - 8}{4 - x^2} \cdot \dfrac{x^2 - x - 6}{3x^2 + 6x + 12} \quad \substack{\text{Take the}\\ \text{reciprocal.}}$$

Multiply the first fraction by the reciprocal of the second fraction.

$$= \dfrac{(x - 2)(x^2 + 2x + 4)}{(2 - x)(2 + x)} \cdot \dfrac{(x - 3)(x + 2)}{3(x^2 + 2x + 4)}$$

Factor the numerator and denominator. Note that $x^3 - 8$ is a difference of cubes.

$$= \dfrac{\overset{(-1)}{\cancel{(x - 2)}}\overset{1}{\cancel{(x^2 + 2x + 4)}} \cdot (x - 3)\overset{1}{\cancel{(x + 2)}}}{\cancel{(2 - x)}\cancel{(2 + x)} \cdot 3\cancel{(x^2 + 2x + 4)}}$$

Apply the multiplication property of fractions. Divide out common factors. Note that $(x - 2)$ and $(2 - x)$ are opposite polynomials, and their ratio is -1.

$$= -\dfrac{x - 3}{3}$$

Avoiding Mistakes

For the expression $\dfrac{x - 3}{3}$ do not be tempted to "divide out" the 3 in the numerator with the 3 in the denominator. The 3's are *terms*, not factors. Only common *factors* can be divided out.

Skill Practice 5   Divide. $\dfrac{y^3 - 27}{9 - y^2} \div \dfrac{5y^2 + 15y + 45}{y^2 + 8y + 15}$

4. Add and Subtract Rational Expressions

Recall that fractions can be added or subtracted if they have a common denominator.

Addition and Subtraction of Algebraic Fractions	
Let a, b, c, and d be real-valued expressions.	**Examples:**
$\dfrac{a}{b} + \dfrac{c}{b} = \dfrac{a + c}{b}$ for $b \neq 0$	• $\dfrac{3}{x} + \dfrac{7}{x} = \dfrac{3 + 7}{x} = \dfrac{10}{x}$
$\dfrac{a}{b} - \dfrac{c}{b} = \dfrac{a - c}{b}$ for $b \neq 0$	• $\dfrac{5}{y - 1} - \dfrac{z}{y - 1} = \dfrac{5 - z}{y - 1}$

If two rational expressions have different denominators, then it is necessary to convert the expressions to equivalent expressions with the same denominator. We do this by applying the property of equivalent fractions, $\dfrac{a}{b} = \dfrac{ac}{bc}$, where $b \neq 0$ and $c \neq 0$. For example, suppose we want to convert the expression $\dfrac{5}{x}$ to an equivalent expression with a denominator of $x^2 y$.

Multiply numerator and denominator by the factors missing from the denominator.

$$\downarrow$$

$$\dfrac{5}{x} = \dfrac{5 \cdot xy}{x \cdot xy} = \dfrac{5xy}{x^2 y} \leftarrow \text{New denominator is } x^2 y.$$

Answer

5. $-\dfrac{y + 5}{5}$

When adding or subtracting numerical fractions or rational expressions, it is customary to use the least common denominator (LCD) of the original expressions. To find the LCD, follow these guidelines.

Finding the LCD of Two Rational Expressions

Step 1 Factor the denominator completely.
Step 2 The LCD is the product of unique prime factors where each factor is raised to the greatest power to which it appears in any denominator.

EXAMPLE 6   Identifying the LCD of Rational Expressions

Identify the LCD for the given rational expressions.

a. $\dfrac{2}{5a^2bc^5}$ and $\dfrac{1}{10a^3c^2}$ 　　　　**b.** $\dfrac{1}{x^2 + 5x}$ and $\dfrac{x + 3}{x^2 + 10x + 25}$

Solution:

a. $\dfrac{2}{5a^2bc^5}$ and $\dfrac{1}{2 \cdot 5a^3c^2}$ 　　　**Step 1:** Factor the denominators.

$\text{LCD} = 2^1 5^1 a^3 b^1 c^5 = 10a^3bc^5$ 　　　**Step 2:** Write the product of unique prime factors. Raise each factor to the greatest power to which it appears.

b. $\dfrac{1}{x(x + 5)}$ and $\dfrac{x + 3}{(x + 5)^2}$ 　　　**Step 1:** Factor the denominators.

$\text{LCD} = x^1(x + 5)^2 = x(x + 5)^2$ 　　　**Step 2:** Write the product of unique prime factors. Raise each factor to the greatest power to which it appears.

Skill Practice 6   Identify the LCD for the given rational expressions.

a. $\dfrac{7}{15c^2d^8}$ and $\dfrac{1}{3c^5d^2e}$ 　　　　**b.** $\dfrac{1}{y^2 - 16y + 64}$ and $\dfrac{y + 2}{y^2 - 8y}$

The procedure to add or subtract fractions is as follows.

Adding and Subtracting Rational Expressions

Step 1 Factor the denominators and determine the LCD of all expressions.
Step 2 Write each expression as an equivalent expression with the LCD as its denominator.
Step 3 Add or subtract the numerators as indicated and write the result over the LCD.
Step 4 Simplify if possible.

EXAMPLE 7   Adding Rational Expressions

Add the rational expressions and simplify the result.　　　$\dfrac{7}{4a} + \dfrac{11}{10a^2}$

Answers
6. a. $15c^5d^8e$ 　　**b.** $y(y - 8)^2$

Solution:

$$\frac{7}{4a} + \frac{11}{10a^2} = \frac{7}{2 \cdot 2a} + \frac{11}{2 \cdot 5a^2}$$

Step 1: Factor the denominators. The LCD is $2^2 \cdot 5a^2$ or $20a^2$.

$$= \frac{7 \cdot (5a)}{2 \cdot 2a \cdot (5a)} + \frac{11 \cdot (2)}{2 \cdot 5a^2 \cdot (2)}$$

Step 2: Multiply numerator and denominator of each expression by the factors missing from the denominators.

$$= \frac{35a}{20a^2} + \frac{22}{20a^2}$$

Step 3: Add the numerators and write the result over the common denominator.

$$= \frac{35a + 22}{20a^2}$$

Step 4: The expression is already simplified.

Skill Practice 7   Add the rational expressions and simplify the result.

$$\frac{8}{9y^2} + \frac{1}{15y}$$

EXAMPLE 8   **Subtracting Rational Expressions**

Subtract the rational expressions and simplify the result.

$$\frac{3x + 5}{x^2 + 4x + 3} - \frac{x - 5}{x^2 + 2x - 3}$$

Solution:

$$\frac{3x + 5}{x^2 + 4x + 3} - \frac{x - 5}{x^2 + 2x - 3}$$

$$= \frac{3x + 5}{(x + 3)(x + 1)} - \frac{x - 5}{(x + 3)(x - 1)}$$

Factor the denominators. The LCD is $(x + 3)(x + 1)(x - 1)$.

$$= \frac{(3x + 5)(x - 1)}{(x + 3)(x + 1)(x - 1)} - \frac{(x - 5)(x + 1)}{(x + 3)(x - 1)(x + 1)}$$

Multiply numerator and denominator of each expression by the factors missing from the denominators.

$$= \frac{(3x + 5)(x - 1) - (x - 5)(x + 1)}{(x + 3)(x + 1)(x - 1)}$$

Subtract the numerators and write the result over the common denominator.

$$= \frac{3x^2 + 2x - 5 - (x^2 - 4x - 5)}{(x + 3)(x + 1)(x - 1)}$$

$$= \frac{3x^2 + 2x - 5 - x^2 + 4x + 5}{(x + 3)(x + 1)(x - 1)}$$

$$= \frac{2x^2 + 6x}{(x + 3)(x + 1)(x - 1)}$$

$$= \frac{2x(\overset{1}{\cancel{x + 3}})}{(\cancel{x + 3})(x + 1)(x - 1)}$$

Factor the numerator and denominator and simplify.

$$= \frac{2x}{(x + 1)(x - 1)}$$

> **Avoiding Mistakes**
>
> It is very important to use parentheses around the second trinomial in the numerator. This will ensure that all terms that follow will be subtracted

---

Skill Practice 8   Subtract the rational expressions and simplify the result.

$$\frac{t}{t^2 + 5t + 6} - \frac{2}{t^2 + 3t + 2}$$

Answers

7. $\dfrac{40 + 3y}{45y^2}$ **8.** $\dfrac{t - 3}{(t + 1)(t + 3)}$

5. Simplify Complex Fractions

A **complex fraction** (also called a **compound fraction**) is an expression that contains one or more fractions in the numerator or denominator. We present two methods to simplify a complex fraction. Method I is an application of the order of operations.

Simplifying a Complex Fraction (Method I)

Step 1   Add or subtract the fractions in the numerator to form a single fraction. Add or subtract the fractions in the denominator to form a single fraction.

Step 2   Divide the resulting expressions by multiplying the rational expression in the numerator by the reciprocal of the expression in the denominator.

Step 3   Simplify if possible.

EXAMPLE 9   Simplifying a Complex Fraction (Method I)

Simplify. $\dfrac{\dfrac{x}{4} - \dfrac{4}{x}}{\dfrac{1}{4} + \dfrac{1}{x}}$

Solution:

$$\frac{\dfrac{x}{4} - \dfrac{4}{x}}{\dfrac{1}{4} + \dfrac{1}{x}} = \frac{\dfrac{x \cdot x}{4 \cdot x} - \dfrac{4 \cdot 4}{x \cdot 4}}{\dfrac{1 \cdot x}{4 \cdot x} + \dfrac{1 \cdot 4}{x \cdot 4}} = \frac{\dfrac{x^2 - 16}{4x}}{\dfrac{x + 4}{4x}}$$

Step 1: Subtract the fractions in the numerator. Add the fractions in the denominator.

$$= \frac{x^2 - 16}{4x} \cdot \frac{4x}{x + 4}$$

Step 2: Multiply the rational expression from the numerator by the reciprocal of the expression from the denominator.

$$= \frac{(x - 4)(x + 4)}{4x} \cdot \frac{\overset{1}{4x}}{x + 4}$$

Step 3: Simplify by factoring and dividing out common factors.

$$= x - 4$$

Skill Practice 9   Simplify. $\dfrac{\dfrac{1}{7} + \dfrac{1}{y}}{\dfrac{y}{7} - \dfrac{7}{y}}$

In Example 10 we demonstrate another method (Method II) to simplify a complex fraction.

Simplifying a Complex Fraction (Method II)

Step 1   Multiply the numerator and denominator of the complex fraction by the LCD of all individual fractions.

Step 2   Apply the distributive property and simplify the numerator and denominator.

Step 3   Simplify the resulting expression if possible.

Answer

9. $\dfrac{1}{y - 7}$

EXAMPLE 10 **Simplifying a Complex Fraction (Method II)**

Simplify. $\dfrac{d^{-2} - c^{-2}}{d^{-1} - c^{-1}}$

Solution:

$$\frac{d^{-2} - c^{-2}}{d^{-1} - c^{-1}} = \frac{\dfrac{1}{d^2} - \dfrac{1}{c^2}}{\dfrac{1}{d} - \dfrac{1}{c}}$$

First write the expression with positive exponents.

$$= \frac{c^2 d^2 \cdot \left(\dfrac{1}{d^2} - \dfrac{1}{c^2}\right)}{c^2 d^2 \cdot \left(\dfrac{1}{d} - \dfrac{1}{c}\right)}$$

Step 1: Multiply numerator and denominator by the LCD of all four individual fractions: $c^2 d^2$.

$$= \frac{\dfrac{c^2 d^2}{1} \cdot \dfrac{1}{d^2} - \dfrac{c^2 d^2}{1} \cdot \dfrac{1}{c^2}}{\dfrac{c^2 d^2}{1} \cdot \dfrac{1}{d} - \dfrac{c^2 d^2}{1} \cdot \dfrac{1}{c}}$$

Step 2: Apply the distributive property.

$$= \frac{c^2 - d^2}{c^2 d - c d^2}$$

$$= \frac{(c - d)(c + d)}{cd(c - d)} = \frac{c + d}{cd}$$

Step 3: Simplify by factoring and dividing out common factors.

Skill Practice 10 Simplify. $\dfrac{4 - 6x^{-1}}{2x^{-1} - 3x^{-2}}$

EXAMPLE 11 **Simplifying a Complex Fraction (Method II)**

Simplify. $\dfrac{\dfrac{2}{1 + h} - 2}{h}$

Solution:

TIP The expression given in Example 11 is a pattern we see in a first semester calculus course.

$$\frac{\dfrac{2}{1 + h} - 2}{h} = \frac{\dfrac{2}{1 + h} - \dfrac{2}{1}}{h} = \frac{(1 + h) \cdot \left(\dfrac{2}{1 + h} - \dfrac{2}{1}\right)}{(1 + h) \cdot (h)}$$

Step 1: Multiply numerator and denominator by the LCD which is $(1 + h)$.

$$= \frac{\dfrac{(1 + h)}{1} \cdot \left(\dfrac{2}{1 + h}\right) - \dfrac{(1 + h)}{1} \cdot \left(\dfrac{2}{1}\right)}{(1 + h) \cdot (h)}$$

Step 2: Apply the distributive property.

$$= \frac{2 - 2(1 + h)}{h(1 + h)}$$

Step 3: Simplify.

$$= \frac{2 - 2 - 2h}{h(1 + h)} = \frac{-2h}{h(1 + h)} = \frac{-2}{1 + h} \quad \text{or} \quad -\frac{2}{1 + h}$$

Answer

10. $2x$

Skill Practice 11   Simplify. $\dfrac{\dfrac{5}{1+h} - 5}{h}$

6. Rationalize the Denominator of a Radical Expression

The same principle that applies to simplifying rational expressions also applies to simplifying algebraic fractions. For example, $\frac{5}{\sqrt{x}}$ is an algebraic fraction, but not a rational expression because the denominator is not a polynomial.

From Section R.4, we outlined the criteria for a radical expression to be simplified. Conditions 2 and 3 are stated here.

- No fraction may appear in the radicand.
- No denominator of a fraction may contain a radical.

In Example 12, we use the property of equivalent fractions to remove a radical from the denominator of a fraction. This is called **rationalizing the denominator.**

EXAMPLE 12   **Rationalizing the Denominator**

Simplify. Assume that the variables represent positive real numbers.

a. $\dfrac{5}{\sqrt{x}}$ **b.** $\sqrt[3]{\dfrac{21}{14a^2}}$

Solution:

a. $\dfrac{5}{\sqrt{x}} = \dfrac{5 \cdot \sqrt{x}}{\sqrt{x} \cdot \sqrt{x}}$ Multiply numerator and denominator by $\sqrt{x}$ so that the radicand in the denominator is a perfect square.

$= \dfrac{5\sqrt{x}}{\sqrt{x^2}}$ Apply the product property of radicals.

$= \dfrac{5\sqrt{x}}{x}$ Simplify the radical in the denominator.

> **Avoiding Mistakes**
>
> A factor within a radicand cannot be simplified with a factor outside the radicand. For example, $\dfrac{5\sqrt{x}}{x}$ cannot be simplified further.

b. $\sqrt[3]{\dfrac{21}{14a^2}} = \sqrt[3]{\dfrac{3}{2a^2}}$ Simplify the fraction.

$= \dfrac{\sqrt[3]{3}}{\sqrt[3]{2a^2}}$ Apply the division property of radicals to write the expression as the quotient of two radicals.

$= \dfrac{\sqrt[3]{3} \cdot \sqrt[3]{2^2 a}}{\sqrt[3]{2a^2} \cdot \sqrt[3]{2^2 a}}$ Multiply numerator and denominator by $\sqrt[3]{2^2 a}$ so that the radicand in the denominator is a perfect cube.

$= \dfrac{\sqrt[3]{3 \cdot 2^2 a}}{\sqrt[3]{2^3 a^3}}$ Apply the product property of radicals.

$= \dfrac{\sqrt[3]{12a}}{2a}$ Simplify.

Skill Practice 12   Simplify. Assume that the variables represent positive real numbers.

a. $\dfrac{\sqrt{5}}{\sqrt{7}}$ **b.** $\sqrt[4]{\dfrac{5}{15x^3}}$

Answers

11. $-\dfrac{5}{1+h}$

12. a. $\dfrac{\sqrt{35}}{7}$ **b.** $\dfrac{\sqrt[4]{27x}}{3x}$

In Section R.5, we multiplied conjugate pairs. The product $(a + b)(a - b)$ results in a difference of squares, $a^2 - b^2$. If either a or b has a square root factor, then the product will simplify to an expression without square roots. This observation is important when rationalizing the denominator of an expression with two terms involving square roots.

EXAMPLE 13   **Rationalizing the Denominator**

Rationalize the denominator. $\dfrac{4}{\sqrt{7} - \sqrt{5}}$

Solution:

> **TIP** Keep the numerator in factored form until the denominator is simplified completely. By so doing, it will be easier to identify common factors in the numerator and denominator.

$$\dfrac{4}{\sqrt{7} - \sqrt{5}} = \dfrac{4 \cdot (\sqrt{7} + \sqrt{5})}{(\sqrt{7} - \sqrt{5}) \cdot (\sqrt{7} + \sqrt{5})}$$

Multiply numerator and denominator by the conjugate of the denominator.

$$= \dfrac{4(\sqrt{7} + \sqrt{5})}{(\sqrt{7})^2 - (\sqrt{5})^2}$$

Recall that $(a - b)(a + b) = a^2 - b^2$.

$$= \dfrac{4(\sqrt{7} + \sqrt{5})}{7 - 5}$$

Simplify the radicals in the denominator.

$$= \dfrac{\overset{2}{\cancel{4}}(\sqrt{7} + \sqrt{5})}{\cancel{2}}$$

With the numerator and denominator in factored form, simplify the fraction.

$$= 2(\sqrt{7} + \sqrt{5}) \quad \text{or} \quad 2\sqrt{7} + 2\sqrt{5}$$

Skill Practice 13   Rationalize the denominator. $\dfrac{12}{\sqrt{13} - \sqrt{10}}$

EXAMPLE 14   **Simplifying an Expression Containing Radicals**

Simplify. Assume that x is a positive real number. $\dfrac{5}{\sqrt{2x}} + \dfrac{\sqrt{2x}}{x}$

Solution:

$$\dfrac{5}{\sqrt{2x}} + \dfrac{\sqrt{2x}}{x} = \dfrac{5 \cdot \sqrt{2x}}{\sqrt{2x} \cdot \sqrt{2x}} + \dfrac{\sqrt{2x}}{x}$$

Rationalize the denominator of the first expression.

$$= \dfrac{5\sqrt{2x}}{2x} + \dfrac{\sqrt{2x}}{x}$$

The LCD is $2x$.

$$= \dfrac{5\sqrt{2x}}{2x} + \dfrac{\sqrt{2x} \cdot 2}{x \cdot 2}$$

Multiply numerator and denominator of the second expression by 2 to obtain a common denominator.

$$= \dfrac{5\sqrt{2x}}{2x} + \dfrac{2\sqrt{2x}}{2x} = \dfrac{5\sqrt{2x} + 2\sqrt{2x}}{2x}$$

Add the fractions by adding the numerators and writing the result over the common denominator.

$$= \dfrac{7\sqrt{2x}}{2x}$$

Simplify.

Skill Practice 14   Simplify. Assume that x is a positive real number.

$$\dfrac{3\sqrt{5}}{\sqrt{x}} + \dfrac{2\sqrt{5x}}{3x}$$

Answers

13. $4(\sqrt{13} + \sqrt{10})$ or $4\sqrt{13} + 4\sqrt{10}$

14. $\dfrac{11\sqrt{5x}}{3x}$

SECTION R.7   Practice Exercises

Review Exercises

For Exercises 1–8, factor completely.

1. $30x^3 - 65x^2 - 25x$

2. $40y^3 - 132y^2 - 28y$

3. $t^4 - t$

4. $y^5 + 64y^2$

5. $2x^3 + 3x^2 - 32x - 48$

6. $3t^3 + t^2 - 75t - 25$

7. $25w^4 - 40w^2u + 16u^2$

8. $49v^4 + 42v^2w + 9w^2$

Concept Connections

9. A _____ expression is a ratio of two polynomials.

10. The restricted values of the variable for a rational expression are those that make the denominator equal to _____.

11. The expression $\dfrac{5(x + 2)}{(x + 2)(x - 1)}$ equals $\dfrac{5}{x - 1}$ provided that $x \neq$ _____ and $x \neq$ _____.

12. The ratio of a polynomial and its opposite equals _____.

13. A _____ fraction is an expression that contains one or more fractions in the numerator or denominator.

14. The process to remove a radical from the denominator of a fraction is called _____ the denominator.

Objective 1: Determine Restricted Values for a Rational Expression

For Exercises 15–22, determine the restrictions on the variable. (See Example 1)

15. $\dfrac{x - 4}{x + 7}$

16. $\dfrac{y - 1}{y + 10}$

17. $\dfrac{a}{a^2 - 81}$

18. $\dfrac{t}{t^2 - 16}$

19. $\dfrac{a}{a^2 + 81}$

20. $\dfrac{t}{t^2 + 16}$

21. $\dfrac{6c}{7a^3b^2}$

22. $\dfrac{11z}{8x^5y}$

Objective 2: Simplify Rational Expressions

23. Determine which expressions are equal to $-\dfrac{5}{x - 3}$.

   a. $\dfrac{-5}{x - 3}$ **b.** $\dfrac{5}{3 - x}$

   c. $-\dfrac{5}{3 - x}$ **d.** $\dfrac{-5}{3 - x}$

24. Determine which expressions are equal to $\dfrac{-2}{a + b}$.

   a. $\dfrac{-2}{a - b}$ **b.** $-\dfrac{2}{a + b}$

   c. $\dfrac{2}{-a - b}$ **d.** $\dfrac{2}{a - b}$

For Exercises 25–34, simplify the expression and state the restrictions on the variable. (See Examples 2–3)

25. $\dfrac{x^2 - 9}{x^2 - 4x - 21}$

26. $\dfrac{y^2 - 64}{y^2 - 7y - 8}$

27. $-\dfrac{12a^2bc}{3ab^5}$

28. $-\dfrac{15tu^5v}{3t^3u}$

29. $\dfrac{10 - 5\sqrt{6}}{15}$

30. $\dfrac{12 + 4\sqrt{3}}{8}$

31. $\dfrac{2y^2 - 16y}{64 - y^2}$

32. $\dfrac{81 - t^2}{7t^2 - 63t}$

33. $\dfrac{4b - 4a}{ax - xb - 2a + 2b}$

34. $\dfrac{2z - 2y}{xy - xz + 3y - 3z}$

Objective 3: Multiply and Divide Rational Expressions

For Exercises 35–42, multiply or divide as indicated. The restrictions on the variables are implied. (See Examples 4–5)

35. $\dfrac{3a^5b^7}{a - 5b} \cdot \dfrac{2a - 10b}{12a^4b^{10}}$

36. $\dfrac{8x - 3y}{x^3y^4} \cdot \dfrac{6xy^8}{24x - 9y}$

37. $\dfrac{c^2 - d^2}{cd^{11}} \div \dfrac{8c^2 + 4cd - 4d^2}{8c^4d^{10}}$

38. $\dfrac{m^{11}n^2}{m^2 - n^2} \div \dfrac{18m^9n^5}{9m^2 + 6mn - 15n^2}$

39. $\dfrac{2a^2b - ab^2}{8b^2 + ab} \cdot \dfrac{a^2 + 16ab + 64b^2}{2a^2 + 15ab - 8b^2}$

40. $\dfrac{2c^2 - 2cd}{3c^2d + 2c^3} \cdot \dfrac{4c^2 + 12cd + 9d^2}{2c^2 + cd - 3d^2}$

41. $\dfrac{x^3 - 64}{16x - x^3} \div \dfrac{2x^2 + 8x + 32}{x^2 + 2x - 8}$

42. $\dfrac{3y^2 + 21y + 147}{25y - y^3} \div \dfrac{y^3 - 343}{y^2 - 12y + 35}$

Objective 4: Add and Subtract Rational Expressions

For Exercises 43–48, identify the least common denominator for each pair of expressions. (See Example 6)

43. $\dfrac{7}{6x^5yz^4}$ and $\dfrac{3}{20xy^2z^3}$

44. $\dfrac{12}{35b^4cd^3}$ and $\dfrac{8}{25b^2c^3d}$

45. $\dfrac{2t + 1}{(3t + 4)^3(t - 2)}$ and $\dfrac{4}{t(3t + 4)^2(t - 2)}$

46. $\dfrac{5y - 7}{y(2y - 5)(y + 6)^4}$ and $\dfrac{6}{(2y - 5)^3(y + 6)^2}$

47. $\dfrac{x + 3}{x^2 + 20x + 100}$ and $\dfrac{3}{2x^2 + 20x}$

48. $\dfrac{z - 4}{4z^2 - 20z + 25}$ and $\dfrac{5}{12z^2 - 30z}$

For Exercises 49–60, add or subtract as indicated. (See Examples 7–8)

49. $\dfrac{m^2}{m + 3} + \dfrac{6m + 9}{m + 3}$

50. $\dfrac{n^2}{n + 5} + \dfrac{7n + 10}{n + 5}$

51. $\dfrac{2}{9c} + \dfrac{7}{15c^3}$

52. $\dfrac{6}{25x} + \dfrac{7}{10x^4}$

53. $\dfrac{9}{2x^2y^4} - \dfrac{11}{xy^5}$

54. $\dfrac{-2}{3m^3n} - \dfrac{5}{m^2n^4}$

55. $\dfrac{1}{x^2 + xy} - \dfrac{2}{x^2 - y^2}$

56. $\dfrac{4}{4a^2 - b^2} - \dfrac{1}{2a^2 - ab}$

57. $\dfrac{5}{y} + \dfrac{2}{y + 1} - \dfrac{6}{y^2}$

58. $\dfrac{5}{t^2} + \dfrac{4}{t + 2} - \dfrac{3}{t}$

59. $\dfrac{3w}{w - 4} + \dfrac{2w + 4}{4 - w}$

60. $\dfrac{2x - 1}{x - 7} + \dfrac{x + 6}{7 - x}$

Objective 5: Simplify Complex Fractions

For Exercises 61–70, simplify the complex fraction. (See Examples 9–11)

61. $\dfrac{\dfrac{1}{27x} + \dfrac{1}{9}}{\dfrac{1}{3} + \dfrac{1}{9x}}$

62. $\dfrac{\dfrac{1}{8x} + \dfrac{1}{4}}{\dfrac{1}{2} + \dfrac{1}{4x}}$

63. $\dfrac{\dfrac{x}{6} - \dfrac{5x + 14}{6x}}{\dfrac{1}{6} - \dfrac{7}{6x}}$

64. $\dfrac{\dfrac{x}{3} - \dfrac{2x + 3}{3x}}{\dfrac{1}{3} + \dfrac{1}{3x}}$

65. $\dfrac{2a^{-1} - b^{-1}}{4a^{-2} - b^{-2}}$

66. $\dfrac{3u^{-1} - v^{-1}}{9u^{-2} - v^{-2}}$

67. $\dfrac{\dfrac{3}{1 + h} - 3}{h}$

68. $\dfrac{\dfrac{4}{1 + h} - 4}{h}$

69. $\dfrac{\dfrac{7}{x + h} - \dfrac{7}{x}}{h}$

70. $\dfrac{\dfrac{8}{x + h} - \dfrac{8}{x}}{h}$

Objective 6: Rationalize the Denominator of a Radical Expression

For Exercises 71–90, simplify the expression. Assume that the variable expressions represent positive real numbers.
(See Examples 12–14)

71. $\dfrac{4}{\sqrt{y}}$

72. $\dfrac{7}{\sqrt{z}}$

73. $\dfrac{4}{\sqrt[3]{y}}$

74. $\dfrac{7}{\sqrt[4]{z}}$

75. $\sqrt[3]{\dfrac{18}{12w}}$

76. $\sqrt[3]{\dfrac{10}{25p}}$

77. $\dfrac{12}{\sqrt[4]{8wx^2}}$

78. $\dfrac{12}{\sqrt[4]{27a^2b}}$

79. $\dfrac{\sqrt{12}}{\sqrt{x}+1}$

80. $\dfrac{\sqrt{50}}{\sqrt{x}-2}$

81. $\dfrac{8}{\sqrt{15}-\sqrt{11}}$

82. $\dfrac{12}{\sqrt{6}-\sqrt{2}}$

83. $\dfrac{x-5}{\sqrt{x}+\sqrt{5}}$

84. $\dfrac{y-3}{\sqrt{y}+\sqrt{3}}$

85. $\dfrac{2\sqrt{10}+3\sqrt{5}}{4\sqrt{10}+2\sqrt{5}}$

86. $\dfrac{3\sqrt{3}+\sqrt{6}}{5\sqrt{3}-2\sqrt{6}}$

87. $\dfrac{7}{\sqrt{3x}}+\dfrac{\sqrt{3x}}{x}$

88. $\dfrac{4}{\sqrt{11y}}+\dfrac{\sqrt{11y}}{y}$

89. $\dfrac{5}{w\sqrt{7}}-\dfrac{\sqrt{7}}{w}$

90. $\dfrac{13}{t\sqrt{2}}-\dfrac{\sqrt{2}}{t}$

Mixed Exercises

91. The average round trip speed S (in mph) of a vehicle traveling a distance of d miles each way is given by

$$S = \dfrac{2d}{\dfrac{d}{r_1}+\dfrac{d}{r_2}}.$$

In this formula, r_1 is the average speed going one way, and r_2 is the average speed on the return trip.

a. Simplify the complex fraction.

b. If a plane flies 400 mph from Orlando to Albuquerque and 460 mph on the way back, compute the average speed of the round trip. Round to 1 decimal place.

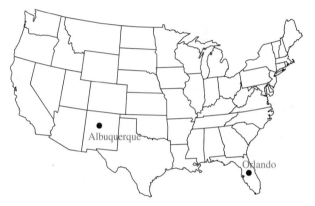

92. The formula $R = \dfrac{1}{\dfrac{1}{R_1}+\dfrac{1}{R_2}}$ gives the total electrical resistance R (in ohms, Ω) when two resistors of resistance R_1 and R_2 are connected in parallel.

a. Simplify the complex fraction on the right.

b. Find the total resistance when $R_1 = 12\ \Omega$ and $R_2 = 20\ \Omega$.

93. The concentration C (in ng/mL) of a drug in the bloodstream t hours after ingestion is modeled by $C = \dfrac{600t}{t^3 + 125}$.

a. Determine the concentration at 1 hr, 4 hr, and 12 hr. Round to 1 decimal place.

b. From the graph, what is the limiting concentration (that is, the concentration of the drug in the bloodstream for large values of t)?

Concentration of Drug in Bloodstream vs. Time

$C = \dfrac{600t}{t^3 + 125}$

94. An object that is originally 35°C is placed in a freezer. The temperature T (in °C) of the object can be approximated by the model $T = \dfrac{350}{t^2 + 3t + 10}$, where t is the time in hours after the object is placed in the freezer.

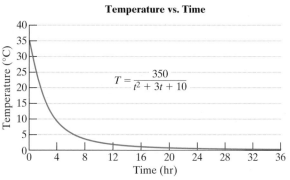

Temperature vs. Time

a. Determine the temperature at 3 hr and 24 hr. Round to 1 decimal place.

b. From the graph, what is the limiting temperature (that is, the temperature for large values of t)?

For Exercises 95–98, write a simplified expression for the perimeter or area as indicated.

95. Perimeter

96. Perimeter

97. Area

98. Area

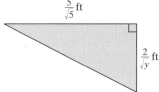

For Exercises 99–116, simplify the expression.

99. $\dfrac{2x^3 y}{x^2 y + 3xy} \cdot \dfrac{x^2 + 6x + 9}{2x + 6} \div 5xy^4$

100. $\dfrac{2y^2 + 20y + 50}{12 - 4y} \cdot \dfrac{y - 3}{y^2 + 12y + 35} \div (3y + 15)$

101. $\left(\dfrac{4}{2t + 1} - \dfrac{t}{2t^2 + 17t + 8} \right)(t + 8)$

102. $\left(\dfrac{2m}{6m + 3} - \dfrac{1}{m + 4} \right)(2m + 1)$

103. $\dfrac{n - 2}{n - 4} + \dfrac{2n^2 - 15n + 12}{n^2 - 16} - \dfrac{2n - 5}{n + 4}$

104. $\dfrac{c^2 + 13c + 18}{c^2 - 9} + \dfrac{c + 1}{c + 3} - \dfrac{c + 8}{c - 3}$

105. $\dfrac{1 - a^{-1} - 6a^{-2}}{1 - 4a^{-1} + 3a^{-2}}$

106. $\dfrac{1 + t^{-1} - 12t^{-2}}{1 - 4t^{-1} + 3t^{-2}}$

107. $\dfrac{34}{2\sqrt{5} - \sqrt{3}}$

108. $\dfrac{13}{2\sqrt{7} + \sqrt{2}}$

109. $\dfrac{8 - \sqrt{48}}{6}$

110. $\dfrac{10 - \sqrt{50}}{15}$

111. $\dfrac{14}{\sqrt{7x}} - \dfrac{\sqrt{7x}}{x}$

112. $\dfrac{6y}{\sqrt{xy}} + \dfrac{10\sqrt{xy}}{x}$

113. $\dfrac{45 + 9x - 5x^2 - x^3}{x^3 - 3x^2 - 25x + 75}$

114. $\dfrac{98 - 49x - 2x^2 + x^3}{7x^2 - x^3 - 28 + 4x}$

115. $\dfrac{t + 6}{1 + \dfrac{2}{t}} - t - 4$

116. $\dfrac{m - 4}{1 - \dfrac{2}{m}} - m + 2$

Write About It

117. Explain why the expression $\dfrac{x}{x-y}$ is not defined for $x = y$.

118. Is the statement $\dfrac{3(x-4)}{(x+2)(x-4)} = \dfrac{3}{x+2}$ true for all values of x? Explain why or why not.

119. Compare the process to rationalize the denominator for the following expressions.

$$\dfrac{1}{\sqrt{x}} \quad \text{and} \quad \dfrac{1}{\sqrt[3]{x}}$$

120. For the given expression, explain why multiplying the numerator and denominator by the conjugate of the denominator will rationalize the denominator.

$$\dfrac{7}{\sqrt{5} - \sqrt{3}}$$

Expanding Your Skills

121. The numbers 1, 2, 4, 5, 10, and 20 are natural numbers that are factors of 20. There are other factors of 20 within the set of rational numbers and the set of irrational numbers. For example:

  a. Show that $\dfrac{14}{3}$ and $\dfrac{30}{7}$ are factors of 20 over the set of rational numbers.

  b. Show that $(5 - \sqrt{5})$ and $(5 + \sqrt{5})$ are factors of 20 over the set of irrational numbers.

122. a. Show that $\dfrac{15}{2}$ and $\dfrac{4}{5}$ are factors of 6 over the set of rational numbers.

  b. Show that $(3 - \sqrt{3})$ and $(3 + \sqrt{3})$ are factors of 6 over the set of irrational numbers.

For Exercises 123–130, simplify the expression.

123. $\dfrac{w^{3n+1} - w^{3n}z}{w^{n+2} - w^n z^2}$

124. $\dfrac{x^{2n+1} - x^{2n}y}{x^{n+3} - x^n y^3}$

125. $\sqrt{\dfrac{x-y}{x+y}}$

126. $\sqrt{\dfrac{m-3}{m+3}}$

127. $\dfrac{\sqrt{5}}{\sqrt[3]{2}}$

128. $\dfrac{\sqrt{7}}{\sqrt[4]{3}}$

129. $\dfrac{a-b}{\sqrt[3]{a} - \sqrt[3]{b}}$ (*Hint:* Factor the numerator as a difference of cubes over the set of irrational numbers.)

130. $\dfrac{x+y}{\sqrt[3]{x} + \sqrt[3]{y}}$

For Exercises 131–132, rationalize the numerator by multiplying numerator and denominator by the conjugate of the numerator.

131. $\dfrac{\sqrt{4+h} - 2}{h}$

132. $\dfrac{\sqrt{x+h} - \sqrt{x}}{h}$

Technology Connections

133. The expression $\dfrac{x^2 - 9}{x - 3}$ is undefined at $x = 3$. Use a calculator or spreadsheet to evaluate the expression for values of x *close* to 3. What number does the expression seem to approach as x gets close to 3?

x	2.9	2.99	2.999	2.9999
$\dfrac{x^2 - 9}{x - 3}$				

x	3.1	3.01	3.001	3.0001
$\dfrac{x^2 - 9}{x - 3}$				

134. Evaluate the expression $\dfrac{2x - 4}{x}$ for large values of x. What number does the expression seem to approach as x gets large (approaches infinity)?

x	100	1000	10,000	100,000
$\dfrac{2x - 4}{x}$				

CHAPTER R   KEY CONCEPTS

SECTION R.1 Sets and the Real Number Line	Reference
Natural Numbers: $\mathbb{N} = \{1, 2, 3, \dots\}$ **Whole Numbers:** $\mathbb{W} = \{0, 1, 2, 3, \dots\}$ **Integers:** $\mathbb{Z} = \{\dots, -3, -2, -1, 0, 1, 2, 3, \dots\}$ **Rational Numbers:** $\mathbb{Q} = \{\frac{p}{q} \mid p, q \in \mathbb{Z} \text{ and } q \neq 0\}$ **Irrational Numbers:** $\mathbb{H}$ is the set of real numbers that cannot be expressed as a ratio of integers.	p. 5
For a real number x, the **absolute value of x** is $\lvert x \rvert = \begin{cases} x & \text{if } x \geq 0 \\ -x & \text{if } x < 0 \end{cases}$	p. 7
The distance between two points a and b on a number line is given by $\lvert a - b \rvert$ or $\lvert b - a \rvert$.	p. 9

SECTION R.2 Models, Algebraic Expressions, and Properties of Real Numbers	Reference
• Commutative property of addition $\qquad\qquad$ $a + b = b + a$ • Commutative property of multiplication $\qquad$ $a \cdot b = b \cdot a$ • Associative property of addition $\qquad\qquad$ $(a + b) + c = a + (b + c)$ • Associative property of multiplication $\qquad$ $(a \cdot b) \cdot c = a \cdot (b \cdot c)$ • Identity property of addition $\qquad\qquad$ $a + 0 = a \quad \text{and} \quad 0 + a = a$ • Identity property of multiplication $\qquad$ $a \cdot 1 = a \quad \text{and} \quad 1 \cdot a = a$ • Inverse property of addition $\qquad\qquad$ $a + (-a) = 0 \quad \text{and} \quad (-a) + a = 0$ • Inverse property of multiplication $\qquad$ $a \cdot \frac{1}{a} = 1 \quad \text{and} \quad \frac{1}{a} \cdot a = 1 \text{ where } a \neq 0$ • Distributive property of multiplication over addition $\quad a \cdot (b + c) = a \cdot b + a \cdot c$	p. 20

SECTION R.3 Integer Exponents and Scientific Notation	Reference
Properties of exponents and key definitions $\quad b^0 = 1 \quad \text{and} \quad b^{-n} = \dfrac{1}{b^n}$	p. 30
• Product rule for exponents $\qquad\qquad$ $b^m \cdot b^n = b^{m+n}$	
• Quotient rule for exponents $\qquad\qquad$ $\dfrac{b^m}{b^n} = b^{m-n}$	
• Power rule for exponents $\qquad\qquad$ $(b^m)^n = b^{m \cdot n}$	
• Power of a product $\qquad\qquad$ $(ab)^m = a^m b^m$	
• Power of a quotient $\qquad\qquad$ $\left(\dfrac{a}{b}\right)^m = \dfrac{a^m}{b^m}$	
A number expressed in the form $a \times 10^n$, where $1 \leq \lvert a \rvert < 10$ and n is an integer is said to be in **scientific notation.**	p. 33

SECTION R.4 Rational Exponents and Radicals	Reference
b is an nth-root of a if $b^n = a$. $\sqrt[n]{a}$ represents the principal nth-root of a.	p. 40
If $n > 1$ is an integer and $\sqrt[n]{a}$ is a real number, then • $a^{1/n} = \sqrt[n]{a}$ $\qquad\qquad$ • $a^{m/n} = \left(\sqrt[n]{a}\right)^m$ and $a^{m/n} = \sqrt[n]{a^m}$	p. 41

Let $n > 1$ be an integer and a be a real number. • If n is *even* then $\sqrt[n]{a^n} = \lvert a \rvert$. • If n is *odd* then $\sqrt[n]{a^n} = a$. Product property of radicals: $\sqrt[n]{a} \cdot \sqrt[n]{b} = \sqrt[n]{ab}$. Quotient property of radicals: $\dfrac{\sqrt[n]{a}}{\sqrt[n]{b}} = \sqrt[n]{\dfrac{a}{b}}$. Property of nested radicals: $\sqrt[m]{\sqrt[n]{a}} = \sqrt[m \cdot n]{a}$.	p. 44

SECTION R.5 Polynomials and Multiplication of Radicals | Reference

Special Case Products: $(a + b)(a - b) = a^2 - b^2$ $(a + b)^2 = a^2 + 2ab + b^2$ $(a - b)^2 = a^2 - 2ab + b^2$	p. 58

SECTION R.6 Factoring | Reference

General factoring strategy:
 1. Factor out the GCF.
 2. Identify the number of terms.
    4 terms: Factor by grouping either 2 terms with 2 terms or 3 terms with 1 term.
    3 terms: If the trinomial is a perfect square trinomial, factor as the square of a binomial.
       $a^2 + 2ab + b^2 = (a + b)^2$
       $a^2 - 2ab + b^2 = (a - b)^2$
       Otherwise, factor by trial-and-error.
    2 terms: Determine whether the binomial fits one of the following patterns:
       $a^2 - b^2 = (a + b)(a - b)$
       $a^3 + b^3 = (a + b)(a^2 - ab + b^2)$
       $a^3 - b^3 = (a - b)(a^2 + ab + b^2)$
	p. 71

SECTION R.7 Rational Expressions and More Operations on Radicals | Reference

A **rational expression** is a ratio of two polynomials. Values of the variable that make the denominator equal to zero are called restricted values of the variable.	p. 76
To simplify a rational expression, use the property of equivalent algebraic fractions. $$\dfrac{ac}{bc} = \dfrac{a}{b} \quad \text{for } b \neq 0, c \neq 0$$	p. 77
To multiply or divide rational expressions, $$\dfrac{a}{b} \cdot \dfrac{c}{d} = \dfrac{ac}{bd} \quad \text{for } b \neq 0, d \neq 0 \quad \text{and} \quad \dfrac{a}{b} \div \dfrac{c}{d} = \dfrac{a}{b} \cdot \dfrac{d}{c} \quad \text{for } b \neq 0, c \neq 0, d \neq 0$$	p. 79
To add or subtract rational expressions, write each fraction as an equivalent fraction with a common denominator. Then apply the following properties. $$\dfrac{a}{b} + \dfrac{c}{b} = \dfrac{a + c}{b} \quad \text{and} \quad \dfrac{a}{b} - \dfrac{c}{b} = \dfrac{a - c}{b} \quad \text{for } b \neq 0$$	p. 80
Removing a radical from the denominator of a fraction is called **rationalizing the denominator**.	p. 85

Expanded Chapter Summary available at www.mhhe.com/millerca.

CHAPTER R   Review Exercises

SECTION R.1

1. Given $A = \left\{ \sqrt{6}, 0, -8, 1.\overline{45}, \sqrt{9}, -\dfrac{2}{3}, 3\pi \right\}$, determine which elements belong to the given set.

   a. $\mathbb{N}$ **b.** $\mathbb{W}$ **c.** $\mathbb{Z}$

   d. $\mathbb{Q}$ **e.** $\mathbb{H}$ **f.** $\mathbb{R}$

2. Determine if the statement is true or false.

   a. $\{4, 6, 8\} \subset \{2, 4, 6, 8\}$

   b. $\{2, 4, 6, 8\} \subset \{4, 6, 8\}$

For Exercises 3–4, write each statement as an inequality.

3. x is at least 4.

4. $6y$ is no more than 8.

5. Complete the table.

Graph	Interval Notation	Set-Builder Notation
a. $\xrightarrow{\hspace{0.3cm}\underset{-3}{[}\hspace{2cm}\underset{7}{}\hspace{0.3cm}}$		
b. $\xrightarrow{\hspace{4cm}}$	$(2.1, \infty)$	
c. $\xrightarrow{\hspace{4cm}}$		$\{x \mid 4 \geq x\}$

6. Simplify without absolute value bars.

   a. $|w - 4|$ for $w < 4$

   b. $|w - 4|$ for $w \geq 4$

7. a. Write an absolute value expression to represent the distance between 2 and $\sqrt{5}$ on the number line.

   b. Simplify the expression from part (a) without absolute value bars.

For Exercises 8–12, simplify the expression.

8. a. 16^2 **b.** $(-16)^2$ **c.** -16^2

    d. $\sqrt{16}$ **e.** $-\sqrt{16}$ **f.** $\sqrt{-16}$

9. $\sqrt{\dfrac{25}{4}}$

10. $72 \cdot \left[\left(\dfrac{2}{3} \right)^2 - \left(\dfrac{1}{2} \right)^3 \right]$

11. $\dfrac{32 - |-11 + 3|}{36 \div 2 \div 3 - 2}$

12. $-5 - 3\left[8 - 2\sqrt{4^2 + (2 - 5)^2} \right]$

SECTION R.2

13. Jesse makes \$150 more per week than Ethan.

   a. Write a model for Jesse's salary J in terms of Ethan's salary E.

   b. Write a model for Ethan's salary E in terms of Jesse's salary J.

14. The width of a rectangle is 8 ft less than twice the length. Write a model for the width W in terms of the length L.

15. For a single-story home with a low pitch roof and asphalt shingles, a roofing company charges \$3.60 per square foot to tear off the old shingles and install new shingles. If the plywood underneath is damaged, the roofer charges \$50 per sheet replaced. The cost for high-impact skylights is \$250 each.

   a. Write a formula for the cost C (in \$) for a new roof, based on the square footage s, the number of plywood sheets replaced p, and the number of skylights n.

   b. Compute the cost to replace a 2100-ft^2 low pitch roof that requires four sheets of new plywood and two high-impact skylights.

16. Given $13x^2z^4 - \dfrac{2}{z} + \sqrt{5x + z}$, list the terms of the expression and the coefficients of each term.

For Exercises 17–18, simplify the expression.

17. $15.2c^2d - 11.1cd + 8.7c^2d - 5.4cd$

18. $8 - \left[4x^2 - \dfrac{1}{2}(6 - 4x^2) + 3 \right] + 13x^2$

For Exercises 19–27, identify the property that makes the given statement true. Choose from

   a. Commutative property of addition

   b. Commutative property of multiplication

   c. Associative property of addition

   d. Associative property of multiplication

   e. Identity property of addition

   f. Identity property of multiplication

   g. Inverse property of addition

   h. Inverse property of multiplication

   i. Distributive property of multiplication over addition

19. $5(ab) = (5a)b$ **20.** $\dfrac{1}{5} \cdot 5 = 1$

21. $p + (q + r) = (p + q) + r$

22. $p(q + r) = pq + pr$

23. $-\pi + 0 = -\pi$

24. $-\pi + \pi = 0$

25. $x + (y + z) = (y + z) + x$

26. $1 \cdot x = x$

27. $(ab)c = c(ab)$

28. Evaluate $\sqrt{(x_2 - x_1)^2 + (y_2 - y_1)^2}$ for $x_1 = 5$, $x_2 = -2$, $y_1 = -6$, $y_2 = 3$.

SECTION R.3

For Exercises 29–35, simplify completely. Write the answers with positive exponents only.

29. a. 9^0 **b.** -9^0 **c.** $9x^0$ **d.** $(9x)^0$

30. a. $\dfrac{1}{m^{-5}}$ **b.** m^{-5} **c.** $8m^{-9}n^2$ **d.** $8m^9n^{-2}$

31. $p^{-8} \cdot p^{12} \cdot p^{-1}$

32. $\dfrac{m^{-4}m^{10}}{m^6}$

33. $(-12a^{-3}b^4)^2$

34. $\left(\dfrac{-81x^8y^5}{9x^6y^8}\right)^{-2}$

35. $\left(\dfrac{1}{2u^5v^{-2}}\right)^{-3}\left(\dfrac{4}{u^{-3}v^2}\right)^{-1}$

36. Write the numbers in scientific notation.

   a. 4920   **b.** 0.00492   **c.** 4.92

37. Write the numbers in standard decimal notation.

   a. 9.8×10^{-1} **b.** 9.8×10^0 **c.** 9.8×10^1

For Exercises 38–39, perform the indicated operations.

38. $(9.2 \times 10^4)(3.0 \times 10^5)$

39. $\dfrac{(8.6 \times 10^{-3})(4.1 \times 10^8)}{2.0 \times 10^{-6}}$

40. A healthy adult female will have approximately 5 million red blood cells per 1 μL of blood. If a woman donates 1 pint of blood to a blood bank, approximately how many red blood cells will be present? (*Hint:* 1 μL $= 10^{-6}$ L and 1 pint ≈ 0.47 L.)

SECTION R.4

41. Write the expressions using radical notation.

   a. $x^{2/7}$ **b.** $9x^{2/7}$ **c.** $(9x)^{2/7}$

42. Write the expressions using rational exponents.

   a. $12\sqrt{w}$ **b.** $\sqrt{12w}$

For Exercises 43–47, simplify the expression. Write exponential expressions with positive exponents only. Assume that all variables represent positive real numbers.

43. a. $-\sqrt[4]{256}$ **b.** $\sqrt[4]{-256}$

44. $\sqrt[3]{-\dfrac{8}{125}}$

45. a. $10{,}000^{3/4}$ **b.** $10{,}000^{-3/4}$

   c. $-10{,}000^{3/4}$ **d.** $-10{,}000^{-3/4}$

   e. $(-10{,}000)^{3/4}$ **f.** $(-10{,}000)^{-3/4}$

46. $\dfrac{p^{7/3}p^{-2/3}}{p^{2/3}}$

47. $(9m^{-4}n^{2/3})^{1/2}$

48. Simplify. Assume that t represents any real number.

   a. $\sqrt{(3t - 4)^2}$ **b.** $\sqrt[3]{(3t - 4)^3}$

   c. $\sqrt[4]{(3t - 4)^4}$

For Exercises 49–55, simplify the radical expressions. Assume that all variables represent positive real numbers.

49. $\sqrt[3]{54xy^{12}z^{14}}$

50. $\sqrt[4]{32b^3c^{15}d^8}$

51. $\sqrt{\dfrac{p^{13}}{9}}$

52. $\dfrac{\sqrt[3]{3xy^5}}{\sqrt[3]{81x^7y^2}}$

53. $\sqrt{10} \cdot \sqrt{35}$

54. $(-5\sqrt[5]{a^3})(6\sqrt[5]{a^4})$

55. $\sqrt[4]{cd^2} \cdot \sqrt[3]{c^2d}$

For Exercises 56–58, add or subtract as indicated. Assume that all variables represent positive real numbers.

56. $\dfrac{1}{5}\sqrt{125} + \dfrac{3}{2}\sqrt{20} - \dfrac{1}{4}\sqrt{80}$

57. $-2c\sqrt[3]{54c^2d^3} + 5cd\sqrt[3]{2c^2} - 10d\sqrt[3]{250c^5}$

58. $3\sqrt{5t} + 8t\sqrt{5t}$

SECTION R.5

59. Determine if the expression is a polynomial.

   a. $5a^3 - 4a^2 + 6a - 3$

   b. $\dfrac{7}{a^3} - \dfrac{4}{a} + 6$

   c. $\sqrt{6x} + 5$

60. Write the polynomial in descending order. Identify the leading coefficient and degree of the polynomial.

$$-y^5 + 7.61y^9 + 2.5y^{11}$$

61. Determine the degree of the polynomial.

$$-4ac^2d^3 + 5ac^3d^4 - a^2cd^2$$

62. The revenue R (in $ billions) and operating expenses E (in $ billions) for cellular and wireless communications industries can be approximated by the following polynomial models. (*Source:* U.S. Census Bureau, www.census.gov)

$$R = 14x + 156.67$$
$$E = -x^2 + 8x + 130$$

In each case, x represents the number of years since 2006.

Revenue and Operating Expenses for Cellular and Wireless Communications Industries

$R = 14x + 156.67$

$E = -x^2 + 8x + 130$

($ Billions)

Year ($x = 0$ represents 2006)

a. Write and simplify the polynomial $R - E$.

b. Interpret the meaning of the polynomial from part (a).

c. Evaluate the polynomial $R - E$ for $x = 4$ and interpret the meaning of this value.

For Exercises 63–71, perform the indicated operations.

63. $(-7.2a^2b^3 + 4.1ab^2 - 3.9b) - (0.8a^2b^3 - 3.2ab^2 - b)$

64. $(-8uv^3)\left(\frac{1}{4}u^2v\right)$

65. $(5w^3 + 6y^2)(2w^3 - y^2)$

66. $(4p - 6)\left(\frac{1}{2}p^2 - p + 4\right)$

67. $(9t - 4)(9t + 4)$

68. $\left(\frac{1}{3}m - \frac{1}{4}n^3\right)\left(\frac{1}{3}m + \frac{1}{4}n^3\right)$

69. $(5k - 3)^2$

70. $(6c^2 + 5d^3)^2$

71. $[(2v - 1) + w][(2v - 1) - w]$

For Exercises 72–76, multiply the radicals and simplify. Assume that all variable expressions represent positive real numbers.

72. $4\sqrt{3}(2\sqrt{3} - 5\sqrt{5} + \sqrt{7})$

73. $(6\sqrt{5} - 2\sqrt{3})(2\sqrt{5} + 5\sqrt{3})$

74. $(7\sqrt{2} - 2\sqrt{11})(7\sqrt{2} + 2\sqrt{11})$

75. $(2c^2\sqrt{d} - 5d^2\sqrt{c})^2$

76. $(\sqrt{x + 2} + 4)^2$

77. Write and simplify an expression that represents the volume.

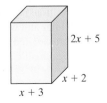

$2x + 5$

$x + 2$

$x + 3$

78. Determine the area of the triangle.

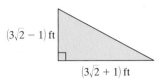

$(3\sqrt{2} - 1)$ ft

$(3\sqrt{2} + 1)$ ft

SECTION R.6

For Exercises 79–94, factor completely.

79. $80m^4n^8 - 48m^5n^3 - 16m^2n$

80. $11p^2(2p + 1) - 22p(2p + 1)$

81. $15ac - 14b - 10a + 21bc$

82. $-t + 12t^2 - 6$

83. $8x^3 - 40x^2y + 50xy^2$

84. $256a^4 - 625$

85. $3k^4 - 81k$

86. $(c + 2)^3 + d^3$

87. $25n^2 - m^2 - 12m - 36$

88. $(x^2 - 7)^2 + 8(x^2 - 7) + 15$

89. $(2p - 5)^2 - (4p + 1)^2$

90. $m^6 + 9m^3 + 8$

91. $x^4 + 6x^2y + 9y^2 - x^2 - 3y$

92. $7w^{-8} + 5w^{-7} + w^{-6}$

93. $12x^{7/2} - 4x^{5/2}$

94. $x(2x + 5)^{-3/4} + (2x + 5)^{1/4}$

SECTION R.7

95. Determine the restrictions on the variable.

  a. $\dfrac{w - 2}{w^2 - 4}$ **b.** $\dfrac{w - 2}{w^2 + 4}$

For Exercises 96–97, simplify and state the restricted values on the variable.

96. $-\dfrac{24a^2c^5d^2}{16c^6d^7}$

97. $\dfrac{m^2 - 16}{m^2 - m - 12}$

For Exercises 98–106, perform the indicated operations.

98. $\dfrac{2x - 5y}{x^3y} \cdot \dfrac{x^5y^7}{6x - 15y}$

99. $\dfrac{4ac}{a^2 + 4ac} \cdot \dfrac{a^2 + 8ac + 16c^2}{8a + 32c}$

100. $\dfrac{5x^2 + 25x + 125}{16x - x^3} \div \dfrac{x^3 - 125}{x^2 - 9x + 20}$

101. $\dfrac{7}{20x} + \dfrac{2}{15x^4}$

102. $\dfrac{6}{9x^2 - y^2} - \dfrac{1}{3x^2 - xy}$

103. $\dfrac{4}{x^2} + \dfrac{3}{x + 3} - \dfrac{2}{x}$

104. $\dfrac{x - 1}{x - 6} + \dfrac{5}{6 - x}$

105. $\dfrac{\dfrac{1}{16x} + \dfrac{1}{8}}{\dfrac{1}{4} + \dfrac{1}{8x}}$

106. $\dfrac{5m^{-1} - n^{-1}}{25m^{-2} - n^{-2}}$

For Exercises 107–112, simplify the expression. Assume that all variable expressions represent positive real numbers.

107. $\dfrac{5}{\sqrt{k}}$

108. $\dfrac{5}{\sqrt[4]{k}}$

109. $\dfrac{6}{\sqrt[4]{8x^2 y}}$

110. $\dfrac{15}{\sqrt{10} - \sqrt{7}}$

111. $\dfrac{x - 4}{\sqrt{x} + 2}$

112. $\dfrac{3}{\sqrt{5y}} + \dfrac{\sqrt{5y}}{y}$

CHAPTER R Test

1. Refer to $B = \left\{ 0, \dfrac{\pi}{6}, \sqrt{-25}, 8, -\dfrac{5}{7}, 2.1, -0.\overline{4}, -3 \right\}$.

Determine which elements belong to the given sets.

   a. $\mathbb{N}$ **b.** $\mathbb{W}$ **c.** $\mathbb{Z}$

   d. $\mathbb{Q}$ **e.** $\mathbb{H}$ **f.** $\mathbb{R}$

2. Max is twice as old as Jonas. If M represents Max's age and J represents Jonas's age, write an expression representing

   a. Max's age in terms of Jonas's age.

   b. Jonas's age in terms of Max's age.

3. The cost to have a room carpeted is \$12/yd^2 of carpet, \$40/hr of labor, and a flat \$30 fee charged by the installation company for gasoline.

   a. Write a formula that represents the total cost C (in \$) in terms of the amount of carpeting A and the number of hours of labor L.

   b. Determine the total cost to have 80 yd^2 of carpet put down if the installers take 2 hr to do the job.

4. Simplify without absolute value bars. $|5 - t|$ for $t > 5$.

5. a. Find the distance between $\sqrt{2}$ and 2 on the number line.

   b. Simplify without absolute value bars.

6. a. Determine the restrictions on y. $\dfrac{2y - 22}{y^2 - 9y - 22}$

   b. Simplify the expression.

For Exercises 7–28, perform the indicated operations and simplify the expression. Assume that all radical expressions represent real numbers.

7. $-\{6 + 4[9x - 2(3x - 5)] + 3\}$

8. $\dfrac{1}{3}a^2 b - \dfrac{1}{2}ab^2 - \dfrac{5}{6}a^2 b + 4ab^2$

9. $\dfrac{7^2 - 4[8 - (-2)] - 4^2}{-2|-4 + 6|}$

10. $(2a^3 b^{-4})^2 (4a^{-2} b^7)^{-1}$

11. $\left(\dfrac{1}{2}\right)^0 + \left(\dfrac{1}{3}\right)^{-3} + \left(\dfrac{1}{4}\right)^{-1}$

12. $\left(\dfrac{t^{2/5} \cdot t^{7/5}}{t^3}\right)^{10}$

13. $\sqrt[3]{80k^{15} m^2 n^7}$

14. $\dfrac{3}{4}\sqrt[4]{8p^2 q^3} \cdot \sqrt[4]{2p^3 q}$

15. $\sqrt{125ab^3} - 3b\sqrt{20ab}$

16. $\sqrt[3]{x^2 y} \cdot \sqrt[3]{xy}$

17. $(12n^2 - 4)\left(\dfrac{1}{2}n^2 - 3n + 5\right)$

18. $[(3a + b) - c][(3a + b) + c]$

19. $\left(\dfrac{1}{4}\sqrt{z} - p^2\right)\left(\dfrac{1}{4}\sqrt{z} + p^2\right)$

20. $\left(5\sqrt{x} + \sqrt{2}\right)\left(3\sqrt{x} - 2\sqrt{2}\right)$

21. $\left(\sqrt{x} - 6z\right)^2$

22. $\dfrac{3x^2}{x^3 + 14x^2 + 49x} \div \dfrac{8x - 4}{4x^2 + 26x - 14}$

23. $\dfrac{x^2}{x - 5} + \dfrac{10x - 25}{5 - x}$

24. $\dfrac{-12}{y^3 + 4y^2} + \dfrac{1}{y} - \dfrac{3}{y^2 + 4y}$

25. $\dfrac{\dfrac{x}{4} - \dfrac{9}{4x}}{\dfrac{1}{4} - \dfrac{3}{4x}}$

26. $\sqrt[3]{\dfrac{8}{2xy^2}}$

27. $\dfrac{6}{\sqrt{13} + \sqrt{10}}$

28. $\dfrac{7}{t\sqrt{2}} - \dfrac{\sqrt{2}}{t}$

For Exercises 29–35, factor completely.

29. $30x^3 + 2x^2 - 4x$

30. $xy + 5ay + 10ac + 2xc$

31. $x^5 + 2x^4 - 81x - 162$

32. $c^2 - 4a^2 - 44a - 121$

33. $27u^3 - v^6$

34. $4w^{-6} + 2w^{-5} + 7w^{-4}$

35. $y(2y - 1)^{-3/4} + (2y - 1)^{1/4}$

36. Determine the volume of the cone using the formula $V = \dfrac{1}{3}\pi r^2 h$. Write the answer in terms of π.

h, 13 in., *r* = 5 in.

37. Write an expression in terms of x that represents the area of the shaded region.

$x - 2$, $x + 6$, $x - 2$, $2x - 5$

38. Write the numbers in the given statement in scientific notation. "China uses 45,000,000,000 pairs of disposable chopsticks per year. This equates to approximately 1.66 million cubic meters of timber."

39. Write the number in the given statement in standard decimal notation. "The Ebola virus is approximately 8×10^{-7} m in length."

40. Perform the indicated operations.
$$\dfrac{(8.4 \times 10^{11})(6.0 \times 10^{-3})}{(4.2 \times 10^{-5})}$$

41. Write the interval notation representing $\{x \mid 2.7 < x\}$.

42. Write the set-builder notation representing the interval $[-3, 5)$.

Equations and Inequalities

1

Chapter Outline

According to legend, while taking a leisurely stroll through his orchard one day, the great astronomer and mathematician Sir Isaac Newton watched an apple fall from a tree. He most likely realized that the apple had no velocity when it was released, and yet it picked up speed as it moved toward the ground. As the legend is told, this event inspired Newton to begin his study on gravity. The resulting ideas incorporate gravity into the acceleration of the apple and may be generalized to any object launched into the air with an initial velocity.

In Chapter 1, we study equations and inequalities that will help us analyze many natural phenomena as well as applications in day-to-day life. The techniques we develop will enable us to solve equations that can be of assistance in making good financial decisions, buying the correct amount of materials for home projects, and even figuring the speed at which Sir Isaac Newton's apple might have hit the ground.

Linear Equations and Rational Equations

OBJECTIVES

1. Solve Linear Equations in One Variable
2. Identify Conditional Equations, Identities, and Contradictions
3. Solve Rational Equations
4. Solve Literal Equations for a Specified Variable

Whether to lease an automobile, to buy an automobile, or to use public transportation is an important financial decision that affects a family's monthly budget. As part of an informed decision, it is useful to create a mathematical model of the cost for each option.

Suppose that a couple has an option to buy a used car for $8800 and that they expect it to last 3 yr without major repair. Another option is to lease a new automobile for an initial down payment of $2500 followed by 36 monthly payments of $225. A mathematical model for the cost C (in $) to lease the car for t months is $C = 225t + 2500$. After how many months will the cost to lease the new car equal the cost to buy the used car? The answer can be found by solving the equation $8800 = 225t + 2500$ (see Example 3).

1. Solve Linear Equations in One Variable

In this section, we present methods to solve an important type of equation called a linear equation in one variable.

Definition of a Linear Equation in One Variable

A **linear equation in one variable** is an equation that can be written in the form $ax + b = 0$, where a and b are real numbers, $a \neq 0$, and x is the variable.

A linear equation in one variable is also called a **first-degree equation** because the degree of the variable term must be exactly one.

Linear equation in one variable	Not a linear equation in one variable	
$5x + 35 = 0$	$5x^2 + 35 = 0$	(not first degree)
$\dfrac{x}{4} - 5 = 0$	$\dfrac{4}{x} - 5 = 0$	(not first degree because $\frac{4}{x}$ is $4x^{-1}$)
$3x + 4 = 7$	$3x + 4y = 7$	(contains two variables)
$0.7x - 0.8 = 0.1$	$0.7x - 0.8 - 0.1$	(This is an expression, not an equation.)

A **solution** to an equation is a value of the variable that makes the equation a true statement. The set of all solutions to an equation is called the **solution set** of the equation. **Equivalent equations** have the same solution set. To solve a linear equation in one variable, we form simpler, equivalent equations until obtaining an equation whose solution is obvious. The properties used to produce equivalent equations include the addition, subtraction, multiplication, and division properties of equality.

Properties of Equality

Let a, b, and c be real numbers.

Property Name	Statement of Property	Algebraic Examples
Addition and subtraction properties of equality	$a = b$ is equivalent to $a + c = b + c$. $a = b$ is equivalent to $a - c = b - c$. Adding or subtracting the same quantity on both sides of an equation results in an equivalent equation.	• $x - 4 = 9$ $x - 4 + 4 = 9 + 4$ $x = 13$ • $3x = 2x + 5$ $3x - 2x = 2x - 2x + 5$ $x = 5$
Multiplication and division properties of equality	$a = b$ is equivalent to $ac = bc$ $(c \neq 0)$. $a = b$ is equivalent to $\frac{a}{c} = \frac{b}{c}$ $(c \neq 0)$. Multiplying or dividing by the same nonzero quantity on both sides of an equation results in an equivalent equation.	• $\frac{1}{3}x = 4$ $3\left(\frac{1}{3}x\right) = 3(4)$ $x = 12$ • $4x = 20$ $\dfrac{4x}{4} = \dfrac{20}{4}$ $x = 5$

The general strategy for solving a linear equation in one variable is to isolate the variable on one side of the equation and to place all other terms on the other side. For equations that require multiple steps to solve, follow these guidelines.

Solving a Linear Equation in One Variable

Step 1 Simplify both sides of the equation.
  • Use the distributive property to clear parentheses.
  • Combine like terms.
  • Consider clearing fractions or decimals by multiplying both sides of the equation by the least common denominator (LCD) of all terms.

Step 2 Use the addition or subtraction property of equality to collect the variable terms on one side of the equation and the constant terms on the other side.

Step 3 Use the multiplication or division property of equality to make the coefficient on the variable term equal to 1.

Step 4 Check the potential solution in the original equation.

Step 5 Write the solution set.

EXAMPLE 1   **Solving a Linear Equation**

Solve. $-3(w - 4) + 5 = 10 - (w + 1)$

Solution:

$$-3(w - 4) + 5 = 10 - (w + 1)$$

$-3w + 12 + 5 = 10 - w - 1$ Apply the distributive property.

$-3w + 17 = 9 - w$ Combine like terms.

$-3w + w + 17 = 9 - w + w$ Add w to both sides of the equation.

$-2w + 17 = 9$ Combine like terms.

$-2w + 17 - 17 = 9 - 17$ Subtract 17 from both sides.

$-2w = -8$ Combine like terms.

$\dfrac{-2w}{-2} = \dfrac{-8}{-2}$ Divide both sides by -2 to obtain a coefficient of 1 for w.

$w = 4$ Check: $-3(w - 4) + 5 = 10 - (w + 1)$

$-3[(4) - 4] + 5 \overset{?}{=} 10 - [(4) + 1]$

$-3(0) + 5 \overset{?}{=} 10 - (5)$

The solution set is {4}. $5 \overset{?}{=} 5 \checkmark$ true

---

Skill Practice 1   Solve. $5(v - 4) - 2 = 2(v + 7) - 3$

TECHNOLOGY CONNECTIONS

Checking a Solution to an Equation in One Variable

A calculator can be used to check the solution to an equation. First note that the variable used within an equation is arbitrary. For instance, the equation from Example 1, $-3(w - 4) + 5 = 10 - (w + 1)$, can also be expressed in terms of x: $-3(x - 4) + 5 = 10 - (x + 1)$.

To check the solution, first store the value 4 in memory within the calculator as the variable x. On a calculator, this is done using the STO feature. Then evaluate both sides of the equation using 4 for x. The right and left sides of the equation should be equal.

```
4→X
                        4
-3(X-4)+5
                        5  ←— left side ⎤
10-(X+1)                              ⎥ equal
                        5  ←— right side ⎦
```

If a linear equation contains fractions, it is often helpful to clear the equation of fractions. This is done by multiplying both sides of the equation by the least common denominator (LCD) of all terms in the equation.

Answer

1. {11}

EXAMPLE 2   **Solving a Linear Equation by Clearing Fractions**

Solve. $\dfrac{m-2}{5} - \dfrac{m-4}{2} = \dfrac{m+5}{15} + 2$

Solution:

TIP To find the least common multiple of 5, 2, and 15, first factor each number into prime factors.

$5 = 5 \cdot 1$

$2 = 2 \cdot 1$

$15 = 3 \cdot 5$

$\text{LCD} = 2 \cdot 3 \cdot 5 = 30$

$$\dfrac{m-2}{5} - \dfrac{m-4}{2} = \dfrac{m+5}{15} + 2$$

The least common denominator is 30.

$$30\left(\dfrac{m-2}{5} - \dfrac{m-4}{2}\right) = 30\left(\dfrac{m+5}{15} + 2\right)$$

Clear fractions by multiplying both sides by the LCD, 30.

$$\dfrac{30^6}{1}\left(\dfrac{m-2}{5_1}\right) - \dfrac{30^{15}}{1}\left(\dfrac{m-4}{2_1}\right) = \dfrac{30^2}{1}\left(\dfrac{m+5}{15_1}\right) + \dfrac{30}{1}\left(\dfrac{2}{1}\right)$$

Apply the distributive property.

$$6(m-2) - 15(m-4) = 2(m+5) + 60$$

Apply the distributive property.

$$6m - 12 - 15m + 60 = 2m + 10 + 60$$

$$-9m + 48 = 2m + 70$$

Combine like terms.

$$-9m - 2m + 48 - 48 = 2m - 2m + 70 - 48$$

Subtract $2m$ and 48 from both sides.

$$-11m = 22$$

Combine like terms.

$$\dfrac{-11m}{-11} = \dfrac{22}{-11}$$

Divide both sides by -11 to obtain a coefficient of 1 for m.

$$m = -2$$

The value -2 checks in the original equation.

The solution set is $\{-2\}$.

Skill Practice 2   Solve. $\dfrac{y+5}{2} - \dfrac{y-2}{4} = \dfrac{y+7}{3} + 1$

In Example 3, we use a linear equation to solve the application given at the beginning of the section.

EXAMPLE 3   **Using a Linear Equation in an Application**

A couple must decide whether to buy a used car for $8800 or lease a new car. The cost C (in $) to lease a car for t months is given by $C = 225t + 2500$. After how many months will the cost to lease a new car equal the cost to buy the used car?

Solution:

$$C = 225t + 2500$$

$$8800 = 225t + 2500$$

Substitute 8800 for the cost C.

$$8800 - 2500 = 225t + 2500 - 2500$$

Subtract 2500 from both sides.

$$6300 = 225t$$

$$\dfrac{6300}{225} = \dfrac{225t}{225}$$

Divide both sides by 225.

$$28 = t$$

In 28 months the cost to lease a new car will be equal to the cost to buy a used car.

Answer

2. $\{-4\}$

> **Skill Practice 3**   The cost C (in $) to rent a storage unit for t months is given by $C = 150 + 52.50t$. If Winston has $1200 budgeted for storage, for how many months can he rent the unit?

2. Identify Conditional Equations, Identities, and Contradictions

The linear equations examined thus far have all had exactly one solution. These equations are examples of conditional equations. A **conditional equation** is true for some values of the variable and false for other values.

An equation that is true for all values of the variable for which the expressions in an equation are defined is called an **identity.** An equation that is false for all values of the variable is called a **contradiction.** Example 4 presents each of these three types of equations.

EXAMPLE 4   **Identifying Conditional Equations, Contradictions, and Identities**

Identify each equation as a conditional equation, a contradiction, or an identity. Then give the solution set.

a. $3(2x - 1) = 2(3x - 2)$ **b.** $3(2x - 1) = 2(3x - 2) + 1$

c. $3(2x - 1) = 5x - 4$

Solution:

a. $3(2x - 1) = 2(3x - 2)$

$\qquad 6x - 3 = 6x - 4$ Apply the distributive property.

$\qquad\quad -3 = -4$ Subtract $6x$ from both sides. Contradiction

This equation is a contradiction.
The solution set is the empty set $\{\ \}$.

b. $3(2x - 1) = 2(3x - 2) + 1$

$\qquad 6x - 3 = 6x - 4 + 1$ Apply the distributive property.

$\qquad 6x - 3 = 6x - 3$ Combine like terms.

$\qquad\quad 0 = 0$ Subtract $6x$ from both sides. Add 3 to both sides.

This equation is an identity.
The solution set is the set of all real numbers, $\mathbb{R}$.

c. $3(2x - 1) = 5x - 4$

$\qquad 6x - 3 = 5x - 4$ Apply the distributive property.

$\qquad\quad x = -1$ Subtract $5x$ from both sides. Add 3 to both sides.

This is a conditional equation.
The solution set is $\{-1\}$.   Conditional equation. The statement is true under the condition that $x = -1$.

> **Skill Practice 4**   Identify each equation as a conditional equation, a contradiction, or an identity. Then give the solution set.
>
> **a.** $4x + 1 - x = 6x - 2$ **b.** $2(-5x - 1) = 2x - 12x + 6$
>
> **c.** $2(3x - 1) = 6(x + 1) - 8$

Answers

3. He can rent the unit for 20 months.

4. a. Conditional equation; $\{1\}$

   b. Contradiction; $\{\ \}$

   c. Identity; $\mathbb{R}$

3. Solve Rational Equations

One of the powerful features of mathematics is that methods used to solve one type of equation can sometimes be adapted to solve other types of equations. Two equations are shown here. The equation on the left is a linear equation. The equation on the right is a rational equation. A **rational equation** is an equation in which each term contains a rational expression. All linear equations are rational equations, but not all rational equations are linear. For example:

Linear Equation with Constants in the Denominator

$$\frac{x}{2} = \frac{2x}{3} - 1$$

Rational Equation with Variables in the Denominator

$$\frac{12}{x} = \frac{6}{2x} + 3$$

The linear equation can be solved by first multiplying both sides of the equation by the least common denominator of all the fractions. This is the same strategy used in Example 5 to solve a rational equation with a variable in the denominator. However, when a variable appears in the denominator of a fraction, we must restrict the values of the variable to avoid division by zero.

EXAMPLE 5   **Solving a Rational Equation**

Solve the equation and check the solution. $\dfrac{12}{x} = \dfrac{6}{2x} + 3$

Solution:

$\dfrac{12}{x} = \dfrac{6}{2x} + 3$	Restrict x so that $x \neq 0$. The LCD is $2x$.
$2x\left(\dfrac{12}{x}\right) = 2x\left(\dfrac{6}{2x} + \dfrac{3}{1}\right)$	Clear fractions by multiplying both sides by the LCD, $2x$. Since $x \neq 0$, this will produce an equivalent equation.
$\dfrac{2x}{1}\left(\dfrac{12}{x}\right) = \dfrac{2x}{1}\left(\dfrac{6}{2x}\right) + \dfrac{2x}{1}\left(\dfrac{3}{1}\right)$	Apply the distributive property.
$24 = 6 + 6x$	Simplify.
$18 = 6x$	Subtract 6 from both sides.
$3 = x$	

Avoiding Mistakes

Be sure to note the restrictions on the variable before solving the equation. In Example 5, we have the restriction $x \neq 0$.

Check: $\dfrac{12}{x} = \dfrac{6}{2x} + \dfrac{3}{1}$

$\dfrac{12}{(3)} \overset{?}{=} \dfrac{6}{2(3)} + \dfrac{3}{1}$

$4 \overset{?}{=} 1 + 3 \checkmark$ true

The solution set is $\{3\}$.

Skill Practice 5   Solve the equation and check the solution. $\dfrac{15}{y} = \dfrac{21}{3y} + 2$

In Example 6, we demonstrate the importance of determining restricted values of the variable in an equation and checking the potential solutions. You will see that for some equations, a potential solution does not check.

Answer
5. $\{4\}$

EXAMPLE 6   **Solving a Rational Equation**

Solve the equation and check the solution. $\dfrac{x}{x-4} = \dfrac{4}{x-4} - \dfrac{4}{5}$

Solution:

$$\dfrac{x}{x-4} = \dfrac{4}{x-4} - \dfrac{4}{5}$$
Restrict x so that $x \neq 4$.
The LCD is $5(x-4)$.

$$5(x-4)\left(\dfrac{x}{x-4}\right) = 5(x-4)\left(\dfrac{4}{x-4} - \dfrac{4}{5}\right)$$
Clear fractions by multiplying both sides by the LCD $5(x-4)$.

$$\dfrac{5\cancel{(x-4)}}{1}\left(\dfrac{x}{\cancel{x-4}}\right) = \dfrac{5\cancel{(x-4)}}{1}\left(\dfrac{4}{\cancel{x-4}}\right) + \dfrac{5(x-4)}{1}\left(-\dfrac{4}{\cancel{5}}\right)$$
Apply the distributive property.

$$5x = 20 - 4(x-4)$$
Simplify.

$$5x = 20 - 4x + 16$$
Apply distributive property.

$$9x = 36$$
Combine like terms.
Add $4x$ to both sides.

  This is a restricted value of x. Substituting 4 for x in the original equation results in division by 0.

Check: $\dfrac{x}{x-4} = \dfrac{4}{x-4} - \dfrac{4}{5}$

$$\underbrace{\dfrac{(4)}{(4)-4}}_{\text{undefined}} \overset{?}{=} \underbrace{\dfrac{4}{(4)-4}}_{\text{undefined}} - \dfrac{4}{5}$$

The solution set is $\{\ \}$.

Skill Practice 6   Solve the equation and check the solution.

$$\dfrac{y}{y+5} = \dfrac{-5}{y+5} + \dfrac{5}{4}$$

EXAMPLE 7   **Solving a Rational Equation**

Solve the equation and check the solution. $\dfrac{6}{y^2 + 8y + 15} - \dfrac{2}{y+3} = \dfrac{-4}{y+5}$

Solution:

$$\dfrac{6}{y^2 + 8y + 15} - \dfrac{2}{y+3} = \dfrac{-4}{y+5}$$

$$\dfrac{6}{(y+3)(y+5)} - \dfrac{2}{y+3} = \dfrac{-4}{y+5}$$
Restrict y so that $y \neq -3$, $y \neq -5$.
Clear fractions by multiplying both sides by the LCD $(y+3)(y+5)$.

$$(y+3)(y+5)\left(\dfrac{6}{(y+3)(y+5)} - \dfrac{2}{y+3}\right) = (y+3)(y+5)\left(\dfrac{-4}{y+5}\right)$$

$$\dfrac{\cancel{(y+3)(y+5)}}{1}\left(\dfrac{6}{\cancel{(y+3)(y+5)}}\right) - \dfrac{\cancel{(y+3)}(y+5)}{1}\left(\dfrac{2}{\cancel{y+3}}\right)$$

$$= \dfrac{(y+3)\cancel{(y+5)}}{1}\left(\dfrac{-4}{\cancel{y+5}}\right)$$

$$6 - 2(y + 5) = -4(y + 3)$$
$$6 - 2y - 10 = -4y - 12$$
$$-2y - 4 = -4y - 12$$
$$2y = -8$$
$$y = -4$$

The value -4 is *not* a restricted value.

Apply the distributive property.

Combine like terms.

Check: $\dfrac{6}{y^2 + 8y + 15} - \dfrac{2}{y + 3} = \dfrac{-4}{y + 5}$

$\dfrac{6}{(-4)^2 + 8(-4) + 15} - \dfrac{2}{(-4) + 3} \overset{?}{=} \dfrac{-4}{(-4) + 5}$

$-6 + 2 \overset{?}{=} -4 \checkmark$ true

The solution set is $\{-4\}$.

Skill Practice 7   Solve the equation and check the solution.

$$\frac{11}{x^2 + 5x + 4} - \frac{3}{x + 4} = \frac{1}{x + 1}$$

---

4. Solve Literal Equations for a Specified Variable

Sometimes an equation contains multiple variables. For example, $d = rt$ relates the distance that an object travels to the rate of travel and time of travel. Such an equation is called a literal equation (an equation with many letters). We often want to manipulate a literal equation to solve for a specified variable. In such a case, we use the same techniques as we would with an equation containing one variable.

EXAMPLE 8   **Solving an Equation for a Specified Variable**

Solve for the indicated variable.

a. $d = rt$ for t **b.** $3x + 2y = 6$ for y

c. $A = \dfrac{1}{2}h(B + b)$ for B

Solution:

a. $d = rt$ for t

$\dfrac{d}{r} = \dfrac{rt}{r}$

$\dfrac{d}{r} = t$ or $t = \dfrac{d}{r}$

The relationship between r and t is multiplication. Therefore, perform the inverse operation. Divide both sides by r.

b. $3x + 2y = 6$ for y

$2y = -3x + 6$

Subtract $3x$ from both sides to isolate the y term on one side of the equation.

$\dfrac{2y}{2} = \dfrac{-3x + 6}{2}$

Divide both sides by 2 to isolate y.

$y = \dfrac{-3x + 6}{2}$ or $y = -\dfrac{3}{2}x + 3$ Simplify.

c. $A = \dfrac{1}{2}h(B + b)$ for B

First note that letters in algebra are case sensitive. The letters b and B represent different variables.

$2(A) = 2\left[\dfrac{1}{2}h(B + b)\right]$

Multiply by 2 to clear fractions.

$2A = h(B + b)$

$\dfrac{2A}{h} = \dfrac{h(B + b)}{h}$

Divide by h.

$\dfrac{2A}{h} = B + b$

$\dfrac{2A}{h} - b = B$ or $B = \dfrac{2A}{h} - b$

Subtract b from both sides to isolate B.

Skill Practice 8 Solve for the indicated variable.

a. $I = Prt$ for t **b.** $4x + 3y = 12$ for y

c. $A = \dfrac{1}{2}h(B + b)$ for b

In Example 9, multiple occurrences of the variable x appear within the equation. Factoring is required to combine x terms so that we can isolate x.

EXAMPLE 9 Solving an Equation for a Specified Variable

Solve the equation for x. $ax + by = cx + d$

Solution:

$ax + by = cx + d$ Subtract cx from both sides to combine the x terms on one side.

$ax - cx = d - by$ Subtract by from both sides to combine the non-x terms on the other side.

$x(a - c) = d - by$ Factor out x as the GCF on the left side of the equation.

$\dfrac{x(a - c)}{a - c} = \dfrac{d - by}{a - c}$ Divide by $(a - c)$.

$x = \dfrac{d - by}{a - c}$

Skill Practice 9 Solve the equation for x. $3x - w = ax + z$

Answers

8. a. $t = \dfrac{I}{Pr}$

b. $y = \dfrac{-4x + 12}{3}$ or

$y = -\dfrac{4}{3}x + 4$

c. $b = \dfrac{2A}{h} - B$

9. $x = \dfrac{w + z}{3 - a}$ or $x = -\dfrac{w + z}{a - 3}$

TIP In Example 9, the answer can be expressed in different forms. For example, if we had isolated x on the right side of the equation, the solution for x would be

$ax + by = cx + d$

$by - d = cx - ax$

$\dfrac{by - d}{(c - a)} = \dfrac{x(c - a)}{(c - a)}$

$x = \dfrac{by - d}{c - a}$

To show that $\dfrac{by - d}{c - a} = \dfrac{d - by}{a - c}$ multiply either expression by $\dfrac{-1}{-1}$.

$\dfrac{(by - d)}{(c - a)} \cdot \dfrac{(-1)}{(-1)} = \dfrac{-by + d}{-c + a} = \dfrac{d - by}{a - c}$

SECTION 1.1   Practice Exercises

Concept Connections

1. An equation that can be written in the form $ax + b = 0$ where a and b are real numbers and $a \neq 0$ is called a _____ equation in one variable.

2. A linear equation is also called a _____-degree equation because the degree of the variable is 1.

3. A _____ to an equation is the value of the variable that makes the equation a true statement.

4. The solution _____ to an equation is the set of all solutions to the equation.

5. Two equations are _____ equations if they have the same solution set.

6. The _____ property of equality indicates that adding the same real number to both sides of an equation results in an equivalent equation.

7. The _____ property of equality indicates that if $a = b$, then $\dfrac{a}{c} = \dfrac{b}{c}$ provided that $c \neq 0$.

8. A _____ equation is one that is true for some values of the variable and false for others.

9. An _____ is an equation that is true for all values of the variable for which the expressions in the equation are defined.

10. A _____ is an equation that is false for all values of the variable.

11. A _____ equation is an equation in which each term contains a rational expression.

12. If an equation has no solution, then the solution set is the _____ set and is denoted by _____.

Objective 1: Solve Linear Equations in One Variable

For Exercises 13–14, determine if the equation is linear or nonlinear. If the equation is linear, find the solution set.

13. **a.** $-2x = 8$ **b.** $\dfrac{-2}{x} = 8$ **c.** $-\dfrac{1}{2}x = 8$

    d. $-2|x| = 8$ **e.** $x - 2 = 8$

14. **a.** $12 = 4x$ **b.** $12 = \dfrac{4}{x}$ **c.** $12 = \dfrac{1}{4}x$

    d. $12 = 4\sqrt{x}$ **e.** $12 = 4 + x$

For Exercises 15–34, solve the equation. (See Examples 1–2)

15. $-6x - 4 = 20$

16. $-8y + 6 = 22$

17. $4 = 7 - 3(4t + 1)$

18. $11 = 7 - 2(5p - 2)$

19. $-6(v - 2) + 3 = 9 - (v + 4)$

20. $-5(u - 4) + 2 = 11 - (u - 3)$

21. $2.3 = 4.5x + 30.2$

22. $9.4 = 3.5p - 0.4$

23. $0.05y + 0.02(6000 - y) = 270$

24. $0.06x + 0.04(10{,}000 - x) = 520$

25. $2(5x - 6) = 4[x - 3(x - 10)]$

26. $4(y - 3) = 3[y + 2(y - 2)]$

27. $\dfrac{1}{4}x - \dfrac{3}{2} = 2$

28. $\dfrac{1}{6}x - \dfrac{5}{3} = 1$

29. $\dfrac{1}{2}w - \dfrac{3}{4} = \dfrac{2}{3}w + 2$

30. $\dfrac{2}{5}p - \dfrac{3}{10} = \dfrac{7}{15}p - 1$

31. $\dfrac{y - 1}{5} + \dfrac{y}{4} = \dfrac{y + 3}{2} + 1$

32. $\dfrac{x - 6}{3} + \dfrac{x}{7} = \dfrac{x + 1}{3} + 2$

33. $\dfrac{n + 3}{4} - \dfrac{n - 2}{5} = \dfrac{n + 1}{10} - 1$

34. $\dfrac{t - 2}{3} - \dfrac{t + 7}{5} = \dfrac{t - 4}{10} + 2$

35. A scientist measures the density of a piece of glacial ice to be 920 kg/m^3 and that of the surrounding seawater to be 1025 kg/m^3. Because the densities are different, approximately one-ninth of the volume of the iceberg is above water. The volume seen above water V_s can be approximated by $V_s = \frac{1}{9}V_t$, where V_t is the total volume of the iceberg.

    a. Determine the volume of the portion of an iceberg seen above water if the total volume is 50,040 m^3.

    b. Determine the total volume of an iceberg if the portion above water is estimated to be 9000 m^3.

36. At one point during difficult economic times in the United States, $1 American was worth €0.78 (euro). Therefore, the model $E = 0.78d$ gives the number of euros E that can be exchanged for d American dollars.

a. Determine the number of euros that can be exchanged for $500.

b. Determine the number of dollars that can be exchanged for €800. Round to the nearest dollar.

37. The total revenue R (in $ billions) for the motion picture and video production industries in the United States can be modeled by $R = 4.25x + 93.9$, where x is the number of years since 2005. (*Source*: U.S. Census Bureau, www.census.gov) (**See Example 3**)

a. Determine the revenue for the year 2011.

b. Determine the year in which the revenue was $110.9 billion.

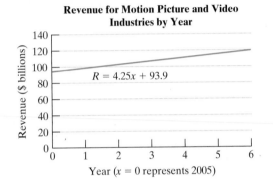

Revenue for Motion Picture and Video Industries by Year

38. The total revenue R (in $ billions) for cellular and other wireless telecommunications industries in the United States can be modeled by $R = 17.5x + 138.5$, where x is the number of years since 2005. (*Source*: www.census.gov)

a. Determine the revenue for the year 2007.

b. Determine the year in which the revenue was $226 billion.

Total Revenue for Cellular and Other Wireless Telecommunications by Year

39. In the mid-nineteenth century, explorers used the boiling point of water to estimate altitude. The boiling temperature of water T (in °F) can be approximated by the model $T = -1.83a + 212$, where a is the altitude in thousands of feet.

a. Determine the temperature at which water boils at an altitude of 4000 ft.

b. Two campers hiking in Colorado boil water for tea. If the water boils at 193°F, approximate the altitude of the campers. Give the result to the nearest hundred feet.

40. For a recent year, the cost C (in $) for tuition and fees for x credit-hours at a public college was given by $C = 167.95x + 94$.

a. Determine the cost to take 9 credit-hours.

b. If Jenna spent $2445.30 for her classes, how many credit-hours did she take?

41. The annual per capita consumer expenditure E (in $) for prescription drugs can be modeled by $E = 46.2x + 446.2$, where x is the number of years since the year 2000. In what year did the average per capita expenditure for prescription drugs equal $862 per year? (*Source*: www.census.gov)

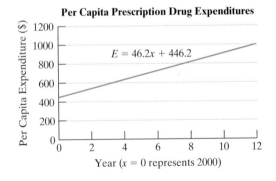

Per Capita Prescription Drug Expenditures

42. The annual per capita consumer expenditure E (in $) for nursing home care can be modeled by $E = 13.7x + 338$, where x is the number of years since the year 2000. In what year did the average per capita expenditure for nursing home care equal $475? (*Source*: www.census.gov)

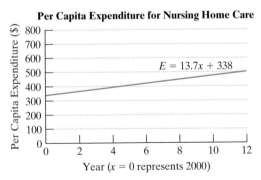

Per Capita Expenditure for Nursing Home Care

Objective 2: Identify Conditional Equations, Identities, and Contradictions

For Exercises 43–48, identify the equation as a conditional equation, a contradiction, or an identity. Then give the solution set. (See Example 4)

43. $2x - 3 = 4(x - 1) - 1 - 2x$

44. $4(3 - 5n) + 1 = -4n - 8 - 16n$

45. $-(6 - 2w) = 4(w + 1) - 2w - 10$

46. $-5 + 3x = 3(x - 1) - 2$

47. $\frac{1}{2}x + 3 = \frac{1}{4}x + 1$

48. $\frac{2}{3}y - 5 = \frac{1}{6}y - 4$

Objective 3: Solve Rational Equations

For Exercises 49–52, determine the restrictions on x.

49. $\frac{3}{x - 5} + \frac{2}{x + 4} = \frac{5}{7}$

50. $\frac{2}{x + 1} - \frac{5}{x - 7} = \frac{2}{3}$

51. $\frac{3}{2x^2 + 7x - 15} - \frac{1}{6} = \frac{1}{x^2 - 25}$

52. $\frac{6}{3x^2 - 11x - 4} - \frac{1}{3} = \frac{1}{x^2 - 16}$

For Exercises 53–68, solve the equation. (See Examples 5–7)

53. $\frac{1}{2} - \frac{7}{2y} = \frac{5}{y}$

54. $\frac{1}{3} - \frac{4}{3t} = \frac{7}{t}$

55. $\frac{w + 3}{4w} + 1 = \frac{w - 5}{w}$

56. $\frac{x + 2}{6x} + 1 = \frac{x - 7}{x}$

57. $\frac{c}{c - 3} = \frac{3}{c - 3} - \frac{3}{4}$

58. $\frac{7}{d - 7} - \frac{7}{8} = \frac{d}{d - 7}$

59. $\frac{1}{t - 1} = \frac{3}{t^2 - 1}$

60. $\frac{1}{w + 2} = \frac{5}{w^2 - 4}$

61. $\frac{2}{x - 5} - \frac{1}{x + 5} = \frac{11}{x^2 - 25}$

62. $\frac{2}{c + 3} - \frac{1}{c - 3} = \frac{10}{c^2 - 9}$

63. $\frac{5}{x^2 - x - 2} - \frac{2}{x^2 - 4} = \frac{4}{x^2 + 3x + 2}$

64. $\frac{4}{x^2 - 2x - 8} - \frac{1}{x^2 - 16} = \frac{2}{x^2 + 6x + 8}$

65. $\frac{5}{m - 2} = \frac{3m}{m^2 + 2m - 8} - \frac{2}{m + 4}$

66. $\frac{10}{n - 6} = \frac{15n}{n^2 - 2n - 24} - \frac{6}{n + 4}$

67. $\frac{5x}{3x^2 - 5x - 2} - \frac{1}{3x + 1} = \frac{3}{2 - x}$

68. $\frac{3x}{2x^2 + x - 3} - \frac{2}{2x + 3} = \frac{4}{1 - x}$

Objective 4: Solve Literal Equations for a Specified Variable

For Exercises 69–90, solve for the specified variable. (See Examples 8–9)

69. $A = lw$ for l

70. $E = IR$ for R

71. $P = a + b + c$ for c

72. $W = K - T$ for K

73. $\Delta s = s_2 - s_1$ for s_1

74. $\Delta t = t_f - t_i$ for t_i

75. $7x + 2y = 8$ for y

76. $3x + 5y = 15$ for y

77. $5x - 4y = 2$ for y

78. $7x - 2y = 5$ for y

79. $\frac{1}{2}x + \frac{1}{3}y = 1$ for y

80. $\frac{1}{4}x - \frac{2}{3}y = 2$ for y

81. $S = \frac{n}{2}(a + d)$ for d

82. $S = \frac{n}{2}[2a + (n - 1)d]$ for a

83. $V = \frac{1}{3}\pi r^2 h$ for h

84. $V = \frac{1}{3}Bh$ for B

85. $6 = 4x + tx$ for x

86. $8 = 3x + kx$ for x

87. $6x + ay = bx + 5$ for x

88. $3x + 2y = cx + d$ for x

89. $A = P + Prt$ for P

90. $C = A + Ar$ for A

Mixed Exercises

For Exercises 91–104, solve the equation.

91. $\dfrac{5}{2n + 1} = \dfrac{-2}{3n - 4}$

92. $\dfrac{4}{5z - 3} = \dfrac{-2}{4z + 7}$

93. $5 - 2\{3 - [5v + 3(v - 7)]\} = 8v + 6(3 - 4v) - 61$

94. $6 - \{4 - 2[8u - 2(u - 3)]\} = -4u + 3(2 - u) + 8$

95. $(x - 7)(x + 2) = x^2 + 4x + 13$

96. $(m + 3)(2m - 5) = 2m^2 + 4m - 3$

97. $\dfrac{3}{c^2 - 4c} - \dfrac{9}{2c^2 + 3c} = \dfrac{2}{2c^2 - 5c - 12}$

98. $\dfrac{4}{d^2 - d} - \dfrac{5}{2d^2 + 5d} = \dfrac{2}{2d^2 + 3d - 5}$

99. $\dfrac{1}{3}x + \dfrac{1}{2} = \dfrac{1}{2}(x + 1) - \dfrac{1}{6}x$

100. $\dfrac{1}{2}x + \dfrac{2}{5} = \dfrac{2}{5}(x + 1) + \dfrac{1}{10}x$

101. $(t + 2)^2 = (t - 4)^2$

102. $(y - 3)^2 = (y + 1)^2$

103. $\dfrac{3}{3a + 4} = \dfrac{5}{5a - 1}$

104. $\dfrac{8}{8x - 3} = \dfrac{2}{2x + 5}$

105. Suppose that 40 deer are introduced in a protected wilderness area. The population of the herd P can be approximated by $P = \dfrac{40 + 20x}{1 + 0.05x}$, where x is the time in years since introducing the deer. Determine the time required for the deer population to reach 200.

106. Starting from rest, an automobile's velocity v (in ft/sec) is given by $v = \dfrac{180t}{2t + 10}$, where t is the time in seconds after the car begins forward motion. Determine the time required for the car to reach a speed of 60 ft/sec ($\approx$ 41 mph).

107. Brianna's SUV gets 22 mpg in the city and 30 mpg on the highway. The amount of gas she uses A (in gal) is given by $A = \dfrac{1}{22}c + \dfrac{1}{30}h$, where c is the number of city miles driven and h is the number of highway miles driven. If Brianna drove 165 mi on the highway and used 7 gal of gas, how many city miles did she drive?

108. Dexter's truck gets 32 mpg on the highway and 24 mpg in the city. The amount of gas he uses A (in gal) is given by $A = \dfrac{1}{24}c + \dfrac{1}{32}h$, where c is the number of city miles driven and h is the number of highway miles driven. If Dexter drove 60 mi in the city and used 9 gal of gas, how many highway miles did he drive?

Write About It

109. Explain why the value 5 is not a solution to the equation $\dfrac{x}{x - 5} + \dfrac{1}{5} = \dfrac{5}{x - 5}$.

110. Explain why the value 2 is not the only solution to the equation $2x + 4 = 2(x - 3) + 10$.

111. Explain why $\dfrac{3}{x} + 12 = 0$ is not a linear equation in one variable.

112. Explain why $2\sqrt{x} + 6 = 0$ is not a linear equation in one variable.

113. Explain why the equation $x + 1 = x + 2$ has no solution.

114. Explain the difference in the process to clear fractions between the two equations.

$$\dfrac{x}{3} + \dfrac{1}{2} = 1 \quad \text{and} \quad \dfrac{3}{x} + \dfrac{1}{2} = 1$$

Expanding Your Skills

For Exercises 115–118, find the value of a so that the equation has the given solution set.

115. $ax + 6 = 4x + 14$ $\{4\}$

116. $ax - 3 = 2x + 9$ $\{3\}$

117. $a(2x - 5) + 6 = 5x + 7$ $\{16\}$

118. $a(2x + 4) + 12x = 3(2 - x)$ $\{34\}$

In Section R.1, we learned that a repeating decimal is a rational number (a ratio of two integers). For any repeating decimal, a corresponding ratio of two integers can be found by solving a linear equation. For example, to find two integers that represent $0.1\overline{92}$, let x represent $0.1\overline{92}$. The fractional value of x can be found as follows.

Let x represent $0.1\overline{92}$.
Then $10x = 1.\overline{92}$.
Then $1000x = 192.\overline{92}$.

$1000x = 192.\overline{92}$ Multiply x by two powers of 10 sufficient to line up the repeating digits to the right of the decimal point.
$\underline{-10x \quad -1.\overline{92}}$ When these values are subtracted, the digits to the right of the decimal point are zero.
$990x = 191.00$

$$x = \frac{191}{990} = 0.1\overline{92}$$

For Exercises 119–122, find a ratio of two integers that represents the given number.

119. $0.5\overline{16}$ **120.** $0.8\overline{26}$ **121.** $0.5\overline{34}$ **122.** $0.\overline{761}$

SECTION 1.2   Applications and Modeling with Linear Equations

OBJECTIVES

1. Solve Applications Involving Geometry
2. Solve Applications Involving Simple Interest
3. Solve Applications Involving Mixtures
4. Solve Applications Involving Uniform Motion
5. Solve Applications Involving Linear Models
6. Solve Applications Involving Rate of Work Done
7. Solve Applications Involving Proportions

1. Solve Applications Involving Geometry

In Examples 1–6, we use linear and rational equations to model physical situations to solve applications. While there is no magic formula to apply to all word problems, we do offer the following guidelines to help you organize the given information and to form a useful model.

> **Problem-Solving Strategy**
>
> 1. Read the problem carefully. Determine what the problem is asking for, and assign variables to the unknown quantities.
> 2. Make an appropriate figure or table if applicable. Label the given information and variables in the figure or table.
> 3. Write an equation that represents the verbal model. The equation may be a known formula or one that you create that is unique to the problem.
> 4. Solve the equation from step 3.
> 5. Interpret the solution to the equation and check that it is reasonable in the context of the problem.

In Example 1, we present an application involving a rectangular figure. Refer to the inside back cover of the text to familiarize yourself with several common formulas from the study of geometry.

EXAMPLE 1   Solving an Application Involving Geometry

An 8 in. by 10 in. rectangular photograph is in a frame that adds a border of x inches on all sides. If the perimeter of the frame is 48 in., determine the width of the frame border x.

Solution:

1. After reading the problem carefully, we see that the size of the border x is the unknown quantity.

2. A figure is provided with the given dimensions of the photograph and the unknown value of the border labeled as x.

3. To build an equation use the fact that the perimeter of the frame is 48 in. We can use the formula for the perimeter of a rectangle.

$$P = 2l + 2w$$

$$48 = 2(\underbrace{10 + 2x}_{\text{length}}) + 2(\underbrace{8 + 2x}_{\text{width}})$$

The length of the frame is $l = 10 + 2x$

The width of the frame is $w = 8 + 2x$

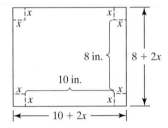

4. $48 = 20 + 4x + 16 + 4x$ Solve the equation.

   $48 = 8x + 36$

   $12 = 8x$ Subtract 36 from both sides.

   $1.5 = x$ Divide by 8.

5. The frame border is 1.5 in.

   <u>Check that the answer is reasonable</u>:

   The length of the frame would be $10 + 2x = 10$ in. $+ 2(1.5$ in.$) = 13$ in.

   The width of the frame would be $8 + 2x = 8$ in. $+ 2(1.5$ in.$) = 11$ in.

   The perimeter of the frame is $P = 2(13$ in.$) + 2(11$ in.$)$

   $= 26$ in. $+ 22$ in.

   $= 48$ in. ✓

Skill Practice 1   A café has a 12 yd by 15 yd patio with a surrounding walkway that is x yards wide. The perimeter around the outside of the walkway is 64 yd. Determine the value of x.

---

2. Solve Applications Involving Simple Interest

Simple interest I for a loan or an investment is based on the principal P (amount of money invested or borrowed), the annual interest rate r, and the time of the loan t in years. The relationship among the variables is given by $I = Prt$.

For example, if $5000 is invested at 4% simple interest for 18 months (1.5 yr), then the amount of simple interest earned is

$$I = P \cdot r \cdot t$$
$$I = (\$5000)(0.04)(1.5)$$
$$= \$300$$

The formula for simple interest is used in Example 2.

Answer
1. The walkway is 1.25 yd wide.

| EXAMPLE 2 | **Solving an Application Involving Simple Interest** |

Kent invested a total of $8000. He invested part of the money for 2 yr in a stock fund that earned the equivalent of 6.5% simple interest. He put the remaining money in an 18-month certificate of deposit (CD) that earned 2.5% simple interest. If the total interest from both investments was $855, determine the amount invested in each account.

Solution:

We can assign a variable to *either* the amount invested in the stock fund or the amount invested in the CD.

Let x represent the principal invested in the stock fund.
Then, $(8000 - x)$ is the remaining amount in the CD.

The interest from each account is computed from the formula $I = Prt$. Consider organizing this information in a table.

	Stock Fund (6.5% yield)	CD (2.5% yield)	Total
Principal	x	$8000 - x$	$8000
Interest ($I = Prt$)	$x(0.065)(2)$	$(8000 - x)(0.025)(1.5)$	$855

To build an equation, note that

$$\left(\begin{array}{c}\text{Interest from} \\ \text{stock fund}\end{array}\right) + \left(\begin{array}{c}\text{Interest} \\ \text{from CD}\end{array}\right) = \left(\begin{array}{c}\text{Total} \\ \text{interest}\end{array}\right)$$

$x(0.065)(2) + (8000 - x)(0.025)(1.5) = 855$	Second row of table
$0.13x + 0.0375(8000 - x) = 855$	Simplify.
$0.13x + 300 - 0.0375x = 855$	Apply the distributive property.
$0.0925x + 300 = 855$	Combine like terms.
$0.0925x = 555$	Subtract 300 from both sides.
$x = 6000$	

The amount invested in the stock fund is x: $6000.
The amount invested in the CD is $8000 - x = \$8000 - \$6000 = \$2000$.

Skill Practice 2   Franz borrowed a total of $10,000. Part of the money was borrowed from a lending institution that charged 5.5% simple interest. The rest of the money was borrowed from a friend to whom Franz paid 2.5% simple interest. Franz paid his friend back after 9 months (0.75 yr) and paid the lending institution after 2 yr. If the total amount Franz paid in interest was $735, how much did he borrow from each source?

3. Solve Applications Involving Mixtures

In Example 2, we "mixed" money between two different investments. We had to find the correct distribution of principal between two accounts to produce the given amount of interest. Example 3 presents a similar type of application that involves mixing different concentrations of a bleach solution to produce a third mixture of a given concentration.

Answer

2. Franz borrowed $4000 from his friend and $6000 from the lending institution.

For example, household bleach contains 6% sodium hypochlorite (active ingredient). This means that the remaining 94% of liquid is some other mixing agent such as water. Therefore, given 200 cL of household bleach, 6% would be pure sodium hypochlorite, and 94% would be some other mixing agent.

$$\text{Pure sodium hypochlorite} = (0.06)(200 \text{ cL}) = 12 \text{ cL}$$
$$\text{Other mixing agent} = (0.94)(200 \text{ cL}) = 188 \text{ cL}$$

To find the amount of pure sodium hypochlorite, we multiplied the concentration rate by the amount of solution.

EXAMPLE 3   **Solving an Application Involving Mixtures**

Household bleach contains 6% sodium hypochlorite. How much household bleach should be combined with 70 L of a weaker 1% hypochlorite solution to form a solution that is 2.5% sodium hypochlorite?

Solution:

Let x represent the amount of 6% sodium hypochlorite solution (in liters).
70 L is the amount of 1% sodium hypochlorite solution.
Therefore, $x + 70$ is the amount of the resulting mixture (2.5% solution).

The amount of pure sodium hypochlorite in each mixture is found by multiplying the concentration rate by the amount of solution.

	6% Solution	1% Solution	2.5% Solution
Amount of solution	x	70	$x + 70$
Pure sodium hypochlorite	$0.06x$	$0.01(70)$	$0.025(x + 70)$

Check that the answer is reasonable. The total amount of the resulting solution is 30 L + 70 L, which is 100 L.

Amount of sodium hypochlorite:
$\dfrac{\begin{array}{l} 0.06(30 \text{ L}) = 1.8 \text{ L} \\ 0.01(70 \text{ L}) = 0.7 \text{ L} \end{array}}{0.025(100 \text{ L}) = 2.5 \text{ L} \checkmark}$

To build an equation, note that

$$\left(\begin{array}{c} \text{Amount of sodium} \\ \text{hypochlorite in} \\ \text{6\% solution} \end{array} \right) + \left(\begin{array}{c} \text{Amount of sodium} \\ \text{hypochlorite in} \\ \text{1\% solution} \end{array} \right) = \left(\begin{array}{c} \text{Amount of sodium} \\ \text{hypochlorite in} \\ \text{2.5\% solution} \end{array} \right)$$

$$0.06x + 0.01(70) = 0.025(x + 70) \qquad \text{Second row in the table}$$
$$0.06x + 0.7 = 0.025x + 1.75 \qquad \text{Solve the equation.}$$
$$0.035x = 1.05$$
$$x = 30$$

The amount of household bleach (6% sodium hypochlorite solution) needed is 30 L.

Skill Practice 3   How much 4% acid solution should be mixed with 200 mL of a 12% acid solution to make a 9% acid solution?

4. Solve Applications Involving Uniform Motion

Example 4 involves uniform motion. Recall that the distance that an object travels is given by

$$d = rt \qquad \text{Distance} = (\text{Rate})(\text{Time})$$

Answer

3. 120 mL of the 4% acid solution should be used.

EXAMPLE 4   **Solving an Application Involving Uniform Motion**

Donna participated in a 41-mi biathlon that included running and bicycling. She spent 1 hr 45 min on the bike and 45 min running. If her average speed on the bicycle was 12 mph faster than her average speed running, find her average speed running and her average speed riding.

Solution:

There are two unknowns: Donna's average speed on the bike and her average speed running.

Let x represent Donna's average speed running.
Then $x + 12$ represents her speed on the bicycle.

The remaining information can be organized in a table.

	Distance	Rate	Time
Run	$0.75x$	x	0.75 hr
Bike	$1.75(x + 12)$	$x + 12$	1.75 hr

The expressions in this column are found by $d = rt$.

Note that consistency in the units of measurement is important. The speed is given in miles per *hour*. Therefore, we want the time to be in hours.

1 hr 45 min = 1.75 hr
45 min = 0.75 hr

$$\begin{pmatrix} \text{Total} \\ \text{distance} \end{pmatrix} = \begin{pmatrix} \text{Distance} \\ \text{running} \end{pmatrix} + \begin{pmatrix} \text{Distance} \\ \text{riding} \end{pmatrix}$$

$$41 = 0.75x + 1.75(x + 12)$$
$$41 = 0.75x + 1.75x + 21$$
$$20 = 2.5x$$
$$8 = x$$

To build an equation, note that the total distance equals the sum of the distance running and the distance riding.

Solve the equation.

Donna's speed running is 8 mph.
Her speed on the bicycle is $8 + 12 = 20$ mph.

Interpret the solution in the context of the problem.

Avoiding Mistakes

Check that the answer is reasonable by verifying that the total distance traveled is 41 mi.

Distance running:
(8 mph)(0.75 hr) = 6 mi

Distance riding:
(20 mph)(1.75 mi) = 35 mi

Total: 6 mi + 35 mi = 41 mi

Skill Practice 4   Rene drove from Miami to Orlando, a total distance of 240 mi. He drove for 1 hr in city traffic and for 3 hr on the highway. If his average speed on the highway was 20 mph faster than his speed in the city, determine his average speed driving in the city and his average speed driving on the highway.

Point of Interest

The relationship $d = rt$ is a familiar formula indicating that distance equals rate times time, or equivalently that $t = \frac{d}{r}$. However, suppose that a spaceship travels to a distant planet and then returns to Earth. Einstein's theory of special relativity indicates that $t = \frac{d}{r}$ only represents the trip's duration for an observer on Earth. For a person on the spaceship, the time will be shorter by a factor of $\sqrt{1 - \frac{r^2}{c^2}}$, where r is the speed of the spaceship and c is the speed of light.

For example, suppose that a spaceship travels to a planet 10 light-years away (a light-year is the distance that light travels in 1 yr) and then returns. The round trip is 20 light-years. Further suppose that the spaceship travels at half the speed of light, that is, $r = 0.5c$.

To an observer on Earth, the elapsed time of travel (in yr) is

$$t_E = \frac{d}{r} = \frac{20}{0.5} = 40$$

To an observer on the spaceship, the elapsed time (in yr) is

$$t_S = \frac{d}{r}\sqrt{1 - \frac{r^2}{c^2}} = \frac{20}{0.5}\sqrt{1 - \frac{(0.5c)^2}{c^2}} \approx 34.6$$

The unit of measurement in each case is years. Thus, the observer on Earth perceives the time of travel to be 40 yr, whereas to an observer on the spaceship the time of travel is only 34.6 yr.

Answer

4. Rene drove 45 mph in the city and 65 mph on the highway.

5. Solve Applications Involving Linear Models

The examples and exercises in Section R.2 provided practice forming algebraic models given a description of a situation in words. This skill is revisited in Example 5.

EXAMPLE 5   Solving an Application Involving Linear Models

In the year 2000, the average cost C_{ave} for electricity in the United States was 8.24¢ per kWh (kilowatt-hour) and has been increasing by approximately 0.334¢ per year. (*Source*: U.S. Energy Information Administration, www.eia.gov)

Jose noted that the cost per kWh in his area was 7.58¢ in the year 2000, and has been increasing at a rate of 0.4¢ per year.

a. Write a model representing the average cost for electricity C_{ave} (in ¢/kWh) in the United States t years after the year 2000.

b. Write a model representing the cost for electricity C_J (in ¢/kWh) in Jose's area t years after the year 2000.

c. In what year will the cost per kWh in Jose's area equal the national average?

Solution:

Let t represent the number of years since the year 2000.

a. $C_{ave} = 8.24 + 0.334t$

b. $C_J = 7.58 + 0.4t$

c. To determine the year in which the cost for electricity in Jose's area will equal the national average, equate C_J and C_{ave}.

$$C_J = C_{ave}$$
$$7.58 + 0.4t = 8.24 + 0.334t$$
$$0.066t = 0.66$$
$$t = 10$$

In the year 2010 (10 yr after the year 2000), the cost for electricity in Jose's area was equal to the national average.

Skill Practice 5   A candidate for mayor needs to purchase yard signs. Company A charges $1.20 per sign. Company B charges $1.10 per sign along with a flat fee of $15.90 for the design of the sign.

a. Write a model representing the cost C_A for x signs from Company A.

b. Write a model representing the cost C_B for x signs from Company B.

c. Determine the number of signs for which the cost from each company will be the same.

6. Solve Applications Involving Rate of Work Done

EXAMPLE 6   Solving an Application Involving "Work" Rates

At a mail-order company, Derrick can process 100 orders in 4 hr. Miguel can process 100 orders in 3 hr.

a. How long would it take them to process 100 orders if they work together?

b. How long would it take them to process 1400 orders if they work together?

Answers
5. a. $C_A = 1.20x$
  b. $C_B = 1.10x + 15.90$
  c. 159 signs

Solution:

a. Let t represent the amount of time required to process 100 orders working together.

One method to approach this problem is to add the rates of speed at which each person works.

$$\begin{pmatrix} \text{Derrick's} \\ \text{speed} \end{pmatrix} + \begin{pmatrix} \text{Miguel's} \\ \text{speed} \end{pmatrix} = \begin{pmatrix} \text{Speed working} \\ \text{together} \end{pmatrix}$$

$$\frac{1 \text{ job}}{4 \text{ hr}} + \frac{1 \text{ job}}{3 \text{ hr}} = \frac{1 \text{ job}}{t \text{ hr}} \qquad \text{1 job = 100 orders.}$$

$$12t \cdot \left(\frac{1}{4} + \frac{1}{3} \right) = 12t \cdot \left(\frac{1}{t} \right) \qquad \text{Multiply both sides by the LCD, } 12t.$$

$$3t + 4t = 12 \qquad \text{Apply the distributive property.}$$

$$7t = 12$$

$$t = \frac{12}{7} \quad \text{or} \quad 1\frac{5}{7}$$

Derrick and Miguel can process 100 orders in $1\frac{5}{7}$ hr working together.

b. The time required to process 1400 orders is 14 times as long as the time to process 100 orders. $(\frac{12}{7} \text{ hr})(14) = 24 \text{ hr.}$

Skill Practice 6   Sheldon and Penny were awarded a contract to paint 16 classrooms in the new math building at a university. Once all the preparation work is complete, Sheldon can paint an office in 30 min and Penny can paint an office in 45 min.

   a. How long would it take them to paint one office working together?
   b. How long would it take them to paint all 16 offices?

7. Solve Applications Involving Proportions

An equation that equates two ratios or rates is called a **proportion.** Symbolically, we define a proportion as an equation of the form

$$\frac{a}{b} = \frac{c}{d}, \text{ where } b \neq 0 \text{ and } d \neq 0.$$

The method of clearing fractions can be used to solve proportions.

EXAMPLE 7   Solving an Application Involving a Proportion

In a jury pool, there are 8 more men than women. If the ratio of men to women is 8 to 7, determine the number of men and women in the pool.

Solution:

Let x represent the number of women.   Label the variables.
Then $x + 8$ represents the number of men.

$$\underset{\text{number of women}}{\overset{\text{number of men}}{\longrightarrow}} \frac{x + 8}{x} = \frac{8}{7} \overset{\longleftarrow \text{ men}}{\underset{\longleftarrow \text{ women}}{}} \qquad \text{Set up a proportion.}$$

$$7x \left(\frac{x + 8}{x} \right) = 7x \left(\frac{8}{7} \right) \qquad \text{Multiply by the LCD of } 7x.$$

$$7(x + 8) = x(8)$$

$$7x + 56 = 8x \qquad \text{Apply the distributive property.}$$

$$56 = x$$

The number of women is 56. The number of men is $56 + 8 = 64$.

Answer

7. There were 52 Republicans and 48 Democrats.

> **Skill Practice 7**   For the 104th Congress, there were 4 more Republicans than Democrats in the U.S. Senate. This resulted in a ratio of 13 Republicans to 12 Democrats. How many senators were Republican and how many were Democrat?

SECTION 1.2   Practice Exercises

Review Exercises

For Exercises 1–4, write each phrase as an algebraic expression. Use x as the variable unless otherwise indicated.

1. Two less than five times a number

2. Ten subtracted from four times a number

3. 6% of a number

4. 60% of a number

5. The sum of two numbers is 40. If one number is x, write an expression for the other number.

6. The total of two numbers is 54. If one number is x, write an expression for the other number.

7. If x represents the smaller of two consecutive integers, write an expression for the next larger consecutive integer.

8. If x represents the larger of two consecutive odd integers, write an expression for the next smaller consecutive odd integer.

Concept Connections

For Exercises 9–12, refer to the inside back cover.

9. The formula for the perimeter P of a rectangle with length l and width w is given by _____.

10. The sum of the measures of the angles inscribed inside a triangle is _____.

11. If the measure of an angle is represented by x, then _____ represents the measure of its complement.

12. If the measure of an angle is represented by x, then _____ represents the measure of its supplement.

13. If $6000 is borrowed at 7.5% simple interest for 2 yr, then the amount of interest is _____.

14. Suppose that 8% of a solution is fertilizer by volume and the remaining 92% is water. How much fertilizer is in a 2-L bucket of solution?

15. If $d = rt$, then $t = \dfrac{\square}{\square}$

16. If $d = rt$, then $r = \dfrac{\square}{\square}$

Objective 1: Solve Applications Involving Geometry

17. The perimeter of a rectangular lot of land is 440 ft. This includes an easement of x feet of uniform width inside the lot on which no building can be done. If the buildable area is 128 ft by 60 ft, determine the width of the easement. (**See Example 1**)

18. The Arthur Ashe Stadium tennis court is center court to the U.S. Open tennis tournament. The dimensions of the court are 78 ft by 36 ft, with a uniform border of x feet around the outside for additional play area. If the perimeter of the entire play area is 396 ft, determine the value of x.

19. A contractor must tile a rectangular kitchen that is 4 ft longer than it is wide, and the perimeter of the kitchen is 48 ft.

   a. Find the dimensions of the kitchen.

   b. How many square feet of tile should be ordered if the contractor adds an additional 10% to account for waste?

   c. Determine the total cost if the tile costs $12/ft^2 and sales tax is 6%.

20. Max and Molly plan to put down all-weather carpeting on their porch. The length of the porch is 2 ft longer than twice the width, and the perimeter is 64 ft.

   a. Find the dimensions of the porch.

   b. How many square feet of carpeting should they buy if they add an additional 10% for waste?

   c. Determine the total cost if the carpeting costs $5.85/ft^2 and sales tax is 7.5%.

For Exercises 21–24, write an expression in terms of x that represents the measure of angle designated by the ? symbol.

21.

22.

23.

24.

25. A ladder leans against a wall. The angle between the ladder and the ground is 22° more than the angle that the ladder makes with the wall. Find the measure of each angle.

26. Stakes are fixed in the ground with ropes attached to support a newly planted tree. The angle that a rope makes with the ground is 1.5 times the measure of the angle that the rope makes with the tree. Find the measure of each angle.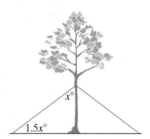

Objective 2: Solve Applications Involving Simple Interest

27. Rocco borrowed a total of $5000 from two student loans. One loan charged 3% simple interest and the other charged 2.5% simple interest, both payable after graduation. If the interest he owed after 1 yr was $132.50, determine the amount of principal for each loan. (**See Example 2**)

28. Laura borrowed a total of $22,000 from two different banks to start a business. One bank charged the equivalent of 4% simple interest, and the other charged 5.5% interest. If the total interest after 1 yr was $910, determine the amount borrowed from each bank.

29. Fernando invested money in a 3-yr CD (certificate of deposit) that returned the equivalent of 4.4% simple interest. He invested $2000 less in an 18-month CD that had a 3% return. If the total amount of interest from these investments was $706.50, determine how much was invested in each CD.

30. Ebony bought a 5-yr Treasury note that paid the equivalent of 2.8% simple interest. She invested $5000 more in a 10-yr bond earning 3.6% than she did in the Treasury note. If the total amount of interest from these investments was $5300, determine the amount of principal for each investment.

Objective 3: Solve Applications Involving Mixtures

31. Ethanol fuel mixtures have "E" numbers that indicate the percentage of ethanol in the mixture by volume. For example, E10 is a mixture of 10% ethanol and 90% gasoline. How much E5 should be mixed with 5000 gal of E10 to make an E9 mixture? (**See Example 3**)

32. A nurse mixes 60 cc of a 50% saline solution with a 10% saline solution to produce a 25% saline solution. How much of the 10% solution should he use?

33. The density and strength of concrete are determined by the ratio of cement and aggregate (aggregate is sand, gravel, or crushed stone). Suppose that a contractor has 480 ft^3 of a dry concrete mixture that is 70% sand by volume. How much pure sand must be added to form a new mixture that is 75% sand by volume?

34. Antifreeze is a compound added to water to reduce the freezing point of a mixture. In extreme cold (less than −35°F), one car manufacturer recommends that a mixture of 65% antifreeze be used. How much 50% antifreeze solution should be drained from a 4-gal tank and replaced with pure antifreeze to produce a 65% antifreeze mixture?

Objective 4: Solve Applications Involving Uniform Motion

35. Two passengers leave the airport at Kansas City, Missouri. One flies to Los Angeles, California, in 3.4 hr and the other flies in the opposite direction to New York City in 2.4 hr. With prevailing westerly winds, the speed of the plane to New York City is 60 mph faster than the speed of the plane to Los Angeles. If the total distance traveled by both planes is 2464 mi, determine the average speed of each plane. (**See Example 4**)

36. Two planes leave from Atlanta, Georgia. One makes a 5.2-hr flight to Seattle, Washington, and the other makes a 2.5-hr flight to Boston, Massachusetts. The plane to Boston averages 44 mph slower than the plane to Seattle. If the total distance traveled by both planes is 3124 mi, determine the average speed of each plane.

37. Darren drives to school in rush hour traffic and averages 32 mph. He returns home in mid-afternoon when there is less traffic and averages 48 mph. What is the distance between his home and school if the total traveling time is 1 hr 15 min?

38. Peggy competes in a biathlon by running and bicycling around a large loop through a city. She runs the loop one time and bicycles the loop five times. She can run 8 mph and she can ride 16 mph. If the total time it takes her to complete the race is 1 hr 45 min, determine the distance of the loop.

Objective 5: Solve Applications Involving Linear Models

39. Helene considers two jobs. One pays $45,000/yr with an anticipated yearly raise of $2250. A second job pays $48,000/yr with yearly raises averaging $2000.

   a. Write a model representing the salary S_1 (in $) for the first job in x years. (**See Example 5**)

   b. Write a model representing the salary S_2 (in $) for the second job in x years.

   c. In how many years will the salary from the first job equal the salary from the second?

40. Tasha considers two sales jobs for different pharmaceutical companies. One pays a base salary of $25,000 with a 16% commission on sales. The other pays $30,000 with a 15% commission on sales.

   a. Write a model representing the salary S_1 (in $) for the first job based on x dollars in sales.

   b. Write a model representing the salary S_2 (in $) for the second job based on x dollars in sales.

   c. For how much in sales will the two jobs result in equal salaries?

41. A motorist drives on State Road 417 to and from work each day and pays $3.50 in tolls one-way.

   a. Write a model for the cost for tolls C (in $) for x working days.

   b. The department of transportation has a prepaid toll program that discounts tolls for high-volume use. The motorist can buy a pass for $105 per month. How many working days are required for the motorist to save money by buying the pass?

42. A subway ride is $2.25 per ride.

   a. Write a model for the cost C (in $) for x rides on the subway.

   b. A commuter can purchase an unlimited-ride MetroCard for $89 per month. How many rides are required for a commuter to save money by buying the MetroCard?

Objective 6: Solve Applications Involving Rate of Work Done

43. Joel can run around a $\frac{1}{4}$-mi track in 66 sec, and Jason can run around the track in 60 sec. If the runners start at the same point on the track and run in opposite directions, how long with it take the runners to cover $\frac{1}{4}$ mi? (**See Example 6**)

44. Marta can vacuum the house in 40 min. It takes her daughter 1 hr to vacuum the house. How long would it take them if they worked together?

45. One pump can fill a pool in 10 hr. Working with a second slower pump, the two pumps together can fill the pool in 6 hr. How fast can the second pump fill the pool by itself?

46. Brad and Angelina can mow their yard together with two lawn mowers in 30 min. When Brad works alone, it takes him 50 min. How long would it take Angelina to mow the lawn by herself?

Objective 7: Solve Applications Involving Proportions

47. At a construction site, cement, sand, and gravel are mixed to make concrete. The ratio of cement to sand to gravel is 1 to 2.4 to 3.6. If a 150-lb bag of sand is used, how much cement and gravel must be used? (**See Example 7**)

48. The property tax on a $180,000 house is $1296. At this rate, what is the property tax on a house that is $240,000?

49. In addition to measuring a person's individual HDL and LDL cholesterol levels, doctors also compute the ratio of total cholesterol to HDL cholesterol. Doctors recommend that the ratio of total cholesterol to HDL cholesterol be kept under 4. Suppose that the ratio of a patient's total cholesterol to HDL is 3.4 and her HDL is 60 mg/dL. Determine the patient's LDL level and total cholesterol. (Assume that total cholesterol is the sum of the LDL and HDL levels.)

50. For a recent Congress, there were 10 more Democrats than Republicans in the U.S. Senate. This resulted in a ratio of 11 Democrats to 9 Republicans. How many senators were Democrat and how many were Republican?

51. When studying wildlife populations, biologists sometimes use a technique called "mark-recapture." For example, a researcher captured and tagged 30 deer in a wildlife management area. Several months later, the researcher observed a new sample of 80 deer and determined that 5 were tagged. What is the total number of deer in the population?

52. To estimate the number of bass in a lake, a biologist catches and tags 24 bass. Several weeks later, the biologist catches a new sample of 40 bass and finds that 4 are tagged. How many bass are in the lake?

Mixed Exercises

53. Seismographs can record two types of wave energy (P waves and S waves) that travel through the Earth after an earthquake. Traveling through granite, P waves travel approximately 5 km/sec and S waves travel approximately 3 km/sec. If a geologist working at a seismic station measures a time difference of 40 sec between an earthquake's P waves and S waves, how far from the epicenter of the earthquake is the station?

54. Suppose that a shallow earthquake occurs in which the P waves travel 8 km/sec and the S waves travel 4.8 km/sec. If a seismologist measures a time difference of 20 sec between the arrival of the P waves and the S waves, how far is the seismologist from the epicenter of the earthquake?

55. Suppose that a merchant buys a patio set from the wholesaler for $180. At what price should the merchant mark the patio set so that it may be offered at a discount of 25% but still give the merchant a 40% profit on his $180 investment?

56. Suppose that a bookstore buys a textbook from the publisher for $80. At what price should the bookstore mark the textbook so that it may be offered at a discount of 10% but still give the bookstore a 35% profit on the $80 investment?

57. Henri needs to have a toilet repaired in his house. The cost of the new plumbing fixtures is $110 and labor is $60/hr.

    a. Write a model that represents the cost of the repair C (in $) in terms of the number of hours of labor x.

    b. After how many hours of labor would the cost of the repair job equal the cost of a new toilet of $350?

58. After a hurricane, repairs to a roof will cost $2400 for materials and $80/hr in labor.

    a. Write a model that represents the cost of the repair C (in $) in terms of the number of hours of labor x.

    b. If an estimate for a new roof is $5520, after how many hours of labor would the cost to repair the roof equal the cost of a new roof?

59. A student 5 ft tall measures the length of the shadow of the Washington Monument to be 444 ft. At the same time, her shadow is 4 ft. Approximate the height of the Washington Monument.

60. A 6-ft man is standing 40 ft from a light post. If the man's shadow is 20 ft, determine the height of the light post.

61. A vertical pole is placed in the ground at a campsite outside Salt Lake City, Utah. One winter day, $\frac{1}{8}$ of the pole is in the ground, $\frac{2}{3}$ of the pole is covered in snow, and 1.5 ft is above the snow. How long is the pole, and how deep is the snow?

62. The formula to convert temperature in Fahrenheit F to temperature in Celsius C is given by $C = \frac{5}{9}(F - 32)$. Determine the temperature at which the Celsius and Fahrenheit temperature readings are the same.

63. A tank contains 40 L of a mixture of plant fertilizer and water in which 20% of the mixture is fertilizer. How much of the mixture should be drained and replaced by an equal amount of water to dilute the mixture to 15% fertilizer?

64. How much water must be evaporated from 200 mL of a 5% salt solution to produce a 25% salt solution?

65. Two angles are supplementary. If the measure of one angle is 18° more than 5 times the other, find the measure of each angle.

66. Two angles are complementary. If the measure of one angle is 24° more than 21 times the other, find the measure of each angle.

67. Aliyah earned an $8000 bonus from her sales job for exceeding her sales goals. After paying taxes at a 28% rate, she invested the remaining money in two stocks. One stock returned the equivalent of 11% simple interest after 1 yr, and the other returned 5% at the end of 1 yr. If her investments returned $453.60 (excluding commissions) how much did she invest in each stock?

68. Caitlin invested money in two mutual funds—a stock fund and a balanced fund. She invested twice as much in the stock fund as in the balanced fund. At the end of 1 yr, the stock fund earned the equivalent of 17% simple interest and the balanced fund earned 3.5%. If her total gain was $1125, determine how much she invested in each fund.

69. The perimeter of a triangle is 4 times the length of the shortest side. The length of the longest side is 5 ft more than the length of the shortest side. The length of the middle side is 1 ft longer than the length of the shortest side. Find the lengths of the sides.

70. The perimeter of a triangle is 5 times the length of the shortest side. The length of the longer side is 9 cm longer than the length of the shortest side. The length of the middle side is 4 cm less than the length of the longest side. Find the lengths of the sides.

Proportions are used in geometry with similar triangles. If two triangles are similar, then the lengths of the corresponding sides are proportional. For the similar triangles shown, $\frac{a}{x} = \frac{b}{y} = \frac{c}{z}$.

For Exercises 71–72, the triangles are similar with the corresponding sides oriented as shown. Solve for x and y.

71.

72.

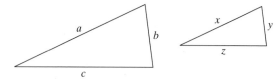

Write About It

73. Is it possible for the measures of the angles in a triangle to be represented by three consecutive odd integers? Explain.

74. Is it possible for the measures of two complementary angles to be consecutive integers? Explain.

75. Bob wants to change a $100 bill into an equal number of $20 bills, $10 bills, and $5 bills. Is this possible? Explain.

76. Is it possible for the length of one side of a triangle to be one-half the perimeter? Explain.

Expanding Your Skills

77. One number is 16 more than another number. The quotient of the larger number and smaller number is 3 and the remainder is 2. Find the numbers.

78. One number is 25 more than another number. The quotient of the larger number and the smaller number is 4 and the remainder is 1. Find the numbers.

79. The sum of the digits of a two-digit number is 14. If the digits are reversed, the new number is 18 more than the original number. Determine the original number.

80. The sum of the digits of a two-digit number is 9. If the digits are reversed, the new number is 45 less than the original number. Determine the original number.

Consider a seesaw with two children of masses m_1 and m_2 on either side. Suppose that the position of the fulcrum (pivot point) is labeled as the origin, $x = 0$. Further suppose that the position of each child relative to the origin is x_1 and x_2, respectively. The seesaw will be in equilibrium if $m_1x_1 + m_2x_2 = 0$. Use this equation for Exercises 81–84.

81. Find x_2 so that the system of masses is in equilibrium.

$m_1 = 30$ kg, $x_1 = -1.2$ m and $m_2 = 20$ kg, $x_2 = ?$

82. Find x_1 so that the system of masses is in equilibrium.

$m_1 = 64$ kg, $x_1 = ?$ and $m_2 = 80$ kg, $x_2 = 2$ m

83. Find the missing mass so that the system is in equilibrium. (*Hint*: Recall that positions to the left of 0 on the number line are negative.)

84. Find the missing mass so that the system is in equilibrium.

SECTION 1.3   Complex Numbers

1. Simplify Imaginary Numbers

In our study of algebra thus far, we have worked exclusively with real numbers. However, as we encounter new types of equations, we need to look outside the set of real numbers to find solutions. For example, the equation $x^2 = 1$ has two solutions: 1 and -1. But what about the equation $x^2 = -1$? There is no real number x for which $x^2 = -1$. For this reason, mathematicians defined a new number i such that $i^2 = -1$. The number i is called an *imaginary number* and is used to represent $\sqrt{-1}$. Furthermore, the square root of any negative real number is an imaginary number that can be expressed in terms of i.

> **The Imaginary Number i**
>
> - $i = \sqrt{-1}$ and $i^2 = -1$
> - If b is a positive real number, then $\sqrt{-b} = i\sqrt{b}$.

EXAMPLE 1   **Writing Imaginary Numbers in Terms of i**

Write each expression in terms of i.

a. $\sqrt{-25}$ **b.** $\sqrt{-12}$ **c.** $\sqrt{-13}$

Solution:

a. $\sqrt{-25} = i\sqrt{25} = 5i$

b. $\sqrt{-12} = i\sqrt{12} = i \cdot 2\sqrt{3}$ The value $i \cdot 2\sqrt{3}$ can be written as $2i\sqrt{3}$ or as
    $= 2i\sqrt{3}$ or $2\sqrt{3}i$ $2\sqrt{3}i$. Note, however, that the factor i is written *outside* the radical.

c. $\sqrt{-13} = i\sqrt{13}$ or $\sqrt{13}i$

Skill Practice 1   Write each expression in terms of i.
a. $\sqrt{-81}$ **b.** $\sqrt{-50}$ **c.** $\sqrt{-11}$

In Example 2, we multiply and divide the square roots of negative real numbers. However, note that the multiplication and division properties of radicals can be used only if the radicals represent real-valued expressions.

$$\sqrt{a} \cdot \sqrt{b} = \sqrt{ab}$$ provided that the roots represent real numbers.

$$\frac{\sqrt{a}}{\sqrt{b}} = \sqrt{\frac{a}{b}}$$ provided that the roots represent real numbers.

For this reason, in Example 2 it is important to write the radical expressions in terms of i first, before applying the multiplication or division property of radicals.

EXAMPLE 2   **Simplifying Imaginary Numbers in Terms of i**

Multiply or divide as indicated.

a. $\sqrt{-9} \cdot \sqrt{-25}$ **b.** $\sqrt{-15} \cdot \sqrt{-3}$ **c.** $\dfrac{\sqrt{-50}}{\sqrt{-2}}$

Answers
1. a. $9i$ **b.** $5i\sqrt{2}$ **c.** $i\sqrt{11}$

Solution:

a. $\sqrt{-9} \cdot \sqrt{-25} = i\sqrt{9} \cdot i\sqrt{25}$ Write each radical in terms of i first, *before* multiplying.

$\qquad\qquad\qquad = 3i \cdot 5i$ Simplify the radicals.

$\qquad\qquad\qquad = 15i^2$ Multiply.

$\qquad\qquad\qquad = 15(-1)$ By definition, $i^2 = -1$.

$\qquad\qquad\qquad = -15$ Simplify.

b. $\sqrt{-15} \cdot \sqrt{-3} = i\sqrt{15} \cdot i\sqrt{3}$ Write each radical in terms of i first, *before* multiplying.

$\qquad\qquad\qquad = i^2\sqrt{45}$ Apply the multiplication property of radicals.

$\qquad\qquad\qquad = (-1)\sqrt{3^2 \cdot 5}$ Simplify.

$\qquad\qquad\qquad = -3\sqrt{5}$

c. $\dfrac{\sqrt{-50}}{\sqrt{-2}} = \dfrac{i\sqrt{50}}{i\sqrt{2}}$ Write each radical in terms of i first, *before* dividing.

$\qquad\qquad = \dfrac{\overset{1}{i}\sqrt{50}}{i\sqrt{2}}$ Simplify the ratio of common factors to 1.

$\qquad\qquad = \sqrt{\dfrac{50}{2}}$ Apply the division property of radicals.

$\qquad\qquad = \sqrt{25} = 5$ Simplify.

Skill Practice 2 Multiply or divide as indicated.

a. $\sqrt{-16} \cdot \sqrt{-49}$ $\qquad$ **b.** $\sqrt{-10}\sqrt{-2}$ $\qquad$ **c.** $\dfrac{\sqrt{-48}}{\sqrt{-3}}$

---

2. Write Complex Numbers in the Form $a + bi$

We now define a new set of numbers that includes the real numbers and the imaginary numbers. This is called the set of complex numbers.

Complex Numbers

Given real numbers a and b, a number written in the form $a + bi$ is called a **complex number.** The value a is called the **real part** of the complex number and the value b is called the **imaginary part.**

Real part: 5   Imaginary part: -8

$$5 - 8i = 5 + (-8)i$$

Notes	Examples
• If $b = 0$, then $a + bi$ equals the real number a. This tells us that all real numbers are complex numbers.	The real number 4 can be written as $4 + 0i$.
• If $b \neq 0$, then $a + bi$ is called an **imaginary number.**	The numbers $9 + 2i$ and $4i$ are imaginary numbers.
• If $a = 0$, and $b \neq 0$, then $a + bi = bi$ which we say is **pure imaginary.**	The number $8i$ is a pure imaginary number.

Answers

2. a. -28 $\quad$ **b.** $-2\sqrt{5}$ $\quad$ **c.** 4

The set of complex numbers, denoted by $\mathbb{C}$, is made up of the elements of the set of real numbers and the set of imaginary numbers. The relationship among these sets of numbers is given in Figure 1-1.

Complex Numbers	
Real numbers	Imaginary numbers
$a + 0i$	$a + bi \; (b \neq 0)$
Examples: $-5, \frac{1}{2}, \pi$	Examples: $4 + 7i$ $-3i$

Figure 1-1

A complex number written in the form $a + bi$ is said to be in **standard form.** That being said, we sometimes write $a - bi$ in place of $a + (-b)i$. Furthermore, a number such as $5 + \sqrt{3}i$ is sometimes written as $5 + i\sqrt{3}$ to emphasize that the factor of i is not under the radical. In Example 3, we practice writing complex numbers in standard form.

EXAMPLE 3   **Writing Complex Numbers in Standard Form**

Simplify each expression and write the result in the form $a + bi$.

a. -11 **b.** $-3\sqrt{-4}$ **c.** $3 - \sqrt{-100}$

d. $\dfrac{2 + 7i}{5}$ **e.** $\dfrac{-6 + \sqrt{-18}}{9}$

Solution:

a. $-11 = -11 + 0i$ — The real part is -11 and the imaginary part is 0.

b. $-3\sqrt{-4} = -3 \cdot 2i = -6i$ — Simplify the expression.
$\qquad\qquad\quad = 0 + (-6)i$ — Write the result in standard form.

c. $3 - \sqrt{-100} = 3 - 10i$ — Simplify the expression.
$\qquad\qquad\quad = 3 + (-10)i$ — Although $3 + (-10)i$ is written in standard
$\qquad\qquad\quad = 3 - 10i$ — form, $3 - 10i$ is also acceptable.

d. $\dfrac{2 + 7i}{5} = \dfrac{2}{5} + \dfrac{7}{5}i$ — Write the fraction as two separate terms.

e. $\dfrac{-6 + \sqrt{-18}}{9} = \dfrac{-6 + 3i\sqrt{2}}{9}$ — Simplify the radical.
$\qquad\qquad\qquad\qquad\qquad\quad$ $\sqrt{-18} = i\sqrt{18} = i\sqrt{3^2 \cdot 2} = 3i\sqrt{2}$

$\qquad\qquad\quad = \dfrac{-6}{9} + \dfrac{3i\sqrt{2}}{9}$ — Write the fraction as two separate terms.

$\qquad\qquad\quad = -\dfrac{2}{3} + \dfrac{\sqrt{2}}{3}i$ — Simplify each fraction and write the result in the form $a + bi$.

Skill Practice 3   Simplify each expression and write the result in the form $a + bi$.

a. 3 **b.** $5\sqrt{-36}$ **c.** $4 + \sqrt{-49}$ **d.** $\dfrac{3 - 8i}{7}$ **e.** $\dfrac{10 + \sqrt{-75}}{20}$

Answers

3. a. $3 + 0i$ **b.** $0 + 30i$

c. $4 + 7i$ **d.** $\dfrac{3}{7} + \left(-\dfrac{8}{7}\right)i$

e. $\dfrac{1}{2} + \dfrac{\sqrt{3}}{4}i$

3. Perform Operations on Complex Numbers

By definition, $i^2 = -1$, but what about other powers of i? Consider the following pattern.

TIP Notice that even powers of i simplify to 1 or -1.
- If the exponent is a multiple of 4, then the expression equals 1.
- If the exponent is even but *not* a multiple of 4, then the expression equals -1.

$$i^1 = i$$
$$i^2 = -1$$
$$i^3 = i^2 \cdot i = (-1)i = -i$$
$$i^4 = i^2 \cdot i^2 = (-1)(-1) = 1$$
$$i^5 = i^4 \cdot i = (1)i = i$$
$$i^6 = i^4 \cdot i^2 = (1)(-1) = -1$$
$$i^7 = i^4 \cdot i^2 \cdot i = (1)(-1)i = -i$$
$$i^8 = i^4 \cdot i^4 = (1)(1) = 1$$

$$i^1 = i$$
$$i^2 = -1$$
$$i^3 = -i$$
$$i^4 = 1$$
Pattern: $i, -1, -i, 1$

$$i^5 = i$$
$$i^6 = -1$$
$$i^7 = -i$$
$$i^8 = 1$$
Pattern repeats: $i, -1, -i, 1, \ldots$

Notice that the fourth powers of i (i^4, i^8, i^{12}, ...) equal the real number 1. For other powers of i, we can write the expression as a product of a fourth power of i and a factor of i, i^2, or i^3, which equals i, -1, or $-i$, respectively.

EXAMPLE 4   Simplifying Powers of i

Simplify.

a. i^{48} **b.** i^{23} **c.** i^{50} **d.** i^{-19}

Solution:

a. $i^{48} = 1$ Since 48 is a multiple of 4, then i^{48} is a fourth power of i, and is equal to 1.

b. $i^{23} = i^{20} \cdot i^3$ Write i^{23} as a product of the largest fourth power of i and
$= (1) \cdot i^3 = -i$ a remaining factor.

c. $i^{50} = i^{48} \cdot i^2$
$= (1)(-1) = -1$

d. $i^{-19} = i^{-20} \cdot i^1$
$= (1)i = i$

TIP To simplify i^n, divide the exponent, n, by 4. The remainder is the exponent of the remaining factor of i once the fourth power of i has been extracted.

Example: $i^{50} = i^{48} \cdot i^2 = (1)i^2$

$$\begin{array}{r} 12 \\ 4\overline{)50} \\ \underline{48} \\ 2 \end{array}$$

So $i^{50} = (1) \cdot i^2 = -1$

Skill Practice 4   Simplify.

a. i^{13} **b.** i^{103} **c.** i^{64} **d.** i^{-30}

To add or subtract complex numbers, add or subtract their real parts, and add or subtract their imaginary parts. That is,

$$(a + bi) + (c + di) = (a + c) + (b + d)i$$
$$(a + bi) - (c + di) = (a - c) + (b - d)i$$

EXAMPLE 5   Adding and Subtracting Complex Numbers

Add or subtract as indicated. Write the answer in the form $a + bi$.

a. $(-2 - 4i) + (5 + 2i) - (3 - 6i)$

b. Subtract $\left(\dfrac{1}{2} + \dfrac{2}{3}i\right)$ from $\left(\dfrac{3}{4} + \dfrac{9}{5}i\right)$.

Answers
4. a. i **b.** $-i$ **c.** 1 **d.** -1

Solution:

a. $(-2 - 4i) + (5 + 2i) - (3 - 6i)$ Combine the real parts and combine the

$= (-2 + 5 - 3) + [-4 + 2 - (-6)]i$ imaginary parts.

$= 0 + 4i$ Write the result in the form $a + bi$.

b. Subtract $\left(\dfrac{1}{2} + \dfrac{2}{3}i\right)$ from $\left(\dfrac{3}{4} + \dfrac{9}{5}i\right)$.

$\left(\dfrac{3}{4} + \dfrac{9}{5}i\right) - \left(\dfrac{1}{2} + \dfrac{2}{3}i\right)$ The statement "subtract x from y" is equivalent to $y - x$. The order is important.

$= \left(\dfrac{3}{4} - \dfrac{1}{2}\right) + \left(\dfrac{9}{5} - \dfrac{2}{3}\right)i$ Subtract the real parts. Subtract the imaginary parts.

$= \left(\dfrac{3}{4} - \dfrac{2}{4}\right) + \left(\dfrac{27}{15} - \dfrac{10}{15}\right)i$ Write using common denominators.

$= \dfrac{1}{4} + \dfrac{17}{15}i$ Write the result in the form $a + bi$.

Skill Practice 5   Add or subtract as indicated. Write the answer in the form $a + bi$.

a. $(8 - 3i) - (2 + 4i) + (5 + 7i)$ **b.** Subtract $\left(\dfrac{1}{10} + \dfrac{1}{3}i\right)$ from $\left(\dfrac{3}{5} + \dfrac{5}{6}i\right)$

In Examples 6 and 7, we multiply complex numbers using a process similar to multiplying polynomials.

EXAMPLE 6   **Multiplying Complex Numbers**

Multiply. Write the results in the form $a + bi$.

a. $-\dfrac{1}{2}i(4 + 6i)$ **b.** $(-2 + 6i)(4 - 3i)$

Solution:

a. $-\dfrac{1}{2}i(4 + 6i) = -2i - 3i^2$ Apply the distributive property.

$= -2i - 3(-1)$ Recall that $i^2 = -1$.

$= 3 - 2i$ or $3 + (-2)i$ Write the result in the form $a + bi$.

b. $(-2 + 6i)(4 - 3i)$ Apply the distributive property.

$= -2(4) + (-2)(-3i) + 6i(4) + 6i(-3i)$

$= -8 + 6i + 24i - 18i^2$

$= -8 + 30i - 18(-1)$ Recall that $i^2 = -1$.

$= -8 + 30i + 18$

$= 10 + 30i$ Write the result in the form $a + bi$.

Skill Practice 6   Multiply. Write the result in the form $a + bi$.

a. $-\dfrac{1}{3}i(9 - 15i)$ **b.** $(-5 + 4i)(3 - i)$

Answers

5. a. $11 + 0i$ **b.** $\dfrac{1}{2} + \dfrac{1}{2}i$

6. a. $-5 + (-3)i$ **b.** $-11 + 17i$

In Example 7, we make use of the special case products:

$$(a \pm b)^2 = a^2 \pm 2ab + b^2 \quad \text{and} \quad (a + b)(a - b) = a^2 - b^2$$

> **EXAMPLE 7** **Evaluating Special Products with Complex Numbers**
>
> Multiply. Write the results in the form $a + bi$.
>
> **a.** $(3 + 4i)^2$ **b.** $(5 + 2i)(5 - 2i)$
>
> **Solution:**
>
> **a.** $(3 + 4i)^2 = (3)^2 + 2(3)(4i) + (4i)^2$ Apply the property
> $= 9 + 24i + 16i^2$ $(a + b)^2 = a^2 + 2ab + b^2$.
> $= 9 + 24i + 16(-1)$
> $= 9 + 24i - 16$
> $= -7 + 24i$ Write the result in the form $a + bi$.
>
> **b.** $(5 + 2i)(5 - 2i) = (5)^2 - (2i)^2$ Apply the property
> $= 25 - 4i^2$ $(a + b)(a - b) = a^2 - b^2$.
> $= 25 - 4(-1)$
> $= 25 + 4$
> $= 29 \quad \text{or} \quad 29 + 0i$ Write the result in the form $a + bi$.

> **Skill Practice 7** Multiply. Write the result in the form $a + bi$.
>
> **a.** $(4 - 7i)^2$ **b.** $(10 - 3i)(10 + 3i)$

In Section R.5 we noted that the expressions $(a + b)$ and $(a - b)$ are conjugates. Similarly, the expressions $(a + bi)$ and $(a - bi)$ are called **complex conjugates.** Furthermore, as illustrated in Example 7(b), the product of complex conjugates is a real number.

$$
\begin{aligned}
(a + bi)(a - bi) &= (a)^2 - (bi)^2 \\
&= a^2 - b^2 i^2 \\
&= a^2 - b^2(-1) \\
&= a^2 + b^2
\end{aligned}
$$

> **Product of Complex Conjugates**
>
> If a and b are real numbers, then $(a + bi)(a - bi) = a^2 + b^2$.
>
> | Number | Standard Form | Conjugate | Product |
> |---|---|---|---|
> | $3 + 7i$ | $3 + 7i$ | $3 - 7i$ | $(3 + 7i)(3 - 7i) = (3)^2 + (7)^2 = 58$ |
> | $\sqrt{-5}$ | $0 + \sqrt{5}i$ | $0 - \sqrt{5}i$ | $(0 + \sqrt{5}i)(0 - \sqrt{5}i) = (0)^2 + (\sqrt{5})^2 = 5$ |

In Example 8, we demonstrate division of complex numbers such as $\frac{8 + 2i}{3 - 5i}$. The goal is to make the denominator a real number so that the quotient can be written in standard form $a + bi$. This can be accomplished by multiplying the denominator by its complex conjugate. Of course, this means that we must also multiply the numerator by the same quantity.

EXAMPLE 8   **Dividing Complex Numbers**

Divide. Write the result in the form $a + bi$.

a. $\dfrac{8 + 2i}{3 - 5i}$ **b.** $\left(2 + \sqrt{3}i\right)^{-1}$ **c.** $\dfrac{-2}{5i}$

Solution:

a. $\dfrac{8 + 2i}{3 - 5i} = \dfrac{(8 + 2i) \cdot (3 + 5i)}{(3 - 5i) \cdot (3 + 5i)}$ Multiply numerator and denominator by the conjugate of the denominator.

$= \dfrac{24 + 40i + 6i + 10i^2}{(3)^2 + (5)^2}$ Apply the distributive property in the numerator.
Multiply conjugates in the denominator.

$= \dfrac{24 + 46i + 10(-1)}{9 + 25}$ Replace i^2 by -1.

$= \dfrac{14 + 46i}{34}$

$= \dfrac{14}{34} + \dfrac{46}{34}i = \dfrac{7}{17} + \dfrac{23}{17}i$ Write the result in the form $a + bi$.

b. $\left(2 + \sqrt{3}i\right)^{-1} = \dfrac{1 \cdot \left(2 - \sqrt{3}i\right)}{\left(2 + \sqrt{3}i\right) \cdot \left(2 - \sqrt{3}i\right)}$ Multiply numerator and denominator by the conjugate of the denominator.

$= \dfrac{2 - \sqrt{3}i}{(2)^2 + \left(\sqrt{3}\right)^2}$

$= \dfrac{2 - \sqrt{3}i}{4 + 3} = \dfrac{2}{7} - \dfrac{\sqrt{3}}{7}i$ Simplify.

TIP In Example 8(b) we left the answer as $\frac{2}{7} - \frac{\sqrt{3}}{7}i$ rather than as $\frac{2}{7} + \left(-\frac{\sqrt{3}}{7}\right)i$ because the expression written using addition is more cumbersome. Both answers are acceptable.

c. $\dfrac{-2}{5i} = \dfrac{-2 \cdot i}{5i \cdot i}$ In this example, it is sufficient to multiply numerator and denominator by i (rather than by the conjugate $-5i$) to produce a real number in the denominator.

$= \dfrac{-2i}{5i^2} = \dfrac{-2i}{5(-1)} = \dfrac{-2i}{-5} = \dfrac{2}{5}i$

$= 0 + \dfrac{2}{5}i$ Write the result in the form $a + bi$.

Skill Practice 8   Divide. Write the result in the form $a + bi$.

a. $\dfrac{5 + 6i}{2 - 7i}$ **b.** $\left(5 + \sqrt{7}i\right)^{-1}$ **c.** $\dfrac{-7}{10i}$

Answers

8. a. $-\dfrac{32}{53} + \dfrac{47}{53}i$ **b.** $\dfrac{5}{32} - \dfrac{\sqrt{7}}{32}i$

c. $0 + \dfrac{7}{10}i$

TECHNOLOGY CONNECTIONS

Operations on Complex Numbers

Most graphing calculators and some scientific calculators can perform operations on complex numbers. A graphing calculator may have two different modes: one for operations over the set of real numbers and one for operations over the set of complex numbers. Choose the "$a + bi$" mode on your calculator. Then evaluate the expressions.

a. $\sqrt{-9}$ **b.** $(8 + 3i) - (2 - 7i)$ **c.** $(5 - 2i)(10 - 2i)$

SECTION 1.3   Practice Exercises

Review Exercises

For Exercises 1–8, perform the indicated operation and simplify.

1. $(3x + 2) - (5x + 1)$

2. $(4y - 5) - (10y - 7)$

3. $(3a - 4)(5a + 2)$

4. $(2c - 5)(7c + 1)$

5. $\left(\dfrac{1}{6}m - \dfrac{2}{5}n\right)\left(\dfrac{1}{6}m + \dfrac{2}{5}n\right)$

6. $\left(\dfrac{1}{2}x - \dfrac{2}{3}y\right)\left(\dfrac{1}{2}x + \dfrac{2}{3}y\right)$

7. $(z + 2)^2$

8. $(b - 7)^2$

Concept Connections

9. The imaginary number i is defined so that $i = \sqrt{-1}$ and $i^2 =$ _____.

10. For a positive real number b, the value $\sqrt{-b} =$ _____.

11. Given a complex number $a + bi$, the value of a is called the _____ part and the value of b is called the _____ part.

12. Given a complex number $a + bi$, if $b \neq 0$, then the number is called an _____ number.

13. Given a complex number $a + bi$, if $a = 0$ and $b \neq 0$, then the number is called a _____ imaginary number.

14. A complex number written in the form $a + bi$ is said to be written in standard _____.

15. The set of _____ numbers denoted by $\mathbb{C}$ includes real numbers and imaginary numbers.

16. Given a complex number $a + bi$, the expression $a - bi$ is called the complex _____.

Objective 1: Simplify Imaginary Numbers

For Exercises 17–34, write each expression in terms of i and simplify. (See Examples 1–2)

17. $\sqrt{-121}$

18. $\sqrt{-100}$

19. $\sqrt{-98}$

20. $\sqrt{-63}$

21. $\sqrt{-19}$

22. $\sqrt{-23}$

23. $-\sqrt{-16}$

24. $-\sqrt{-25}$

25. $\sqrt{-4}\sqrt{-9}$

26. $\sqrt{-1}\sqrt{-36}$

27. $\sqrt{-10}\sqrt{-5}$

28. $\sqrt{-6}\sqrt{-15}$

29. $\sqrt{-6}\sqrt{-14}$

30. $\sqrt{-10}\sqrt{-15}$

31. $\dfrac{\sqrt{-98}}{\sqrt{-2}}$

32. $\dfrac{\sqrt{-45}}{\sqrt{-5}}$

33. $\dfrac{\sqrt{-63}}{\sqrt{7}}$

34. $\dfrac{\sqrt{-80}}{\sqrt{5}}$

Objective 2: Write Complex Numbers in the Form $a + bi$

For Exercises 35–40, determine the real and imaginary parts of the complex number.

35. $3 - 7i$ **36.** $2 - 4i$ **37.** $19i$

38. $40i$ **39.** $-\dfrac{1}{4}$ **40.** $-\dfrac{4}{7}$

For Exercises 41–44, determine if the statement is true or false.

41. a. $\mathbb{R} \subset \mathbb{C}$ **b.** $\mathbb{C} \subset \mathbb{R}$ **42. a.** $4 - 5i \in \mathbb{R}$ **b.** $4 - 5i \in \mathbb{C}$

43. a. $6 \in \mathbb{R}$ **b.** $6 \in \mathbb{C}$ **44. a.** $9i \in \mathbb{R}$ **b.** $9i \in \mathbb{C}$

For Exercises 45–54, simplify each expression and write the result in standard form, $a + bi$. (See Example 3)

45. 5 **46.** -4 **47.** $4\sqrt{-4}$ **48.** $2\sqrt{-144}$

49. $2 + \sqrt{-12}$ **50.** $6 - \sqrt{-24}$ **51.** $\dfrac{8 + 3i}{14}$ **52.** $\dfrac{4 + 5i}{6}$

53. $\dfrac{-18 + \sqrt{-48}}{4}$ **54.** $\dfrac{-10 + \sqrt{-125}}{5}$

Objective 3: Perform Operations on Complex Numbers

For Exercises 55–58, simplify the powers of i. (See Example 4)

55. a. i^{20} **b.** i^{29} **c.** i^{50} **d.** i^{-41}

56. a. i^{32} **b.** i^{47} **c.** i^{66} **d.** i^{-27}

57. a. i^{37} **b.** i^{-37} **c.** i^{82} **d.** i^{-82}

58. a. i^{103} **b.** i^{-103} **c.** i^{52} **d.** i^{-52}

For Exercises 59–82, perform the indicated operations. Write the answers in standard form, $a + bi$. (See Examples 5–7)

59. $(2 - 7i) + (8 - 3i)$ **60.** $(6 - 10i) + (8 + 4i)$ **61.** $(15 + 21i) - (18 - 40i)$

62. $(250 + 100i) - (80 + 25i)$ **63.** $\left(\dfrac{1}{2} + \dfrac{2}{3}i\right) - \left(\dfrac{5}{6} + \dfrac{1}{12}i\right)$ **64.** $\left(\dfrac{3}{5} - \dfrac{1}{8}i\right) - \left(\dfrac{7}{10} + \dfrac{1}{6}i\right)$

65. $(2.3 + 4i) - (8.1 - 2.7i) + (4.6 - 6.7i)$ **66.** $(0.05 - 0.03i) + (-0.12 + 0.08i) - (0.07 + 0.05i)$

67. $-\dfrac{1}{8}(16 + 24i)$ **68.** $-\dfrac{1}{6}(60 - 30i)$ **69.** $2i(5 + i)$

70. $4i(6 + 5i)$ **71.** $\sqrt{-3}\left(\sqrt{11} - \sqrt{-7}\right)$ **72.** $\sqrt{-2}\left(\sqrt{13} + \sqrt{-5}\right)$

73. $(3 - 6i)(10 + i)$ **74.** $(2 - 5i)(8 + 2i)$ **75.** $(3 - 7i)^2$

76. $(10 - 3i)^2$ **77.** $\left(3 - \sqrt{-5}\right)\left(4 + \sqrt{-5}\right)$ **78.** $\left(2 + \sqrt{-7}\right)\left(10 + \sqrt{-7}\right)$

79. $4(6 + 2i) - 5i(3 - 7i)$ **80.** $-3(8 - 3i) - 6i(2 + i)$ **81.** $(2 - i)^2 + (2 + i)^2$

82. $(3 - 2i)^2 + (3 + 2i)^2$

For Exercises 83–86, for each given number, (a) identify the complex conjugate and (b) determine the product of the number and its conjugate.

83. $3 - 6i$ **84.** $4 - 5i$ **85.** $8i$ **86.** $9i$

For Exercises 87–102, perform the indicated operations. Write the answers in standard form, $a + bi$. (See Examples 7–8)

87. $(10 - 4i)(10 + 4i)$ **88.** $(3 - 9i)(3 + 9i)$ **89.** $(7i)(-7i)$

90. $(-5i)(5i)$ **91.** $\left(\sqrt{2} + \sqrt{3}i\right)\left(\sqrt{2} - \sqrt{3}i\right)$ **92.** $\left(\sqrt{5} + \sqrt{7}i\right)\left(\sqrt{5} - \sqrt{7}i\right)$

93. $\dfrac{6 + 2i}{3 - i}$ **94.** $\dfrac{5 + i}{4 - i}$ **95.** $\dfrac{8 - 5i}{13 + 2i}$

96. $\dfrac{10 - 3i}{11 + 4i}$

97. $(6 + \sqrt{5}i)^{-1}$

98. $(4 - \sqrt{3}i)^{-1}$

99. $\dfrac{5}{13i}$

100. $\dfrac{6}{7i}$

101. $\dfrac{-1}{\sqrt{-3}}$

102. $\dfrac{-2}{\sqrt{-11}}$

Mixed Exercises

For Exercises 103–106, evaluate $\sqrt{b^2 - 4ac}$ for the given values of a, b, and c, and simplify.

103. $a = 2$, $b = 4$, and $c = 6$

104. $a = 5$, $b = -5$, and $c = 10$

105. $a = 2$, $b = -6$, and $c = 5$

106. $a = 2$, $b = 4$, and $c = 4$

For Exercises 107–110, verify by substitution that the given values of x are solutions to the given equation.

107. $x^2 + 25 = 0$

   a. $x = 5i$

   b. $x = -5i$

108. $x^2 + 49 = 0$

   a. $x = 7i$

   b. $x = -7i$

109. $x^2 - 4x + 7 = 0$

   a. $x = 2 + i\sqrt{3}$

   b. $x = 2 - i\sqrt{3}$

110. $x^2 - 6x + 11 = 0$

   a. $x = 3 + i\sqrt{2}$

   b. $x = 3 - i\sqrt{2}$

111. Prove that $(a + bi)(c + di) = (ac - bd) + (ad + bc)i$.

112. Prove that $(a + bi)^2 = (a^2 - b^2) + (2ab)i$.

Write About It

113. Explain the flaw in the following logic.
$$\sqrt{-9} \cdot \sqrt{-4} = \sqrt{(-9)(-4)} = \sqrt{36} = 6$$

114. Discuss the difference between the products $(a + b)(a - b)$ and $(a + bi)(a - bi)$.

115. Give an example of a complex number that is its own conjugate.

116. Give an example of two complex numbers whose product is a real number.

Expanding Your Skills

The variable z is often used to denote a complex number and $\bar{z}$ is used to denote its conjugate. If $z = a + bi$, simplify the expressions in Exercises 117–118.

117. $z \cdot \bar{z}$

118. $z^2 - \bar{z}^2$

For Exercises 119–124, factor the expressions over the set of complex numbers. For assistance, consider these examples.

- In Chapter R we saw that some expressions factor over the set of integers. For example: $x^2 - 4 = (x + 2)(x - 2)$.
- Some expressions factor over the set of irrational numbers. For example: $x^2 - 5 = (x + \sqrt{5})(x - \sqrt{5})$.
- To factor an expression such as $x^2 + 4$, we need to factor over the set of complex numbers. For example, verify that $x^2 + 4 = (x + 2i)(x - 2i)$.

119. a. $x^2 - 9$

   b. $x^2 + 9$

120. a. $x^2 - 100$

   b. $x^2 + 100$

121. a. $x^2 - 64$

   b. $x^2 + 64$

122. a. $x^2 - 25$

   b. $x^2 + 25$

123. a. $x^2 - 3$

   b. $x^2 + 3$

124. a. $x^2 - 11$

   b. $x^2 + 11$

Technology Connections

For Exercises 125–128, use a calculator to perform the indicated operations.

125. a. $\sqrt{-16}$

   b. $(4 - 5i) - (2 + 3i)$

   c. $(12 - 15i)(-2 + 9i)$

126. a. $\sqrt{-169}$

   b. $(-11 - 2i) + (-4 + 9i)$

   c. $(8 + 12i)(-3 - 7i)$

127. a. $(4 - 9i)^2$

   b. $\dfrac{7}{2i}$

   c. $\dfrac{14 + 8i}{3 - i}$

128. a. $(11 + 4i)^2$

   b. $\dfrac{11}{10i}$

   c. $\dfrac{5 + 7i}{6 + 8i}$

SECTION 1.4   Quadratic Equations

1. Solve Quadratic Equations by Using the Zero Product Property

A linear equation in one variable is an equation of the form $ax + b = 0$, where $a \neq 0$. A linear equation is also called a first-degree equation. We now turn our attention to a quadratic equation. This is identified as a second-degree equation.

Definition of a Quadratic Equation

Let a, b, and c represent real numbers where $a \neq 0$. A **quadratic equation** in the variable x is an equation of the form

$$ax^2 + bx + c = 0$$

To solve a quadratic equation, we make use of the zero product property.

Zero Product Property

If $mn = 0$, then $m = 0$ or $n = 0$.

Verbal Explanation	Example
If the product of two factors is zero, then at least one factor is zero.	$(x + 4)(x - 2) = 0$ implies that $x + 4 = 0$ or $x - 2 = 0$, indicating that $x = -4$ or $x = 2$.

EXAMPLE 1   Applying the Zero Product Property

Solve. $2x(2x - 7) = -12$

Solution:

$$2x(2x - 7) = -12$$
$$4x^2 - 14x = -12 \qquad \text{Apply the distributive property.}$$
$$4x^2 - 14x + 12 = 0 \qquad \text{Set one side of the equation equal to zero.}$$

$$2(2x^2 - 7x + 6) = 0 \qquad \text{Factor.}$$
$$2(x - 2)(2x - 3) = 0$$
$$2 = 0 \quad \text{or} \quad x - 2 = 0 \quad \text{or} \quad 2x - 3 = 0 \qquad \text{Set each factor equal to zero.}$$
$$\uparrow$$
contradiction $\qquad\qquad x = 2 \qquad\qquad x = \dfrac{3}{2}$

Both solutions check.

The solution set is $\left\{2, \dfrac{3}{2}\right\}$.

Check: $2x(2x - 7) = -12$
$x = 2$

$2(2)[2(2) - 7] \overset{?}{=} -12$
$\qquad\qquad 4(-3) \overset{?}{=} -12 \checkmark$

$x = \frac{3}{2}$

$2(\frac{3}{2})[2(\frac{3}{2}) - 7] \overset{?}{=} -12$
$\qquad 3(-4) \overset{?}{=} -12 \checkmark$

TIP After applying the zero product property in Example 1, we have three equations. The first equation does not contain the variable x. It is a contradiction and does not yield a solution for x.

Skill Practice 1   Solve. $10(3x^2 - 13x) = -40$

Answer

1. $\left\{4, \dfrac{1}{3}\right\}$

2. Solve Quadratic Equations by Using the Square Root Property

The zero product property can be used to solve equations of the form $x^2 = k$.

$$x^2 = k$$
$$x^2 - k = 0$$
$$(x - \sqrt{k})(x + \sqrt{k}) = 0$$
$$x - \sqrt{k} = 0 \quad \text{or} \quad x + \sqrt{k} = 0$$
$$x = \sqrt{k} \qquad\qquad x = -\sqrt{k}$$

The solutions can also be written as $x = \pm\sqrt{k}$. This is read as "x equals plus or minus the square root of k."

The solution set is $\{\pm\sqrt{k}\}$.

This result is formalized as the square root property.

Square Root Property

If $x^2 = k$, then $x = \pm\sqrt{k}$.

The solution set is $\{\sqrt{k}, -\sqrt{k}\}$ or more concisely $\{\pm\sqrt{k}\}$.

EXAMPLE 2 **Applying the Square Root Property**

Solve the equations by using the square root property.

a. $x^2 = 64$ **b.** $2y^2 + 36 = 0$ **c.** $(w + 3)^2 = 8$

Solution:

a. $x^2 = 64$

$x = \pm\sqrt{64}$ Apply the square root property.

$x = \pm 8$ Both solutions check in the original equation.

The solution set is $\{\pm 8\}$.

TIP The solutions to the equation in Example 2(b) are written concisely as $\pm 3i\sqrt{2}$. Do not forget that this actually represents two solutions:

$$y = 3i\sqrt{2} \quad \text{and}$$
$$y = -3i\sqrt{2}$$

b. $2y^2 + 36 = 0$

$2y^2 = -36$ Isolate the square term.

$y^2 = -18$ Write the equation in the form $y^2 = k$.

$y = \pm\sqrt{-18}$ Apply the square root property.

$y = \pm 3i\sqrt{2}$ Simplify the radical.

The solution set is $\{\pm 3i\sqrt{2}\}$. Both solutions check in the original equation.

c. $(w + 3)^2 = 8$

$w + 3 = \pm\sqrt{8}$ Apply the square root property.

$w = -3 \pm\sqrt{8}$ Subtract 3 from both sides to isolate w.

$w = -3 \pm 2\sqrt{2}$ Simplify the radical. $\sqrt{8} = \sqrt{2^3} = 2\sqrt{2}$

The solution set is $\{-3 \pm 2\sqrt{2}\}$. Both solutions check.

Skill Practice 2 Solve the equations by using the square root property.

a. $a^2 = 49$ **b.** $2c^2 + 80 = 0$ **c.** $(t + 4)^2 = 24$

Answers

2. a. $\{\pm 7\}$ **b.** $\{\pm 2i\sqrt{10}\}$

c. $\{-4 \pm 2\sqrt{6}\}$

Point of Interest

Unfortunate names? In the long history of mathematics, number systems have been expanded to accommodate meaningful solutions to equations. But the negative connotation of their names may suggest a reluctance by early mathematicians to accept these new concepts. Negative numbers for example are not unpleasant or disagreeable. Irrational numbers are not illogical or absurd, and imaginary numbers are not "fake." Instead these sets of numbers are necessary to render solutions to such equations as

$$2x + 10 = 0 \qquad x^2 - 5 = 0 \qquad x^2 + 4 = 0$$

3. Complete the Square

In Example 2(c), the left side of the equation is the square of a binomial and the right side is a constant. We can manipulate a quadratic equation $ax^2 + bx + c = 0$ $(a \neq 0)$ to write it as the square of a binomial equal to a constant. First look at the relationship between a perfect square trinomial and its factored form.

Perfect Square Trinomial	**Factored Form**
$x^2 + 10x + 25$ $\longrightarrow$	$(x + 5)^2$
$t^2 - 6t + 9$ $\longrightarrow$	$(t - 3)^2$
$p^2 - 14p + 49$ $\longrightarrow$	$(p - 7)^2$

For a perfect square trinomial with a leading coefficient of 1, the constant term is the square of one-half the linear term coefficient. For example:

$$x^2 + 10x + 25$$
$$\left[\tfrac{1}{2}(10)\right]^2$$

In general, an expression of the form $x^2 + bx + n$ is a perfect square trinomial if $n = \left(\tfrac{1}{2}b\right)^2$. The process to create a perfect square trinomial is called **completing the square.**

EXAMPLE 3   **Completing the Square**

Determine the value of n that makes the polynomial a perfect square trinomial. Then factor the expression as the square of a binomial.

   a. $x^2 + 18x + n$ **b.** $x^2 - 13x + n$ **c.** $x^2 + \dfrac{4}{7}x + n$

Solution:

a. $x^2 + 18x + n$ To find n, take $\tfrac{1}{2}$ of 18, and square the result.

$= x^2 + 18x + 81$ $n = \left[\tfrac{1}{2}(18)\right]^2 = [9]^2 = 81$

$= (x + 9)^2$ Factor.

b. $x^2 - 13x + n$ To find n, take $\tfrac{1}{2}$ of -13, and square the result.

$= x^2 - 13x + \dfrac{169}{4}$ $n = \left[\tfrac{1}{2}(-13)\right]^2 = \left[-\tfrac{13}{2}\right]^2 = \tfrac{169}{4}$

$= \left(x - \dfrac{13}{2}\right)^2$ Factor.

c. $x^2 + \dfrac{4}{7}x + n$ To find n, take $\tfrac{1}{2}$ of $\tfrac{4}{7}$, and square the result.

$= x^2 + \dfrac{4}{7}x + \dfrac{4}{49}$ $n = \left[\tfrac{1}{2}\left(\tfrac{4}{7}\right)\right]^2 = \left[\tfrac{2}{7}\right]^2 = \tfrac{4}{49}$

$= \left(x + \dfrac{2}{7}\right)^2$ Factor.

TIP When factoring a perfect square trinomial, the constant term in the binomial will always be one-half the x term coefficient.

$$x^2 + 18x + 81$$
$$= (x + 9)^2$$

Note: $9 = \tfrac{1}{2}(18)$

Skill Practice 3 Determine the value of n that makes the polynomial a perfect square trinomial. Then factor the expression as the square of a binomial.

   a. $x^2 + 12x + n$ **b.** $x^2 + 5x + n$ **c.** $x^2 - \dfrac{2}{3}x + n$

We can solve a quadratic equation $ax^2 + bx + c = 0$ $(a \neq 0)$ by completing the square and then applying the square root property.

Solving a Quadratic Equation $ax^2 + bx + c = 0$ by Completing the Square and Applying the Square Root Property

Step 1 Divide both sides by a to make the leading coefficient 1.

Step 2 Isolate the variable terms on one side of the equation.

Step 3 Complete the square.
- Add the square of one-half the linear term coefficient to both sides.
- Factor the resulting perfect square trinomial.

Step 4 Apply the square root property and solve for x.

EXAMPLE 4 **Completing the Square and Solving a Quadratic Equation**

Solve the equation by completing the square and applying the square root property. $\quad x^2 - 3 = -10x$

Solution:

$x^2 - 3 = -10x$	Write the equation in the form $ax^2 + bx + c = 0$.
$x^2 + 10x - 3 = 0$	**Step 1:** Notice that the leading coefficient is already 1.
$x^2 + 10x + \underline{\quad} = 3 + \underline{\quad}$	**Step 2:** Add 3 to both sides to isolate the variable terms.
$x^2 + 10x + 25 = 3 + 25$	**Step 3:** Add $\left[\frac{1}{2}(10)\right]^2 = [5]^2 = 25$ to both sides.
$(x + 5)^2 = 28$	Factor.
$x + 5 = \pm\sqrt{28}$	**Step 4:** Apply the square root property and solve for x.
$x = -5 \pm 2\sqrt{7}$	Both solutions check in the original equation.
$\left\{-5 \pm 2\sqrt{7}\right\}$	Write the solution set.

Skill Practice 4 Solve the equation by completing the square and applying the square root property. $\quad x^2 - 2 = 8x$

In Example 5, we encounter a quadratic equation in which the leading coefficient is not 1. The first step is to divide both sides by the leading coefficient.

Answers

3. a. $n = 36; (x + 6)^2$

  b. $n = \dfrac{25}{4}; \left(x + \dfrac{5}{2}\right)^2$

  c. $n = \dfrac{1}{9}; \left(x - \dfrac{1}{3}\right)^2$

4. $\left\{4 \pm 3\sqrt{2}\right\}$

EXAMPLE 5   **Completing the Square and Solving a Quadratic Equation**

Solve the equation by completing the square and applying the square root property. $-2x^2 - 3x - 5 = 0$

Solution:

$-2x^2 - 3x - 5 = 0$	The equation is in the form $ax^2 + bx + c = 0$.
$\dfrac{-2x^2}{-2} - \dfrac{3x}{-2} - \dfrac{5}{-2} = \dfrac{0}{-2}$	**Step 1:** Divide by the leading coefficient, -2.
$x^2 + \dfrac{3}{2}x + \dfrac{5}{2} = 0$	The new leading coefficient is 1.
$x^2 + \dfrac{3}{2}x + \underline{\quad} = -\dfrac{5}{2} + \underline{\quad}$	**Step 2:** Subtract $\frac{5}{2}$ from both sides to isolate the variable terms.
$x^2 + \dfrac{3}{2}x + \dfrac{9}{16} = -\dfrac{5}{2} + \dfrac{9}{16}$	**Step 3:** Add $\left[\frac{1}{2}\left(\frac{3}{2}\right)\right]^2 = \left[\frac{3}{4}\right]^2 = \frac{9}{16}$ to both sides.
$\left(x + \dfrac{3}{4}\right)^2 = -\dfrac{40}{16} + \dfrac{9}{16}$	Factor.
$\left(x + \dfrac{3}{4}\right)^2 = -\dfrac{31}{16}$	
$x + \dfrac{3}{4} = \pm\sqrt{-\dfrac{31}{16}}$	**Step 4:** Apply the square root property and solve for x.
$x = -\dfrac{3}{4} \pm i\dfrac{\sqrt{31}}{4}$	Simplify the radical. The solutions both check in the original equation.
$\left\{ -\dfrac{3}{4} \pm \dfrac{\sqrt{31}}{4}i \right\}$	Write the solution set.

Skill Practice 5   Solve the equation by completing the square and applying the square root property. $-3x^2 + 5x - 7 = 0$

4. Solve Quadratic Equations by Using the Quadratic Formula

If we solve a general quadratic equation $ax^2 + bx + c = 0$ $(a \neq 0)$ by completing the square and using the square root property, the result is a formula that gives the solutions for x in terms of a, b, and c.

$ax^2 + bx + c = 0$	Begin with a quadratic equation in standard form with $a > 0$.
$\dfrac{ax^2}{a} + \dfrac{bx}{a} + \dfrac{c}{a} = \dfrac{0}{a}$	Divide by the leading coefficient.
$x^2 + \dfrac{b}{a}x + \dfrac{c}{a} = 0$	
$x^2 + \dfrac{b}{a}x = -\dfrac{c}{a}$	Isolate the terms containing x.
$x^2 + \dfrac{b}{a}x + \left(\dfrac{1}{2} \cdot \dfrac{b}{a}\right)^2 = \left(\dfrac{1}{2} \cdot \dfrac{b}{a}\right)^2 - \dfrac{c}{a}$	Add the square of $\frac{1}{2}$ the linear term coefficient to both sides of the equation.
$\left(x + \dfrac{b}{2a}\right)^2 = \dfrac{b^2}{4a^2} - \dfrac{c}{a}$	Factor the left side as a perfect square.

Answer

5. $\left\{ \dfrac{5}{6} \pm \dfrac{\sqrt{59}}{6}i \right\}$

$$\left(x + \frac{b}{2a}\right)^2 = \frac{b^2 - 4ac}{4a^2}$$

Combine fractions on the right side by finding a common denominator.

$$x + \frac{b}{2a} = \pm\sqrt{\frac{b^2 - 4ac}{4a^2}}$$

Apply the square root property.

$$x + \frac{b}{2a} = \pm\frac{\sqrt{b^2 - 4ac}}{2a}$$

Simplify the denominator.

$$x = -\frac{b}{2a} \pm \frac{\sqrt{b^2 - 4ac}}{2a}$$

Subtract $\frac{b}{2a}$ from both sides.

$$= \frac{-b \pm \sqrt{b^2 - 4ac}}{2a}$$

Combine fractions.

The result is called the quadratic formula.

TIP When applying the quadratic formula, note that a, b, and c are constants. The variable is x.

The Quadratic Formula

For a quadratic equation of the form $ax^2 + bx + c = 0$ $(a \neq 0)$, the solutions are

$$x = \frac{-b \pm \sqrt{b^2 - 4ac}}{2a}$$

EXAMPLE 6   Using the Quadratic Formula

Solve the equation by applying the quadratic formula. $x(x - 6) = 3$

Solution:

$$x(x - 6) = 3$$
$$x^2 - 6x - 3 = 0$$

Write the equation in the form $ax^2 + bx + c = 0$.

$$a = 1, b = -6, c = -3$$

Identify the values of a, b, and c.

$$x = \frac{-(-6) \pm \sqrt{(-6)^2 - 4(1)(-3)}}{2(1)}$$

Apply the quadratic formula.
$$x = \frac{-b \pm \sqrt{b^2 - 4ac}}{2a}$$

$$= \frac{6 \pm \sqrt{48}}{2}$$

Simplify.

$$= \frac{6 \pm 4\sqrt{3}}{2}$$

Simplify the radical.
$$\sqrt{48} = \sqrt{2^4 \cdot 3} = 2^2\sqrt{3} = 4\sqrt{3}$$

$$= \frac{2(3 \pm 2\sqrt{3})}{2}$$

Factor the numerator.

$$= 3 \pm 2\sqrt{3}$$

Simplify the fraction.

The solution set is $\{3 \pm 2\sqrt{3}\}$.

The solutions both check in the original equation.

Avoiding Mistakes

When writing the quadratic formula, note that the fraction bar extends under both terms in the numerator.

$$x = \frac{-b \pm \sqrt{b^2 - 4ac}}{2a} \quad \text{yes}$$

$$x = -b \pm \frac{\sqrt{b^2 - 4ac}}{2a} \quad \text{no}$$

Skill Practice 6   Solve the equation by applying the quadratic formula.
$x(x - 8) = 3$

Answer
6. $\{4 \pm \sqrt{19}\}$

TECHNOLOGY CONNECTIONS

Checking a Solution to an Equation

To check a potential solution to an equation, store the value in the variable x in the calculator. Then evaluate the expressions on both sides of the equation to confirm that they are equal for the given value of x.

```
3+2√(3)→X
        6.464101615
X(X-6)
              3
```

```
3-2√(3)→X
        -.4641016151
X(X-6)
              3
```

If a quadratic equation has fractional or decimal coefficients, we have the option of clearing fractions or decimals to create integer coefficients. This makes the application of the quadratic formula easier, as demonstrated in Example 7.

EXAMPLE 7   Using the Quadratic Formula

Solve the equation by applying the quadratic formula. $\dfrac{3}{10}x^2 - \dfrac{2}{5}x + \dfrac{7}{10} = 0$

Solution:

$$\frac{3}{10}x^2 - \frac{2}{5}x + \frac{7}{10} = 0$$
The equation is in the form $ax^2 + bx + c = 0$.

$$10 \cdot \left(\frac{3}{10}x^2 - \frac{2}{5}x + \frac{7}{10}\right) = 10 \cdot (0)$$
Multiply by 10 to clear fractions.

$$3x^2 - 4x + 7 = 0$$

$$a = 3, \, b = -4, \, c = 7$$
Identify the values of a, b, and c.

$$x = \frac{-(-4) \pm \sqrt{(-4)^2 - 4(3)(7)}}{2(3)}$$
Apply the quadratic formula.
$$x = \frac{-b \pm \sqrt{b^2 - 4ac}}{2a}$$

$$= \frac{4 \pm \sqrt{-68}}{6}$$
Simplify.

$$= \frac{4 \pm 2i\sqrt{17}}{6}$$
Simplify the radical.

$$= \frac{2(2 \pm i\sqrt{17})}{2 \cdot 3}$$
Factor the numerator and denominator.

$$= \frac{2 \pm i\sqrt{17}}{3}$$
Simplify the fraction.

$$= \frac{2}{3} \pm \frac{\sqrt{17}}{3}i$$
The solutions are imaginary numbers. Write the solutions in standard form, $a + bi$.

The solution set is $\left\{\dfrac{2}{3} \pm \dfrac{\sqrt{17}}{3}i\right\}$.
The solutions both check in the original equation.

Skill Practice 7   Solve the equation by applying the quadratic formula.
$$\frac{5}{12}x^2 - \frac{1}{2}x + \frac{1}{4} = 0$$

Answer

7. $\left\{\dfrac{3}{5} \pm \dfrac{\sqrt{6}}{5}i\right\}$

Three methods have been presented to solve a quadratic equation. We offer these guidelines to choose an appropriate and efficient method to solve a given quadratic equation.

Methods to Solve a Quadratic Equation	
Method/Notes	**Example**
Apply the Zero Product Property • Set one side of the equation equal to zero and factor the other side. Then apply the zero product property.	$x^2 - x = 12$ $x^2 - x - 12 = 0$ $(x - 4)(x + 3) = 0$ $x = 4$ or $x = -3$
Complete the Square and Apply the Square Root Property • Good choice if the equation is in the form $x^2 = k$. • Good choice if the equation is in the form $ax^2 + bx + c = 0$, where $a = 1$ and b is an even real number.	$c^2 = -6$ $c = \pm\sqrt{-6}$ $c = \pm i\sqrt{6}$ $x^2 + 6x + 2 = 0$ $x^2 + 6x + 9 = -2 + 9$ $(x + 3)^2 = 7$ $x + 3 = \pm\sqrt{7}$ $x = -3 \pm \sqrt{7}$
Apply the Quadratic Formula • Applies in all situations. • Consider clearing fractions or decimals if the coefficients are not integer values.	$0.2x^2 + 0.5x + 0.1 = 0$ $10(0.2x^2 + 0.5x + 0.1) = 10(0)$ $2x^2 + 5x + 1 = 0$ $x = \dfrac{-(5) \pm \sqrt{(5)^2 - 4(2)(1)}}{2(2)}$ $x = \dfrac{-5 \pm \sqrt{17}}{4}$

5. Use the Discriminant

The solutions to a quadratic equation are given by $x = \dfrac{-b \pm \sqrt{b^2 - 4ac}}{2a}$. The radicand, $b^2 - 4ac$, is called the *discriminant*. The value of the discriminant tells us the number and type of solutions to the equation. We examine three different cases.

Using the Discriminant to Determine the Number and Type of Solutions to a Quadratic Equation

Given a quadratic equation $ax^2 + bx + c = 0$ $(a \neq 0)$, the quantity $b^2 - 4ac$ is called the **discriminant.**

Discriminant $b^2 - 4ac$	Number and Type of Solutions	Examples	Result of Quadratic Formula
$b^2 - 4ac < 0$	2 imaginary solutions	$2x^2 - 3x + 5 = 0$ $b^2 - 4ac = (-3)^2 - 4(2)(5)$ $= -31$	$x = \dfrac{3 \pm \sqrt{-31}}{4}$
$b^2 - 4ac = 0$	1 real solution	$x^2 + 6x + 9 = 0$ $b^2 - 4ac = (6)^2 - 4(1)(9)$ $= 0$	$x = \dfrac{-6 \pm \sqrt{0}}{2} = -3$
$b^2 - 4ac > 0$	2 real solutions	$x^2 - x - 12 = 0$ $b^2 - 4ac = (-1)^2 - 4(1)(-12)$ $= 49$ $2x^2 + 7x - 1 = 0$ $b^2 - 4ac = (7)^2 - 4(2)(-1)$ $= 57$	$x = \dfrac{1 \pm \sqrt{49}}{2}$ $(x = 4, x = -3)$ $x = \dfrac{-7 \pm \sqrt{57}}{4}$

EXAMPLE 8 Using the Discriminant

Use the discriminant to determine the number and type of solutions for each equation.

   a. $5x^2 - 3x + 1 = 0$ **b.** $2x^2 = 3 - 6x$ **c.** $4x^2 + 12x = -9$

Solution:

Equation	$b^2 - 4ac$	Solution Type and Number
a. $5x^2 - 3x + 1 = 0$	$(-3)^2 - 4(5)(1)$ $= -11$	Because $-11 < 0$, there are two imaginary solutions.
b. $2x^2 = 3 - 6x$ $2x^2 + 6x - 3 = 0$	$(6)^2 - 4(2)(-3)$ $= 60$	Because $60 > 0$, there are two real solutions.
c. $4x^2 + 12x = -9$ $4x^2 + 12x + 9 = 0$	$(12)^2 - 4(4)(9)$ $= 0$	Because the discriminant is 0, there is one real solution.

Skill Practice 8 Use the discriminant to determine the number and type of solutions for each equation.

   a. $2x^2 - 4x + 5 = 0$ **b.** $25x^2 = 10x - 1$ **c.** $x^2 + 10x = -9$

Answers

8. a. Discriminant: -24 (2 imaginary solutions)
  b. Discriminant: 0 (1 real solution)
  c. Discriminant: 64 (2 real solutions)

6. Solve an Equation for a Specified Variable

In Examples 9 and 10, we manipulate literal equations to solve for a specified variable.

EXAMPLE 9   Solving an Equation for a Specified Variable

Solve for r. $V = \dfrac{1}{3}\pi r^2 h$ $(r > 0)$

Solution:

> **TIP** The equation $V = \frac{1}{3}\pi r^2 h$ is linear in the variables V and h, and quadratic in the variable r.

$$V = \frac{1}{3}\pi r^2 h \qquad \text{This equation is quadratic in the variable } r. \text{ The strategy in this example is to isolate } r^2 \text{ and then apply the square root property.}$$

$$3(V) = 3\left(\frac{1}{3}\pi r^2 h\right) \qquad \text{Multiply both sides by 3 to clear fractions.}$$

$$3V = \pi r^2 h$$

$$\frac{3V}{\pi h} = \frac{\pi r^2 h}{\pi h} \qquad \text{Divide both sides by } \pi h \text{ to isolate } r^2.$$

> **TIP** The formula $V = \frac{1}{3}\pi r^2 h$ gives the volume of a right circular cone with radius r. Therefore, $r > 0$.

$$\frac{3V}{\pi h} = r^2$$

$$r = \sqrt{\frac{3V}{\pi h}} \text{ or } r = \frac{\sqrt{3V\pi h}}{\pi h} \qquad \text{Apply the square root property. Since } r > 0, \text{ we take the positive square root only.}$$

Skill Practice 9   Solve for v. $E = \dfrac{1}{2}mv^2$ $(v > 0)$

EXAMPLE 10   Solving an Equation for a Specified Variable

Solve for t. $mt^2 + nt = z$

Solution:

This equation is quadratic in the variable t. The strategy is to write the polynomial in descending order by powers of t. Then since there are two t terms with different exponents, we cannot isolate t directly. Instead we apply the quadratic formula.

$$mt^2 + nt = z$$
$$mt^2 + nt - z = 0 \qquad \text{Write the polynomial in descending order by } t.$$

> **Avoiding Mistakes**
>
> In the equation $mt^2 + nt - z = 0$, t is the variable, and m, n, and z are the coefficients.

$$a = m, b = n, c = -z \qquad \text{Identify the coefficients of each term.}$$

$$t = \frac{-(n) \pm \sqrt{(n)^2 - 4(m)(-z)}}{2m} \qquad \text{Apply the quadratic formula.}$$

$$t = \frac{-n \pm \sqrt{n^2 + 4mz}}{2m} \qquad \text{Simplify.}$$

Skill Practice 10   Solve for p. $cp^2 - dp = k$

Answers

9. $v = \sqrt{\dfrac{2E}{m}}$ or $v = \dfrac{\sqrt{2Em}}{m}$

10. $p = \dfrac{d \pm \sqrt{d^2 + 4ck}}{2c}$

SECTION 1.4   Practice Exercises

Review Exercises

For Exercises 1–4, factor completely.

1. $5t^2 + 7t - 6$

2. $4y^2 + y - 5$

3. $x^2 + 14x + 49$

4. $z^2 - 16z + 64$

For Exercises 5–6, simplify.

5. $\dfrac{8 + \sqrt{-44}}{4}$

6. $\dfrac{9 - \sqrt{-27}}{6}$

Concept Connections

7. A _____ equation is a second-degree equation of the form $ax^2 + bx + c = 0$ where $a \neq 0$.

8. A _____ equation is a first-degree equation of the form $ax + b = 0$ where $a \neq 0$.

9. The zero product property indicates that if $ab = 0$, then _____ = 0 or _____ = 0.

10. The zero product property indicates that if $(5x + 1)(x - 4) = 0$, then _____ = 0 or _____ = 0.

11. The square root property indicates that if $x^2 = k$, then $x =$ _____.

12. The value of n that would make the trinomial $x^2 + 20x + n$ a perfect square trinomial is _____.

13. Given $ax^2 + bx + c = 0$ $(a \neq 0)$, write the quadratic formula.

14. For a quadratic equation $ax^2 + bx + c = 0$, the discriminant is given by the expression _____.

Objective 1: Solve Quadratic Equations by Using the Zero Product Property

For Exercises 15–22, solve by applying the zero product property. (See Example 1)

15. $n^2 + 5n = 24$

16. $y^2 = 18 - 7y$

17. $8t(t + 3) = 2t - 5$

18. $6m(m + 4) = m - 15$

19. $40p^2 - 90 = 0$

20. $32n^2 - 162 = 0$

21. $3x^2 = 12x$

22. $z^2 = 25z$

Objective 2: Solve Quadratic Equations by Using the Square Root Property

For Exercises 23–34, solve by using the square root property. (See Example 2)

23. $x^2 = 81$

24. $w^2 = 121$

25. $5y^2 - 35 = 0$

26. $6v^2 - 30 = 0$

27. $4u^2 + 64 = 0$

28. $8p^2 + 72 = 0$

29. $(k + 2)^2 = 28$

30. $(z + 11)^2 = 40$

31. $(w - 5)^2 = 9$

32. $(c - 3)^2 = 49$

33. $\left(t - \dfrac{1}{2}\right)^2 = -\dfrac{17}{4}$

34. $\left(a - \dfrac{1}{3}\right)^2 = -\dfrac{47}{9}$

Objective 3: Complete the Square

For Exercises 35–42, determine the value of n that makes the polynomial a perfect square trinomial. Then factor as the square of a binomial. (See Example 3)

35. $x^2 + 14x + n$

36. $y^2 + 22y + n$

37. $p^2 - 26p + n$

38. $u^2 - 4u + n$

39. $w^2 - 3w + n$

40. $v^2 - 11v + n$

41. $m^2 + \dfrac{2}{9}m + n$

42. $k^2 + \dfrac{2}{5}k + n$

For Exercises 43–52, solve by completing the square and applying the square root property. (See Examples 4–5)

43. $y^2 + 22y - 4 = 0$

44. $x^2 + 14x - 3 = 0$

45. $t^2 - 8t = -24$

46. $p^2 - 24p = -156$

47. $4z^2 + 24z = -160$

48. $2m^2 + 20m = -70$

49. $2x(x - 3) = 4 + x$

50. $5c(c - 2) = 6 + 3c$

51. $-4y^2 - 12y + 5 = 0$

52. $-2x^2 - 14x + 5 = 0$

Objective 4: Solve Quadratic Equations by Using the Quadratic Formula

For Exercises 53–56, determine whether the statement is true or false.

53. The equation $5x^2 + 3x = 0$ cannot be solved by using the quadratic formula.

54. The equation $2x^2 - 18 = 0$ cannot be solved by using the quadratic formula.

55. Given the equation $2x^2 - 18 = 0$, the quadratic formula can be applied by using $a = 2$, $b = 0$, and $c = -18$.

56. Given the equation $5x^2 + 3x = 0$, the quadratic formula can be applied by using $a = 5$, $b = 3$, and $c = 0$.

For Exercises 57–72, solve by using the quadratic formula. (See Examples 6–7)

57. $x^2 - 3x - 7 = 0$

58. $x^2 - 5x - 9 = 0$

59. $y^2 = -4y - 6$

60. $z^2 = -8z - 19$

61. $t(t - 6) = -10$

62. $m(m + 10) = -34$

63. $-7c + 3 = -5c^2$

64. $-5d + 2 = -6d^2$

65. $(6x + 5)(x - 3) = -2x(7x + 5) + x - 12$

66. $(5c + 7)(2c - 3) = -2c(c + 15) - 35$

67. $9x^2 + 49 = 0$

68. $121x^2 + 4 = 0$

69. $\dfrac{1}{2}x^2 - \dfrac{2}{7} = \dfrac{5}{14}x$

70. $\dfrac{1}{3}x^2 - \dfrac{7}{6} = \dfrac{3}{2}x$

71. $0.4y^2 = 2y - 2.5$

72. $0.09n^2 = 0.42n - 0.49$

Mixed Exercises

For Exercises 73–80, determine if the equation is linear, quadratic, or neither. If the equation is linear or quadratic, find the solution set.

73. $2y + 4 = 0$

74. $3z - 9 = 0$

75. $2y^2 + 4y = 0$

76. $3z^2 - 9z = 0$

77. $5x(x + 6) = 5x^2 + 27x + 3$

78. $3x(x - 4) = 3x^2 - 11x + 4$

79. $2x^2(x + 7) = x^2 + 3x + 1$

80. $-x(x^2 - 5) + 4 = x^2 + 5$

For Exercises 81–98, solve the equation by using any method.

81. $(3x - 4)^2 = 0$

82. $(2x + 1)^2 = 0$

83. $m^2 + 4m = -2$

84. $n^2 + 8n = -3$

85. $\dfrac{x^2 - 4x}{6} - \dfrac{5x}{3} = 1$

86. $\dfrac{m^2 + 2m}{7} - \dfrac{9m}{14} = \dfrac{3}{2}$

87. $2(x + 4) + x^2 = x(x + 2) + 8$

88. $3(y - 5) + y^2 = y(y + 3) - 15$

89. $\dfrac{3}{5}x^2 - \dfrac{1}{10}x = \dfrac{1}{2}$

90. $\dfrac{1}{12}x^2 - \dfrac{11}{24}x = -\dfrac{1}{2}$

91. $x^2 - 5x = 5x(x - 1) - 4x^2 + 1$

92. $p^2 - 4p = 4p(p - 1) - 3p^2 + 2$

93. $(2y + 7)(y + 1) = 2y^2 - 11$

94. $(3z - 8)(z + 2) = 3z^2 + 10$

95. $7d^2 + 5 = 0$

96. $11t^2 + 3 = 0$

97. $x^2 - \sqrt{5} = 0$

98. $y^2 - \sqrt{11} = 0$

Objective 5: Use the Discriminant

For Exercises 99–106, (a) evaluate the discriminant and (b) determine the number and type of solutions to each equation. (See Example 8)

99. $3x^2 - 4x + 6 = 0$

100. $5x^2 - 2x + 4 = 0$

101. $-2w^2 + 8w = 3$

102. $-6d^2 + 9d = 2$

103. $3x(x - 4) = x - 4$

104. $2x(x - 2) = x + 3$

105. $-1.4m + 0.1 = -4.9m^2$

106. $3.6n + 0.4 = -8.1n^2$

Objective 6:   Solve an Equation for a Specified Variable

For Exercises 107–120, solve for the indicated variable. (See Examples 9–10)

107. $A = \pi r^2$ for $r > 0$

108. $A = \pi r^2 h$ for $r > 0$

109. $s = \frac{1}{2}gt^2$ for $t > 0$

110. $V = \frac{1}{3}x^2 h$ for $x > 0$

111. $a^2 + b^2 = c^2$ for $a > 0$

112. $a^2 + b^2 + c^2 = d^2$ for $c > 0$

113. $L = c^2 I^2 Rt$ for $I > 0$

114. $I = cN^2 r^2 s$ for $N > 0$

115. $kw^2 - cw = r$ for w

116. $dy^2 + my = p$ for y

117. $s = v_0 t + \frac{1}{2}at^2$ for t

118. $S = 2\pi rh + \pi r^2 h$ for r

119. $LI^2 + RI + \frac{1}{C} = 0$ for I

120. $A = \pi r^2 + \pi rs$ for r

Write About It

121. Explain why the zero product property cannot be applied directly to solve the equation $(2x - 3)(x + 1) = 6$.

122. Given a quadratic equation, what is the discriminant and what information does it provide about the given quadratic equation?

123. Explain how the discriminant can be used to determine if the solutions to a quadratic equation are imaginary numbers.

124. How is the quadratic formula derived?

Expanding Your Skills

For Exercises 125–126, solve for the indicated variable.

125. $x^2 - xy - 2y^2 = 0$ for x

126. $3a^2 + 2ab - b^2 = 0$ for a

For Exercises 127–136, write an equation with integer coefficients and the variable x that has the given solution set.
[*Hint*: Apply the zero product property in reverse. For example, to build an equation whose solution set is $\{2, -\frac{5}{2}\}$ we have $(x - 2)(2x + 5) = 0$, or simply $2x^2 + x - 10 = 0$.]

127. $\{4, -2\}$

128. $\{7, -1\}$

129. $\left\{\frac{2}{3}, \frac{1}{4}\right\}$

130. $\left\{\frac{3}{5}, \frac{1}{7}\right\}$

131. $\{\sqrt{5}, -\sqrt{5}\}$

132. $\{\sqrt{2}, -\sqrt{2}\}$

133. $\{2i, -2i\}$

134. $\{9i, -9i\}$

135. $\{1 \pm 2i\}$

136. $\{2 \pm 9i\}$

The solutions to the equation $ax^2 + bx + c = 0$ $(a \neq 0)$ are $x_1 = \dfrac{-b + \sqrt{b^2 - 4ac}}{2a}$ and $x_2 = \dfrac{-b - \sqrt{b^2 - 4ac}}{2a}$.
For Exercises 137–138, prove the given statements.

137. Prove that $x_1 + x_2 = -\dfrac{b}{a}$.

138. Prove that $x_1 x_2 = \dfrac{c}{a}$.

For Exercises 139–140, a quadratic equation $ax^2 + bx = c = 0$ is given. Show that the solutions x_1 and x_2 meet the conditions that $x_1 + x_2 = -\frac{b}{a}$ and $x_1 x_2 = \frac{c}{a}$.

139. $x^2 + 3x - 10 = 0$;
$x_1 = 2$ and $x_2 = -5$

140. $x^2 - 2x + 5 = 0$;
$x_1 = 1 + 2i$ and $x_2 = 1 - 2i$

Technology Connections

It is important to understand the difference between an exact solution to an equation and an approximate solution. For Exercises 141–142, find the exact solutions and the approximate solutions to 4 decimal places.

141. $9x^2 - 5x - 7 = 0$

142. $11x^2 - 7x - 6 = 0$

For Exercises 143–144, use a calculator to determine if the given value is a solution to the equation. Store the value in the variable x in the calculator. Then evaluate the expressions on both sides of the equation to determine if they are equal for the given value of x.

143. $3x^2 = 7x - 1$; $x = \dfrac{7 + \sqrt{37}}{6}$

144. $3x^2 = 7x - 1$; $x = \dfrac{7 - \sqrt{37}}{6}$

PROBLEM RECOGNITION EXERCISES

Simplifying Expressions Versus Solving Equations

For Exercises 1–8, identify the statement as an expression or as an equation. Then simplify the expression or solve the equation.

1. a. $(2x - 5)(3x + 1)$

   b. $(2x - 5)(3x + 1) = 0$

2. a. $\dfrac{5}{x - 3} - \dfrac{1}{x + 7} - \dfrac{2}{x^2 + 4x - 21}$

   b. $\dfrac{5}{x - 3} - \dfrac{1}{x + 7} = \dfrac{2}{x^2 + 4x - 21}$

3. a. $(2x - 3)^2 = 8$

   b. $(2x - 3)^2 - 8$

4. a. $5 - \{6 + 3[2 - 5(y - 2)] + 1\} = 7$

   b. $5 - \{6 + 3[2 - 5(y - 2)] + 1\}$

5. a. $x^2 - 11x + 28 = 0$

   b. $x^2 - 11x - 28 = 0$

6. a. $3x(x + 9) = 20 - x$

   b. $3(x + 9) = 20 - x$

7. a. $\dfrac{35}{x} + 12 + x = 0$

   b. $\dfrac{35}{x} + 12 + x$

8. a. $\dfrac{x}{x - 2} + \dfrac{2}{3} = \dfrac{2}{x - 2}$

   b. $\dfrac{x}{x - 2} + \dfrac{2}{3} - \dfrac{2}{x - 2}$

SECTION 1.5 Applications of Quadratic Equations

OBJECTIVES

1. Solve Applications Involving Quadratic Equations and Geometry
2. Solve Applications Involving Quadratic Models

1. Solve Applications Involving Quadratic Equations and Geometry

In this section, we solve applications that involve quadratic equations. Examples 1–3 involve applications with geometric figures.

EXAMPLE 1   Solving an Application Involving Volume

A trough at the end of a gutter spout is meant to direct water away from a house. The homeowner makes the trough from a rectangular piece of aluminum that is 20 in. long and 12 in. wide. He makes a fold along the two long sides a distance of x inches from the edge. If he wants the trough to hold 360 in.^{3} of water, how far from the edge should he make the fold?

Solution:

Let x represent the distance between the edge of the sheet and the fold.

Information is given about the volume of the trough. When the fold is made, the trough will be in the shape of a rectangular solid with the ends missing. The volume is given by the product of length, width, and height.

20 in.

x

$12 - 2x$

$V = lwh$	
$360 = (20)(12 - 2x)(x)$	The length is 20 in., the width is $12 - 2x$, and the height is x.
$360 = 240x - 40x^2$	Apply the distributive property.
$40x^2 - 240x + 360 = 0$	Set one side equal to zero.
$40(x^2 - 6x + 9) = 0$	Factor.
$40(x - 3)^2 = 0$	
$40 \neq 0$ or $x - 3 = 0$	Apply the zero product property. Set each factor equal to zero.
$x = 3$	The first equation is a contradiction. The only solution is 3.

The sheet of aluminum should be folded 3 in. from the edges.

> **TIP** In Example 1, we choose to move the terms to the left side of the equation so that the leading coefficient is positive. This often makes the polynomial easier to factor.

Skill Practice 1   A box is to be formed by taking a sheet of cardboard and cutting away four 2 in. by 2 in. squares from each corner. Then the sides are turned up to form a box that holds 56 in.³ If the length of the original piece of cardboard is 3 in. more than the width, find the dimensions of the original sheet of cardboard.

x

$x + 3$

2 in.

2 in.

In Example 2, we investigate an application involving the area of a triangle.

EXAMPLE 2   **Solving an Application Involving Area**

A sail on a sailboat is in the shape of two adjacent triangles (see figure) that share a common base. The height of the upper triangle is 6 ft less than the base. The height of the lower triangle is 4 ft less than the base. If the total sail area is 50 ft², find the base and height of each triangle.

$x - 6$

x

$x - 4$

Answer

1. The sheet of cardboard is 8 in. by 11 in.

Solution:

Let x represent the common base of the triangles.

Then $x - 6$ represents the height of the upper triangle.

The expression $x - 4$ represents the height of the lower triangle.

$\left(\begin{array}{c}\text{Area of upper}\\\text{triangle}\end{array}\right) + \left(\begin{array}{c}\text{Area of lower}\\\text{triangle}\end{array}\right) = \left(\begin{array}{c}\text{Total}\\\text{area}\end{array}\right)$ Recall that the area of a triangle is given by $A = \frac{1}{2}bh$.

$$\frac{1}{2}x(x - 6) + \frac{1}{2}x(x - 4) = 50$$

Substitute x for the base and $x - 6$ and $x - 4$ for the heights of the triangles.

$$2 \cdot \left[\frac{1}{2}x(x - 6) + \frac{1}{2}x(x - 4)\right] = 2 \cdot [50]$$

Multiply both sides by 2 to clear fractions.

$$x(x - 6) + x(x - 4) = 100$$

$$x^2 - 6x + x^2 - 4x = 100 \qquad \text{Apply the distributive property.}$$

$$2x^2 - 10x - 100 = 0 \qquad \text{Set one side equal to zero.}$$

$$2(x^2 - 5x - 50) = 0 \qquad \text{Factor.}$$

$$2(x - 10)(x + 5) = 0$$

$2 \neq 0$ or $x - 10 = 0$ or $x + 5 = 0$ Apply the zero product property.

       $x = 10$ or $x \neq -5$ Since x represents the base of a triangle, x must be positive.

The base is 10 ft.   Interpret the solution in the context of the problem.

The upper triangle height is 10 ft $-$ 6 ft $=$ 4 ft.

The lower triangle height is 10 ft $-$ 4 ft $=$ 6 ft.

Skill Practice 2   A large stunt kite is in the shape of a diamond with a small upper triangle and a larger lower triangle. The total area of the kite is 36 ft^2. The value of x in the figure represents the base of each triangle. The height of the lower triangle is 2 ft less than the base. Find the base and height of the lower triangle.

In Example 3, we use the Pythagorean theorem and a quadratic equation to find the lengths of the sides of a right triangle.

EXAMPLE 3   **Solving an Application Involving the Pythagorean Theorem**

A window is in the shape of a rectangle with an adjacent right triangle above (see figure). The length of one leg of the right triangle is 2 ft less than the length of the hypotenuse. The length of the other leg is 1 ft less than the length of the hypotenuse. Find the lengths of the sides.

Solution:

Let x represent the length of the hypotenuse.

Then $x - 1$ represents the length of the longer leg.

And $x - 2$ represents the length of the shorter leg.

Use the Pythagorean theorem to relate the lengths of the sides.

$$a^2 + b^2 = c^2 \qquad\qquad\text{Pythagorean theorem}$$

$$(x - 1)^2 + (x - 2)^2 = (x)^2 \qquad\text{Substitute } x - 1, x - 2, \text{ and } x \text{ for the lengths of the sides.}$$

$$x^2 - 2x + 1 + x^2 - 4x + 4 = x^2$$

$$x^2 - 6x + 5 = 0 \qquad\text{Set one side of the equation equal to zero.}$$

$$(x - 1)(x - 5) = 0 \qquad\text{Factor.}$$

$$x - 1 = 0 \quad\text{or}\quad x - 5 = 0 \qquad\text{Apply the zero product property.}$$

$$\cancel{x = 1} \quad\text{or}\quad x = 5 \qquad\text{Reject } x = 1 \text{ because if } x \text{ were 1, the lengths of the legs would be 0 ft and } -1 \text{ ft, which is impossible.}$$

The hypotenuse is 5 ft.

The length of the longer leg is given by $x - 1$: 5 ft − 1 ft = 4 ft.

The length of the shorter leg is given by $x - 2$: 5 ft − 2 ft = 3 ft.

> **Avoiding Mistakes**
>
> In Example 3, be sure to square the binomials correctly. Recall that $(a - b)^2 = a^2 - 2ab + b^2$.
>
> Therefore,
> $(x - 1)^2 = x^2 - 2x + 1$
> $(x - 2)^2 = x^2 - 4x + 4$

Skill Practice 3   A sail on a sailboat is in the shape of two adjacent right triangles. The hypotenuse of the lower triangle is 10 ft, and one leg is 2 ft shorter than the other leg. Find the lengths of the legs of the lower triangle.

2. Solve Applications Involving Quadratic Models

In Example 4, we study a quadratic model that involves the average annual expenditure for cellular service according to the age of the individual using the service.

EXAMPLE 4   **Analyzing Expenditure for Cellular Service**

The model $E = -0.475a^2 + 37.0a - 44.6$ represents the annual expenditure for cellular service E (in $) for individuals a years old. (*Source*: U.S. Bureau of Labor Statistics, www.bls.gov) Use the formula to determine the age(s) at which the average annual expenditure for cellular service is $600. Round the solutions to the nearest year.

Solution:

$$E = -0.475a^2 + 37.0a - 44.6$$

$$600 = -0.475a^2 + 37.0a - 44.6 \qquad\text{Substitute 600 for } E.$$

$$0.475a^2 - 37.0a + 644.6 = 0$$

$$a = \frac{-(-37.0) \pm \sqrt{(-37.0)^2 - 4(0.475)(644.6)}}{2(0.475)} \qquad\begin{array}{l}\text{Apply the quadratic}\\\text{formula.}\end{array}$$

$$a = \frac{37.0 \pm \sqrt{144.26}}{0.95}$$

$$a = \frac{37.0 + \sqrt{144.26}}{0.95} \approx 52$$

$$a = \frac{37.0 - \sqrt{144.26}}{0.95} \approx 26$$

Answer

3. The longer leg is 8 ft and the shorter leg is 6 ft.

For individuals of age 26 and age 52, the average annual expenditure for cellular service is approximately $600. See Figure 1-2.

Annual Expenditure ($) for Cellular Service by Age Group

$E = -0.475a^2 + 37.0a - 44.6$

Figure 1-2

> **Skill Practice 4** Use the formula from Example 4 to determine the age(s) at which the average annual expenditure for cellular service is $650. Round to the nearest year.

In the study of physical science, a common model used to represent the vertical position s of an object moving vertically under the influence of gravity is given in Table 1-1.

Table 1-1 **Vertical Position for an Object Traveling Upward or Downward Under the Influence of Gravity**

Suppose that an object has an initial vertical position of s_0 and initial velocity v_0 straight upward or downward. Then the vertical position s of the object is given by $$s = -\frac{1}{2}gt^2 + v_0t + s_0, \text{ where}$$	
g	is the acceleration due to gravity • at sea level on Earth, $g = 32$ ft/sec² or $g = 9.8$ m/sec²
t	is the time of travel
v_0	is the initial velocity • positive if the object initially travels upward • negative if the object initially travels downward
s_0	is the initial vertical position
s	is the vertical position of the object at time t

> **TIP** The value of g is chosen to be consistent with the units for position and velocity. In this case, the initial height is given in ft. The initial velocity is given in ft/sec. Therefore, we choose g in ft/sec² rather than m/sec².

For example, suppose that a child tosses a ball straight upward from a height of 1.5 ft, with an initial velocity of 48 ft/sec.

The initial height is $s_0 = 1.5$ ft.

The initial velocity is $v_0 = 48$ ft/sec.

The acceleration due to gravity is $g = 32$ ft/sec².

The vertical position of the ball is given by

$$s = -\frac{1}{2}gt^2 + v_0t + s_0$$

$$s = -\frac{1}{2}(32)t^2 + (48)t + (1.5)$$

$$= -16t^2 + 48t + 1.5$$

Answer

4. For individuals of age 32 and age 46, the average annual expenditure is $650.

EXAMPLE 5   **Analyzing an Object Moving Vertically**

A toy rocket is shot straight upward from a launch pad of 1 m above ground level with an initial velocity of 24 m/sec.

   a. Write a model to express the height of the rocket s (in meters) above ground level.

   b. Find the time(s) at which the rocket is at a height of 20 m. Round to 1 decimal place.

   c. Find the time(s) at which the rocket is at a height of 40 m.

Solution:

a. $s = -\dfrac{1}{2}gt^2 + v_0 t + s_0$ In this example,

     $s_0 = 1$ m

$s = -\dfrac{1}{2}(9.8)t^2 + (24)t + (1)$ $v_0 = 24$ m/sec

                       $g = 9.8$ m/sec^2

$= -4.9t^2 + 24t + 1$

> **TIP** Choose $g = 9.8$ m/sec^2 because the height is given in meters and velocity is given in meters per second.

b. $20 = -4.9t^2 + 24t + 1$ Substitute 20 for s.

    $4.9t^2 - 24t + 19 = 0$ Set one side equal to zero.

$t = \dfrac{-(-24) \pm \sqrt{(-24)^2 - 4(4.9)(19)}}{2(4.9)}$ Apply the quadratic formula.

$t = \dfrac{24 \pm \sqrt{203.6}}{9.8}$

$t = \dfrac{24 + \sqrt{203.6}}{9.8} \approx 3.9$

$t = \dfrac{24 - \sqrt{203.6}}{9.8} \approx 1.0$

The rocket will be at a height of 20 m at 1 sec and 3.9 sec after launch.

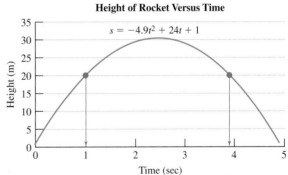

Height of Rocket Versus Time

$s = -4.9t^2 + 24t + 1$

c. $40 = -4.9t^2 + 24t + 1$ Substitute 40 for s.

    $4.9t^2 - 24t + 39 = 0$

$t = \dfrac{-(-24) \pm \sqrt{(-24)^2 - 4(4.9)(39)}}{2(4.9)}$ Apply the quadratic formula.

$t = \dfrac{24 \pm \sqrt{-188.4}}{9.8}$ The solutions are imaginary numbers.

There is no real number t for which the height of the rocket will be 40 m. The rocket will not reach a height of 40 m.

> **Skill Practice 5** A fireworks mortar is launched straight upward from a pool deck 2 m off the ground at an initial velocity of 40 m/sec.
>
> **a.** Write a model to express the height of the mortar s (in meters) above ground level.
>
> **b.** Find the time(s) at which the mortar is at a height of 60 m. Round to 1 decimal place.
>
> **c.** Find the time(s) at which the rocket is at a height of 100 m.

Answers

5. a. $s = -4.9t^2 + 40t + 2$
  b. The mortar will be at a height of 60 m at 1.9 sec and 6.3 sec after launch.
  c. The mortar will not reach a height of 100 m.

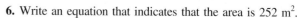

SECTION 1.5 Practice Exercises

Review Exercises

1. Write a formula for the area of a triangle of base b and height h.

2. Write a formula for the area of a circle of radius r.

3. Write a formula for the volume of a rectangular solid of length l, width w, and height h.

4. Write the Pythagorean theorem for a right triangle with the lengths of the legs given by a and b and the length of the hypotenuse given by c.

Concept Connections

For Exercises 5–14, write an equation in terms of x that represents the relationship between the labeled quantities in the given figure. Refer to the formulas given in the inside back cover if necessary.

5. Write an equation that indicates that the area is 629 yd^2.

6. Write an equation that indicates that the area is 252 m^2.

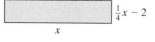

7. Write an equation that indicates that the area is 88π in.^{2}

8. Write an equation that indicates that the area is 212π cm^2.

9. Write an equation that indicates that the area is 50 ft^2.

10. Write an equation that indicates that the area is 220 yd^2.

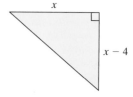

11. Write an equation that indicates that the volume is 640 in.^{3}

12. Write an equation that indicates that the volume is 312 ft^3.

13. Write an equation that relates the lengths of the sides of the given right triangle.

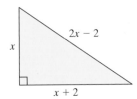

14. Write an equation that relates the lengths of the sides of the given right triangle.

15. If the smaller of two consecutive even integers is given by x, then the next larger consecutive even integer is given by _____.

16. If the larger of two consecutive integers is given by x, then the next smaller consecutive integer is given by _____.

Objective 1: Solve Applications Involving Quadratic Equations and Geometry

17. a. Write an equation representing the fact that the product of two consecutive even integers is 120.

   b. Solve the equation from part (a) to find the two integers.

18. a. Write an equation representing the fact that the product of two consecutive odd integers is 35.

   b. Solve the equation from part (a) to find the two integers.

19. a. Write an equation representing the fact that the sum of the squares of two consecutive integers is 113.

   b. Solve the equation from part (a) to find the two integers.

20. a. Write an equation representing the fact that the sum of the squares of two consecutive integers is 181.

   b. Solve the equation from part (a) to find the two integers.

21. On moving day, Jorge needs to rent a truck. The length of the cargo space is 12 ft, and the height is 1 ft less than the width. The brochure indicates that the truck can hold 504 ft³. What are the dimensions of the cargo space? Assume that the cargo space is in the shape of a rectangular solid. (**See Example 1**)

22. Loreen plans to make several open-topped boxes in which to carry plants. She makes the boxes from rectangular sheets of cardboard from which she cuts out 6-in. squares from each corner. The length of the original piece of cardboard is 12 in. more than the width. If the volume of the box is 1728 in.³, determine the dimensions of the original piece of cardboard.

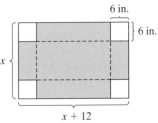

23. A sprinkler rotates 360° to water a circular region. If the total area watered is approximately 2000 yd², determine the radius of the region (the radius is length of the stream of water). Round the answer to the nearest yard.

24. An earthquake could be felt over a 46,000-mi² area. Up to how many miles from the epicenter could the earthquake be felt? Round to the nearest mile.

25. A patio is configured from a rectangle with two right triangles of equal size attached at the two ends. The length of the rectangle is 20 ft. The base of the right triangle is 3 ft less than the height of the triangle. If the total area of the patio is 348 ft², determine the base and height of the triangular portions. (**See Example 2**)

26. The front face of a house is in the shape of a rectangle with a Queen post roof truss above. The length of the rectangular region is 3 times the height of the truss. The height of the rectangle is 2 ft more than the height of the truss. If the total area of the front face of the house is 336 ft², determine the length and width of the rectangular region.

27. A baseball diamond is in the shape of a square with 90-ft sides. How far is it from home plate to second base? Give the exact value and give an approximation to the nearest tenth of a foot.

Second base

90 ft

90 ft

Home plate

28. The figure shown is a cube with 6-in. sides. Find the exact length of the diagonal through the interior of the cube d by following these steps.

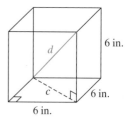

d

6 in.

c

6 in.

6 in.

a. Apply the Pythagorean theorem using the sides on the base of the cube to find the length of diagonal c.

b. Apply the Pythagorean theorem using c and the height of the cube as the legs of the triangle through the interior of the cube.

29. The sail on a sailboat is in the shape of two adjacent right triangles. In the lower triangle, the shorter leg is 2 ft less than the longer leg. The hypotenuse is 2 ft more than the longer leg. **(See Example 3)**

4 ft

$x + 2$

$x - 2$

x

a. Find the lengths of the sides of the lower triangle.

b. Find the total sail area.

30. A portion of a roof truss is given in the figure. The triangle on the left is configured such that the longer leg is 7 ft longer than the shorter leg, and the hypotenuse is 1 ft more than twice the shorter leg.

$2x + 1$

$x + 7$

9 ft

x

a. Find the lengths of the sides of the triangle on the left.

b. Find the lengths of the sides of the triangle on the right.

31. The display area on a cell phone has a 3.5-in. diagonal.

a. If the aspect ratio of length to width is 1.5 to 1, determine the length and width of the display area. Round the values to the nearest hundredth of an inch.

b. If the phone has 326 pixels per inch, approximate the dimensions in pixels.

32. The display area on a computer has a 15-in. diagonal. If the aspect ratio of length to width is 1.6 to 1, determine the length and width of the display area. Round the values to the nearest hundredth of an inch.

Objective 2: Solve Applications Involving Quadratic Models

33. In a round-robin tennis tournament, each player plays every other player exactly one time. The number of matches N is given by $N = \frac{1}{2}n(n - 1)$, where n is the number of players in the tournament. If 28 matches were played, how many players were in the tournament?

34. The sum of the first n natural numbers, $S = 1 + 2 + 3 + \cdots + n$, is given by $S = \frac{1}{2}n(n + 1)$. If the sum of the first n natural numbers is 171, determine the value of n.

35. The population P of a culture of *Pseudomonas aeruginosa* bacteria is given by $P = -1718t^2 + 82{,}000t + 10{,}000$, where t is the time in hours since the culture was started. Determine the time(s) at which the population was 600,000. Round to the nearest hour. **(See Example 4)**

36. The gas mileage for a certain vehicle can be approximated by $m = -0.04x^2 + 3.6x - 49$, where x is the speed of the vehicle in mph. Determine the speed(s) at which the car gets 30 mpg. Round to the nearest mph.

37. The distance d (in ft) required to stop a car that was traveling at speed v (in mph) before the brakes were applied depends on the amount of friction between the tires and the road and the driver's reaction time. After an accident, a legal team hired an engineering firm to collect data for the stretch of road where the accident occurred. Based on the data, the stopping distance is given by $d = 0.05v^2 + 2.2v$.

a. Determine the distance required to stop a car going 50 mph.

b. Up to what speed (to the nearest mph) could a motorist be traveling and still have adequate stopping distance to avoid hitting a deer 330 ft away?

38. Leptin is a hormone that has a central role in fat metabolism. One study published in the *New England Journal of Medicine* measured serum leptin concentrations versus the percentage of body fat for 275 individuals. The concentration of leptin c (in ng/mL) is approximated by $c = 219x^2 - 26.7x + 1.64$, where x is percentage of body fat.

a. Determine the concentration of leptin in an individual with 22% body fat ($x = 0.22$). Round to 1 decimal place.

b. If an individual has 3 ng/mL of leptin, determine the percentage of body fat. Round to the nearest whole percent.

(*Source*: "Serum Immunoreactive-Leptin Concentrations in Normal-Weight and Obese Humans," *New England Journal of Medicine*, Feb., 1996)

For Exercises 39–42, use the model $s = -\frac{1}{2}gt^2 + v_0 t + s_0$. (See Example 5)

39. NBA basketball legend Michael Jordan had a 48-in. vertical leap. Suppose that Michael jumped from ground level with an initial velocity of 16 ft/sec.

a. Write a model to express Michael's height (in ft) above ground level t seconds after leaving the ground.

b. Use the model from part (a) to determine how long it would take Michael to reach his maximum height of 48 in. (4 ft).

40. At the time of this printing, the highest vertical leap on record is 60 in., held by Kadour Ziani. For this record-setting jump, Kadour left the ground with an initial velocity of $8\sqrt{5}$ ft/sec.

a. Write a model to express Kadour's height (in ft) above ground level t seconds after leaving the ground.

b. Use the model from part (a) to determine how long it would take Kadour to reach his maximum height of 60 in. (5 ft). Round to the nearest hundredth of a second.

41. A bad punter on a football team kicks a football approximately straight upward with an initial velocity of 75 ft/sec.

a. If the ball leaves his foot from a height of 4 ft, write an equation for the vertical height s (in ft) of the ball t seconds after being kicked.

b. Find the time(s) at which the ball is at a height of 80 ft. Round to 1 decimal place.

42. In a classic *Seinfeld* episode, Jerry tosses a loaf of bread (a marble rye) straight upward to his friend George who is leaning out of a third-story window.

a. If the loaf of bread leaves Jerry's hand at a height of 1 m with an initial velocity of 18 m/sec, write an equation for the vertical position of the bread s (in meters) t seconds after release.

b. How long will it take the bread to reach George if he catches the bread on the way up at a height of 16 m? Round to the nearest tenth of a second.

Expanding Your Skills

43. A **golden rectangle** is a rectangle in which the ratio of its length to its width is equal to the ratio of the sum of its length and width to its length: $\frac{L}{W} = \frac{L+W}{L}$ (values of L and W that meet this condition are said to be in the **golden ratio**).

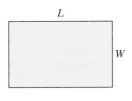

a. Suppose that a golden rectangle has a width of 1 unit. Solve the equation to find the exact value for the length. Then give a decimal approximation to 2 decimal places.

b. To create a golden rectangle with a width of 9 ft, what should be the length? Round to 1 decimal place.

44. An artist has been commissioned to make a stained glass window in the shape of a regular octagon. The octagon must fit inside an 18-in. square space. Determine the length of each side of the octagon. Round to the nearest hundredth of an inch.

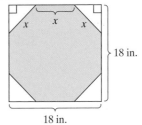

45. A farmer has 160 yd of fencing material and wants to enclose three rectangular pens. Suppose that x represents the length of each pen and y represents the width as shown in the figure.

a. Assuming that the farmer uses all 160 yd of fencing, write an expression for y in terms of x.

b. Write an expression in terms of x for the area of one individual pen.

c. If the farmer wants to design the structure so that each pen encloses 250 yd², determine the dimensions of each pen.

46. At noon, a ship leaves a harbor and sails south at 10 knots. Two hours later, a second ship leaves the harbor and sails east at 15 knots. When will the ships be 100 nautical miles apart? Round to the nearest minute.

SECTION 1.6   More Equations and Applications

1. Solve Polynomial Equations

In this section, we expand our repertoire of equations that we can recognize and solve. First, we use the zero product property to solve polynomial equations. The goal is to set one side of the equation equal to zero and factor the other side into linear or quadratic factors.

EXAMPLE 1   Solving a Polynomial Equation

Solve the equation. $4x^3 + 12x^2 - 9x - 27 = 0$

Solution:

$$4x^3 + 12x^2 - 9x - 27 = 0$$ This is a polynomial equation with one side already equal to zero.

$$4x^2(x + 3) - 9(x + 3) = 0$$ Factor by grouping.

$$(x + 3)(4x^2 - 9) = 0$$

$$(x + 3)(2x - 3)(2x + 3) = 0$$

$$x + 3 = 0 \quad \text{or} \quad 2x - 3 = 0 \quad \text{or} \quad 2x + 3 = 0$$ Apply the zero product property. Set each factor equal to zero.

$$x = -3 \quad \text{or} \quad x = \frac{3}{2} \quad \text{or} \quad x = -\frac{3}{2}$$

The solution set is $\left\{-3, \dfrac{3}{2}, -\dfrac{3}{2}\right\}$.   The solutions all check in the original equation.

Skill Practice 1   Solve the equation. $25y^3 + 100y^2 - y - 4 = 0$

EXAMPLE 2   Solving a Polynomial Equation

Solve the equation. $2x^5 = 16x^2$

Solution:

$$2x^5 = 16x^2$$

$$2x^5 - 16x^2 = 0$$ Set one side equal to zero.

$$2x^2(x^3 - 8) = 0$$ Factor out the GCF.

$$2x^2(x - 2)(x^2 + 2x + 4) = 0$$ Factor as a difference of cubes.

$$2x^2 = 0 \quad \text{or} \quad x - 2 = 0 \quad \text{or} \quad x^2 + 2x + 4 = 0$$ The third equation is a quadratic equation and the expression on the left is not factorable over the rational numbers. Use the quadratic formula.

$$x = 0 \quad \text{or} \quad x = 2 \quad \text{or}$$

$$x = \frac{-(2) \pm \sqrt{(2)^2 - 4(1)(4)}}{2(1)}$$

$$= \frac{-2 \pm \sqrt{-12}}{2}$$

$$= \frac{-2 \pm 2i\sqrt{3}}{2}$$ Simplify the radical expression. $\sqrt{-12} = i\sqrt{2^2 \cdot 3} = 2i\sqrt{3}$

$$= -1 \pm i\sqrt{3}$$ The solutions all check in the original equation.

The solution set is $\{0, 2, -1 \pm i\sqrt{3}\}$.

Answer

1. $\left\{-4, \dfrac{1}{5}, -\dfrac{1}{5}\right\}$

Skill Practice 2 Solve the equation. $w^4 = 27w$

---

2. Solve Rational Equations

In Section 1.1, we solved rational equations by multiplying both sides of the equation by the LCD to clear fractions. We review this process in Example 3.

EXAMPLE 3 **Solving a Rational Equation**

Solve. $\dfrac{2x}{x-4} - \dfrac{3}{x+2} = \dfrac{x^2+14}{x^2-2x-8}$

Solution:

$\dfrac{2x}{x-4} - \dfrac{3}{x+2} = \dfrac{x^2+14}{x^2-2x-8}$

$\dfrac{2x}{x-4} - \dfrac{3}{x+2} = \dfrac{x^2+14}{(x-4)(x+2)}$ Factor the denominators.

The variable x has the restrictions that $x \neq 4$ and $x \neq -2$.

$(x-4)(x+2)\left(\dfrac{2x}{x-4} - \dfrac{3}{x+2}\right) = (x-4)(x+2)\left[\dfrac{x^2+14}{(x-4)(x+2)}\right]$ Multiply both sides by the LCD to clear fractions.

$2x(x+2) - 3(x-4) = x^2 + 14$ The resulting equation is quadratic.

$2x^2 + 4x - 3x + 12 = x^2 + 14$

$x^2 + x - 2 = 0$

$(x+2)(x-1) = 0$ Apply the zero product property.

$x = -2$ or $x = 1$ The value −2 is not a solution because it is a restricted value. It does not check.

Check: $x = -2$

$\dfrac{2(-2)}{(-2)-4} - \underbrace{\dfrac{3}{(-2)+2}}_{\text{undefined}} \overset{?}{=} \underbrace{\dfrac{(-2)^2+14}{(-2)^2-2(-2)-8}}_{\text{undefined}}$

Check: $x = 1$

$\dfrac{2(1)}{(1)-4} - \dfrac{3}{(1)+2} \overset{?}{=} \dfrac{(1)^2+14}{(1)^2-2(1)-8}$

$\dfrac{2}{-3} - 1 \overset{?}{=} \dfrac{15}{-9}$

$-\dfrac{5}{3} \overset{?}{=} -\dfrac{5}{3}$ ✓ true

The solution set is $\{1\}$. The value -2 does not check.

Skill Practice 3 Solve. $\dfrac{3x}{x-5} = \dfrac{2}{x+1} + \dfrac{2x^2+40}{x^2-4x-5}$

In Example 4, we solve a uniform motion application that can be modeled by a rational equation.

Answers

2. $\left\{0, 3, \dfrac{-3 \pm 3i\sqrt{3}}{2}\right\}$

3. $\{-6\}$; The value 5 does not check.

EXAMPLE 4   Solving an Application Involving Uniform Motion

Trent takes his boat 6 mi downstream with a 1.5-mph current. The return trip against the current takes 1 hr longer. Find the speed of the boat in still water (in the absence of current).

Solution:

Let b represent the speed of the boat in still water.

Assign a variable to the unknown quantity.

	Distance (mi)	Rate (mph)	Time
With current	6	$b + 1.5$	$\dfrac{6}{b + 1.5}$
Against current	6	$b - 1.5$	$\dfrac{6}{b - 1.5}$

Organize the given information in a figure or chart.

$$\left(\begin{array}{c}\text{Time of trip}\\\text{against current}\end{array}\right) - \left(\begin{array}{c}\text{Time of trip}\\\text{with current}\end{array}\right) = 1 \longleftarrow$$

The return trip against the current takes longer. The difference in time between the return trip and the original trip is 1 hr.

$$\frac{6}{b - 1.5} - \frac{6}{b + 1.5} = 1$$

The restrictions on b are $b \neq 1.5$ and $b \neq -1.5$.

$$(b - 1.5)(b + 1.5) \cdot \left(\frac{6}{b - 1.5} - \frac{6}{b + 1.5}\right) = (b - 1.5)(b + 1.5) \cdot 1$$

$$6(b + 1.5) - 6(b - 1.5) = (b - 1.5)(b + 1.5)$$

Apply the distributive property.

$$6b + 9 - 6b + 9 = b^2 - 2.25$$

$$20.25 = b^2$$

$$b = \pm\sqrt{20.25}$$

Apply the square root property.

$$b = 4.5$$

Reject the negative solution because b represents the speed of the boat.

The speed of the boat in still water is 4.5 mph.

Skill Practice 4   A fishing boat can travel 60 km with a 2.5-km/hr current in 2 hr less time than it can travel 60 km against the current. Determine the speed of the fishing boat in still water.

3. Solve Radical Equations and Equations with Rational Exponents

An equation with one or more radicals containing a variable (such as $\sqrt[3]{x} = 5$) is called a **radical equation.** We can eliminate the radical by raising both sides of the equation to a power equal to the index of the radical.

$$\sqrt[3]{x} = 5$$
$$\left(\sqrt[3]{x}\right)^3 = (5)^3$$
$$x = 125$$

The index is 3. Therefore, raise both sides to the third power.

By raising each side of a radical equation to a power equal to the index, a new equation is produced. However, some (or all) of the solutions to the new equation may *not* be solutions to the original equation. These are called **extraneous solutions.** For this reason, it is necessary to check all potential solutions in the original equation. For example, consider the equation $\sqrt{x} = -10$. By inspection, this equation

Answer

4. The boat travels 12.5 km/hr in still water.

has no solution because the principal square root of x must be nonnegative. However, if we square both sides of the equation, it appears as though a solution exists:

Square both sides.

$$\sqrt{x} = -10$$
$$\left(\sqrt{x}\right)^2 = (-10)^2$$
$$x = 100$$

Solution set: { }

The value 100 does not check in the original equation. Therefore, 100 is an extraneous solution.

Solving a Radical Equation

Step 1 Isolate the radical. If an equation has more than one radical, choose one of the radicals to isolate.

Step 2 Raise each side of the equation to a power equal to the index of the radical.

Step 3 Solve the resulting equation. If the equation still has a radical, repeat steps 1 and 2.

***Step 4** Check the potential solutions in the original equation.

*In solving radical equations, extraneous solutions potentially arise when both sides of the equation are raised to an even power. Therefore, an equation with only odd-indexed roots will not have extraneous solutions. However, it is still recommended that all potential solutions be checked.

EXAMPLE 5   Solving a Radical Equation

Solve. $\sqrt{x + 10} - 4 = x$

Solution:

$$\sqrt{x + 10} - 4 = x$$

$$\sqrt{x + 10} = x + 4 \qquad \text{Isolate the radical.}$$

$$\left(\sqrt{x + 10}\right)^2 = (x + 4)^2 \qquad \text{The index is 2. Therefore, raise both sides to the second power.}$$

$$x + 10 = x^2 + 8x + 16 \qquad \text{The resulting equation is quadratic.}$$

$$0 = x^2 + 7x + 6 \qquad \text{Set one side equal to zero.}$$

$$0 = (x + 6)(x + 1) \qquad \text{Factor.}$$

$$x = -6 \quad \text{or} \quad x = -1 \qquad \text{Apply the zero product rule.}$$

Avoiding Mistakes

When raising both sides of an equation to a power, be sure to enclose both sides of the equation in parentheses.

Both sides of the equation were raised to an even power. Therefore, it is necessary to check the potential solutions.

Check: $x = -6$	Check: $x = -1$
$\sqrt{x + 10} - 4 = x$	$\sqrt{x + 10} - 4 = x$
$\sqrt{(-6) + 10} - 4 \overset{?}{=} (-6)$	$\sqrt{(-1) + 10} - 4 \overset{?}{=} (-1)$
$\sqrt{4} - 4 \overset{?}{=} -6$	$\sqrt{9} - 4 \overset{?}{=} -1$
$2 - 4 \overset{?}{=} -6$	$3 - 4 \overset{?}{=} -1$
$-2 \overset{?}{=} -6$ false	$-1 \overset{?}{=} -1$ ✓ true

The solution set is $\{-1\}$. The value -6 does not check.

Skill Practice 5   Solve the equation. $\sqrt{t + 7} = t - 5$

In Example 6, we solve the equation $\sqrt{m - 1} - \sqrt{3m + 1} = -2$. The first step is to isolate one of the radicals. However, the presence of the constant term, -2, makes it impossible to isolate both radicals simultaneously. As a result, it is necessary to square both sides of the equation twice.

Answer

5. $\{9\}$; The value 2 does not check.

EXAMPLE 6 Solving an Equation Containing Two Radicals

Solve. $\sqrt{m-1} - \sqrt{3m+1} = -2$

Solution:

$$\sqrt{m-1} - \sqrt{3m+1} = -2$$

$$\sqrt{m-1} = \sqrt{3m+1} - 2 \qquad \text{Isolate one of the radicals.}$$

$$(\sqrt{m-1})^2 = (\sqrt{3m+1} - 2)^2 \qquad \begin{array}{l}\text{The index is 2. Therefore,}\\\text{raise both sides to the}\\\text{second power.}\end{array}$$

$$m - 1 = 3m + 1 - 4\sqrt{3m+1} + 4$$

$$m - 1 = 3m + 5 - 4\sqrt{3m+1}$$

$$4\sqrt{3m+1} = 2m + 6$$

$$2\sqrt{3m+1} = m + 3 \qquad \text{Divide both sides by 2 to simplify.}$$

$$(2\sqrt{3m+1})^2 = (m+3)^2 \qquad \begin{array}{l}\text{The resulting equation has another}\\\text{radical. Isolate the radical, and square}\\\text{both sides again.}\end{array}$$

$$4(3m+1) = m^2 + 6m + 9$$

$$12m + 4 = m^2 + 6m + 9 \qquad \text{The resulting equation is quadratic.}$$

$$0 = m^2 - 6m + 5$$

$$0 = (m-5)(m-1) \qquad \text{Apply the zero product property.}$$

$$m = 5 \quad \text{or} \quad m = 1 \qquad \begin{array}{l}\text{Both sides of the equation were raised to}\\\text{an even power. Check both potential}\\\text{solutions.}\end{array}$$

<u>Check:</u> $m = 5$

$$\sqrt{m-1} - \sqrt{3m+1} = -2$$

$$\sqrt{(5)-1} - \sqrt{3(5)+1} \stackrel{?}{=} -2$$

$$\sqrt{4} - \sqrt{16} \stackrel{?}{=} -2$$

$$2 - 4 \stackrel{?}{=} -2 \ \checkmark \ \text{true}$$

<u>Check:</u> $m = 1$

$$\sqrt{m-1} - \sqrt{3m+1} = -2$$

$$\sqrt{(1)-1} - \sqrt{3(1)+1} \stackrel{?}{=} -2$$

$$\sqrt{0} - \sqrt{4} \stackrel{?}{=} -2$$

$$0 - 2 \stackrel{?}{=} -2 \ \checkmark \ \text{true}$$

Both solutions check. The solution set is $\{1, 5\}$.

Avoiding Mistakes

Exercise caution when squaring the two-term expression on the right.

$$(\sqrt{3m+1} - 2)^2$$
$$= (\sqrt{3m+1})^2$$
$$\quad - 2(\sqrt{3m+1})(2) + (2)^2$$
$$= 3m + 1$$
$$\quad -4\sqrt{3m+1} + 4$$

Skill Practice 6 Solve. $1 + \sqrt{n+4} = \sqrt{3n+1}$

In Example 7, we solve equations containing rational exponents. First recall the definition of $b^{m/n}$.

$$b^{m/n} = (\sqrt[n]{b})^m = \sqrt[n]{b^m} \text{ provided that } \sqrt[n]{b} \text{ is a real number.}$$

This means that an equation such as $\sqrt[3]{x} = 2$ can also be written as $x^{1/3} = 2$. To solve the equation, we cube both sides. Notice that raising the expression $x^{1/3}$ to the third power will result in x^1. This is because the exponents are reciprocals.

$$x^{1/3} = 2 \qquad \text{3 is the reciprocal of } \tfrac{1}{3}.$$
$$(x^{1/3})^3 = (2)^3$$
$$x^1 = 8$$

From this observation and the power rule of exponents, we make the following generalization.

Answer

6. $\{5\}$; The value 0 does not check.

Avoiding Mistakes

The $\pm$ sign is necessary when m is even. This is because all positive numbers have two even-indexed roots. For example:

$$x^2 = 25$$
$$x^{2/1} = 25$$
$$(x^{2/1})^{1/2} = \pm(25)^{1/2}$$
$$x = \pm 5$$

Solving an Equation of the Form $u^{m/n} = k$

Step 1 Isolate the expression with the rational exponent.

Step 2 Raise each side of the equation to a power equal to the reciprocal of the rational exponent. This yields the following solutions.

- If m is odd:

$$u^{m/n} = k$$
$$(u^{m/n})^{n/m} = (k)^{n/m}$$
$$u = k^{n/m}$$

- If m is even:

$$u^{m/n} = k$$
$$(u^{m/n})^{n/m} = \pm(k)^{n/m}$$
$$u = \pm k^{n/m}$$

Step 3 Check the potential solutions in the original equation.

EXAMPLE 7   Solving Equations Containing Rational Exponents

Solve.   **a.** $5(y + 1)^{3/4} = 30$ **b.** $w^{2/3} = \dfrac{1}{64}$

Solution:

a.

$$5(y + 1)^{3/4} = 30$$

$$(y + 1)^{3/4} = 6 \qquad \text{Divide both sides by 5 to isolate } (y + 1)^{3/4}.$$

$$[(y + 1)^{3/4}]^{4/3} = (6)^{4/3} \qquad \text{The original rational exponent is } \tfrac{3}{4}. \text{ The reciprocal is } \tfrac{4}{3}.$$

$$y + 1 = 6^{4/3} \qquad \text{The } \pm \text{ sign is not needed because we are taking an odd-indexed root.}$$

$$y = 6^{4/3} - 1 \qquad \underline{\text{Check:}} \qquad 5[(6^{4/3} - 1) + 1]^{3/4} \stackrel{?}{=} 30$$

The solution checks.
The solution set is $\{6^{4/3} - 1\}$.

$$5(6^{4/3})^{3/4} \stackrel{?}{=} 30$$
$$5(6) \stackrel{?}{=} 30 \ \checkmark \ \text{true}$$

b.

$$w^{2/3} = \dfrac{1}{64} \qquad \text{The expression with the rational exponent is already isolated.}$$

$$(w^{2/3})^{3/2} = \pm\left(\dfrac{1}{64}\right)^{3/2} \qquad \text{The original rational exponent is } \tfrac{2}{3}. \text{ The reciprocal is } \tfrac{3}{2}.$$

$$w = \pm\left(\sqrt{\dfrac{1}{64}}\right)^{3} \qquad \text{The } \pm \text{ sign is necessary because raising the right side to the } \tfrac{3}{2} \text{ power means that we are cubing the expression and taking a square root. There are two real-valued square roots of a positive real number— one positive and one negative.}$$

$$w = \pm\left(\dfrac{1}{8}\right)^{3} = \pm\dfrac{1}{512} \qquad \text{The solutions both check in the original equation.}$$

$$\underline{\text{Check:}}$$

$$\left(\dfrac{1}{512}\right)^{2/3} \stackrel{?}{=} \dfrac{1}{64} \ \checkmark \ \text{true} \qquad \left(-\dfrac{1}{512}\right)^{2/3} \stackrel{?}{=} \dfrac{1}{64} \ \checkmark \ \text{true}$$

The solution set is $\left\{\pm\dfrac{1}{512}\right\}$.

Skill Practice 7   Solve.   **a.** $2(t - 3)^{5/6} = 10$ **b.** $m^{4/5} = \dfrac{1}{16}$

Answers

7. a. $\{5^{6/5} + 3\}$ **b.** $\left\{\pm\dfrac{1}{32}\right\}$

EXAMPLE 8 Solving an Application Involving an Equation with Rational Exponents

The number of hours t needed to slow roast a stuffed turkey that weighs x pounds can be approximated by $t = 0.9x^{3/5}$.

a. Approximately how long would it take to cook a 15-lb turkey? Round to the nearest tenth of an hour.

b. If a turkey needs to cook for 5.4 hr, how many pounds is the turkey?

Solution:

a. $t = 0.9x^{3/5}$

$t = 0.9(15)^{3/5}$ Substitute 15 for x.

≈ 4.6

It would take approximately 4.6 hr.

b. $t = 0.9x^{3/5}$

$5.4 = 0.9x^{3/5}$ Substitute 5.4 for t.

$6 = x^{3/5}$ Isolate the expression $x^{3/5}$ (divide both sides by 0.9).

$(6)^{5/3} = (x^{3/5})^{5/3}$ The original rational exponent is $\frac{3}{5}$. The reciprocal is $\frac{5}{3}$.

$x = 6^{5/3} \approx 19.8$

The turkey weighs approximately 19.8 lb.

Skill Practice 8 Suppose that P dollars in principal is invested in an account that earns compound interest annually and grows to A dollars in t years. The annual interest rate r is given by $r = (\frac{A}{P})^{1/t} - 1$.

a. Determine the annual interest rate if \$2000 grows to \$2375.37 after 5 yr.

b. If \$5000 is invested at 5% determine the amount in the account after 6 yr.

4. Solve Equations in Quadratic Form

In Section 1.4, we learned to solve quadratic equations by applying the quadratic formula or by completing the square and applying the square root property. This is particularly important because many other equations are quadratic in form. That is, with a simple substitution, these equations can be expressed as quadratic equations in a new variable. For example:

TIP For an equation written in quadratic form, notice that the expression for u is taken to be the variable expression from the middle term.

Equation in Quadratic Form		New Equation
$\left(2 + \dfrac{3}{x}\right)^2 - \left(2 + \dfrac{3}{x}\right) - 12 = 0$	$\xrightarrow{\text{Let } u = 2 + \frac{3}{x}}$	$u^2 - u - 12 = 0$
$2w^{2/3} - 3w^{1/3} - 20 = 0$	$\xrightarrow{\text{Let } u = w^{1/3}}$	$2u^2 - 3u - 20 = 0$

The equations on the right are quadratic and easily solved. Then using back substitution, we can solve for the original variable.

Answers

8. a. 3.5%   **b.** \$6700.48

EXAMPLE 9   **Solving an Equation in Quadratic Form**

Solve. $(2x^2 - 3)^2 + 36(2x^2 - 3) + 35 = 0$

Solution:

$(2x^2 - 3)^2 + 36(2x^2 - 3) + 35 = 0$	The equation is in quadratic form.
$u^2 + 36u + 35 = 0$	Let $u = 2x^2 - 3$.
$(u + 35)(u + 1) = 0$	Set one side equal to zero and factor the other side.
$u = -35$ or $u = -1$	Apply the zero product property.
$2x^2 - 3 = -35$ or $2x^2 - 3 = -1$	Back substitute. Replace u by $2x^2 - 3$.
$x^2 = -16$ or $x^2 = 1$	Isolate the square term.
$x = \pm 4i$ or $x = \pm 1$	Apply the square root property.

The solution set is $\{\pm 4i, \pm 1\}$.   The solutions all check in the original equation.

Skill Practice 9   Solve. $(x^2 - 6)^2 + 33(x^2 - 6) + 62 = 0$

EXAMPLE 10   **Solving an Equation in Quadratic Form**

Solve. $2w^{2/3} = 3w^{1/3} + 20$

Solution:

$2w^{2/3} = 3w^{1/3} + 20$	Set one side equal to zero, and write the expression on the left in descending order.
$2w^{2/3} - 3w^{1/3} - 20 = 0$	
$2(w^{1/3})^2 - 3(w^{1/3}) - 20 = 0$	The equation is in quadratic form.
$2u^2 - 3u - 20 = 0$	Let $u = w^{1/3}$.
$(2u + 5)(u - 4) = 0$	Factor.
$u = -\dfrac{5}{2}$ or $u = 4$	Apply the zero product property.
$w^{1/3} = -\dfrac{5}{2}$ or $w^{1/3} = 4$	Back substitute. Replace u by $w^{1/3}$.
$(w^{1/3})^3 = \left(-\dfrac{5}{2}\right)^3$ or $(w^{1/3})^3 = (4)^3$	Cube both sides.
$w = -\dfrac{125}{8}$ or $w = 64$	Both solutions check in the original equation.

The solution set is $\left\{-\dfrac{125}{8}, 64\right\}$.

Skill Practice 10   Solve. $2t^{2/3} = 15 - 7t^{1/3}$

TIP Consider the equation from Example 10:

$2w^{2/3} - 3w^{1/3} - 20 = 0$

As an alternative to using substitution, the expression on the left can be factored directly.

$(2w^{1/3} + 5)(w^{1/3} - 4) = 0$

Applying the zero product property results in the same solutions.

Answers

9. $\{\pm 5i, \pm 2\}$ **10.** $\left\{-125, \dfrac{27}{8}\right\}$

Review Exercises

For Exercises 1–2, factor.

1. $x^3 + 27$

2. $2x^3 + 5x^2 - 8x - 20$

For Exercises 3–4, identify the restrictions on x.

3. $\dfrac{2x + 5}{4x^2 - 25}$

4. $\dfrac{2x - 15}{x^2 - 2x - 35}$

For Exercises 5–6, simplify.

5. $27^{2/3}$

6. $81^{3/4}$

Concept Connections

7. A _____ equation is an equation that has one or more radicals containing a variable.

8. Given an equation of the form $u^{m/n} = k$, raise both sides to the _____ power to isolate u (that is, to obtain u^1 on the left side).

9. The equation $m^{2/3} + 10m^{1/3} + 9 = 0$ is said to be in _____ form, because making the substitution $u = $ _____ results in a new equation that is quadratic.

10. Consider the equation $(4x^2 + 1)^2 + 4(4x^2 + 1) + 4 = 0$. If the substitution $u = $ _____ is made, then the equation becomes $u^2 + 4u + 4 = 0$.

Objective 1: Solve Polynomial Equations

For Exercises 11–18, solve the equation. (See Examples 1–2)

11. $75y^3 + 100y^2 - 3y - 4 = 0$

12. $98t^3 - 49t^2 - 8t + 4 = 0$

13. $2x^4 - 32 = 0$

14. $5m^4 - 5 = 0$

15. $2x^4 = -128x$

16. $10x^5 = -1250x^2$

17. $3n^2(n^2 + 3) = 20 - 2n^2$

18. $2y^2(y^2 - 2) = 18 + y^2$

Objective 2: Solve Rational Equations

For Exercises 19–26, solve the equation. (See Example 3)

19. $\dfrac{3x}{x + 2} - \dfrac{5}{x - 4} = \dfrac{2x^2 - 14x}{x^2 - 2x - 8}$

20. $\dfrac{4c}{c - 5} - \dfrac{1}{c + 1} = \dfrac{3c^2 + 3}{c^2 - 4c - 5}$

21. $\dfrac{m}{2m + 1} + 1 = \dfrac{2}{m - 3}$

22. $\dfrac{n}{n - 3} + 2 = \dfrac{3}{2n - 1}$

23. $2 - \dfrac{3}{y} = \dfrac{5}{y^2}$

24. $7 + \dfrac{20}{z} = \dfrac{3}{z^2}$

25. $\dfrac{18}{m^2 - 3m} + 2 = \dfrac{6}{m - 3}$

26. $\dfrac{48}{m^2 - 4m} + 3 = \dfrac{12}{m - 4}$

27. Jesse takes a 3-day kayak trip and travels 72 km south from Everglades City to a camp area in Everglades National Park. The trip to the camp area with a 2 km/hr current takes 9 hr less time than the return trip against the current. Find the speed that Jesse travels in still water. (**See Example 4**)

28. A plane travels 800 mi from Dallas, Texas, to Atlanta, Georgia, with a prevailing west wind of 40 mph. The return trip against the wind takes $\frac{1}{2}$ hr longer. Find the average speed of the plane in still air.

29. Jean runs 6 mi and then rides 24 mi on her bicycle in a biathlon. She rides 8 mph faster than she runs. If the total time for her to complete the race is 2.25 hr, determine her average speed running and her average speed riding her bicycle.

30. Barbara drives between Miami, Florida, and West Palm Beach, Florida. She drives 50 mi in clear weather and then encounters a thunderstorm for the last 15 mi. She drives 20 mph slower through the thunderstorm than she does in clear weather. If the total time for the trip takes 1.5 hr, determine her average speed in nice weather and her average speed driving in the thunderstorm.

Objective 3: Solve Radical Equations and Equations with Rational Exponents

For Exercises 31–50, solve the equation. (See Examples 5–7)

31. $\sqrt{2x - 4} = 6$

32. $\sqrt{3x + 1} = 11$

33. $\sqrt{m + 18} + 2 = m$

34. $\sqrt{2n + 29} + 3 = n$

35. $-4\sqrt[3]{2x - 5} + 6 = 10$

36. $-3\sqrt[5]{4x - 1} + 2 = 8$

37. $\sqrt[4]{5y - 3} - \sqrt[4]{2y + 1} = 0$

38. $\sqrt[6]{y + 7} - \sqrt[6]{4y + 5} = 0$

39. $\sqrt{8 - p} - \sqrt{p + 5} = 1$

40. $\sqrt{d + 4} - \sqrt{6 + 2d} = -1$

41. $3 - \sqrt{y + 3} = \sqrt{2 - y}$

42. $\sqrt{k - 2} = \sqrt{2k + 3} - 2$

43. a. $m^{3/4} = 5$ b. $m^{2/3} = 5$

44. a. $n^{5/6} = 3$ b. $n^{4/5} = 3$

45. $3(t + 2)^{5/6} = 21$

46. $4(y - 3)^{3/4} = 20$

47. $2p^{4/5} = \dfrac{1}{8}$

48. $5t^{2/3} = \dfrac{1}{5}$

49. $(2v + 7)^{1/3} - (v - 3)^{1/3} = 0$

50. $(5u - 6)^{1/5} - (3u + 1)^{1/5} = 0$

51. The percentage of drug released in the bloodstream t hours after being administered is affected by numerous variables including drug solubility and filler ingredients. For a particular drug and dosage, the percentage of drug released P is given by $P = 48t^{1/5}$ $(0 \le t \le 35)$. For example, the value $P = 50$ represents 50% of the drug released.

    a. Determine the percentage of drug released after 2 hr. Round to the nearest percent.

    b. How many hours is required for 75% of the drug to be released? Round to the nearest tenth of an hour. (**See Example 8**)

Percentage of Drug Released by Time

52. A tomato plant is purchased at a garden supply store. The initial height of the plant is 25.4 in. The height of the plant h (in inches) is approximated by $h = 16(t + 4)^{1/3}$, where t is the time in days after planting.

    a. Determine the height of the plant 14 days after planting. Round to the nearest inch.

    b. How long after the plant is planted will it take for the height to reach 5 ft? Round to the nearest day.

53. If an object is dropped from a height of h meters, the velocity v (in m/sec) at impact is given by $v = \sqrt{2gh}$, where $g = 9.8$ m/sec^2 is the acceleration due to gravity.

    a. Determine the impact velocity for an object dropped from a height of 10 m.

    b. Determine the height required for an object to have an impact velocity of 26.8 m/sec ($\approx$ 60 mph). Round to the nearest tenth of a meter.

54. The yearly depreciation rate for a certain vehicle is modeled by $r = 1 - \left(\frac{V}{C}\right)^{1/n}$, where V is the value of the car after n years, and C is the original cost.

    a. Determine the depreciation rate for a car that originally cost $18,000 and is worth $12,000 after 3 yr. Round to the nearest tenth of a percent.

    b. Determine the original cost of a truck that has a yearly depreciation rate of 15% and is worth $11,000 after 5 yr. Round to the nearest $100.

Objective 4: Solve Equations in Quadratic Form

For Exercises 55–64, make an appropriate substitution and solve the equation. (See Examples 9–10)

55. $(x^2 + 2)^2 + (x^2 + 2) - 42 = 0$

56. $(y^2 - 3)^2 - 9(y^2 - 3) - 52 = 0$

57. $\left(2 + \dfrac{3}{t}\right)^2 - \left(2 + \dfrac{3}{t}\right) = 12$

58. $\left(\dfrac{5}{y} + 3\right)^2 + 6\left(\dfrac{5}{y} + 3\right) = -8$

59. $5c^{2/5} - 11c^{1/5} + 2 = 0$

60. $3d^{2/3} - d^{1/3} - 4 = 0$

61. $x^2(x^2 + 5) = 7$

62. $x^2(x^2 - 2) = x^2 + 13$

63. $30k^{-2} - 23k^{-1} + 2 = 0$

64. $3q^{-2} + 16q^{-1} + 5 = 0$

For Exercises 65–66, solve the equation in two ways.

a. Solve as a radical equation by first isolating the radical.

b. Solve by writing the equation in quadratic form and using an appropriate substitution.

65. $y + 4\sqrt{y} = 21$ **66.** $w - 3\sqrt{w} = 10$

Mixed Exercises

For Exercises 67–78, solve for the indicated variable.

67. $\dfrac{1}{f} = \dfrac{1}{p} + \dfrac{1}{q}$ for p

68. $\dfrac{1}{R} = \dfrac{1}{R_1} + \dfrac{1}{R_2} + \dfrac{1}{R_3}$ for R_3

69. $E = kT^4$ for $T > 0$

70. $V = \dfrac{4}{3}\pi r^3$ for $r > 0$

71. $a = \dfrac{kF}{m}$ for m

72. $V = \dfrac{k}{P}$ for P

73. $16 + \sqrt{x^2 - y^2} = z$ for x

74. $4 + \sqrt{x^2 + y^2} = z$ for y

75. $\dfrac{P_1 V_1}{T_1} = \dfrac{P_2 V_2}{T_2}$ for T_1

76. $\dfrac{t_1}{s_1 v_1} = \dfrac{t_2}{s_2 v_2}$ for v_2

77. $T = 2\pi\sqrt{\dfrac{L}{g}}$ for g

78. $t = \sqrt{\dfrac{2s}{g}}$ for s

Write About It

79. Explain how to determine if an equation is in quadratic form.

80. Explain how the zero product property can be used to solve a polynomial equation.

81. Why must the potential solutions to a radical equation be checked in the original equation?

82. Consider the equation $u^{m/n} = k$, where m is an even integer and k is a positive real number. Explain why the $\pm$ symbol is necessary in the solution set $\{\pm k^{n/m}\}$.

Expanding Your Skills

83. Joan and Henry both work for a mail-order company preparing packages for shipping. It takes Henry approximately 1 hr longer to fill 100 orders than Joan. If they work together, it takes 3 hr to fill 100 orders. Find the amount of time required for each individual to fill 100 orders working alone. Round to the nearest tenth of an hour.

84. Antonio and Jeremy work for a plumbing company that was recently awarded a contract to install the plumbing fixtures in a new office complex. There are 12 bathrooms in the building. It takes Jeremy 4 hr longer than Antonio to complete one bathroom. If they work together it takes 8 hr to complete a bathroom. Find the rate at which each individual can complete a bathroom working alone.

85. Pam is in a canoe on a lake 400 ft from the closest point on a straight shoreline. Her house is 800 ft up the road along the shoreline. She can row 2.5 ft/sec and she can walk 5 ft/sec. If the total time it takes for her to get home is 5 min (300 sec), determine the point along the shoreline at which she landed her canoe.

86. Martha is in a boat in the ocean 48 mi from point A, the closest point along a straight shoreline. She needs to dock the boat at a marina x miles farther up the coast, and then drive along the coast to point B, 96 mi from point A. Her boat travels 20 mph, and she drives 60 mph. If the total trip took 4 hr, determine the distance x along the shoreline.

SECTION 1.7   Linear Inequalities and Compound Inequalities

OBJECTIVES

1. **Solve Linear Inequalities in One Variable**
2. **Determine the Union and Intersection of Sets**
3. **Solve Compound Linear Inequalities**
4. **Solve Applications of Inequalities**

TIP For a review of set-builder notation and interval notation, see Section R.1.

1. Solve Linear Inequalities in One Variable

Emily wants to earn an "A" in her College Algebra course and knows that the average of her tests and assignments must be at least 90. She has five test grades of 96, 84, 80, 98, and 88. She also has a score of 100 for online homework, and this carries the same weight as a test grade. She still needs to take the final exam and the final is weighted as two test grades. To determine the scores on the final exam that would result in an average of 90 or more, Emily would solve the following inequality (See Example 9):

$$\frac{96 + 84 + 80 + 98 + 88 + 100 + 2x}{8} \geq 90, \text{ where } x \text{ is Emily's score on the final.}$$

A linear equation in one variable is an equation that can be written as $ax + b = 0$, where a and b are real numbers and $a \neq 0$. A **linear inequality** is any relationship of the form $ax + b < 0$, $ax + b \leq 0$, $ax + b > 0$, or $ax + b \geq 0$. The solution set to a linear equation consists of a single element that can be represented by a point on the number line. The solution set to a linear inequality contains an infinite number of elements and can be expressed in set-builder notation or in interval notation.

Equation/Inequality	Solution Set	Graph
$x + 4 = 0$	$\{-4\}$	
$x + 4 \geq 0$	$\{x \mid x \geq -4\}$ or $[-4, \infty)$	
$x + 4 < 0$	$\{x \mid x < -4\}$ or $(-\infty, -4)$	

To solve a linear inequality in one variable, we use the following properties of inequality.

Properties of Inequality

Let a, b, and c represent real numbers.

Property	*Statement
Addition and Subtraction Properties of Inequality	1. If $a < b$, then $a + c < b + c$. 2. If $a < b$, then $a - c < b - c$.
Multiplication and Division Properties of Inequality	3. If c is *positive* and $a < b$, then $a \cdot c < b \cdot c$ and $\dfrac{a}{c} < \dfrac{b}{c}$. 4. If c is *negative* and $a < b$, then $a \cdot c > b \cdot c$ and $\dfrac{a}{c} > \dfrac{b}{c}$.

*These properties of inequality are also true for statements expressed with the symbols $\leq$, $>$, and $\geq$.

Property 4 indicates that if both sides of an inequality are multiplied or divided by a negative number, then the direction of the inequality sign must be reversed.

EXAMPLE 1   **Solving a Linear Inequality**

Solve the inequality. Graph the solution set and write the solution set in set-builder notation and in interval notation.

$$-6x + 4 < 34$$

Solution:

$$-6x + 4 < 34$$

$$-6x + 4 - 4 < 34 - 4 \qquad \text{Subtract } 4 \text{ from both sides.}$$

$$-6x < 30$$

$$\frac{-6x}{-6} > \frac{30}{-6} \qquad \text{Divide both sides by } -6. \text{ Reverse the inequality sign.}$$

$$x > -5$$

The solution set is $\{x \mid x > -5\}$.
Interval notation: $(-5, \infty)$

Skill Practice 1   Solve the inequality. Graph the solution set and write the solution set in set-builder notation and in interval notation. $-5t - 6 \geq 24$

TIP   In Example 1, the solution set to the inequality $-6x + 4 < 34$ is $\{x \mid x > -5\}$. This means that all numbers greater than -5 make the inequality a true statement. You can check by taking an arbitrary test point from the interval $(-5, \infty)$. For example, the value $x = -4$ makes the original inequality true.

Test point

Check: $x = -4$

$$-6(-4) + 4 \overset{?}{<} 34$$

$$24 + 4 \overset{?}{<} 34 \checkmark \quad \text{true}$$

EXAMPLE 2   **Solving a Linear Inequality Containing Fractions**

Solve the inequality. Graph the solution set and write the solution set in set-builder notation and in interval notation.

$$\frac{x + 1}{3} - \frac{2x - 4}{6} \leq -\frac{x}{2}$$

Solution:

$$\frac{x + 1}{3} - \frac{2x - 4}{6} \leq -\frac{x}{2}$$

$$6 \cdot \left(\frac{x + 1}{3} - \frac{2x - 4}{6} \right) \leq 6 \cdot \left(-\frac{x}{2} \right) \qquad \text{Multiply both sides by the LCD of } 6 \text{ to clear fractions.}$$

$$2(x + 1) - (2x - 4) \leq -3x$$

$$2x + 2 - 2x + 4 \leq -3x \qquad \text{Apply the distributive property.}$$

$$6 \leq -3x$$

$$\frac{6}{-3} \geq \frac{-3x}{-3} \qquad \text{Divide both sides by } -3. \text{ Since } -3 \text{ is a negative number, reverse the inequality sign.}$$

$$-2 \geq x \quad \text{or} \quad x \leq -2$$

The solution set is $\{x \mid x \leq -2\}$.
Interval notation: $(-\infty, -2]$

Answer

1.

$$\xleftarrow{\hspace{2cm}} \overset{-6}{\rule{0.5cm}{0pt}]} \xrightarrow{\hspace{2cm}}$$

$\{t \mid t \leq -6\}; (-\infty, -6]$

> **Skill Practice 2**   Solve the inequality. Graph the solution set and write the solution set in set-builder notation and in interval notation.
>
> $$\frac{m - 4}{2} - \frac{3m + 4}{10} > -\frac{3m}{5}$$

EXAMPLE 3   **Solving Inequalities with Special Case Solution Sets**

Solve the inequalities.

    a. $3(2x + 1) + 4 \le 6x + 2$ **b.** $9 + 4c > 3(c + 1) + c$

Solution:

    a. $3(2x + 1) + 4 \le 6x + 2$

$6x + 3 + 4 \le 6x + 2$	Apply the distributive property.
$6x + 7 \le 6x + 2$	Combine like terms.
$7 \le 2$ (contradiction)	Subtract $6x$ from both sides. The statement "7 is less than or equal to 2" is false for all real numbers x.

The solution set is { }.

    b. $9 + 4c > 3(c + 1) + c$

$9 + 4c > 3c + 3 + c$	Apply the distributive property.
$9 + 4c > 4c + 3$	Combine like terms.
$9 > 3$ (true for all real numbers)	Subtract $4c$ from both sides. The statement "9 is greater than 3" is true for all real numbers c.

The solution set is $\mathbb{R}$.
Interval notation: $(-\infty, \infty)$

> **Skill Practice 3**   Solve the inequalities.
>
>   **a.** $9(d + 4) < 6(d + 4) + 3d$ **b.** $-4 - 2(x + 1) \ge -2x - 10$

2. Determine the Union and Intersection of Sets

Two or more sets can be combined by the operations of union and intersection.

Union and Intersection of Sets

The **union** of sets A and B, denoted $A \cup B$, is the set of elements that belong to set A or to set B or to both sets A and B. See Figure 1-3.	The **intersection** of sets A and B, denoted $A \cap B$, is the set of elements common to both set A and set B. See Figure 1-4.
	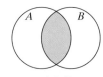
$A \cup B$ A union B The elements in A or B or both	$A \cap B$ A intersection B The elements common to A and B
Figure 1-3	**Figure 1-4**

In Examples 4 and 5, we practice finding the union and intersections of sets.

Answers

2.

$\xleftarrow{\hspace{3cm}} \overset{(}{\underset{3}{}} \xrightarrow{\hspace{2cm}}$

$\{m \,|\, m > 3\}; (3, \infty)$

3. a. { }   **b.** $\mathbb{R}; (-\infty, \infty)$

EXAMPLE 4   **Finding the Union and Intersection of Sets**

Find the union or intersection of sets as indicated, given:

$$A = \{-5, -3, -1, 1\} \qquad B = \{-5, 0, 5\} \qquad C = \{-4, -2, 0, 2, 4\}$$

a. $A \cap B$ **b.** $A \cup B$ **c.** $A \cap C$

Solution:

a. $A \cap B = \{-5\}$ The only element common to both A and B is -5.
                                     $A = \{-5, -3, -1, 1\}, B = \{-5, 0, 5\}$

b. $A \cup B = \{-5, -3, -1, 0, 1, 5\}$ The union of A and B consists of all elements
                                              from A along with all elements from B.

c. $A \cap C = \{\ \}$ Sets A and C have no common elements.

Skill Practice 4   From the sets A, B, and C defined in Example 4, find
   a. $B \cap C$ **b.** $B \cup C$ **c.** $A \cup C$

EXAMPLE 5   **Finding the Union and Intersection of Sets**

Find the union or intersection of sets as indicated, given:

$$D = \{x \mid x < 4\} \qquad E = \{x \mid x \geq -2\} \qquad F = \{x \mid x \leq -3\}$$

a. $D \cap E$ **b.** $D \cup E$ **c.** $D \cup F$ **d.** $E \cap F$

Solution:

a. The intersection of sets
   D and E is the interval
   of overlap.
   $D \cap E = \{x \mid -2 \leq x < 4\}$
   Interval notation: $[-2, 4)$

b. The union of set D and
   set E includes all the
   elements from both sets.
   This is all real numbers.
   $D \cup E = \mathbb{R}$
   Interval notation: $(-\infty, \infty)$

c. The union of set D
   and F includes all the
   elements of D along with
   the elements of F. Since set F
   is contained within set D,
   the union is set D itself.
   $D \cup F = \{x \mid x < 4\}$
   Interval notation: $(-\infty, 4)$

d. There are no elements
   common to both set E
   and set F. The intervals
   do not overlap.
   $E \cap F = \{\ \}$

> **Skill Practice 5**   Given $X = \{x \mid x \geq -1\}$, $Y = \{x \mid x < 2\}$, and $Z = \{x \mid x < -4\}$, find the union or intersection of sets as indicated.
>
> **a.** $X \cap Y$ **b.** $X \cup Y$ **c.** $Y \cap Z$ **d.** $X \cap Z$

3. Solve Compound Linear Inequalities

In Examples 6–8, we solve **compound inequalities.** These are statements with two or more inequalities joined by the word "and" or the word "or." For example, suppose that x represents the glucose level measured from a fasting blood sugar test.

- The normal glucose range is given by $x \geq 70$ mg/dL and $x \leq 100$ mg/dL
- An abnormal glucose level is given by $x < 70$ mg/dL or $x > 100$ mg/dL

To find the solution sets for compound inequalities follow these guidelines.

Solving a Compound Inequality

Step 1 To solve a compound inequality, first solve the individual inequalities.

Step 2 • If two inequalities are joined by the word "and," the solutions are the values of the variable that simultaneously satisfy each inequality. That is, we take the *intersection* of the individual solution sets.

 • If two inequalities are joined by the word "or," the solutions are the values of the variable that satisfy either inequality. Therefore, we take the *union* of the individual solution sets.

EXAMPLE 6   Solving a Compound Inequality "Or"

Solve. $x - 2 \leq 5$ or $\dfrac{1}{2}x > 6$

Solution:

$x - 2 \leq 5$ or $\dfrac{1}{2}x > 6$ First solve the individual inequalities. Then take the *union* of the individual solution sets.

$x \leq 7$ or $x > 12$

The solution set is $\{x \mid x \leq 7 \text{ or } x > 12\}$.

Interval notation: $(-\infty, 7] \cup (12, \infty)$

> **Skill Practice 6**   Solve. $\dfrac{1}{4}y < -1$ or $3 + y \geq 5$

In Example 7, we solve a compound inequality in which the individual inequalities are joined by the word "and." In this case, we take the intersection of the individual solution sets.

EXAMPLE 7   Solving a Compound Inequality "And"

Solve. $-\dfrac{1}{4}t < 2$ and $0.52t \geq 1.3$

Solution:

$-\dfrac{1}{4}t < 2$ and $0.52t \geq 1.3$ | First solve the individual inequalities. Multiply both sides of the first inequality by -4 (reverse the inequality sign). Divide the second inequality by 0.52.

$t > -8$ and $t \geq 2.5$ | Take the *intersection* of the individual solution sets. The intervals overlap for values of t greater than or equal to 2.5.

The solution set is
$\{t \mid t \geq 2.5\}$.

Interval notation: $[2.5, \infty)$

Skill Practice 7   Solve. $0.36w \leq 0.54$ and $-\dfrac{1}{2}w > 3$

Sometimes a compound inequality joined by the word "and" is written as a three-part inequality. For example:

$5 < -2x + 7$ and $-2x + 7 \leq 11$ | In this example, two simultaneous conditions are imposed on the quantity $-2x + 7$.

$5 < -2x + 7 \leq 11$

To solve a three-part inequality, the goal is to isolate x in the middle region. This is demonstrated in Example 8.

EXAMPLE 8   Solving a Three-Part Compound Inequality

Solve. $5 < -2x + 7 \leq 11$

Solution:

$5 < -2x + 7 \leq 11$

$5 - 7 < -2x + 7 - 7 \leq 11 - 7$ | Subtract 7 from all three parts of the inequality.

$-2 < -2x \leq 4$

$\dfrac{-2}{-2} > \dfrac{-2x}{-2} \geq \dfrac{4}{-2}$ | Divide all three parts by -2.

$1 > x \geq -2$ or equivalently $-2 \leq x < 1$

The solution set is $\{x \mid -2 \leq x < 1\}$.
Interval notation: $[-2, 1)$

Skill Practice 8   Solve. $-16 \leq -3y - 4 < 2$

4. Solve Applications of Inequalities

In Example 9, we use a linear inequality to solve an application.

EXAMPLE 9   **Using a Linear Inequality in an Application of Grades**

Emily has test scores of 96, 84, 80, 98, and 88. Her score for online homework is 100 and is weighted as one test grade. Emily still needs to take the final exam, which counts as two test grades. What score does she need on the final exam to have an average of at least 90? (This is the minimum average to earn an "A" in the class.)

Solution:

Let x represent the grade needed on the final exam.

$$\left(\begin{array}{c}\text{Average of} \\ \text{all scores}\end{array}\right) \geq 90 \qquad \text{To earn an "A," Emily's average must be at least 90.}$$

$$\frac{96 + 84 + 80 + 98 + 88 + 100 + 2x}{8} \geq 90 \qquad \text{Take the sum of all grades. Divide by a total of eight grades.}$$

$$\frac{546 + 2x}{8} \geq 90$$

$$8 \cdot \left(\frac{546 + 2x}{8}\right) \geq 8 \cdot (90) \qquad \text{Multiply by 8 to clear fractions.}$$

$$546 + 2x \geq 720$$

$$2x \geq 174 \qquad \text{Subtract 546 from both sides.}$$

$$x \geq 87 \qquad \text{Divide by 2.}$$

Emily must earn a score of at least 87 to earn an "A" in the class.

Skill Practice 9   For a recent year, the monthly snowfall (in inches) for Chicago, Illinois, for November, December, January, and February was 2, 8.4, 11.2, and 7.9, respectively. How much snow would be necessary in March for Chicago to exceed its monthly average snowfall of 7.28 in. for these five months?

Answer

9. Chicago would need more than 6.9 in. of snow in March.

SECTION 1.7   Practice Exercises

Review Exercises

For Exercises 1–4, write the interval notation for the given sets. Refer to Section R.1 for review of set-builder notation and interval notation.

1. $\{x \mid x < -5\}$ **2.** $\{y \mid y > -1\}$ **3.** $\{z \mid 4 \leq z\}$ **4.** $\{m \mid -5 \geq m\}$

For Exercises 5–6, write the given interval in set-builder notation.

5. $\left(-\dfrac{5}{6}, 4\right]$ **6.** $\left[-3, \dfrac{4}{3}\right)$

Concept Connections

7. The _____ of sets A and B, denoted by _____, is the set of elements that belong to A or B or both A and B.

8. The multiplication and division properties of inequality indicate that if both sides of an inequality are multiplied or divided by a negative real number, the direction of the _____ sign must be reversed.

9. The _____ of two sets A and B, denoted by _____, is the set of elements common to both A and B.

10. If a compound inequality consists of two inequalities joined by the word "and," the solution set is the _____ of the solution sets of the individual inequalities.

11. The compound inequality $a < x$ and $x < b$ can be written as the three-part inequality _____.

12. If a compound inequality consists of two inequalities joined by the word "or," the solution set is the _____ of the solution sets of the individual inequalities.

Objective 1: Solve Linear Inequalities in One Variable

For Exercises 13–30, solve the inequality. Graph the solution set, and write the solution set in set-builder notation and interval notation. (See Examples 1–3)

13. $-2x - 5 > 17$

14. $-8t + 1 < 17$

15. $-3 \le -\dfrac{4}{3}w + 1$

16. $8 \ge -\dfrac{5}{2}y - 2$

17. $-1.2 + 0.6a \le 0.4a + 0.5$

18. $-0.7 + 0.3x \le 0.9x - 0.4$

19. $-5 > 6(c - 4) + 7$

20. $-14 < 3(m - 7) + 7$

21. $\dfrac{4 + x}{2} - \dfrac{x - 3}{5} < -\dfrac{x}{10}$

22. $\dfrac{y + 3}{4} - \dfrac{3y + 1}{6} > -\dfrac{1}{12}$

23. $\dfrac{1}{3}(x + 4) - \dfrac{5}{6}(x - 3) \ge \dfrac{1}{2}x + 1$

24. $\dfrac{1}{2}(t - 6) - \dfrac{4}{3}(t + 2) \ge -\dfrac{3}{4}t - 2$

25. $5(7 - x) + 2x < 6x - 2 - 9x$

26. $2(3x + 1) - 4x > 2(x + 8) - 5$

27. $5 - 3[2 - 4(x - 2)] \ge 6\{2 - [4 - (x - 3)]\}$

28. $8 - [6 - 10(x - 1)] \ge 2\{1 - 3[2 - (x + 4)]\}$

29. $4 - 3k > -2(k + 3) - k$

30. $2x - 9 < 6(x - 1) - 4x$

Objective 2: Determine the Union and Intersection of Sets

For Exercise 31, find the union or intersection as indicated, given the following sets:
$A = \{0, 4, 8, 12\}, B = \{0, 3, 6, 9, 12\}, C = \{-2, 4, 8\}$. (See Example 4)

31. a. $A \cup B$ **b.** $A \cap B$ **c.** $A \cup C$ **d.** $A \cap C$ **e.** $B \cup C$ **f.** $B \cap C$

For Exercise 32, find the union or intersection as indicated, given the following sets:
$X = \{-10, -9, -8, -7\}, Y = \{-10, -8, -6, -4\}, Z = \{-6, -5, -4, -3, -2\}$.

32. a. $X \cup Y$ **b.** $X \cap Y$ **c.** $X \cup Z$ **d.** $X \cap Z$ **e.** $Y \cup Z$ **f.** $Y \cap Z$

For Exercise 33, find the union or intersection as indicated, given the following sets:
$C = \{x \mid x < 9\}, D = \{x \mid x \ge -1\}, F = \{x \mid x < -8\}$. (See Example 5)

33. a. $C \cup D$ **b.** $C \cap D$ **c.** $C \cup F$ **d.** $C \cap F$ **e.** $D \cup F$ **f.** $D \cap F$

For Exercise 34, find the union or intersection as indicated, given the following sets:
$M = \{y \mid y \ge -3\}, N = \{y \mid y \ge 5\}, P = \{y \mid y < 0\}$.

34. a. $M \cup N$ **b.** $M \cap N$ **c.** $M \cup P$ **d.** $M \cap P$ **e.** $N \cup P$ **f.** $N \cap P$

For Exercises 35–36, write the union or intersection of the given sets using the roster method.
$A = \{x \mid x \in \mathbb{Z} \text{ and } -2 < x \le 5\}, B = \{x \mid x \in W \text{ and } x < 4\}$.

35. $A \cup B$

36. $A \cap B$

For Exercises 37–38, write the union or intersection of the given sets using the roster method.
$M = \{t \mid t \in \mathbb{N} \text{ and } t \le 5\}, S = \{t \mid t \in \mathbb{Z} \text{ and } -3 \le t < 2\}$.

37. $M \cap S$

38. $M \cup S$

Objective 3: Solve Compound Linear Inequalities

For Exercises 39–46, solve the compound inequality. Graph the solution set, and write the solution set in interval notation. (See Examples 6–7)

39. a. $x < 4$ and $x \ge -2$
    b. $x < 4$ or $x \ge -2$

40. a. $y \le -2$ and $y > -5$
    b. $y \le -2$ or $y > -5$

41. a. $m + 1 \leq 6$ or $\frac{1}{3}m < -2$

   b. $m + 1 \leq 6$ and $\frac{1}{3}m < -2$

42. a. $n - 6 > 1$ or $\frac{3}{4}n \geq 6$

   b. $n - 6 > 1$ and $\frac{3}{4}n \geq 6$

43. a. $-\frac{2}{3}y > -12$ and $2.08 \geq 0.65y$

   b. $-\frac{2}{3}y > -12$ or $2.08 \geq 0.65y$

44. a. $-\frac{4}{5}m < 8$ and $0.85 \leq 0.34m$

   b. $-\frac{4}{5}m < 8$ or $0.85 \leq 0.34m$

45. a. $3(x - 2) + 2 \leq x - 8$ or $4(x + 1) + 2 > -2x + 4$
   b. $3(x - 2) + 2 \leq x - 8$ and $4(x + 1) + 2 > -2x + 4$

46. a. $5(t - 4) + 2 > 3(t + 1) - 3$ or $2t - 6 > 3(t - 4) - 2$
   b. $5(t - 4) + 2 > 3(t + 1) - 3$ and $2t - 6 > 3(t - 4) - 2$

47. Write $-2.8 < y \leq 15$ as two separate inequalities joined by "and."

48. Write $-\frac{1}{2} \leq z < 2.4$ as two separate inequalities joined by "and."

For Exercises 49–54, solve the compound inequality. Graph the solution set, and write the solution set in interval notation. (See Example 8)

49. $-3 < -2x + 1 \leq 9$

50. $-6 \leq -3x + 9 < 0$

51. $1 \leq \frac{5x - 4}{2} < 3$

52. $-2 \leq \frac{4x - 1}{3} \leq 5$

53. $-2 \leq \frac{-2x + 1}{-3} \leq 4$

54. $-4 < \frac{-5x - 2}{-2} < 4$

Objective 4: Solve Applications of Inequalities

For Exercises 55–58, write a three-part inequality to represent the given statement.

55. The normal range for the hemoglobin level x for an adult female is greater than or equal to 12.0 g/dL and less than or equal to 15.2 g/dL.

56. A tennis player must play in the "open" division of a tennis tournament if the player's age a is over 18 yr and under 25 yr.

57. The distance d that Zina hits a 9-iron is at least 90 ft, but no more than 110 ft.

58. A small plane's average speed s is at least 220 mph but not more than 410 mph.

59. Marilee wants to earn an "A" in a class and needs an overall average of at least 92. Her test grades are 88, 92, 100, and 80. The average of her quizzes is 90 and counts as one test grade. The final exam counts as 2.5 test grades. What scores on the final exam would result in Marilee's overall average of 92 or greater? (**See Example 9**)

60. A 10-yr-old competes in gymnastics. For several competitions she received the following "All-Around" scores: 36, 36.9, 37.1, and 37.4. Her coach recommends that gymnasts whose "All-Around" scores average at least 37 move up to the next level. What "All-Around" scores in the next competition would result in the child being eligible to move up?

61. A car travels 50 mph and passes a truck traveling 40 mph. How long will it take the car to be more than 16 mi ahead?

62. A work-study job in the library pays \$10.75/hr and a job in the tutoring center pays \$16.25/hr. How long would it take for a tutor to make over \$500 more than a student working in the library? Round to the nearest hour.

63. A rectangular garden is to be constructed so that the width is 100 ft. What are the possible values for the length of the garden if at most 800 ft of fencing is to be used?

64. The lengths of the sides of a triangle are given by three consecutive integers greater than 1. What are the possible values for the shortest side if the perimeter is not to exceed 24 ft?

65. For a certain bowling league, a beginning bowler computes her handicap by taking 90% of the difference between 220 and her average score in league play. Determine the average scores that would produce a handicap of 72 or less. Also assume that a negative handicap is not possible in this league.

66. Betty has a rectangular kitchen that is 20 ft by 15 ft. She wants to have the kitchen tiled and has budgeted $5600. The contractor charges for tile and for installation. To account for waste, the amount of tile the contractor buys is 10% more than the measured area of the kitchen.

    a. How many square feet of tile will the contractor buy?

    b. The contractor charges $6 per square foot for installation, and the sales tax rate is 6% for tile and labor. What is the maximum cost per square foot of tile that Betty can afford?

For Exercises 67–68, suppose that P dollars in principal is invested at an annual simple interest rate r for t years. Then the amount in the account A (in $) is given by $A = P + Prt$.

67. With a 5% simple interest rate, what is the minimum time required for $4000 to grow to at least $5000?

68. With a 4% simple interest rate, what is the minimum amount of principal required for an investment to grow to at least $10,000 in 8 yr? Round to the nearest cent.

For Exercises 69–70, use the relationship between temperature in Celsius and temperature in Fahrenheit. $C = \dfrac{5}{9}(F - 32)$

69. Hypothermia is a condition in which core body temperature drops below 35°C. Determine the temperatures in Fahrenheit for which hypothermia would set in.

70. Body temperature is usually maintained between 36.5°C and 37.5°C, inclusive. Determine the corresponding range of temperature in Fahrenheit.

71. Donovan has offers for two sales jobs. Job A pays a base salary of $25,000 plus a 10% commission on sales. Job B pays a base salary of $30,000 plus 8% commission on sales.

    a. How much would Donovan have to sell for the salary from Job A to exceed the salary from Job B?

    b. If Donovan routinely sells more than $500,000 in merchandise, which job would result in a higher salary?

72. Nancy wants to vacation in Austin, Texas. Hotel A charges $179 per night with a 14% nightly room tax and free parking. Hotel B charges $169 per night with an 18% nightly room tax plus a one-time $40 parking fee. After how many nights will Hotel B be less expensive?

73. The boiling temperature of water T (in °F) can be approximated by the model $T = -1.83a + 212$, where a is the altitude in thousands of feet. At what altitudes will water boil at less than 200°F? Answer to the nearest hundred feet.

74. The annual per capita consumer expenditure E (in $) for prescription drugs can be modeled by $E = 46.2x + 446.2$, where x is the number of years since the year 2000. In what years will the average per capita expenditure for prescription drugs exceed $1000 assuming that this trend continues?

Mixed Exercises

For Exercises 75–80, determine the set of values for x for which the radical expression would produce a real number. For example, the expression $\sqrt{x - 1}$ is a real number if $x - 1 \geq 0$ or equivalently, $x \geq 1$.

75. a. $\sqrt{x - 2}$ **b.** $\sqrt{2 - x}$ **76. a.** $\sqrt{x - 6}$ **b.** $\sqrt{6 - x}$

77. a. $\sqrt{x + 4}$ **b.** $\sqrt[3]{x + 4}$ **78. a.** $\sqrt{x + 7}$ **b.** $\sqrt[3]{x + 7}$

79. a. $\sqrt{2x - 9}$ **b.** $\sqrt[4]{2x - 9}$ **80. a.** $\sqrt{3x - 7}$ **b.** $\sqrt[4]{3x - 7}$

For Exercises 81–84, answer true or false given that $a > 0$, $b < 0$, $c > 0$, and $d < 0$.

81. $cd > a$ **82.** $ab < c$ **83.** If $a > c$, then $ad < cd$.   **84.** If $a < c$, then $ab < bc$.

For Exercises 85–88, write the set as a single interval.

85. $(-\infty, 2) \cap (-3, 4] \cap [1, 3]$ **86.** $(-\infty, 5) \cap (-1, \infty) \cap [0, 3)$

87. $[(-\infty, -2) \cup (4, \infty)] \cap [-5, 3)$ **88.** $[(-\infty, 6) \cup (10, \infty)] \cap [8, 12)$

For Exercises 89–98, solve the inequality. Write the solution set in interval notation.

89. $2x + 1 < -3$ or $2x + 3 > 3$ **90.** $4m - 2 \leq -1$ or $4m - 2 \geq 1$

91. $-2 \leq 6d - 4 \leq 2$ **92.** $-8 < 3k + 7 < 8$

93. $-11 < 6y + 7$ and $6y + 7 < -5$ **94.** $-13 < 2c - 3$ and $2c - 3 < 5$

95. $6 < -\dfrac{1}{2}p + 4$

96. $-7 < -\dfrac{1}{3}z + 3$

97. $-1 < \dfrac{4 - x}{-2} \le 3$

98. $0 \le \dfrac{6 - x}{-4} < 2$

Write About It

99. How is the process to solve a linear inequality different from the process to solve a linear equation?

100. Explain why $8 < x < 2$ has no solution.

101. Explain why $-3 > w > -1$ has no solution.

102. Explain how to find the solution set for a compound inequality.

SECTION 1.8   Absolute Value Equations and Inequalities

OBJECTIVES

1. **Solve Absolute Value Equations**
2. **Solve Absolute Value Inequalities**
3. **Solve Applications Involving Absolute Value**

In Section R.1, we introduced the concept of absolute value and how it relates to distance on the number line. This concept can be used to express limits on measurement error. For example, suppose that a machine at an orange juice factory is designed to dispense 8 fl oz of orange juice into bottles. No measurement is exact, but the engineers are confident that the machine is in error by no more than 0.05 fl oz.

Suppose that x represents the exact amount of juice poured into a given bottle. This value cannot be determined exactly (no measuring device is accurate to an unlimited number of place values). However, the absolute value inequality $|x - 8| \le 0.05$ represents an interval in which to estimate x. (See Example 7)

1. Solve Absolute Value Equations

Thus far in Chapter 1, we have learned to recognize and solve the following types of equations.

- Linear equations
- Quadratic equations
- Rational equations
- Radical equations
- Equations with rational exponents
- Equations in quadratic form

Now we add absolute value equations to this list. For example, given $|x| = 5$, the solution set is $\{-5, 5\}$. The equation can also be written as $|x - 0| = 5$. The solutions are the values of x that are 5 units from 0 on the number line. See Figure 1-5.

$$\underbrace{\qquad\qquad}_{\text{5 units}} \qquad \underbrace{\qquad\qquad}_{\text{5 units}}$$

5 units   5 units

$-6 \quad -5 \quad -4 \quad -3 \quad -2 \quad -1 \quad 0 \quad 1 \quad 2 \quad 3 \quad 4 \quad 5 \quad 6$

Figure 1-5

Given a nonnegative real number k, the generic absolute value equation $|u| = k$ can be solved directly from the definition of absolute value. Recall that

$$|u| = \begin{cases} u \text{ if } u \ge 0 \\ -u \text{ if } u < 0 \end{cases}$$

Thus, $|u| = k$ means that $u = k$ or $-u = k$. Solving for u, we have $u = k$ or $u = -k$.

This and three other properties summarized in Table 1-2 follow directly from the definition of absolute value.

Table 1-2   Properties Involving Absolute Value Equations

Let k represent a real number.
1. If $k > 0$, $|u| = k$ is equivalent to $u = k$ or $u = -k$.
2. If $k = 0$, $|u| = k$ is equivalent to $u = 0$.
3. If $k < 0$, $|u| = k$ has no solution.
4. $|u| = |w|$ is equivalent to $u = w$ or $u = -w$.

To solve an absolute value equation, first isolate the absolute value. Then solve the equation by rewriting the equation in its equivalent form given in Table 1-2.

EXAMPLE 1   Solving Absolute Value Equations

Solve.   **a.** $2|3 - 2t| + 4 = 10$ **b.** $|7w - 3| + 8 = 2$

Solution:

a. $2|3 - 2t| + 4 = 10$ Isolate the absolute value. Subtract 4 and divide by 2.

$|3 - 2t| = 3$ The equation is in the form $|u| = k$, where $u = 3 - 2t$.

$3 - 2t = 3$ or $3 - 2t = -3$ Rewrite in the equivalent form: $u = k$ or $u = -k$.

$-2t = 0$ or $-2t = -6$

$t = 0$ or $t = 3$

The solution set is $\{0, 3\}$.

Check: $t = 0$ Check: $t = 3$

$2|3 - 2(0)| + 4 \overset{?}{=} 10$ $2|3 - 2(3)| + 4 \overset{?}{=} 10$

$2|3| + 4 \overset{?}{=} 10$ ✓ true $2|-3| + 4 \overset{?}{=} 10$ ✓ true

b. $|7w - 3| + 8 = 2$ Isolate the absolute value. Subtract 8 from both sides.

$|7w - 3| = -6$ By definition, the absolute value of an expression cannot be negative. The equation has no solution.

The solution set is $\{ \ \}$.

Skill Practice 1   Solve.

a. $5|2 - 4t| + 3 = 53$ **b.** $|6c - 7| + 9 = 5$

EXAMPLE 2   Solving an Absolute Value Equation

Solve. $-4 = -\dfrac{1}{3}|m - 2|$

Solution:

$-4 = -\dfrac{1}{3}|m - 2|$ Isolate the absolute value. Multiply by -3.
    The equation is in the form $|u| = k$, where $u = m - 2$.

$12 = |m - 2|$

$m - 2 = 12$ or $m - 2 = -12$ Rewrite in the equivalent form: $u = k$ or $u = -k$.

$m = 14$ or $m = -10$ Both solutions check in the original equation.

The solution set is $\{14, -10\}$.

Skill Practice 2   Solve. $-6 = -\dfrac{1}{2}|p + 3|$

Answers

1. a. $\{-2, 3\}$ **b.** $\{ \ \}$
2. $\{9, -15\}$

In Example 3, we use the property that $|u| = |w|$ is equivalent to $u = w$ or $u = -w$.

EXAMPLE 3   **Solving an Equation with Two Absolute Values**

Solve. $|2x - 6| = |x + 1|$

Solution:

$$|2x - 6| = |x + 1|$$

The equation is in the form $|u| = |w|$, where $u = 2x - 6$ and $w = x + 1$.

$2x - 6 = x + 1$ or $2x - 6 = -(x + 1)$

Write the equivalent form $u = w$ or $u = -w$.

$x = 7$ or $2x - 6 = -x - 1$

Solve the individual equations.

$$3x = 5$$

$$x = \frac{5}{3}$$

The solution set is $\left\{7, \dfrac{5}{3}\right\}$.

Both solutions check in the original equation.

Skill Practice 3   Solve. $|-x + 7| = |2x - 4|$

2. Solve Absolute Value Inequalities

We now investigate the solutions to absolute value inequalities. For example:

Inequality	Graph	Solution Set
$\|x\| < 3$		$\{x \mid -3 < x < 3\}$
$\|x\| > 3$		$\{x \mid x < -3 \text{ or } x > 3\}$

We can generalize these observations with the following properties involving absolute value inequalities.

Properties Involving Absolute Value Inequalities

For a real number $k > 0$,

1. $|u| < k$ is equivalent to $-k < u < k$.
2. $|u| > k$ is equivalent to $u < -k$ or $u > k$.

Note: The statements also hold true for the inequality symbols $\leq$ and $\geq$, respectively.

Properties (1) and (2) follow directly from the definition: $|u| = \begin{cases} u \text{ if } u \geq 0 \\ -u \text{ if } u < 0 \end{cases}$

By definition, $|u| < k$ is equivalent to

$$u < k \quad \text{and} \quad -u < k$$
$$u < k \quad \text{and} \quad u > -k$$
$$-k < u < k \qquad (1)$$

By definition, $|u| > k$ is equivalent to

$$u > k \quad \text{or} \quad -u > k$$
$$u > k \quad \text{or} \quad u < -k$$
$$u < -k \quad \text{or} \quad u > k \qquad (2)$$

TIP The solution set to $|x| < 3$ is the set of real numbers within 3 units of zero on the number line.

The solution set to $|x| > 3$ is the set of real numbers more than 3 units from zero on the number line.

Answer

3. $\left\{\dfrac{11}{3}, -3\right\}$

EXAMPLE 4 **Solving an Absolute Value Inequality**

Solve the inequality and write the solution set in interval notation.

$$2|6 - m| - 3 < 7$$

Solution:

$2|6 - m| - 3 < 7$	First isolate the absolute value. Add 3 and divide by 2.
$|6 - m| < 5$	The inequality is in the form $|u| < k$ where $u = 6 - m$.
$-5 < 6 - m < 5$	Write the equivalent compound inequality: $-k < u < k$
$-11 < -m < -1$	Subtract 6 from all three parts.
$\dfrac{-11}{-1} > \dfrac{-m}{-1} > \dfrac{-1}{-1}$	Divide by -1 and reverse the inequality signs.

$11 > m > 1$ or equivalently $1 < m < 11$.

The solution set is $\{m \mid 1 < m < 11\}$.
Interval notation: $(1, 11)$

Skill Practice 4 Solve the inequality and write the solution set in interval notation. $3|5 - x| + 2 \le 14$

EXAMPLE 5 **Solving an Absolute Value Inequality**

Solve the inequality and write the solution set in interval notation.

$$-4 \ge -2|3x + 1|$$

Solution:

$-4 \ge -2|3x + 1|$	First isolate the absolute value.
$\dfrac{-4}{-2} \le \dfrac{-2|3x + 1|}{-2}$	Divide both sides by -2 and reverse the inequality sign.
$2 \le |3x + 1|$	Write the absolute value on the left. Notice that the direction of the inequality sign is also changed. The inequality is now in the form $|u| \ge k$, where $u = 3x + 1$.
$|3x + 1| \ge 2$	
$3x + 1 \le -2$ or $3x + 1 \ge 2$	Write the equivalent form $u \le -k$ or $u \ge k$.
$x \le -1$ or $x \ge \dfrac{1}{3}$	Take the union of the solution sets of the individual inequalities.

The solution set is $\left\{ x \mid x \le -1 \quad \text{or} \quad x \ge \dfrac{1}{3} \right\}$.

Interval notation: $(-\infty, -1] \cup \left[\dfrac{1}{3}, \infty \right)$

Skill Practice 5 Solve the inequality and write the solution set in interval notation. $-18 > -3|2y - 4|$

Answers
4. $[1, 9]$ **5.** $(-\infty, -1) \cup (5, \infty)$

In Example 1(b) we saw that the equation $|7w - 3| = -6$ has no solution because an absolute value cannot be equal to a negative number. We must also exercise caution when an absolute value is compared to a negative number or zero within an inequality. This is demonstrated in Example 6.

EXAMPLE 6   Solving Absolute Value Inequalities with Special Case Solution Sets

Solve the inequality and write the solution set in interval notation where appropriate.

a. $|x + 2| < -4$ **b.** $|x + 2| \geq -4$
c. $|x - 5| \leq 0$ **d.** $|x - 5| > 0$

Solution:

a. $|x + 2| < -4$
   The solution set is { }.

By definition an absolute value is greater than or equal to zero. Therefore, the absolute value of an expression cannot be less than zero or any negative number. This inequality has no solution.

b. $|x + 2| \geq -4$
   The solution set is $\mathbb{R}$.
   Interval notation: $(-\infty, \infty)$

An absolute value of any real number is greater than or equal to zero. Therefore, it is also greater than every negative number. This inequality is true for all real numbers, x.

c. $|x - 5| \leq 0$
   $|x - 5| = 0$
   $x - 5 = 0$
   $x = 5$
   The solution set is $\{5\}$.

The absolute value of x minus 5 cannot be less than zero, but it can be *equal* to zero.

d. $|x - 5| > 0$

$|x - 5| > 0$ for all values of x except 5. When $x = 5$, we have $|5 - 5| = 0$, and this is not greater than zero. The solution set is all real numbers excluding 5.

   The solution set is $\{x \mid x < 5 \text{ or } x > 5\}$.
   Interval notation: $(-\infty, 5) \cup (5, \infty)$

5

Skill Practice 6   Solve.

a. $|x - 3| < -2$ **b.** $|x - 3| > -2$
c. $|x + 1| \leq 0$ **d.** $|x + 1| > 0$

---

3. Solve Applications Involving Absolute Value

EXAMPLE 7   Solving an Application Involving an Absolute Value Inequality

Suppose that a machine is calibrated to dispense 8 fl oz of orange juice into a plastic bottle, with a measurement error of no more than 0.05 fl oz. Let x represent the actual amount of orange juice poured into the bottle.

a. Write an absolute value inequality that represents an interval in which to estimate x.

b. Solve the inequality and interpret the answer.

Answers
6. a. { }   **b.** $\mathbb{R}; (-\infty, \infty)$
   c. $\{-1\}$ **d.** $(-\infty, -1) \cup (-1, \infty)$

Solution:

a. The measurement error is ± 0.05 fl oz. This means that the value of x can deviate from 8 fl oz by as much as ± 0.05 fl oz.

$|x - 8| \leq 0.05$ The distance between x and 8 is no more than 0.05 unit.

b. $|x - 8| \leq 0.05$
$-0.05 \leq x - 8 \leq 0.05$ The amount of orange juice in the bottle is between
$7.95 \leq x \leq 8.05$ 7.95 fl oz and 8.05 fl oz, inclusive.

Skill Practice 7   A board is to be cut to a length of 24 in. The measurement error is no more than 0.02 in. Let x represent the actual length of the board.

a. Write an absolute value inequality that represents an interval in which to estimate x.

b. Solve the inequality from part (a) and interpret the meaning.

Answers

7. a. $|x - 24| \leq 0.02$
b. $23.98 \leq x \leq 24.02$; The actual length of the board is between 23.98 in. and 24.02 in., inclusive.

SECTION 1.8   Practice Exercises

Review Exercises

1. Write an absolute value expression representing the distance between x and 4 on the number line.

2. Write an absolute value expression representing the distance between -1 and x on the number line.

For Exercises 3–6, solve the inequality. Write the solution set in set-builder notation and interval notation.

3. $-4 < 2x - 10 < 4$

4. $-1 \leq 5t + 1 \leq 1$

5. $5m \leq -20$ or $5m \geq 20$

6. $7c < -14$ or $7c > 14$

Concept Connections

7. An _____ value equation is an equation of the form $|u| = k$. If k is a positive real number then the solution set is _____.

8. If u and w represent real-valued expressions, then the equation $|u| = |w|$ can be written in an equivalent form without absolute value bars as _____.

9. If k is a positive real number, then the inequality $|x| < k$ is equivalent to _____ $< x <$ _____.

10. If k is a positive real number, then the inequality $|x| > k$ is equivalent to $x <$ _____ or x _____ k.

11. If k is a positive real number, then the solution set to the inequality $|x| > -k$ is _____.

12. If k is a positive real number, then the solution set to the inequality $|x| < -k$ is _____.

Objective 1: Solve Absolute Value Equations

For Exercises 13–32, solve the equations. (See Examples 1–3)

13. a. $|p| = 6$
b. $|p| = 0$
c. $|p| = -6$

14. a. $|w| = 2$
b. $|w| = 0$
c. $|w| = -2$

15. a. $|x - 3| = 4$
b. $|x - 3| = 0$
c. $|x - 3| = -7$

16. a. $|m + 1| = 5$
b. $|m + 1| = 0$
c. $|m + 1| = -1$

17. $2|3x - 4| + 7 = 9$

18. $4|2t + 7| + 2 = 22$

19. $-3 = -|c - 7| + 1$

20. $-4 = -|z + 8| - 3$

21. $2 = 8 + |11y + 4|$

22. $6 = 7 + |9z - 3|$

23. $\left|4 - \frac{1}{2}w\right| - \frac{1}{3} = \frac{1}{2}$

24. $\left|2 - \frac{1}{3}p\right| - \frac{7}{6} = \frac{1}{2}$

25. $|3y + 5| = |y + 1|$

26. $|2a - 3| = |a + 2|$

27. $\left|\frac{1}{4}w\right| = |4w|$

28. $|3z| = \left|\frac{1}{3}z\right|$

29. $|x + 4| = |x - 7|$

30. $|k - 3| = |k + 3|$

31. $|2p - 1| = |1 - 2p|$

32. $|4d - 3| = |3 - 4d|$

Objective 2: Solve Absolute Value Inequalities

For Exercises 33–36, solve the equation or inequality. Write the solution set to each inequality in interval notation.

33. a. $|x| = 7$
   b. $|x| < 7$
   c. $|x| > 7$

35. a. $|a + 9| + 2 = 6$
   b. $|a + 9| + 2 \leq 6$
   c. $|a + 9| + 2 \geq 6$

34. a. $|y| = 8$
   b. $|y| < 8$
   c. $|y| > 8$

36. a. $|b + 1| - 4 = 1$
   b. $|b + 1| - 4 \leq 1$
   c. $|b + 1| - 4 \geq 1$

For Exercises 37–48, solve the inequality, and write the solution set in interval notation. (See Examples 4–5)

37. $3|4 - x| - 2 < 16$

38. $2|7 - y| + 1 < 17$

39. $2|x + 3| - 4 \geq 6$

40. $5|x + 1| - 9 \geq -4$

41. $-11 \leq 5 - |2p + 4|$

42. $-18 \leq 6 - |3z + 3|$

43. $10 < |-5c - 4| + 2$

44. $15 < |-2d - 3| + 6$

45. $\left| \dfrac{y + 3}{6} \right| < 2$

46. $\left| \dfrac{m - 4}{2} \right| < 14$

47. $\left| \dfrac{1}{2}p - 6 \right| \geq 0.01$

48. $\left| \dfrac{1}{4}q - 2 \right| \geq 0.05$

For Exercises 49–56, write the solution set. (See Example 6)

49. a. $|x| = -9$
   b. $|x| < -9$
   c. $|x| > -9$

53. a. $|z| = 0$
   b. $|z| < 0$
   c. $|z| \leq 0$
   d. $|z| > 0$
   e. $|z| \geq 0$

50. a. $|y| = -2$
   b. $|y| < -2$
   c. $|y| > -2$

54. a. $|2w| = 0$
   b. $|2w| < 0$
   c. $|2w| \leq 0$
   d. $|2w| > 0$
   e. $|2w| \geq 0$

51. a. $18 = 4 - |y + 7|$
   b. $18 \leq 4 - |y + 7|$
   c. $18 \geq 4 - |y + 7|$

55. a. $|k + 4| = 0$
   b. $|k + 4| < 0$
   c. $|k + 4| \leq 0$
   d. $|k + 4| > 0$
   e. $|k + 4| \geq 0$

52. a. $15 = 2 - |p - 3|$
   b. $15 \leq 2 - |p - 3|$
   c. $15 \geq 2 - |p - 3|$

56. a. $|c - 3| = 0$
   b. $|c - 3| < 0$
   c. $|c - 3| \leq 0$
   d. $|c - 3| > 0$
   e. $|c - 3| \geq 0$

Objective 3: Solve Applications Involving Absolute Value

For Exercises 57–62,

a. Write an absolute value equation or inequality to represent each statement.

b. Solve the equation or inequality. Write the solution set to the inequalities in interval notation.

57. The distance between a number x and 4 on the number line is 6.

58. The distance between a number x and 3 on the number line is 8.

59. The variation between the measured value v and 16 oz is less than 0.01 oz.

60. The variation between the measured value t and 60 min is less than 0.2 min.

61. The value of x differs from 4 by more than 1 unit.

62. The value of y differs from 10 by more than 2 units.

For Exercises 63–64, write an inequality that represents the statement.

63. The distance between x and c is less than δ and greater than 0 (δ is the lowercase Greek letter "delta").

64. The distance between y and L is less than ε (ε is the Greek letter "epsilon").

65. A refrigerator manufacturer recommends that the temperature t (in °F) inside a refrigerator be 36.5°F. If the thermostat has a margin of error of no more than 1.5°F,

   a. Write an absolute value inequality that represents an interval in which to estimate t. (**See Example 7**)

   b. Solve the inequality and interpret the answer.

67. The results of a political poll indicate that the leading candidate will receive 51% of the votes with a margin of error of no more than 3%. Let x represent the true percentage of votes received by this candidate.

   a. Write an absolute value inequality that represents an interval in which to estimate x.

   b. Solve the inequality and interpret the answer.

66. A box of cereal is labeled to contain 16 oz. A consumer group takes a sample of 50 boxes and measures the contents of each box. The individual content of each box differs slightly from 16 oz, but by no more than 0.5 oz.

   a. If x represents the exact weight of the contents of a box of cereal, write an absolute value inequality that represents an interval in which to estimate x.

   b. Solve the inequality and interpret the answer.

68. A police officer uses a radar detector to determine that a motorist is traveling 34 mph in a 25 mph school zone. The driver goes to court and argues that the radar detector is not accurate. The manufacturer claims that the radar detector is calibrated to be in error by no more than 3 mph.

   a. If x represents the motorist's actual speed, write an inequality that represents an interval in which to estimate x.

   b. Solve the inequality and interpret the answer. Should the motorist receive a ticket?

69. Suppose that over the course of 3 months, a court system selects 1000 jurors from a large jury pool having an equal number of males and females. If males and females are selected at random, there should be approximately 500 males and 500 females selected. However, these values may vary slightly. If 1000 people are selected at random from the large jury pool, the inequality $\left|\dfrac{x - 500}{\sqrt{250}}\right| < 1.96$ gives the "reasonable" range for the number of women selected, x.

   a. Solve the inequality and interpret the answer in the context of this problem. (*Hint:* Round so that the endpoints of the interval are whole numbers, but still within the interval defined by the inequality.)

   b. If the group of 1000 jurors has 560 women, does it appear that there may be some bias toward women jurors?

70. A die is a six-sided cube with sides labeled with 1, 2, 3, 4, 5, or 6 dots. The die is a "fair" die if when rolled, each outcome is equally likely. Therefore, the probability that it lands on "1" is $\frac{1}{6}$. If a fair die is rolled 360 times, we would expect it to land as a "1" roughly 60 times. Let x represent the number of times a "1" is rolled. The inequality $\left|\dfrac{x - 60}{\sqrt{50}}\right| < 1.96$ gives the "reasonable" range for the number of times that a "1" comes up in 360 rolls.

   a. Solve the inequality and interpret the answer in the context of this problem.

   b. If the die is rolled 360 times, and a "1" comes up 30 times, does it appear that the die is a fair die?

Mixed Exercises

For Exercises 71–74, write an absolute value inequality that represents the statement.

71. $3x - 1 < -7$ or $3x - 1 > 7$

73. $-4 \le 2z \le 4$

72. $7 - y < -1$ or $7 - y > 1$

74. $-11 \le 8p \le 11$

For Exercises 75–78, write an absolute value inequality whose solution set is shown in the graph.

75.

77.

76.

78.

Write About It

79. Explain why the equation $|x| = -5$ has no solution.

80. Explain why the inequality $|x| > -5$ is true for all real numbers x.

81. Explain the difference between the solution sets for the following inequalities:
$$|x - 3| \leq 0 \quad \text{and} \quad |x - 3| > 0$$

82. Explain why $x^2 = 4$ is equivalent to the equation $|x| = 2$.

Expanding Your Skills

For Exercises 83–88, solve the inequality and write the solution set in interval notation.

83. $|x| + x < 11$ (*Hint:* Use the definition of $|x|$ to consider two cases.
Case 1: $x + x < 11$ if $x \geq 0$.
Case 2: $-x + x < 11$ if $x < 0$.

84. $|x| - x > 10$

85. $1 < |x| < 9$

86. $2 < |y| < 11$

87. $5 \leq |2x + 1| \leq 7$

88. $7 \leq |3x - 5| \leq 13$

89. Solve the inequality for p: $|p - \hat{p}| < z\sqrt{\dfrac{\hat{p}\hat{q}}{n}}$. (Do not rationalize the denominator.)

90. Solve the inequality for μ: $|\mu - \bar{x}| < \dfrac{z\sigma}{\sqrt{n}}$. (Do not rationalize the denominator.)

PROBLEM RECOGNITION EXERCISES

Recognizing and Solving Equations and Inequalities

For Exercises 1–20,

  a. Identify the type of equation or inequality (some may fit more than one category).
  b. Solve the equation or inequality. Write the solution sets to the inequalities in interval notation if possible.

- Linear equation or inequality
- Quadratic equation
- Rational equation
- Absolute value equation or inequality

- Radical equation
- Equation in quadratic form
- Polynomial equation (degree > 2)
- Compound inequality

1. $(x^2 - 5)^2 - 5(x^2 - 5) + 4 = 0$

2. $2 \leq |3t - 1| - 6$

3. $\sqrt[3]{2y - 5} - 4 = -1$

4. $-9|3z - 7| + 1 = 4$

5. $\dfrac{2}{w - 3} + \dfrac{5}{w + 1} = 1$

6. $48x^3 + 80x^2 - 3x - 5 = 0$

7. $-2(m + 2) < -m + 5$ and $6 \geq m + 3$

8. $6 \leq -2c + 8$ or $\dfrac{1}{3}c - 2 < 2$

9. $(2p + 1)(p + 5) = 2p + 40$

10. $2x(x - 4) + 7 = 2x^2 - 3[x + 5 - (2 + x)]$

11. $\dfrac{a - 4}{2} - \dfrac{3a + 1}{4} \leq -\dfrac{a}{8}$

12. $3x^2 + 11 = 4$

13. $-1 \leq \dfrac{6 - x}{-5} \leq 7$

14. $5 = \sqrt{5 + 2n} + \sqrt{2 + n}$

15. $|4x - 5| = |3x - 2|$

16. $\dfrac{1}{d} - \dfrac{1}{2d - 1} + \dfrac{2d}{2d - 1} = 0$

17. $-|x + 4| + 8 > 3$

18. $y - 4\sqrt{y} - 12 = 0$

19. $c^{2/3} = 16$

20. $2|z - 14| + 8 > 4$

CHAPTER 1   KEY CONCEPTS

SECTION 1.1 Linear Equations and Rational Equations	Reference
A **linear equation in one variable** is an equation that can be written in the form $ax + b = 0$, where a and b are real numbers and $a \neq 0$.	p. 100
A **conditional equation** is an equation that is true for some values of the variable but false for others. A **contradiction** is false for all values of the variable. An **identity** is true for all values of the variable for which the expressions in the equation are well defined.	p. 104
Solve a rational equation by multiplying both sides of the equation by the LCD of all fractions in the equation.	p. 105

SECTION 1.2 Applications and Modeling with Linear Equations	Reference
Equations in algebra can be used to organize information from a physical situation.	p. 113

SECTION 1.3 Complex Numbers	Reference
$i = \sqrt{-1}$ and $i^2 = -1$. For a real number $b > 0$, $\sqrt{-b} = i\sqrt{b}$.	p. 125
To add or subtract complex numbers, combine the real parts, and combine the imaginary parts.	p. 128
Multiply complex numbers by using the distributive property.	p. 129
The product of complex conjugates: $(a + bi)(a - bi) = a^2 + b^2$	p. 130
Divide complex numbers by multiplying the numerator and denominator by the conjugate of the denominator.	p. 131

SECTION 1.4 Quadratic Equations	Reference
Let a, b, and c represent real numbers. A **quadratic equation** in the variable x is an equation of the form $ax^2 + bx + c = 0$, where $a \neq 0$.	p. 135
Zero product property: If $mn = 0$, then $m = 0$ or $n = 0$.	p. 135
Square root property: If $x^2 = k$, then $x = \pm\sqrt{k}$.	p. 136
A quadratic equation can be solved by completing the square and applying the square root property.	p. 138
The solutions to $ax^2 + bx + c = 0$ $(a \neq 0)$ are given by the quadratic formula. $$x = \frac{-b \pm \sqrt{b^2 - 4ac}}{2a}$$	p. 140
The discriminant to the equation $ax^2 + bx + c = 0$ $(a \neq 0)$ is given by $b^2 - 4ac$. The discriminant indicates the number of and type of solutions to the equation. • If $b^2 - 4ac < 0$, the equation has 2 imaginary solutions. • If $b^2 - 4ac = 0$, the equation has 1 rational solution. • If $b^2 - 4ac > 0$, the equation has 2 real solutions.	p. 143

SECTION 1.5 Applications of Quadratic Equations	Reference
Quadratic equations are used to model applications with the Pythagorean theorem, volume, area, and objects moving vertically under the influence of gravity.	p. 148
The vertical position s of an object moving vertically under the influence of gravity is approximated by $s = -\frac{1}{2}gt^2 + v_0t + s_0$, where • g is the acceleration due to gravity (at sea level on Earth: $g = 32$ ft/sec^2 or 9.8 m/sec^2). • t is the time after the start of the experiment. • v_0 is the initial velocity. • s_0 is the initial position (height). • s is the position of the object at time t.	p. 152

SECTION 1.6 More Equations and Applications	Reference
A polynomial equation with one side equal to zero and the other factored as a product of linear or quadratic factors can be solved by applying the zero product property.	p. 158
Solving radical equations: 1. Isolate the radical. If an equation has more than one radical, choose one of the radicals to isolate. 2. Raise each side of the equation to a power equal to the index of the radical. 3. Solve the resulting equation. If the equation still has a radical, repeat steps 1 and 2. 4. Check the potential solutions in the original equation.	p. 161
Solving an equation of the form $u^{m/n} = k$: If m is odd: If m is even: $\quad u^{m/n} = k \qquad\qquad\qquad u^{m/n} = k$ $(u^{m/n})^{n/m} = (k)^{n/m} \qquad (u^{m/n})^{n/m} = \pm(k)^{n/m}$ $\quad u = k^{n/m} \qquad\qquad\qquad u = \pm k^{n/m}$	p. 163
Substitution can be used to solve equations that are in quadratic form.	p. 164

SECTION 1.7 Linear Inequalities and Compound Inequalities	Reference
An inequality that can be written in one of the following forms is a **linear inequality in one variable.** $ax + b < 0$, $ax + b \leq 0$, $ax + b > 0$, or $ax + b \geq 0$	p. 169
$A \cup B$ is the **union** of A and B. This is the set of elements that belong to set A or set B or to both sets A and B. $A \cap B$ is the **intersection** of A and B. This is the set of elements common to both A and B.	p. 171
Solving compound inequalities: • If two inequalities are joined by the word "and," take the *intersection* of the individual solution sets. • The inequality $a < x < b$ is equivalent to $a < x$ and $x < b$. • If two inequalities are joined by the word "or," take the *union* of the individual solution sets.	p. 173

SECTION 1.8 Absolute Value Equations and Inequalities	Reference
Let k represent a real number. 1. If $k > 0$, $|u| = k$ is equivalent to $u = k$ or $u = -k$. 2. If $k = 0$, $|u| = k$ is equivalent to $u = 0$. 3. If $k < 0$, $|u| = k$ has no solution. 4. $|u| = |w|$ is equivalent to $u = w$ or $u = -w$.	p. 180
5. $|u| < k$ is equivalent to $-k < u < k$. 6. $|u| > k$ is equivalent to $u < -k \quad$ or $\quad u > k$.	p. 181

Expanded Chapter Summary available at www.mhhe.com/millerca.

CHAPTER 1   Review Exercises

SECTION 1.1

1. Determine the restrictions on x for the equation

$$\frac{3}{x^2 - 4} + \frac{4}{2x - 7} = \frac{2}{3}$$

For Exercises 2–9, solve the equation.

2. $-8(t - 4) + 7 = 4[t - 3(1 - t)] + 6$

3. $\frac{4}{5}x - \frac{2}{3} = \frac{7}{10}x - 2$

4. $\frac{m + 2}{3} - \frac{m - 4}{4} = \frac{m + 1}{6} - 1$

5. $x - 5 + 2(x - 4) = 3(x + 1) - 5$

6. $0.2x + 1.6 = x - 0.8(x - 2)$

7. $(y - 4)^2 = (y + 3)^2$

8. $\frac{x + 3}{5x} + 2 = \frac{x - 4}{x}$

9. $\frac{1}{m - 1} = \frac{5m}{m^2 + 3m - 4} - \frac{3}{m + 4}$

For Exercises 10–12, solve for the indicated variable.

10. $4x - 3y = 6$ for y

11. $t_a = \frac{t_1 + t_2}{2}$ for t_2

12. $4x + 6y = ax + c$ for x

13. Dexter's hybrid car gets 41 mpg in the city and 36 mpg on the highway. The amount of gas he uses A (in gal) is given by $A = \frac{1}{41}c + \frac{1}{36}h$, where c is the number of city miles driven and h is the number of highway miles driven. If Dexter drove 288 mi on the highway and used 11 gal of gas, how many city miles did he drive?

SECTION 1.2

14. Shawna invested a total of $12,000 in two mutual funds: an international fund and a real estate fund. After 1 yr, the international fund earned the equivalent of 8.2% simple interest and the real estate fund returned 1.5%. If the total earnings at the end of the year was $749.50, determine the amount invested in each fund.

15. Cassandra bought a 10-yr Treasury note that paid the equivalent of 3.5% simple interest. She invested $4000 more in a 15-yr bond earning 4.1% than she did in the Treasury note. If the total amount of interest from these investments is $10,180, determine the amount of principal for each investment. Assume that each investment was held to maturity.

16. A chemist mixed 100 cc of a 60% acid solution with a 20% acid solution to produce a 25% acid solution. How much of the 20% solution did he use?

17. Suppose that 250 ft^3 of dry concrete mixture is 50% sand by volume. How much pure sand must be added to form a new mixture that is 70% sand by volume?

18. When Kevin commuted to work one morning, his average speed was 45 mph. He averaged only 30 mph for the return trip because of an accident on the highway. If the total time for the round trip was 50 min ($\frac{5}{6}$ hr), determine the distance between his place of work and his home.

19. Two boats leave a marina at the same time. One travels south and the other travels north. The southbound boat travels 6 mph faster than the northbound boat. After 3 hr, the distance between the boats is 66 mi. Determine the speed of each boat.

20. Monique plans to join a gym so that she can use weights and participate in fitness classes. Gym A costs $300/yr plus $4 for each fitness class. Gym B costs $360/yr plus $2 for each class.

   a. Write a model representing the cost C_A (in $) for Gym A if Monique attends x fitness classes.

   b. Write a model representing the cost C_B (in $) for Gym B if Monique attends x fitness classes.

   c. For how many fitness classes will the cost for the two gyms be the same?

21. At a dance studio, each social dance has a $5 door fee.

   a. Write a model for the cost C (in $) for door fees to attend x social dances.

   b. A VIP membership at the studio costs $80 for 3 months, but the door fee is waived for all social dances. How many social dances would be required for a patron to save money by buying the VIP membership?

22. Petra and Dawn are typesetters for a publishing company. Petra can typeset 50 pages in 4 days and Dawn can typeset 50 pages in 3.5 days. How long would it take them to typeset a 150-page manuscript if they work together?

23. One pump can drain a pond in 22 hr. Working with a second pump, the two pumps together can drain the pond in 10 hr. How fast can the second pump drain the pond by itself?

24. On a police force, there are 60 more male officers than female officers. If the ratio of male to female officers is 10:7, determine the number of male and female officers on the force.

25. To estimate the number of turtles in a large pond, a biologist catches and tags 12 turtles. Several weeks later the biologist catches a new sample of 36 turtles from the pond and finds that 3 are tagged. How many turtles are in the pond?

SECTION 1.3

For Exercises 26–28, write each expression in terms of i and simplify.

26. $-\sqrt{-169}$ **27.** $\sqrt{-12}$ **28.** $\sqrt{-16} \cdot \sqrt{-4}$

29. Identify the real and imaginary parts of the complex number.

   a. $3 - 7i$ **b.** $2i$

30. Simplify the powers of i.

   a. i^{35} **b.** i^{56} **c.** i^{62}

   d. i^{17} **e.** i^{-5}

For Exercises 31–40, perform the indicated operations.

31. $\left(\dfrac{2}{3} + \dfrac{3}{5}i\right) - \left(\dfrac{1}{6} + \dfrac{2}{5}i\right)$ **32.** $3i(7 + 2i)$

33. $\sqrt{-5}\left(\sqrt{11} + \sqrt{-3}\right)$ **34.** $(4 - 7i)(5 + i)$

35. $(4 - 6i)^2$ **36.** $\left(2 + \sqrt{-2}\right)\left(4 + \sqrt{-2}\right)$

37. $(8 - 3i)(8 + 3i)$ **38.** $\dfrac{4 + 3i}{3 - i}$

39. $\left(6 - \sqrt{5}i\right)^{-1}$ **40.** $\dfrac{7}{4i}$

SECTION 1.4

For Exercises 41–46, solve the equation.

41. $3y^2 - 4y = 8 - 6y$ **42.** $(2v + 3)^2 - 1 = 6$

43. $10t^2 + 1210 = 0$ **44.** $2d(d - 3) = 1 + 4d$

45. $x^2 - 5 = (x + 2)(x - 4)$ **46.** $\dfrac{1}{5}x^2 - \dfrac{2}{3} = \dfrac{7}{15}x$

For Exercises 47–48, determine the value of n that makes the polynomial a perfect square trinomial. Then factor as the square of a binomial.

47. $x^2 + 18x + n$ **48.** $x^2 + \dfrac{2}{7}x + n$

For Exercises 49–50, solve the equation by using three methods.

a. Factoring and applying the zero product property.

b. Completing the square and applying the square root property.

c. Applying the quadratic formula.

49. $x^2 - 10x = -9$ **50.** $2x^2 - 3x - 5 = 0$

For Exercises 51–52, answer true or false.

51. The equation $(x - 4)^2 = 25$ is equivalent to $x - 4 = 5$.

52. The equation $(x + 1)^2 = 9$ is equivalent to $x + 1 = \pm3$.

For Exercises 53–55, (a) evaluate the discriminant and (b) determine the number and type of solutions to each equation.

53. $4x^2 - 20x + 25 = 0$

54. $-2y^2 = 5y - 1$

55. $5t(t + 1) = 4t - 11$

For Exercises 56–58, solve for the indicated variable.

56. $H = kl^2 Rt$ for $I > 0$

57. $(x - h)^2 + (y - k)^2 = r^2$ for y

58. $s = a_0t^2 + v_0t + s_0$ for t

SECTION 1.5

59. A rectangular rug has a decorative interior with a $\frac{1}{2}$-ft border of uniform width around the outside. The length of the decorative area is 3 ft more than the width. If the area of the rug (including the border) is 108 ft², find the dimensions of the rug (including the border).

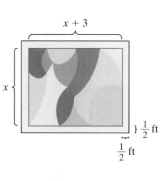

60. At a textile factory, rectangular pieces of cloth are cut to make tablecloths in which the width is 2 ft less than the length. However, the machine cuts the cloth with an additional 0.5 ft added to both the length and width to account for the hems on all sides. If the piece of cloth is 19.25 ft², determine the dimensions of the cloth.

61. A television has a 50-in. diagonal screen. If the aspect ratio (length to width) is 1.6 to 1, determine the length and width of the screen. Round to 1 decimal place.

62. A tablet computer has a 7-in. diagonal screen. The length is 2.7 in. more than the width. Find the length and width of the screen. Round to 1 decimal place.

63. The sum S of the first n natural numbers ($S = 1 + 2 + 3 + 4 + \cdots + n$) is given by $S = \frac{1}{2}n(n + 1)$. If the sum of the first n natural numbers is 4186, determine the value of n.

64. The stopping distance d (in ft) for a car on a certain road is given by $d = 0.048v^2 + 2.2v$, where v is the speed of the car in mph the instant before the brakes were applied.

   a. If the car was traveling 50 mph before the brakes were applied, find the stopping distance.

   b. If the stopping distance is 390 ft, how fast was the car traveling before the brakes were applied? Round to the nearest mile per hour.

65. A fireworks mortar is shot straight upward with an initial velocity of 200 ft/sec from a platform 2 ft off the ground.

   a. Use the formula $s = -\frac{1}{2}gt^2 + v_0t + s_0$ to write a model for the height of the mortar s (in ft) at a time t seconds after launch. Assume that $g = 16$ ft/sec².

   b. How long will it take the mortar (on the way up) to clear a tree line that is 80 ft high? Round to the nearest tenth of a second.

66. The population of the United States since the year 1950 can be approximated by $P = 0.009t^2 + 2.05t + 182$, where P is the population in millions and t represents the number of years since 1950. Use this model to approximate the year in which the population reached 300 million. Round to the nearest year.

SECTION 1.6

For Exercises 67–82, solve the equation.

67. $4x^3 - 6x^2 - 20x + 30 = 0$

68. $3x^2(x^2 + 2) = 20 - x^2$

69. $\sqrt{k + 7} - \sqrt{3 - k} = 2$

70. $\dfrac{n}{3n + 2} + 1 = \dfrac{4}{n - 2}$

71. $11v^{-2} + 23v^{-1} + 2 = 0$

72. $\sqrt[3]{4 - x} - \sqrt[3]{2x + 1} = 0$

73. $-2\sqrt{3m + 4} - 3 = 5$

74. $\sqrt{51 - 14x} + 4 = x - 2$

75. $p^{2/3} = 7$

76. $p^{3/4} = 7$

77. $2(y - 5)^{5/4} = 22$

78. $10w^{2/3} = \dfrac{1}{10}$

79. $6d^{2/3} - 7d^{1/3} - 3 = 0$

80. $(2u^2 - 1)^2 - 10(2u^2 - 1) + 9 = 0$

81. $2\left(\dfrac{4}{w} + 1\right)^2 - 10\left(\dfrac{4}{w} + 1\right) = 0$

82. $\dfrac{4v}{5v - 25} - \dfrac{10}{v - 5} = v + \dfrac{4}{5}$

For Exercises 83–85, solve for the indicated variable.

83. $m = \dfrac{1}{2}\sqrt{2a^2 + 2b^2 - 2c^2}$ for $a > 0$

84. $\dfrac{1}{a} = \dfrac{1}{b} + \dfrac{1}{c}$ for b

85. $\dfrac{a_1 t_1}{v_1} = \dfrac{a_2 t_2}{v_2}$ for v_2

SECTION 1.7

For Exercises 86–89, solve the inequality. Graph the solution set and write the solution set in set-builder notation and interval notation.

86. $-4 \le -\dfrac{2}{3}p + 14$

87. $-0.6 + 0.2x < 0.8x - 1.8$

88. $\dfrac{2 + y}{3} - \dfrac{y - 1}{4} < \dfrac{y}{6}$

89. $9 - [5 - 4(t - 1)] \ge 3\{2 - [5 - (t + 2)]\}$

90. Given $A = \{10, 11, 12, 13\}$, $B = \{10, 12, 14, 16\}$, and $C = \{7, 8, 9, 10, 11\}$, find

a. $A \cup B$ **b.** $A \cap B$ **c.** $A \cup C$

d. $A \cap C$ **e.** $B \cup C$ **f.** $B \cap C$

91. Given $X = \{x \mid x < 7\}$, $Y = \{x \mid x \ge -2\}$, and $Z = \{x \mid x < -3\}$, find

a. $X \cup Y$ **b.** $X \cap Y$ **c.** $X \cup Z$

d. $X \cap Z$ **e.** $Y \cup Z$ **f.** $Y \cap Z$

For Exercises 92–95, solve the compound inequality. Graph the solution set and write the solution set in interval notation.

92. a. $t + 2 \le 8$ or $\dfrac{1}{3}t < -4$

b. $t + 2 \le 8$ and $\dfrac{1}{3}t < -4$

93. a. $-2(x - 1) + 4 < x + 3$ or $5(x + 2) - 3 \le 4x + 1$

b. $-2(x - 1) + 4 < x + 3$ and $5(x + 2) - 3 \le 4x + 1$

94. $-11 \le -4x - 1 \le 7$ **95.** $0 < \dfrac{-3x + 9}{-4} < 6$

96. Write an inequality to represent the following statement. A pilot is instructed to keep a plane at an altitude a of over 29,000 ft, but not to exceed 31,000 ft.

97. The months of June, July, August, and September are the wettest months in Miami, Florida, averaging 7.83 in./month. If Miami gets 8.54 in. in June, 5.79 in. in July, and 8.63 in. in August, how much rain is needed in September to exceed the monthly average for these 4 months?

98. A homeowner wants to resod her 2000 ft^2 lawn. Sod varies in price from \$0.10/ft^2 to \$0.30/ft^2 depending on the type of grass. The cost of labor for her gardener to put down the sod is \$400. If the homeowner has budgeted \$850 for the project, determine the price range per square foot of sod that she can afford.

For Exercises 99–100, determine the set of x values for which the radical expression would produce a real number.

99. a. $\sqrt{x - 12}$ **b.** $\sqrt{12 - x}$

100. a. $\sqrt{5x + 7}$ **b.** $\sqrt[3]{5x + 7}$

SECTION 1.8

For Exercises 101–110, solve the equation or inequality. Write the solution set to the inequalities in interval notation if possible.

101. a. $|w + 2| + 1 = 6$ **102. a.** $3 = |7x + 1| + 4$

b. $|w + 2| + 1 < 6$ **b.** $3 < |7x + 1| + 4$

c. $|w + 2| + 1 \ge 6$ **c.** $3 \ge |7x + 1| + 4$

103. a. $|y + 5| - 3 = -3$ **104. a.** $|x - 1| = |3x + 5|$

b. $|y + 5| - 3 < -3$ **b.** $|x - 1| = |x + 5|$

c. $|y + 5| - 3 \le -3$ **c.** $|x - 1| = |1 - x|$

d. $|y + 5| - 3 > -3$

e. $|y + 5| - 3 \ge -3$

105. $-5 = -|5x + 1| - 4$

106. $\left|\dfrac{1}{2}x + \dfrac{2}{3}\right| - \dfrac{1}{6} = 1$

107. $|2x| = \left|\dfrac{1}{2}x\right|$ **108.** $4|x + 2| - 10 \geq -6$

109. $|0.5x - 8| < 0.01$ **110.** $-9 \leq 4 - |2k - 1|$

For Exercises 111–112, (a) write an absolute value inequality that represents the given statement and (b) solve the inequality.

111. The distance between x and 3 on a number line is no more than 0.5.

112. The distance between t and -2 on a number line exceeds 0.01.

CHAPTER 1   Test

1. Write the expression in terms of i and simplify.
$\sqrt{-25} \cdot \sqrt{-4}$

2. Simplify the powers of i.
   a. i^{89} **b.** i^{46} **c.** i^{35} **d.** i^{120} **e.** i^{-11}

For Exercises 3–5, perform the indicated operations. Write the answers in the form $a + bi$.

3. $(4 - 7i)(6 + 2i)$ **4.** $(3 - 5i)^2$ **5.** $\dfrac{4 + 3i}{2 - 5i}$

For Exercises 6–8, (a) evaluate the discriminant and (b) determine the number and type of solutions to the equation.

6. $2x^2 - 4x + 7 - 0$

7. $x^2 + 25 = 10x$

8. $3x(x + 4) = 2x - 2$

For Exercises 9–24, solve the equation.

9. $3y + 2[5(y - 4) - 2] = 5y + 6(7 + y) - 3$

10. $\dfrac{2 + t}{6} - \dfrac{3t - 1}{4} = 1 - \dfrac{2t - 5}{3}$

11. $0.4(w + 1) + 0.8 = 0.1w + 0.3(4 + w)$

12. $\dfrac{-11}{2x^2 + x - 15} - \dfrac{2}{2x - 5} = \dfrac{1}{x + 3}$

13. $(3x - 4)^2 - 2 = 11$

14. $y^2 + 10y = 4$

15. $6t(2t + 1) = 5 - 5t$

16. $\dfrac{3x^2}{4} - x = -\dfrac{1}{2}$

17. $12y^3 + 24y^2 = 3y + 6$

18. $(2y - 3)^{1/3} - (4y + 5)^{1/3} = 0$

19. $\sqrt{2d} = 1 - \sqrt{d + 7}$

20. $\dfrac{c}{c + 6} - 4 = \dfrac{72}{c^2 - 36}$

21. $w^{4/5} - 11 = 0$

22. $\left(5 - \dfrac{2}{k}\right)^2 - 6\left(5 - \dfrac{2}{k}\right) - 27 = 0$

23. $-2 = |x - 3| - 6$

24. $|2v + 5| = |2v - 1|$

For Exercises 25–27, solve for the indicated variable.

25. $aP - 4 = Pt + 2$ for P

26. $\sqrt{a^2 - b^2} = c$ for $b > 0$

27. $-16t^2 + v_0 t + 2 = 0$ for t

28. Given $A = \{x \mid x < 2\}$, $B = \{x \mid x \geq 0\}$, and $C = (x \mid x < -1\}$, find
   a. $A \cup B$ **b.** $A \cap B$
   c. $A \cup C$ **d.** $A \cap C$
   e. $B \cup C$ **f.** $B \cap C$

For Exercises 29–31, solve the compound inequality. Write the answer in interval notation if possible.

29. $-2 \leq \dfrac{4 - x}{3} \leq 6$

30. $-\dfrac{4}{3}y < -24$ or $y + 7 \leq 2y - 3$

31. $3(x - 5) + 1 \leq 4(x + 2) + 6$ and $0.3x - 1.6 > 0.2$

For Exercises 32–35, solve the equations and inequalities. Write the answers to the inequalities in interval notation if possible.

32. $2 < -1 + |4w - 3|$ **33.** $-|8 - v| \geq -6$

34. a. $|7x + 4| + 11 = 2$ **b.** $|7x + 4| + 11 < 2$
    c. $|7x + 4| + 11 > 2$

35. a. $|x - 13| + 4 = 4$ **b.** $|x - 13| + 4 < 4$
    c. $|x - 13| + 4 \leq 4$ **d.** $|x - 13| + 4 > 4$
    e. $|x - 13| + 4 \geq 4$

36. How much of an 80% antifreeze solution should be mixed with 2 gal of a 50% antifreeze solution to make a 60% antifreeze solution?

37. Two passengers leave the airport at Denver, Colorado. One takes a 2.3-hr flight to Seattle, Washington, and the other takes a 3.3-hr flight to New York City. The plane flying to New York flies 60 mph faster than the plane flying to Seattle. If the total distance traveled by both planes is 2662 mi, determine the average speed of each plane.

38. Kelly has an aboveground swimming pool. Using water from one hose requires 3 hr to fill the pool. If a second hose is turned on, the pool can be filled in 1.2 hr. How long would it take the second hose to fill the pool if it worked alone?

39. Total cholesterol is made up of LDL and HDL cholesterol. Suppose that the ratio of a patient's total cholesterol to HDL cholesterol is 3.8 and her HDL is 70 mg/dL. Determine the patient's LDL cholesterol level and total cholesterol.

40. A garden area is configured in the shape of a rectangle with two right triangles of equal size attached at the ends. The length of the rectangle is 18 ft. The height of the right triangles is 7 ft longer than the base. If the total area of the garden is 276 ft^2, determine the base and height of the triangular portions.

41. A varsity soccer player kicks a soccer ball approximately straight upward with an initial velocity of 60 ft/sec. The ball leaves the player's foot at a height of 2 ft.

   a. Use the formlua
   $$s = -\tfrac{1}{2}gt^2 + v_0 t + s_0$$
   to write a model representing the height of the ball s (in ft), t seconds after being kicked. Assume that the acceleration due to gravity is $g = 32$ ft/sec^2.

   b. Determine the times at which the ball is 52 ft in the air.

42. A golfer plays 5 rounds of golf with the following scores: 92, 88, 85, 90, and 89. What score would he need on his sixth round to have an average below 88?

CHAPTER 1 Cumulative Review Exercises

For Exercises 1–7, perform the indicated operations and simplify the expression.

1. $[(5x + 3)^2 - (5x - 3)^2]^2$

2. $\left(4\sqrt{3} + 2\sqrt{2}\right)\left(4\sqrt{3} - 2\sqrt{2}\right)$

3. $\dfrac{3x^2 - x - 4}{4x^2 - 8x - 12} \div \dfrac{3x - 4}{6x^2 - 54}$

4. $\dfrac{6}{x + 2} - \dfrac{5}{x - 2} + \dfrac{x}{x^2 - 4}$

5. $\dfrac{\dfrac{1}{5x} - \dfrac{3}{5}}{\dfrac{2}{x} + \dfrac{1}{5}}$

6. $\dfrac{2}{\sqrt{7} + \sqrt{3}}$

7. $\sqrt[3]{81y^5 z^2 w^{12}}$

8. a. Write an absolute value expression that represents the distance between 4π and 11 on the number line.

   b. Simplify the expression from part (a) without absolute value bars.

9. Factor. $4x^3 - 32y^6$

10. Divide and write the answer in the form $a + bi$.
   $$\dfrac{3 - 7i}{2 + 5i}$$

11. Stephan borrowed a total of $8000 in two student loans. One loan charged 4% simple interest and the other charged 5% simple interest, both payable after graduation. If the interest he owed after 1 yr was $380, determine the amount of principal for each loan.

For Exercises 12–17, solve the equation.

12. $(4x - 1)^2 + 3 = 6$

13. $2x(x - 4) = 2x + 5$

14. $2\left(\dfrac{x}{3} + 1\right)^2 + 5\left(\dfrac{x}{3} + 1\right) - 12 = 0$

15. $\sqrt{x + 4} - 2 = x$

16. $-|5 - x| + 6 = 4$

17. $x - 9 = \dfrac{72}{x - 8}$

18. Given $A = \{x \mid x < 11\}$, $B = \{x \mid x \geq 4\}$, and $C = \{x \mid x < 2\}$, find

   a. $A \cup B$ **b.** $A \cap B$ **c.** $A \cup C$

   d. $A \cap C$ **e.** $B \cup C$ **f.** $B \cap C$

For Exercises 19–20, solve the inequality and write the solution set in interval notation.

19. $|2x - 11| + 1 \leq 12$

20. $-\dfrac{3}{5}y < 15$

Functions and Graphs

Each year the IRS (Internal Revenue Service) publishes tax rates that tell us how much federal income tax we need to pay based on our adjusted gross income. For example, a single person with adjusted gross income of more than $8375 but not more than $34,000 is taxed at a rate of 15%. However, finding adjusted gross income is not always trivial. There are numerous variables that come into play. The IRS takes into account exemptions, deductions, and tax credits among other things.

In Chapter 2, we will look at mathematical relationships involving two or more variables. To fully appreciate the connection among several variables, we will investigate their relationships to each other algebraically, numerically, and graphically.

Schedule X—If your filling status is Single

| If your taxable income is: | | The tax is: | |
Over—	But not over—		of the amount over—
$0	$8,375	——— 10%	$0
8,375	34,000	$837.50 + 15%	8,375
34,000	82,400	4,681.25 + 25%	34,000
82,400	171,850	16,781.25 + 28%	82,400
171,850	373,650	41,827.25 + 33%	171,850
373,650	———	108,421.25 + 35%	373,650

(*Source*: Internal Revenue Service, www.irs.gov)

The Rectangular Coordinate System and Graphing Utilities

OBJECTIVES

1. Plot Points on a Rectangular Coordinate System
2. Use the Distance and Midpoint Formulas
3. Graph Equations by Plotting Points
4. Identify x- and y-Intercepts
5. Graph Equations Using a Graphing Utility

Websites, newspapers, sporting events, and the workplace all utilize graphs and tables to present data. Therefore, it is important to learn how to create and interpret meaningful graphs. Understanding how points are located relative to a fixed origin is important for many graphing applications. For example, computer game developers use a rectangular coordinate system to define the locations of objects moving around the screen.

1. Plot Points on a Rectangular Coordinate System

Mathematician, René Descartes (pronounced "day cart") (1597–1650) was the first to identify points in a plane by a pair of coordinates. He did this by intersecting two perpendicular number lines with the point of intersection called the **origin.** These lines form a **rectangular coordinate system** (also known in his honor as the **Cartesian coordinate system**) or simply a **coordinate plane.** The horizontal line is called the **x-axis** and the vertical line is called the **y-axis.** The x- and y-axes divide the plane into four **quadrants.** The quadrants are labeled counterclockwise as I, II, III, and IV (Figure 2-1).

Every point in the plane can be uniquely identified by using an ordered pair (x, y) to specify its coordinates with respect to the origin. In an ordered pair, the first coordinate is called the **x-coordinate,** and the second is called the **y-coordinate.** The origin is identified as (0, 0). In Figure 2-2, six points have been graphed. The point (−3, 5), for example, is placed 3 units in the negative x direction (to the left) and 5 units in the positive y direction (upward).

Figure 2-1

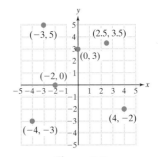

Figure 2-2

2. Use the Distance and Midpoint Formulas

Recall that the distance between two points A and B on a number line can be represented by $|A - B|$ or $|B - A|$. Now we want to find the distance between two points in a coordinate plane. For example, consider the points (1, 5) and (4, 9). The distance d between the points is labeled in Figure 2-3. The dashed horizontal and vertical line segments form a right triangle with hypotenuse d.

The horizontal distance between the points is $|4 - 1| = 3$.
The vertical distance between the points is $|9 - 5| = 4$.

Figure 2-3

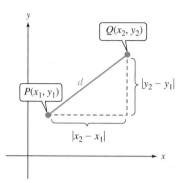

Figure 2-4

Applying the Pythagorean theorem, we have

$$d^2 = (3)^2 + (4)^2$$

$$d = \sqrt{(3)^2 + (4)^2} = \sqrt{25} = 5$$

Since d is a distance, reject the negative square root.

The distance between the points is 5 units.

We can make this process generic by labeling the points $P(x_1, y_1)$ and $Q(x_2, y_2)$. See Figure 2-4.

- The horizontal leg of the right triangle is $|x_2 - x_1|$ or equivalently $|x_1 - x_2|$.
- The vertical leg of the right triangle is $|y_2 - y_1|$ or equivalently $|y_1 - y_2|$.

Applying the Pythagorean theorem, we have

$$d^2 = (x_2 - x_1)^2 + (y_2 - y_1)^2$$

$$d = \sqrt{(x_2 - x_1)^2 + (y_2 - y_1)^2}$$

We can drop the absolute value bars because $|a|^2 = (a)^2$ for all real numbers a. Likewise $|x_2 - x_1|^2 = (x_2 - x_1)^2$ and $|y_2 - y_1|^2 = (y_2 - y_1)^2$.

> **TIP** Since
> $$(x_2 - x_1)^2 = (x_1 - x_2)^2$$
> and
> $$(y_2 - y_1)^2 = (y_1 - y_2)^2,$$
> the distance formula can also be expressed as
> $$d = \sqrt{(x_1 - x_2)^2 + (y_1 - y_2)^2}.$$

Distance Formula

The distance between points (x_1, y_1) and (x_2, y_2) is given by

$$d = \sqrt{(x_2 - x_1)^2 + (y_2 - y_1)^2}$$

EXAMPLE 1   Finding the Distance Between Two Points

Find the distance between the points $(-5, 1)$ and $(7, -3)$. Give the exact distance and an approximation to 2 decimal places.

Solution:

$$(-5, 1) \quad \text{and} \quad (7, -3)$$
$$(x_1, y_1) \quad \text{and} \quad (x_2, y_2)$$

Label the points. Note that the choice for (x_1, y_1) and (x_2, y_2) will not affect the outcome.

$$d = \sqrt{[7 - (-5)]^2 + (-3 - 1)^2}$$

Apply the distance formula.
$$d = \sqrt{(x_2 - x_1)^2 + (y_2 - y_1)^2}$$

$$= \sqrt{(12)^2 + (-4)^2}$$

Simplify the radical.

$$= \sqrt{160}$$

$$= 4\sqrt{10} \approx 12.65$$

The exact distance is $4\sqrt{10}$ units. This is approximately 12.65 units.

> **Skill Practice 1**   Find the distance between the points $(-1, 4)$ and $(3, -6)$. Give the exact distance and an approximation to 2 decimal places.

> **Avoiding Mistakes**
>
> A statement of the form "if p, then q" is called a **conditional statement**. Its **converse** is the statement "if q, then p." The converse of a statement is not necessarily true. However, in the case of the Pythagorean theorem, the converse is a true statement.

The Pythagorean theorem tells us that if a right triangle has legs of lengths a and b and a hypotenuse of length c, then $a^2 + b^2 = c^2$. The following related statement is also true: If $a^2 + b^2 = c^2$, then a triangle with sides of lengths a, b, and c is a right triangle. We use this important concept in Example 2.

Answer

1. $2\sqrt{29}$ units ≈ 10.77 units

EXAMPLE 2   **Determining if Three Points Form the Vertices of a Right Triangle**

Determine if the points $M(-2, -3)$, $P(4, 1)$, and $Q(-1, 7)$ form the vertices of a right triangle.

Solution:

Determine the distance between each pair of points.

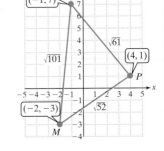

$$d(M, P) = \sqrt{[4 - (-2)]^2 + [1 - (-3)]^2} = \sqrt{52}$$
$$d(P, Q) = \sqrt{(-1 - 4)^2 + (7 - 1)^2} = \sqrt{61}$$
$$d(M, Q) = \sqrt{[-1 - (-2)]^2 + [7 - (-3)]^2} = \sqrt{101}$$

The line segment $\overline{MQ}$ is the longest and would potentially be the hypotenuse, c. Label the shorter sides as a and b.

Check the condition that $a^2 + b^2 = c^2$.

$$(\sqrt{52})^2 + (\sqrt{61})^2 \overset{?}{=} (\sqrt{101})^2$$
$$52 + 61 \neq 101$$

The points M, P, and Q do not form the vertices of a right triangle.

Skill Practice 2   Determine if the points $X(-6, -4)$, $Y(2, -2)$, and $Z(0, 5)$ form the vertices of a right triangle.

Now suppose that we want to find the midpoint of the line segment between the distinct points (x_1, y_1) and (x_2, y_2). The **midpoint** of a line segment is the point equidistant (the same distance) from the endpoints (Figure 2-5).

The x-coordinate of the midpoint is the average of the x-coordinates from the endpoints. Likewise, the y-coordinate of the midpoint is the average of the y-coordinates from the endpoints.

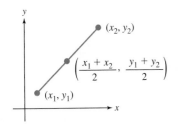

Figure 2-5

Midpoint Formula

The midpoint of the line segment with endpoints (x_1, y_1) and (x_2, y_2) is

$$M = \left(\frac{x_1 + x_2}{2}, \frac{y_1 + y_2}{2} \right)$$

average of   average of
x-coordinates y-coordinates

Avoiding Mistakes

The midpoint of a line segment is an ordered pair (with two coordinates), not a single number.

EXAMPLE 3   **Finding the Midpoint of a Line Segment**

Find the midpoint of the line segment with endpoints $(4.2, -4)$ and $(-2.8, 3)$.

Solution:

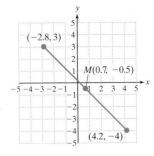

$(4.2, -4)$ and $(-2.8, 3)$

(x_1, y_1) and (x_2, y_2) Label the points.

$$M = \left(\frac{4.2 + (-2.8)}{2}, \frac{-4 + 3}{2} \right)$$ Apply the midpoint formula.

$$= \left(0.7, -\frac{1}{2} \right) \quad \text{or} \quad (0.7, -0.5)$$ Simplify.

Answer

2. No

> **Skill Practice 3**   Find the midpoint of the line segment with endpoints $(-1.5, -9)$ and $(-8.7, 4)$.

3. Graph Equations by Plotting Points

The relationship between two variables can often be expressed as a graph or expressed algebraically as an equation. For example, suppose that two variables, x and y, are related such that y is 2 more than x. An equation to represent this relationship is $y = x + 2$. A **solution to an equation** in the variables x and y is an ordered pair (x, y) that when substituted into the equation makes the equation a true statement.

For example, the following ordered pairs are solutions to the equation $y = x + 2$.

Solution	$y = x + 2$
$(0, 2)$	$2 = 0 + 2$ ✓
$(-4, -2)$	$-2 = -4 + 2$ ✓
$(2, 4)$	$4 = 2 + 2$ ✓

The set of all solutions to an equation is called the **solution set of the equation.** The graph of all solutions to an equation is called the **graph of the equation.** The graph of $y = x + 2$ is shown in Figure 2-6.

One of the goals of this text is to identify families of equations and the characteristics of their graphs. As we proceed through the text, we will develop tools to graph equations efficiently. For now, we present the **point-plotting method** to graph the solution set of an equation. In Example 4, we start by selecting several values of x and using the equation to calculate the corresponding values of y. Then we plot the points to form a general outline of the curve and connect the points to form a smooth line or curve.

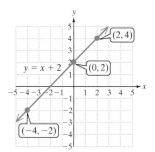

Figure 2-6

> **EXAMPLE 4**   **Graphing an Equation by Plotting Points**
>
> Graph the equation by plotting points. $y - |x| = -1$
>
> **Solution:**
>
> $y - |x| = -1$ Solve for y in terms of x.
> $\quad\quad y = |x| - 1$ Arbitrarily select negative and positive values for x such as -3, -2, -1, 0, 1, 2, and 3. Then use the equation to calculate the corresponding y values.
>
> | x | y | $y = |x| - 1$ | Ordered pair |
> |---|---|---|---|
> | -3 | 2 | $y = |-3| - 1 = 2$ | $(-3, 2)$ |
> | -2 | 1 | $y = |-2| - 1 = 1$ | $(-2, 1)$ |
> | -1 | 0 | $y = |-1| - 1 = 0$ | $(-1, 0)$ |
> | 0 | -1 | $y = |0| - 1 = -1$ | $(0, -1)$ |
> | 1 | 0 | $y = |1| - 1 = 0$ | $(1, 0)$ |
> | 2 | 1 | $y = |2| - 1 = 1$ | $(2, 1)$ |
> | 3 | 2 | $y = |3| - 1 = 2$ | $(3, 2)$ |
>
>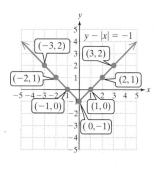
>
> **Skill Practice 4**   Graph the equation by plotting points. $x^2 + y = 4$

Answers

3. $\left(-5.1, -\dfrac{5}{2}\right)$ or $(-5.1, -2.5)$

4.

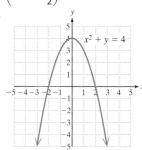

The graph of an equation in the variables x and y represents a relationship between a real number x and a corresponding real number y. Therefore, the values of x must be chosen so that when substituted into the equation, they produce a real number for y. Sometimes the values of x must be restricted to produce real numbers for y. This is demonstrated in Example 5.

EXAMPLE 5   **Graphing an Equation by Plotting Points**

Graph the equation by plotting points. $y^2 - 1 = x$

Solution:

$$y^2 - 1 = x \qquad \text{Solve for } y \text{ in terms of } x.$$
$$y^2 = x + 1$$
$$y = \pm\sqrt{x + 1} \qquad \text{Apply the square root property.}$$

Choose $x \geq -1$ so that the radicand is nonnegative.

TIP In Example 5, we chose several convenient values of x such as $-1, 0, 3,$ and 8 so that the radicand would be a perfect square.

x	y	$y = \pm\sqrt{x + 1}$	Ordered pairs
-1	0	$y = \pm\sqrt{(-1) + 1} = 0$	$(-1, 0)$
0	± 1	$y = \pm\sqrt{(0) + 1} = \pm 1$	$(0, 1), (0, -1)$
1	$\pm\sqrt{2}$	$y = \pm\sqrt{(1) + 1} = \pm\sqrt{2}$ ≈ 1.4	$(1, \sqrt{2}), (1, -\sqrt{2})$
3	± 2	$y = \pm\sqrt{(3) + 1} = \pm 2$	$(3, 2), (3, -2)$
8	± 3	$y = \pm\sqrt{(8) + 1} = \pm 3$	$(8, 3), (8, -3)$

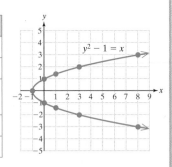

Skill Practice 5   Graph the equation by plotting points. $x + y^2 = 2$

---

4. Identify x- and y-Intercepts

When analyzing graphs, we want to examine their most important features. Two key features are the x- and y-intercepts of a graph. These are the points where a graph intersects the x- and y-axes.

Any point on the x-axis has a y-coordinate of zero. Therefore, an **x-intercept** is a point $(a, 0)$ where a graph intersects the x-axis (Figure 2-7). Any point on the y-axis has an x-coordinate of zero. Therefore, a **y-intercept** is a point $(0, b)$ where a graph intersects the y-axis (Figure 2-7).

Figure 2-7

TIP In some applications, we may refer to an x-intercept as the x-*coordinate* of a point of intersection that a graph makes with the x-axis. For example, if an x-intercept is $(-4, 0)$, then the x-intercept may be stated simply as -4 (the y-coordinate is understood to be zero). Similarly, we may refer to a y-intercept as the y-*coordinate* of a point of intersection that a graph makes with the y-axis. For example, if a y-intercept is $(0, 2)$, then it may be stated simply as 2.

Answer

5.

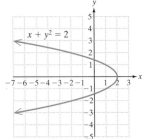

To find the x- and y-intercepts from an equation in x and y, follow these steps.

Determining x- and y-Intercepts from an Equation

Given an equation in x and y,

- Find the x-intercept(s) by substituting 0 for y in the equation and solving for x.
- Find the y-intercept(s) by substituting 0 for x in the equation and solving for y.

> ### EXAMPLE 6   Finding *x*- and *y*-Intercepts
>
> Given the equation $y = |x| - 1$,
>
> **a.** Find the *x*-intercept(s).   **b.** Find the *y*-intercept(s).
>
> **Solution:**
>
> **a.** $y = |x| - 1$
>
> $\quad\quad 0 = |x| - 1$ To find the *x*-intercept(s), substitute 0 for *y* and solve for *x*.
>
> $\quad\quad |x| = 1$ Isolate the absolute value.
>
> $\quad\quad x = 1 \quad \text{or} \quad x = -1$ Recall that for $k > 0$, $|x| = k$ is equivalent to $x = k$ or $x = -k$.
>
> The *x*-intercepts are $(1, 0)$ and $(-1, 0)$.
>
> **b.** $y = |x| - 1$
>
> $\quad = |0| - 1$ To find the *y*-intercept(s), substitute 0 for *x* and solve for *y*.
>
> $\quad = -1$
>
> The *y*-intercept is $(0, -1)$.
>
> The intercepts $(1, 0)$, $(-1, 0)$, and $(0, -1)$ are consistent with the graph of the equation $y = |x| - 1$ found in Example 4 (Figure 2-8).

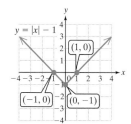

Figure 2-8

> **Skill Practice 6**   Given the equation $y = x^2 - 4$,
>
> **a.** Find the *x*-intercept(s).   **b.** Find the *y*-intercept(s).

> **TIP** Sometimes when solving for an *x*- or *y*-intercept, we encounter an equation with an imaginary solution. In such a case, the graph has no *x*- or *y*-intercept.
>
>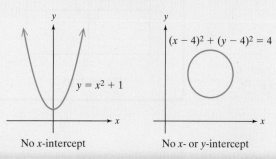
>
> No *x*-intercept   No *x*- or *y*-intercept

5. Graph Equations Using a Graphing Utility

Graphing by the point-plotting method should only be considered a beginning strategy for creating the graphs of equations in two variables. We will quickly enhance this method with other techniques that are less cumbersome and use more analysis and strategy.

One weakness of the point-plotting method is that it may be slow to execute by pencil and paper. Also, the selected points must fairly represent the shape of the graph. Otherwise the sketch will be inaccurate. Graphing utilities can help with both of these weaknesses. They can graph many points quickly, and the more points that are plotted, the greater the likelihood that we see the key features of the graph. Graphing utilities include graphing calculators, spreadsheets, specialty graphing programs, and apps on phones.

Figures 2-9 and 2-10 show a table and a graph for $y = x^2 - 3$.

TECHNOLOGY CONNECTIONS

Using the Table Feature and Graphing an Equation

Figure 2-9

In Figure 2-9, we first enter the equation into the graphing editor. Notice that the calculator expects the equation represented with the y variable isolated.

To set up a table, enter the starting value for x, in this case, -3. Then set the increment by which to increase x, in this case 1. The x-increment is entered as ΔTbl (read "delta table"). Using the "Auto" setting means that the table of values for the independent and dependent variables will be automatically generated.

The table shows seven x-y pairs but more can be accessed by using the up and down arrow keys on the keypad.

> **TIP** The Greek letter Δ ("delta") written before a variable represents an increment of change in that variable. In this context, it represents the change from one value of x to the next.

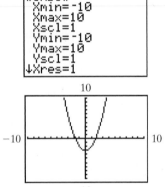

Figure 2-10

> **TIP** The calculator plots a large number of points and then connects the points. So instead of graphing a single smooth curve, it graphs a series of short line segments. This may give the graph a jagged look (Figure 2-10).

The graph in Figure 2-10 is shown between x- and y-values from -10 to 10. The tick marks on the axes are 1 unit apart. The viewing window with these parameters is denoted $[-10, 10, 1]$ by $[-10, 10, 1]$.

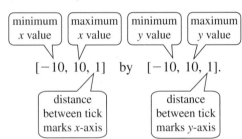

EXAMPLE 7   Graphing Equations Using a Graphing Utility

Use a graphing utility to graph $y = |x| - 15$ and $y = -x^2 + 12$ on the viewing window defined by $[-20, 20, 2]$ by $[-15, 15, 3]$.

Solution:

Enter the equations using the Y= editor.

Use the WINDOW editor to change the viewing window parameters. The variables Xmin, Xmax, and Xscl relate to $[-20, 20, 2]$. The variables Ymin, Ymax, and Yscl relate to $[-15, 15, 3]$.

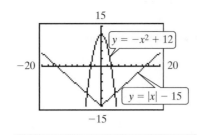

Select the GRAPH feature. Notice that the graphs of both equations appear. This provides us with a tool for visually examining two different models at the same time.

Answer

7.

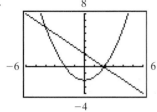

Skill Practice 7   Use a graphing utility to graph $y = -x + 2$ and $y = -0.5x^2 - 2$ on the viewing window $[-6, 6, 1]$ by $[-4, 8, 1]$.

| SECTION 2.1 | Practice Exercises |

Concept Connections

1. In a rectangular coordinate system, the point where the x- and y-axes meet is called the _____.

2. The x- and y-axes divide the coordinate plane into four regions called _____.

3. The distance between two distinct points (x_1, y_1) and (x_2, y_2) is given by the formula _____.

4. The midpoint of the line segment with endpoints (x_1, y_1) and (x_2, y_2) is given by the formula _____.

5. A _____ to an equation in the variables x and y is an ordered pair (x, y) that makes the equation a true statement.

6. An x-intercept of a graph has a y-coordinate of _____.

7. A y-intercept of a graph has an x-coordinate of _____.

8. Given an equation in the variables x and y, find the y-intercept by substituting _____ for x and solving for _____.

Objective 1: Plot Points on a Rectangular Coordinate System

For Exercises 9–10, plot the points on a rectangular coordinate system.

9. $A(-3, -4)$ $B\left(\dfrac{5}{3}, \dfrac{7}{4}\right)$ $C(-1.2, 3.8)$ $D(\pi, -5)$ $E(0, 4.5)$ $F\left(\sqrt{5}, 0\right)$

10. $A(-2, -5)$ $B\left(\dfrac{9}{2}, \dfrac{7}{3}\right)$ $C(-3.6, 2.1)$ $D(5, -\pi)$ $E(3.4, 0)$ $F\left(0, \sqrt{3}\right)$

Objective 2: Use the Distance and Midpoint Formulas

For Exercises 11–18,

a. Find the exact distance between the points. (**See Example 1**)

b. Find the midpoint of the line segment whose endpoints are the given points. (**See Example 3**)

11. $(-2, 7)$ and $(-4, 11)$ **12.** $(-1, -3)$ and $(3, -7)$ **13.** $(-7, -4)$ and $(2, 5)$

14. $(3, 6)$ and $(-4, -1)$ **15.** $(2.2, -2.4)$ and $(5.2, -6.4)$ **16.** $(37.1, -24.7)$ and $(31.1, -32.7)$

17. $\left(\sqrt{5}, -\sqrt{2}\right)$ and $\left(4\sqrt{5}, -7\sqrt{2}\right)$ **18.** $\left(\sqrt{7}, -3\sqrt{5}\right)$ and $\left(2\sqrt{7}, \sqrt{5}\right)$

For Exercises 19–22, determine if the given points form the vertices of a right triangle. (See Example 2)

19. $(1, 3)$, $(3, 1)$, and $(0, -2)$ **20.** $(1, 2)$, $(3, 0)$, and $(-3, -2)$

21. $(-2, 4)$, $(5, 0)$, and $(-5, 1)$ **22.** $(-6, 2)$, $(3, 1)$, and $(1, -2)$

Objective 3: Graph Equations by Plotting Points

For Exercises 23–24, determine if the given points are solutions to the equation.

23. $x^2 + y = 1$

   a. $(-2, -3)$ **b.** $(4, -17)$ **c.** $\left(\dfrac{1}{2}, \dfrac{3}{4}\right)$

24. $|x - 3| - y = 4$

   a. $(1, -2)$ **b.** $(-2, -3)$ **c.** $\left(\dfrac{1}{10}, -\dfrac{11}{10}\right)$

For Exercises 25–30, identify the set of values x for which y will be a real number.

25. $y = \dfrac{2}{x - 3}$ **26.** $y = \dfrac{2}{x + 7}$ **27.** $y = \sqrt{x - 10}$

28. $y = \sqrt{x + 11}$ **29.** $y = \sqrt{1.5 - x}$ **30.** $y = \sqrt{2.2 - x}$

For Exercises 31–44, graph the equations by plotting points. (See Examples 4–5)

31. $y = x$ **32.** $y = x^2$ **33.** $y = \sqrt{x}$

34. $y = |x|$ **35.** $y = x^3$ **36.** $y = \dfrac{1}{x}$

37. $y - |x| = 2$ **38.** $|x| + y = 3$ **39.** $y^2 - x - 2 = 0$

40. $y^2 - x + 1 = 0$ **41.** $x = |y| + 1$ **42.** $x = |y| - 3$

43. $y = |x + 1|$ **44.** $y = |x - 2|$

Objective 4: Identify *x*- and *y*-Intercepts

For Exercises 45–52, estimate the *x*- and *y*-intercepts from the graph.

45.

46.

47.

48.

49.

50.

51.

52.

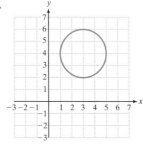

For Exercises 53–54, determine the *x*- and *y*-intercepts of the graph whose points are defined in the spreadsheet.

53.

	A	B	C	D	E	F	G	H
1	x	-1	0	1	2	3	4	5
2	y	-4	-2	0	2	4	6	8

54.

	A	B	C	D	E	F	G	H
1	x	-10	-5	0	5	10	15	20
2	y	-3	0	4	9	15	22	30

For Exercises 55–66, find the *x*- and *y*-intercepts. (See Example 6)

55. $-2x + 4y = 12$

56. $-3x - 5y = 60$

57. $x^2 + y = 9$

58. $x^2 = -y + 16$

59. $y = |x - 5| - 2$

60. $y = |x + 4| - 3$

61. $x = y^2 - 1$

62. $x = y^2 - 4$

63. $|x| = |y|$

64. $x = |5y|$

65. $\dfrac{(x - 3)^2}{4} + \dfrac{(y - 4)^2}{9} = 1$

66. $\dfrac{(x + 6)^2}{16} + \dfrac{(y + 3)^2}{4} = 1$

Mixed Exercises

67. A map of a wilderness area is drawn with the origin placed at the parking area. Two fire observation platforms are located at points *A* and *B*. If a fire is located at point *C*, which observation tower is closer to the fire?

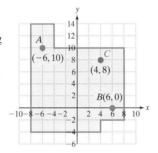

68. A map of a state park is drawn so that the origin is placed at the visitor center. The distance between grid lines is 1 mi. Suppose that two hikers are located at points *A* and *B*.

  a. Determine the distance between the hikers.

  b. If the hikers want to meet for lunch, determine the location of the midpoint between the hikers.

For Exercises 69–70, assume that the units shown in the grid are in feet.

a. Determine the exact length and width of the rectangle shown.

b. Determine the perimeter and area.

69.

70.

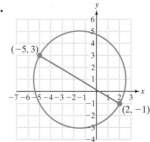

For Exercises 71–72, the endpoints of a diameter of a circle are shown. Find the center and radius of the circle.

71.

72.

For Exercises 73–74, an isosceles triangle is shown (an isosceles triangle has two sides of equal length). **Find the area of the triangle. Assume that the units shown in the grid are in meters.** (*Hint*: Find the midpoint of the base of the triangle. Then use the distance formula to find the base and height.)

73.

74.

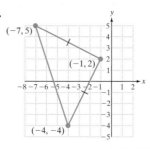

For Exercises 75–80, read the scenario given and **select a graph (a–f) that best models the situation.**

75. Average daily temperature (*y*) for Albuquerque, New Mexico, versus the number of days (*x*) after January 1. Assume that the *x*-axis represents a period of 1 yr.

76. Temperature of a cake (*y*) versus the number of minutes (*x*) after the cake has come out of the oven.

77. Average number of doctors visits per year (*y*) versus the age of patient (*x*).

78. Speed of a car (*y*) versus time (*x*). Assume that the experiment begins at a time at which the car begins merging onto a highway until the time when the driver merges off the highway.

79. Speed of a shopping cart (*y*) versus time (*x*). Assume that the shopping cart starts at rest, and then is blown across a parking lot by the wind until it finally comes to rest after hitting a dumpster.

80. The weight of an individual (*y*) versus the age (*x*) of the individual over the individual's lifetime.

a.

b.

c.

d.

e.

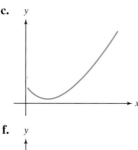

f.

81. The graph shows average life expectancy for males in the United States based on an individual's birth year. The average life expectancy for a man born in 1975 is 68.8 yr. The average life expectancy for a man born in 1995 is 72.5 yr. Assuming a linear trend, estimate the life expectancy for a man born in 1985. (*Source*: U.S. National Center for Health Statistics, www.cdc.gov/nchs)

82. The city of Guayaquil in Ecuador is located on the coast and has an altitude of 10 m above sea level. The city of Quito, located in the mountains of Ecuador, has an altitude of 2810 m above sea level. The high temperature for each city is given for a day in November. Assuming a linear relationship between altitude and temperature, estimate the November high temperature for a city in Ecuador that is 1410 m.

For Exercises 83–86, determine if points A, B, and C are collinear. Three points are collinear if they all fall on the same line. There are several ways that we can determine if three points, A, B, and C are collinear. One method is to determine if the sum of the lengths of the line segments $\overline{AB}$ and $\overline{BC}$ equals the length of $\overline{AC}$.

83. $(2, 2)$, $(4, 3)$, and $(8, 5)$

84. $(2, 1.5)$, $(4, 2)$, and $(8, 3)$

85. $(-2, 8)$, $(1, 2)$, and $(4, -3)$

86. $(-1, 5)$, $(0, 3)$, and $(5, -13)$

Write About It

87. Suppose that d represents the distance between two points (x_1, y_1) and (x_2, y_2). Explain how the distance formula is developed from the Pythagorean theorem.

88. Explain how you might remember the midpoint formula to find the midpoint of the line segment between (x_1, y_1) and (x_2, y_2).

89. Explain how to find the x- and y-intercepts from an equation in the variables x and y.

90. Given an equation in the variables x and y, what does the graph of the equation represent?

Expanding Your Skills

A point in three-dimensional space can be represented in a three-dimensional coordinate system. In such a case, a z-axis is taken perpendicular to both the x- and y-axes. A point A is assigned an ordered triple $A(x, y, z)$ relative to a fixed origin where the three axes meet. For Exercises 91–94, determine the distance between the two given points in space. Use the distance formula

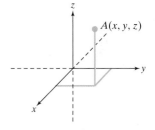

$$d = \sqrt{(x_2 - x_1)^2 + (y_2 - y_1)^2 + (z_2 - z_1)^2}.$$

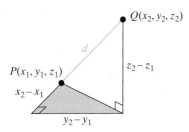

91. $(5, -3, 2)$ and $(4, 6, -1)$

92. $(6, -4, -1)$ and $(2, 3, 1)$

93. $(3, 7, -2)$ and $(0, -5, 1)$

94. $(9, -5, -3)$ and $(2, 0, 1)$

In advanced courses, a complex number $a + bi$ is represented by an ordered pair (a, b). In such a case, we can graph a complex number in a plane in which the horizontal axis represents the real part and the vertical axis represents the imaginary part. This is called the **complex plane**.

For Exercises 95–96, graph the complex number in the complex plane.

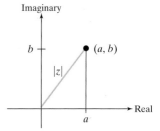

95. a. $3 + 4i$ **b.** $-2 - i$ **c.** 5 **d.** $4i$

96. a. $2 - 3i$ **b.** $-4 - i$ **c.** 3 **d.** $2i$

The absolute value of a complex number $z = a + bi$ is defined as $|z| = \sqrt{a^2 + b^2}$. Geometrically, this is the distance from the point (a, b) in the complex plane to the origin.

For Exercises 97–100, find the absolute value of the complex number.

97. $3 - 4i$

98. $-6 + 8i$

99. $2 - 7i$

100. $1 + 9i$

Objective 5: Graph Equations Using a Graphing Utility (Technology Connections)

101. What is meant by a viewing window on a graphing device?

102. Which of the viewing windows would show both the x- and y-intercepts of the graph of $780x - 42y = 5460$?

    a. $[-20, 20, 2]$ by $[-40, 40, 10]$

    b. $[-10, 10, 1]$ by $[-10, 10, 1]$

    c. $[-10, 10, 1]$ by $[-10, 150, 10]$

    d. $[-10, 10, 1]$ by $[-150, 10, 10]$

For Exercises 103–106, graph the equation with a graphing utility on the given viewing window. (See Example 7)

103. $y = 2x - 5$ on $[-10, 10, 1]$ by $[-10, 10, 1]$

104. $y = -4x + 1$ on $[-10, 10, 1]$ by $[-10, 10, 1]$

105. $y = 1400x^2 - 1200x$ on $[-5, 5, 1]$ by $[-1000, 2000, 500]$

106. $y = -800x^2 + 600x$ on $[-5, 5, 1]$ by $[-1000, 500, 200]$

For Exercises 107–108, graph the equations on the standard viewing window. (See Example 7)

107. a. $y = x^3$

    b. $y = |x| - 9$

108. a. $y = \sqrt{x + 4}$

    b. $y = |x - 2|$

For Exercises 109–110, use a graphing device to create a table of values for the given values of x. Then identify the x- and y-intercepts shown in the table.

109. $y = x^3 - 3x^2 - x + 3$ for $x = -2, -1, 0, 1, 2, 3, 4$

110. $y = x^3 - x^2 - 4x + 4$ for $x = -3, -2, -1, 0, 1, 2, 3$

SECTION 2.2   Circles

OBJECTIVES

1. Write an Equation of a Circle in Standard Form

2. Write the General Form of an Equation of a Circle

1. Write an Equation of a Circle in Standard Form

In addition to graphing equations by plotting points, we will learn to recognize specific categories of equations and the characteristics of their graphs. We begin by presenting the definition of a circle.

> **Definition of a Circle**
>
> A **circle** is the set of all points in a plane that are equidistant from a fixed point called the **center.** The fixed distance from any point on the circle to the center is called the **radius.**

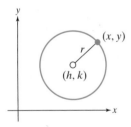

Figure 2-11

The radius of a circle is often denoted by r, where $r > 0$. It is also important to note that the center is not actually part of the graph of a circle. It will be drawn in the text as an open dot for reference only.

Suppose that a circle is centered at the point (h, k) and has radius r (Figure 2-11). The distance formula can be used to derive an equation of the circle. Let (x, y) be an arbitrary point on the circle. Then by definition the distance between (h, k) and (x, y) must be r.

Apply the distance formula. $\sqrt{(x_2 - x_1)^2 + (y_2 - y_1)^2} = d$

$$\sqrt{(x - h)^2 + (y - k)^2} = r \qquad \text{Distance between } (h, k) \text{ and } (x, y)$$
$$(x - h)^2 + (y - k)^2 = r^2 \qquad \text{Standard form of an equation of a circle}$$

Standard Form of an Equation of a Circle

Given a circle centered at (h, k) with radius r, the **standard form** of an equation of the circle (also called **center-radius form**) is given by

$$(x - h)^2 + (y - k)^2 = r^2 \quad \text{where } r > 0$$

Examples	Standard form	Center	Radius
$(x - 4)^2 + (y + 3)^2 = 25$	$(x - 4)^2 + [y - (-3)]^2 = (5)^2$	$(4, -3)$	5
$x^2 + \left(y - \frac{1}{2}\right)^2 = 12$	$(x - 0)^2 + \left(y - \frac{1}{2}\right)^2 = \left(\sqrt{12}\right)^2$	$\left(0, \frac{1}{2}\right)$	$2\sqrt{3}$
$x^2 + y^2 = 7$	$(x - 0)^2 + (y - 0)^2 = \left(\sqrt{7}\right)^2$	$(0, 0)$	$\sqrt{7}$

In Example 1, we write an equation of a circle in standard form.

EXAMPLE 1   Writing an Equation of a Circle in Standard Form

a. Write the standard form of an equation of the circle with center $(-4, 6)$ and radius 2.

b. Graph the circle.

Solution:

a. $(h, k) = (-4, 6)$ and $r = 2$ Label the center (h, k) and the radius r.

$[x - (-4)]^2 + (y - 6)^2 = (2)^2$ Standard form: $(x - h)^2 + (y - k)^2 = r^2$

$(x + 4)^2 + (y - 6)^2 = 4$ Simplify.

b.

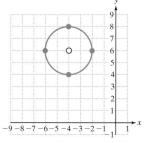

To graph the circle, first locate the center and draw a small open dot. Then plot points r units to the left, right, above, and below the center.

Draw the circle through the points.

Skill Practice 1

a. Write an equation of the circle with center $(3, -1)$ and radius 4.

b. Graph the circle.

EXAMPLE 2   Writing an Equation of a Circle in Standard Form

Write the standard form of an equation of the circle with endpoints of a diameter $(-1, 0)$ and $(3, 4)$.

Solution:

A sketch of this scenario is given in Figure 2-12 on page 210. Notice that the midpoint of the diameter is the center of the circle.

$(-1, 0)$ and $(3, 4)$

(x_1, y_1) and (x_2, y_2) Label the points.

The center is $\left(\dfrac{-1 + 3}{2}, \dfrac{0 + 4}{2}\right) = (1, 2)$.

Answers

1. a. $(x - 3)^2 + (y + 1)^2 = 16$

   b.

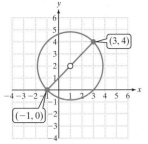

Figure 2-12

The radius of the circle is the distance between either endpoint of the diameter and the center. Using the endpoint $(-1, 0)$ as (x_1, y_1) and the center $(1, 2)$ as (x_2, y_2), apply the distance formula.

$$d = \sqrt{(x_2 - x_1)^2 + (y_2 - y_1)^2}$$
$$r = \sqrt{[1 - (-1)]^2 + (2 - 0)^2} = \sqrt{(2)^2 + (2)^2} = \sqrt{8}$$

An equation of the circle is: $(x - h)^2 + (y - k)^2 = r^2$.

$$(x - 1)^2 + (y - 2)^2 = \left(\sqrt{8}\right)^2$$
$$(x - 1)^2 + (y - 2)^2 = 8 \quad \text{(Standard form)}$$

Skill Practice 2 Write the standard form of an equation of the circle with endpoints of a diameter $(-3, 3)$ and $(-1, -1)$.

2. Write the General Form of an Equation of a Circle

In Example 2 we have the equation $(x - 1)^2 + (y - 2)^2 = 8$. If we expand the binomials and combine like terms, we can write the equation in *general form*.

$$(x - 1)^2 + (y - 2)^2 = 8 \qquad \text{Standard form (center-radius form)}$$
$$x^2 - 2x + 1 + y^2 - 4y + 4 = 8 \qquad \text{Expand the binomials}$$
$$x^2 + y^2 - 2x - 4y - 3 = 0 \qquad \text{General form}$$

General Form of an Equation of a Circle

An equation of a circle written in the form $x^2 + y^2 + Ax + By + C = 0$ is called the **general form** of an equation of a circle.

By completing the square we can write an equation of a circle given in general form as an equation in standard form. The purpose of writing an equation of a circle in standard form is to identify the radius and center. This is demonstrated in Example 3.

EXAMPLE 3 Writing an Equation of a Circle in Standard Form

Write the equation of the circle in standard form. Then identify the center and radius.

$$x^2 + y^2 + 10x - 6y + 25 = 0$$

Solution:

$$x^2 + y^2 + 10x - 6y + 25 = 0$$
$$(x^2 + 10x \quad) + (y^2 - 6y \quad) = -25 \qquad \begin{array}{l}\text{Group the } x \text{ terms. Group the } y \text{ terms.}\\ \text{Move the constant term to the right.}\end{array}$$
$$(x^2 + 10x + 25) + (y^2 - 6y + 9) \qquad \begin{array}{l}\text{Complete the squares.}\\ \text{\textit{Note}: } [\tfrac{1}{2}(10)]^2 = 25, [\tfrac{1}{2}(-6)]^2 = 9\end{array}$$
$$= -25 + 25 + 9$$
$$(x + 5)^2 + (y - 3)^2 = 9 \qquad \text{Factor.}$$

The center is $(-5, 3)$, and the radius is $\sqrt{9} = 3$. See Figure 2-13.

Figure 2-13

Skill Practice 3 Write the equation of the circle in standard form. Then identify the center and radius. $x^2 + y^2 - 8x + 2y - 8 = 0$

Answers

2. $(x + 2)^2 + (y - 1)^2 = 5$
3. $(x - 4)^2 + (y + 1)^2 = 25$;
   Center: $(4, -1)$; Radius: 5

Note that not all equations of the form $x^2 + y^2 + Ax + By + C = 0$ represent the graph of a circle. Completing the square results in an equation of the form $(x - h)^2 + (y - k)^2 = r^2$. In the case where $r^2 > 0$, the graph of the equation will be a circle with radius r. However, if $r^2 = 0$, or if $r^2 < 0$, then the graph will be a single point or nonexistent. These are called **degenerate cases.**

- If $r^2 > 0$, then the graph will be a circle with radius r.
- If $r^2 = 0$, then the graph will be a single point, (h, k). The solution set is $\{(h, k)\}$.
- If $r^2 < 0$, then the solution set is the empty set, { }.

EXAMPLE 4   **Determining if an Equation Represents the Graph of a Circle**

Write the equation in the form $(x - h)^2 + (y - k)^2 = r^2$, and identify the solution set.

$$x^2 + y^2 - 14y + 49 = 0$$

Solution:

$x^2 + y^2 - 14y + 49 = 0$	
$x^2 + (y^2 - 14y\quad) = -49$	Group the y terms and complete the square. Note that the x^2 term is already a perfect square: $(x - 0)^2$.
$x^2 + (y^2 - 14y + 49) = -49 + 49$	Complete the square: $\left[\frac{1}{2}(-14)\right]^2 = 49$.
$x^2 + (y - 7)^2 = 0$	Factor.

Since $r^2 = 0$, the solution set is $\{(0, 7)\}$. The sum of two squares will equal zero only if each individual term is zero. Therefore, $x = 0$ and $y = 7$.

Skill Practice 4   Write the equation in the form $(x - h)^2 + (y - k)^2 = r^2$, and identify the solution set. $x^2 + y^2 + 2x + 5 = 0$

TECHNOLOGY CONNECTIONS

Setting a Square Viewing Window and Graphing a Circle

A graphing calculator expects an equation with the y variable isolated. Therefore, to graph an equation of a circle such as $(x + 5)^2 + (y - 3)^2 = 9$, from Example 3, we first solve for y.

$$(x + 5)^2 + (y - 3)^2 = 9$$
$$(y - 3)^2 = 9 - (x + 5)^2$$
$$y - 3 = \pm\sqrt{9 - (x + 5)^2}$$
$$y = 3 \pm \sqrt{9 - (x + 5)^2}$$

Notice that the graph looks more oval-shaped than circular. This is because the calculator has a rectangular screen. If the scaling is the same on the x- and y-axes, the graph will appear elongated horizontally. To eliminate this distortion, use a ZSquare option, located in the Zoom menu.

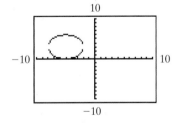

Also notice that the calculator display does not show the upper and lower semicircles connecting at their endpoints when in fact the semicircles should "hook up." This is due to the calculator's limited resolution.

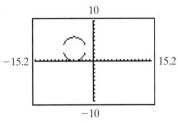

SECTION 2.2	Practice Exercises

Review Exercises

For Exercises 1–2, (a) find the distance between the given points and (b) find the midpoint of the line segment whose endpoints are the given points.

1. $(-5, 2)$ and $(6, 7)$

2. $(4, -3)$ and $(2, -1)$

For Exercises 3–4, find the x- and y-intercepts of the graph of the equation.

3. $x^2 + y^2 = 16$

4. $x^2 + y^2 = 25$

5. If the diameter of a circle is 10 ft, what is the radius?

6. If the radius of a circle is 4.2 in., what is the diameter?

Concept Connections

7. A _____ is the set of all points in a plane equidistant from a fixed point called the _____.

8. The distance from the center of a circle to any point on the circle is called the _____ and is often denoted by r.

9. The standard form of an equation of a circle with center (h, k) and radius r is given by _____.

10. An equation of a circle written in the form $x^2 + y^2 + Ax + By + C = 0$ is called the _____ form of an equation of a circle.

Objective 1: Write an Equation of a Circle in Standard Form

11. Is the point $(2, 7)$ on the circle defined by $(x - 2)^2 + (y - 7)^2 = 4$?

12. Is the point $(3, 5)$ on the circle defined by $(x - 3)^2 + (y - 5)^2 = 36$?

13. Is the point $(-4, 7)$ on the circle defined by $(x + 1)^2 + (y - 3)^2 = 25$?

14. Is the point $(2, -7)$ on the circle defined by $(x + 6)^2 + (y + 1)^2 = 100$?

For Exercises 15–22, determine the center and radius of the circle.

15. $(x - 4)^2 + (y + 2)^2 = 81$

16. $(x + 3)^2 + (y - 1)^2 = 16$

17. $x^2 + (y - 2.5)^2 = 6.25$

18. $(x - 1.5)^2 + y^2 = 2.25$

19. $x^2 + y^2 = 20$

20. $x^2 + y^2 = 28$

21. $\left(x - \dfrac{3}{2}\right)^2 + \left(y + \dfrac{3}{4}\right)^2 = \dfrac{81}{49}$

22. $\left(x + \dfrac{1}{7}\right)^2 + \left(y - \dfrac{3}{5}\right)^2 = \dfrac{25}{9}$

For Exercises 23–36, information about a circle is given.

a. Write an equation of the circle in standard form.

b. Graph the circle. (**See Examples 1–2**)

23. Center: $(-2, 5)$; Radius: 1

24. Center: $(-3, 2)$; Radius: 4

25. Center: $(-4, -3)$; Radius: $\sqrt{11}$

26. Center: $(-5, -2)$; Radius: $\sqrt{21}$

27. Center: $(0, 0)$; Radius: 2.6

28. Center: $(0, 0)$; Radius: 4.2

29. The endpoints of a diameter are $(-2, 4)$ and $(6, -2)$.

30. The endpoints of a diameter are $(7, 3)$ and $(5, -1)$.

31. The center is $(-2, -1)$ and another point on the circle is $(6, 5)$.

32. The center is $(3, 1)$ and another point on the circle is $(6, 5)$.

33. The center is $(4, 6)$ and the circle is tangent to the y-axis. (Informally, a line is tangent to a circle if it touches the circle in exactly one point.)

34. The center is $(-2, -4)$ and the circle is tangent to the x-axis.

35. The center is in quadrant IV, the radius is 5, and the circle is tangent to both the x- and y-axes.

36. The center is in quadrant II, the radius is 3, and the circle is tangent to both the x- and y-axes.

37. Write an equation that represents the set of points that are 5 units from $(8, -11)$.

38. Write an equation that represents the set of points that are 9 units from $(-4, 16)$.

Objective 2: Write the General Form of an Equation of a Circle

39. Determine the solution set for the equation
$(x + 1)^2 + (y - 5)^2 = 0$.

40. Determine the solution set for the equation
$(x - 3)^2 + (y + 12)^2 = 0$.

41. Determine the solution set for the equation
$(x - 17)^2 + (y + 1)^2 = -9$.

42. Determine the solution set for the equation
$(x + 15)^2 + (y - 3)^2 = -25$.

For Exercises 43–54, write the equation in standard form: $(x - h)^2 + (y - k)^2 = r^2$. Then if possible identify the center and radius of the circle. If the equation represents a degenerate case, give the solution set. (See Examples 3–4)

43. $x^2 + y^2 + 6x - 2y + 6 = 0$

44. $x^2 + y^2 + 12x - 14y + 84 = 0$

45. $x^2 + y^2 - 20y - 4 = 0$

46. $x^2 + y^2 + 22x - 4 = 0$

47. $10x^2 + 10y^2 - 80x + 200y + 920 = 0$
(*Hint*: Divide by 10 to make the x^2 and y^2
term coefficients equal to 1.)

48. $2x^2 + 2y^2 - 32x + 12y + 90 = 0$

49. $x^2 + y^2 - 4x - 18y + 89 = 0$

50. $x^2 + y^2 - 10x - 22y + 155 = 0$

51. $4x^2 + 4y^2 - 20y + 25 = 0$

52. $4x^2 + 4y^2 - 12x + 9 = 0$

53. $x^2 + y^2 - x - \dfrac{3}{2}y - \dfrac{3}{4} = 0$

54. $x^2 + y^2 - \dfrac{2}{3}x - \dfrac{5}{3}y - \dfrac{5}{9} = 0$

Mixed Exercises

55. A cell tower is a site where antennas, transmitters, and receivers are placed to create a cellular network. Suppose that a cell tower is located at a point $A(4, 6)$ on a map and its range is 1.5 mi. Write an equation that represents the boundary of the area that can receive a signal from the tower. Assume that all distances are in miles.

56. A radar transmitter on a ship has a range of 20 nautical miles. If the ship is located at a point $(-32, 40)$ on a map, write an equation for the boundary of the area within the range of the ship's radar. Assume that all distances on the map are represented in nautical miles.

57. Suppose that three geological study areas are set up on a map at points $A(-4, 12)$, $B(11, 3)$, and $C(0, 1)$, where all units are in miles. Based on the speed of compression waves, scientists estimate the distances from the study areas to the epicenter of an earthquake to be 13 mi, 5 mi, and 10 mi, respectively. Graph three circles whose centers are located at the study areas and whose radii are the given distances to the earthquake. Then estimate the location of the earthquake.

58. Three fire observation towers are located at points $A(-6, -14)$, $B(14, 10)$, and $C(-3, 13)$ on a map where all units are in kilometers. A fire is located at distances of 17 km, 15 km, and 13 km, respectively, from the observation towers. Graph three circles whose centers are located at the observation towers and whose radii are the given distances to the fire. Then estimate the location of the fire.

Expanding Your Skills

59. Find all values of y such that the distance between $(4, y)$ and $(-2, 6)$ is 10 units.

60. Find all values of x such that the distance between $(x, -1)$ and $(4, 2)$ is 5 units.

61. Find all points on the line $y = x$ that are 6 units from $(2, 4)$.

62. Find all points on the line $y = -x$ that are 4 units from $(-4, 6)$.

The general form of an equation of a circle is $(x - h)^2 + (y - k)^2 = r^2$. If we solve the equation for x we get equations of the form $x = h \pm \sqrt{r^2 - (y - k)^2}$. The equation $x = h + \sqrt{r^2 - (y - k)^2}$ represents the graph of the corresponding right-side semicircle, and the equation $x = h - \sqrt{r^2 - (y - k)^2}$ represents the graph of the left-side semicircle. Likewise, if we solve for y, we have $y = k \pm \sqrt{r^2 - (x - h)^2}$. These equations represent the top and bottom semicircles. For Exercises 63–66, graph the equations.

63. a. $y = \sqrt{16 - x^2}$
   b. $y = -\sqrt{16 - x^2}$
   c. $x = \sqrt{16 - y^2}$
   d. $x = -\sqrt{16 - y^2}$

64. a. $y = \sqrt{9 - x^2}$
   b. $y = -\sqrt{9 - x^2}$
   c. $x = \sqrt{9 - y^2}$
   d. $x = -\sqrt{9 - y^2}$

65. a. $x = -1 - \sqrt{9 - (y - 2)^2}$

   b. $x = -1 + \sqrt{9 - (y - 2)^2}$

   c. $y = 2 - \sqrt{9 - (x + 1)^2}$

   d. $y = 2 + \sqrt{9 - (x + 1)^2}$

66. a. $x = 3 - \sqrt{4 - (y + 2)^2}$

   b. $x = 3 + \sqrt{4 - (y + 2)^2}$

   c. $y = -2 - \sqrt{4 - (x - 3)^2}$

   d. $y = -2 + \sqrt{4 - (x - 3)^2}$

Write About It

67. State the definition of a circle.

68. What are the advantages of writing an equation of a circle in standard form?

69. The screen shot shows the graphs of $y = \pm\sqrt{36 - x^2}$. Why does the calculator show a gap between the top and bottom semicircles?

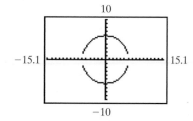

70. The screen shot shows the graph of $x^2 + y^2 = 49$. Why does the graph appear more like an ellipse (an oval shape) than a circle?

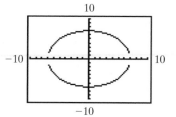

Technology Connections

For Exercises 71–74, use a graphing calculator to graph the circles on an appropriate square viewing window.

71. $x^2 + y^2 = 36$

72. $x^2 + y^2 = 49$

73. $(x - 18)^2 + (y + 20)^2 = 80$

74. $(x + 0.04)^2 + (y - 0.02)^2 = 0.01$

SECTION 2.3   Functions and Relations

OBJECTIVES

1. **Determine Whether a Relation Is a Function**
2. **Apply Function Notation**
3. **Determine x- and y-Intercepts of a Function Defined by** $y = f(x)$
4. **Determine Domain and Range of a Function**
5. **Interpret a Function Graphically**

1. Determine Whether a Relation Is a Function

In the physical world, many quantities that are subject to change are related to other variables. For example:

- The cost of mailing a package is related to the weight of a package.
- The minimum braking distance of a car depends on the speed of the car.
- The perimeter of a rectangle is a function of its length and width.
- The test score that a student earns is related to the number of hours of study.

In mathematics we can express the relationship between two values as a set of ordered pairs.

> ### Definition of a Relation
>
> A set of ordered pairs (x, y) is called a **relation** in x and y.
>
> - The set of x values in the ordered pairs is called the **domain** of the relation.
> - The set of y values in the ordered pairs is called the **range** of the relation.

EXAMPLE 1   Writing a Relation from Observed Data Points

Table 2-1 shows the score x that a student earned on an algebra test based on the number of hours y spent studying one week prior to the test.

Hours of Study, x	Test Score, y
8	92
3	58
11	98
5	72
8	86

Table 2-1

a. Write the set of ordered pairs that defines the relation given in Table 2-1.

b. Write the domain.

c. Write the range.

Solution:

a. Relation: {(8, 92), (3, 58), (11, 98), (5, 72), (8, 86)}

b. Domain: {8, 3, 11, 5}

c. Range: {92, 58, 98, 72, 86}

Skill Practice 1   For the table shown,

x	3	−2	5	1
y	−4	0	3	0

a. Write the set of ordered pairs that defines the relation.

b. Write the domain.

c. Write the range.

The data in Table 2-1 show two different test scores for 8 hr of study. That is, for $x = 8$, there are two different y values. In many applications, we prefer to work with relations that assign one and only one y value for a given of x. Such a relation is called a function.

Definition of a Function

Given a relation in x and y, we say that **y is a function of x** if for each value of x in the domain, there is exactly one value of y in the range.

EXAMPLE 2   Determining if a Relation Is a Function

Determine if the relation defines y as a function of x.

a. {(3, 1), (2, 5), (−4, 2), (−1, 0), (3, −4)}

b. {(−1, 4), (2, 3), (3, 4), (−4, 5)}

Solution:

a.   same x values

{(3, 1), (2, 5), (−4, 2), (−1, 0), (3, −4)}

different y values

When $x = 3$, there are two different y values: $y = 1$ and $y = −4$.

This relation is *not* a function.

b. {(−1, 4), (2, 3), (3, 4), (−4, 5)}

No two ordered pairs have the same x value but different y values.

This relation *is* a function.

Answers

1. a. {(3, −4), (−2, 0), (5, 3), (1, 0)}
   b. Domain: {3, −2, 5, 1}
   c. Range: {−4, 0, 3}
2. a. Yes   **b.** No

Skill Practice 2   Determine if the relation defines y as a function of x.

a. {(8, 4), (3, −1), (5, 4)}   **b.** {(−3, 2), (9, 5), (1, 0), (−3, 1)}

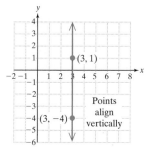

Figure 2-14

A relation that is not a function has at least one domain element x paired with more than one range element y. For example, the ordered pairs $(3, 1)$ and $(3, -4)$ do not make up a function. On a graph, these two points are aligned vertically. A vertical line drawn through one point also intersects the other point (Figure 2-14). This observation leads to the vertical line test.

Using the Vertical Line Test

Consider a relation defined by a set of points (x, y) graphed on a rectangular coordinate system. The graph defines y as a function of x if no vertical line intersects the graph in more than one point.

EXAMPLE 3   Applying the Vertical Line Test

The graphs of three relations are given. In each case, determine if the relation defines y as a function of x.

Solution:

a.

This is a function

No vertical line intersects the graph in more than one point.

b.

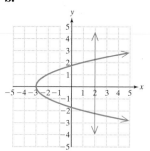

This is not a function.

There is at least one vertical line that intersects the graph in more than one point.

c.

This is a function.

No vertical line intersects the graph in more than one point.

TIP In Example 3(c) there is only one y value assigned to $x = 1$. This is because the point $(1, 2)$ is *not* included in the graph of the function as denoted by the open dot.

Skill Practice 3   Determine if the given relation defines y as a function of x.

a.

b.

c.

A relation can also be defined by a figure showing a "mapping" between x and y, or by an equation in x and y.

Answers
3. a. No   **b.** Yes   **c.** No

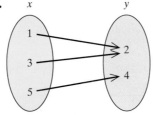

EXAMPLE 4   **Determining if a Relation Is a Function**

Determine if the relation defines y as a function of x.

a. x y
b. $y^2 = x$ **c.** $(x - 2)^2 + (y + 1)^2 = 9$

Solution:

a. This mapping defines the set of ordered pairs: $\{(1, 2), (3, 2), (5, 4)\}$. This relation *is* a function.

No two ordered pairs have the same x value but different y values.

b. $y^2 = x$

$\quad y = \pm\sqrt{x}$

Solve the equation for y. For any $x > 0$, there are two corresponding y values.

x	y	Ordered pairs
0	0	$(0, 0)$
1	$1, -1$	$(1, 1), (1, -1)$
4	$2, -2$	$(4, 2), (4, -2)$
9	$3, -3$	$(9, 3), (9, -3)$

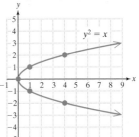

This relation is *not* a function.

c. $(x - 2)^2 + (y + 1)^2 = 9$

This equation represents the graph of a circle with center $(2, -1)$ and radius 3.

This relation is *not* a function because it fails the vertical line test.

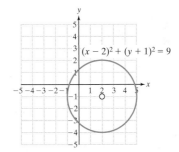

Skill Practice 4   Determine if the relation defines y as a function of x.

a. x y
b. $|y + 1| = x$ **c.** $x^2 + y^2 = 25$

2. Apply Function Notation

A function may be defined by an equation with two variables. For example, the equation $y = x - 2$ defines y as a function of x. This is because for any real number x, the value of y is the unique number that is 2 less than x.

When a function is defined by an equation, we often use function notation. For example, the equation $y = x - 2$ may be written in function notation as

$$f(x) = x - 2 \text{ read as "}f \text{ of } x \text{ equals } x - 2\text{."}$$

Answers
4. a. Yes   **b.** No   **c.** No

With function notation,

- f is the name of the function,
- x is an input variable from the domain,
- $f(x)$ is the function value (or y value) corresponding to x.

A function may be evaluated at different values of x by using substitution.

$$f(x) = x - 2$$
$$f(4) = (4) - 2 = 2 \qquad f(4) = 2 \text{ can be interpreted as } (4, 2).$$
$$f(1) = (1) - 2 = -1 \qquad f(1) = -1 \text{ can be interpreted as } (1, -1).$$

EXAMPLE 5 **Evaluating a Function**

Evaluate the function defined by $g(x) = 2x + 1$ for the given values of x.

a. $g(-2)$ **b.** $g(-1)$ **c.** $g(0)$ **d.** $g(1)$ **e.** $g(2)$

Solution:

a. $g(-2) = 2(-2) + 1$ Substitute -2 for x.
$ = -3$ $g(-2) = -3$

b. $g(-1) = 2(-1) + 1$ Substitute -1 for x.
$ = -1$ $g(-1) = -1$

c. $g(0) = 2(0) + 1$ Substitute 0 for x.
$ = 1$ $g(0) = 1$

d. $g(1) = 2(1) + 1$ Substitute 1 for x.
$ = 3$ $g(1) = 3$

e. $g(2) = 2(2) + 1$ Substitute 2 for x.
$ = 5$ $g(2) = 5$

The function values represent the ordered pairs $(-2, -3), (-1, -1), (0, 1), (1, 3)$, and $(2, 5)$. The line through the points represents all ordered pairs defined by this function. This is the graph of the function.

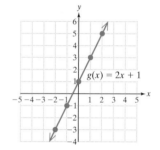

TIP The name of a function can be represented by any letter or symbol. However, lowercase letters such as f, g, h, and so on are often used.

Skill Practice 5 Evaluate the function defined by $h(x) = 4x - 3$ for the given values of x.

a. $h(-3)$ **b.** $h(-1)$ **c.** $h(0)$ **d.** $h(1)$ **e.** $h(3)$

EXAMPLE 6 **Evaluating a Function**

Evaluate the function defined by $k(x) = 3x^2 + 2x$ for the given values of x.

a. $k(a)$ **b.** $k(x + h)$

Solution:

a. $k(a) = 3a^2 + 2a$ Substitute a for x.

b. $k(x + h) = 3(x + h)^2 + 2(x + h)$ Substitute $x + h$ for x.
$ = 3(x^2 + 2xh + h^2) + 2x + 2h$ Simplify.
$ $ Recall: $(a + b)^2 = a^2 + 2ab + b^2$
$ = 3x^2 + 6xh + 3h^2 + 2x + 2h$

Answers
5. a. $h(-3) = -15$
    b. $h(-1) = -7$ **c.** $h(0) = -3$
    d. $h(1) = 1$ **e.** $h(3) = 9$
6. a. $m(t) = -t^2 + 4t$
    b. $m(a + h)$
        $= -a^2 - 2ah - h^2 + 4a + 4h$

Skill Practice 6 Evaluate the function defined by $m(x) = -x^2 + 4x$ for the given values of x.

a. $m(t)$ **b.** $m(a + h)$

3. Determine *x*- and *y*-Intercepts of a Function Defined by *y* = *f*(*x*)

Recall that to find an *x*-intercept(s) of the graph of an equation, we substitute 0 for *y* in the equation and solve for *x*. Using function notation, $y = f(x)$, this is equivalent to finding the real solutions of the equation $f(x) = 0$. To find the *y*-intercept, substitute 0 for *x* and solve the equation for *y*. Using function notation, this is equivalent to finding $f(0)$.

Finding Intercepts Using Function Notation

Given a function defined by $y = f(x)$,

- The *x*-intercepts are the real solutions to the equation $f(x) = 0$.
- The *y*-intercept is given by $f(0)$.

EXAMPLE 7   **Finding the *x*- and *y*-Intercepts of a Function**

Find the *x*- and *y*-intercepts of the function defined by $f(x) = x^2 - 4$.

Solution:

To find the *x*-intercept(s), solve the equation $f(x) = 0$.

$$f(x) = x^2 - 4$$
$$0 = x^2 - 4$$
$$x^2 = 4$$
$$x = \pm 2 \qquad \text{The } x\text{-intercepts are } (2, 0) \text{ and } (-2, 0).$$

To find the *y*-intercept, evaluate $f(0)$.

$$f(0) = (0)^2 - 4$$
$$= -4 \qquad \text{The } y\text{-intercept is } (0, -4).$$

Skill Practice 7   Find the *x*- and *y*-intercepts of the function defined by $f(x) = |x| - 5$.

---

4. Determine Domain and Range of a Function

Given a relation defining *y* as a function of *x*, the **domain** is the set of *x* values in the function, and the **range** is the set of *y* values in the function. In Example 8, we find the domain and range from the graph of a function.

EXAMPLE 8   **Determining Domain and Range**

Determine the domain and range for the functions shown.

a.

b.

c.
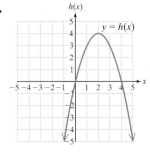

Answer

7. *x*-intercepts: (5, 0) and (−5, 0);
   y-intercept: (0, −5)

Solution:

a. The graph defines the set of ordered pairs:
$\{(-3, -4), (-1, 3), (0, 1), (2, 4), (4, 4)\}$

Domain: $\{-3, -1, 0, 2, 4\}$ The domain is the set of x values.

Range: $\{-4, 1, 3, 4\}$ The range is the set of y values.

b.

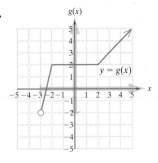

The domain is shown on the x-axis in green tint.
Domain: $\{x \mid x > -3\}$ or in interval notation: $(-3, \infty)$.

The range is shown on the y-axis in red tint.
Range: $\{y \mid y > -2\}$ or in interval notation: $(-2, \infty)$.

c.

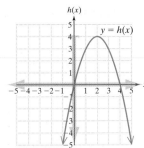

The graph extends infinitely far downward and infinitely far to the left and right. Therefore, the domain is the set of all real numbers, x.

The domain is shown on the x-axis in green tint.
Domain: $\mathbb{R}$ or in interval notation: $(-\infty, \infty)$.

The range is shown on the y-axis in red tint.
Range: $\{y \mid y \le 4\}$ or in interval notation: $(-\infty, 4]$.

Skill Practice 8 Determine the domain and range for the functions shown.

a.

b.

In some cases, a function may have restrictions on the domain. For example, consider the function defined by:

$$f(x) = x^2 + 2 \quad \text{for} \quad x \ge 0$$

The restriction on x (that is, $x \ge 0$) is explicitly stated along with the definition of the function. If no such restriction is stated, then by default, the domain is all real numbers that when substituted into the function produce real numbers in the range. To determine the implied domain of a function defined by $y = f(x)$, keep these guidelines in mind.

- Exclude values of x that make the denominator of a fraction zero.
- Exclude values of x that make the radicand negative within an even-indexed root.

Answers
8. a. Domain: $\{-4, -2, 0, 3, 4\}$;
     Range: $\{-3, 0, 1, 5\}$
  b. Domain: $\{x \mid x \le 4\}$ or $(-\infty, 4]$;
      Range: $\{y \mid y \ge -4\}$ or $[-4, \infty)$

EXAMPLE 9 **EXAMPLE 9**   **Determining the Domain of a Function**

Write the domain of each function in interval notation.

a. $f(x) = \dfrac{x + 3}{2x - 5}$ **b.** $g(x) = \dfrac{x}{x^2 + 4}$

c. $h(t) = \sqrt{2 - t}$ **d.** $m(a) = |4 + a|$

Solution:

a. $f(x) = \dfrac{x + 3}{2x - 5}$ The domain is all real numbers except those that make the denominator zero.

The variable x has the restriction that $2x - 5 \neq 0$. Therefore, $x \neq \frac{5}{2}$.

Domain: $\left(-\infty, \dfrac{5}{2}\right) \cup \left(\dfrac{5}{2}, \infty\right)$

b. $g(x) = \dfrac{x}{x^2 + 4}$ ⟵ Denominator always positive (never zero)

The expression $x^2 \geq 0$ for all real numbers x. Therefore, $x^2 + 4 > 0$ for all real numbers x.

Domain: $(-\infty, \infty)$

c. $h(t) = \sqrt{2 - t}$ The domain is restricted to the real numbers that make the radicand greater than or equal to zero.

$2 - t \geq 0$

$-t \geq -2$ Divide by -1 and reverse the inequality sign.

$t \leq 2$

Domain: $(-\infty, 2]$

d. $m(a) = |4 + a|$ There are no fractions or radicals that would restrict the domain.

Domain: $(-\infty, \infty)$ The expression $|4 + a|$ is a real number for all real numbers a.

Skill Practice 9   Write the domain of each function in interval notation.

a. $f(x) = \dfrac{x - 2}{3x + 1}$ **b.** $g(x) = \dfrac{x^2}{5}$

c. $k(x) = \sqrt{x + 3}$ **d.** $p(x) = 2x^2 + 3x$

5. Interpret a Function Graphically

In Example 10, we will review the key concepts studied in this section by identifying characteristics of a function based on its graph.

EXAMPLE 10 **EXAMPLE 10**   **Identifying Characteristics of a Function**

Use the function f pictured to answer the questions.

a. Determine $f(2)$.

b. Determine $f(-5)$.

c. Find all x for which $f(x) = 0$.

d. Find all x for which $f(x) = 3$.

e. Determine the x-intercept(s).

f. Determine the y-intercept.

g. Determine the domain of f.

h. Determine the range of f.

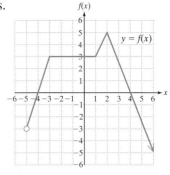

Answers

9. a. $\left(-\infty, -\dfrac{1}{3}\right) \cup \left(-\dfrac{1}{3}, \infty\right)$

b. $(-\infty, \infty)$

c. $[-3, \infty)$

d. $(-\infty, \infty)$

Solution:

a. $f(2) = 5$ $f(2) = 5$ because the function contains the point (2, 5).

b. $f(-5)$ is not defined.   The point $(-5, -3)$ is not included in the function as indicated by the open dot.

c. $f(x) = 0$ for $x = -4$ and $x = 4$.   The points $(-4, 0)$ and $(4, 0)$ represent the points where $f(x) = 0$.

d. $f(x) = 3$ for all x on the interval $[-3, 1]$ and for $x = \frac{14}{5}$.

e. The x-intercepts are $(-4, 0)$ and $(4, 0)$.

f. The y-intercept is $(0, 3)$.

g. The domain is $(-5, \infty)$.

h. The range is $(-\infty, 5]$.

Skill Practice 10   Use the function f pictured to find:

a. $f(-2)$.

b. $f(4)$.

c. All x for which $f(x) = 3$.

d. All x for which $f(x) = 1$.

e. The x-intercept(s).

f. The y-intercept.

g. The domain of f.

h. The range of f.

Answers

10. a. $f(-2) = 1$

b. $f(4)$ is not defined.

c. $x = -4$

d. All x on the interval $[-3, -1]$

e. (0, 0)

f. (0, 0)

g. $(-\infty, 4)$

h. $(-4, \infty)$

SECTION 2.3   Practice Exercises

Review Exercises

For Exercises 1–2, graph the equation.

1. $x^2 + (y + 1)^2 = 4$

2. $(x - 3)^2 + y^2 = 9$

3. The points (2, 7) and $(-1, 3)$ define the endpoints of a diameter of a circle. Find the center and radius.

4. The points $(-3, -5)$ and (4, 1) define the endpoints of a diameter of a circle. Find the center and radius.

For Exercises 5–6, determine the x- and y-intercepts of the graph of the equation.

5. $y = x^3 + 5x^2 - 4x - 20$

6. $y = -x^3 + 3x^2 + x - 3$

Concept Connections

7. A set of ordered pairs (x, y) is called a _____ in x and y. The set of x values in the relation is called the _____ of the relation. The set of _____ values is called the range of the relation.

8. Explain what it means for a relation to define y as a function of x.

9. If the graph of a set of points (x, y) has two points aligned vertically then the relation (does/does not) define y as a function of x.

10. Given a function defined by $y = f(x)$, the statement $f(2) = 4$ is equivalent to what ordered pair?

11. Given a function defined by $y = f(x)$, to find the _____-intercept, evaluate $f(0)$.

12. Given a function defined by $y = f(x)$, to find the x-intercept(s), substitute 0 for _____ and solve for x.

13. Given $f(x) = \dfrac{x + 1}{x + 5}$, the domain is restricted so that $x \neq$ _____.

14. Given $g(x) = \sqrt{x - 5}$, the domain is restricted so that $x \geq$ _____.

Objective 1: Determine Whether a Relation Is a Function

For Exercises 15–18,

a. Write a set of ordered pairs (x, y) that defines the relation.

b. Write the domain of the relation.

c. Write the range of the relation.

d. Determine if the relation defines y as a function of x. (**See Examples 1–2**)

15.

Actor x	Number of Oscar Nominations y
Tom Hanks	5
Jack Nicholson	12
Sean Penn	5
Dustin Hoffman	7

16.

City x	Elevation at Airport (ft) y
Albany	285
Denver	5883
Miami	11
San Francisco	11

17.

18.

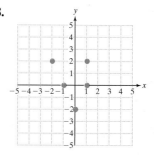

19. Answer true or false. All relations are functions.

20. Answer true or false. All functions are relations.

For Exercises 21–38, determine if the relation defines y as a function of x. (See Examples 3–4)

21.

22.

23.

24.

25.

26.

27.

28.

29.

30.

31.

32.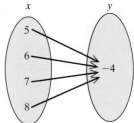

33. $(x + 1)^2 + (y + 5)^2 = 25$

34. $(x + 3)^2 + (y + 4)^2 = 1$

35. $y = x + 3$

36. $y = x - 4$

37. a. $y = x^2$

   b. $x = y^2$

38. a. $y = |x|$

   b. $x = |y|$

Objective 2: Apply Function Notation

39. The statement $f(4) = 1$ corresponds to what ordered pair?

40. The statement $g(7) = -5$ corresponds to what ordered pair?

For Exercises 41–60, evaluate the function for the given value of x. (See Examples 5–6)

$$f(x) = x^2 + 3x \qquad g(x) = \frac{1}{x} \qquad h(x) = 5 \qquad k(x) = \sqrt{x + 1}$$

41. a. $f(-2)$ **b.** $f(-1)$ **c.** $f(0)$ **d.** $f(1)$ **e.** $f(2)$

42. a. $g(-2)$ **b.** $g(-1)$ **c.** $g\left(-\frac{1}{2}\right)$ **d.** $g\left(\frac{1}{2}\right)$ **e.** $g(2)$

43. a. $h(-2)$ **b.** $h(-1)$ **c.** $h(0)$ **d.** $h(1)$ **e.** $h(2)$

44. a. $k(-2)$ **b.** $k(-1)$ **c.** $k(0)$ **d.** $k(1)$ **e.** $k(3)$

45. $g(3)$ **46.** $h(-7)$ **47.** $g\left(\frac{1}{3}\right)$

48. $h(7)$ **49.** $k(-5)$ **50.** $f(5)$

51. $k(8)$ **52.** $f(-5)$ **53.** $g(t)$

54. $f(a)$ **55.** $k(a + b)$ **56.** $h(a + b)$

57. $f(a + 4)$ **58.** $f(t - 3)$ **59.** $g(0)$

60. $k(-10)$

For Exercises 61–68, refer to the function $f = \{(2, 3), (9, 7), (3, 4), (-1, 6)\}$.

61. Determine $f(9)$.   **62.** Determine $f(-1)$.   **63.** Determine $f(3)$.

64. Determine $f(2)$.   **65.** For what value of x is $f(x) = 6$?   **66.** For what value of x is $f(x) = 7$?

67. For what value of x is $f(x) = 3$?   **68.** For what value of x is $f(x) = 4$?

69. Joe rides his bicycle an average of 18 mph. The distance Joe rides $d(t)$ (in mi) is given by $d(t) = 18t$, where t is the time in hours that he rides.

   a. Evaluate $d(2)$ and interpret the meaning.

   b. Determine the distance Joe travels in 40 min.

70. Frank needs to drive 250 mi from Daytona Beach to Miami. After having driven x miles, the distance remaining $r(x)$ (in mi) is given by $r(x) = 250 - x$.

   a. Evaluate $r(50)$ and interpret the meaning.

   b. Determine the distance remaining after 122 mi.

71. At a restaurant, if a party has eight or more people, the gratuity is automatically added to the bill. If x is the cost of the meal, then the total bill $C(x)$ with an 18% gratuity and a 6% sales tax is given by: $C(x) = x + 0.06x + 0.18x$. Evaluate $C(225)$ and interpret the meaning in the context of this problem.

72. A bookstore marks up the price of a book by 40% of the cost from the publisher. Therefore, the bookstore's price to the student, $P(x)$ (in $) after a 7.5% sales tax, is given by $P(x) = 1.075(x + 0.40x)$, where x is the cost of the book from the publisher. Evaluate $P(60)$ and interpret the meaning in the context of this problem.

Objective 3: Determine *x*- and *y*-Intercepts of a Function Defined by $y = f(x)$

For Exercises 73–82, determine the *x*- and *y*-intercepts for the given function. (See Example 7)

73. $f(x) = 2x - 4$

74. $g(x) = 3x - 12$

75. $h(x) = |x| - 8$

76. $k(x) = -|x| + 2$

77. $p(x) = -x^2 + 12$

78. $q(x) = x^2 - 8$

79. $r(x) = |x - 8|$

80. $s(x) = |x + 3|$

81. $f(x) = \sqrt{x} - 2$

82. $g(x) = -\sqrt{x} + 3$

83. The amount spent on video games per person in the United States has been increasing since 2006. (*Source*: www.census.gov) The function defined by $f(x) = 9.4x + 35.7$ represents the amount spent $f(x)$ (in \$) *x* years since 2006. Determine the *y*-intercept and interpret its meaning in context.

84. The number of Botox injection procedures $B(x)$ (in millions) in the United States by year can be approximated by $B(x) = -0.12x^2 + 0.86x + 1.6$ where *x* is the number of years since 2002. (*Source*: www.census.gov) Determine the *y*-intercept and interpret its meaning in context.

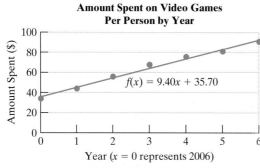

**Amount Spent on Video Games
Per Person by Year**

$f(x) = 9.40x + 35.70$

Year (*x* = 0 represents 2006)

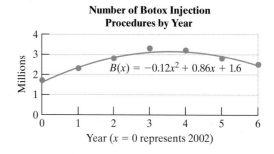

**Number of Botox Injection
Procedures by Year**

$B(x) = -0.12x^2 + 0.86x + 1.6$

Year (*x* = 0 represents 2002)

Objective 4: Determine Domain and Range of a Function

For Exercises 85–94, determine the domain and range of the function. (See Example 8)

85.

86.

87.

88.

89.

90.

91.

92.

93.

94.

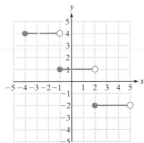

For Exercises 95–108, write the domain in interval notation. (See Example 9)

95. $f(x) = \dfrac{x - 3}{x - 4}$

96. $g(x) = \dfrac{x + 6}{x - 2}$

97. $h(t) = \dfrac{2t}{2t + 7}$

98. $k(a) = \dfrac{4a}{3a + 4}$

99. $m(x) = \dfrac{6}{|x| + 4}$

100. $n(x) = \dfrac{-7}{x^2 + 3}$

101. $r(a) = \sqrt{a + 15}$

102. $f(c) = \sqrt{c + 12}$

103. $t(x) = \dfrac{\sqrt{3 - x}}{5}$

104. $k(x) = \dfrac{\sqrt{6 - x}}{-3}$

105. $s(x) = \dfrac{5}{\sqrt{3 - x}}$

106. $h(x) = \dfrac{-3}{\sqrt{6 - x}}$

107. $p(x) = 3x^2 - 4x + 1$

108. $q(x) = -2x^2 + 8x - 3$

Objective 5: Interpret a Function Graphically

For Exercises 109–112, use the graph of $y = f(x)$ to answer the following. (See Example 10)

    a. Determine $f(-2)$.

    b. Determine $f(3)$.

    c. Find all x for which $f(x) = -1$.

    d. Find all x for which $f(x) = -4$.

    e. Determine the x-intercept(s).

    f. Determine the y-intercept.

    g. Determine the domain of f.

    h. Determine the range of f.

109.

110.

111.

112.

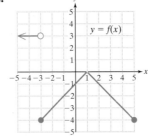

Mixed Exercises

For Exercises 113–120, write a function that represents the given statement.

113. Suppose that a phone card has 400 min. Write a relationship that represents the number of minutes remaining $r(x)$ as a function of the number of minutes already used x.

114. Suppose that a roll of wire has 200 ft. Write a relationship that represents the amount of wire remaining $w(x)$ as a function of the number of feet of wire x already used.

115. Given an equilateral triangle with sides of length x, write a relationship that represents the perimeter $P(x)$ as a function of x.

116. In an isosceles triangle, two angles are equal in measure. If the third angle is x degrees, write a relationship that represents the measure of one of the equal angles $A(x)$ as a function of x.

117. Two adjacent angles form a right angle. If the measure of one angle is x degrees, write a relationship representing the measure of the other angle $C(x)$ as a function of x.

118. Two adjacent angles form a straight angle (180°). If the measure of one angle is x degrees, write a relationship representing the measure of the other angle $S(x)$ as a function of x.

119. Write a relationship for a function whose $f(x)$ values are 2 less than three times the square of x.

120. Write a relationship for a function whose $f(x)$ values are 3 more than the principal square root of x.

Write About It

121. If two points align vertically then the points do not define y as a function of x. Explain why.

122. Given a function defined by $y = f(x)$, explain how to determine the x- and y-intercepts.

Expanding Your Skills

123. Given a square with sides of length s, diagonal of length d, perimeter P, and area A,

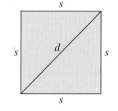

  a. Write P as a function of s.
  b. Write A as a function of s.
  c. Write A as a function of P.
  d. Write P as a function of A.
  e. Write d as a function of s.
  f. Write s as a function of d.
  g. Write P as a function of d.
  h. Write A as a function of d.

124. Given a circle with radius r, diameter d, circumference C, and area A,

  a. Write C as a function of r.
  b. Write A as a function of r.
  c. Write r as a function of d.
  d. Write d as a function of r.
  e. Write C as a function of d.
  f. Write A as a function of d.
  g. Write A as a function of C.
  h. Write C as a function of A.

SECTION 2.4   Linear Equations in Two Variables and Linear Functions

1. Graph Linear Equations in Two Variables

The median income for men and women has increased since the year 1980. Although there are year-to-year fluctuations in income, the general trend appears to be upward (Figure 2-15). (*Source*: U.S. Census Bureau, www.census.gov)

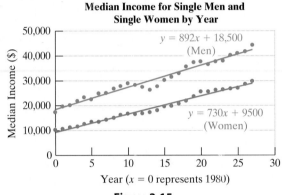

Median Income for Single Men and Single Women by Year

$y = 892x + 18{,}500$ (Men)

$y = 730x + 9500$ (Women)

Year ($x = 0$ represents 1980)

Figure 2-15

The graph in Figure 2-15 is called a scatter plot. A **scatter plot** is a visual representation of a set of points. In this case, the x values represent the number of years since 1980, and the y values represent the median income in dollars. The line that models each set of data is called a **regression line** and is found by using techniques taught in a first course in statistics. The equations that represent the two lines are called linear equations in two variables.

TIP For an equation in standard form, the value of A, B, and C are usually taken to be integers and relatively prime.

Linear Equation in Two Variables

Let A, B, and C represent real numbers such that A and B are not both zero. A **linear equation** in the variables x and y is an equation that can be written in the form:

$Ax + By = C$ This is called the **standard form** of an equation of a line.

Note: A linear equation $Ax + By = C$ has variables x and y each of first degree.

In Example 1, we demonstrate that the graph of a linear equation $Ax + By = C$ is a line. The line may be slanted, horizontal, or vertical depending on the coefficients A, B, and C.

EXAMPLE 1   Graphing Linear Equations

Graph the line represented by each equation.

a. $2x + 3y = 6$ **b.** $x = -3$ **c.** $2y = 4$

Solution:

a. Solve the equation for y. Then substitute arbitrary values of x into the equation and solve for the corresponding values of y.

$2x + 3y = 6$ Solve the equation for y.

$$3y = -2x + 6$$

$$y = -\frac{2}{3}x + 2$$

In the table we have selected convenient values of x that are multiples of 3.

x	y
-3	4
0	2
3	0
6	-2

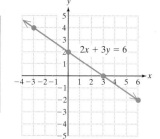

b. $x = -3$

The solutions to this equation must have an x-coordinate of -3. The y variable can be *any* real number.

x	y
-3	-2
-3	0
-3	2
-3	4

↑ x must be -3. ↑ y can be any real number.

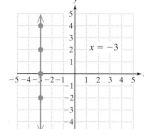

c. $2y = 4$ Solve for y.

  $y = 2$

The solutions to this equation must have a y-coordinate of 2. The x variable can be *any* real number.

x	y
-2	2
0	2
2	2
4	2

↑ x can be any real number. ↑ y must be 2.

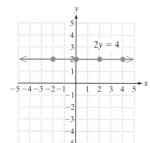

Skill Practice 1   Graph the line represented by each equation.

  a. $4x + 2y = 2$ **b.** $y = 1$ **c.** $-3x = 12$

2. Determine the Slope of a Line

One of the important characteristics of a nonvertical line is that for every 1 unit change in x the y value will change by a constant amount, m. See Figure 2-16 and Figure 2-17.

Answer

1. a.–c.

Figure 2-16

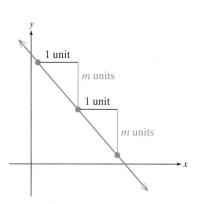

Figure 2-17

The value of the constant m is the slope of the line. Slope is an important concept because it represents the average rate of change between the y and x variables. For example, consider the line representing the median income for single women since 1980. The line in Figure 2-18 has a slope of 730. This means that women's median income increased by $730 per year during this time period.

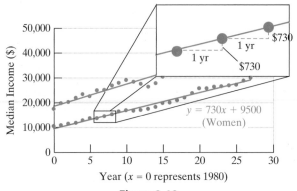

Figure 2-18

Consider any two distinct points (x_1, y_1) and (x_2, y_2) on a line (Figure 2-19). The slope m of the line through the points is the ratio between the change in the y values $(y_2 - y_1)$ and the change in the x values $(x_2 - x_1)$. In many applications in the sciences, the change in a variable is denoted by the Greek letter Δ (delta). Therefore, $(y_2 - y_1)$ can be represented by Δy and $(x_2 - x_1)$ can be represented by Δx.

Figure 2-19

Slope Formula

The **slope** of a line passing through the distinct points (x_1, y_1) and (x_2, y_2) is

$$m = \frac{\Delta y}{\Delta x} = \frac{y_2 - y_1}{x_2 - x_1} \text{ provided that } x_2 - x_1 \neq 0$$

change in y (rise)

change in x (run)

EXAMPLE 2 **Finding the Slope of a Line Through Two Points**

Find the slope of the line passing through the given points.

a. $(-3, -2)$ and $(2, 5)$ **b.** $\left(-\dfrac{5}{2}, 0\right)$ and $(1, -7)$

Solution:

a. $(-3, -2)$ and $(2, 5)$

(x_1, y_1) and (x_2, y_2) Label the points.

$$m = \frac{y_2 - y_1}{x_2 - x_1} = \frac{5 - (-2)}{2 - (-3)} = \frac{7}{5}$$

A line with a positive slope "*rises*" upward from left to right.

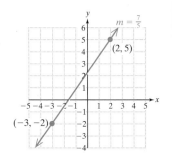

b. $\left(-\dfrac{5}{2}, 0\right)$ and $(1, -7)$

(x_1, y_1) and (x_2, y_2) Label the points.

$$m = \frac{y_2 - y_1}{x_2 - x_1} = \frac{-7 - 0}{1 - \left(-\frac{5}{2}\right)} = \frac{-7}{\frac{7}{2}} = -7 \cdot \frac{2}{7} = -2$$

A line with a negative slope "*falls*" downward from left to right.

Skill Practice 2   Find the slope of the line passing through the given points.

   a. $(-4, 1)$ and $(2, -2)$ **b.** $\left(\dfrac{3}{4}, 2\right)$ and $(-3, 17)$

EXAMPLE 3   **Finding the Slope of Horizontal and Vertical Lines**

Find the slope of each line.

                  Solution:

a.

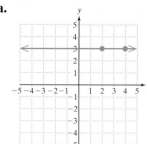

By inspection, we see that between any two points on the graph, the vertical change is zero, so the slope is zero.

   To compute this numerically, select any two points on the line such as $(2, 3)$ and $(4, 3)$.

$$m = \frac{y_2 - y_1}{x_2 - x_1} = \frac{3 - 3}{4 - 2} = \frac{0}{2} = 0$$

b.

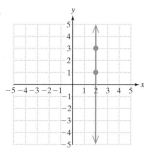

To find the slope, select any two points on the line such as $(2, 1)$ and $(2, 3)$.

$$m = \frac{y_2 - y_1}{x_2 - x_1} = \frac{3 - 1}{2 - 2} = \frac{2}{0} \quad \text{(undefined)}$$

By inspection, we see that between any two points on the line, the change in x is zero. This makes the slope undefined because the ratio representing the slope has a divisor of zero.

Skill Practice 3   Fill in the blank.

   a. The slope of a vertical line is _____.
   b. The slope of a horizontal line is _____.

From Example 1, we see that a linear equation may represent the graph of a slanted line, a horizontal line, or a vertical line. From Examples 2 and 3, we see that a line may have a positive slope, a negative slope, a zero slope, or an undefined slope.

Answers

2. a. $-\dfrac{1}{2}$ **b.** -4

3. a. Undefined   **b.** 0

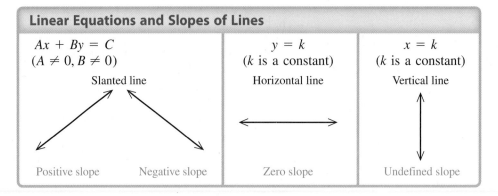

Linear Equations and Slopes of Lines

$Ax + By = C$ $(A \neq 0, B \neq 0)$	$y = k$ (k is a constant)	$x = k$ (k is a constant)
Slanted line	Horizontal line	Vertical line
Positive slope Negative slope	Zero slope	Undefined slope

3. Apply the Slope-Intercept Form of a Line

The slope formula can be used to develop the slope-intercept form of a line. Suppose that a line has a slope m and y-intercept $(0, b)$. Let (x, y) be any other point on the line. From the slope formula, we have:

$$\frac{y - b}{x - 0} = m \qquad \text{Slope formula}$$

$$y - b = mx \qquad \text{Multiply by } x.$$

$$y = mx + b \qquad \text{Slope-intercept form}$$

Avoiding Mistakes

An equation of a vertical line takes the form $x = k$, where k is a constant. Because there is no y variable and because the slope is undefined, an equation of a vertical line cannot be written in slope-intercept form.

Slope-Intercept Form of a Line

Given a line with slope m and y-intercept $(0, b)$, the **slope-intercept form** of the line is given by $y = mx + b$.

The slope-intercept form of a line is particularly useful because we can identify the slope and y-intercept by inspection. For example:

$$y = \frac{2}{3}x - 5 \qquad\qquad m = \frac{2}{3} \qquad y\text{-intercept: } (0, -5)$$

$$y = x + 4 \qquad\qquad m = 1 \qquad y\text{-intercept: } (0, 4)$$

$$y = 2x \quad (\text{or } y = 2x + 0) \qquad m = 2 \qquad y\text{-intercept: } (0, 0)$$

$$y = 6 \quad (\text{or } y = 0x + 6) \qquad m = 0 \qquad y\text{-intercept: } (0, 6)$$

If the slope and y-intercept of a graph are known, we can graph the line. This is demonstrated in Example 4.

EXAMPLE 4   **Using the Slope and y-Intercept to Graph a Line**

Given $3x + 4y = 4$,

    a. Write the equation in slope-intercept form.

    b. Determine the slope and y-intercept.

    c. Graph the line by using the slope and y-intercept.

Solution:

    a. $3x + 4y = 4$

$$4y = -3x + 4 \qquad \text{To write an equation in slope-intercept form, isolate the } y \text{ variable.}$$

$$y = -\frac{3}{4}x + 1 \qquad \text{Slope-intercept form}$$

    b. $m = -\dfrac{3}{4}$ and the y-intercept is $(0, 1)$.   The slope is the coefficient on x.

                                               The constant term gives the y-intercept.

c.

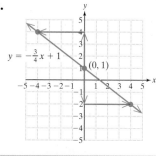

$y = -\frac{3}{4}x + 1$ (0, 1)

To graph the line, first plot the *y*-intercept (0, 1).

Then begin at the *y*-intercept, and use the slope to find a second point on the line. In this case, the slope can be interpreted as the following two ratios:

$$m = \frac{-3}{4} \begin{array}{l}\longleftarrow \text{Move down 3 units.}\\ \longleftarrow \text{Move right 4 units.}\end{array}$$

$$m = \frac{3}{-4} \begin{array}{l}\longleftarrow \text{Move up 3 units.}\\ \longleftarrow \text{Move left 4 units.}\end{array}$$

Skill Practice 4   Given $2x + 4y = 8$,

   a. Write the equation in slope-intercept form.
   b. Determine the slope and *y*-intercept.
   c. Graph the line by using the slope and *y*-intercept.

Notice that the slope-intercept form of a line $y = mx + b$ has the *y* variable isolated and defines *y* in terms of *x*. Therefore, an equation written in slope-intercept form defines *y* as a function of *x*. In Example 4, $y = -\frac{3}{4}x + 1$ can be written using function notation as $f(x) = -\frac{3}{4}x + 1$.

Definition of Linear and Constant Functions

Let *m* and *b* represent real numbers where $m \neq 0$. Then,

- A function defined by $f(x) = mx + b$ is a **linear function.** The graph of a linear function is a slanted line.
- A function defined by $f(x) = b$ is a **constant function.** The graph of a constant function is a horizontal line.

The slope-intercept form of a line can be used as a tool to define a linear function given a point on the line and the slope.

EXAMPLE 5   Writing an Equation of a Line Given a Point and the Slope

Write an equation of the line that passes through the point $(2, -3)$ and has slope -4. Then write the linear equation using function notation, where $y = f(x)$.

Solution:

Given $m = -4$ and $(2, -3)$.   We need to find an equation of the form $y = mx + b$. The goal is to use the given information to find *m* and *b*.

$y = mx + b$

$y = -4x + b$ The value of *m* is given as -4.

$-3 = -4(2) + b$ Substitute $x = 2$ and $y = -3$ from the given point $(2, -3)$.

$-3 = -8 + b$ Solve for *b*.

$b = 5$

$y = mx + b$

$y = -4x + 5$ Substitute $m = -4$ and $b = 5$ into the equation $y = mx + b$.

$f(x) = -4x + 5$ Write the relation using function notation.

From the graph, we see that the graph of
$f(x) = -4x + 5$ does indeed pass through the point $(2, -3)$ and has slope -4.

> **Skill Practice 5**   Write an equation of the line that passes through the point $(-1, -4)$ and has slope 3. Then write the equation using function notation.

4. Compute Average Rate of Change

The graphs of many functions are not linear. However, we often use linear approximations to analyze nonlinear functions on small intervals. For example, the graph in Figure 2-20 shows the blood alcohol concentration (BAC) for an individual over a period of 9 hr.

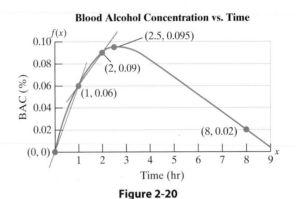

Figure 2-20

A line drawn through two points on a graph is called a **secant line.** In Figure 2-20, the average rate of change in BAC between two points on the graph is the slope of the secant line through the points. Notice that the slope of the secant line between $x = 0$ and $x = 1$ (shown in red) is greater than the slope of the secant line between $x = 1$ and $x = 2$ (shown in green). This means that the average increase in BAC is greater over the first hour than over the second hour.

Average Rate of Change of a Function

Suppose that the points (x_1, y_1) and (x_2, y_2) are points on the graph of a function f. Using function notation, these are the points $(x_1, f(x_1))$ and $(x_2, f(x_2))$.

If f is defined on the interval $[x_1, x_2]$, then the **average rate of change** of f on the interval $[x_1, x_2]$ is the slope of the secant line containing $(x_1, f(x_1))$ and $(x_2, f(x_2))$.

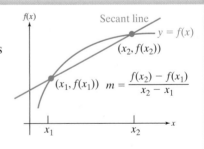

Average rate of change: $m = \dfrac{\Delta y}{\Delta x} = \dfrac{y_2 - y_1}{x_2 - x_1}$ or $m = \dfrac{f(x_2) - f(x_1)}{x_2 - x_1}$

Answer

5. $y = 3x - 1;\ f(x) = 3x - 1$

EXAMPLE 6   Computing Average Rate of Change

Determine the average rate of change of blood alcohol level

a. from $x_1 = 0$ to $x_2 = 1$.

b. from $x_1 = 1$ to $x_2 = 2$.

c. Interpret the results from parts (a) and (b).

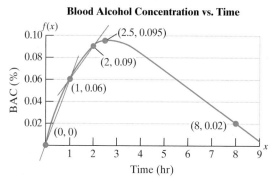

Blood Alcohol Concentration vs. Time

Solution:

a. Average rate of change $= \dfrac{f(x_2) - f(x_1)}{x_2 - x_1}$

$= \dfrac{f(1) - f(0)}{1 - 0} = \dfrac{0.06 - 0}{1} = 0.06$

b. Average rate of change $= \dfrac{f(x_2) - f(x_1)}{x_2 - x_1}$

$= \dfrac{f(2) - f(1)}{2 - 1} = \dfrac{0.09 - 0.06}{1} = 0.03$

c. The blood alcohol concentration rose by an average of 0.06% per hour during the first hour.

The blood alcohol concentration rose by an average of 0.03% per hour during the second hour.

Skill Practice 6   Refer to the graph in Example 6.

a. Determine the average rate of change of blood alcohol level from $x_1 = 2.5$ to $x_2 = 8$. Round to 3 decimal places.

b. Interpret the results from part (a).

EXAMPLE 7   Computing Average Rate of Change

Given the function defined by $f(x) = x^2 - 1$, determine the average rate of change from $x_1 = -2$ to $x_2 = 0$.

Solution:

Average rate of change $= \dfrac{f(x_2) - f(x_1)}{x_2 - x_1}$

$= \dfrac{f(0) - f(-2)}{0 - (-2)} = \dfrac{-1 - 3}{2} = -2$

The average rate of change is -2.

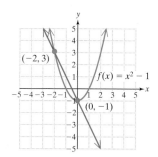

Answers

6. a. -0.014

   b. The blood alcohol concentration decreased by an average of 0.014% per hour during this time interval.

7. 9

Skill Practice 7   Given the function defined by $f(x) = x^3 + 2$, determine the average rate of change from $x_1 = -3$ to $x_2 = 0$.

5. Solve Equations and Inequalities Graphically

In many settings, the use of technology can provide a numerical and visual interpretation of an algebraic problem. For example, consider the equation $-x - 1 = x + 5$.

$$-x - 1 = x + 5$$
$$-6 = 2x$$
$$-3 = x \qquad \text{The solution set is } \{-3\}.$$

Now suppose that we create two functions from the left and right sides of the equation: $f(x) = -x - 1$ and $g(x) = x + 5$. Figure 2-21 shows that the graphs of f and g intersect at $(-3, 2)$. The x-coordinate of the point of intersection is the solution to the equation $-x - 1 = x + 5$. That is, $f(x) = g(x)$ when $x = -3$.

The graphs of f and g can also be used to find the solution sets to the related inequalities.

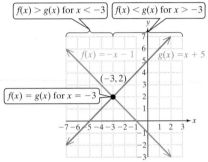

Figure 2-21

$-x - 1 < x + 5$ The solution set is the set of x values for which $f(x) < g(x)$. This is the interval where the blue line is below the red line. The solution set is $(-3, \infty)$.

$-x - 1 > x + 5$ The solution set is the set of x values for which $f(x) > g(x)$. This is the interval where the blue line is *above* the red line. The solution set is $(-\infty, -3)$.

EXAMPLE 8 **Solving Equations and Inequalities Graphically**

Solve the equations and inequalities graphically.

a. $2x - 3 = x - 1$ **b.** $2x - 3 < x - 1$ **c.** $2x - 3 > x - 1$

Solution:

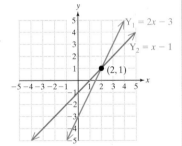

a. The left side of the equation is graphed as $Y_1 = 2x - 3$. The right side of the equation is graphed as $Y_2 = x - 1$. The point of intersection is $(2, 1)$. Therefore, $Y_1 = Y_2$ for $x = 2$.
The solution set is $\{2\}$.

b. $Y_1 < Y_2$ to the *left* of $x = 2$. (That is, the blue line is below the red line for $x < 2$.)
In interval notation the solution set is $(-\infty, 2)$.

c. $Y_1 > Y_2$ to the *right* of $x = 2$. (That is, the blue line is above the red line for $x > 2$.)
In interval notation the solution set is $(2, \infty)$.

TIP The solution set to the inequality $2x - 3 \leq x - 1$ includes equality, so the right endpoint would be included: $(-\infty, 2]$.
The solution set to the inequality $2x - 3 \geq x - 1$ includes equality, so the left endpoint would be included: $[2, \infty)$.

Skill Practice 8 Use the graph to solve the equations and inequalities.

a. $x + 1 = 2x - 2$
b. $x + 1 \leq 2x - 2$
c. $x + 1 \geq 2x - 2$

Answers
8. a. $\{3\}$ **b.** $[3, \infty)$ **c.** $(-\infty, 3]$

TECHNOLOGY CONNECTIONS

Verifying Solutions to an Equation

We can verify the solutions to the equations and inequalities from Example 8 on a graphing calculator.

The solutions can be verified numerically by using the **Table** feature on the calculator. First enter $Y_1 = 2x - 3$ and $Y_2 = x - 1$.

Then display the table values for Y_1 and Y_2 for $x = 2$ and for x values less than and greater than 2.

Display the graphs of Y_1 and Y_2 and use the **Intersect** feature to determine the point of intersection.

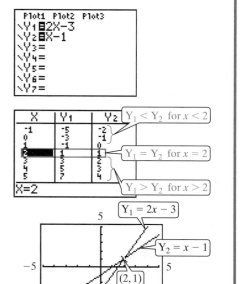

In Example 9 we solve the equation $6x - 2(x + 2) - 5 = 0$. Notice that one side is zero. We can check the solution graphically by determining where the related function $Y_1 = 6x - 2(x + 2) - 5$ intersects the x-axis.

EXAMPLE 9   Solving Equations and Inequalities Graphically

a. Solve the equation $6x - 2(x + 2) - 5 = 0$ and verify the solution graphically on a graphing utility.

b. Use the graph to find the solution set to the inequality
$6x - 2(x + 2) - 5 \leq 0$.

c. Use the graph to find the solution set to the inequality
$6x - 2(x + 2) - 5 \geq 0$.

Solution:

a.
$$6x - 2(x + 2) - 5 = 0$$
$$6x - 2x - 4 - 5 = 0$$
$$4x - 9 = 0$$
$$x = \frac{9}{4}$$

The solution set is $\left\{ \dfrac{9}{4} \right\}$.

To verify the solution graphically enter the left side of the equation as $Y_1 = 6x - 2(x + 2) - 5$.

Using the **Zero** feature, we have $Y_1 = 0$ for $x = 2.25$. This is consistent with the solution $x = \frac{9}{4}$.

b. To solve $6x - 2(x + 2) - 5 \leq 0$ determine the values of x for which $Y_1 \leq 0$ (where the function is on or below the x-axis).

The solution set is $\left(-\infty, \dfrac{9}{4}\right]$.

c. To solve $6x - 2(x + 2) - 5 \geq 0$ determine the values of x for which $Y_1 \geq 0$ (where the function is on or above the x-axis).

The solution set is $\left[\dfrac{9}{4}, \infty\right)$.

Answers

9. a. $\left\{\dfrac{5}{2}\right\}$

b. $\left(-\infty, \dfrac{5}{2}\right]$

c. $\left[\dfrac{5}{2}, \infty\right)$

Skill Practice 9

a. Solve the equation $3x - (x + 4) - 1 = 0$ and verify the solution graphically on a graphing utility.

b. Use the graph to find the solution set to the inequality $3x - (x + 4) - 1 \leq 0$.

c. Use the graph to find the solution set to the inequality $3x - (x + 4) - 1 \geq 0$.

SECTION 2.4   Practice Exercises

Review Exercises

For Exercises 1–4,

a. Determine if the graph defines y as a function of x.

b. Write the domain of the relation in interval notation.

c. Write the range of the relation in interval notation.

d. Identify the x-intercept.

e. Identify the y-intercept.

1.   **2.**   **3.**   **4.**

For Exercises 5–6,

a. Find the midpoint of the line segment whose endpoints are the two given points.

b. Determine the distance between the points.

5. $\left(3\sqrt{2},\ \sqrt{5}\right)$ and $\left(\sqrt{2},\ -4\sqrt{5}\right)$

6. $\left(\sqrt{6},\ \sqrt{3}\right)$ and $\left(2\sqrt{6},\ 5\sqrt{3}\right)$

Concept Connections

7. A _____ diagram is a visual representation of a set of data points represented as ordered pairs.

8. A _____ equation in the variables x and y can be written in the form $Ax + By = C$, where A and B are not both zero.

9. An equation of the form $x = k$ where k is a constant represents the graph of a _____ line.

10. An equation of the form $y = k$ where k is a constant represents the graph of a _____ line.

11. True or false: The slope between any two distinct points on a nonvertical line is a constant.

12. Write the formula for the slope of a line between the two distinct points (x_1, y_1) and (x_2, y_2).

13. The slope of a horizontal line is _____.

14. The slope of a vertical line is _____.

15. An equation written in the form $y = mx + b$ is said to be written in _____-_____ form.

16. A function f is a linear function if $f(x) =$ _____, where m represents the slope and $(0, b)$ represents the y-intercept.

17. If f is defined on the interval $[x_1, x_2]$, then the average rate of change of f on the interval $[x_1, x_2]$ is given by the formula _____.

18. The graph of a constant function defined by $f(x) = b$ is a (horizontal/vertical) line.

Objective 1: Graph Linear Equations in Two Variables

For Exercises 19–30, graph the equation and identify the x- and y-intercepts. (See Example 1)

19. $-3x + 4y = 12$ **20.** $-2x + y = 4$ **21.** $2y = -5x + 2$

22. $3y = -4x + 6$ **23.** $x = -6$ **24.** $y = 4$

25. $5y + 1 = 11$ **26.** $3x - 2 = 4$ **27.** $0.02x + 0.05y = 0.1$

28. $0.03x + 0.07y = 0.21$ **29.** $2x = 3y$ **30.** $2x = -5y$

Objective 2: Determine the Slope of a Line

31. Find the average slope of the hill.

1000 ft

300 ft

32. Find the absolute value of the slope of the storm drainage pipe.

5 ft

80 ft

33. The road sign shown in the figure indicates the percent grade of a hill. This gives the slope of the road as the change in elevation per 100 horizontal feet. Given a 2.5% grade, write this as a slope in fractional form.

2.5% Grade

34. The pitch of a roof is defined as $\dfrac{\text{rafter rise}}{\text{rafter run}}$ and the fraction is typically written with a denominator of 12.

Determine the pitch of the roof from point A to point C.

Rafter C

A 7 ft B

Span 24 ft

For Exercises 35–44, determine the slope of the line passing through the given points. (See Example 2)

35. $(4, -7)$ and $(2, -1)$

36. $(-9, 4)$ and $(-1, -6)$

37. $(30, -52)$ and $(-22, -39)$

38. $(-100, -16)$ and $(84, 30)$

39. $(2.6, 4.1)$ and $(9.5, -3.7)$

40. $(8.5, 6.2)$ and $(-5.1, 7.9)$

41. $\left(\dfrac{3}{4}, 6\right)$ and $\left(\dfrac{5}{2}, 1\right)$

42. $\left(-3, \dfrac{2}{5}\right)$ and $\left(4, \dfrac{3}{10}\right)$

43. $\left(3\sqrt{6}, 2\sqrt{5}\right)$ and $\left(\sqrt{6}, \sqrt{5}\right)$

44. $\left(2\sqrt{11}, -3\sqrt{3}\right)$ and $\left(\sqrt{11}, -5\sqrt{3}\right)$

For Exercises 45–50, determine the slope of the line. (See Examples 2–3)

45.

46.

47.

48.

49.

50.

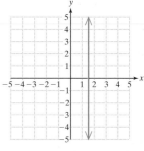

51. What is the slope of a line perpendicular to the x-axis?

52. What is the slope of a line parallel to the x-axis?

53. What is the slope of a line defined by $y = -7$?

54. What is the slope of a line defined by $x = 2$?

55. If the slope of a line is $\frac{4}{5}$, how much vertical change will be present for a horizontal change of 52 ft?

56. If the slope of a line is $\frac{5}{8}$, how much horizontal change will be present for a vertical change of 216 m?

57. Suppose that $y = P(t)$ represents the population of a city at time t. What does $\frac{\Delta P}{\Delta t}$ represent?

58. Suppose that $y = d(t)$ represents the distance that an object travels in time t. What does $\frac{\Delta d}{\Delta t}$ represent?

Objective 3: Apply the Slope-Intercept Form of a Line

For Exercises 59–70,

a. Write the equation in slope-intercept form if possible, and determine the slope and y-intercept.

b. Graph the equation using the slope and y-intercept. (**See Example 4**)

59. $2x - 4y = 8$

60. $3x - y = 6$

61. $3x = 2y - 4$

62. $5x = 3y - 6$

63. $3x = 4y$

64. $-2x = 3y$

65. $2y - 6 = 8$

66. $3y + 9 = 6$

67. $0.02x + 0.06y = 0.06$

68. $0.03x + 0.04y = 0.12$

69. $\dfrac{x}{4} + \dfrac{y}{7} = 1$

70. $\dfrac{x}{3} + \dfrac{y}{4} = 1$

For Exercises 71–72, determine if the function is linear, constant, or neither.

71. a. $f(x) = -\dfrac{3}{4}x$

b. $g(x) = -\dfrac{3}{4}x - 3$

c. $h(x) = -\dfrac{3}{4x}$

d. $k(x) = -\dfrac{3}{4}$

72. a. $m(x) = 5x + 1$

b. $n(x) = \dfrac{5}{x} + 1$

c. $p(x) = 5$

d. $q(x) = 5x$

For Exercises 73–82,

a. Use slope-intercept form to write an equation of the line that passes through the given point and has the given slope.

b. Write the equation using function notation where $y = f(x)$. (**See Example 5**)

73. $(0, 9)$; $m = \dfrac{1}{2}$ **74.** $(0, -4)$; $m = \dfrac{1}{3}$ **75.** $(1, -6)$; $m = -3$ **76.** $(2, -8)$; $m = -5$

77. $(-5, -3)$; $m = \dfrac{2}{3}$ **78.** $(-4, -2)$; $m = \dfrac{3}{2}$ **79.** $(2, 5)$; $m = 0$ **80.** $(-1, -3)$; $m = 0$

81. $(3.6, 5.1)$; $m = 1.2$ **82.** $(1.2, 2.8)$; $m = 2.4$

For Exercises 83–86,

a. Use slope-intercept form to write an equation of the line that passes through the two given points.

b. Then write the equation using function notation where $y = f(x)$.

83. $(4, 2)$ and $(0, -6)$ **84.** $(-8, 1)$ and $(0, -3)$ **85.** $(7, -3)$ and $(4, 1)$ **86.** $(2, -4)$ and $(-1, 3)$

Objective 4: Compute Average Rate of Change

For Exercises 87–88, find the slope of the secant line pictured in red. (See Example 6)

87.

88.

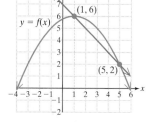

89. The function given by $y = f(x)$ shows the value of $5000 invested at 5% interest compounded continuously, x years after the money was originally invested.

   a. Find the average amount earned per year between the 5th year and 10th year.

   b. Find the average amount earned per year between the 20th year and the 25th year.

   c. Based on the answers from parts (a) and (b), does it appear that the rate at which annual income increases is increasing or decreasing with time?

90. The function given by $y = f(x)$ shows the average monthly temperature (°F) for Cedar Key. The value of x is the month number and $x = 1$ represents January.

   a. Find the average rate of change in temperature between months 3 and 5 (March and May).

   b. Find the average rate of change in temperature between months 9 and 11 (September and November).

   c. Comparing the results in parts (a) and (b), what does a positive rate of change mean in the context of this problem? What does a negative rate of change mean?

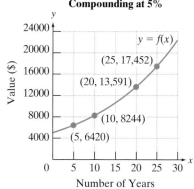

Value of $5000 with Continuous Compounding at 5%

Average Monthly Temperature for Cedar Key, Florida

91. The population of the United States since the year 1960 can be approximated by $f(t) = 0.009t^2 + 2.10t + 182$, where $f(t)$ is the population in millions and t represents the number of years since 1960.

   a. Find the average rate of change in U.S. population between 1960 and 1970. Round to 1 decimal place.

   b. Find the average rate of change in U.S. population between 2000 and 2010. Round to 1 decimal place.

   c. Based on the answers from parts (a) and (b), does it appear that the rate at which U.S. population increases is increasing or decreasing with time?

92. The world population since the year 1980 can be approximated by $f(t) = -0.2t^2 + 86t + 4450$, where $f(t)$ is the population in millions and t represents the number of years since 1980.

   a. Find the average rate of change in world population between 1980 and 1990.

   b. Find the average rate of change in world population between 2000 and 2010.

   c. Based on the answers from parts (a) and (b), does it appear that the rate at which world population increases is increasing or decreasing with time?

For Exercises 93–98, determine the average rate of change of the function on the given interval. (See Example 7)

93. $f(x) = x^2 - 3$

   a. on $[0, 1]$

   b. on $[1, 3]$

   c. on $[-2, 0]$

94. $g(x) = 2x^2 + 2$

   a. on $[0, 1]$

   b. on $[1, 3]$

   c. on $[-2, 0]$

95. $h(x) = x^3$

   a. on $[-1, 0]$

   b. on $[0, 1]$

   c. on $[1, 2]$

96. $k(x) = x^3 - 2$

   a. on $[-1, 0]$

   b. on $[0, 1]$

   c. on $[1, 2]$

97. $m(x) = \sqrt{x}$

   a. $[0, 1]$

   b. $[1, 4]$

   c. $[4, 9]$

98. $n(x) = \sqrt{x - 1}$

   a. $[1, 2]$

   b. $[2, 5]$

   c. $[5, 10]$

Objective 5: Solve Equations and Inequalities Graphically

For Exercises 99–106, use the graph to solve the equation and inequalities. Write the solutions to the inequalities in interval notation. (See Examples 8–9)

99. a. $2x + 4 = -x + 1$

   b. $2x + 4 < -x + 1$

   c. $2x + 4 \geq -x + 1$

100. a. $4x - 2 = -3x + 5$

   b. $4x - 2 < -3x + 5$

   c. $4x - 2 \geq -3x + 5$

101. a. $-3x + 1 = -x - 3$

   b. $-3x + 1 > -x - 3$

   c. $-3x + 1 \leq -x - 3$

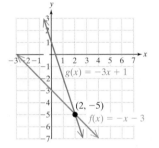

102. a. $-x - 2 = 2x - 5$

   b. $-x - 2 \leq 2x - 5$

   c. $-x - 2 > 2x - 5$

103. a. $-3(x + 2) + 1 = -x + 5$

   b. $-3(x + 2) + 1 \leq -x + 5$

   c. $-3(x + 2) + 1 \geq -x + 5$

104. a. $-4(x - 5) + 3x = -3x + 1$

   b. $-4(x - 5) + 3x \leq -3x + 1$

   c. $-4(x - 5) + 3x \geq -3x + 1$

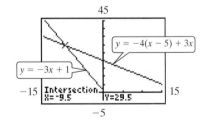

105. a. $4 - 2(x + 1) + 12 + x = 0$

  b. $4 - 2(x + 1) + 12 + x < 0$

  c. $4 - 2(x + 1) + 12 + x > 0$

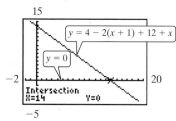

106. a. $8 - 4(1 - x) - 7 - 2x = 0$

  b. $8 - 4(1 - x) - 7 - 2x < 0$

  c. $8 - 4(1 - x) - 7 - 2x > 0$

107. The graph shows the enrollment in U.S. colleges and universities by gender and by year from 1970 to 2010. (*Source*: www.census.gov) The function defined by $F(x) = 0.17x + 3.8$ represents the number of women in college (in millions), x years after 1970. $M(x) = 0.086x + 4.48$ represents the number of men in college (in millions), x years after 1970. Solve the equation and inequalities and interpret the meaning of the solution sets in the context of this problem.

  a. $F(x) = M(x)$

  b. $F(x) < M(x)$

  c. $F(x) > M(x)$

108. The graph shows the annual per capita consumption of pork and chicken in the United States by year from 1980 to 2010. (*Source*: U.S. Department of Agriculture, www.usda.gov) The function defined by $P(x) = -0.11x + 49.7$ represents the amount of pork eaten (in lb), x years after 1980. $C(x) = 1.13x + 31.5$ represents the amount of chicken eaten (in lb), x years after 1980. Solve the equation and inequalities and interpret the meaning of the solution sets in the context of this problem.

  a. $P(x) = C(x)$

  b. $P(x) < C(x)$

  c. $P(x) > C(x)$

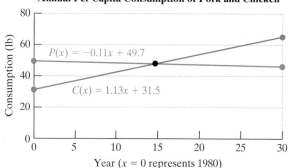

Write About It

109. Explain how you can determine from a linear equation $Ax + By = C$ (A and B not both zero) whether the line is slanted, horizontal, or vertical.

111. What is the benefit of writing an equation of a line in slope-intercept form?

110. Explain how you can determine from a linear equation $Ax + By = C$ (A and B not both zero) whether the line passes through the origin.

112. Explain how the average rate of change of a function f on the interval $[x_1, x_2]$ is related to slope.

Expanding Your Skills

113. Determine the area in the second quadrant enclosed by $y = 2x + 4$ and the x- and y-axes.

114. Determine the area enclosed by

$$y = x + 6$$
$$y = -2x + 6$$
$$y = 0$$

115. Determine the area enclosed by

$$y = -\frac{1}{2}x - 2$$
$$y = \frac{1}{3}x - 2$$
$$y = 0$$

116. Determine the area enclosed by

$$y = \sqrt{4 - (x - 2)^2}$$
$$y = 0$$

117. Consider the standard form of a linear equation $Ax + By = C$ in the case where $B \neq 0$.

    a. Write the equation in slope-intercept form.

    b. Identify the slope in terms of the coefficients A and B.

    c. Identify the y-intercept in terms of the coefficients B and C.

118. Use the results from Exercise 117 to determine the slope and y-intercept for the graphs of the lines.

    a. $5x - 9y = 6$

    b. $0.052x - 0.013y = 0.39$

Technology Connections

For Exercises 119–124, solve the equation in part (a) and verify the solution on a graphing calculator. Then use the graph to find the solution set to the inequalities in parts (b) and (c). Write the solution sets to the inequalities in interval notation. (See Example 9)

119. a. $3.1 - 2.2(t + 1) = 6.3 + 1.4t$

    b. $3.1 - 2.2(t + 1) > 6.3 + 1.4t$

    c. $3.1 - 2.2(t + 1) < 6.3 + 1.4t$

120. a. $-11.2 - 4.6(c - 3) + 1.8c = 0.4(c + 2)$

    b. $-11.2 - 4.6(c - 3) + 1.8c > 0.4(c + 2)$

    c. $-11.2 - 4.6(c - 3) + 1.8c < 0.4(c + 2)$

121. a. $|2x - 3.8| - 4.6 = 7.2$

    b. $|2x - 3.8| - 4.6 \geq 7.2$

    c. $|2x - 3.8| - 4.6 \leq 7.2$

122. a. $|x - 1.7| + 4.95 = 11.15$

    b. $|x - 1.7| + 4.95 \geq 11.15$

    c. $|x - 1.7| + 4.95 \leq 11.15$

123. a. $2\sqrt{4z - 3} - 14 = 0$

    b. $2\sqrt{4z - 3} - 14 > 0$

    c. $2\sqrt{4z - 3} - 14 < 0$

124. a. $2\sqrt{y + 1} - 3 = 0$

    b. $2\sqrt{y + 1} - 3 > 0$

    c. $2\sqrt{y + 1} - 3 < 0$

For Exercises 125–126, graph the lines in (a)–(c) on the standard viewing window. Compare the graphs. Are they exactly the same? If not, how are they different?

125. a. $y = 3x + 1$

    b. $y = 2.99x + 1$

    c. $y = 3.01x + 1$

126. a. $y = x + 3$

    b. $y = x + 2.99$

    c. $y = x + 3.01$

SECTION 2.5   Applications of Linear Equations and Modeling

OBJECTIVES

1. Apply the Point-Slope Formula
2. Determine the Slopes of Parallel and Perpendicular Lines
3. Create Linear Functions to Model Data
4. Create Models Using Linear Regression

1. Apply the Point-Slope Formula

The slope formula can be used to develop the point-slope form of an equation of a line. Suppose that a line has a slope m and passes through a known point (x_1, y_1). Let (x, y) be any other point on the line. From the slope formula, we have

$$\frac{y - y_1}{x - x_1} = m \qquad \text{Slope formula.}$$

$$\left(\frac{y - y_1}{x - x_1}\right)(x - x_1) = m(x - x_1) \qquad \text{Clear fractions.}$$

$$y - y_1 = m(x - x_1) \qquad \text{This is called the point slope formula for a line.}$$

The point-slope formula is useful to build an equation of a line given a point on the line and the slope of the line.

> **Point-Slope Formula**
>
> The point-slope formula for a line is given by $y - y_1 = m(x - x_1)$, where m is the slope of the line and (x_1, y_1) is a point on the line.

EXAMPLE 1   **Writing an Equation of a Line Given a Point on the Line and Slope**

Use the point-slope formula to find an equation of the line passing through the point $(2, -3)$ and having slope -4. Write the answer in slope-intercept form.

Solution:

Label $(2, -3)$ as (x_1, y_1) and $m = -4$.

$$y - y_1 = m(x - x_1)$$ Apply the point-slope formula.

$$y - (-3) = -4(x - 2)$$ Substitute $x_1 = 2$, $y_1 = -3$, and $m = -4$.

$$y + 3 = -4x + 8$$ Simplify.

$$y = -4x + 5 \text{ (slope-intercept form)}$$

Skill Practice 1   Use the point-slope formula to find an equation of the line passing through the point $(-5, 2)$ and having slope -3. Write the answer in slope-intercept form.

EXAMPLE 2   **Writing an Equation of a Line Given Two Points**

Use the point-slope formula to write an equation of the line passing through the points $(4, -6)$ and $(-1, 2)$. Write the answer in slope-intercept form.

Solution:

To apply the point-slope formula, we first need to know the slope of the line.

$(4, -6)$ and $(-1, 2)$ Label the points.

(x_1, y_1) and (x_2, y_2)

$$m = \frac{y_2 - y_1}{x_2 - x_1} = \frac{2 - (-6)}{-1 - 4} = \frac{8}{-5} = -\frac{8}{5}$$ Apply the slope formula using either given point as (x_1, y_1).

$$y - y_1 = m(x - x_1)$$ Apply the point-slope formula.

$$y - (-6) = -\frac{8}{5}(x - 4)$$ Substitute $y_1 = -6$, $x_1 = 4$, and $m = -\frac{8}{5}$.

$$y + 6 = -\frac{8}{5}x + \frac{32}{5}$$

$$y = -\frac{8}{5}x + \frac{32}{5} - 6$$

$$y = -\frac{8}{5}x + \frac{32}{5} - \frac{30}{5}$$

$$y = -\frac{8}{5}x + \frac{2}{5} \text{ (slope-intercept form)}$$

To check, we see that the graph of the line passes through $(4, -6)$ and $(-1, 2)$ as expected.

Skill Practice 2   Write an equation of the line passing through the points $(2, -5)$ and $(7, -3)$.

Answers

1. $y = -3x - 13$

2. $y = \dfrac{2}{5}x - \dfrac{29}{5}$

2. Determine the Slopes of Parallel and Perpendicular Lines

Lines in the same plane that do not intersect are **parallel lines.** Nonvertical parallel lines have the same slope and different y-intercepts (Figure 2-22).

Lines that intersect at a right angle are **perpendicular lines.** If two nonvertical lines are perpendicular, then the slope of one line is the opposite of the reciprocal of the slope of the other line (Figure 2-23).

Figure 2-22

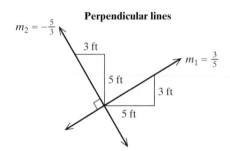

Figure 2-23

Slopes of Parallel and Perpendicular Lines

- If m_1 and m_2 represent the slopes of two nonvertical parallel lines, then $m_1 = m_2$.
- If m_1 and m_2 represent the slopes of two nonvertical perpendicular lines, then $m_1 = -\dfrac{1}{m_2}$ or equivalently $m_1 m_2 = -1$.

EXAMPLE 3   **Finding Slopes of Parallel and Perpendicular Lines**

The slope of a line is given. Find the slope of a line parallel to the given line, and the slope of a line perpendicular to the given line.

a. $m = \dfrac{4}{3}$ **b.** $m = -2$ **c.** $m = 0$

Solution:

a. $m = \dfrac{4}{3}$ Slope of a parallel line: $\frac{4}{3}$ Slope of a perpendicular line: $-\frac{3}{4}$

b. $m = -2$ Slope of a parallel line: -2 Slope of a perpendicular line: $\frac{1}{2}$

c. $m = 0$ Slope of a parallel line: 0 Slope of a perpendicular line: Undefined

---

Skill Practice 3   The slope of a line is given. Find the slope of a line parallel to the given line, and the slope of a line perpendicular to the given line.

a. $-\dfrac{2}{5}$ **b.** $m = 5$ **c.** $m = 1$

Answers

3. **a.** $-\dfrac{2}{5}; \dfrac{5}{2}$ **b.** $5; -\dfrac{1}{5}$ **c.** $1; -1$

In Examples 4 and 5, we use the point-slope formula to find an equation of a line through a specified point and parallel or perpendicular to another line.

EXAMPLE 4   Writing an Equation of a Line Parallel to Another Line

Write an equation of the line passing through the point $(-4, 1)$ and parallel to the line defined by $x + 4y = 3$. Write the answer in slope-intercept form and in standard form.

Solution:

$$x + 4y = 3$$

The slope of the given line can be found from its slope-intercept form. Solve for y.

$$4y = -x + 3$$

$$y = -\frac{1}{4}x + \frac{3}{4}$$

The slope of both lines is $-\frac{1}{4}$.

Apply the point-slope formula with $x_1 = -4$, $y_1 = 1$, and $m = -\frac{1}{4}$.

$$y - y_1 = m(x - x_1)$$

$$y - 1 = -\frac{1}{4}[x - (-4)]$$

$$y - 1 = -\frac{1}{4}(x + 4)$$

$$y - 1 = -\frac{1}{4}x - 1$$

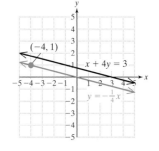

$$y = -\frac{1}{4}x \text{ (slope-intercept form)}$$

From the graph, we see that the line passes through the point $(-4, 1)$ and is parallel to the graph of $x + 4y = 3$.

$$4(y) = 4\left(-\frac{1}{4}x\right)$$

$$4y = -x$$

$$x + 4y = 0 \text{ (standard form)}$$

Clearing fractions, and collecting the x and y terms on one side of the equation gives us standard form.

Skill Practice 4   Write an equation of the line passing through the point $(-3, 2)$ and parallel to the line defined by $x + 3y = 6$. Write the answer in slope-intercept form and in standard form.

EXAMPLE 5   Writing an Equation of a Line Perpendicular to Another Line

Write an equation of the line passing through the point $(2, -3)$ and perpendicular to the line defined by $y = \frac{1}{2}x - 4$. Write the answer in slope-intercept form and in standard form.

Answer

4. $y = -\frac{1}{3}x + 1; x + 3y = 3$

Avoiding Mistakes

The solution to Example 5 can be checked by graphing both lines and verifying that they are perpendicular and that the line $y = -2x + 1$ passes through the point $(2, -3)$.

Solution:

From the slope-intercept form, $y = \frac{1}{2}x - 4$, the slope of given line is $\frac{1}{2}$.

$y - y_1 = m(x - x_1)$	The slope of a line perpendicular to the given line is -2.
$y - (-3) = -2(x - 2)$	Apply the point-slope formula with $x_1 = 2$, $y_1 = -3$, and $m = -2$.
$y + 3 = -2x + 4$	Simplify.

$y = -2x + 1$ (slope-intercept form)	Write the equation in slope-intercept form by solving for y.
$2x + y = 1$ (standard form)	Write the equation in standard form by collecting the x and y terms on one side of the equation.

Skill Practice 5 Write an equation of the line passing through the point $(-8, -4)$ and perpendicular to the line defined by $y = \frac{1}{6}x + 3$.

3. Create Linear Functions to Model Data

In many day-to-day applications, two variables are related linearly. By finding an equation of the line, we produce a model that relates the two variables. This is demonstrated in Example 6.

EXAMPLE 6 **Using a Linear Function in an Application**

A family plan for a cell phone has a monthly base price of $99 plus $12.99 for each additional family member added beyond the primary account holder.

a. Write a linear function to model the monthly cost $C(x)$ (in $) of a family plan for x additional family members added.

b. Evaluate $C(4)$ and interpret the meaning in the context of this problem.

Solution:

a. $C(x) = mx + b$	The base price $99 is the fixed cost with zero additional family members added. So the constant b is 99.
$C(x) = 12.99x + 99$	The rate of increase, $12.99 per additional family member, is the slope.

b. $C(4) = 12.99(4) + 99$	Substitute 4 for x.
$= 150.96$	

The total monthly cost of the plan with 4 additional family members beyond the primary account holder is $150.96.

Skill Practice 6 A speeding ticket is $100 plus $5 for every 1 mph over the speed limit.

a. Write a linear function to model the cost $S(x)$ (in $) of a speeding ticket for a person caught driving x mph over the speed limit.

b. Evaluate $S(15)$ and interpret the meaning in the context of this problem.

Answers

5. $y = -6x - 52$; $6x + y = -52$
6. a. $S(x) = 5x + 100$
   b. $S(15) = 175$ means that a ticket costs $175 for a person caught speeding 15 mph over the speed limit.

Linear functions can sometimes be used to model the cost, revenue, and profit of producing and selling x items.

Linear Cost, Revenue, and Profit Functions

A **linear cost function** models the cost $C(x)$ to produce x items.

$C(x) = mx + b$ m is the variable cost per item. b is the fixed cost.	The fixed cost does not change relative to the number of items produced. For example, the cost to rent an office is a fixed cost. The variable cost per item is the rate at which cost increases for each additional unit produced. Variable costs include labor, material, and shipping.

A **linear revenue function** models revenue $R(x)$ for selling x items.

$R(x) = px$	p is the price per item.

A **linear profit function** models the profit for producing and selling x items.

$P(x) = R(x) - C(x)$	Subtract the cost to produce x items from the revenue brought in from selling x items.

EXAMPLE 7   Writing Linear Cost, Revenue, and Profit Functions

At a summer art show a vendor sells lemonade for $2.00 per cup. The cost to rent the booth is $120. Furthermore, the vendor knows that the lemons, sugar, and cups collectively cost $0.50 for each cup of lemonade produced.

a. Write a linear cost function to produce x cups of lemonade.
b. Write a linear revenue function for selling x cups of lemonade.
c. Write a linear profit function for producing and selling x cups of lemonade.
d. How much profit will the vendor make if 50 cups of lemonade are produced and sold?
e. How much profit will be made for producing and selling 128 cups?
f. Determine the break-even point.

Solution:

a. $C(x) = 0.50x + 120$

The fixed cost is $120 because it does not change relative to the number of cups of lemonade produced. The variable cost is $0.50 per lemonade.

b. $R(x) = 2.00x$

The price per cup of lemonade is $2.00. Therefore, the product $2.00x$ gives the amount of revenue for x cups of lemonade sold.

c. $P(x) = R(x) - C(x)$

Profit is defined as the difference of revenue and cost.

$P(x) = 2.00x - (0.50x + 120)$

$P(x) = 1.50x - 120$

d. $P(50) = 1.50(50) - 120$ Substitute 50 for x.

$\qquad = -45$ The vendor will lose \$45.

e. $P(128) = 1.50(128) - 120$ Substitute 128 for x.

$\qquad = 72$ The vendor will make \$72.

f. For what value of x will   The break-even point is defined as the point where
$R(x) = C(x)$ or $P(x) = 0$?   revenue equals cost. Alternatively, this can be stated
        as the point where profit equals zero: $P(x) = 0$.

$$P(x) = 0$$
$$1.50x - 120 = 0 \qquad \text{Solve for } x.$$
$$1.50x = 120$$
$$x = 80$$

If the vendor produces and sells 80 cups of lemonade, the cost and revenue
will be equal, resulting in a profit of \$0. This is the break-even point.

Skill Practice 7   Repeat Example 7 in the case where the vendor can cut
the cost to \$0.40 per cup of lemonade, and sell lemonades for \$1.50 per cup.

Figure 2-24 shows the graphs of the revenue and cost functions from Example 7.
Notice that R and C intersect at (80, 160). This means that if 80 cups of lemonade
are produced and sold, the revenue and cost are both \$160. That is, $R(x) = C(x)$ and
the company breaks even. The graph of the profit function P is consistent with this
result. The value of $P(x)$ is 0 for 80 lemonades produced and sold (Figure 2-25).

Figure 2-24

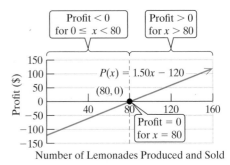

Figure 2-25

From Figures 2-24 and 2-25, we can draw the following conclusions.

- The company experiences a loss if fewer than 80 cups of lemonade are
  produced and sold. That is, $R(x) < C(x)$, or equivalently $P(x) < 0$.

- The company experiences a profit if more than 80 cups of lemonade are
  produced and sold. That is, $R(x) > C(x)$, or equivalently $P(x) > 0$.

- The company breaks even if exactly 80 cups of lemonade are produced and
  sold. That is, $R(x) = C(x)$, or equivalently $P(x) = 0$.

Answers

7. a. $C(x) = 0.40x + 120$
b. $R(x) = 1.50x$
c. $P(x) = 1.10x - 120$
d. $-\$65$
e. \$20.80
f. Approximately 109 cups

EXAMPLE 8   **Writing a Linear Model to Relate Two Variables**

The data shown in the graph represent the age and systolic blood pressure for a sample of 12 randomly selected healthy adults.

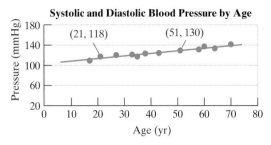

Systolic and Diastolic Blood Pressure by Age

a. Suppose that x represents the age of an adult (in yr), and y represents the systolic blood pressure (in mmHg). Use the points (21, 118) and (51, 130) to write a linear model relating y as a function of x.

b. Interpret the meaning of the slope in the context of this problem.

c. Use the model to estimate the systolic blood pressure for a 55-year-old. Round to the nearest whole unit.

> **TIP**   The equation
> $y = -0.4x + 109.6$ can also be expressed in function notation. For example, we can rename y as $S(x)$.
>
> $S(x) = -0.4x + 109.6$
>
> The value $S(x)$ represents the estimated systolic blood pressure for an adult of age x years.

Solution:

a. (21, 118) and (51, 130)

  (x_1, y_1) and (x_2, y_2) Label the points.

  $m = \dfrac{130 - 118}{51 - 21} = 0.4$ Determine the slope of the line.

  $y - y_1 = m(x - x_1)$ Apply the point-slope formula.
  $y - 118 = 0.4(x - 21)$
  $y = 0.4x + 109.6$ The equation $y = 0.4x + 109.6$ relates an individual's age to an estimated systolic blood pressure for that age.

b. The slope is 0.4. This means that the average increase in systolic blood pressure for adults is 0.4 mmHg per year of age.

c. $y = 0.4x + 109.6$
  $y = 0.4(55) + 109.6$ Substitute 55 for x.
  $y = 131.6$

  Based on the sample of data, the estimated systolic blood pressure for a 55-year-old is 132 mmHg.

Skill Practice 8   Suppose that y represents the average consumer spending on television services per year (in dollars), and that x represents the number of years since 2004.

a. Use the data points (2, 308) and (6, 408) to write a linear equation relating y to x.

b. Interpret the meaning of the slope in the context of this problem.

c. Interpret the meaning of the y-intercept in the context of this problem.

d. Use the model from part (a) to estimate the average consumer spending on television services for the year 2007.

Answers

8. a. $y = 25x + 258$
  b. The slope is 25 and means that consumer spending on television services rose $25 per year during this time period.
  c. (0, 258); The average consumer spending on television services for the year 2004 was $258.
  d. $333

4. Create Models Using Linear Regression

In Example 8, we used two given data points to determine a linear model for systolic blood pressure versus age. There are two drawbacks to this method. First, the equation is not necessarily unique. If we use two different data points, we may get a different equation. Second, it is generally preferable to write a model that is based on *all* the data points, rather than just two points. One such model is called the least-squares regression line.

The procedure to find the least-squares regression line is discussed in detail in a statistics course. Here we will give the basic premise and use a graphing utility to perform the calculations. Consider a set of data points $(x_1, y_1), (x_2, y_2), (x_3, y_3), \ldots, (x_n, y_n)$. The **least-squares regression line,** $\hat{y} = mx + b$, is the unique line that minimizes the sum of the squared vertical deviations from the observed data points to the line (Figure 2-26).

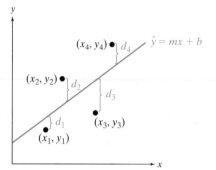

Figure 2-26

On a calculator or spreadsheet, the equation $\hat{y} = mx + b$ may be denoted as $y = ax + b$ or as $y = b_0 + b_1 x$. In any event, the coefficient of x is the slope of the line, and the constant gives us the y-intercept. Although the exact keystrokes on different calculators and graphing utilities may vary, we will use the following guidelines to find the least-squares regression line.

Creating a Linear Regression Model

1. Graph the data in a scatter plot.
2. Inspect the data visually to determine if the data suggest a linear trend.
3. Invoke the linear regression feature on a calculator, graphing utility, or spreadsheet.
4. Check the result by graphing the line with the data points to verify that the line passes through or near the data points.

EXAMPLE 9   Finding a Least-Squares Regression Line

The data given in the table represent the age and systolic blood pressure for a sample of 12 randomly selected healthy adults.

Age (yr)	17	21	27	33	35	38	43	51	58	60	64	70
Systolic blood pressure (mmHg)	110	118	121	122	118	124	125	130	132	138	134	142

a. Make a scatter plot of the data using age as the independent variable, x, and systolic pressure as the dependent variable y.

b. Based on the graph, does a linear model seem appropriate?

c. Determine the equation of the least-squares regression line.

d. Use the least-squares regression line to approximate the systolic blood pressure for a healthy 55-year-old. Round to the nearest whole unit.

Solution:

a. On a graphing calculator hit the STAT button and select EDIT to enter the x and y data into two lists (shown here as L1 and L2).

Select the STAT PLOT option and turn Plot1 to On. For the type of graph, select the scatter plot image.

Be sure that the window is set to accommodate x values between 17 and 70, and y values between 110 and 142, inclusive. Then hit the GRAPH key. The window settings shown here are [0, 80, 10] by [0, 200, 20].

b. From the graph, the data appear to follow a linear trend.

c. Under the STAT menu, select CALC and then the LinReg(ax + b) option.

The command LinReg(ax + b) prompts the user to enter the list names (L_1 and L_2) containing the x and y data values. Then highlight Calculate and hit ENTER.

In the regression model $y = ax + b$, the values for the coefficients a and b are placed on the home screen.

Rounding the values of a and b gives us $y = 0.511x + 104$.

Enter the equation $Y_1 = 0.511x + 104$ into the equation editor and hit the GRAPH key. The graph of the regression line passes near or through the observed data points.

d. $y = 0.511x + 104$
$y = 0.511(55) + 104$ To approximate the systolic blood pressure for a 55-year-old, substitute 55 for x.
$= 132.105$

The systolic blood pressure for a healthy 55-year-old would be approximately 132 mmHg.

TIP The linear equation found in Example 8 was based on two data points. The least-squares regression line is based on all available data points. The estimate from each model for systolic blood pressure for a 55-year-old rounds to 132 mmHg.

> **Skill Practice 9**   The data given represent the class averages for individual students based on the number of absences from class.
>
> | Number of Absences (x) | 3 | 7 | 1 | 11 | 2 | 14 | 2 | 5 |
> |---|---|---|---|---|---|---|---|---|
> | Average in Class (y) | 88 | 67 | 96 | 62 | 90 | 56 | 97 | 82 |
>
> **a.** Find the equation of the least-squares regression line.
>
> **b.** Use the model from part (a) to approximate the average for a student who misses 6 classes.

Answers

9. a. $y = -3.27x + 98.1$
 b. The student's average would be approximately 78.5.

SECTION 2.5   Practice Exercises

Review Exercises

For Exercises 1–2, use slope-intercept form to write an equation of a line with the given slope and that passes through the given point.

1. $(-4, 2); \; m = \dfrac{3}{2}$

2. $(-12, 3); \; m = \dfrac{5}{6}$

For Exercises 3–4, identify the slope and y-intercept.

3. $-6x + 3y = y + 3$

4. $2x = 3y + 1$

For Exercises 5–6,

a. State whether the graph of the equation is a horizontal line or vertical line.

b. Identify the slope.

c. Identify the y-intercept.

5. $2x + 1 = 11$

6. $-3y - 9 = 6$

Concept Connections

7. Given a point (x_1, y_1) on a line with slope m, the point-slope formula is given by _____.

8. If two nonvertical lines have the same slope but different y-intercepts, then the lines are (parallel/perpendicular).

9. If m_1 and m_2 represent the slopes of two nonvertical perpendicular lines, then $m_1 m_2 =$ _____.

10. Suppose that $y = C(x)$ represents the cost to produce x items, and that $y = R(x)$ represents the revenue for selling x items. The profit $P(x)$ of producing and selling x items is defined by $P(x) =$ _____.

Objective 1: Apply the Point-Slope Formula

For Exercises 11–26, use the point-slope formula to write an equation of the line having the given conditions. Write the answer in slope-intercept form (if possible). (See Examples 1–2)

11. Passes through $(-3, 5)$ and $m = -2$.

12. Passes through $(4, -6)$ and $m = 3$.

13. Passes through $(-1, 0)$ and $m = \dfrac{2}{3}$.

14. Passes through $(-4, 0)$ and $m = \dfrac{3}{5}$.

15. Passes through $(3.4, 2.6)$ and $m = 1.2$.

16. Passes through $(2.2, 4.1)$ and $m = 2.4$.

17. Passes through $(6, 2)$ and $(-3, 1)$.

18. Passes through $(-4, 8)$ and $(-7, -3)$.

19. Passes through $(0, 8)$ and $(5, 0)$.

20. Passes through $(0, -6)$ and $(11, 0)$.

21. Passes through $(2.3, 5.1)$ and $(1.9, 3.7)$.

22. Passes through $(1.6, 4.8)$ and $(0.8, 6)$.

23. Passes through $(3, -4)$ and $m = 0$.

24. Passes through $(-5, 1)$ and $m = 0$.

25. Passes through $\left(\dfrac{2}{3}, \dfrac{1}{5}\right)$ and the slope is undefined.

26. Passes through $\left(-\dfrac{4}{7}, \dfrac{3}{10}\right)$ and the slope is undefined.

27. Given a line defined by $x = 4$, what is the slope of the line?

28. Given a line defined by $y = -2$, what is the slope of the line?

Objective 2: Determine the Slopes of Parallel and Perpendicular Lines

For Exercises 29–34, the slope of a line is given. (See Example 3)

a. Determine the slope of a line parallel to the given line, if possible.

b. Determine the slope of a line perpendicular to the given line, if possible.

29. $m = \dfrac{3}{11}$

30. $m = \dfrac{6}{7}$

31. $m = -6$

32. $m = -10$

33. $m = 1$

34. m is undefined

For Exercises 35–42, determine if the lines defined by the given equations are parallel, perpendicular, or neither.

35. $y = 2x - 3$
$y = -\dfrac{1}{2}x + 7$

36. $y = \dfrac{4}{3}x - 1$
$y = -\dfrac{3}{4}x + 5$

37. $8x - 5y = 3$
$2x = \dfrac{5}{4}y + 1$

38. $2x + 3y = 7$
$4x = -6y + 2$

39. $2x = 6$
$5 = y$

40. $3y = 5$
$x = 1$

41. $6x = 7y$
$\dfrac{7}{2}x - 3y = 0$

42. $5y = 2x$
$\dfrac{5}{2}x - y = 0$

For Exercises 43–50, write an equation of the line satisfying the given conditions. Write the answer in slope-intercept form (if possible) and in standard form with no fractional coefficients. (See Examples 4–5)

43. Passes through $(2, 5)$ and is parallel to the line defined by $2x + y = 6$.

44. Passes through $(3, -1)$ and is parallel to the line defined by $-3x + y = 4$.

45. Passes through $(6, -4)$ and is perpendicular to the line defined by $x - 5y = 1$.

46. Passes through $(5, 4)$ and is perpendicular to the line defined by $x - 2y = 7$.

47. Passes through $(6, 8)$ and is parallel to the line defined by $3x = 7y + 5$.

48. Passes through $(7, -6)$ and is parallel to the line defined by $2x = 5y - 4$.

49. Passes through $(2.2, 6.4)$ and is perpendicular to the line defined by $2x = 4 - y$.

50. Passes through $(3.6, 1.2)$ and is perpendicular to the line defined by $4x = 9 - y$.

For Exercises 51–56, write an equation of the line that satisfies the given conditions.

51. Passes through $(8, 6)$ and is parallel to the x-axis.

52. Passes through $(-11, 13)$ and is parallel to the y-axis.

53. Passes through $\left(\dfrac{5}{11}, -\dfrac{3}{4}\right)$ and is perpendicular to the y-axis.

54. Passes through $\left(-\dfrac{7}{9}, \dfrac{7}{3}\right)$ and is perpendicular to the x-axis.

55. Passes through $(-61.5, 47.6)$ and is parallel to the line defined by $x = -12$.

56. Passes through $(-0.004, 0.009)$ and is parallel to the line defined by $y = 6$.

Objective 3: Create Linear Functions to Model Data

57. A sales person makes a base salary of $400 per week plus 12% commission on sales. (**See Example 6**)

    a. Write a linear function to model the sales person's weekly salary $S(x)$ for x dollars in sales.

    b. Evaluate $S(8000)$ and interpret the meaning in the context of this problem.

58. At a parking garage in a large city, the charge for parking consists of a flat fee of $2.00 plus $1.50/hr.

    a. Write a linear function to model the cost for parking $P(t)$ for t hours.

    b. Evaluate $P(1.6)$ and interpret the meaning in the context of this problem.

59. Suppose that an aircraft has an initial mass at take-off of 120,000 kg (this includes passengers, cargo, and fuel). Further suppose that the aircraft burns fuel at an average rate of 2400 gal/hr. (The burn rate is actually not constant. An aircraft burns fuel at a lesser rate as fuel burns and the aircraft becomes lighter towards the end of a flight. However, we will consider an average burn rate of 2400 gal/hr.)

   a. If jet fuel weighs 2.7 kg/gal, write a linear function that represents the weight of the aircraft $W(t)$ at a time t hours into a 4.5 hr flight.

   b. Evaluate $W(2.5)$ and interpret the meaning in the context of this problem.

60. The average water level in a retention pond is 6.8 ft. During a time of drought, the water level decreases at a rate of 3 in./day.

   a. Write a linear function W that represents the water level $W(t)$ (in ft) t days after a drought begins.

   b. Evaluate $W(20)$ and interpret the meaning in the context of this problem.

61. Millage rate is the amount per $1000 that is often used to calculate property tax. For example, a home with a $60,000 taxable value in a municipality with a 19 mil tax rate would require $(0.019)(\$60,000) = \$1140$ in property taxes. In one county, homeowners pay a flat tax of $172 plus a rate of 19 mil on the taxable value of a home.

   a. Write a linear function that represents the total property tax $T(x)$ for a home with a taxable value of x dollars.

   b. Evaluate $T(80,000)$ and interpret the meaning in the context of this problem.

62. Jorge borrows $2400 from his grandmother and pays the money back in monthly payments of $150.

   a. Write a linear function that represents the remaining money owed $L(x)$ after x months.

   b. Evaluate $L(12)$ and interpret the meaning in the context of this problem.

For Exercises 63–64, the fixed and variable costs to produce an item are given along with the price at which an item is sold. (See Example 7)

a. Write a linear cost function that represents the cost $C(x)$ to produce x items.

b. Write a linear revenue function that represents the revenue $R(x)$ for selling x items.

c. Write a linear profit function that represents the profit $P(x)$ for producing and selling x items.

d. Determine the break-even point.

63. Fixed cost: $2275
   Variable cost per item: $34.50
   Price at which the item is sold: $80.00

64. Fixed cost: $5625
   Variable cost per item: $0.40
   Price at which the item is sold: $1.30

65. The profit function P is shown for producing and selling x items. Determine the values of x for which

   a. $P(x) = 0$ (the company breaks even)

   b. $P(x) < 0$ (the company experiences a loss)

   c. $P(x) > 0$ (the company makes a profit)

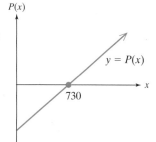

66. The cost and revenue functions C and R are shown for producing and selling x items. Determine the values of x for which

   a. $R(x) = C(x)$ (the company breaks even)

   b. $R(x) < C(x)$ (the company experiences a loss)

   c. $R(x) > C(x)$ (the company makes a profit)

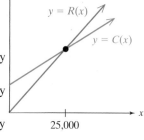

67. A small business makes cookies and sells them at the farmer's market. The fixed monthly cost for use of a Health Department–approved kitchen and rental space at the farmer's market is $790. The cost of labor, taxes, and ingredients for the cookies amounts to $0.24 per cookie, and the cookies sell for $6.00 per dozen. **(See Example 7)**

   a. Write a linear cost function representing the cost $C(x)$ to produce x dozen cookies per month.

   b. Write a linear revenue function representing the revenue $R(x)$ for selling x dozen cookies.

   c. Write a linear profit function representing the profit for producing and selling x dozen cookies in a month.

   d. Determine the number of cookies (in dozens) that must be produced and sold for a monthly profit.

   e. If 150 dozen cookies are sold in a given month, how much money will the business make or lose?

68. A lawn service company charges $60 for each lawn maintenance call. The fixed monthly cost of $680 includes telephone service and depreciation of equipment. The variable costs include labor, gasoline, and taxes and amount to $36 per lawn.

   a. Write a linear cost function representing the monthly cost $C(x)$ for x maintenance calls.

   b. Write a linear revenue function representing the monthly revenue $R(x)$ for x maintenance calls.

   c. Write a linear profit function representing the monthly profit $P(x)$ for x maintenance calls.

   d. Determine the number of lawn maintenance calls needed per month for the company to make money.

   e. If 42 maintenance calls are made for a given month, how much money will the lawn service make or lose?

69. The Centers for Disease Control tracks teenage alcohol usage. The graph shows the percentage of high school students y who used alcohol during the month prior to the time that the data were taken. (*Source*: www.cdc.gov) The x variable represents the number of years since 1990. (**See Example 8**)

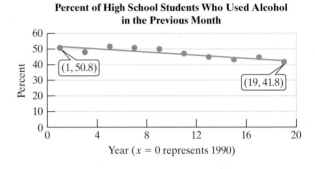

   a. Use the points $(1, 50.8)$ and $(19, 41.8)$ to write a linear model for these data.

   b. Interpret the meaning of the slope in the context of this problem.

   c. Interpret the meaning of the y-intercept in the context of this problem.

   d. Use the model from part (a) to approximate the percentage of high school students who used alcohol 1 month prior to the CDC survey during the year 2010.

   e. Would it be reasonable to use the model from part (a) to predict the percentage of high school students who use alcohol in the year 2050?

70. The graph shows the number of lung transplants y in the United States for selected years. (*Source*: U.S. Department of Health and Human Services, www.hhs.gov) The x variable represents the number of years since 1990.

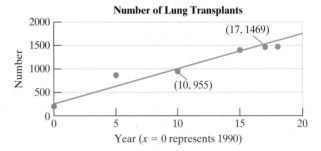

   a. Use the points $(10, 955)$ and $(17, 1469)$ to write a linear model for these data. Round the slope to 1 decimal place and the y-intercept to the nearest whole unit.

   b. Interpret the meaning of the slope in the context of this problem.

   c. Interpret the meaning of the y-intercept in the context of this problem.

   d. Use the model from part (a) to approximate the number of lung transplants performed in the year 2002.

   e. Would it be reasonable to use the model from part (a) to determine the number of lung transplants in the year 2050?

71. The graph shows the number of students enrolled in public colleges for selected years (*Source*: U.S. National Center for Education Statistics, www.nces.ed.gov). The x variable represents the number of years since 1990 and the y variable represents the number of students (in millions).

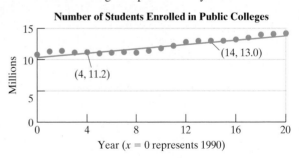

   a. Use the points $(4, 11.2)$ and $(14, 13.0)$ to write a linear model for these data.

   b. Interpret the meaning of the slope in the context of this problem.

   c. Interpret the meaning of the y-intercept in the context of this problem.

   d. In the event that the linear trend continues beyond the last observed data point, use the model in part (a) to predict the number of students enrolled in public colleges for the year 2015.

72. The graph shows the consumption of cigarettes (in billions) in the United States for selected years. (*Source*: www.cdc.gov) The x variable represents the number of years since 1990 and the y variable represents the number of cigarettes consumed in billions.

Cigarette Consumption (billions) in the United States for Selected Years

a. Use the points (4, 486) and (13, 400) to write a linear model for these data. (Round the slope to 2 decimal places and round the y-intercept to the nearest whole unit.)

b. Interpret the meaning of the slope in the context of this problem.

c. Interpret the meaning of the y-intercept in the context of this problem.

d. In the event that the linear trend continues beyond the last observed data point, use the model in part (a) to predict the number of cigarettes consumed in the United States for the year 2015.

73. The table gives the number of calories and the amount of cholesterol for selected fast food hamburgers.

a. Graph the data in a scatter plot using the number of calories as the independent variable x and the amount of cholesterol as the dependent variable y.

b. The amount of cholesterol is approximately linearly related to the number of calories. Use the data points (480, 60) and (720, 90) to write a linear function that defines the amount of cholesterol $c(x)$ as a linear function of the number of calories x.

c. Interpret the meaning of the slope in the context of this problem.

d. Use the model from part (b) to predict the amount of cholesterol for a hamburger with 650 calories.

Hamburger Calories	Cholesterol (mg)
220	35
420	50
460	50
480	60
560	70
590	105
610	65
680	80
720	90
800	95
1050	150

74. The table gives the average gestation period or incubation period for selected animals and their corresponding average longevity.

a. Graph the data in a scatter plot using the number of days for gestation or incubation as the independent variable x and the longevity as the dependent variable y.

b. Longevity is approximately linearly related to the length of the gestation or incubation period. Use the data points (44, 8.5) and (620, 35) to write a linear function that defines longevity $L(x)$ as a linear function of the length of the gestation/incubation period x. Round the slope to 3 decimal places and the y-intercept to 2 decimal places.

c. Interpret the meaning of the slope in the context of this problem.

d. Use the model from part (b) to predict the longevity for an animal with an 80-day gestation period. Round to the nearest whole unit.

Animal	Gestation/Incubation Period (days)	Longevity (yr)
Chicken	22	7.5
Duck	28	10
Rabbit	33	7
Squirrel	44	8.5
Fox	57	9
Cat	60	11
Dog	62	11
Wolf	62	11
Lion	109	10
Pig	115	10
Goat	148	12
Sheep	148	12
Horse	337	23
Elephant	620	35

Objective 4: Create Models Using Linear Regression

For Exercises 75–78, use the scatter plot to determine if a linear regression model appears to be appropriate.

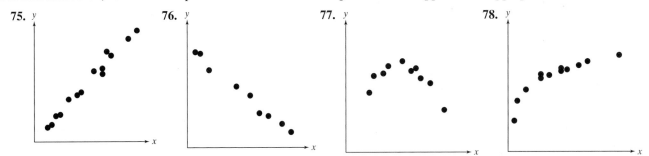

75. **76.** **77.** **78.**

For Exercises 79–84, use a graphing utility to determine the least-squares regression line for the given data.
(See Example 9)

79. The graph in Exercise 69 shows the percentage of high school seniors who used alcohol during the month prior to the time that the data were taken for selected years.

   a. Use the data in the table to find the least-squares regression line. Round the slope and y-intercept to 1 decimal place.

   b. Use a graphing utility to graph the regression line and the observed data.

   c. Use the model in part (a) to approximate the percentage of high school seniors who used alcohol within 1 month prior to the CDC study during the year 2010. Compare the result to the result obtained in Exercise 69(d).

Years Since 1990 (x)	Percent (y)
1	50.8
3	48.0
5	51.6
7	50.8
9	50.0
11	47.1
13	44.9
15	43.3
17	44.7
19	41.8

80. The graph in Exercise 70 shows the number of lung transplants performed in the United States for selected years.

   a. Use the data in the table to find the least-squares regression line. Round the slope and y-intercept to 1 decimal place.

   b. Use a graphing utility to graph the regression line and the observed data.

   c. Use the model from part (a) to approximate the number of lung transplants performed in the year 2002. Compare the result to the result obtained in Exercise 70(d).

Years Since 1990 (x)	Number Lung Transplants (y)
0	203
5	869
10	955
15	1406
17	1469
18	1478

81. The graph in Exercise 71 shows the number of students enrolled in public colleges for selected years. The graph is based on the data given in the table. The x variable represents the number of years since 1990, and the y variable represents the enrollment in public colleges in millions.

   a. Use the data in the table to find the least-squares regression line. Round the slope to 3 decimal places and y-intercept to 2 decimal places.

   b. Use a graphing utility to graph the regression line and the observed data.

   c. In the event that the linear trend continues beyond the last observed data point, use the model in part (a) to predict the number of students enrolled in public colleges for the year 2015.

x	y	x	y
0	10.8	11	12.2
1	11.3	12	12.8
2	11.4	13	12.9
3	11.2	14	13.0
4	11.2	15	13.0
5	11.0	16	13.2
6	11.1	17	13.5
7	11.2	18	14.0
8	11.1	19	14.1
9	11.4	20	14.2
10	11.8		

82. The graph in Exercise 72 shows the number of cigarettes consumed in the United States for selected years. The graph is based on the data given in the table. The *x* variable represents the number of years since 1990, and the *y* variable represents the number of cigarettes consumed in billions.

x	y		x	y
0	525		9	435
1	510		10	430
2	500		11	425
3	485		12	415
4	486		13	400
5	487		14	388
6	487		15	376
7	480		16	372
8	465		17	364

   a. Use the data in the table to find the least-squares regression line. Round the slope to 2 decimal places and *y*-intercept to the nearest whole number.

   b. Use a graphing utility to graph the regression line and the observed data.

   c. In the event that the linear trend continues beyond the last observed data point, use the model in part (a) to predict the number of cigarettes consumed for the year 2015. Round to the nearest billion.

83. The data given in Exercise 73 give the amount of cholesterol *y* for a hamburger with *x* calories.

   a. Use these data to find the least-squares regression line. Round the slope to 3 decimal places and the *y*-intercept to 2 decimal places.

   b. Use a graphing utility to graph the regression line and the observed data.

   c. Use the regression line to predict the amount of cholesterol in a hamburger with 650 calories. Round to the nearest milligram.

84. The data given in Exercise 74 gives the average gestation period or incubation period *x* (in days) for selected animals and their corresponding average longevity *y* (in yr).

   a. Use these data to find the least-squares regression line. Round the slope to 3 decimal places and the *y*-intercept to 2 decimal places.

   b. Use a graphing utility to graph the regression line and the observed data.

   c. Use the regression line to predict the longevity for an animal with an 80-day gestation period. Round to the nearest year.

Mixed Exercises

85. Suppose that a line passes through the points $(4, -6)$ and $(2, -1)$. Where will it pass through the *x*-axis?

86. Suppose that a line passes through the points $(2, -5)$ and $(-4, 7)$. Where will it pass through the *x*-axis?

87. Write a rule for a linear function $y = f(x)$, given that $f(0) = 4$ and $f(3) = 11$.

88. Write a rule for a linear function $y = g(x)$, given that $g(0) = 7$ and $g(-2) = 4$.

89. Write a rule for a linear function $y = h(x)$, given that $h(1) = 6$ and $h(-3) = 2$.

90. Write a rule for a linear function $y = k(x)$, given that $k(-2) = 10$ and $k(5) = -18$.

Write About It

91. Explain how you can use slope to determine if two nonvertical lines are parallel or perpendicular.

92. State one application of using the point-slope formula.

93. Explain how cost and revenue are related to profit.

94. Explain how to determine the break-even point.

Expanding Your Skills

95. Find an equation of line *L*.

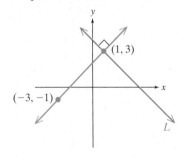

96. In geometry, it is known that the tangent line to a circle at a given point *A* on the circle is perpendicular to the radius drawn to point *A*. Suppose that line *L* is tangent to the given circle at the point $(4, 3)$. Write an equation representing line *L*.

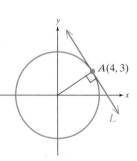

97. In calculus, we can show that the slope of the line drawn tangent to the curve $y = x^3 + 1$ at the point $(c, c^3 + 1)$ is given by $3c^2$. Find an equation of the line tangent to $y = x^3 + 1$ at the point $(-2, -7)$.

98. In calculus, we can show that the slope of the line drawn tangent to the curve $y = \frac{1}{x}$ at the point $\left(c, \frac{1}{c}\right)$ is given by $-\frac{1}{c^2}$. Find an equation of the line tangent to $y = \frac{1}{x}$ at the point $\left(2, \frac{1}{2}\right)$.

A median of a triangle is a line segment drawn from a vertex of the triangle to the midpoint of the opposite side of the triangle.

99. Find an equation of the median of a triangle drawn from vertex $A(5, -2)$ to the side formed by $B(-2, 9)$ and $C(4, 7)$.

100. Find an equation of the median of a triangle drawn from vertex $A(6, -5)$ to the side formed by $B(-4, 1)$ and $C(12, 3)$.

PROBLEM RECOGNITION EXERCISES

Comparing Graphs of Equations

In Section 2.6, we will learn additional techniques to graph functions by recognizing characteristics of the functions. In many cases, we can also graph families of functions by relating them to one of several basic graphs called "parent" functions. To prepare for the discussion in Section 2.6, use a graphing utility or plot points to graph the basic functions in Exercises 1–8.

1. $y = 1$

2. $y = x$

3. $y = x^2$

4. $y = x^3$

5. $y = \sqrt{x}$

6. $y = \sqrt[3]{x}$

7. $y = |x|$

8. $y = \dfrac{1}{x}$

For Exercises 9–18, graph the functions by plotting points or by using a graphing utility. Explain how the graphs are related.

9. **a.** $f(x) = x^2$
 b. $g(x) = x^2 + 2$
 c. $h(x) = x^2 - 4$

10. **a.** $f(x) = |x|$
 b. $g(x) = |x| + 2$
 c. $h(x) = |x| - 4$

11. **a.** $f(x) = \sqrt{x}$
 b. $g(x) = \sqrt{x - 2}$
 c. $h(x) = \sqrt{x + 4}$

12. **a.** $f(x) = x^2$
 b. $g(x) = (x - 2)^2$
 c. $h(x) = (x + 3)^2$

13. **a.** $f(x) = |x|$
 b. $g(x) = -|x|$

14. **a.** $f(x) = \sqrt{x}$
 b. $g(x) = -\sqrt{x}$

15. **a.** $f(x) = x^2$
 b. $g(x) = \dfrac{1}{2}x^2$
 c. $h(x) = 2x^2$

16. **a.** $f(x) = |x|$
 b. $g(x) = \dfrac{1}{3}|x|$
 c. $h(x) = 3|x|$

17. **a.** $f(x) = \sqrt{x}$
 b. $g(x) = \sqrt{-x}$

18. **a.** $f(x) = \sqrt[3]{x}$
 b. $g(x) = \sqrt[3]{-x}$

| SECTION 2.6 | Transformations of Graphs |

OBJECTIVES

1. Recognize Basic Functions
2. Apply Vertical and Horizontal Shifts
3. Apply Vertical and Horizontal Shrinking and Stretching
4. Apply Reflections Across the *x*- and *y*-Axes
5. Summarize Transformations of Graphs

1. Recognize Basic Functions

A function defined by $f(x) = mx + b$ is a linear function and its graph is a line in a rectangular coordinate system. In addition to linear functions, we will learn to identify other categories of functions and the shapes of their graphs (Table 2-2).

TIP The functions given in Table 2-2 were introduced in Section 2.1, Exercises 31–36, and in the Problem Recognition Exercises on page 261.

Table 2-2 Basic Functions and Their Graphs

1. Linear functions   Constant functions
   $f(x) = mx + b$ $f(x) = b$

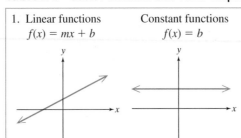

2. Identity function: $f(x) = x$

x	f(x)
-2	-2
-1	-1
0	0
1	1
2	2

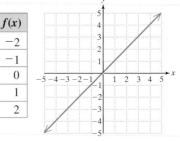

3. Quadratic function: $f(x) = x^2$
   (graph is a parabola)

x	f(x)
-2	4
-1	1
0	0
1	1
2	4

4. Cube function: $f(x) = x^3$

x	f(x)
-2	-8
-1	-1
0	0
1	1
2	8

5. Square root function: $f(x) = \sqrt{x}$

x	f(x)
0	0
1	1
4	2
9	3
16	4

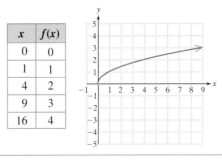

6. Cube root function: $f(x) = \sqrt[3]{x}$

x	f(x)
-8	-2
-1	-1
0	0
1	1
8	2

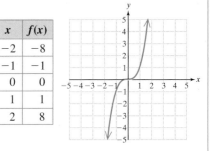

7. Absolute value function: $f(x) = |x|$

x	f(x)
-2	2
-1	1
0	0
1	1
2	2

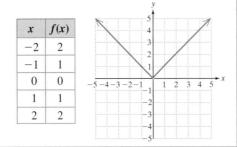

8. Reciprocal function: $f(x) = \dfrac{1}{x}$

x	f(x)
-2	-½
-1	-1
-½	-2
½	2
1	1
2	½

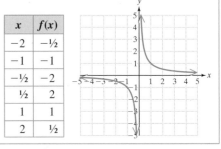

Notice that the graph of $f(x) = \frac{1}{x}$ gets close to (but never touches) the y-axis as x gets close to zero. Likewise, as x approaches ∞ and $-\infty$, the graph approaches the x-axis without touching the x-axis. The x- and y-axes are called **asymptotes** of f and will be studied in detail in Section 3.5.

2. Apply Vertical and Horizontal Shifts

We will call the eight basic functions pictured in Table 2-2 "parent" functions. Other functions that share the characteristics of a parent function are grouped as a "family" of functions. For example, consider the functions defined by $g(x) = x^2 + 2$ and $h(x) = x^2 - 4$, pictured in Figure 2-27.

x	$f(x) = x^2$	$g(x) = x^2 + 2$	$h(x) = x^2 - 4$
-3	9	11	5
-2	4	6	0
-1	1	3	-3
0	0	2	-4
1	1	3	-3
2	4	6	0
3	9	11	5

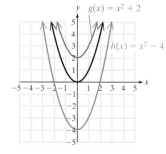

Figure 2-27

The graphs of g and h both resemble the graph of $f(x) = x^2$, but are shifted vertically upward or downward. The table of points reveals that for corresponding x values, the values of $g(x)$ are 2 more than the values of $f(x)$. Thus, the graph is shifted *upward* 2 units. Likewise, the values of $h(x)$ are 4 less than the values of $f(x)$ and the graph is shifted *downward* 4 units. Such shifts are called translations. These observations are consistent with the following rules.

> **TIP** For each ordered pair (x, y) on the graph of $y = f(x)$, the corresponding point
> - $(x, y + k)$ is on the graph of $y = f(x) + k$.
> - $(x, y - k)$ is on the graph of $y = f(x) - k$.

Vertical Translations of Graphs

Consider a function defined by $y = f(x)$. Let k represent a positive real number.

- The graph of $y = f(x) + k$ is the graph of $y = f(x)$ shifted k units *upward*.
- The graph of $y = f(x) - k$ is the graph of $y = f(x)$ shifted k units *downward*.

EXAMPLE 1   Translating a Graph Vertically

Use translations to graph the given functions.

a. $g(x) = |x| - 3$ **b.** $h(x) = x^3 + 2$

Solution:

a.

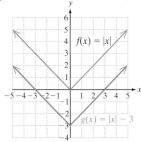

The parent function for $g(x) = |x| - 3$ is $f(x) = |x|$.

The graph of g (shown in blue) is the graph of f shifted *downward* 3 units. For example the point $(0, 0)$ on the graph of $f(x) = |x|$ corresponds to $(0, -3)$ on the graph of $g(x) = |x| - 3$.

b.

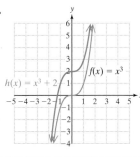

The parent function for $h(x) = x^3 + 2$ is $f(x) = x^3$.

The graph of h (shown in blue) is the graph of f shifted *upward* 2 units. For example:

The point $(0, 0)$ on the graph of $f(x) = x^3$ corresponds to $(0, 2)$ on the graph of $h(x) = x^3 + 2$.

The point $(1, 1)$ on the graph of $f(x) = x^3$ corresponds to $(1, 3)$ on the graph of $h(x) = x^3 + 2$.

Skill Practice 1   Use translations to graph the given functions.

a. $g(x) = \sqrt{x} - 2$ **b.** $h(x) = |x| + 1$

The graph of a function will be shifted to the right or left if a constant is added to or subtracted from the input variable x. In Example 2, we consider $g(x) = (x + 3)^2$.

EXAMPLE 2   **Translating a Graph Horizontally**

Graph the function defined by $g(x) = (x + 3)^2$.

Solution:

Because 3 is added to the x variable, we might expect the graph of $g(x) = (x + 3)^2$ to be the same as the graph of $f(x) = x^2$, but shifted in the x direction (horizontally). To determine whether the shift is to the left or right, we can locate the x-intercept of the graph of $g(x) = (x + 3)^2$. Substituting 0 for $g(x)$, we have:

$$0 = (x + 3)^2$$
$$x = -3 \qquad \text{The } x\text{-intercept is } (-3, 0).$$

Therefore, the new x-intercept (and also the vertex of the parabola) is $(-3, 0)$. This means that the graph is shifted to the left.

Skill Practice 2   Graph the function defined by $g(x) = |x + 2|$.

Using similar logic as outlined in Example 2, we can show that the graph of $h(x) = (x - 3)^2$ is the graph of $f(x) = x^2$ translated to the *right* 3 units. These observations are consistent with the following rules.

Horizontal Translations of Graphs

Consider a function defined by $y = f(x)$. Let h represent a positive real number.

- The graph of $y = f(x - h)$ is the graph of $y = f(x)$ shifted h units to the *right*.
- The graph of $y = f(x + h)$ is the graph of $y = f(x)$ shifted h units to the *left*.

TIP   Consider a positive real number h. To graph $y = f(x - h)$ or $y = f(x + h)$, shift the graph of $y = f(x)$ horizontally in the opposite direction of the sign within parentheses. The graph of $y = f(x - h)$ is a shift in the positive x direction. The graph of $y = f(x + h)$ is a shift in the negative x direction.

Answers

1. a.

b.

2.

EXAMPLE 3   **Translating a Function Horizontally and Vertically**

Use translations to graph the function defined by $p(x) = \sqrt{x - 3} - 2$.

Solution:

The parent function for $p(x) = \sqrt{x - 3} - 2$ is $f(x) = \sqrt{x}$.

The graph of p (shown in blue) is the graph of f shifted to the right 3 units and downward 2 units. We can plot several strategic points as an outline for the new curve.

- The point $(0, 0)$ on the graph of f corresponds to $(3, -2)$ on the graph of p.
- The point $(1, 1)$ on the graph of f corresponds to $(4, -1)$ on the graph of p.
- The point $(4, 2)$ on the graph of f corresponds to $(7, 0)$ on the graph of p.

Skill Practice 3   Use translations to graph the function defined by $q(x) = \sqrt{x + 2} - 5$.

3. Apply Vertical and Horizontal Shrinking and Stretching

Horizontal and vertical translations of functions are called **rigid transformations** because the shape of the graph is not affected. We now look at **nonrigid transformations**. These operations cause a distortion of the graph (either an elongation or contraction in the horizontal or vertical direction). We begin by investigating the functions defined by $y = f(x)$ and $y = a \cdot f(x)$, where a is a positive real number.

EXAMPLE 4   **Graphing a Function with a Vertical Stretch or Shrink**

Graph the functions.

a. $f(x) = |x|$ **b.** $g(x) = 2|x|$ **c.** $h(x) = \dfrac{1}{2}|x|$

Solution:

Answers

3.

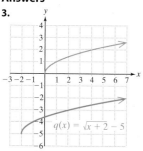

x	$f(x) = |x|$	$g(x) = 2|x|$	$h(x) = \frac{1}{2}|x|$
-3	3	6	$\frac{3}{2}$
-2	2	4	1
-1	1	2	$\frac{1}{2}$
0	0	0	0
1	1	2	$\frac{1}{2}$
2	2	4	1
3	3	6	$\frac{3}{2}$

double

multiply by $\frac{1}{2}$

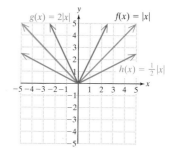

For a given value of x, the value of $g(x)$ is twice the value of $f(x)$. Therefore, the graph of g is elongated or stretched vertically by a factor of 2.

For a given value of x, the value of $h(x)$ is one-half that of $f(x)$. Therefore, the graph of h is shrunk vertically.

4.

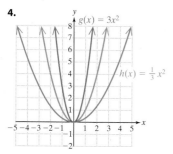

Skill Practice 4   Graph the functions.

a. $f(x) = x^2$ **b.** $g(x) = 3x^2$ **c.** $h(x) = \dfrac{1}{3}x^2$

Vertical Shrinking and Stretching of Graphs

Consider a function defined by $y = f(x)$. Let a represent a positive real number.

- If $a > 1$, then the graph of $y = af(x)$ is the graph of $y = f(x)$ stretched vertically by a factor of a.
- If $0 < a < 1$, then the graph of $y = af(x)$ is the graph of $y = f(x)$ shrunk vertically by a factor of a.

Note: For any point (x, y) on the graph of $y = f(x)$, the point (x, ay) is on the graph of $y = af(x)$.

A function may also be stretched or shrunk horizontally.

Horizontal Shrinking and Stretching of Graphs

Consider a function defined by $y = f(x)$. Let a represent a positive real number.

- If $a > 1$, then the graph of $y = f(ax)$ is the graph of $y = f(x)$ shrunk horizontally by a factor of a.
- If $0 < a < 1$, then the graph of $y = f(ax)$ is the graph of $y = f(x)$ stretched horizontally by a factor of a.

Note: For any point (x, y) on the graph of $y = f(x)$, the point $(\frac{x}{a}, y)$ is on the graph of $y = f(ax)$.

EXAMPLE 5   Graphing a Function with a Horizontal Shrink or Stretch

The graph of $y = f(x)$ is shown. Graph

a. $y = f(2x)$

b. $y = f\left(\frac{1}{2}x\right)$

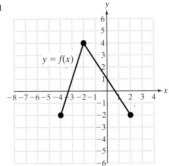

Solution:

a. $f(2x)$ is in the form $f(ax)$ with $a = 2 > 1$. The graph of $y = f(2x)$ is the graph of $y = f(x)$ horizontally compressed.

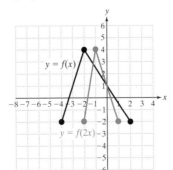

The graph of f has the following "strategic" points that define the shape of the function: $(-4, -2), (-2, 4),$ and $(2, -2)$.

To graph $y = f(2x)$, divide each x value by 2. This results in the points: $(-2, -2), (-1, 4),$ and $(1, -2)$.

The graph of $y = f(2x)$ is shown in blue.

b. $f\left(\frac{1}{2}x\right)$ is in the form $f(ax)$ with $a = \frac{1}{2}$. The graph of $y = f\left(\frac{1}{2}x\right)$ is the graph of $y = f(x)$ stretched horizontally.

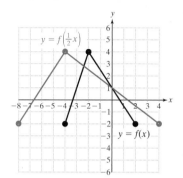

The strategic points on the graph of f are: $(-4, -2)$, $(-2, 4)$, and $(2, -2)$.

To graph $y = f\left(\frac{1}{2}x\right)$ divide each x value by $\frac{1}{2}$. The strategic points are: $(-8, -2)$, $(-4, 4)$, and $(4, -2)$.

The graph of $y = f\left(\frac{1}{2}x\right)$ is shown in red.

Skill Practice 5 The graph of $y = f(x)$ is shown.

Graph. **a.** $y = f(2x)$ **b.** $y = f\left(\dfrac{1}{2}x\right)$

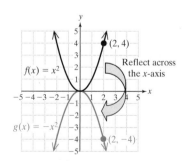

4. Apply Reflections Across the *x*- and *y*-Axes

The graphs of $f(x) = x^2$ (in black) and $g(x) = -x^2$ (in blue) are shown in Figure 2-28. Notice that a point (x, y) on the graph of f corresponds to the point $(x, -y)$ on the graph of g. Therefore, the graph of g is the graph of f reflected across the *x*-axis.

The graphs of $f(x) = \sqrt{x}$ (in black) and $g(x) = \sqrt{-x}$ (in blue) are shown in Figure 2-29. Notice that a point (x, y) on the graph of f corresponds to the point $(-x, y)$ on g. Therefore, the graph of g is the graph of f reflected across the *y*-axis.

Answers

5. a.

b.

Figure 2-28

Figure 2-29

Reflections Across the *x*- and *y*-Axes

Consider a function defined by $y = f(x)$.

- The graph of $y = -f(x)$ is the graph of $y = f(x)$ reflected across the *x*-axis.
- The graph of $y = f(-x)$ is the graph of $y = f(x)$ reflected across the *y*-axis.

EXAMPLE 6   **Reflecting the Graph of a Function Across the *x*- and *y*-Axes**

The graph of $y = f(x)$ is given.

  a. Graph $y = -f(x)$.
  b. Graph $y = f(-x)$.

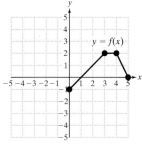

Solution:

  a. Reflect $y = f(x)$ across the *x*-axis.   **b.** Reflect $y = f(x)$ across the *y*-axis.

    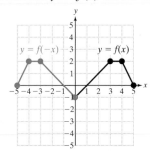

Skill Practice 6   The graph of $y = f(x)$ is given.

  a. Graph $y = -f(x)$.
  b. Graph $y = f(-x)$.

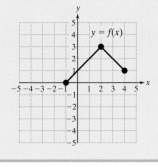

5. Summarize Transformations of Graphs

The operations of reflecting a graph of a function about an axis and shifting, stretching, and shrinking a graph are called **transformations.** Transformations give us tools to graph families of functions that are built from basic "parent" functions.

Answers

6. a.

b.

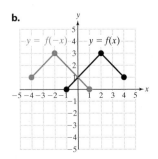

Transformations of Functions		
Consider a function defined by $y = f(x)$. Let k, h, and a represent positive real numbers. The graphs of the following functions are related to $y = f(x)$ as follows.		
Vertical shift	$y = f(x) + k$ and $y = f(x) - k$	Shift upward Shift downward
Horizontal shift	$y = f(x - h)$ and $y = f(x + h)$	Shift right Shift left
Vertical stretch/shrink	$y = af(x)$	Vertical stretch (if $a > 1$) Vertical shrink (if $0 < a < 1$)
Horizontal stretch/shrink	$y = f(ax)$	Horizontal shrink (if $a > 1$) Horizontal stretch (if $0 < a < 1$)
Reflection	$y = -f(x)$ $y = f(-x)$	Reflection across the *x*-axis Reflection across the *y*-axis

To graph a function requiring multiple transformations on the parent function, the sequence of transformations is important. We recommend the following guidelines:

- Perform horizontal transformations first. These are operations on x.
- Perform vertical transformations next. These are operations on $f(x)$.

Horizontal transformations

$$y = a \cdot f[\overbrace{b(x - c)}] + d$$

Vertical transformations

Order of transformations:
1. Horizontal shrink/stretch/reflection "b."
2. Horizontal shift "c."
3. Vertical shrink/stretch/reflection "a."
4. Vertical shift "d."

It is important to note that horizontal transformations are performed "outside-in," that is, in the reverse order as the customary order of operations. For example, to transform the graph of $y = f(x)$ to $y = f[b(x - c)]$, we have

$$f(x) \xrightarrow[\substack{\text{Horizontal shrink/} \\ \text{stretch/reflection}}]{\text{Replace } x \text{ by } bx.} f(bx) \xrightarrow[\text{Horizontal shift}]{\text{Replace } x \text{ by } (x - c).} f[b(x - c)]$$

The recommended sequence of transformations is demonstrated in Examples 7 and 8.

EXAMPLE 7   Using Transformations to Graph a Function

Use transformations to graph the function defined by $n(x) = \frac{1}{2}(x - 1)^2 - 3$.

Solution:

The graph of $n(x) = \frac{1}{2}(x - 1)^2 - 3$ is the same as the graph of $f(x) = x^2$, with three transformations in the following order.

1. Shift the graph to the right 1 unit.
2. Apply a vertical shrink (multiply the y values by $\frac{1}{2}$).
3. Shift the graph downward 3 units.

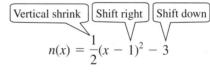

$$n(x) = \frac{1}{2}(x - 1)^2 - 3$$

Shift right

Vertical shrink

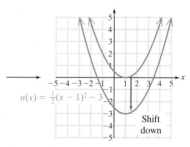

Shift down

Skill Practice 7   Use transformations to graph the function defined by $m(x) = 3|x - 2| - 4$.

Answer

7.

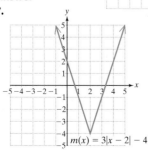

EXAMPLE 8 **Using Transformations to Graph a Function**

Use transformations to graph the function defined by $v(x) = \sqrt{-x - 2}$.

Solution:

$v(x) = \sqrt{-x - 2}$ can be written as $v(x) = \sqrt{-(x + 2)}$.

To visualize the horizontal transformations, write the radicand in factored form:
$\sqrt{b(x + c)}$

The graph of $v(x) = \sqrt{-(x + 2)}$ is the same as the graph of $f(x) = \sqrt{x}$, with two transformations in the following order.

1. Reflect the graph across the y-axis.
2. Shift the graph to the left 2 units.

$$v(x) = \sqrt{-(x + 2)}$$

Answer

8.

Skill Practice 8 Use transformations to graph the function defined by $r(x) = \sqrt[3]{-x + 1}$.

We make one final comment regarding transformations of graphs. Transformations also apply to relations that are not functions. For example, the equation $x^2 + y^2 = r^2$ represents the graph of a circle centered at the origin with radius r. The equation $(x - h)^2 + (y - k)^2 = r^2$ is the graph of $x^2 + y^2 = r^2$, shifted horizontally h units and vertically k units.

SECTION 2.6 **Practice Exercises**

Review Exercises

1. Given $f(x) = -\frac{3}{2}x + 1$,

   a. Determine the slope of the line.

   b. Determine the y-intercept.

   c. Graph the line.

2. Given $f(x) = -\frac{3}{2}$

   a. Determine the slope of the line.

   b. Determine the y-intercept.

   c. Graph the line.

3. Graph $y = x + 1$, $y = x + 2$, and $y = x + 3$ on the same rectangular coordinate system. How do the graphs differ?

4. Graph $x^2 + y^2 = 4$ and $(x - 4)^2 + (y - 3)^2 = 4$ on the same rectangular coordinate system. How do the graphs differ?

Concept Connections

5. A function defined by $f(x) = mx + b$ is a _____ function and its graph is a line in a rectangular coordinate system.

6. Let c represent a positive real number. The graph of $y = f(x) + c$ is the graph of $y = f(x)$ shifted (up/down/left/right) c units.

7. Let c represent a positive real number. The graph of $y = f(x + c)$ is the graph of $y = f(x)$ shifted (up/down/left/right) c units.

8. Let c represent a positive real number. The graph of $y = f(x - c)$ is the graph of $y = f(x)$ shifted (up/down/left/right) c units.

9. Let c represent a positive real number. The graph of $y = f(x) - c$ is the graph of $y = f(x)$ shifted (up/down/left/right) c units.

10. The graph of $y = 3f(x)$ is the graph of $y = f(x)$ with a (choose one: vertical stretch, vertical shrink, horizontal stretch, horizontal shrink).

11. The graph of $y = f(3x)$ is the graph of $y = f(x)$ with a (choose one: vertical stretch, vertical shrink, horizontal stretch, horizontal shrink).

12. The graph of $y = f(\frac{1}{3}x)$ is the graph of $y = f(x)$ with a (choose one: vertical stretch, vertical shrink, horizontal stretch, horizontal shrink).

13. The graph of $y = \frac{1}{3}f(x)$ is the graph of $y = f(x)$ with a (choose one: vertical stretch, vertical shrink, horizontal stretch, horizontal shrink).

14. The graph of $y = -f(x)$ is the graph of $y = f(x)$ reflected across the _____ -axis.

Objective 1: Recognize Basic Functions

For Exercises 15–20, from memory match the equation with its graph.

15. $f(x) = \sqrt{x}$

16. $f(x) = \sqrt[3]{x}$

17. $f(x) = x^3$

18. $f(x) = x^2$

19. $f(x) = |x|$

20. $f(x) = \dfrac{1}{x}$

a.

b.

c.

d.

e.

f.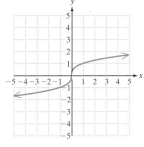

Objective 2: Apply Vertical and Horizontal Shifts

For Exercises 21–32, use translations to graph the given functions. (See Examples 1–3)

21. $f(x) = |x| + 1$

22. $g(x) = \sqrt{x} + 2$

23. $k(x) = x^3 - 2$

24. $h(x) = \dfrac{1}{x} - 2$

25. $g(x) = \sqrt{x + 5}$

26. $m(x) = |x + 1|$

27. $r(x) = (x - 4)^2$

28. $t(x) = \sqrt[3]{x - 2}$

29. $a(x) = \sqrt{x + 1} - 3$

30. $b(x) = |x - 2| + 4$

31. $c(x) = (x - 3)^2 + 1$

32. $d(x) = \sqrt{x + 4} - 1$

Objective 3: Apply Vertical and Horizontal Shrinking and Stretching

For Exercises 33–38, use transformations to graph the functions. (See Example 4)

33. $m(x) = 4\sqrt[3]{x}$

34. $n(x) = 3|x|$

35. $r(x) = \dfrac{1}{2}x^2$

36. $t(x) = \dfrac{1}{3}|x|$

37. $p(x) = |2x|$

38. $q(x) = \sqrt{2x}$

For Exercises 39–46, use the graphs of $y = f(x)$ and $y = g(x)$ to graph the given function. (See Example 5)

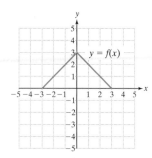

39. $y = \dfrac{1}{3}f(x)$

40. $y = \dfrac{1}{2}g(x)$

41. $y = 3f(x)$

42. $y = 2g(x)$

43. $y = f(3x)$

44. $y = g(2x)$

45. $y = f\left(\dfrac{1}{3}x\right)$

46. $y = g\left(\dfrac{1}{2}x\right)$

Objective 4: Apply Reflections Across the *x*- and *y*-Axes

For Exercises 47–52, graph the function by applying an appropriate reflection.

47. $f(x) = -\dfrac{1}{x}$

48. $g(x) = -\sqrt{x}$

49. $h(x) = -x^3$

50. $k(x) = -|x|$

51. $p(x) = (-x)^3$

52. $q(x) = \sqrt[3]{-x}$

For Exercises 53–56, use the graphs of $y = f(x)$ and $y = g(x)$ to graph the given function. (See Example 6)

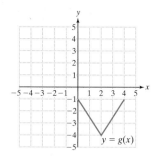

53. $y = f(-x)$

54. $y = g(-x)$

55. $y = -f(x)$

56. $y = -g(x)$

For Exercises 57–60, use the graphs of $y = f(x)$ and $y = g(x)$ to graph the given function. (See Example 6)

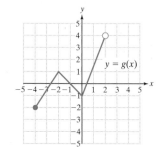

57. $y = f(-x)$

58. $y = g(-x)$

59. $y = -f(x)$

60. $y = -g(x)$

Objective 5: Summarize Transformations of Graphs

For Exercises 61–72, use transformations to graph the functions. (See Examples 7–8)

61. $v(x) = -(x + 2)^2 + 1$ **62.** $u(x) = -(x - 1)^2 - 2$ **63.** $f(x) = 2\sqrt{x + 3} - 1$ **64.** $g(x) = 2\sqrt{x - 1} + 3$

65. $p(x) = \dfrac{1}{2}|x - 1| - 2$ **66.** $q(x) = \dfrac{1}{3}|x + 2| - 1$ **67.** $r(x) = -\sqrt{-x} + 1$ **68.** $s(x) = -\sqrt{-x} - 2$

69. $f(x) = \sqrt{-x + 3}$ **70.** $g(x) = \sqrt{-x - 4}$ **71.** $n(x) = (2x + 6)^2$ **72.** $m(x) = |2x - 4|$

Mixed Exercises

For Exercises 73–80, the graph of $y = f(x)$ is given. Graph the indicated function.

73. Graph $y = -f(x - 1) + 2$.

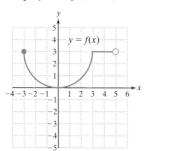

74. Graph $y = -f(x + 1) - 2$.

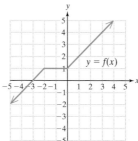

75. Graph $y = 2f(x - 2) - 3$.

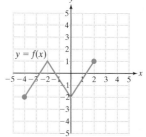

76. Graph $y = 2f(x + 2) - 4$.

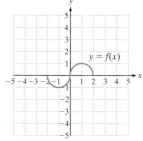

77. Graph $y = -3f(2x)$.

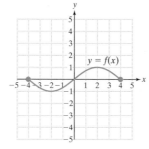

78. Graph $y = -\dfrac{1}{2}f\left(\dfrac{1}{2}x\right)$.

79. Graph $y = f(-x) - 2$.

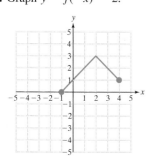

80. Graph $y = f(-x) + 3$.

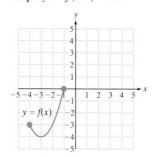

For Exercises 81–83, by inspection select the function given in a, b, or c, that best models the trend of the data in the scatter plot over the interval [40, 250].

a. $f(x) = 0.00034(x - 33.4)^2 + 9.3$ **b.** $f(x) = 0.087x + 5.3$ **c.** $f(x) = 1.78\sqrt{x - 19.8}$

81.

82.

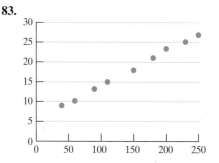

83.

Write About It

84. Explain why the graph of $g(x) = |2x|$ can be interpreted as a horizontal shrink of the graph of $f(x) = |x|$ or as a vertical stretch of the graph of $f(x) = |x|$.

85. Explain why the graph of $h(x) = \sqrt{\frac{1}{2}x}$ can be interpreted as a horizontal stretch of the graph of $f(x) = \sqrt{x}$ or as a vertical shrink of the graph of $f(x) = \sqrt{x}$.

86. Explain the difference between the graphs of $f(x) = |x - 2| - 3$ and $g(x) = |x - 3| - 2$.

Expanding Your Skills

For Exercises 87–92, use transformations on the basic functions presented in Table 2-2 to write a rule $y = f(x)$ that would produce the given graph.

87.

88.

89.

90.

91.

92.

Technology Connections

93. a. Graph the functions on the viewing window $[-5, 5, 1]$ by $[-2, 8, 1]$.

$$y = x^2$$
$$y = x^4$$
$$y = x^6$$

c. Describe the general shape of the graph of $y = x^n$ where n is an even number greater than 1.

b. Graph the functions on the viewing window $[-4, 4, 1]$ by $[-10, 10, 1]$.

$$y = x^3$$
$$y = x^5$$
$$y = x^7$$

d. Describe the general shape of the graph of $y = x^n$ where n is an odd number greater than 1.

<table>
<tr><td>

SECTION 2.7

</td><td>

Analyzing Graphs of Functions and Piecewise-Defined Functions

</td></tr>
</table>

1. Test for Symmetry

The photos in Figures 2-30 through 2-32 each show a type of symmetry.

Figure 2-30

Figure 2-31

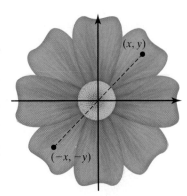

Figure 2-32

The photo of the roseate spoonbill (Figure 2-30) shows an image of the bird reflected in the water. Suppose that we superimpose the x-axis at the waterline. Every point (x, y) on the bird has a mirror image $(x, -y)$ below the x-axis. Therefore, this image is symmetric with respect to the x-axis.

A human face is symmetric with respect to a vertical line through the center (Figure 2-31). If we place the y-axis along this line, a point (x, y) on one side has a mirror image at $(-x, y)$. This image is symmetric with respect to the y-axis.

The flower shown in Figure 2-32 is symmetric with respect to the point at its center. Suppose that we place the origin at the center of the flower. Then any point (x, y) has a mirror image at the point $(-x, -y)$. This image is symmetric with respect to the origin.

Given an equation in the variables x and y, use the following rules to determine if the graph is symmetric with respect to the x-axis, the y-axis, or the origin.

Tests for Symmetry

Consider an equation in the variables x and y.

- The graph of the equation is symmetric with respect to the y-axis if substituting $-x$ for x in the equation results in an equivalent equation.
- The graph of the equation is symmetric with respect to the x-axis if substituting $-y$ for y in the equation results in an equivalent equation.
- The graph of the equation is symmetric with respect to the origin if substituting $-x$ for x and $-y$ for y in the equation results in an equivalent equation.

EXAMPLE 1 Testing for Symmetry

Determine whether the graph is symmetric to the y-axis, x-axis, or origin.

a. $y = |x|$ **b.** $x = y^2 - 4$

Solution:

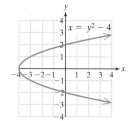

a.

$y = |x|$
$y = |-x|$ same
$y = |x|$

Test for symmetry with respect to the y-axis.
Replace x by $-x$. Note that $|-x| = |x|$.
This equation *is* equivalent to the original equation.

$y = |x|$
$-y = |x|$ not the same
$y = -|x|$

Test for symmetry with respect to the x-axis.
Replace y by $-y$.
This equation is *not* equivalent to the original equation.

$y = |x|$
$-y = |-x|$ not the same
$-y = |x|$
$y = -|x|$

Test for symmetry with respect to the origin.
Replace x by $-x$ and y by $-y$.
Note that $|-x| = |x|$.
This equation is *not* equivalent to the original equation.

The graph is symmetric with respect to the y-axis only.

b.

$x = y^2 - 4$
$-x = y^2 - 4$ not the same
$x = -y^2 + 4$

Test for symmetry with respect to the y-axis.
Replace x by $-x$.
This equation is *not* equivalent to the original equation.

$x = y^2 - 4$
$x = (-y)^2 - 4$ same
$x = y^2 - 4$

Test for symmetry with respect to the x-axis.
Replace y by $-y$.
This equation *is* equivalent to the original equation.

$x = y^2 - 4$
$-x = (-y)^2 - 4$ not the same
$-x = y^2 - 4$
$x = -y^2 + 4$

Test for symmetry with respect to the origin.
Replace x by $-x$ and y by $-y$.

This equation is *not* equivalent to the original equation.

The graph is symmetric with respect to the x-axis only (Figure 2-33).

Figure 2-33

Skill Practice 1 Determine whether the graph is symmetric to the y-axis, x-axis, or origin.

a. $y = x^2$ **b.** $|y| = x + 1$

EXAMPLE 2 Testing for Symmetry

Determine whether the graph is symmetric to the y-axis, x-axis, or origin.

$$x^2 + y^2 = 9$$

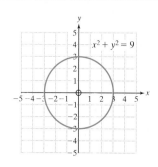

Solution:

The graph of $x^2 + y^2 = 9$ is a circle with center at the origin and radius 3. By inspection, we can see that the graph is symmetric with respect to both axes and the origin.

Answers
1. a. y-axis symmetry
　　b. x-axis symmetry

Test for y-axis symmetry.
Replace x by $-x$.

$x^2 + y^2 = 9$
$(-x)^2 + y^2 = 9$ } same
$x^2 + y^2 = 9$

Test for x-axis symmetry.
Replace y by $-y$.

$x^2 + y^2 = 9$
$x^2 + (-y)^2 = 9$ } same
$x^2 + y^2 = 9$

Test for origin symmetry.
Replace x and y by $-x$ and $-y$.

$x^2 + y^2 = 9$
$(-x)^2 + (-y)^2 = 9$ } same
$x^2 + y^2 = 9$

The graph is symmetric with respect to the y-axis, the x-axis, and the origin.

> **Skill Practice 2**   Determine whether the graph is symmetric to the y-axis, x-axis, or origin.
>
> $$\frac{x^2}{4} + \frac{y^2}{9} = 1$$

2. Identify Even and Odd Functions

A function may be symmetric with respect to the y-axis or to the origin. A function that is symmetric with respect to the y-axis is called an *even* function. A function that is symmetric with respect to the origin is called an *odd* function.

> **Even and Odd Functions**
>
> - A function f is an **even function** if $f(-x) = f(x)$ for all x in the domain of f. The graph of an even function is symmetric to the y-axis.
> - A function f is an **odd function** if $f(-x) = -f(x)$ for all x in the domain of f. The graph of an odd function is symmetric to the origin.

> **EXAMPLE 3**   **Identifying Even and Odd Functions**
>
> By inspection determine if the function is even, odd, or neither.

Solution:

a.

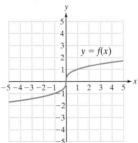

The function is symmetric to the origin. Therefore, the function is an *odd* function.

b.

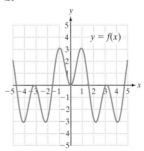

The function is symmetric to the y-axis. Therefore, the function is an *even* function.

c.

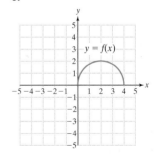

The function is not symmetric with respect to either the y-axis or the origin. Therefore, the function is *neither* even nor odd.

Answer

2. Symmetric with respect to the y-axis, x-axis, and origin

Skill Practice 3 Determine if the function is even, odd, or neither.

a.

b.

c.

EXAMPLE 4 **Identifying Even and Odd Functions**

Determine if the function is even, odd, or neither.

a. $f(x) = -2x^4 + 5|x|$ **b.** $g(x) = 4x^3 - x$ **c.** $h(x) = 2x^2 + x$

Solution:

> **TIP** In Example 4(a) we suspect that f is an even function because each term is of the form x^{even} or $|x|$. In each case, replacing x by $-x$ results in an equivalent term.

a. $f(x) = -2x^4 + 5|x|$ ⟵ | Determine whether the function is even.

$f(-x) = -2(-x)^4 + 5|-x|$ same | Replace x by $-x$ to determine if $f(-x) = f(x)$.

$f(-x) = -2x^4 + 5|x|$ ⟵

Since $f(-x) = f(x)$, the function f is an even function.

There is no need to test whether f is an odd function because a function cannot be both even and odd.

> **TIP** In Example 4(b) we suspect that g is an odd function because each term is of the form x^{odd}. In each case, replacing x by $-x$ results in the *opposite* of the original term.

b. $g(x) = 4x^3 - x$ Each term has x raised to an odd power. Therefore, replacing x by $-x$ will result in the *opposite* of the original term. Therefore, test whether g is an odd function. That is, test whether $g(-x) = -g(x)$.

Evaluate: $g(-x)$

Evaluate: $-g(x)$

$g(-x) = 4(-x)^3 - (-x)$

$-g(x) = -(4x^3 - x)$

$= -4x^3 + x$ ⟵ same ⟶ $= -4x^3 + x$

Since $g(-x) = -g(x)$, the function g is an odd function.

> **TIP** In Example 4(c) $h(x)$ has a mixture of terms of the form x^{odd} and x^{even}. Therefore, we might suspect that the function is neither even nor odd.

c. $h(x) = 2x^2 + x$ ⟵ | Determine whether the function is even.

$h(-x) = 2(-x)^2 + (-x)$ not the same | Replace x by $-x$ to determine if $h(-x) = h(x)$.

$h(-x) = 2x^2 - x$ ⟵

Since $h(-x) \neq h(x)$, the function is not even.

Next, test whether h is an odd function. Test whether $h(-x) = -h(x)$.

Evaluate: $h(-x)$

Evaluate: $-h(x)$

$h(-x) = 2(-x)^2 + (-x)$

$-h(x) = -(2x^2 + x)$

$= 2x^2 - x$ ⟵ not the same ⟶ $= -2x^2 - x$

Since $h(-x) \neq -h(x)$, the function is not an odd function. Therefore, h is neither even nor odd.

Answers

3. a. Even function
b. Odd function
c. Neither even nor odd
4. a. Odd function
b. Even function
c. Neither even nor odd

Skill Practice 4 Determine if the function is even, odd, or neither.

a. $m(x) = -x^5 + x^3$ **b.** $n(x) = x^2 - |x| + 1$ **c.** $p(x) = 2|x| + x$

3. Graph Piecewise-Defined Functions

Suppose that a car is stopped for a red light. When the light turns green, the car undergoes a constant acceleration for 20 sec until it reaches a speed of 45 mph. It travels 45 mph for 1 min (60 sec), and then decelerates for 30 sec to stop at another red light. The graph of the car's speed y (in mph) versus the time x (in sec) after leaving the first red light is shown in Figure 2-34.

Figure 2-34

Notice that the graph can be segmented into three pieces. The first 20 sec is represented by a linear function with a positive slope, $y = 2.25x$. The next 60 sec is represented by the constant function $y = 45$. And the last 30 sec is represented by a linear function with a negative slope, $y = -1.5x + 165$.

To write a rule defining this function we use a **piecewise-defined function** in which we define each "piece" on a restricted domain.

$$f(x) = \begin{cases} 2.25x & \text{for } 0 \le x \le 20 \\ 45 & \text{for } 20 < x < 80 \\ -1.5x + 165 & \text{for } 80 \le x \le 110 \end{cases}$$

EXAMPLE 5   **Interpreting a Piecewise-Defined Function**

Evaluate the function for the given values of x.

$$f(x) = \begin{cases} -x - 1 & \text{for } -4 \le x < -1 \\ -3 & \text{for } -1 \le x < 2 \\ \sqrt{x - 2} & \text{for } x \ge 2 \end{cases}$$

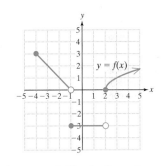

a. $f(-3)$ **b.** $f(-1)$

c. $f(2)$ **d.** $f(6)$

Solution:

a. $f(x) = -x - 1$ $x = -3$ is on the interval $-4 \le x < -1$. Use the first rule
$f(-3) = -(-3) - 1$ in the function: $f(x) = -x - 1$.
$f(-3) = 2$

b. $f(x) = -3$ $x = -1$ is on the interval $-1 \le x < 2$. Use the second rule
$f(-1) = -3$ in the function: $f(x) = -3$.

c. $f(x) = \sqrt{x - 2}$ $x = 2$ is on the interval $x \ge 2$. Use the third rule in the
$f(2) = \sqrt{2 - 2}$ function: $f(x) = \sqrt{x - 2}$.
$f(2) = 0$

d. $f(x) = \sqrt{x - 2}$ $x = 6$ is on the interval $x \ge 2$. Use the third rule in the
$f(6) = \sqrt{6 - 2}$ function: $f(x) = \sqrt{x - 2}$.
$f(6) = 2$

Skill Practice 5   Evaluate the function for the given values of x.

$$f(x) = \begin{cases} x + 7 & \text{for } x < -2 \\ x^2 & \text{for } -2 \le x < 1 \\ 3 & \text{for } 1 \le x \le 4 \end{cases}$$

a. $f(-3)$ **b.** $f(-2)$ **c.** $f(1)$ **d.** $f(4)$

Answers

5. a. 4   **b.** 4   **c.** 3   **d.** 3

TECHNOLOGY CONNECTIONS

Graphing a Piecewise-Defined Function

A graphing calculator can be used to graph a piecewise-defined function. The key is to enter each "piece" of the function in the equation editor, along with its domain restriction in parentheses. In this context, the backslash symbol (the same as the division bar on the calculator) is used to separate the function from its domain. Furthermore, the inequalities in parentheses are either assigned a value of 1 or 0 depending on whether the inequality is true or false. If an inequality is true, then the function is multiplied by 1 and is "turned on." If an inequality is false, then the function is multiplied by 0 and is "turned off."

Consider the function from Example 5.

$$f(x) = \begin{cases} -x - 1 & \text{for } -4 \le x < -1 \\ -3 & \text{for } -1 \le x < 2 \\ \sqrt{x - 2} & \text{for } x \ge 2 \end{cases}$$

The inequality symbols are found under the TEST menu, and the function is entered as:

$$Y_1 = (-x - 1)/(x \ge -4)/(x < -1)$$
$$Y_2 = -3/(x \ge -1)/(x < 2)$$
$$Y_3 = \sqrt{(x - 2)}/(x \ge 2)$$

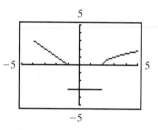

Notice that the inclusion or exclusion of the endpoints of each piece of the function is ambiguous on the calculator display.

In Examples 6 and 7, we graph piecewise-defined functions.

EXAMPLE 6 Graphing a Piecewise-Defined Function

Graph the function defined by $f(x) = \begin{cases} -3x & \text{for } x < 1 \\ -3 & \text{for } x \ge 1 \end{cases}$.

Solution:

- The first rule $f(x) = -3x$ defines a line with slope -3 and y-intercept $(0, 0)$. This line should be graphed only to the left of $x = 1$. The point $(1, -3)$ is graphed as an open dot, because the point is not part of the rule $f(x) = -3x$. See the blue portion of the graph in Figure 2-35.
- The second rule $f(x) = -3$ is a horizontal line for $x \ge 1$. The point $(1, -3)$ is a closed dot to show that it is part of the rule $f(x) = -3$. The closed dot from the red segment of the graph "overrides" the open dot from the blue segment. Taken together, the closed dot "plugs" the hole in the graph.

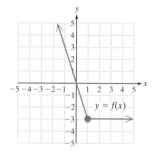

Figure 2-35

Skill Practice 6 Graph the function.

$$f(x) = \begin{cases} 2 & \text{for } x \le -1 \\ -2x & \text{for } x > -1 \end{cases}$$

TIP The function in Example 6 has no "gaps," and therefore we say that the function is **continuous.** Informally, this means that we can draw the function without lifting our pencil from the page. The formal definition of a continuous function will be studied in calculus.

EXAMPLE 7 **Graphing a Piecewise-Defined Function**

Graph the function. $f(x) = \begin{cases} x + 3 & \text{for } x < -1 \\ x^2 & \text{for } -1 \le x < 2 \end{cases}$

Solution:

The first rule $f(x) = x + 3$ defines a line with slope 1 and y-intercept $(0, 3)$. This line should be graphed only for $x < -1$ (that is to the left of $x = -1$). The point $(-1, 2)$ is graphed as an open dot, because the point is not part of the function. See the red portion of the graph in Figure 2-36.

The second rule $f(x) = x^2$ is one of the basic functions learned in Section 2.6. It is a parabola with vertex at the origin. We sketch this function only for x values on the interval $-1 \le x < 2$. The point $(-1, 1)$ is a closed dot to show that it is part of the function. The point $(2, 4)$ is displayed as an open dot to indicate that it is not part of the function.

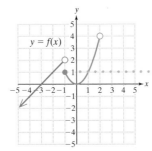

TIP The function in Example 7 has a gap at $x = -1$, and therefore, we say that f is **discontinuous** at -1.

Avoiding Mistakes

Note that the function cannot have a closed dot at both $(-1, 1)$ and $(-1, 2)$ because it would not pass the vertical line test.

Figure 2-36

Skill Practice 7 Graph the function.

$$f(x) = \begin{cases} |x| & \text{for } -4 \le x < 2 \\ -x + 2 & \text{for } x \ge 2 \end{cases}$$

We now look at a special category of piecewise-defined functions called **step functions.** The graph of a step function is a series of discontinuous "steps." One important step function is called the **greatest integer function** or **floor function.** It is defined by

$$f(x) = [\![x]\!] \text{ where } [\![x]\!] \text{ is the greatest integer less than or equal to } x.$$

The operation $[\![x]\!]$ may also be denoted as **int(x)** or by **floor(x).** These alternative notations are often used in computer programming.

In Example 8, we graph the greatest integer function.

Answers

6.

7.

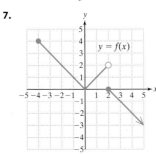

EXAMPLE 8   Graphing the Greatest Integer Function

Graph the function defined by $f(x) = [\![x]\!]$.

Solution:

x	$f(x) = [\![x]\!]$
-1.7	-2
-1	-1
-0.6	-1
0	0
0.4	0
1	1
1.8	1
2	2
2.5	2

Evaluate f for several values of x.

Greatest integer less than or equal to -1.7 is -2.

Greatest integer less than or equal to -1 is -1.

Greatest integer less than or equal to -0.6 is -1.

Greatest integer less than or equal to 0 is 0.

Greatest integer less than or equal to 0.4 is 0.

Greatest integer less than or equal to 1 is 1.

Greatest integer less than or equal to 1.8 is 1.

Greatest integer less than or equal to 2 is 2.

Greatest integer less than or equal to 2.5 is 2.

> **TIP** On many graphing calculators, the greatest integer function is denoted by int( ) and is found under the MATH menu followed by NUM.

From the table, we see a pattern and from the pattern, we form the graph.

If $0 \le x < 1$, then $[\![x]\!] = 0$
If $1 \le x < 2$, then $[\![x]\!] = 1$
If $2 \le x < 3$, then $[\![x]\!] = 2$
...
If $-3 \le x < -2$, then $[\![x]\!] = -3$
If $-2 \le x < -1$, then $[\![x]\!] = -2$
If $-1 \le x < 0$,   then $[\![x]\!] = -1$
...

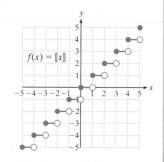

$f(x) = [\![x]\!]$

Skill Practice 8   Evaluate $f(x) = [\![x]\!]$ for the given values of x.

a. $f(1.7)$ **b.** $f(5.5)$ **c.** $f(-4)$ **d.** $f(-4.2)$

In Example 9, we use a piecewise-defined function to model an application.

EXAMPLE 9   Using a Piecewise-Defined Function in an Application

For the year 2010, the federal income tax owed by a taxpayer (single—no dependents) was based on the individual's taxable income. (*Source*: Internal Revenue Service, www.irs.gov)

At Least	But Less Than	Base Tax	+ Rate	Of the Amount Over
$0	$8,375	$0	10%	$0
$8,375	$34,000	$837.50	15%	$8,375
$34,000	$82,400	$4681.25	25%	$34,000

Write a piecewise-defined function that expresses an individual's federal income tax $f(x)$ (in $) as a function of the individual's taxable income x (in $).

Answers
8. a. 1   **b.** 5
   c. -4 **d.** -5

Solution:

First row: If an individual has a taxable income of $0 \leq x < \$8375$, then the individual will pay 10% of x dollars. This can be expressed as:

$$y = 0.10x \qquad \text{for } \$0 \leq x < \$8375$$

Second row: If an individual has a taxable income of $\$8375 \leq x < \$34,000$, then the individual will pay $837.50 plus 15% of the money earned above $8375. This can be expressed as:

$$y = 837.50 + 0.15(x - 8375) \qquad \text{for } \$8375 \leq x < \$34,000$$

Third row: If an individual has a taxable income of $\$34,000 \leq x < \$82,400$, then the individual will pay $4681.25 plus 25% of the money earned above $34,000. This can be expressed as:

$$y = \$4681.25 + 0.25(x - 34,000) \qquad \text{for } \$34,000 \leq x < \$82,400$$

The piecewise-defined function f expresses all three cases.

$$f(x) = \begin{cases} 0.10x & \text{for } 0 \leq x < 8375 \\ 837.50 + 0.15(x - 8375) & \text{for } 8375 \leq x < 34,000 \\ 4681.25 + 0.25(x - 34,000) & \text{for } 34,000 \leq x < 82,400 \end{cases}$$

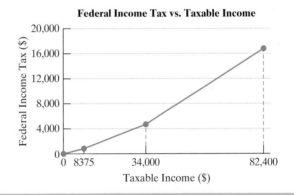

Federal Income Tax vs. Taxable Income

Skill Practice 9   A retail store buys T-shirts from the manufacturer. The cost is $7.99 per shirt for 1 to 100 shirts, inclusive. Then the price is decreased to $6.99 per shirt thereafter. Write a piecewise-defined function that expresses the cost $C(x)$ (in $) to buy x shirts.

4. Investigate Increasing, Decreasing, and Constant Behavior of a Function

The graph in Figure 2-37 approximates the altitude of an airplane, $f(t)$, at a time t minutes after takeoff.

Answer

9. $C(x) = \begin{cases} 7.99x & \text{for } 1 \leq x \leq 100 \\ 799 + 6.99(x - 100) & \text{for } x > 100 \end{cases}$

Figure 2-37

Notice that the plane increased in altitude up to the first 40 min of the flight. So we say that the function f is increasing on the interval $(0, 40)$. The plane flew at a constant altitude for the next 1 hr 20 min, so we say that f is constant on the interval $(40, 120)$. Finally, the plane decreased in altitude for the last 40 min, and we say that f is decreasing on the interval $(120, 160)$.

Informally, a function is increasing on an interval in its domain if its graph rises from left to right. A function is decreasing on an interval in its domain if it falls from left to right. A function is constant on an interval in its domain if it is horizontal over the interval. These ideas are stated formally using mathematical notation.

Intervals of Increasing, Decreasing, and Constant Behavior

Suppose that I is an interval contained within the domain of a function f.

- f is increasing on I if $f(x_1) < f(x_2)$ for all $x_1 < x_2$ on I.
- f is decreasing on I if $f(x_1) > f(x_2)$ for all $x_1 < x_2$ on I.
- f is constant on I if $f(x_1) = f(x_2)$ for all x_1 and x_2 on I.

  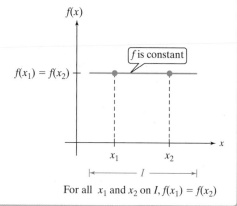

For all $x_1 < x_2$ on I, $f(x_1) < f(x_2)$ For all $x_1 < x_2$ on I, $f(x_1) > f(x_2)$ For all x_1 and x_2 on I, $f(x_1) = f(x_2)$

EXAMPLE 10   **Determining the Intervals Over Which a Function Is Increasing, Decreasing, and Constant**

Use interval notation to write the interval(s) over which f is

  a. Increasing   **b.** Decreasing

  c. Constant

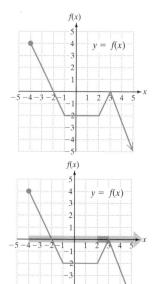

Solution:

  a. f is increasing on the interval $(2, 3)$.
     (Highlighted in red tint.)

  b. f is decreasing on the interval
     $(-4, -1) \cup (3, \infty)$.
     (Highlighted in orange tint.)

  c. f is constant on the interval $(-1, 2)$.
     (Highlighted in green tint.)

Skill Practice 10   Use interval notation to write the interval(s) over which f is

a. Increasing
b. Decreasing
c. Constant

5. Determine Relative Minima and Maxima of a Function

The intervals over which a function changes from increasing to decreasing behavior or vice versa tell us where to look for relative maximum values and relative minimum values of a function. Consider the function pictured in Figure 2-38.

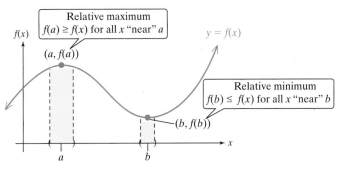

Figure 2-38

- The function has a relative maximum of $f(a)$. Informally, this means that $f(a)$ is the greatest function value relative to other points on the function nearby.
- The function has a relative minimum of $f(b)$. Informally, this means that $f(b)$ is the smallest function value relative to other points on the function nearby.

This is stated formally in the following definition.

TIP   The plural of maximum and minimum are **maxima** and **minima.**

Note that relative maxima and minima are also called *local* maxima and minima.

Relative Minimum and Relative Maximum Values

- $f(a)$ is a **relative maximum** of f if there exists an open interval containing a such that $f(a) \geq f(x)$ for all x in the interval.
- $f(b)$ is a **relative minimum** of f if there exists an open interval containing b such that $f(b) \leq f(x)$ for all x in the interval.

Note: An open interval is an interval in which the endpoints are not included.

Answers
10. a. $(-5, -3) \cup (-1, 2)$
   b. $(2, \infty)$ **c.** $(-3, -1)$

EXAMPLE 11 Finding Relative Maxima and Minima

For the graph of $y = g(x)$ shown,

   a. Determine the relative maxima.

   b. Determine the relative minima.

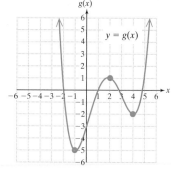

Solution:

   a. The point $(2, 1)$ is the highest point in a small interval surrounding $x = 2$.

      A relative maximum occurs at $x = 2$, and the value of the relative maximum is $g(2) = 1$.

   b. The points $(-1, -5)$ and $(4, -2)$ are the lowest points in small intervals surrounding $x = -1$ and $x = 4$, respectively.

      Therefore, relative minima occur at $x = -1$ and $x = 4$. The values of the relative minima are $g(-1) = -5$ and $g(4) = -2$.

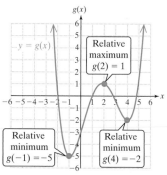

Avoiding Mistakes

Be sure to note that the value of a relative minimum or relative maximum is the *y* value of a function, not the *x* value.

Skill Practice 11 For the graph shown,

   a. Determine the relative maxima.

   b. Determine the relative minima.

TECHNOLOGY CONNECTIONS

Determining Relative Maxima and Minima

Relative maxima and relative minima are often difficult to find analytically and require techniques from calculus. However, a graphing utility can be used to approximate the location and value of relative maxima and minima. To do so, we use the Minimum and Maximum features.

Enter the function defined by $Y_1 = x^3 - 4x^2 + 3x$. Then access the Maximum feature.

Answers

11. a. Relative maximum: $f(-2) = 3$

   b. Relative minimum: $f(2) = 0$

The calculator asks for a left bound. This is a point slightly to the left of the relative maximum. Then hit ENTER.

The calculator asks for a right bound. This is a point slightly to the right of the relative maximum. Hit ENTER.

The calculator asks for a guess. This is a point close to the relative maximum. Hit ENTER and the approximate coordinates of the maximum point are shown (0.45, 0.63).

To find the relative minimum, repeat these steps using the Minimum feature. The coordinates are approximately $(2.22, -2.11)$.

SECTION 2.7   Practice Exercises

Review Exercises

For Exercises 1–4, graph the equation.

1. $y = 3x - 4$ for $x \geq 1$

2. $y = 2(x - 1)^2 - 4$ for $x \geq 0$

3. $(x - 2)^2 + (y + 3)^2 = 4$

4. $y = \sqrt{x + 4}$

5. Given $f(x) = -3x^2 - 5x + 1$, find $f(-x)$.

6. Given $g(x) = |2x| - x^2 + 3$, find $g(-x)$.

Concept Connections

7. A graph of an equation is symmetric with respect to the _____-axis if replacing x by $-x$ results in an equivalent equation.

8. A graph of an equation is symmetric with respect to the _____-axis if replacing y by $-y$ results in an equivalent equation.

9. A graph of an equation is symmetric with respect to the _____ if replacing x by $-x$ and y by $-y$ results in an equivalent equation.

10. An even function is symmetric with respect to the _____.

11. An odd function is symmetric with respect to the _____.

12. The expression _____ represents the greatest integer, less than or equal to x.

Objective 1: Test for Symmetry

For Exercises 13–24, determine whether the graph of the equation is symmetric with respect to the *x*-axis, *y*-axis, origin, or none of these. (See Examples 1–2)

13. $y = x^2 + 3$ **14.** $y = -|x| - 4$ **15.** $x = -|y| - 4$ **16.** $x = y^2 + 3$

17. $x^2 + y^2 = 3$ **18.** $|x| + |y| = 4$ **19.** $y = |x| + 2x + 7$ **20.** $y = x^2 + 6x + 1$

21. $x^2 = 5 + y^2$ **22.** $y^4 = 2 + x^2$ **23.** $y = \dfrac{1}{2}x - 3$ **24.** $y = \dfrac{2}{5}x + 1$

Objective 2: Identify Even and Odd Functions

25. What type of symmetry does an even function have?

26. What type of symmetry does an odd function have?

For Exercises 27–32, use the graph to determine if the function is even, odd, or neither. (See Example 3)

27.

28.

29.

30.

31.

32.

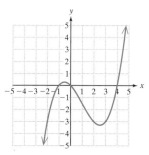

33. a. Given $f(x) = 4x^2 - 3|x|$, find $f(-x)$.

   b. Is $f(-x) = f(x)$?

   c. Is this function even, odd, or neither?

35. a. Given $h(x) = 4x^3 - 2x$, find $h(-x)$.

   b. Find $-h(x)$.

   c. Is $h(-x) = -h(x)$?

   d. Is this function even, odd, or neither?

37. a. Given $m(x) = 4x^2 + 2x - 3$, find $m(-x)$.

   b. Find $-m(x)$.

   c. Is $m(-x) = m(x)$?

   d. Is $m(-x) = -m(x)$?

   e. Is this function even, odd, or neither?

34. a. Given $g(x) = -x^8 + |3x|$, find $g(-x)$.

   b. Is $g(-x) = g(x)$?

   c. Is this function even, odd, or neither?

36. a. Given $k(x) = -8x^5 - 6x^3$, find $k(-x)$.

   b. Find $-k(x)$.

   c. Is $k(-x) = -k(x)$?

   d. Is this function even, odd, or neither?

38. a. Given $n(x) = 7|x| + 3x - 1$, find $n(-x)$.

   b. Find $-n(x)$.

   c. Is $n(-x) = n(x)$?

   d. Is $n(-x) = -n(x)$?

   e. Is this function even, odd, or neither?

For Exercises 39–48, determine if the function is even, odd, or neither. (See Example 4)

39. $f(x) = 3x^6 + 2x^2 + |x|$

40. $p(x) = -|x| + 12x^{10} + 5$

41. $k(x) = 13x^3 + 12x$

42. $m(x) = -4x^5 + 2x^3 + x$

43. $n(x) = \sqrt{16 - (x - 3)^2}$

44. $r(x) = \sqrt{81 - (x + 2)^2}$

45. $q(x) = \sqrt{16 + x^2}$

46. $z(x) = \sqrt{49 + x^2}$

47. $h(x) = 5x$

48. $g(x) = -x$

Objective 3: Graph Piecewise-Defined Functions

For Exercises 49–52, evaluate the function for the given values of x. (See Example 5)

49. $f(x) = \begin{cases} -3x + 7 & \text{for } x < -1 \\ x^2 + 3 & \text{for } -1 \le x < 4 \\ 5 & \text{for } x \ge 4 \end{cases}$

    a. $f(3)$ **b.** $f(-2)$ **c.** $f(-1)$

    d. $f(4)$ **e.** $f(5)$

50. $g(x) = \begin{cases} -2|x| - 3 & \text{for } x \le -2 \\ 5x + 6 & \text{for } -2 < x < 3 \\ 4 & \text{for } x \ge 3 \end{cases}$

    a. $g(-3)$ **b.** $g(3)$ **c.** $g(-2)$

    d. $g(0)$ **e.** $g(4)$

51. $h(x) = \begin{cases} 2 & \text{for } -3 \le x < -2 \\ 1 & \text{for } -2 \le x < -1 \\ 0 & \text{for } -1 \le x < 0 \\ -1 & \text{for } 0 \le x < 1 \end{cases}$

    a. $h(-1.7)$ **b.** $h(-2.5)$ **c.** $h(0.05)$

    d. $h(-2)$ **e.** $h(0)$

52. $t(x) = \begin{cases} x & \text{for } 0 < x \le 1 \\ 2x & \text{for } 1 < x \le 2 \\ 3x & \text{for } 2 < x \le 3 \\ 4x & \text{for } 3 < x \le 4 \end{cases}$

    a. $t(1.99)$ **b.** $t(0.4)$ **c.** $t(3)$

    d. $t(1)$ **e.** $t(3.001)$

For Exercises 53–56, match the function with its graph.

53. $f(x) = x + 1$ for $x < 2$

54. $f(x) = x + 1$ for $-1 < x \le 2$

55. $f(x) = x + 1$ for $-1 \le x < 2$

56. $f(x) = x + 1$ for $x \ge 2$

a.

b.

c.

d.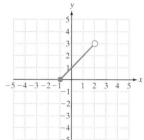

57. a. Graph $p(x) = x + 2$ for $x \le 0$.
  (See Examples 6–7)

  b. Graph $q(x) = -x^2$ for $x > 0$.

  c. Graph $r(x) = \begin{cases} x + 2 & \text{for } x \le 0 \\ -x^2 & \text{for } x > 0 \end{cases}$

58. a. Graph $f(x) = |x|$ for $x < 0$.

  b. Graph $g(x) = \sqrt{x}$ for $x \ge 0$.

  c. Graph $h(x) = \begin{cases} |x| & \text{for } x < 0 \\ \sqrt{x} & \text{for } x \ge 0 \end{cases}$

59. a. Graph $m(x) = \dfrac{1}{2}x - 2$ for $x \le -2$.

  b. Graph $n(x) = -x + 1$ for $x > -2$.

  c. Graph $t(x) = \begin{cases} \dfrac{1}{2}x - 2 & \text{for } x \le -2 \\ -x + 1 & \text{for } x > -2 \end{cases}$

60. a. Graph $a(x) = x$ for $x < 1$.

  b. Graph $b(x) = \sqrt{x - 1}$ for $x \ge 1$.

  c. Graph $c(x) = \begin{cases} x & \text{for } x < 1 \\ \sqrt{x - 1} & \text{for } x \ge 1 \end{cases}$

For Exercises 61–70, graph the function. (See Examples 6–7)

61. $f(x) = \begin{cases} |x| & \text{for } x < 2 \\ -x + 4 & \text{for } x \ge 2 \end{cases}$

62. $h(x) = \begin{cases} -2x & \text{for } x < 0 \\ \sqrt{x} & \text{for } x \ge 0 \end{cases}$

63. $g(x) = \begin{cases} x + 2 & \text{for } x < -1 \\ -x + 2 & \text{for } x \ge -1 \end{cases}$

64. $k(x) = \begin{cases} 3x & \text{for } x < 1 \\ -3x & \text{for } x \ge 1 \end{cases}$

65. $r(x) = \begin{cases} x^2 - 4 & \text{for } x \le 2 \\ 2x - 4 & \text{for } x > 2 \end{cases}$

66. $s(x) = \begin{cases} -x - 1 & \text{for } x \le -1 \\ \sqrt{x + 1} & \text{for } x > -1 \end{cases}$

67. $t(x) = \begin{cases} -3 & \text{for } -4 \le x < -2 \\ -1 & \text{for } -2 \le x < 0 \\ 1 & \text{for } 0 \le x < 2 \end{cases}$

68. $z(x) = \begin{cases} -1 & \text{for } -3 < x \le -1 \\ 1 & \text{for } -1 < x \le 1 \\ 3 & \text{for } 1 < x \le 3 \end{cases}$

69. $m(x) = \begin{cases} 3 & \text{for } -4 < x < -1 \\ -x & \text{for } -1 \le x < 3 \\ \sqrt{x - 3} & \text{for } x \ge 3 \end{cases}$

70. $n(x) = \begin{cases} -4 & \text{for } -3 < x < -1 \\ x & \text{for } -1 \le x < 2 \\ -x^2 + 4 & \text{for } x \ge 2 \end{cases}$

71. a. Graph $f(x) = \begin{cases} -x & \text{for } x < 0 \\ x & \text{for } x \ge 0 \end{cases}$

    b. To what basic function from Section 2.6 is the graph of f equivalent?

For Exercises 72–80, evaluate the step function defined by $f(x) = [\![x]\!]$ for the given values of x. (See Example 8)

72. $f(-3.7)$ **73.** $f(-4.2)$ **74.** $f(-0.5)$ **75.** $f(-0.09)$ **76.** $f(0.5)$

77. $f(0.09)$ **78.** $f(6)$ **79.** $f(-9)$ **80.** $f(-5)$

For Exercises 81–84, graph the function. (See Example 8)

81. $f(x) = [\![x + 3]\!]$ **82.** $g(x) = [\![x - 3]\!]$ **83.** $k(x) = \text{int}\left(\dfrac{1}{2}x\right)$ **84.** $h(x) = \text{int}(2x)$

85. For a recent year, the rate for first class postage was as follows. (**See Example 9**)

Weight not Over	Price
1 oz	$0.44
2 oz	$0.61
3 oz	$0.78
3.5 oz	$0.95

    a. Write a piecewise-defined function to model the cost $C(x)$ to mail a letter first class if the letter is x ounces.

    b. Graph the function.

86. The water level in a retention pond started at 5 ft (60 in.) and decreased at a rate of 2 in./day during a 14-day drought. A tropical depression moved through at the beginning of the 15th day and produced rain at an average rate of 2.5 in./day for 5 days.

    a. Write a piecewise-defined function to model the water level $L(x)$ (in inches) as a function of the number of days x since the beginning of the drought.

    b. Graph the function.

87. A sales person makes a base salary of $2000 per month. Once he reaches $40,000 in total sales, he earns an additional 5% commission on the amount in sales over $40,000. Write a piecewise-defined function to model the sales person's total monthly salary $S(x)$ (in $) as a function of the amount in sales x.

88. A cell phone plan charges $49.95 per month plus $14.02 in taxes, plus $0.40 per minute for calls beyond the 600-min monthly limit. Write a piecewise-defined function to model the monthly cost $C(x)$ (in $) as a function of the number of minutes used x for the month.

Objective 4: Investigate Increasing, Decreasing, and Constant Behavior of a Function

For Exercises 89–96, use interval notation to write the intervals over which f is (a) increasing, (b) decreasing, and (c) constant. (See Example 10)

89.

90.

91.

92.

93.

94.

95.

96.

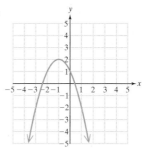

Objective 5: Determine Relative Minima and Maxima of a Function

For Exercises 97–102, identify the location and value of any relative maxima or minima of the function. (See Example 11)

97.

98.

99.

100.

101.

102.

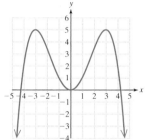

103. The unemployment rate for the civilian labor force for selected years is shown in the graph. (*Source*: U.S. Bureau of Labor Statistics, www.bls.gov) The *x*-axis represents the number of years since the year 2000.

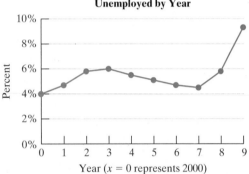

a. Over what interval(s) did the unemployment rate increase?

b. Over what interval(s) did the unemployment rate decrease?

c. Estimate the values of any relative maxima or minima on the interval (0, 9).

104. The number of births from teenage mothers aged 15–17 yr for selected years is shown in the graph. (*Source*: www.cdc.gov) The *x*-axis represents the number of years since 1980.

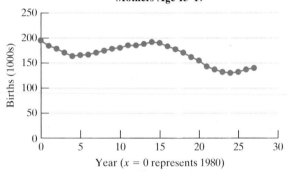

a. Approximate the interval(s) over which the number of births from teenage mothers increased.

b. Approximate the interval(s) over which the number of births from teenage mothers decreased.

c. Estimate the values of any relative maxima or minima on the interval (0, 27).

Mixed Exercises

For Exercises 105–110, produce a rule for the function whose graph is shown. (*Hint*: Consider using the basic functions learned in Section 2.6 and transformations of their graphs.)

105.

106.

107.

108.

109.

110.

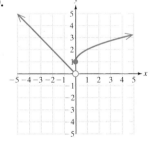

111. A sled accelerates down a hill and then slows down after it reaches a flat portion of ground. The speed of the sled $s(t)$ (in ft/sec) at a time t (in sec) after movement begins can be approximated by:

$$s(t) = \begin{cases} 1.5t & \text{for } 0 \le t \le 20 \\ \dfrac{30}{t-19} & \text{for } 20 < t \le 40 \end{cases}$$

Determine the speed of the sled after 10 sec, 20 sec, 30 sec, and 40 sec. Round to 1 decimal place if necessary.

112. A car starts from rest and accelerates to a speed of 60 mph in 12 sec. It travels 60 mph for 1 min and then decelerates for 20 sec until it comes to rest. The speed of the car $s(t)$ (in mph) at a time t (in sec) after the car begins motion can be modeled by:

$$s(t) = \begin{cases} \dfrac{5}{12}t^2 & \text{for } 0 \le t \le 12 \\ 60 & \text{for } 12 < t \le 72 \\ \dfrac{3}{20}(92 - t)^2 & \text{for } 72 < t \le 92 \end{cases}$$

Determine the speed of the car 6 sec, 12 sec, 45 sec, and 80 sec after the car begins motion.

113. A math tutor makes $14 per hour in the tutoring lab at her school. During final exam week, she earns overtime at $21 per hour for the work exceeding her normal 40-hr work week. Which graph best depicts her total salary for the week as a function of the number of hours worked?

a.

b.

c.

d.
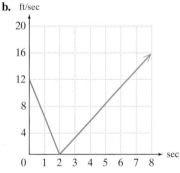

114. A ball rolls along the ground toward a child for 2 sec, and then the child kicks the ball. Which graph best represents the speed of the ball as a function of time?

a.

b.

c.

d.

In computer programming the greatest integer function is sometimes called the "floor" function. Programmers also make use of the "ceiling" function which returns the smallest integer not less than x. For example: ceil(3.1) = 4. For Exercises 115–116, evaluate the floor and ceiling functions for the given value of x.

floor(x) is the greatest integer less than or equal to x.
ceil(x) is the smallest integer not less than x.

115. a. floor(2.8)   **b.** floor(-3.1)   **c.** floor(4)
      d. ceil(2.8)   **e.** ceil(-3.1)   **f.** ceil(4)

116. a. floor(5.5)   **b.** floor(-0.1)   **c.** floor(-2)
      d. ceil(5.5)   **e.** ceil(-0.1)   **f.** ceil(-2)

Write About It

117. From an equation in x and y, explain how to determine whether the graph of the equation is symmetric with respect to the x-axis, y-axis, or origin.

118. From the graph of a function, how can you determine if the function is even or odd?

119. Explain why the relation defined by
$$y = \begin{cases} 2x & \text{for } x \le 1 \\ 3 & \text{for } x \ge 1 \end{cases}$$
is not a function.

120. Explain why the function is discontinuous at $x = 1$.
$$f(x) = \begin{cases} 3x & \text{for } x < 1 \\ 3 & \text{for } x > 1 \end{cases}$$

121. Provide an informal explanation of a relative maximum.

122. Explain what it means for a function to be increasing on an interval.

Expanding Your Skills

123. Suppose that the average rate of change of a continuous function between any two points to the left of $x = a$ is negative, and the average rate of change of the function between any two points to the right of $x = a$ is positive. Does the function have a relative minimum or maximum at a?

124. Suppose that the average rate of change of a continuous function between any two points to the left of $x = a$ is positive, and the average rate of change of the function between any two points to the right of $x = a$ is negative. Does the function have a relative minimum or maximum at a?

A graph is *concave up* on a given interval if it "bends" upward. A graph is *concave down* on a given interval if it "bends" downward. For Exercises 125–128, determine whether the curve is (a) concave up or concave down and (b) increasing or decreasing.

125.   **126.**   **127.**   **128.**

Technology Connections

For Exercises 129–134, use a graphing utility to graph the piecewise-defined function.

129. $f(x) = \begin{cases} 2.5x + 2 & \text{for } x \le 1 \\ x^2 - x - 1 & \text{for } x > 1 \end{cases}$

130. $g(x) = \begin{cases} -3.1x - 4 & \text{for } x < -2 \\ -x^3 + 4x - 1 & \text{for } x \ge -2 \end{cases}$

131. $k(x) = \begin{cases} -2.7x - 4.1 & \text{for } x \le -1 \\ -x^3 + 2x + 5 & \text{for } -1 < x < 2 \\ 1 & \text{for } x \ge 2 \end{cases}$

    Is there actually a "gap" in the graph at $x = 2$?

132. $z(x) = \begin{cases} 2.5x + 8 & \text{for } x < -2 \\ -2x^2 + x + 4 & \text{for } -2 \le x < 2 \\ -2 & \text{for } x \ge 2 \end{cases}$

    Is there actually a "gap" in the graph at $x = 2$?

133. $h(x) = \text{int}(0.4x - 1)$

134. $p(x) = \text{int}(0.6x + 2)$

For Exercises 135–136, use a graphing utility to approximate the relative maxima and relative minima of the function on the standard viewing window. Round to 3 decimal places.

135. $f(x) = -0.6x^2 + 2x + 3$

136. $g(x) = 0.4x^2 - 3x - 2.2$

Algebra of Functions and Function Composition

1. Perform Operations on Functions

In Section 2.5, we learned that a profit function can be constructed from the difference of a revenue function and a cost function according to the following rule.

$$P(x) = R(x) - C(x)$$

As this example illustrates, the difference of two functions makes up a new function. New functions can also be formed from the sum, product, and quotient of two functions.

Sum, Difference, Product, and Quotient of Functions

Given functions f and g, the functions $f + g$, $f - g$, $f \cdot g$, and $\frac{f}{g}$ are defined by:

$$(f + g)(x) = f(x) + g(x)$$
$$(f - g)(x) = f(x) - g(x)$$
$$(f \cdot g)(x) = f(x) \cdot g(x)$$
$$\left(\frac{f}{g}\right)(x) = \frac{f(x)}{g(x)} \text{ provided that } g(x) \neq 0$$

The domains of the functions $f + g$, $f - g$, $f \cdot g$, and $\frac{f}{g}$ are all real numbers in the intersection of the domains of the individual functions f and g. For $\frac{f}{g}$, we further restrict the domain to exclude values of x for which $g(x) = 0$.

EXAMPLE 1   **Adding Two Functions**

Given $f(x) = \sqrt{25 - x^2}$ and $g(x) = 5$, find $(f + g)(x)$.

Solution:

By definition $(f + g)(x) = f(x) + g(x)$.
$$= \sqrt{25 - x^2} + 5$$

Skill Practice 1   Given $m(x) = -|x|$ and $n(x) = 4$, find $(m + n)(x)$.

In Example 1, the graph of function f is a semicircle and the graph of function g is a horizontal line (Figure 2-39). Therefore, the graph of $y = (f + g)(x)$ is the graph of f with a vertical shift (shown in blue). Notice that each y value on $f + g$ is the sum of the y values from the individual functions f and g.

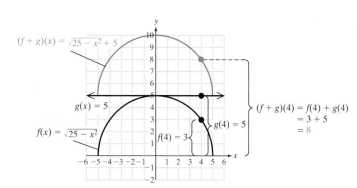

Figure 2-39

Answer

1. $(m + n)(x) = -|x| + 4$

In Example 2, we evaluate the difference, product, and quotient of functions for given values of x.

EXAMPLE 2 **Evaluating Functions for Given Values of x**

Given $m(x) = 4x$, $n(x) = |x - 3|$, and $p(x) = \dfrac{1}{x + 1}$, determine the function values if possible.

a. $(m - n)(-2)$ **b.** $(m \cdot p)(1)$ **c.** $\left(\dfrac{p}{n}\right)(3)$

Solution:

a. $(m - n)(-2) = m(-2) - n(-2)$
$= 4(-2) - |-2 - 3|$
$= -8 - 5$
$= -13$

b. $(m \cdot p)(1) = m(1) \cdot p(1)$
$= 4(1) \cdot \dfrac{1}{1 + 1}$
$= 2$

c. $\left(\dfrac{p}{n}\right)(3) = \dfrac{p(3)}{n(3)} = \dfrac{\frac{1}{3 + 1}}{|3 - 3|}$ The domain of $\dfrac{p}{n}$ excludes any values of x that make $n(x) = 0$. In this case, $x = 3$ is excluded from the domain.

$= \dfrac{\frac{1}{4}}{0}$ (undefined)

Skill Practice 2 Use the functions defined in Example 2 to find

a. $(n - m)(-6)$ **b.** $(n \cdot p)(0)$ **c.** $\left(\dfrac{p}{m}\right)(0)$

When combining two or more functions to create a new function, always be sure to determine the domain of the new function. In Example 2(c), the function $\frac{p}{n}$ is not defined for $x = -1$ or for $x = 3$.

$\left(\dfrac{p}{n}\right)(x) = \dfrac{p(x)}{n(x)} = \dfrac{\frac{1}{x + 1}}{|x - 3|}$ ⟵ —— Denominator is zero for $x = -1$.
⟵ —— Denominator of the complex fraction is zero for $x = 3$.

EXAMPLE 3 **Combining Functions and Determining Domain**

Given $g(x) = 2x$, $h(x) = x^2 - 4x$, and $k(x) = \sqrt{x - 1}$,

a. Find $(g - h)(x)$ and write the domain of $g - h$ in interval notation.
b. Find $(g \cdot k)(x)$ and write the domain of $g \cdot k$ in interval notation.
c. Find $\left(\dfrac{k}{h}\right)(x)$ and write the domain of $\dfrac{k}{h}$ in interval notation.

Solution:

a. $(g - h)(x) = g(x) - h(x)$
$= 2x - (x^2 - 4x)$
$= -x^2 + 6x$

The domain of g is $(-\infty, \infty)$.
The domain of h is $(-\infty, \infty)$.
Therefore, the intersection of their domains is $(-\infty, \infty)$.

The domain is $(-\infty, \infty)$.

Answers
2. a. 33 **b.** 3 **c.** Undefined

b. $(g \cdot k)(x) = g(x) \cdot k(x)$

$\qquad\qquad = 2x\sqrt{x-1}$

The domain is $[1, \infty)$.

The domain of g is $(-\infty, \infty)$.
The domain of k is $[1, \infty)$.
Therefore, the intersection of their domains is $[1, \infty)$.

c. $\left(\dfrac{k}{h}\right)(x) = \dfrac{k(x)}{h(x)} = \dfrac{\sqrt{x-1}}{x^2 - 4x}$

$\qquad\qquad = \dfrac{\sqrt{x-1}}{x(x-4)}$

The domain is $[1, 4) \cup (4, \infty)$.

The domain of k is $[1, \infty)$.
The domain of h is $(-\infty, \infty)$.
The intersection of their domains is $[1, \infty)$.

However, we must also exclude values of x that make the denominator zero. In this case, exclude $x = 0$ and $x = 4$. The value $x = 0$ is already excluded because it is not on the interval $[1, \infty)$. Excluding $x = 4$, the domain of $\frac{k}{h}$ is $[1, 4) \cup (4, \infty)$.

Skill Practice 3   Given $m(x) = x + 3$, $n(x) = x^2 - 9$, and $p(x) = \sqrt{x+1}$

a. Find $(n - m)(x)$ and write the domain of $n - m$ in interval notation.

b. Find $(m \cdot p)(x)$ and write the domain of $m \cdot p$ in interval notation.

c. Find $\left(\dfrac{p}{n}\right)(x)$ and write the domain of $\dfrac{p}{n}$ in interval notation.

---

2. Evaluate a Difference Quotient

In Section 2.4, we learned that if f is defined on an interval $[x_1, x_2]$, then the average rate of change of f between $(x_1, f(x_1))$ and $(x_2, f(x_2))$ is given by:

$$m = \frac{f(x_2) - f(x_1)}{x_2 - x_1} \quad \text{(Figure 2-40)}$$

Now we look at a related idea. Let P be an arbitrary point $(x, f(x))$ on the function f. Let h be a positive real number and let Q be the point $(x + h, f(x + h))$. See Figure 2-41. The average rate of change between P and Q is the slope of the secant line and is given by:

$$m = \frac{f(x + h) - f(x)}{(x + h) - x}$$

$$= \frac{f(x + h) - f(x)}{h} \quad \text{(Difference quotient)}$$

TIP h is taken to be a positive real number, implying that $h \neq 0$.

Figure 2-40

Figure 2-41

Answers

3. a. $(n - m)(x) = x^2 - x - 12$;
   Domain: $(-\infty, \infty)$
b. $(m \cdot p)(x) = (x + 3)\sqrt{x + 1}$;
   Domain: $[-1, \infty)$
c. $\left(\dfrac{p}{n}\right)(x) = \dfrac{\sqrt{x + 1}}{x^2 - 9}$;
   Domain: $[-1, 3) \cup (3, \infty)$

The expression on the right is called the **difference quotient** and is very important for the foundation of calculus. In Examples 4 and 5, we practice evaluating the difference quotient for two functions.

EXAMPLE 4 Finding a Difference Quotient

Given $f(x) = 3x - 5$,

a. Find $f(x + h)$.

b. Find the difference quotient, $\dfrac{f(x + h) - f(x)}{h}$.

Solution:

a. $f(x + h) = 3(x + h) - 5$ Substitute $(x + h)$ for x.

          $= 3x + 3h - 5$

$$\overbrace{\qquad}^{f(x+h)} \qquad \overbrace{\qquad}^{f(x)}$$

b. $\dfrac{f(x + h) - f(x)}{h} = \dfrac{(3x + 3h - 5) - (3x - 5)}{h}$

          $= \dfrac{3x + 3h - 5 - 3x + 5}{h}$ Clear parentheses.

          $= \dfrac{3h}{h}$ Combine like terms.

          $= 3$ Simplify the fraction.

Skill Practice 4   Given $f(x) = 4x - 2$,

a. Find $f(x + h)$.

b. Find the difference quotient, $\dfrac{f(x + h) - f(x)}{h}$.

EXAMPLE 5 Finding a Difference Quotient

Given $f(x) = -2x^2 + 4x - 1$,

a. Find $f(x + h)$.

b. Find the difference quotient, $\dfrac{f(x + h) - f(x)}{h}$.

Solution:

a. $f(x + h) = -2(x + h)^2 + 4(x + h) - 1$ Substitute $(x + h)$ for x.

          $= -2(x^2 + 2xh + h^2) + 4x + 4h - 1$

          $= -2x^2 - 4xh - 2h^2 + 4x + 4h - 1$

$$\overbrace{\qquad}^{f(x+h)} \qquad\qquad\qquad \overbrace{\qquad}^{f(x)}$$

b. $\dfrac{f(x + h) - f(x)}{h} = \dfrac{(-2x^2 - 4xh - 2h^2 + 4x + 4h - 1) - (-2x^2 + 4x - 1)}{h}$

      $= \dfrac{-2x^2 - 4xh - 2h^2 + 4x + 4h - 1 + 2x^2 - 4x + 1}{h}$ Clear parentheses.

      $= \dfrac{-4xh - 2h^2 + 4h}{h}$ Combine like terms.

      $= \dfrac{\overset{1}{\cancel{h}}(-4x - 2h + 4)}{\cancel{h}}$ Factor numerator and denominator, and simplify the fraction.

      $= -4x - 2h + 4$

Answers

4. a. $4x + 4h - 2$ **b.** 4

> **Skill Practice 5**   Given $f(x) = -x^2 - 5x + 2$,
>
> **a.** Find $f(x + h)$.
>
> **b.** Find the difference quotient, $\dfrac{f(x + h) - f(x)}{h}$.

3. Compose and Decompose Functions

The next operation on functions we present is called the composition of functions. Informally, this involves a substitution process in which the output from one function becomes the input to another function.

> **Composition of Functions**
>
> The **composition of f and g,** denoted $f \circ g$ is defined by $(f \circ g)(x) = f(g(x))$. The domain of $f \circ g$ is the set of real numbers x in the domain of g such that $g(x)$ is in the domain of f.

To visualize the composition of functions, consider Figure 2-42.

Figure 2-42

EXAMPLE 6   **Composing Functions**

Given $f(x) = x^2 + 2x$ and $g(x) = x - 4$, find

a. $f(g(6))$ **b.** $g(f(-3))$ **c.** $(f \circ g)(0)$ **d.** $(g \circ f)(5)$

Solution:

a. $f(g(6)) = f(2)$ Evaluate $g(6)$ first. $g(6) = (6) - 4 = 2$.
     $= 8$ $f(2) = (2)^2 + 2(2) = 8$

b. $g(f(-3)) = g(3)$ Evaluate $f(-3)$ first. $f(-3) = (-3)^2 + 2(-3) = 3$.
     $= -1$ $g(3) = (3) - 4 = -1$

c. $(f \circ g)(0) = f(g(0))$ Evaluate $g(0)$ first. $g(0) = (0) - 4 = -4$.
     $= f(-4)$ $f(-4) = (-4)^2 + 2(-4)$
     $= 8$

d. $(g \circ f)(5) = g(f(5))$ Evaluate $f(5)$ first. $f(5) = (5)^2 + 2(5) = 35$.
     $= g(35)$ $g(35) = (35) - 4 = 31$
     $= 31$

> **TIP** When composing functions, apply the order of operations. In Example 6(a), the value of $g(6)$ is found first.

Skill Practice 6   Refer to functions f and g given in Example 6. Find

a. $f(g(-4))$ **b.** $g(f(-5))$ **c.** $(f \circ g)(9)$ **d.** $(g \circ f)(10)$

In Example 7, we practice composing functions and identifying the domain of the composite function. This example also illustrates that function composition is not commutative. That is, $(f \circ g)(x) \neq (g \circ f)(x)$ for all functions f and g.

Answers

5. a. $-x^2 - 2xh - h^2 - 5x - 5h + 2$
   b. $-2x - h - 5$
6. a. 48   **b.** 11   **c.** 35
   d. 116

EXAMPLE 7 **Composing Functions and Determining Domain**

Given $f(x) = 2x - 6$ and $g(x) = \frac{1}{x + 4}$, write a rule for each function and write the domain in interval notation.

a. $(f \circ g)(x)$ **b.** $(g \circ f)(x)$

Solution:

a. $(f \circ g)(x) = f(g(x)) = 2(g(x)) - 6$

$$= 2\left(\frac{1}{x + 4}\right) - 6$$

Function g has the restriction that $x \neq -4$.

$$= \frac{2}{x + 4} - 6 \quad \text{provided } x \neq -4$$

The domain of f is all real numbers. Therefore, no further restrictions need to be imposed.

The domain is $(-\infty, -4) \cup (-4, \infty)$.

b. $(g \circ f)(x) = g(f(x)) = \dfrac{1}{f(x) + 4}$

The domain of f has no restrictions.

$$= \frac{1}{(2x - 6) + 4} \qquad f(x) \neq -4$$

However, function g must not have an input value of -4. Therefore, we have the restriction:

$$= \frac{1}{2x - 2} \quad \text{provided } x \neq 1$$

The domain is $(-\infty, 1) \cup (1, \infty)$.

$$f(x) \neq -4$$
$$2x - 6 \neq -4$$
$$2x \neq 2$$
$$x \neq 1$$

Skill Practice 7 Given $f(x) = 3x + 4$ and $g(x) = \frac{1}{x - 1}$, write a rule for each function and write the domain in interval notation.

a. $(f \circ g)(x)$ **b.** $(g \circ f)(x)$

EXAMPLE 8 **Composing Functions and Determining Domain**

Given $m(x) = \frac{1}{x - 5}$ and $p(x) = \sqrt{x - 2}$, find $(m \circ p)(x)$ and write the domain in interval notation.

Solution:

$$(m \circ p)(x) = m(p(x)) = \frac{1}{p(x) - 5}$$

First note that function p has the restriction that $x \geq 2$.

$$p(x) \neq 5$$

The input value for function m must not be 5. Therefore, $p(x) \neq 5$. We have

$$= \frac{1}{\sqrt{x - 2} - 5}$$

$$\sqrt{x - 2} \neq 5$$
$$(\sqrt{x - 2})^2 \neq (5)^2$$

$$(m \circ p)(x) = \frac{1}{\sqrt{x - 2} - 5}$$

$$x - 2 \neq 25$$
$$x \neq 27$$

The domain is $[2, 27) \cup (27, \infty)$.

Answers

7. a. $(f \circ g)(x) = \dfrac{3}{x - 1} + 4;$

Domain: $(-\infty, 1) \cup (1, \infty)$

b. $(g \circ f)(x) = \dfrac{1}{3x + 3};$

Domain: $(-\infty, -1) \cup (-1, \infty)$

8. $(g \circ f)(x) = \dfrac{1}{\sqrt{x - 1} - 3};$

Domain: $[1, 10) \cup (10, \infty)$

Skill Practice 8 Given $f(x) = \sqrt{x - 1}$ and $g(x) = \frac{1}{x - 3}$, find $(g \circ f)(x)$ and write the domain of $g \circ f$ in interval notation.

In Example 9, we use function composition in an application.

EXAMPLE 9   Applying Function Composition

At a popular website, the cost to download individual songs is $1.49 per song. In addition, a first-time visitor to the website has a one-time coupon for $1.00 off.

a. Write a function to represent the cost $C(x)$ (in $) for a first-time visitor to purchase x songs.

b. The sales tax for online purchases depends on the location of the business and customer. If the sales tax rate on a purchase is 6%, write a function to represent the total cost $T(a)$ for a first-time visitor who buys a dollars in songs.

c. Find $(T \circ C)(x)$ and interpret the meaning in context.

d. Evaluate $(T \circ C)(10)$ and interpret the meaning in context.

Solution:

a. $C(x) = 1.49x - 1.00;\ x \geq 1$ The cost function is a linear function with $1.49 as the variable rate per song.

b. $T(a) = a + 0.06a$ The total cost is the sum of the cost of the songs plus the sales tax.

     $= 1.06a$

c. $(T \circ C)(x) = T(C(x))$

     $= 1.06(C(x))$

     $= 1.06(1.49x - 1.00)$ Substitute $1.49x - 1.00$ for $C(x)$.

     $= 1.5794x - 1.06$

$(T \circ C)(x) = 1.5794x - 1.06$ represents the total cost to buy x songs for a first-time visitor to the website.

d. $(T \circ C)(x) = 1.5794x - 1.06$

     $(T \circ C)(10) = 1.5794(10) - 1.06$

             $= 14.734$

The total cost for a first-time visitor to buy 10 songs is $14.73.

Skill Practice 9   An artist shops online for tubes of watercolor paint. The cost is $16 for each 14-mL tube.

a. Write a function representing the cost $C(x)$ (in $) for x tubes of paint.

b. There is a 5.5% sales tax on the cost of merchandise and a fixed cost of $4.99 for shipping. Write a function representing the total cost $T(a)$ for a dollars spent in merchandise.

c. Find $(T \circ C)(x)$ and interpret the meaning in context.

d. Evaluate $(T \circ C)(18)$ and interpret the meaning in context.

The composition of two functions creates a new function in which the output from one function becomes the input to the other. We can also reverse this process. That is, we can decompose a composite function into two or more simpler functions.

For example, consider the function h defined by: $h(x) = (x - 3)^2$. To write h as a composition of two functions, we have $h(x) = (f \circ g)(x) = f(g(x))$. The function g is the "inside" function and f is the "outside" function. So one natural choice for g and f would be:

        $g(x) = x - 3$ Function g subtracts 3 from the input value.

        $f(x) = x^2$ Function f squares the result.

    $h(x) = f(g(x)) = (g(x))^2 = (x - 3)^2$

TIP The decomposition of functions is not unique. For example, $h(x) = (x - 3)^2$ can also be written as $h(x) = f(g(x))$ where $g(x) = x^2 - 6x$ and $f(x) = x + 9$.

Answers

9. a. $C(x) = 16x$

   b. $T(a) = 1.055a + 4.99$

   c. $(T \circ C)(x) = 16.88x + 4.99$ represents the total cost to buy x tubes of paint.

   d. $(T \circ C)(18) = \$308.83$; The total cost to buy 18 tubes of paint is $308.83.

EXAMPLE 10   Decomposing Two Functions

Given $h(x) = |2x^2 - 5|$, find two functions f and g such that $h(x) = (f \circ g)(x)$.

Solution:

We need to find two functions f and g such that $h(x) = (f \circ g)(x) = f(g(x))$.
The function h first evaluates the expression $2x^2 - 5$, and then takes the absolute value. Therefore, it would be natural to take the absolute value of $g(x) = 2x^2 - 5$.

We have: $g(x) = 2x^2 - 5$ and $f(x) = |x|$

Check: $h(x) = (f \circ g)(x) = f(g(x)) = |g(x)|$
         $= |2x^2 - 5|$

Skill Practice 10   Given $m(x) = \sqrt[3]{5x + 1}$, find two functions f and g such that $m(x) = (f \circ g)(x)$.

In Example 11, we have the graphs of two functions, and we apply function addition, subtraction, multiplication, and composition for selected values of x.

EXAMPLE 11   Estimating Function Values from a Graph

The graphs of f and g are shown. Evaluate the functions at the given values of x if possible.

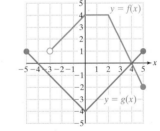

a. $(f + g)(1)$
b. $(fg)(0)$
c. $(g - f)(-3)$
d. $(f \circ g)(3)$
e. $(g \circ f)(4)$
f. $f(g(1))$

Solution:

a. $(f + g)(1) = f(1) + g(1)$
$= 4 + (-3)$
$= 1$

b. $(fg)(0) = f(0) \cdot g(0)$
$= (4)(-4)$
$= -16$

c. $(g - f)(-3) = g(-3) - \underbrace{f(-3)}_{f(-3) \text{ is undefined.}}$

$(g - f)(-3)$ is undefined.

d. $(f \circ g)(3) = f(g(3))$
$= f(-1)$
$= 3$

e. $(g \circ f)(4) = g(f(4))$
$= g(0)$
$= -4$

f. $f(g(1)) = f(-3)$ is undefined.   The open dot at $(-3, 1)$ indicates that -3 is not in the domain of f. The value $g(1) = -3$, but $f(-3)$ is undefined. Therefore, $f(g(1))$ is undefined.

Skill Practice 11   Refer to the functions f and g pictured in Example 11. Evaluate the functions at the given values of x if possible.

Answers
10. $g(x) = 5x + 1$ and $f(x) = \sqrt[3]{x}$
11. a. 4   **b.** -2 **c.** -2
    d. -2 **e.** 4   **f.** Undefined

a. $(f - g)(-2)$ **b.** $\left(\dfrac{f}{g}\right)(3)$ **c.** $(gf)(5)$ **d.** $(g \circ f)(5)$

e. $(f \circ g)(5)$ **f.** $f(g(0))$

SECTION 2.8   Practice Exercises

Review Exercises

For Exercises 1–4, write the domain of the function in interval notation.

1. $f(x) = \sqrt{5 - 2x}$ **2.** $g(x) = \sqrt{1 + 4x}$ **3.** $h(x) = \dfrac{1}{81 - x^2}$ **4.** $k(x) = \dfrac{1}{49 - x^2}$

For Exercises 5–6, evaluate $f(x) = 3x^2 + 5x - 1$ for the given values of x.

5. $f(t + 2)$ **6.** $f(a - 4)$

Concept Connections

7. The function $f + g$ is defined by $(f + g)(x) = $ _____ $+$ _____.

8. The function $\dfrac{f}{g}$ is defined by $\left(\dfrac{f}{g}\right)(x) = $ _____ provided that _____ $\neq 0$.

9. Let h represent a positive real number. Given a function defined by $y = f(x)$, the difference quotient is given by _____.

10. The composition of f and g, denoted by $f \circ g$, is defined by $(f \circ g)(x) = $ _____.

Objective 1: Perform Operations on Functions

For Exercises 11–14, find $(f + g)(x)$ and identify the graph of $f + g$. **(See Example 1)**

11. $f(x) = |x|$ and $g(x) = 3$ **12.** $f(x) = |x|$ and $g(x) = -4$

13. $f(x) = x^2$ and $g(x) = -4$ **14.** $f(x) = x^2$ and $g(x) = 3$

a.   **b.**   **c.**   **d.**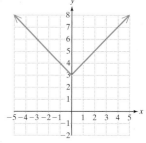

For Exercises 15–24, evaluate the functions for the given values of x. **(See Example 2)**

$$f(x) = -2x \qquad g(x) = |x + 4| \qquad h(x) = \frac{1}{x - 3}$$

15. $(f - g)(3)$ **16.** $(g - h)(2)$ **17.** $(f \cdot g)(-1)$ **18.** $(h \cdot g)(4)$ **19.** $(g + h)(0)$

20. $(f + h)(5)$ **21.** $\left(\dfrac{f}{g}\right)(8)$ **22.** $\left(\dfrac{h}{f}\right)(7)$ **23.** $\left(\dfrac{g}{f}\right)(0)$ **24.** $\left(\dfrac{h}{g}\right)(-4)$

For Exercises 25–36, refer to the functions r, p, and q. Evaluate the function and write the domain in interval notation. **(See Example 3)**

$$r(x) = -3x \qquad p(x) = x^2 + 3x \qquad q(x) = \sqrt{1 - x}$$

25. $(r - p)(x)$ **26.** $(p - r)(x)$ **27.** $(p \cdot q)(x)$ **28.** $(r \cdot q)(x)$

29. $\left(\dfrac{q}{p}\right)(x)$ **30.** $\left(\dfrac{q}{r}\right)(x)$ **31.** $\left(\dfrac{p}{q}\right)(x)$ **32.** $\left(\dfrac{r}{q}\right)(x)$

33. $(r + q)(x)$ **34.** $(p + q)(x)$ **35.** $\left(\dfrac{p}{r}\right)(x)$ **36.** $\left(\dfrac{r}{p}\right)(x)$

Objective 2: Evaluate a Difference Quotient

For Exercises 37–40, a function is given. (See Examples 4–5)

  a. Find $f(x + h)$.   **b.** Find $\dfrac{f(x + h) - f(x)}{h}$.

37. $f(x) = 5x + 9$ **38.** $f(x) = 8x + 4$ **39.** $f(x) = x^2 + 4x$ **40.** $f(x) = x^2 - 3x$

For Exercises 41–48, find the difference quotient and simplify. (See Examples 4–5)

41. $f(x) = -2x + 5$ **42.** $f(x) = -3x + 8$ **43.** $f(x) = -5x^2 - 4x + 2$ **44.** $f(x) = -4x^2 - 2x + 6$

45. $f(x) = x^3$ **46.** $f(x) = x^3 - 2$ **47.** $f(x) = \dfrac{1}{x}$ **48.** $f(x) = \dfrac{1}{x + 2}$

49. Given $f(x) = 4\sqrt{x}$,
  a. Find the difference quotient (do not simplify).
  b. Evaluate the difference quotient for $x = 1$, and the following values of h: $h = 1$, $h = 0.1$, $h = 0.01$, and $h = 0.001$. Round to 4 decimal places.
  c. What value does the difference quotient seem to be approaching as h gets close to 0?

50. Given $f(x) = \dfrac{12}{x}$,
  a. Find the difference quotient (do not simplify).
  b. Evaluate the difference quotient for $x = 2$, and the following values of h: $h = 0.1$, $h = 0.01$, $h = 0.001$, and $h = 0.0001$. Round to 4 decimal places.
  c. What value does the difference quotient seem to be approaching as h gets close to 0?

Objective 3: Compose and Decompose Functions

For Exercises 51–62, refer to functions f, g, and h. Evaluate the functions for the given values of x. (See Example 6)

$$f(x) = x^3 - 4x \qquad g(x) = \sqrt{2x} \qquad h(x) = 2x + 3$$

51. $f(g(8))$ **52.** $h(g(2))$ **53.** $h(f(1))$ **54.** $g(f(3))$

55. $(f \circ g)(18)$ **56.** $(f \circ h)(-1)$ **57.** $(g \circ f)(5)$ **58.** $(h \circ f)(-2)$

59. $(h \circ f)(-3)$ **60.** $(h \circ g)(72)$ **61.** $(g \circ f)(1)$ **62.** $(g \circ f)(-4)$

63. Given $f(x) = 2x + 4$ and $g(x) = x^2$,
  a. Find $(f \circ g)(x)$.   **b.** Find $(g \circ f)(x)$.   **c.** Is the operation of function composition commutative?

64. Given $k(x) = -3x + 1$ and $m(x) = \dfrac{1}{x}$,
  a. Find $(k \circ m)(x)$.   **b.** Find $(m \circ k)(x)$.   **c.** Is $(k \circ m)(x) = (m \circ k)(x)$?

For Exercises 65–76, refer to the functions m, n, p, q, and r. Evaluate the function and write the domain in interval notation. (See Examples 7–8)

$$m(x) = \sqrt{x + 8} \qquad n(x) = x - 5 \qquad p(x) = x^2 - 9x \qquad q(x) = \dfrac{1}{x - 10} \qquad r(x) = |2x + 3|$$

65. $(n \circ p)(x)$ **66.** $(p \circ n)(x)$ **67.** $(m \circ n)(x)$ **68.** $(n \circ m)(x)$

69. $(q \circ n)(x)$ **70.** $(q \circ p)(x)$ **71.** $(q \circ r)(x)$ **72.** $(q \circ m)(x)$

73. $(n \circ r)(x)$ **74.** $(r \circ n)(x)$ **75.** $(n \circ n)(x)$ **76.** $(p \circ p)(x)$

77. A law office orders business stationery. The cost is $21.95 per box. **(See Example 9)**
  a. Write a function that represents the cost $C(x)$ (in $) for x boxes of stationery.
  b. There is a 6% sales tax on the cost of merchandise and $10.99 for shipping. Write a function that represents the total cost $T(a)$ for a dollars spent in merchandise and shipping.
  c. Find $(T \circ C)(x)$.
  d. Find $(T \circ C)(4)$ and interpret its meaning in the context of this problem.

78. The cost to buy tickets online for a dance show is $60 per ticket.
  a. Write a function that represents the cost $C(x)$ (in $) for x tickets to the show.
  b. There is a sales tax of 5.5% and a processing fee of $8.00 for a group of tickets. Write a function that represents the total cost $T(a)$ for a dollars spent on tickets.
  c. Find $(T \circ C)(x)$.
  d. Find $(T \circ C)(6)$ and interpret its meaning in the context of this problem.

79. A bicycle wheel turns at a rate of 80 revolutions per minute (rpm).

   a. Write a function that represents the number of revolutions $r(t)$ in t minutes.

   b. For each revolution of the wheels, the bicycle travels 7.2 ft. Write a function that represents the distance traveled $d(r)$ (in ft) for r revolutions of the wheel.

   c. Evaluate $(d \circ r)(t)$ and interpret the meaning in the context of this problem.

   d. Evaluate $(d \circ r)(30)$ and interpret the meaning in the context of this problem.

80. While on vacation in France, Sadie bought a box of almond croissants. Each croissant cost €2.4 (euros).

   a. Write a function that represents the cost $C(x)$ (in euros) for x croissants.

   b. At the time of the purchase, the exchange rate was $\$1 = €0.80$. Write a function that represents the amount $D(C)$ (in \$) for C euros spent.

   c. Evaluate $(D \circ C)(x)$ and interpret the meaning in the context of this problem.

   d. Evaluate $(D \circ C)(12)$ and interpret the meaning in the context of this problem.

For Exercises 81–88, find two functions f and g such that $h(x) = (f \circ g)(x)$. (See Example 10)

81. $h(x) = (x + 7)^2$

82. $h(x) = (x - 8)^2$

83. $h(x) = \sqrt[3]{2x + 1}$

84. $h(x) = \sqrt[4]{9x - 5}$

85. $h(x) = |2x^2 - 3|$

86. $h(x) = |4 - x^2|$

87. $h(x) = \dfrac{5}{x + 4}$

88. $h(x) = \dfrac{11}{x - 3}$

Mixed Exercises

For Exercises 89–92, the graphs of f and g are shown. Find the function values for the given values of x, if possible. (See Example 11)

89. a. $(f + g)(0)$

   b. $(g - f)(2)$

   c. $(g \cdot f)(-1)$

   d. $\left(\dfrac{g}{f}\right)(1)$

   e. $(f \circ g)(4)$

   f. $(g \circ f)(0)$

   g. $g(f(4))$

90. a. $(f + g)(0)$

   b. $(g - f)(1)$

   c. $(g \cdot f)(2)$

   d. $\left(\dfrac{f}{g}\right)(-3)$

   e. $(f \circ g)(3)$

   f. $(g \circ f)(0)$

   g. $g(f(-4))$

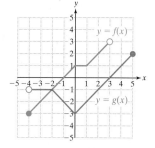

91. a. $(h + k)(-1)$

   b. $(h \cdot k)(4)$

   c. $\left(\dfrac{k}{h}\right)(-3)$

   d. $(k - h)(1)$

   e. $(k \circ h)(4)$

   f. $(h \circ k)(-2)$

   g. $h(k(3))$

92. a. $(m + p)(1)$

   b. $(p - m)(-4)$

   c. $\left(\dfrac{m}{p}\right)(3)$

   d. $(m \cdot p)(3)$

   e. $(m \circ p)(0)$

   f. $(p \circ m)(0)$

   g. $p(m(-4))$

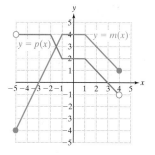

For Exercises 93–100, refer to the functions f and g and evaluate the functions for the given values of x.

$$f = \{(2, 4), (6, -1), (4, -2), (0, 3), (-1, 6)\} \quad \text{and} \quad g = \{(4, 3), (0, 6), (5, 7), (6, 0)\}$$

93. $(f + g)(4)$

94. $(g \cdot f)(0)$

95. $(g \circ f)(2)$

96. $(f \circ g)(0)$

97. $(g \circ g)(6)$

98. $(f \circ f)(-1)$

99. $(f \circ g)(5)$

100. $(g \circ f)(0)$

For Exercises 101–106, refer to the values of $k(x)$ and $p(x)$ in the spreadsheet, and evaluate the functions for the given values of x.

101. $(k + p)(4)$

102. $(p - k)(0)$

103. $(k \circ p)(2)$

104. $(p \circ k)(2)$

105. $(k \circ k)(0)$

106. $(p \circ p)(5)$

	A	B	C
1	x	k(x)	p(x)
2	0	4	-3
3	2	5	4
4	4	6	2
5	5	-1	0

107. In the graph, $y = M(x)$ and $y = W(x)$ give the number of males and females, respectively, on probation, on parole, or incarcerated in the United States. The variable x represents the number of years since 2000. (*Source*: U.S. Department of Justice, www.justice.gov) Find $T(x) = (M + W)(x)$ and interpret its meaning in the context of this problem.

Number of Adults on Probation or Parole or Incarcerated (millions)

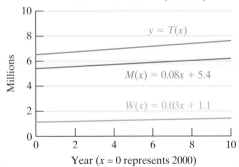

108. In the graph, $y = P(x)$ and $y = R(x)$ give the total enrollment (in millions) in public and private schools, respectively, in the United States. The variable x represents the number of years since 1990. (*Source*: U.S. Center for Education Statistics, http://nces.ed.gov) Find $T(x) = (P + R)(x)$ and interpret its meaning in the context of this problem.

Enrollment in All Levels of School

109. A website designer creates videos on how to create websites. She sells the videos in 10-hr packages for $40 each. Her one-time initial cost to produce each 10-hr video package is $5000 (this includes labor and the cost of computer supplies). The cost to package and ship each CD is $2.80.

   a. Write a linear cost function that represents the cost $C(x)$ to produce, package, and ship x 10-hr video packages.

   b. Write a linear revenue function to represent the revenue $R(x)$ for selling x 10-hr video packages.

   c. Evaluate $(R - C)(x)$ and interpret its meaning in the context of this problem.

   d. Determine the profit if the website designer produces and sells 2400 video packages in the course of one year.

110. An artist makes jewelry from polished stones. The rent for her studio, Internet service, and phone come to $640 per month. She also estimates that it costs $3.50 in supplies to make one necklace. At art shows and online, she sells the necklaces for $25 each.

   a. Write a linear cost function that represents the cost $C(x)$ to produce x necklaces during a one-month period.

   b. Write a linear revenue function to represent the revenue $R(x)$ for selling x necklaces.

   c. Evaluate $(R - C)(x)$ and interpret its meaning in the context of this problem.

   d. Determine the profit if the artist sells 212 necklaces during a one-month period.

111. Suppose that a function H gives the high temperature $H(x)$ (in °F) for day x. Suppose that a function L gives the low temperature $L(x)$ (in °F) for day x. What does $\left(\dfrac{H + L}{2}\right)(x)$ represent?

112. For the given figure,

   a. What does $A_1(x) = \pi(x + 5)^2$ represent?

   b. What does $A_2(x) = \pi x^2$ represent?

   c. Find $(A_1 - A_2)(x)$ and interpret its meaning.

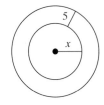

113. For the given figure,

   a. Write an expression $S_1(x)$ that represents the area of the rectangle.

   b. Write an expression $S_2(x)$ that represents the area of the semicircle.

   c. Find $(S_1 - S_2)(x)$ and interpret its meaning.

Write About It

114. Given functions f and g, explain how to determine the domain of $\left(\dfrac{f}{g}\right)(x)$.

115. Given functions f and g, explain how to determine the domain of $(f \circ g)(x)$.

116. Explain what the difference quotient represents.

Expanding Your Skills

117. Given $f(x) = \sqrt{x + 3}$,

    a. Find the difference quotient.

    b. Rationalize the numerator of the expression in part (a) and simplify.

    c. Evaluate the expression in part (b) for $h = 0$.

118. Given $f(x) = \sqrt{x - 4}$,

    a. Find the difference quotient.

    b. Rationalize the numerator of the expression in part (a) and simplify.

    c. Evaluate the expression in part (b) for $h = 0$.

119. A car traveling 60 mph (88 ft/sec) undergoes a constant deceleration until it comes to rest approximately 9.09 sec later. The distance $d(t)$ (in ft) that the car travels t seconds after the brakes are applied is given by $d(t) = -4.84t^2 + 88t$, where $0 \le t \le 9.09$. (**See Example 5**)

    a. Find the difference quotient $\dfrac{d(t + h) - d(t)}{h}$.

    Use the difference quotient to determine the average rate of speed on the following intervals for t:

    b. $[0, 2]$ (*Hint*: $t = 0$ and $h = 2$)

    c. $[2, 4]$ (*Hint*: $t = 2$ and $h = 2$)

    d. $[4, 6]$ (*Hint*: $t = 4$ and $h = 2$)

    e. $[6, 8]$ (*Hint*: $t = 6$ and $h = 2$)

120. A car accelerates from 0 to 60 mph (88 ft/sec) in 8.8 sec. The distance $d(t)$ (in ft) that the car travels t seconds after motion begins is given by $d(t) = 5t^2$, where $0 \le t \le 8.8$.

    a. Find the difference quotient $\dfrac{d(t + h) - d(t)}{h}$.

    Use the difference quotient to determine the average rate of speed on the following intervals for t:

    b. $[0, 2]$

    c. $[2, 4]$

    d. $[4, 6]$

    e. $[6, 8]$

121. The number of cigarettes, $N(x)$ (in billions), produced in the United States can be approximated by $N(x) = -0.28x^2 + 20.8x + 194$ where x is the number of years since 1940. (*Source*: Centers for Disease Control, www.cdc.gov)

    a. Determine the difference quotient. $\dfrac{N(x + h) - N(x)}{h}$

    b. Evaluate the difference quotient on the interval $[10, 20]$, and interpret its meaning in the context of this problem.

    c. Evaluate the difference quotient on the interval $[50, 60]$, and interpret its meaning in the context of this problem.

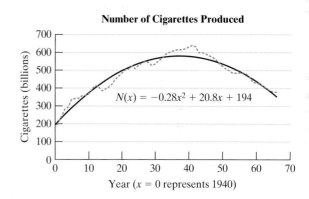

Number of Cigarettes Produced

$N(x) = -0.28x^2 + 20.8x + 194$

Cigarettes (billions) vs. Year ($x = 0$ represents 1940)

122. The amount of CO_2 emitted per year $A(x)$ (in tons) for a vehicle that burns x miles per gallon of gas, can be approximated by $A(x) = 0.0092x^2 - 0.805x + 21.9$. (*Source*: U.S. Department of Energy, http://energy.gov)

    a. Determine the difference quotient. $\dfrac{A(x + h) - A(x)}{h}$

    b. Evaluate the difference quotient on the interval $[20, 25]$, and interpret its meaning in the context of this problem.

    c. Evaluate the difference quotient on the interval $[35, 40]$, and interpret its meaning in the context of this problem.

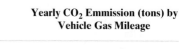

Yearly CO_2 Emmission (tons) by Vehicle Gas Mileage

$A(x) = 0.0092x^2 - 0.805x + 21.9$

CO_2 (tons) vs. Mileage (mpg)

123. Given $f(x) = \dfrac{1}{x - 2}$, evaluate $(f \circ f)(x)$ and write the domain in interval notation.

124. Given $h(x) = \dfrac{1}{x - 6}$, evaluate $(h \circ h)(x)$ and write the domain in interval notation.

125. Given $g(x) = \sqrt{x - 3}$, evaluate $(g \circ g)(x)$ and write the domain in interval notation.

126. Given $m(x) = \sqrt{x - 4}$, evaluate $(m \circ m)(x)$ and write the domain in interval notation.

For Exercises 127–130, refer to the functions f, g, and h and evaluate the given functions.

$$f(x) = 2x + 1 \qquad g(x) = x^2 \qquad h(x) = \sqrt[3]{x}$$

127. $(f \circ g \circ h)(x)$

128. $(g \circ f \circ h)(x)$

129. $(h \circ g \circ f)(x)$

130. $(g \circ h \circ f)(x)$

131. Given $f(x) = \sqrt[3]{4x^2 + 1}$, define functions m, n, h, and k such that $f(x) = (m \circ n \circ h \circ k)(x)$.

132. Given $f(x) = |{-2x^3 - 4}|$, define functions m, n, h, and k such that $f(x) = (m \circ n \circ h \circ k)(x)$.

CHAPTER 2   KEY CONCEPTS

SECTION 2.1 The Rectangular Coordinate System and Graphing Utilities	Reference
The **distance** between two points (x_1, y_1) and (x_2, y_2) in a rectangular coordinate system is given by $$d = \sqrt{(x_2 - x_1)^2 + (y_2 - y_1)^2}.$$	p. 197
The **midpoint** between the points is given by $M = \left(\dfrac{x_1 + x_2}{2}, \dfrac{y_1 + y_2}{2} \right).$	p. 198
• To find an x-intercept $(a, 0)$ of the graph of an equation, substitute 0 for y and solve for x. • To find a y-intercept $(0, b)$ of the graph of an equation, substitute 0 for x and solve for y.	p. 200

SECTION 2.2 Circles	Reference
The **standard form** of an equation of a circle with radius r and center (h, k) is $(x - h)^2 + (y - k)^2 = r^2$.	p. 209
An equation of a circle written in the form $x^2 + y^2 + Ax + By + C = 0$ is called the **general form** of an equation of a circle.	p. 210

SECTION 2.3 Functions and Relations	Reference
A set of ordered pairs (x, y) is called a **relation** in x and y. The set of x values is the **domain** of the relation, and the set of y values is the **range** of the relation.	p. 214
Given a relation in x and y, we say that **y is a function of x** if for each value of x in the domain, there is exactly one value of y in the range.	p. 215
The vertical line test tells us that the graph of a relation defines y as a function of x if no vertical line intersects the graph in more than one point.	p. 216
Given a function defined by $y = f(x)$, • The x-intercept(s) are the real solutions to $f(x) = 0$. • The y-intercept is given by $f(0)$.	p. 219
Given $y = f(x)$, the domain of f is the set of real numbers x that when substituted into the function produce a real number. This excludes • Values of x that make the denominator zero. • Values of x that make a radicand negative within an even-indexed root.	p. 220

SECTION 2.4 Linear Equations in Two Variables and Linear Functions	Reference
Let A, B, and C represent real numbers where A and B are not both zero. A **linear equation** in the variables x and y is an equation that can be written as $Ax + By = C$.	p. 228
The slope of a line passing through the distinct points (x_1, y_1) and (x_2, y_2) is given by $m = \dfrac{\Delta y}{\Delta x} = \dfrac{y_2 - y_1}{x_2 - x_1}$	p. 230
Given a line with slope m and y-intercept $(0, b)$, the **slope-intercept form** of the line is given by $y = mx + b$	p. 232
If f is defined on the interval $[x_1, x_2]$, then the **average rate of change** of f on the interval $[x_1, x_2]$ is the slope of the secant line containing $(x_1, f(x_1))$ and $(x_2, f(x_2))$ and is given by $$m = \frac{f(x_2) - f(x_1)}{x_2 - x_1}$$	p. 234
The x-coordinates of the points of intersection between the graphs of $y = f(x)$ and $y = g(x)$ are the solutions to the equation $f(x) = g(x)$.	p. 236

SECTION 2.5 Applications of Linear Equations and Modeling	Reference
The **point-slope formula** for a line is given by $y - y_1 = m(x - x_1)$ where m is the slope of the line and (x_1, y_1) is a point on the line.	p. 244
• If m_1 and m_2 represent the slopes of two nonvertical parallel lines, then $m_1 = m_2$. • If m_1 and m_2 represent the slopes of two nonvertical perpendicular lines, then $m_1 = -\dfrac{1}{m_2}$ or equivalently $m_1 m_2 = -1$.	p. 246
In many-day-to-day applications, two variables are related linearly.	p. 251
• A linear model can be made from two data points that represent the general trend of the data.	p. 252
• Alternatively, the least-squares regression line is a model that utilizes *all* observed data points.	

SECTION 2.6 Transformations of Graphs	Reference
Consider a function defined by $y = f(x)$. Let k, h, and a represent positive real numbers. The graphs of the following functions are related to $y = f(x)$ as follows.	pp. 263–264
• Vertical shift: $y = f(x) + k$ Shift upward $y = f(x) - k$ Shift downward • Horizontal shift: $y = f(x - h)$ Shift to the right $y = f(x + h)$ Shift to the left	

• Vertical stretch/shrink
 $y = af(x)$ Vertical stretch (if $a > 0$)
            Vertical shrink (if $0 < a < 1$)
 • Horizontal stretch/shrink
 $y = f(ax)$ Horizontal shrink (if $a > 0$)
            Horizontal stretch (if $0 < a < 1$)
	p. 266

• Reflection $y = -f(x)$ Reflection across the x-axis $y = f(-x)$ Reflection across the y-axis	p. 267

SECTION 2.7 Analyzing Graphs of Functions and Piecewise-Defined Functions	Reference
Consider the graph of an equation in x and y.	p. 275
• The graph of the equation is symmetric to the y-axis if substituting $-x$ for x results in an equivalent equation. • The graph of the equation is symmetric to the x-axis if substituting $-y$ for y results in an equivalent equation. • The graph of the equation is symmetric to the origin if substituting $-x$ for x and $-y$ for y results in an equivalent equation.	

• f is an **even function** if $f(-x) = f(x)$ for all x in the domain of f. • f is an **odd function** if $f(-x) = -f(x)$ for all x in the domain of f.	p. 277
To graph a piecewise-defined function, graph each individual function on its domain.	p. 279
The **greatest integer function**, denoted by the rule $f(x) = [\![x]\!]$ or $f(x) = \text{int}(x)$ or $f(x) = \text{floor}(x)$ defines $f(x)$ as the greatest integer less than or equal to x.	p. 281
Suppose that I is an interval contained within the domain of a function f. • f is **increasing** on I if $f(x_1) < f(x_2)$ for all $x_1 < x_2$ on I. • f is **decreasing** on I if $f(x_1) > f(x_2)$ for all $x_1 < x_2$ on I. • f is **constant** on I if $f(x_1) = f(x_2)$ for all x_1 and x_2 on I.	p. 284
• $f(a)$ is a **relative maximum** of f if there exists an open interval containing a such that $f(a) \geq f(x)$ for all x in the interval. • $f(b)$ is a **relative minimum** of f if there exists an open interval containing b such that $f(b) \leq f(x)$ for all x in the interval.	p. 285

SECTION 2.8 Algebra of Functions and Function Composition	Reference
Given functions f and g, the functions $f + g$, $f - g$, $f \cdot g$, and $\frac{f}{g}$ are defined by $(f + g)(x) = f(x) + g(x)$ $(f - g)(x) = f(x) - g(x)$ $(f \cdot g)(x) = f(x) \cdot g(x)$ $\left(\dfrac{f}{g}\right)(x) = \dfrac{f(x)}{g(x)}$ provided that $g(x) \neq 0$	p. 295
The **difference quotient** represents the average rate of change of a function f between two points $(x, f(x))$ and $(x + h, f(x + h))$. $$\dfrac{f(x + h) - f(x)}{h} \quad \text{Difference quotient}$$	p. 297
The **composition of f and g,** denoted $f \circ g$ is defined by $(f \circ g)(x) = f(g(x))$. The domain of $f \circ g$ is the set of real numbers x in the domain of g such that $g(x)$ is in the domain of f.	p. 299

Expanded Chapter Summary available at www.mhhe.com/millerca.

CHAPTER 2   Review Exercises

SECTION 2.1

For Exercises 1–2,

a. Find the exact distance between the points.

b. Find the midpoint of the line segment whose endpoints are the given points.

1. $(-1, 8)$ and $(4, -2)$

2. $\left(\sqrt{3}, -\sqrt{6}\right)$ and $\left(3\sqrt{3}, 4\sqrt{6}\right)$

3. Determine if the given ordered pair is a solution to the equation $4|x - 1| + y = 18$.

   a. $(-3, 2)$ b. $(5, -2)$

For Exercises 4–6, determine the x- and y-intercepts of the graph of the equation.

4. $-3y + 4x = 6$

5. $x = |y + 7| - 3$

6. $\dfrac{(x + 4)^2}{9} + \dfrac{y^2}{4} = 1$

7. Graph the equation by plotting points.
    $y = x^2 - 2x$

8. Find the length of the diagonal shown.

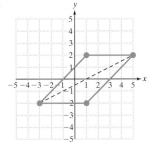

SECTION 2.2

For Exercises 9–10, determine the center and radius of the circle.

9. $(x - 4)^2 + (y + 3)^2 = 4$

10. $x^2 + \left(y - \dfrac{3}{2}\right)^2 = 17$

For Exercises 11–14, information about a circle is given.

a. Write an equation of the circle in standard form.

b. Graph the circle.

   11. Center: $(-3, 1)$; Radius: $\sqrt{11}$

   12. Center: $(0, 0)$; Radius: 4.2

   13. Endpoints of a diameter $(7, 5)$ and $(1, -3)$

   14. The center is in quadrant IV, the radius is 4, and the circle is tangent to both the x- and y-axes.

For Exercises 15–16, (a) write the equation of the circle in standard form and (b) identify the center and radius.

   15. $x^2 + y^2 + 10x - 2y + 17 = 0$

   16. $x^2 + y^2 - 8y + 3 = 0$

For Exercises 17–18, determine the solution set to the equation.

   17. $(x + 3)^2 + (y - 5)^2 = 0$

   18. $x^2 + y^2 + 6x - 4y + 15 = 0$

SECTION 2.3

   19. The table lists four Olympic athletes and the number of Olympic medals won by the athlete.

Athlete (x)	Number of Medals (y)
Dara Torres (swimming)	12
Carl Lewis (track and field)	10
Bonnie Blair (speed skating)	6
Michael Phelps (swimming)	16

   a. Write a set of ordered pairs (x, y) that defines the relation.

   b. Write the domain of the relation.

   c. Write the range of the relation.

   d. Determine if the relation defines y as a function of x.

For Exercises 20–24, determine if the relation defines y as a function of x.

20.

21.

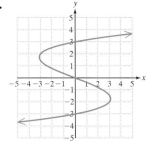

22. $x^2 + (y - 3)^2 = 4$ **23.** $x^2 + y - 3 = 4$

24. Evaluate $f(x) = -2x^2 + 4x$ for the values of x given.

   a. $f(0)$ **b.** $f(-1)$ **c.** $f(3)$

   d. $f(t)$ **e.** $f(x + 4)$

25. Given $f = \{(3, -1), (1, 5), (-2, 4), (0, 4)\}$,

   a. Determine $f(1)$.

   b. Determine $f(0)$.

   c. For what value(s) of x is $f(x) = -1$?

26. A department store marks up the price of a power drill by 32% of the price from the manufacturer. The price $P(x)$ (in \$) to a customer after a 6.5% sales tax is given by $P(x) = 1.065(x + 0.32x)$ where x is the cost of the drill from the manufacturer. Evaluate $P(189)$ and interpret the meaning in the context of this problem.

For Exercises 27–28, determine the x- and y-intercepts for the given function.

   27. $p(x) = |x - 3| - 1$

   28. $q(x) = -\sqrt{x} + 2$

For Exercises 29–30, determine the domain and range of the function.

29.

30.

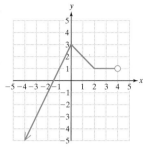

For Exercises 31–34, write the domain in interval notation.

31. $f(x) = \dfrac{x-2}{x-5}$

32. $g(x) = \dfrac{6}{|x|-3}$

33. $m(x) = 2x^2 - 4x + 1$

34. $n(x) = \dfrac{10}{\sqrt{2-x}}$

35. Use the graph of $y = f(x)$ to

   a. Determine $f(-2)$.

   b. Determine $f(3)$.

   c. Find all x for which
$f(x) = -1$.

   d. Find all x for which
$f(x) = -4$.

   e. Determine the
x-intercept(s).

   f. Determine the y-intercept.

   g. Determine the domain of f.

   h. Determine the range of f.

36. Write a relationship for a function whose $f(x)$ value is
4 less than two times the square of x.

SECTION 2.4

**For Exercises 37–40, graph the equation and determine the
x- and y-intercepts.**

37. $-2x + 4y = 8$

38. $-4x = 5y$

39. $y = 2$

40. $3x = 5$

**For Exercises 41–43, determine the slope of the line passing
through the given points.**

41. $(4, -2)$ and $(-12, -4)$

42. $\left(-3, \dfrac{2}{3}\right)$ and $\left(1, -\dfrac{4}{3}\right)$

43. $(a, f(a))$ and $(b, f(b))$

44. What is the slope of a line parallel to the x-axis?

45. What is the slope of a line with equation $x = -2$?

46. What is the slope of a line perpendicular to a line with
equation $y = 1$?

47. Suppose that $y = C(t)$ represents the average cost of a
gallon of milk in the United States t years since 1980.
What does $\dfrac{\Delta C}{\Delta t}$ represent?

48. Determine if the function is linear, constant, or neither.

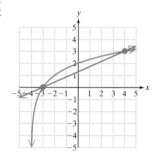

   a. $f(x) = -\dfrac{3}{2}x$ **b.** $g(x) = -\dfrac{3}{2x}$ **c.** $h(x) = -\dfrac{3}{2}$

**For Exercises 49–50, use slope-intercept form to write an
equation of the line that passes through the given point and
has the given slope. Then write the equation using function
notation where $y = f(x)$.**

49. $(1, -5)$ and $m = -\dfrac{2}{3}$ **50.** $\left(2, \dfrac{1}{4}\right)$ and $m = 0$

51. Find the slope of the secant
line pictured in red.

52. The function given by $y = f(x)$ shows the value of $8000
invested at 6% interest compounded continuously,
x years after the money was originally invested.

**Value of $8000 with Continuous
Compounding at 6%**

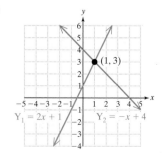

   a. Find the average amount earned per year between the
5th year and the 10th year.

   b. Find the average amount earned per year between the
20th year and the 25th year.

   c. Based on the answers from parts (a) and (b), does it
appear that the rate at which annual income increases
is increasing or decreasing with time?

53. Given $f(x) = -x^3 + 4$, determine the average rate of
change of the function on the given intervals.

   a. $[0, 2]$ **b.** $[2, 4]$

54. Use the graph to solve the
equation and inequalities.
Write the solutions to the
inequalities in interval
notation.

   a. $2x + 1 = -x + 4$

   b. $2x + 1 < -x + 4$

   c. $2x + 1 \geq -x + 4$

SECTION 2.5

55. If the slope of a line is $\frac{2}{3}$,

    a. Determine the slope of a line parallel to the given line.

    b. Determine the slope of a line perpendicular to the given line.

56. Given a line L_1 defined by L_1: $2x - 4y = 3$, determine if the equations given in parts (a)–(c) represent a line parallel to L_1, perpendicular to L_1, or neither parallel nor perpendicular to L_1.

    a. $12x + 6y = 6$ **b.** $3y = 1.5x - 5$

    c. $4x + 8y = 8$

For Exercises 57–63, write an equation of the line having the given conditions. Write the answer in slope-intercept form if possible.

57. Passes through $(-2, -7)$ and $m = 3$.

58. Passes through $(0, 5)$ and $m = -\dfrac{2}{5}$.

59. Passes through $(1.1, 5.3)$ and $(-0.9, 7.1)$.

60. Passes through $(5, -7)$ and the slope is undefined.

61. Passes through $(2, -6)$ and the line is parallel to the line defined by $2x - y = 4$.

62. Passes through $(-2, 3)$ and is perpendicular to the line defined by $5y = 2x$.

63. The line is perpendicular to the y-axis and the y-intercept is $(0, 7)$.

64. A car has a 15-gal tank for gasoline and gets 30 mpg on a highway while driving 60 mph. Suppose that the driver starts a trip with a full tank of gas and travels 450 mi on the highway at an average speed of 60 mph.

    a. Write a linear model representing the amount of gas $G(t)$ left in the tank t hours into a trip.

    b. Evaluate $G(4.5)$ and interpret the meaning in the context of this problem.

65. A dance studio has fixed monthly costs of $1500 that include rent, utilities, insurance, and advertising. The studio charges $60 for each private lesson, but has a variable cost for each lesson of $35 to pay the instructor.

    a. Write a linear cost function representing the cost to the studio $C(x)$ to hold x private lessons for a given month.

    b. Write a linear revenue function representing the revenue $R(x)$ for holding x private lessons for the month.

    c. Write a linear profit function representing the profit $P(x)$ for holding x private lessons for the month.

    d. Determine the number of private lessons that must be held for the studio to make a profit.

    e. If 82 private lessons are held during a given month, how much money will the studio make or lose?

66. The data in the table represent the enrollment y at a college x years since the year 2000.

Year (x)	Enrollment (y)
0	22,100
2	22,800
4	23,600
6	24,300
8	25,300
10	25,700
12	26,500

    a. Graph the data in a scatter plot.

    b. Use the points $(2, 22800)$ and $(12, 26500)$ to write a linear function that defines the enrollment $E(x)$ as a linear function of the number of years x since 2000.

    c. Interpret the meaning of the slope in the context of this problem.

    d. Use the model in part (b) to predict the enrollment for the year 2015 if this linear trend continues.

67. Refer to the data given in Exercise 66.

    a. Use a graphing utility to find the least-squares regression line. Round the slope to 1 decimal place and the y-intercept to the nearest whole unit.

    b. Use a graphing utility to graph the regression line and the observed data.

    c. In the event that the linear trend continues beyond the last observed data point, use the model from part (a) to predict the enrollment for the year 2015.

SECTION 2.6

68. Suppose that a, b, c, and d are real numbers. Given $y = a \cdot f[b(x - c)] + d$, explain the effect of a, b, c, and d on the graph of $y = f(x)$.

For Exercises 69–78, use translations to graph the given functions.

69. $f(x) = |x| - 4$ **70.** $g(x) = \sqrt{x} + 1$

71. $h(x) = (x - 4)^2$ **72.** $k(x) = \sqrt[3]{x} + 1$

73. $r(x) = \sqrt{x - 3} + 1$ **74.** $s(x) = (x + 2)^2 - 3$

75. $t(x) = -2|x|$ **76.** $v(x) = -\dfrac{1}{2}|x|$

77. $m(x) = \sqrt{-x} + 5$ **78.** $n(x) = \sqrt{-x} - 4$

For Exercises 79–84, use the graph of $y = f(x)$ to graph the given function.

79. $y = f(2x)$

80. $y = f(\frac{1}{2}x)$

81. $y = -f(x + 1) - 3$

82. $y = -f(x - 4) - 1$

83. $y = 2f(x - 3) + 1$

84. $y = \frac{1}{2}f(x + 2) - 3$

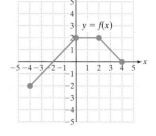

SECTION 2.7

For Exercises 85–88, determine if the graph of the equation is symmetric to the *y*-axis, *x*-axis, origin, or none of these.

85. $y = x^4 - 3$

86. $x = |y| + y^2$

87. $y = \dfrac{1}{3}x - 1$

88. $x^2 = y^2 + 1$

For Exercises 89–94, determine if the function is even, odd, or neither.

89. $f(x) = -4x^3 + x$

90. $g(x) = \sqrt[3]{x}$

91. $p(x) = \sqrt{4 - x^2}$

92. $q(x) = -|x|$

93. $k(x) = (x - 3)^2$

94. $m(x) = |x + 2|$

95. Evaluate the function for the given values of *x*.

$$f(x) = \begin{cases} -4x + 2 & \text{for } x < -1 \\ x^2 & \text{for } -1 \le x \le 2 \\ 5 & \text{for } x > 2 \end{cases}$$

    a. $f(-4)$ **b.** $f(-1)$ **c.** $f(3)$ **d.** $f(2)$

For Exercises 96–98, graph the function.

96. $f(x) = \begin{cases} -4x - 3 & \text{for } x < 0 \\ x^2 & \text{for } x \ge 0 \end{cases}$

97. $g(x) = \begin{cases} |x| & \text{for } x \le 2 \\ 2 & \text{for } x > 2 \end{cases}$

98. $h(x) = \begin{cases} -3 & \text{for } x < -2 \\ 1 & \text{for } -2 \le x < 0 \\ \sqrt{x} & \text{for } x \ge 0 \end{cases}$

99. Evaluate $f(x) = [\![x - 1]\!]$ for the given values of *x*.

    a. $f(-1.5)$ **b.** $f(-2)$ **c.** $f(0.1)$ **d.** $f(6.3)$

For Exercises 100–101, use interval notation to write the interval(s) over which *f* is

    a. Increasing.   **b.** Decreasing.   **c.** Constant.

100.

101.

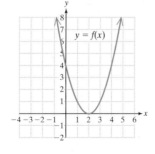

For Exercises 102–103, identify the location and value of any relative maxima or minima of the function.

102.

103.

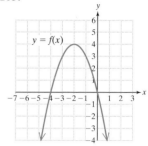

104. Write a rule for the graph of the function. Answers may vary.

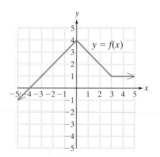

SECTION 2.8

For Exercises 105–109, evaluate the function for the given values of *x*.

$$f(x) = -3x \qquad g(x) = |x - 2| \qquad h(x) = \frac{1}{x + 1}$$

105. $(f - h)(2)$ **106.** $(g \cdot h)(3)$ **107.** $\left(\dfrac{g}{h}\right)(-5)$

108. $(f \circ g)(5)$ **109.** $(g \circ f)(5)$

110. Use the graphs of *f* and *g* to find the function values for the given values of *x*.

    a. $(f + g)(2)$

    b. $(g \cdot f)(-4)$

    c. $\left(\dfrac{g}{f}\right)(-3)$

    d. $f[g(4)]$

    e. $(g \circ f)(-4)$

    f. $(g \circ f)(5)$

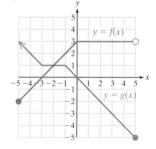

For Exercises 111–116, refer to the functions *m*, *n*, *p*, and *q*. Evaluate the function and write the domain in interval notation.

$$m(x) = -4x \qquad n(x) = x^2 - 4x$$
$$p(x) = \sqrt{x - 2} \qquad q(x) = \frac{1}{x - 5}$$

111. $(n - m)(x)$ **112.** $\left(\dfrac{p}{n}\right)(x)$ **113.** $\left(\dfrac{n}{p}\right)(x)$

114. $(m \cdot p)(x)$ **115.** $(q \circ n)(x)$ **116.** $(q \circ p)(x)$

For Exercises 117–118, evaluate the difference quotient,
$$\frac{f(x + h) - f(x)}{h}.$$

117. $f(x) = -6x - 5$ **118.** $f(x) = 3x^2 - 4x + 9$

For Exercises 119–120, find two functions, f and g such that $h(x) = (f \circ g)(x)$.

119. $h(x) = (x - 4)^2$ **120.** $h(x) = \dfrac{12}{x + 5}$

121. A car traveling 60 mph on the highway gets 28 mpg.

    a. Write a function that represents the distance $d(t)$ (in miles) that the car travels in t hours.

    b. Write a function that represents the number of gallons of gasoline $n(d)$ used for d miles traveled.

    c. Evaluate $(n \circ d)(t)$ and interpret the meaning in the context of this problem.

    d. Evaluate $(n \circ d)(7)$ and interpret the meaning in the context of this problem.

CHAPTER 2   Test

1. The endpoints of a diameter of a circle are $(-2, 3)$ and $(8, -5)$.

    a. Determine the center of the circle.

    b. Determine the radius of the circle.

    c. Write an equation of the circle in standard form.

2. Given $x = |y| - 4$,

    a. Determine the x- and y-intercepts of the graph of the equation.

    b. Does the equation define y as a function of x?

3. Given $x^2 + y^2 + 14x - 10y + 70 = 0$,

    a. Write the equation of the circle in standard form.

    b. Identify the center and radius.

For Exercises 4–5, determine if the relation defines y as a function of x.

4.

5.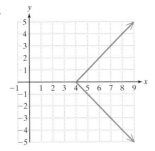

6. Given $f(x) = -2x^2 + 7x - 3$, find

    a. $f(-1)$.

    b. $f(x + h)$.

    c. The difference quotient: $\dfrac{f(x + h) - f(x)}{h}$.

    d. The x-intercepts of the graph of f.

    e. The y-intercept of the graph of f.

    f. The average rate of change of f on the interval $[1, 3]$.

7. Use the graph of $y = f(x)$ to estimate

    a. $f(0)$.

    b. $f(-4)$.

    c. The values of x for which $f(x) = 2$.

    d. The interval(s) over which f is increasing.

    e. The interval(s) over which f is decreasing.

    f. The value(s) of any relative minima.

    g. The value(s) of any relative maxima.

    h. The domain.

    i. The range.

    j. Whether f is even, odd, or neither.

For Exercises 8–9, write the domain in interval notation.

8. $f(w) = \dfrac{2w}{3w + 7}$

9. $f(c) = \sqrt{4 - c}$

10. Given $3x = -4y + 8$,

    a. Identify the slope.

    b. Identify the y-intercept.

    c. Graph the line.

    d. What is the slope of a line perpendicular to this line?

    e. What is the slope of a line parallel to this line?

11. Write an equation of the line passing through the point $(-2, 6)$ and perpendicular to the line defined by $x + 3y = 4$.

12. Use the graph to solve the equation and inequalities.

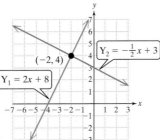

a. $2x + 8 = -\dfrac{1}{2}x + 3$

b. $2x + 8 < -\dfrac{1}{2}x + 3$

c. $2x + 8 \geq -\dfrac{1}{2}x + 3$

For Exercises 13–16, graph the equation.

13. $x^2 + \left(y + \dfrac{5}{2}\right)^2 = 9$

14. $f(x) = 2|x + 3|$

15. $g(x) = -\sqrt{x + 4} + 3$

16. $h(x) = \begin{cases} -x + 3 & \text{for } x < 1 \\ \sqrt{x - 1} & \text{for } x \geq 1 \end{cases}$

17. Determine if the graph of the equation is symmetric to the y-axis, x-axis, origin, or none of these.

$$x^2 + |y| = 8$$

For Exercises 18–19, determine if the function is even, odd, or neither.

18. $f(x) = x^3 - x$ **19.** $g(x) = x^4 + x^3 + x$

20. Evaluate the greatest integer function for the following values of x.

a. 4.27 **b.** −4.27

For Exercises 21–26, refer to the functions f, g, and h defined here.

$$f(x) = x - 4 \quad g(x) = \dfrac{1}{x - 3} \quad h(x) = \sqrt{x - 5}$$

21. Evaluate $(f - h)(6)$. **22.** Evaluate $(g \cdot h)(5)$.

23. Evaluate $(h \circ f)(1)$.

24. Evaluate $(f \cdot g)(x)$ and state the domain in interval notation.

25. Evaluate $\left(\dfrac{g}{f}\right)(x)$ and state the domain in interval notation.

26. Evaluate $(g \circ h)(x)$ and state the domain in interval notation.

27. Write two functions f and g such that $h(x) = (f \circ g)(x)$.

$$h(x) = \sqrt[3]{x - 7}$$

28. For f and g pictured, estimate the following.

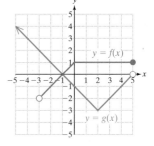

a. $(f + g)(3)$

b. $(f \cdot g)(0)$

c. $g(f(3))$

d. $(f \circ g)(2)$

e. The interval(s) over which $f(x)$ is increasing.

f. The interval(s) over which $g(x)$ is decreasing.

29. The graph shows U.S. expenditures (in $ millions) for national parks for selected years. In the graph, $x = 0$ represents the year 2000. (*Source:* National Park System, www.npca.org)

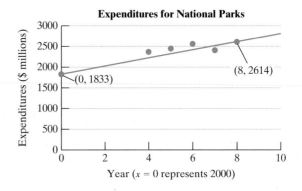

a. Use the points (0, 1833) and (8, 2614) to find a linear function representing the expenditures $E(x)$ for national parks, x years since 2000. Round the slope to the nearest whole unit.

b. If the linear trend continues, use the model from part (a) to estimate the expenditures for U.S. national parks for the year 2015. Round to the nearest million.

30. The data from Exercise 29 representing expenditures for U.S. national parks for selected years are given in the table.

Number of Years Since 2000	Expenditures ($ millions)
0	1833
4	2371
5	2451
6	2563
7	2412
8	2614

a. Use a graphing utility to find the least-squares regression line to fit the data. Round the slope to 1 decimal place and the y-intercept to the nearest whole unit.

b. Use the regression line to estimate the expenditures for national parks for the year 2015. Round to the nearest million.

CHAPTER 2   Cumulative Review Exercises

1. Use the graph of $y = f(x)$ to

a. Evaluate $f(2)$.

b. Find all x such that $f(x) = 0$.

c. Determine the domain of f.

d. Determine the range of f.

e. Determine the interval(s) over which f is increasing.

f. Determine the interval(s) over which f is decreasing.

g. Determine the intervals(s) over which f is constant.

h. Evaluate $(f \circ f)(-1)$.

2. Given the equation of the circle $x^2 + y^2 + 12x - 4y + 31 = 0$,

a. Write the equation in standard form.

b. Identify the center and radius.

For Exercises 3–7, refer to the functions f, g, and h defined here.

$$f(x) = -x^2 + 3x \qquad g(x) = \frac{1}{x} \qquad h(x) = \sqrt{x + 2}$$

3. Evaluate $(g \circ f)(x)$ and write the domain in interval notation.

4. Evaluate $(g \cdot h)(x)$ and write the domain in interval notation.

5. Evaluate the difference quotient. $\dfrac{f(x + h) - f(x)}{h}$

6. Find the average rate of change of f over the interval $[0, 3]$.

7. Determine the x- and y-intercepts of f.

For Exercises 8–9, graph the function.

8. $f(x) = -\sqrt{x + 3}$

9. $g(x) = \begin{cases} -4 & \text{for } x < -2 \\ 1 & \text{for } -2 \le x < 0 \\ x^2 + 1 & \text{for } x \ge 0 \end{cases}$

10. Write an equation of the line passing through the points $(8, -3)$ and $(-2, 1)$. Write the final answer in slope-intercept form.

11. Write an absolute value expression that represents the distance between the points x and 7 on the number line.

12. Factor. $2x^3 - 128$

For Exercises 13–17, solve the equation or inequality. Write the solutions to the inequalities in interval notation.

13. $-3t(t - 1) = 2t + 6$

14. $7 = |4x - 2| + 5$

15. $x^{2/5} - 3x^{1/5} + 2 = 0$

16. $|3a + 1| - 2 \le 9$

17. $3 \le -2x + 1 < 7$

For Exercises 18–20, perform the indicated operations and simplify.

18. $\dfrac{6}{\sqrt{15} + \sqrt{11}}$

19. $3c\sqrt{8c^2 d^3} + c^2\sqrt{50d^3} - 2d\sqrt{2c^4 d}$

20. $\dfrac{2u^{-1} - w^{-1}}{4u^{-2} - w^{-2}}$

Polynomial and Rational Functions

3

Chapter Outline

Meteorology and the study of weather have a strong basis in mathematics. The factors impacting weather are not constant and change over time. For example, during the summer months, hot ocean temperatures in the Atlantic Ocean often produce breeding grounds for hurricanes off the coast of Africa or in the Caribbean. To predict the path of a hurricane, meteorologists collect data from satellites, weather stations around the world, and weather buoys in the ocean. Piecing together the data requires a variety of techniques of mathematical modeling using powerful computers. In the end, scientists combine a series of simple curves to approximate weather patterns that closely fit complicated models.

In this chapter, we study polynomial and rational functions. Both types of functions represent simple curves that can be used for modeling in a wide range of applications, including predictions for the path of a hurricane.

<table>
<tr><td>

SECTION 3.1

</td><td>

Quadratic Functions and Applications

</td></tr>
</table>

OBJECTIVES

1. Graph a Quadratic Function Written in Vertex Form
2. Write $f(x) = ax^2 + bx + c$ $(a \neq 0)$ in Vertex Form
3. Find the Vertex of a Parabola by Using the Vertex Formula
4. Solve Applications Involving Quadratic Functions
5. Create Quadratic Models Using Regression

1. Graph a Quadratic Function Written in Vertex Form

In Chapter 2, we defined a function of the form $f(x) = mx + b$ ($m \neq 0$) as a linear function. The function defined by $f(x) = ax^2 + bx + c$ ($a \neq 0$) is called a *quadratic function*. Notice that a quadratic function has a leading term of second degree. We are already familiar with the graph of $f(x) = x^2$ (Figure 3-1). The graph is a parabola opening upward with vertex at the origin. Also note that the graph is symmetric with respect to the vertical line through the vertex called the **axis of symmetry**.

We can write $f(x) = ax^2 + bx + c$ ($a \neq 0$) in the form $f(x) = a(x - h)^2 + k$ by completing the square. Furthermore, from Section 2.6 we know that the graph of $f(x) = a(x - h)^2 + k$ is related to the graph of $y = x^2$ by a vertical shrink or stretch determined by a, a horizontal shift determined by h, and a vertical shift determined by k. Therefore, the graph of a quadratic function is a parabola with vertex at (h, k).

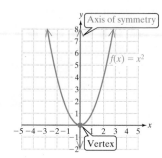

Figure 3-1

TIP A quadratic function is often used as a model for projectile motion. This is motion followed by an object influenced by an initial force and by the force of gravity.

Quadratic Function

A function defined by $f(x) = ax^2 + bx + c$ ($a \neq 0$) is called a **quadratic function.** By completing the square, $f(x)$ can be expressed in **vertex form** as $f(x) = a(x - h)^2 + k$.

- The graph of f is a parabola with vertex (h, k).
- If $a > 0$, the parabola opens upward, and the vertex is the minimum point. The minimum *value* of f is k.
- If $a < 0$, the parabola opens downward, and the vertex is the maximum point. The maximum *value* of f is k.
- The axis of symmetry is $x = h$. This is the vertical line that passes through the vertex.

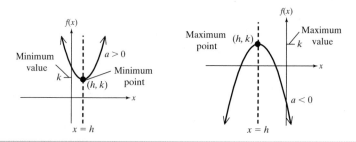

In Example 1, we analyze and graph a quadratic function by identifying the vertex, axis of symmetry, and x- and y-intercepts. From the graph, the minimum or maximum value of the function is readily apparent.

> **EXAMPLE 1**   **Analyzing and Graphing a Quadratic Function**
>
> Given $f(x) = -2(x - 1)^2 + 8$,
>
>   **a.** Determine whether the graph of the parabola opens upward or downward.
>   **b.** Identify the vertex.
>   **c.** Determine the x-intercept(s).
>   **d.** Determine the y-intercept.
>   **e.** Sketch the function.
>   **f.** Determine the axis of symmetry.
>   **g.** Determine the maximum or minimum value of f.
>   **h.** Determine the domain and range.
>
> **Solution:**
>
> **a.** $f(x) = -2(x - 1)^2 + 8$ The function is written as $f(x) = a(x - h)^2 + k$,
>   The parabola opens downward.   where $a = -2$, $h = 1$, and $k = 8$. Since $a < 0$,
>   the parabola opens downward.
>
> **b.** The vertex is $(1, 8)$.   The vertex is (h, k), which is $(1, 8)$.
>
> **c.** $f(x) = -2(x - 1)^2 + 8$
> $0 = -2(x - 1)^2 + 8$ To find the x-intercept(s), find all real solutions
> $-8 = -2(x - 1)^2$ to the equation $f(x) = 0$.
> $4 = (x - 1)^2$
> $\pm\sqrt{4} = x - 1$
> $1 \pm 2 = x$
> $x = 3$ or $x = -1$
>   The x-intercepts are $(3, 0)$ and $(-1, 0)$.
>
> **d.** $f(0) = -2(0 - 1)^2 + 8$ To find the y-intercept, evaluate $f(0)$.
> $= 6$
>   The y-intercept is $(0, 6)$.
>
> **e.** The graph of f is shown in Figure 3-2.
>
> **f.** The axis of symmetry is the vertical
>   line through the vertex: $x = 1$.
>
> **g.** The maximum value is 8.
>
> **h.** The domain is $(-\infty, \infty)$.
>   The range is $(-\infty, 8]$.

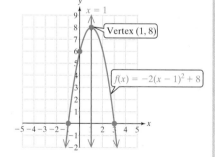

Figure 3-2

> **Skill Practice 1**   Repeat Example 1 with $g(x) = (x + 2)^2 - 1$.

Answers

1. a. Upward   **b.** $(-2, -1)$
  c. $(-3, 0)$ and $(-1, 0)$ **d.** $(0, 3)$
  e.

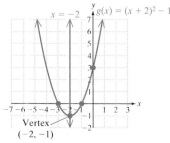

  f. $x = -2$
  g. The minimum value is -1.
  h. The domain is $(-\infty, \infty)$.
     The range is $[-1, \infty)$.

2. Write $f(x) = ax^2 + bx + c$ ($a \neq 0$) in Vertex Form

In Section 2.2, we learned how to complete the square to write an equation of a circle $x^2 + y^2 + Ax + By + C = 0$ in standard form $(x - h)^2 + (y - k)^2 = r^2$. We use the same process to write a quadratic function $f(x) = ax^2 + bx + c$ ($a \neq 0$) in vertex form $f(x) = a(x - h)^2 + k$. However, we will work on the right side of the equation only. This is demonstrated in Example 2.

EXAMPLE 2   **Writing a Quadratic Function in Vertex Form**

Given $f(x) = 3x^2 + 12x + 5$,

a. Write the function in vertex form: $f(x) = a(x - h)^2 + k$.

b. Identify the vertex.

c. Identify the x-intercept(s).

d. Identify the y-intercept.

e. Sketch the function.

f. Determine the axis of symmetry.

g. Determine the minimum or maximum value of f.

h. State the domain and range.

Solution:

a. $f(x) = 3x^2 + 12x + 5$ Factor out the leading coefficient of the x^2 term from the two terms containing x.

$f(x) = 3(x^2 + 4x \qquad) + 5$ The leading term within parentheses now has a coefficient of 1.

$f(x) = 3(x^2 + 4x + 4 - 4) + 5$ Complete the square within parentheses. Add and subtract $\left[\frac{1}{2}(4)\right]^2 = 4$ within parentheses.

$f(x) = 3(x^2 + 4x + 4) + 3(-4) + 5$ Remove -4 from within parentheses, along with a factor of 3.

$f(x) = 3(x + 2)^2 - 7$ (vertex form)

b. The vertex is $(-2, -7)$.

c. $f(x) = 3x^2 + 12x + 5$ To find the x-intercept(s), find the real solutions to the equation $f(x) = 0$.

$0 = 3x^2 + 12x + 5$

$x = \dfrac{-12 \pm \sqrt{(12)^2 - 4(3)(5)}}{2(3)}$ The right side is not factorable. Apply the quadratic formula.

$= \dfrac{-12 \pm \sqrt{84}}{6}$ The x-intercepts are $\left(\dfrac{-6 + \sqrt{21}}{3}, 0\right)$

$= \dfrac{-12 \pm 2\sqrt{21}}{6}$ and $\left(\dfrac{-6 - \sqrt{21}}{3}, 0\right)$ or approximately $(-0.47, 0)$ and $(-3.53, 0)$.

$x = \dfrac{-6 \pm \sqrt{21}}{3}$ $\longrightarrow x \approx -0.47$
                $\longrightarrow x \approx -3.53$

d. $f(0) = 3(0)^2 + 12(0) + 5$ To find the y-intercept, evaluate $f(0)$.

$= 5$ The y-intercept is $(0, 5)$.

e. The graph of f is shown in Figure 3-3.

f. The axis of symmetry is $x = -2$.

g. The minimum value is -7.

h. The domain is $(-\infty, \infty)$.

The range is $[-7, \infty)$.

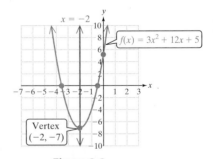

Figure 3-3

Skill Practice 2   Repeat Example 2 with $f(x) = 3x^2 - 6x + 1$.

Answers

2. a. $f(x) = 3(x - 1)^2 - 2$ **b.** $(1, -2)$

c. $\left(\dfrac{3 + \sqrt{6}}{3}, 0\right)$ and $\left(\dfrac{3 - \sqrt{6}}{3}, 0\right)$

d. $(0, 1)$

e.

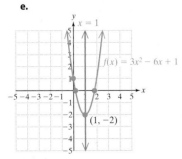

f. $x = 1$

g. The minimum value is -2.

h. The domain is $(-\infty, \infty)$.
The range is $[-2, \infty)$.

3. Find the Vertex of a Parabola by Using the Vertex Formula

Completing the square and writing a quadratic function in the form $f(x) = a(x - h)^2 + k$ is one method to find the vertex of a parabola. Another method is to use the vertex formula. The vertex formula can be derived by completing the square on $f(x) = ax^2 + bx + c$.

$f(x) = ax^2 + bx + c \ (a \neq 0)$

$= a\left(x^2 + \dfrac{b}{a}x + \dfrac{b^2}{4a^2} - \dfrac{b^2}{4a^2}\right) + c$

Factor out a from the x terms, and complete the square within parentheses.

$$\left[\dfrac{1}{2}\left(\dfrac{b}{a}\right)\right]^2 = \dfrac{b^2}{4a^2}$$

$= a\left(x^2 + \dfrac{b}{a}x + \dfrac{b^2}{4a^2}\right) + a\left(-\dfrac{b^2}{4a^2}\right) + c$

Remove the term $-\dfrac{b^2}{4a^2}$ from within parentheses along with a factor of a.

$= a\left(x + \dfrac{b}{2a}\right)^2 - \dfrac{b^2}{4a} + c$

Factor the trinomial.

$= a\left(x + \dfrac{b}{2a}\right)^2 + \dfrac{4ac - b^2}{4a}$

Obtain a common denominator and add the terms outside parentheses.

$= a\left[x - \left(\dfrac{-b}{2a}\right)\right]^2 + \dfrac{4ac - b^2}{4a}$

$f(x)$ is now written in vertex form.

$\underset{\downarrow}{\ } \qquad \underset{\downarrow}{\ }$

$f(x) = a(x - h)^2 \quad + \quad k$

$h = \dfrac{-b}{2a}$ and $k = \dfrac{4ac - b^2}{4a}$

The vertex is $\left(\dfrac{-b}{2a}, \dfrac{4ac - b^2}{4a}\right)$.

The y-coordinate of the vertex is given by $\dfrac{4ac - b^2}{4a}$ and is often hard to remember. Therefore, it is usually easier to evaluate the x-coordinate first from $\dfrac{-b}{2a}$, and then evaluate $f\left(\dfrac{-b}{2a}\right)$.

Vertex Formula to Find the Vertex of a Parabola

For $f(x) = ax^2 + bx + c \ (a \neq 0)$, the vertex is given by $\left(\dfrac{-b}{2a}, f\left(\dfrac{-b}{2a}\right)\right)$.

EXAMPLE 3   Using the Vertex Formula

Given $f(x) = -x^2 + 4x - 5$,

a. State whether the graph of the parabola opens upward or downward.

b. Determine the vertex of the parabola by using the vertex formula.

c. Determine the x-intercept(s).

d. Determine the y-intercept.

e. Sketch the graph.

f. Determine the axis of symmetry.

g. Determine the minimum or maximum value of f.

h. State the domain and range.

Solution:

a. $f(x) = -x^2 + 4x - 5$

The parabola opens downward.

The function is written as $f(x) = ax^2 + bx + c$ where $a = -1$. Since $a < 0$, the parabola opens downward.

b. x-coordinate: $\dfrac{-b}{2a} = \dfrac{-(4)}{2(-1)} = 2$

y-coordinate: $f(2) = -(2)^2 + 4(2) - 5$
$$= -1$$

The vertex is $(2, -1)$.

c. Since the vertex of the parabola is below the x-axis and the parabola opens downward, the parabola cannot cross or touch the x-axis.

Therefore, there are no x-intercepts.

Solving the equation $f(x) = 0$ to find the x-intercepts results in imaginary solutions:

$$0 = -x^2 + 4x - 5$$

$$x = \dfrac{-(4) \pm \sqrt{(4)^2 - 4(-1)(-5)}}{2(-1)}$$

$$x = 2 \pm i$$

d. To find the y-intercept, evaluate $f(0)$.

$f(0) = -(0)^2 + 4(0) - 5 = -5$

The y-intercept is $(0, -5)$.

e. The graph of f is shown in Figure 3-4.

f. The axis of symmetry is $x = 2$.

g. The maximum value of f is -1.

h. The domain is $(-\infty, \infty)$.

The range is $(-\infty, -1]$.

Figure 3-4

Skill Practice 3 Repeat Example 3 with $f(x) = -x^2 - 4x - 7$.

4. Solve Applications Involving Quadratic Functions

Quadratic functions can be used in a variety of applications in which a variable is optimized. That is, the vertex of a parabola gives the maximum or minimum value of the dependent variable. We show three such applications in Examples 4–6.

EXAMPLE 4 Using a Quadratic Function for Projectile Motion

A stone is thrown from a 100-m mesa at an initial velocity of 20 m/sec at an angle of 30° from the horizontal. The height of the stone can be modeled by $h(t) = -4.9t^2 + 10t + 100$, where $h(t)$ is the height in meters and t is the time in seconds after the stone is released.

a. Determine the time at which the stone will be at its maximum height. Round to 2 decimal places.

b. Determine the maximum height. Round to the nearest meter.

c. Determine the time at which the stone will hit the ground.

Answers

3. a. Downward   **b.** $(-2, -3)$
   c. No x-intercepts   **d.** $(0, -7)$
   e.

f. $x = -2$
g. The maximum value is -3.
h. The domain is $(-\infty, \infty)$.
   The range is $(-\infty, -3]$.

Solution:

a. The time at which the stone will be at its maximum height is the *t*-coordinate of the vertex.

$$t = \frac{-b}{2a} = \frac{-10}{2(-4.9)} \approx 1.02$$

The stone will be at its maximum height approximately 1.02 sec after release.

b. The maximum height is the value of $h(t)$ at the vertex.

$$h(1.02) = -4.9(1.02)^2 + 10(1.02) + 100$$
$$\approx 105 \text{ The maximum height is 105 m.}$$

c. The stone will hit the ground when $h(t) = 0$.

$$h(t) = -4.9t^2 + 10t + 100$$
$$0 = -4.9t^2 + 10t + 100$$
$$t = \frac{-10 \pm \sqrt{(10)^2 - 4(-4.9)(100)}}{2(-4.9)}$$

$t \approx 5.65$ or $t \approx -3.61$ Reject the negative solution. The stone will hit the ground in approximately 5.65 sec.

Given $h(t) = -4.9t^2 + 10t + 100$, the coefficients are $a = -4.9$, $b = 10$, and $c = 100$.

The vertex is given by:
$$\left(\frac{-b}{2a}, h\left(\frac{-b}{2a} \right) \right).$$

Skill Practice 4   A quarterback throws a football with an initial velocity of 72 ft/sec at an angle of 25°. The height of the ball can be modeled by $h(t) = -16t^2 + 30.4t + 5$ where $h(t)$ is the height (in ft) and t is the time in seconds after release.

a. Determine the time at which the ball will be at its maximum height.
b. Determine the maximum height of the ball.
c. Determine the amount of time required for the ball to reach the receiver's hands if the receiver catches the ball at a point 3 ft off the ground.

In Example 5, we present a type of application called an optimization problem. The goal is to maximize or minimize the value of the dependent variable by finding an optimal value of the independent variable.

EXAMPLE 5   Applying a Quadratic Function to Geometry

A parking area is to be constructed adjacent to a road. The developer has purchased 340 ft of fencing. Determine dimensions for the parking lot that would maximize the area. Then find the maximum area.

Answers
4. a. 0.95 sec   **b.** 19.44 ft
   c. Approximately 1.96 sec

Solution:

Let x represent the width of the parking area.

Read the problem carefully, draw a representative diagram, and label the unknowns.

Let y represent the length.

Let A represent the area.

$A = xy$

We need to find the values of x and y that would maximize area.

$2x + y = 340$

To write the area as a function of one variable only, we need an equation that relates x and y. We know that the three sides of the parking area are limited by a fixed amount of fencing, 340 ft.

Solve for y.

The equation $2x + y = 340$ is called a **constraint equation.** This equation gives an implied restriction on x and y due to the limited amount of fencing.

$y = 340 - 2x$

Solve the constraint equation, $2x + y = 340$ for either x or y. In this case, we have solved for y.

$A(x) = x(340 - 2x)$

Substitute $340 - 2x$ for y in the equation $A = xy$.

$A(x) = -2x^2 + 340x$

Function A is a quadratic function with a negative leading coefficient. The graph of the parabola opens downward, so the vertex is the maximum point on the function.

x-coordinate of vertex:

$$x = \frac{-b}{2a} = \frac{-340}{2(-2)} = 85$$

$y = 340 - 2(85) = 170$

The x-coordinate of the vertex $\frac{-b}{2a}$ is the value of x that will maximize the area.

The second dimension of the parking lot can be determined from the constraint equation.

The values of x and y that would maximize the area are $x = 85$ ft and $y = 170$ ft.

$A(85) = -2(85)^2 + 340(85) = 14{,}450$

The value of the function at $x = 85$ gives the maximum area.

The maximum area is 14,450 ft^2.

> **Avoiding Mistakes**
>
> To check, verify that the value $A(85)$ is the same as the product of length and width, xy:
>
> $A(85) = 14{,}450 \text{ ft}^2$
>
> $xy = (85 \text{ ft})(170 \text{ ft})$
>
> $ = 14{,}450 \text{ ft}^2 \checkmark$

Skill Practice 5 A farmer has 200 ft of fencing and wants to build three adjacent rectangular corrals. Determine the dimensions that should be used to maximize the area, and find the area of each individual corral.

TECHNOLOGY CONNECTIONS

Using a Table to Verify Maxima or Minima

A graphing calculator or spreadsheet can be used to support an answer to an optimization problem. From Example 5, we have the area of a rectangle represented as:

$A = xy$, where $y = 340 - 2x$.

In the calculator enter:

$Y_1 = 340 - 2x$ (Represents y in terms of x.)

$Y_2 = x(340 - 2x)$ (Represents the area.)

```
Plot1 Plot2 Plot3
\Y1 ▤340-2X
\Y2 ▤X*(340-2X)
\Y3  TABLE SETUP
\Y4   TblStart=70
\Y5   ΔTbl=5
\Y6  Indpnt:  Auto  Ask
\Y7  Depend:  Auto  Ask
```

Answer

5. The dimensions should be $x = 25$ ft and $y = 50$ ft. The area of each individual corral is $\frac{1250}{3} = 416.\overline{6}$ ft^2.

Then create a table of values beginning at $x = 70$ with $\Delta \text{Tbl} = 5$.

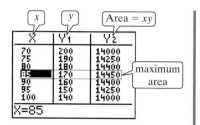

	A	B	C	D	E
1	x	y (340 - 2x)	Area x(340 - 2x)		
2	70	200	14000		=a2*b2
3	75	190	14250		=340 - 2*a2
4	80	180	14400		
5	85	170	14450		
6	90	160	14400		
7	95	150	14250		
8	100	140	14000		

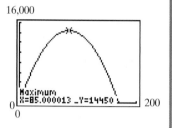

maximum area

The maximum area occurs when x is selected as 85 ft. The value of the maximum area is 14,450 ft^2.

The maximum value of the graph of $A(x) = x(340 - x)$ can also be approximated by using the Maximum feature on a calculator.

5. Create Quadratic Models Using Regression

In Section 2.5, we introduced linear regression. A regression line is a linear model based on all observed data points. In a similar fashion, we can create a quadratic function using regression. For example, suppose that a scientist growing bacteria measures the population of bacteria as a function of time. A scatter plot reveals that the data follow a curve that is approximately parabolic (Figure 3-5). In Example 6, we use a graphing calculator to find a quadratic function that models the population of the bacteria as a function of time.

Population of Bacteria vs. Time

Figure 3-5

EXAMPLE 6   Creating a Quadratic Function Using Regression

The data in the table represent the population of bacteria $P(t)$ (in 1000s) versus the number of hours t since the culture was started.

a. Use regression to find a quadratic function to model the data. Round the coefficients to 3 decimal places.

b. Use the model to determine the time at which the population is the greatest. Round to the nearest hour.

c. What is the maximum population? Round to the nearest hundred.

Time (hr) t	Population (1000s) $P(t)$
5	37.7
10	60.9
15	85.3
20	96.3
25	98.6
30	92.4
35	77.5
40	54.1

Solution:

   a. From the graph in Figure 3-5, it appears that the data follow a parabolic curve. Therefore, a quadratic model would be reasonable.

Enter the data into two lists.

Select the quadratic regression option.

Select Calculate.

The regression model is $P(t) = -0.173t^2 + 8.312t - 1.386$

   b. From the graph, the time when the population is greatest is the t-coordinate of the vertex.

$$t = \frac{-b}{2a} = \frac{-(8.312)}{2(-0.173)} \approx 24$$

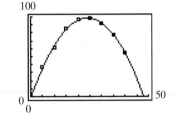

The population is greatest 24 hr after the culture is started.

   c. The maximum population of the bacteria is the $P(t)$ value at the vertex.

$$P(24) = -0.173(24)^2 + 8.312(24) - 1.386$$

$$\approx 98.5 \text{ The maximum number of bacteria is approximately } 98{,}500.$$

Skill Practice 6   The funding $f(t)$ (in $ millions) for a drug rehabilitation center is given in the table for selected years t.

t	0	3	6	9	12	15
$f(t)$	3.5	2.2	2.1	3	4.9	8

   a. Use regression to find a quadratic function to model the data.

   b. During what year is the funding the least? Round to the nearest year.

   c. What is the minimum yearly amount of funding received? Round to the nearest million.

Answers

6. a. $f(t) = 0.060t^2 - 0.593t + 3.486$

   b. Year 5   **c.** $2 million

SECTION 3.1   Practice Exercises

Concept Connections

   1. A function defined by $f(x) = ax^2 + bx + c$ $(a \neq 0)$ is called a _____ function.

   2. The vertical line drawn through the vertex of a quadratic function is called the _____ of symmetry.

   3. A quadratic function given by $f(x) = a(x - h)^2 + k$ is said to be written in _____ form.

   4. Given $f(x) = a(x - h)^2 + k$ $(a \neq 0)$, the vertex of the parabola is the point _____.

   5. Given $f(x) = a(x - h)^2 + k$, if $a < 0$, then the parabola opens _____.

   6. The graph of $f(x) = a(x - h)^2 + k$ $(a \neq 0)$ is a parabola and the axis of symmetry is the line given by $x =$ _____.

   7. Given $f(x) = a(x - h)^2 + k$, if $a > 0$, then the minimum value of f is _____.

   8. Given $f(x) = a(x - h)^2 + k$, if $a < 0$, then the maximum of f is _____.

Objective 1: Graph a Quadratic Function Written in Vertex Form

For Exercises 9–16,

a. Determine whether the graph of the parabola opens upward or downward.

b. Identify the vertex.

c. Determine the x-intercept(s).

d. Determine the y-intercept.

e. Sketch the function.

f. Determine the axis of symmetry.

g. Determine the minimum or maximum value of the function.

h. Determine the domain and range. (**See Example 1**)

9. $f(x) = -(x - 4)^2 + 1$

10. $g(x) = -(x + 2)^2 + 4$

11. $h(x) = 2(x + 1)^2 - 8$

12. $k(x) = 2(x - 3)^2 - 2$

13. $m(x) = 3(x - 1)^2$

14. $n(x) = \frac{1}{2}(x + 2)^2$

15. $p(x) = -\frac{1}{5}(x + 4)^2 + 1$

16. $q(x) = -\frac{1}{3}(x - 1)^2 + 1$

Objective 2: Write $f(x) = ax^2 + bx + c$ $(a \neq 0)$ in Vertex Form

For Exercises 17–22,

a. Write the function in vertex form.

b. Identify the vertex.

c. Identify the x-intercepts.

d. Identify the y-intercept.

e. Sketch the function.

f. Determine the axis of symmetry.

g. Determine the minimum or maximum value of the function.

h. State the domain and range. (**See Example 2**)

17. $f(x) = x^2 + 6x + 5$

18. $g(x) = x^2 + 8x + 7$

19. $p(x) = 3x^2 - 12x - 7$

20. $q(x) = 2x^2 - 4x - 3$

21. $c(x) = -2x^2 - 10x + 4$

22. $d(x) = -3x^2 - 9x + 8$

Objective 3: Find the Vertex of a Parabola by Using the Vertex Formula

For Exercises 23–26, find the vertex of the parabola by applying the vertex formula.

23. $f(x) = 3x^2 - 42x - 91$

24. $g(x) = 4x^2 - 64x + 107$

25. $k(a) = -\frac{1}{3}a^2 + 6a + 1$

26. $j(t) = -\frac{1}{4}t^2 + 10t - 5$

For Exercises 27–30,

a. State whether the graph of the parabola opens upward or downward.

b. Determine the vertex of the parabola.

c. Determine the x-intercept(s).

d. Determine the y-intercept.

e. Sketch the graph.

f. Determine the axis of symmetry.

g. Determine the minimum or maximum value of the function.

h. State the domain and range. (**See Example 3**)

27. $g(x) = -x^2 + 2x - 4$

28. $h(x) = -x^2 - 6x - 10$

29. $f(x) = 5x^2 - 15x + 3$

30. $k(x) = 2x^2 - 10x - 5$

Objective 4: Solve Applications Involving Quadratic Functions

31. The population $P(t)$ of a culture of the bacterium *Pseudomonas aeruginosa* is given by $P(t) = -1718t^2 + 82,000t + 10,000$, where t is the time in hours since the culture was started. (**See Example 4**)

   a. Determine the time at which the population is at a maximum. Round to the nearest hour.

   b. Determine the maximum population. Round to the nearest thousand.

32. The gas mileage $m(x)$ (in mpg) for a certain vehicle can be approximated by $m(x) = -0.028x^2 + 2.688x - 35.012$, where x is the speed of the vehicle in mph.

   a. Determine the speed at which the car gets its maximum gas mileage.

   b. Determine the maximum gas mileage.

33. A professional skateboarder launches into the air from the rim of a half pipe at an initial velocity of 5.4 m/sec. His path is straight upward and his center of mass can be modeled by $h(t) = -4.9t^2 + 5.4t + 3$, where $h(t)$ is the height in meters from the bottom of the half pipe, and t is the time in seconds after he leaves the rim.

   a. Determine the time at which he reaches his maximum height. Round to 2 decimal places.

   b. What is his maximum height? Round to the nearest tenth of a meter.

34. A fireworks mortar is launched straight upward from a pool deck platform 3 m off the ground at an initial velocity of 42 m/sec. The height of the mortar can be modeled by $h(t) = -4.9t^2 + 42t + 3$, where $h(t)$ is the height in meters and t is the time in seconds after launch.

   a. Determine the time at which the mortar is at its maximum height. Round to 2 decimal places.

   b. What is the maximum height? Round to the nearest meter.

35. A firefighter holds a hose 3 m off the ground and directs a stream of water toward a burning building. The water leaves the hose at an initial speed of 16 m/sec at an angle of 30°. The height of the water can be approximated by $h(x) = -0.026x^2 + 0.576x + 3$, where $h(x)$ is the height of the water in meters at a point x meters horizontally from the firefighter to the building.

   a. Determine the horizontal distance from the firefighter at which the maximum height of the water occurs. Round to 1 decimal place.

   b. What is the maximum height of the water? Round to 1 decimal place.

   c. The flow of water hits the house on the downward branch of the parabola at a height of 6 m. How far is the firefighter from the house? Round to the nearest meter.

36. A long jumper leaves the ground at an angle of 20° above the horizontal, at a speed of 11 m/sec. The height of the jumper can be modeled by $h(x) = -0.046x^2 + 0.364x$, where h is the jumper's height in meters and x is the horizontal distance from the point of launch.

   a. At what horizontal distance from the point of launch does the maximum height occur? Round to 2 decimal places.

   b. What is the maximum height of the long jumper? Round to 2 decimal places.

   c. What is the length of the jump? Round to 1 decimal place.

37. The sum of two positive numbers is 24. What two numbers will maximize the product? (**See Example 5**)

38. The sum of two positive numbers is 1. What two numbers will maximize the product?

39. The difference of two numbers is 10. What two numbers will minimize the product?

40. The difference of two numbers is 30. What two numbers will minimize the product?

41. Suppose that a family wants to fence in an area of their yard for a vegetable garden to keep out deer. One side is already fenced from the neighbor's property. (**See Example 5**)

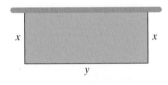

   a. If the family has enough money to buy 160 ft of fencing, what dimensions would produce the maximum area for the garden?

   b. What is the maximum area?

42. Two chicken coops are to be built adjacent to one another from 120 ft of fencing.

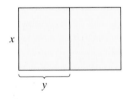

   a. What dimensions should be used to maximize the area of an individual coop?

   b. What is the maximum area of an individual coop?

43. A trough at the end of a gutter spout is meant to direct water away from a house. The homeowner makes the trough from a rectangular piece of aluminum that is 20 in. long and 12 in. wide. He makes a fold along the two long sides a distance of x inches from the edge.

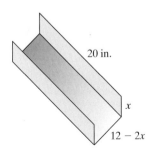

   a. Write a function to represent the volume in terms of x.

   b. What value of x will maximize the volume of water that can be carried by the gutter?

   c. What is the maximum volume?

44. A frame of uniform depth for a shadow box is to be made from a 36-in. piece of wood.

36 in.

x

y

a. Write a function to represent the display area in terms of x.

b. What dimensions should be used to maximize the display area?

c. What is the maximum area?

Objective 5: Create Quadratic Models Using Regression

45. *Tetanus bacillus* bacteria are cultured to produce tetanus toxin used in an inactive form for the tetanus vaccine. The amount of toxin produced per batch increases with time and then decreases as the culture becomes unstable. The variable t is the time in hours after the culture has started, and $y(t)$ is the yield of toxin in grams. (**See Example 6**)

t	8	16	24	32	40	48
$y(t)$	0.60	1.12	1.60	1.78	1.90	2.00

t	56	64	72	80	88	96
$y(t)$	1.94	1.80	1.48	1.30	0.66	0.10

a. Use regression to find a quadratic function to model the data.

b. At what time is the yield the greatest? Round to the nearest hour.

c. What is the maximum yield? Round to the nearest gram.

47. Fluid runs through a drainage pipe with a 10-cm radius and a length of 30 m (3000 cm). The velocity of the fluid gradually decreases from the center of the pipe toward the edges as a result of friction with the walls of the pipe. For the data shown, $v(x)$ is the velocity of the fluid (in cm/sec) and x represents the distance (in cm) from the center of the pipe toward the edge.

x	0	1	2	3	4
$v(x)$	195.6	195.2	194.2	193.0	191.5

x	5	6	7	8	9
$v(x)$	189.8	188.0	185.5	183.0	180.0

a. The pipe is 30 m long (3000 cm). Determine how long it will take fluid to run the length of the pipe through the center of the pipe. Round to 1 decimal place.

b. Determine how long it will take fluid at a point 9 cm from the center of the pipe to run the length of the pipe. Round to 1 decimal place.

c. Use regression to find a quadratic function to model the data.

d. Use the model from part (c) to predict the velocity of the fluid at a distance 5.5 cm from the center of the pipe. Round to 1 decimal place.

46. Gas mileage is tested for a car under different driving conditions. At lower speeds, the car is driven in stop and go traffic. At higher speeds, the car must overcome more wind resistance. The variable x given in the table represents the speed (in mph) for a compact car, and $m(x)$ represents the gas mileage (in mpg).

x	25	30	35	40	45
$m(x)$	22.7	25.1	27.9	30.8	31.9

x	50	55	60	65
$m(x)$	30.9	28.4	24.2	21.9

a. Use regression to find a quadratic function to model the data.

b. At what speed is the gas mileage the greatest? Round to the nearest mile per hour.

c. What is the maximum gas mileage? Round to the nearest mile per gallon.

48. The braking distance required for a car to stop depends on numerous variables such as the speed of the car, the weight of the car, reaction time of the driver, and the coefficient of friction between the tires and the road. For a certain vehicle on one stretch of highway, the braking distances $d(s)$ (in ft) are given for several different speeds s (in mph).

s	30	35	40	45	50
$d(s)$	109	134	162	191	223

s	55	60	65	70	75
$d(s)$	256	291	328	368	409

a. Use regression to find a quadratic function to model the data.

b. Use the model from part (a) to predict the stopping distance for the car if it is traveling 62 mph before the brakes are applied. Round to the nearest foot.

c. Suppose that the car is traveling 53 mph before the brakes are applied. If a deer is standing in the road at a distance of 245 ft from the point where the brakes are applied, would the car hit the deer?

Mixed Exercises

For Exercises 49–52, given a quadratic function defined by $f(x) = ax^2 + bx + c$ $(a \neq 0)$, answer true or false.

49. The graph of f can have two y-intercepts.

50. The graph of f can have two x-intercepts.

51. If $a < 0$, then the vertex of the parabola is the maximum point on the graph of f.

52. The axis of symmetry of the graph of f is the line defined by $y = c$.

For Exercises 53–58, determine the number of x-intercepts of the graph of $f(x) = ax^2 + bx + c$ $(a \neq 0)$, based on the discriminant of the related equation $f(x) = 0$. (*Hint*: Recall that the discriminant is $b^2 - 4ac$.)

53. $f(x) = 4x^2 + 12x + 9$

54. $f(x) = 25x^2 - 20x + 4$

55. $f(x) = -x^2 - 5x + 8$

56. $f(x) = -3x^2 + 4x + 9$

57. $f(x) = -3x^2 + 6x - 11$

58. $f(x) = -2x^2 + 5x - 10$

For Exercises 59–66, given a quadratic function defined by $f(x) = a(x - h)^2 + k$ $(a \neq 0)$, match the graph with the function based on the conditions given.

59. $a > 0, h < 0, k > 0$

60. $a > 0, h < 0, k < 0$

61. $a < 0, h < 0, k < 0$

62. $a < 0, h < 0, k > 0$

63. $a > 0$, axis of symmetry $x = 2, k < 0$

64. $a < 0$, axis of symmetry $x = 2, k > 0$

65. $a < 0, h = 2$, maximum value equals -2

66. $a > 0, h = 2$, minimum value equals 2

a.

b.

c.

d.

e.

f.

g.

h.

Write About It

67. Explain why a parabola opening upward has a minimum value but no maximum value. Use the graph of $f(x) = x^2$ to explain.

68. Explain why a quadratic function whose graph opens downward with vertex $(4, -3)$ has no x-intercept.

69. Explain why a quadratic function given by $f(x) = ax^2 + bx + c$ cannot have two y-intercepts.

70. Explain how to use the discriminant to determine the number of x-intercepts for the graph of $f(x) = ax^2 + bx + c$.

71. If a quadratic function given by $y = f(x)$ has x-intercepts of $(2, 0)$ and $(6, 0)$, explain why the vertex must be $(4, f(4))$.

72. Given an equation of a parabola in the form $y = a \cdot f(x - h)^2 + k$, explain how to determine by inspection if the parabola has no x-intercepts.

Expanding Your Skills

For Exercises 73–76, define a quadratic function $y = f(x)$ that satisfies the given conditions.

73. Vertex $(2, -3)$ and passes through $(0, 5)$

74. Vertex $(-3, 1)$ and passes through $(0, -17)$

75. Axis of symmetry $x = 4$, maximum value 6, passes through $(1, 3)$

76. Axis of symmetry $x = -2$, minimum value 5, passes through $(2, 13)$

For Exercises 77–80, find the value of b or c that gives the function the given minimum or maximum value.

77. $f(x) = 2x^2 + 12x + c$; minimum value -9

78. $f(x) = 3x^2 + 12x + c$; minimum value -4

79. $f(x) = -x^2 + bx + 4$; maximum value 8

80. $f(x) = -x^2 + bx - 2$; maximum value 7

SECTION 3.2   Introduction to Polynomial Functions

OBJECTIVES

1. **Determine the End Behavior of a Polynomial Function**
2. **Identify Zeros and Multiplicities of Zeros**
3. **Apply the Intermediate Value Theorem**
4. **Sketch a Polynomial Function**

1. Determine the End Behavior of a Polynomial Function

The tides are the rise and fall of sea level caused in part by the effect of gravity from the Moon and Sun, and from the rotation of the Earth. The tidal levels for Atlantic City, New Jersey, are given in Figure 3-6 for a day in January for a recent year. The tidal level $h(x)$ measured in feet is given at one-half-hr intervals x starting at midnight. (*Source:* National Oceanic and Atmospheric Administration, www.noaa.gov)

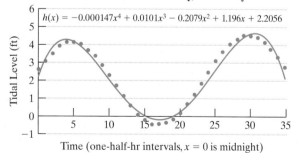

Tidal Levels Atlantic City, New Jersey

$h(x) = -0.000147x^4 + 0.0101x^3 - 0.2079x^2 + 1.196x + 2.2056$

Tidal Level (ft)

Time (one-half-hr intervals, $x = 0$ is midnight)

Figure 3-6

The function defined by

$$h(x) = -0.000147x^4 + 0.0101x^3 - 0.2079x^2 + 1.196x + 2.2056$$

where $0 \le x \le 35$ is an example of a polynomial function of degree 4.

> ### Definition of a Polynomial Function
>
> Let n be a whole number and a_n, a_{n-1}, a_{n-2}, ... , a_1, a_0 be real numbers, where $a_n \neq 0$. Then a function defined by
>
> $$f(x) = a_n x^n + a_{n-1}x^{n-1} + a_{n-2}x^{n-2} + \cdots + a_1 x + a_0$$
>
> is called a **polynomial function of degree n.**

The coefficients of each term of a polynomial function are real numbers, and the exponents on x must be whole numbers.

Polynomial Function	**Not a Polynomial Function**
$f(x) = 4x^5 - 3x^4 + 2x^2$	$f(x) = 4\sqrt{x} - \dfrac{3}{x} + (3 + 2i)x^2$

$\sqrt{x} = x^{1/2}$
Exponent not a whole number

$\dfrac{3}{x} = 3x^{-1}$
Exponent not a whole number

$(3 + 2i)$
Coefficient not a real number

TIP A third-degree polynomial function is referred to as a *cubic* polynomial function.
A fourth-degree polynomial function is referred to as a *quartic* polynomial function.

We have already studied several special cases of polynomial functions. For example:

$f(x) = 2$	constant function	(polynomial function, degree 0)
$g(x) = 3x + 1$	linear function	(polynomial function, degree 1)
$h(x) = 4x^2 + 7x - 1$	quadratic function	(polynomial function, degree 2)

The domain of a polynomial function is all real numbers. Furthermore, the graph of a polynomial function is both continuous and smooth. Informally, a continuous function can be drawn without lifting the pencil from the paper. A smooth function has no sharp corners or points. For example, the first curve shown here could be a polynomial function, but the last three are not polynomial functions.

Smooth and Continuous   Not Smooth   Not Continuous   Not Continuous

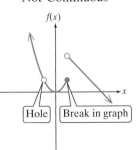

As we analyze polynomial functions, one important characteristic to note is the "end behavior" of the function. That is, in what general direction does the function follow as x approaches ∞ or $-\infty$? Consider the function:

$$f(x) = a_n x^n + a_{n-1} x^{n-1} + a_{n-2} x^{n-2} + \cdots + a_1 x + a_0$$

The leading term has the greatest exponent on x.

The leading term has the greatest exponent on x. Therefore, when $|x|$ gets large (that is, when x approaches ∞ or $-\infty$), the leading term will be relatively larger in absolute value than all other terms. In fact, x^n will eventually be greater in absolute value than the sum of all other terms. Therefore, the "end behavior" of the function is dictated only by the leading term.

The Leading Term Test

Consider a polynomial function given by

$$f(x) = a_n x^n + a_{n-1} x^{n-1} + a_{n-2} x^{n-2} + \cdots + a_1 x + a_0.$$

As x approaches ∞ or $-\infty$, f eventually becomes forever increasing or forever decreasing.

n **is even**		n **is odd**	
a_n positive	a_n negative	a_n positive	a_n negative
			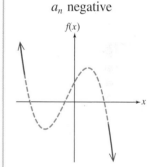
End behavior: up left/up right	End behavior: down left/down right	End behavior: down left/up right	End behavior: up left/down right

EXAMPLE 1   Determining End Behavior

Use the leading term to determine the end behavior of the graph of the function.

a. $f(x) = -4x^5 + 6x^4 + 2x$ **b.** $g(x) = \dfrac{1}{4}x(2x - 3)^3(x + 4)^2$

Solution:

a. $f(x) = -4x^5 + 6x^4 + 2x$

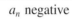

negative   odd

The leading coefficient is negative and the degree is odd. By the leading term test, the end behavior is up to the left and down to the right.

$f(x)$

$f(x) = -4x^5 + 6x^4 + 2x$

b. $g(x) = \frac{1}{4}x(2x - 3)^3(x + 4)^2$

positive even

$g(x) = \frac{1}{4}x(2x - 3)^3(x + 4)^2 = 2x^6 + \cdots$

To determine the leading term, multiply the leading terms from each factor. That is,

$\frac{1}{4}x(2x)^3(x)^2 = 2x^6$.

The leading coefficient is positive and the degree is even. By the leading term test, the end behavior is up to the left and up to the right.

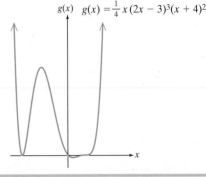

$g(x)$ $g(x) = \frac{1}{4}x(2x - 3)^3(x + 4)^2$

Skill Practice 1   Use the leading term to determine the end behavior of the graph of the function.

a. $f(x) = -0.3x^4 - 5x^2 - 3x + 4$ **b.** $g(x) = \frac{6}{7}(x - 9)^4(x + 4)^2(3x - 5)$

In situations in which a polynomial function is used to model real-world data, we often need to restrict the domain to avoid the end behavior. For example, in Figure 3-7, $h(x) = -0.000147x^4 + 0.0101x^3 - 0.2079x^2 + 1.196x + 2.2056$ is a reasonable model for tidal levels $h(x)$ only for x on the interval $0 \leq x \leq 35$. Outside this range for x, the graph drops inappropriately below the range of the data. In fact, the tidal levels would drop to $-\infty$ if $|x|$ becomes infinitely large.

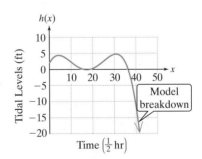

Figure 3-7

2. Identify Zeros and Multiplicities of Zeros

Consider a polynomial function defined by $y = f(x)$. The values of x in the domain of f for which $f(x) = 0$ are called the **zeros** of the function. These are the real solutions (or **roots**) of the equation $f(x) = 0$ and correspond to the x-intercepts of the graph of $y = f(x)$.

Answers

1. a. Down to the left, down to the right
   b. Down to the left, up to the right

EXAMPLE 2   **Determining the Zeros of a Polynomial Function**

Find the zeros of the function defined by $f(x) = x^3 + x^2 - 9x - 9$.

Solution:

$$f(x) = x^3 + x^2 - 9x - 9$$
$$0 = x^3 + x^2 - 9x - 9 \qquad \text{To find the zeros of } f, \text{ set } f(x) = 0 \text{ and solve for } x.$$
$$0 = x^2(x + 1) - 9(x + 1) \qquad \text{Factor by grouping.}$$
$$0 = (x + 1)(x^2 - 9)$$
$$0 = (x + 1)(x - 3)(x + 3) \qquad \text{Factor the difference of squares.}$$
$$x = -1, x = 3, x = -3 \qquad \text{Set each factor equal to zero and solve for } x.$$

The zeros of f are -1, 3, and -3.

The graph of f is shown in Figure 3-8. The zeros of the function are real numbers and correspond to the x-intercepts of the graph. By inspection, we can evaluate $f(0) = -9$, indicating that the y-intercept is $(0, -9)$.

Check:

A table of points can be used to check that $f(-1)$, $f(3)$, and $f(-3)$ all equal 0.

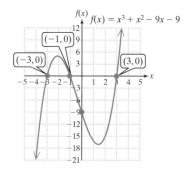

Figure 3-8

Skill Practice 2   Find the zeros of the function defined by
$$f(x) = 4x^3 - 4x^2 - 25x + 25.$$

EXAMPLE 3   **Determining the Zeros of a Polynomial Function**

Find the zeros of the function defined by $f(x) = -x^3 + 8x^2 - 16x$.

Solution:

$$f(x) = -x^3 + 8x^2 - 16x \qquad \text{To find the zeros of } f, \text{ set } f(x) = 0 \text{ and solve for } x.$$
$$0 = -x(x^2 - 8x + 16) \qquad \text{Factor out the GCF.}$$
$$0 = -x(x - 4)^2 \qquad \text{Factor the perfect square trinomial.}$$
$$x = 0, x = 4 \qquad \text{Set each factor equal to zero and solve for } x.$$

The zeros of f are 0 and 4.

The graph of f is shown in Figure 3-9. The zeros of the function are real numbers and correspond to the x-intercepts $(0, 0)$ and $(4, 0)$.

The leading term of $f(x)$ is $-x^3$. The coefficient is negative and the exponent is odd. The graph shows the end behavior up to the left and down to the right as expected.

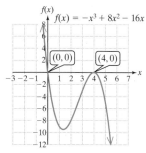

Figure 3-9

Answer

2. $1, \dfrac{5}{2}, -\dfrac{5}{2}$

> **Skill Practice 3**   Find the zeros of the function defined by
> $f(x) = x^3 + 10x^2 + 25x$.

From Example 3, $f(x) = -x^3 + 8x^2 - 16x$ can be written as a product of linear factors:

$$f(x) = -x(x - 4)^2$$

Notice that the factor $(x - 4)$ appears to the second power. Therefore, we say that the corresponding zero, 4, has a multiplicity of 2. In general, we say that if a polynomial function has a factor $(x - c)$ that appears exactly k times, then c is a **zero of multiplicity k.** For example, consider:

$$g(x) = x^2(x - 2)^3(x + 4)^7 \qquad$$

0 is a zero of multiplicity 2.

2 is a zero of multiplicity 3.

-4 is a zero of multiplicity 7.

The graph of a polynomial function behaves in the following manner based on the multiplicity of the zeros.

Touch Points and Cross Points

Let f be a polynomial function and let c be a real zero of f. Then the point $(c, 0)$ is an x-intercept of the graph of f. Furthermore,

- If c is a zero of odd multiplicity, then the graph *crosses* the x-axis at c. The point $(c, 0)$ is called a **cross point.**
- If c is a zero of even multiplicity, then the graph *touches* the x-axis at c and turns back around (does not cross the x-axis). The point $(c, 0)$ is called a **touch point.**

Figure 3-10

To illustrate the behavior of a polynomial function at its real zeros, consider the graph of $f(x) = -x(x - 4)^2$ from Example 3 (Figure 3-10).

- 0 has a multiplicity of 1 (odd multiplicity). The graph *crosses* the x-axis at $(0, 0)$.
- 4 has a multiplicity of 2 (even multiplicity). The graph *touches* the x-axis at $(4, 0)$ and turns back around.

EXAMPLE 4   **Determining Zeros and Multiplicities**

Determine the zeros and their multiplicities for the given functions.

a. $m(x) = \dfrac{1}{10}(x - 4)^2(2x + 5)^3$ **b.** $n(x) = x^4 - 2x^2$

Solution:

a. $m(x) = \dfrac{1}{10}(x - 4)^{\overset{\text{even}}{2}}(2x + 5)^{\overset{\text{odd}}{3}}$ The function is factored into linear factors. The zeros are 4 and $-\frac{5}{2}$.

The function has a zero of 4 with multiplicity 2 (even). The graph has a touch point at $(4, 0)$.

The function has a zero of $-\frac{5}{2}$ with multiplicity 3 (odd). The graph has a cross point at $\left(-\frac{5}{2}, 0\right)$.

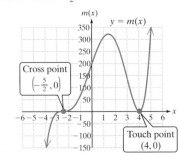

Answer

3. $0, -5$

b. $n(x) = x^4 - 2x^2$
$$= x^2(x^2 - 2)$$
$$= x^2(x - \sqrt{2})^1(x + \sqrt{2})^1$$

The function has a zero of 0 with multiplicity 2 (even). The graph has a touch point at $(0, 0)$.

The function has a zero of $\sqrt{2}$ with multiplicity 1 (odd). The graph has a cross point at $(\sqrt{2}, 0) \approx (1.41, 0)$.

The function has a zero of $-\sqrt{2}$ with multiplicity 1 (odd). The graph has a cross point at $(-\sqrt{2}, 0) \approx (-1.41, 0)$.

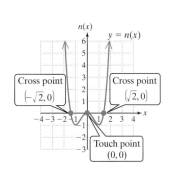

Skill Practice 4   Determine the zeros and their multiplicities for the given functions.

a. $p(x) = -\dfrac{3}{5}(x + 3)^4(5x - 1)^5$ **b.** $q(x) = 2x^6 - 14x^4$

3. Apply the Intermediate Value Theorem

In Examples 2–4, the zeros of the functions were easily identified by first factoring the polynomial. However, in most cases, the real zeros of a polynomial are difficult or impossible to determine algebraically. For example, the function given by $f(x) = x^4 + 6x^3 - 26x + 15$ has zeros of $-1 \pm \sqrt{6}$ and $-2 \pm \sqrt{7}$. At this point, we do not have the tools to find the zeros of this function analytically. However, we can use the intermediate value theorem to help us search for zeros of a polynomial function and approximate their values.

> ### Intermediate Value Theorem
>
> Let f be a polynomial function. For $a < b$, if $f(a)$ and $f(b)$ have opposite signs, then f has at least one zero on the interval $[a, b]$.

EXAMPLE 5   **Applying the Intermediate Value Theorem**

Show that $f(x) = x^4 + 6x^3 - 26x + 15$ has a zero on the interval $[1, 2]$.

Solution:

$f(x) = x^4 + 6x^3 - 26x + 15$
$f(1) = (1)^4 + 6(1)^3 - 26(1) + 15 = -4$
$f(2) = (2)^4 + 6(2)^3 - 26(2) + 15 = 27$

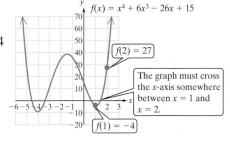

Since $f(1)$ and $f(2)$ have opposite signs, then by the intermediate value theorem, we know that the function must have at least one zero on the interval $[1, 2]$.

The actual value of the zero on the interval $[1, 2]$ is $-1 + \sqrt{6} \approx 1.45$.

Skill Practice 5   Show that $f(x) = x^4 + 6x^3 - 26x + 15$ has a zero on the interval $[-4, -3]$.

Avoiding Mistakes

For a polynomial function f, if $f(a)$ and $f(b)$ have opposite signs, then f must have at least one zero on the interval $[a, b]$. This includes the possibility that f may have more than one zero on $[a, b]$.

TIP   It is important to note that if the signs of $f(a)$ and $f(b)$ are the same, then the intermediate value theorem is inconclusive.

Answers

4. a. -3 (multiplicity 4) and $\dfrac{1}{5}$ (multiplicity 5)
   b. 0 (multiplicity 4), $\sqrt{7}$ (multiplicity 1), and $-\sqrt{7}$ (multiplicity 1)
5. $f(-4) = -9$ and $f(-3) = 12$. Since $f(-4)$ and $f(-3)$ have opposite signs, then the intermediate value theorem guarantees the existence of at least one zero on the interval $[-4, -3]$.

The intermediate value theorem can be used repeatedly in a technique called the bisection method to approximate the value of a zero. See the online group activity "Investigating the Bisection Method for Finding Zeros."

Point of Interest

The modern definition of a computer is a programmable device designed to carry out a sequence of arithmetic or logical operations. However, the word "computer" originally referred to a person who did such calculations using paper and pencil. "Human computers" were notably used in the eighteenth century to predict the path of Halley's comet and to produce astronomical tables critical to surveying and navigation. Later, during World Wars I and II, human computers developed ballistic firing tables that would describe the trajectory of a shell.

Computing tables of values was very time consuming, and the "computers" would often interpolate to find intermediate values within a table. Interpolation is a method by which intermediate values between two numbers are estimated. Often the interpolated values were based on a polynomial function.

4. Sketch a Polynomial Function

TIP Even with advanced techniques from calculus or the use of a graphing utility, it is often difficult or impossible to find the exact location of the turning points of a polynomial function.

The graph of a polynomial function may also have "turning points." For example, consider $f(x) = x(x + 2)(x - 2)^2$. See Figure 3-11.

Multiplying the leading terms within the factors, we have a leading term of $(x)(x)(x)^2 = x^4$. Therefore, the end behavior of the graph is up to the left and up to the right.

Figure 3-11

Starting from the far left, the graph of f decreases to the x-intercept of -2. Since -2 is a zero with an odd multiplicity, the graph must cross the x-axis at -2. For the same reason, the graph must cross the x-axis again at the origin. Therefore, somewhere between $x = -2$ and $x = 0$, the graph must "turn around." This point is called a "turning point."

The turning points of a polynomial function are the points where the function changes from increasing to decreasing or vice versa.

Avoiding Mistakes

A polynomial of degree n may have fewer than $n - 1$ turning points. For example, $f(x) = x^3$ is a degree 3 polynomial function (indicating that it could have a maximum of two turning points), yet the graph has no turning points.

Number of Turning Points of a Polynomial Function

Let f represent a polynomial function of degree n. Then the graph of f has at most $n - 1$ turning points.

At this point we are ready to outline a strategy for sketching a polynomial function.

Graphing a Polynomial Function

To graph a polynomial function defined by $y = f(x)$,

1. Use the leading term to determine the end behavior of the graph.
2. Determine the y-intercept by evaluating $f(0)$.
3. Determine the real zeros of f and their multiplicities (these are the x-intercepts of the graph of f).
4. Plot the x- and y-intercepts and sketch the end behavior.
5. Draw a sketch starting from the left-end behavior. Connect the x- and y-intercepts in the order that they appear from left to right using these rules:
   - The curve will cross the x-axis at an x-intercept if the corresponding zero has an odd multiplicity.
   - The curve will touch but not cross the x-axis at an x-intercept if the corresponding zero has an even multiplicity.
6. Use symmetry to plot additional points. Recall that
   - f is an even function (symmetric to the y-axis) if $f(-x) = f(x)$.
   - f is an odd function (symmetric to the origin) if $f(-x) = -f(x)$.
7. Plot more points if a greater level of accuracy is desired. In particular, to estimate the location of turning points, find several points between two consecutive x-intercepts.

In Examples 6 and 7, we demonstrate the process of graphing a polynomial function.

EXAMPLE 6   Graphing a Polynomial Function

Graph $f(x) = x^3 - 9x$.

Solution:

$f(x) = x^3 - 9x$

1. The leading term is x^3. The end behavior is down to the left and up to the right.

   The exponent on the leading term is odd and the leading coefficient is positive.

2. $f(0) = (0)^3 - 9(0) = 0$

   The y-intercept is $(0, 0)$.

   Determine the y-intercept by evaluating $f(0)$.

3. $0 = x^3 - 9x$

   $0 = x(x^2 - 9)$

   $0 = x(x - 3)(x + 3)$

   Find the real zeros of f by solving for the real solutions to the equation $f(x) = 0$.

   The zeros of the function are 0, 3, and -3, and each has a multiplicity of 1.

   The zeros are real numbers and correspond to x-intercepts on the graph. Since the multiplicity of each zero is an odd number, the graph will cross the x-axis at the zeros.

4.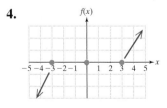

   Plot the x- and y-intercepts and sketch the end behavior.

5. Moving from left to right, the curve increases from the far left and then crosses the *x*-axis at −3. The graph must have a turning point between $x = -3$ and $x = 0$ so that the curve can pass through the next *x*-intercept of (0, 0). ⟶ The graph crosses the *x*-axis at $x = 0$. The graph must then have another turning point between $x = 0$ and $x = 3$ so that the curve can pass through the next *x*-intercept of (3, 0). Finally, the graph crosses the *x*-axis at $x = 3$ and continues to increase to the far right.

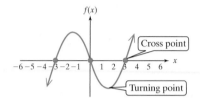

6. $f(x) = x^3 - 9x$

$$f(-x) = (-x)^3 - 9(-x) \qquad -f(x) = -(x^3 - 9x)$$
$$= -x^3 + 9x \xleftarrow{\quad\quad} = -x^3 + 9x$$
$$\underset{f(-x) = -f(x)}{\text{(same)}}$$

Testing for symmetry, we see that $f(-x) = -f(x)$. Therefore, *f* is an odd function and is symmetric with respect to the origin.

TIP The location and *y*-values of the turning points are only approximate. Techniques of calculus are needed to find the exact points.

7. If more accuracy is desired, plot additional points. In this case, since *f* is symmetric to the origin, then if a point (x, y) is on the graph, then so is $(-x, -y)$. The graph of *f* is shown in Figure 3-12.

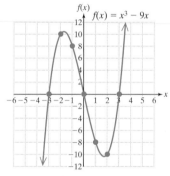

x	$f(x)$
1	−8
2	−10
4	28

Use symmetry.

x	$f(x)$
−1	8
−2	10
−4	−28

Figure 3-12

Skill Practice 6   Graph $g(x) = -x^3 + 4x$.

EXAMPLE 7   **Graphing a Polynomial Function**

Graph $g(x) = -0.1(x - 1)(x + 2)(x - 4)^2$.

Solution:

$g(x) = -0.1(x - 1)(x + 2)(x - 4)^2$

Answer

6.

1. Multiplying the leading terms within the factors, we have a leading term of $-0.1(x)(x)(x)^2 = -0.1x^4$. The end behavior is down to the left and down to the right.

The exponent on the leading term is even and the leading coefficient is negative.

2. $g(0) = -0.1(0 - 1)(0 + 2)(0 - 4)^2 = 3.2$

The *y*-intercept is (0, 3.2).

Determine the *y*-intercept by evaluating $g(0)$.

3. $0 = -0.1(x - 1)(x + 2)(x - 4)^2$

The zeros of the function are 1, −2, and 4.
The multiplicity of 1 is 1.
The multiplicity of −2 is 1.
The multiplicity of 4 is 2.

Find the real zeros of *g* by solving for the real solutions of the equation $g(x) = 0$.

The zeros are real numbers and correspond to *x*-intercepts on the graph: (1, 0), (−2, 0), and (4, 0).

4.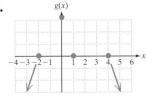

Plot the *x*- and *y*-intercepts and sketch the end behavior.

5. Moving from left to right, the curve increases from the far left. It then crosses the *x*-axis at $x = -2$ and turns back around to pass through the next *x*-intercept at $x = 1$.

The curve has another turning point between $x = 1$ and $x = 4$ so that it can touch the *x*-axis at 4. From there it turns back downward and continues to decrease to the far right.

6. The function is neither even nor odd. There is no symmetry with respect to the *y*-axis or origin.

7. If more accuracy is desired, plot additional points. The graph is shown in Figure 3-13.

x	*g*(*x*)
−3	−19.6
−1	5
2	−1.6
3	−1
5	−2.8

$g(x) = -0.1(x - 1)(x + 2)(x - 4)^2$

Figure 3-13

Skill Practice 7   Graph $h(x) = 0.5x(x - 1)(x + 3)^2$.

TECHNOLOGY CONNECTIONS

Using a Graphing Utility to Graph a Polynomial Function

It is important to have a strong knowledge of algebra to use a graphing utility effectively. For example, consider the graph of $f(x) = 0.005(x - 2)(x + 3)(x - 5)(x + 15)$ on the standard viewing window.

From the leading term, $0.005x^4$, we know that the end behavior should be up to the left and up to the right. Furthermore, the function has four real zeros, (2, −3, 5, and −15), and should have four corresponding *x*-intercepts. Therefore, on the standard viewing window, the calculator does not show the key features of the graph.

By graphing *f* on the window $[-20, 10, 2]$ by $[-35, 10, 5]$, we see the end behavior displayed correctly, all four *x*-intercepts, and the turning points (there should be at most 3).

Answer

7.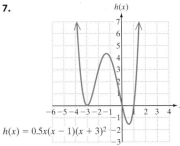

$h(x) = 0.5x(x - 1)(x + 3)^2$

SECTION 3.2   Practice Exercises

Review Exercises

For Exercises 1–2, determine the vertex of the parabola defined by the function.

1. $f(x) = -6x^2 + 18x - 7$

2. $g(x) = 10x^2 - 15x + 5$

For Exercises 3–4, determine the values of x for which $f(x) = 0$.

3. $f(x) = -4x^2 + 18x + 10$

4. $f(x) = -6x^2 - 15x + 36$

For Exercises 5–6, factor completely.

5. $-16x^7 + 48x^6 + 9x^5 - 27x^4$

6. $-98x^6 + 196x^5 + 8x^4 - 16x^3$

Concept Connections

7. A function defined by
$f(x) = a_n x^n + a_{n-1} x^{n-1} + a_{n-2} x^{n-2} + \cdots + a_1 x + a_0$
where $a_n, a_{n-1}, a_{n-2}, \ldots, a_1, a_0$ are real numbers and
$a_n \neq 0$ is called a _____ function.

8. The function given by $f(x) = -3x^5 + \sqrt{2}x + \dfrac{1}{2}x$
(is/is not) a polynomial function.

9. The function given by $f(x) = -3x^5 + 2\sqrt{x} + \dfrac{2}{x}$
(is/is not) a polynomial function.

10. A quadratic function is a polynomial function of degree
_____.

11. A linear function is a polynomial function of degree
_____.

12. Determine if the statement is true or false. The graph of the function defined by $f(x) = |x|$ is smooth.

13. Determine if the statement is true or false. The function defined by $f(x) = \frac{1}{x}$ is continuous.

14. The end behavior of the graph of $f(x) = -6x^2$ is (up/down) to the left and (up/down) to the right.

15. The end behavior of the graph of $f(x) = -8x^3$ is (up/down) to the left and (up/down) to the right.

16. The values of x in the domain of a polynomial function f for which $f(x) = 0$ are called the _____ of the function.

17. Given the function defined by $g(x) = -3(x - 1)^3(x + 5)^4$, the value 1 is a zero with multiplicity _____, and the value -5 is a zero with multiplicity _____.

18. Given the function defined by $h(x) = \frac{1}{2}x^5(x + 0.6)^3$, the value 0 is a zero with multiplicity _____, and the value -0.6 is a zero with multiplicity _____.

19. What is the maximum number of turning points of the graph of $f(x) = -3x^6 - 4x^5 - 5x^4 + 2x^2 + 6$?

20. If the graph of a polynomial function has 3 turning points, what is the minimum degree of the function?

21. If c is a real zero of a polynomial function and the multiplicity is 3, does the graph of the function cross the x-axis or touch the x-axis (without crossing) at $(c, 0)$?

22. If c is a real zero of a polynomial function and the multiplicity is 6, does the graph of the function cross the x-axis or touch the x-axis (without crossing) at $(c, 0)$?

23. Suppose that f is a polynomial function and that $a < b$. If $f(a)$ and $f(b)$ have opposite signs, then what conclusion can be drawn from the intermediate value theorem?

24. An even function is symmetric with respect to the _____ -axis.

25. An odd function is symmetric with respect to the
_____.

26. What is the leading term of
$$f(x) = -\frac{1}{3}(x - 3)^4(3x + 5)^2?$$

27. What is the leading term of
$f(x) = -0.6x^2(10x + 1)^3(x - 1)^4?$

28. If the leading term of a polynomial function is ax^n, where a is negative and n is odd, determine the end behavior.

Objective 1: Determine the End Behavior of a Polynomial Function

For Exercises 29–36, determine the end behavior of the graph of the function. (See Example 1)

29. $f(x) = -3x^4 - 5x^2 + 2x - 6$

30. $g(x) = -\dfrac{1}{2}x^6 + 8x^4 - x^3 + 9$

31. $h(x) = 12x^5 + 8x^4 - 4x^3 - 8x + 1$

32. $k(x) = 11x^7 - 4x^2 + 9x + 3$

33. $m(x) = -4(x - 2)(2x + 1)^2(x + 6)^4$

34. $n(x) = -2(x + 4)(3x - 1)^3(x + 5)$

35. $p(x) = -2x^2(3 - x)(2x - 3)^3$

36. $q(x) = -5x^4(2 - x)^3(2x + 5)$

Objective 2: Identify Zeros and Multiplicities of Zeros

For Exercises 37–48 find the zeros of the function and state the multiplicities. (See Examples 2–4)

37. $f(x) = x^3 + 2x^2 - 25x - 50$ **38.** $g(x) = x^3 + 5x^2 - x - 5$ **39.** $h(x) = -6x^3 - 9x^2 + 60x$

40. $k(x) = -6x^3 + 26x^2 - 28x$ **41.** $m(x) = x^5 - 10x^4 + 25x^3$ **42.** $n(x) = x^6 + 4x^5 + 4x^4$

43. $p(x) = -3x(x + 2)^3(x + 4)$ **44.** $q(x) = -2x^4(x + 1)^3(x - 2)^2$

45. $t(x) = 5x(3x - 5)(2x + 9)(x - \sqrt{3})(x + \sqrt{3})$ **46.** $z(x) = 4x(5x - 1)(3x + 8)(x - \sqrt{5})(x + \sqrt{5})$

47. $c(x) = \left[x - (3 - \sqrt{5})\right]\left[x - (3 + \sqrt{5})\right]$ **48.** $d(x) = \left[x - (2 - \sqrt{11})\right]\left[x - (2 + \sqrt{11})\right]$

Objective 3: Apply the Intermediate Value Theorem

For Exercises 49–50, determine whether the intermediate value theorem guarantees that the function has a zero on the given interval. (See Example 5)

49. $f(x) = 2x^3 - 7x^2 - 14x + 30$

   a. $[1, 2]$ **b.** $[2, 3]$

   c. $[3, 4]$ **d.** $[4, 5]$

50. $g(x) = 2x^3 - 13x^2 + 18x + 5$

   a. $[1, 2]$ **b.** $[2, 3]$

   c. $[3, 4]$ **d.** $[4, 5]$

For Exercises 51–52, a table of values is given for $Y_1 = f(x)$. Determine whether the intermediate value theorem guarantees that the function has a zero on the given interval.

51. $Y_1 = 21x^4 + 46x^3 - 238x^2 - 506x + 77$

   a. $[-4, -3]$

   b. $[-3, -2]$

   c. $[-2, -1]$

   d. $[-1, 0]$

X	Y1
-4	725
-3	-88
-2	105
-1	320
0	77
1	-600
2	-1183

X= -4

52. $Y_1 = 10x^4 + 21x^3 - 119x^2 - 147x + 343$

   a. $[-4, -3]$

   b. $[-3, -2]$

   c. $[-2, -1]$

   d. $[-1, 0]$

X	Y1
-5	1728
-4	243
-3	-44
-2	153
-1	360
0	343
1	108

X= -4

53. Given $f(x) = 4x^3 - 8x^2 - 25x + 50$,

   a. Determine if f has a zero on the interval $[-3, -2]$.

   b. If f has a zero on the interval $[-3, -2]$, find the zero.

54. Given $f(x) = 9x^3 - 18x^2 - 100x + 200$,

   a. Determine if f has a zero on the interval $[-4, -3]$.

   b. If f has a zero on the interval $[-4, -3]$, find the zero.

Objective 4: Sketch a Polynomial Function

For Exercises 55–62, determine if the graph can represent a polynomial function. If so, assume that the end behavior and all turning points are represented in the graph.

a. Determine the minimum degree of the polynomial based on the number of turning points.

b. Determine whether the leading coefficient is positive or negative based on the end behavior and whether the degree of the polynomial is odd or even.

c. Approximate the real zeros of the function, and determine if their multiplicities are even or odd.

55.

56.

57.

58.

59.

60.

61.

62.

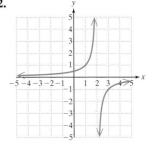

For Exercises 63–74, sketch the function. (See Examples 6–7)

63. $f(x) = x^3 - 5x^2$

64. $g(x) = x^5 - 2x^4$

65. $f(x) = \dfrac{1}{2}(x - 2)(x + 1)(x + 3)$

66. $h(x) = \dfrac{1}{4}(x - 1)(x - 4)(x + 2)$

67. $k(x) = x^4 + 2x^3 - 8x^2$

68. $h(x) = x^4 - x^3 - 6x^2$

69. $k(x) = 0.2(x + 2)^2(x - 4)^3$

70. $m(x) = 0.1(x - 3)^2(x + 1)^3$

71. $p(x) = 9x^5 + 9x^4 - 25x^3 - 25x^2$

72. $q(x) = 9x^5 + 18x^4 - 4x^3 - 8x^2$

73. $t(x) = -x^4 + 11x^2 - 28$

74. $v(x) = -x^4 + 15x^2 - 44$

Mixed Exercises

For Exercises 75–86, determine if the statement is true or false.

75. The function defined by $f(x) = (x + 1)^5(x - 5)^2$ crosses the x-axis at 5.

76. The function defined by $g(x) = -3(x + 4)(2x - 3)^4$ touches but does not cross the x-axis at $\left(\frac{3}{2}, 0\right)$.

77. A third-degree polynomial has three turning points.

78. A third-degree polynomial has two turning points.

79. There is more than one polynomial function with zeros of 1, 2, and 6.

80. There is exactly one polynomial with integer coefficients with zeros of 2, 4, and 6.

81. The graph of an even polynomial function is up to the far left and up to the far right.

82. If c is a real zero of an even polynomial function, then $-c$ is also a zero of the function.

83. The graph of $f(x) = x^2 - 27$ has three x-intercepts.

84. The graph of $f(x) = 3x^2(x - 4)^4$ has no points in quadrants III or IV.

85. The graph of $p(x) = -5x^4(x + 1)^2$ has no points in quadrants I or II.

86. A fourth-degree polynomial has exactly two relative minima and two relative maxima.

87. A rocket will carry a communications satellite into low Earth orbit. Suppose that the thrust during the first 200 sec of flight is provided by solid rocket boosters at different points during liftoff.

The graph shows the acceleration in G-forces (that is, acceleration in 9.8-m/sec² increments) versus time after launch.

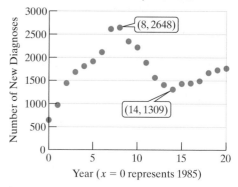

Acceleration in G-Forces vs. Time After Liftoff

a. Approximate the interval(s) over which the acceleration is increasing.

b. Approximate the interval(s) over which the acceleration is decreasing.

c. How many turning points does the graph show?

d. Based on the number of turning points, what is the minimum degree of a polynomial function that could be used to model acceleration versus time? Would the leading coefficient be positive or negative?

e. Approximate the time when the acceleration was the greatest.

f. Approximate the value of the maximum acceleration.

88. The graph represents the number of new AIDS cases diagnosed among adolescents (20–24 yr) in the United States for selected years. (*Source*: Centers for Disease Control, www.cdc.gov)

a. Approximate the interval(s) over which the number of new AIDS cases among adolescents 20–24 yr increased.

b. Approximate the interval(s) over which the number of new AIDS cases among adolescents decreased.

c. How many turning points does the graph show?

d. Based on the number of turning points, what is the minimum degree of a polynomial function that could be used to model the data? Would the leading coefficient be positive or negative?

e. Approximate the year in which the number of new AIDS cases among adolescents 20–24 yr was the greatest.

f. Approximate the value of the maximum number of new cases diagnosed in a single year.

Write About It

89. Given a polynomial defined by $y = f(x)$, explain how to find the x-intercepts.

90. Given a polynomial function, explain how to determine whether an x-intercept is a touch point or a cross point.

91. Write an informal explanation of what it means for a function to be continuous.

92. Write an informal explanation of the intermediate value theorem.

Expanding Your Skills

In calculus, the notation $x \to \infty$ reads as "x approaches infinity." The notation $x \to -\infty$ reads as "x approaches negative infinity." For Exercises 93–96, match the given statement describing the end behavior with the function a, b, c, or d.

a. $y = x^2$ **b.** $y = x^3$ **c.** $y = -x^3$ **d.** $y = -x^2$

93. As $x \to -\infty$, $y \to -\infty$ and as $x \to \infty$, $y \to \infty$

94. As $x \to -\infty$, $y \to -\infty$ and as $x \to \infty$, $y \to -\infty$

95. As $x \to -\infty$, $y \to \infty$ and as $x \to \infty$, $y \to \infty$

96. As $x \to -\infty$, $y \to \infty$ and as $x \to \infty$, $y \to -\infty$

The intermediate value theorem given on page 339 is actually a special case of a broader statement of the theorem. Consider the following:

> Let f be a polynomial function. For $a < b$, if $f(a) \neq f(b)$, then f takes on every value between $f(a)$ and $f(b)$ on the interval $[a, b]$.

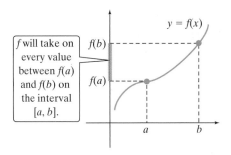

f will take on every value between $f(a)$ and $f(b)$ on the interval $[a, b]$.

Use this broader statement of the intermediate value theorem for Exercises 97–98.

97. Given $f(x) = x^2 - 3x + 2$,

    a. Evaluate $f(3)$ and $f(4)$.

    b. Use the intermediate value theorem to show that there exists at least one value of x for which $f(x) = 4$ on the interval $[3, 4]$.

    c. Find the value(s) of x for which $f(x) = 4$ on the interval $[3, 4]$.

98. Given $f(x) = -x^2 - 4x + 3$,

    a. Evaluate $f(-4)$ and $f(-3)$.

    b. Use the intermediate value theorem to show that there exists at least one value of x for which $f(x) = 5$ on the interval $[-4, -3]$.

    c. Find the value(s) of x for which $f(x) = 5$ on the interval $[-4, -3]$.

Technology Connections

99. For a certain individual, the volume (in liters) of air in the lungs during a 4.5-sec respiratory cycle is shown in the table for 0.5-sec intervals. Graph the points and then find a third-degree polynomial function to model the volume $V(t)$ for t between 0 sec and 4.5 sec. (*Hint*: Use a CubicReg option or polynomial degree 3 option on a graphing utility.)

Time (sec)	Volume (L)
0.0	0.00
0.5	0.11
1.0	0.29
1.5	0.47
2.0	0.63
2.5	0.76
3.0	0.81
3.5	0.75
4.0	0.56
4.5	0.20

100. The torque (in ft-lb) produced by a certain automobile engine turning at x thousand revolutions per minute is shown in the table. Graph the points and then find a third-degree polynomial function to model the torque $T(x)$ for $1 \leq x \leq 5$.

Engine speed (1000 rpm)	Torque (ft-lb)
1.0	165
1.5	180
2.0	188
2.5	190
3.0	186
3.5	176
4.0	161
4.5	142
5.0	120

For Exercises 101–102, graph the family of functions on the standard viewing window. Comment on the end behavior of each graph.

101. a. $y = 0.01x^3$ **b.** $y = 0.01x^5$ **c.** $y = 0.01x^7$ **102. a.** $y = 0.08x^2$ **b.** $y = 0.08x^4$ **c.** $y = 0.08x^6$

For Exercises 103–104, two viewing windows are given for the graph of $y = f(x)$. Choose the window that best shows the key features of the graph.

103. $f(x) = 2(x - 0.5)(x - 0.1)(x + 0.2)$

    a. $[-10, 10, 1]$ by $[-10, 10, 1]$

    b. $[-1, 1, 0.1]$ by $[-0.05, 0.05, 0.01]$

104. $g(x) = 0.08(x - 16)(x + 2)(x - 3)$

    a. $[-10, 10, 1]$ by $[-10, 10, 1]$

    b. $[-5, 20, 5]$ by $[-50, 30, 10]$

For Exercises 105–106, graph the function defined by $y = f(x)$ on an appropriate viewing window.

105. $k(x) = \dfrac{1}{100}(x - 20)(x + 1)(x + 8)(x - 6)$

106. $p(x) = 10(x - 0.4)(x + 0.5)(x + 0.1)(x - 0.8)$

SECTION 3.3 Division of Polynomials and the Remainder and Factor Theorems

OBJECTIVES

1. Divide Polynomials Using Long Division
2. Divide Polynomials Using Synthetic Division
3. Apply the Remainder and Factor Theorems

1. Divide Polynomials Using Long Division

In this section we use the notation $f(x)$, $g(x)$, and so on to represent polynomials in x. We also present two types of polynomial division: long division and synthetic division. Polynomial division can be used to factor a polynomial, solve a polynomial equation, and find the zeros of a polynomial.

When dividing polynomials, if the divisor has two or more terms we can use a long division process similar to the division of real numbers. This is demonstrated in Examples 1–3.

> **EXAMPLE 1** Dividing Polynomials Using Long Division
>
> Use long division to divide. $(6x^3 - 5x^2 - 3) \div (3x + 2)$

Solution:

First note that the dividend can be written as $6x^3 - 5x^2 + 0x - 3$. The term $0x$ is used as a place holder for the missing power of x. The place holder is helpful to keep the powers of x lined up. We also set up long division with both the dividend and divisor written in descending order.

TIP Take a minute to review long division of whole numbers: $2273 \div 5$

$$
\begin{array}{r}
454 \leftarrow \text{Quotient} \\
5\overline{)2273} \\
-20 \\
\hline
27 \\
-25 \\
\hline
23 \\
-20 \\
\hline
3 \leftarrow \text{Remainder}
\end{array}
$$

Answer: $454 + \frac{3}{5}$ or $454\frac{3}{5}$

$3x + 2\overline{)6x^3 - 5x^2 + 0x - 3}$

Divide the leading term in the dividend by the leading term in the divisor.

$\dfrac{6x^3}{3x} = 2x^2$ This is the first term in the quotient.

$$
\begin{array}{r}
2x^2 \phantom{{}- 5x^2 + 0x - 3} \\
3x + 2\overline{)6x^3 - 5x^2 + 0x - 3} \\
-(6x^3 + 4x^2) \phantom{{}+ 0x - 3}
\end{array}
$$

Subtract.

Multiply the divisor by $2x^2$: $2x^2(3x + 2) = 6x^3 + 4x^2$, and subtract the result.

$$
\begin{array}{r}
2x^2 \phantom{{}- 5x^2 + 0x - 3} \\
3x + 2\overline{)6x^3 - 5x^2 + 0x - 3} \\
-(6x^3 + 4x^2) \phantom{{}- 3} \\
\hline
-9x^2 + 0x \phantom{{}- 3}
\end{array}
$$

Bring down the next term from the dividend and repeat the process.

$$
\begin{array}{r}
2x^2 - 3x \phantom{{}- 3} \\
3x + 2\overline{)6x^3 - 5x^2 + 0x - 3} \\
-(6x^3 + 4x^2) \phantom{{}- 3} \\
\hline
-9x^2 + 0x \phantom{{}- 3} \\
-(-9x^2 - 6x) \phantom{{}}
\end{array}
$$

Subtract.

Divide $-9x^2$ by the first term in the divisor.

$\dfrac{-9x^2}{3x} = -3x$

Multiply the divisor by $-3x$: $-3x(3x + 2) = -9x^2 - 6x$, and subtract the result.

$$
\begin{array}{r}
2x^2 - 3x + 2 \\
3x + 2\overline{)6x^3 - 5x^2 + 0x - 3} \\
-(6x^3 + 4x^2) \phantom{{}- 3} \\
\hline
-9x^2 + 0x \phantom{{}- 3} \\
-(-9x^2 - 6x) \phantom{{}} \\
\hline
6x - 3 \\
-(6x + 4) \\
\hline
-7
\end{array}
$$

Bring down the next term from the dividend and repeat the process.

Divide $6x$ by the first term in the divisor. $\frac{6x}{3x} = 2$. This is the next term in the quotient.

Multiply the divisor by 2: $2(3x + 2) = 6x + 4$, and subtract the result.

The remainder is -7.

Long division is complete when the remainder is either zero or has degree less than the degree of the divisor.

The quotient is $2x^2 - 3x + 2$.
The remainder is -7.
The divisor is $3x + 2$.
The dividend is $6x^3 - 5x^2 - 3$.

The result of a long division problem is usually written as the quotient plus the remainder divided by the divisor.

$$\underbrace{\frac{\boxed{\text{Dividend}} \ 6x^3 - 5x^2 - 3}{\boxed{\text{Divisor}} \ 3x + 2}} = \overbrace{2x^2 - 3x + 2}^{\boxed{\text{Quotient}}} + \frac{-7}{3x + 2}$$

-7 — Remainder
$3x + 2$ — Divisor

Skill Practice 1   Use long division to divide $(4x^3 - 23x + 3) \div (2x - 5)$.

By clearing fractions, the result of Example 1 can be checked by multiplication.

$$\text{Dividend} = (\text{Divisor})(\text{Quotient}) \quad + \text{Remainder}$$
$$6x^3 - 5x^2 - 3 \overset{?}{=} (3x + 2)(2x^2 - 3x + 2) + (-7)$$
$$\overset{?}{=} 6x^3 - 5x^2 + 4 + (-7)$$
$$\overset{?}{=} 6x^3 - 5x^2 - 3 \ \checkmark$$

This result illustrates the division algorithm.

Division Algorithm

Suppose that $f(x)$ and $d(x)$ are polynomials where $d(x) \neq 0$ and the degree of $d(x)$ is less than or equal to the degree of $f(x)$. Then there exists unique polynomials $q(x)$ and $r(x)$ such that

$$f(x) = d(x) \cdot q(x) + r(x)$$

where the degree of $r(x)$ is zero or of lesser degree than $d(x)$.

Note: The polynomial $f(x)$ is the **dividend,** $d(x)$ is the **divisor,** $q(x)$ is the **quotient,** and $r(x)$ is the **remainder.**

EXAMPLE 2   Dividing Polynomials Using Long Division

Use long division to divide $(-5 + x + 4x^2 + 2x^3 + 3x^4) \div (x^2 + 2)$.

Solution:

Write the dividend and divisor in descending order and insert place holders for missing powers of x: $(3x^4 + 2x^3 + 4x^2 + x - 5) \div (x^2 + 0x + 2)$

$$
\begin{array}{r}
3x^2 + 2x - 2 \\
x^2 + 0x + 2 \overline{\smash{\big)}\ 3x^4 + 2x^3 + 4x^2 + x - 5} \\
\underline{-(3x^4 + 0x^3 + 6x^2)} \\
2x^3 - 2x^2 + x \\
\underline{-(2x^3 + 0x^2 + 4x)} \\
-2x^2 - 3x - 5 \\
\underline{-(-2x^2 + 0x - 4)} \\
-3x - 1
\end{array}
$$

To begin, divide the leading term in the dividend by the leading term in the divisor.
$\dfrac{3x^4}{x^2} = 3x^2$

Multiply the divisor by $3x^2$ and subtract the result.

Bring down the next term from the dividend and repeat the process.

The process is complete when the remainder is either 0 or has degree less than the degree of the divisor.

The result is $3x^2 + 2x - 2 + \dfrac{-3x - 1}{x^2 + 2}$.

Answer

1. $2x^2 + 5x + 1 + \dfrac{8}{2x - 5}$

Check by using the division algorithm.

$$3x^4 + 2x^3 + 4x^2 + x - 5 \stackrel{?}{=} (x^2 + 2)(3x^2 + 2x - 2) + (-3x - 1)$$
$$\stackrel{?}{=} 3x^4 + 2x^3 - 2x^2 + 6x^2 + 4x - 4 + (-3x - 1)$$
$$\stackrel{?}{=} 3x^4 + 2x^3 + 4x^2 + x - 5 \checkmark$$

Skill Practice 2   Use long division to divide.

$(1 - 7x + 5x^2 - 3x^3 + 2x^4) \div (x^2 + 3)$

In Example 3, we discuss the implications of obtaining a remainder of zero when performing division of polynomials.

EXAMPLE 3   Dividing Polynomials Using Long Division

Use long division to divide. $\dfrac{2x^2 + 3x - 14}{x - 2}$

Solution:

$$
\begin{array}{r}
2x + 7 \\
x - 2 \overline{)2x^2 + 3x - 14} \\
-(2x^2 - 4x) \\
\hline
7x - 14 \\
-(7x - 14) \\
\hline
0
\end{array}
$$

To begin, divide the leading term in the dividend by the leading term in the divisor.

$\dfrac{2x^2}{x} = 2x$

Multiply the divisor by $2x$ and subtract the result.

Bring down the next term from the dividend and repeat the process.

The process is complete when the remainder is either 0 or has degree less than the degree of the divisor.

$\dfrac{2x^2 + 3x - 14}{x - 2} = 2x + 7$

The remainder is zero. This implies that the divisor divides evenly into the dividend. Therefore, both the divisor and quotient are factors of the dividend. This is easily verified by the division algorithm.

| Dividend | | Divisor | Quotient | Remainder |

$$2x^2 + 3x - 14 \stackrel{?}{=} (x - 2)(2x + 7) + 0$$
$$\stackrel{?}{=} (x - 2)(2x + 7)$$

Factored form of $2x^2 + 3x - 14$

Skill Practice 3   Use long division to divide.

$(3x^2 - 14x + 15) \div (x - 3)$

2. Divide Polynomials Using Synthetic Division

When dividing polynomials where the divisor is a binomial of the form $(x - c)$ and c is a constant, we can use synthetic division. Synthetic division enables us to find the quotient and remainder more quickly than long division. It uses an algorithm that manipulates the coefficients of the dividend, divisor, and quotient without the accompanying variable factors.

The division of polynomials from Example 3 is shown on page 351 on the left. The equivalent synthetic division is shown on the right. Notice that the same coefficients are used in both cases.

Answers

2. $2x^2 - 3x - 1 + \dfrac{2x + 4}{x^2 + 3}$

3. $3x - 5$

$$\begin{array}{r} 2x + 7 \\ x - 2\overline{)2x^2 + 3x - 14} \\ \underline{-(2x^2 - 4x)} \\ 7x - 14 \\ \underline{-(7x - 14)} \\ 0 \end{array}$$

Coefficients of dividend

$$\begin{array}{r|rrr} 2 & 2 & 3 & -14 \\ & & 4 & 14 \\ \hline & 2 & 7 & \boxed{0} \end{array}$$ ← Remainder

Coefficients of quotient

In Example 4, we demonstrate the process to divide polynomials by synthetic division.

EXAMPLE 4   **Dividing Polynomials Using Synthetic Division**

Use synthetic division to divide. $(-10x^2 + 2x^3 - 5) \div (x - 4)$

Solution:

As with long division, the terms of the dividend and divisor must be written in descending order with place holders for missing powers of x.

$$(2x^3 - 10x^2 + 0x - 5) \div (x - 4)$$

To use synthetic division, the divisor must be in the form $x - c$. In this case, $c = 4$.

Avoiding Mistakes
It is important to check that the divisor is in the form $(x - c)$ before applying synthetic division. The variable x in the divisor must be of first degree, and its coefficient must be 1.

Step 1: Write the value of c in a box.

Step 2: Write the coefficients of the dividend to the right of the box.

$$\begin{array}{r|rrrr} 4 & 2 & -10 & 0 & -5 \\ & & & & \\ \hline & 2 & & & \end{array}$$

Step 3: Skip a line and draw a horizontal line below the list of coefficients.

Step 4: Bring down the leading coefficient from the dividend and write it below the line.

Step 5: Multiply the value of c by the number below the line ($4 \times 2 = 8$). Write the result in the next column above the line.

$$\begin{array}{r|rrrr} 4 & 2 & -10 & 0 & -5 \\ & & 8 & & \\ \hline & 2 & -2 & & \end{array}$$

Step 6: Add the numbers in the column above the line ($-10 + 8 = -2$), and write the result below the line.

Repeat steps 5 and 6 until all columns have been completed.

$$\begin{array}{r|rrrr} 4 & 2 & -10 & 0 & -5 \\ & & 8 & -8 & -32 \\ \hline & 2 & -2 & -8 & \boxed{-37} \end{array}$$

$x^2 \quad x \quad$ constant

A box is often drawn around the remainder.

The rightmost number below the line is the remainder. The other numbers below the line are the coefficients of the quotient in order by the degree of the term.

Since the divisor is linear (first degree), the degree of the quotient is 1 less than the degree of the dividend. In this case, the dividend is of degree 3. Therefore, the quotient will be of degree 2.

The quotient is $2x^2 - 2x - 8$ and the remainder is -37. Therefore,

$$\frac{2x^3 - 10x^2 - 5}{x - 4} = 2x^2 - 2x - 8 + \frac{-37}{x - 4}$$

Answer

4. $4x^2 + 12x + 8 + \dfrac{17}{x - 3}$

Skill Practice 4   Use synthetic division to divide.

$(4x^3 - 28x - 7) \div (x - 3)$

EXAMPLE 5 **Dividing Polynomials Using Synthetic Division**

Use synthetic division to divide. $(-2x + 4x^3 + 18 + x^4) \div (x + 2)$

Solution:

Write the dividend and divisor in descending order and insert place holders for missing powers of x. $(x^4 + 4x^3 + 0x^2 - 2x + 18) \div (x + 2)$

To use synthetic division, the divisor must be of the form $x - c$. In this case, we have $x + 2 = x - (-2)$. Therefore, $c = -2$.

The dividend is a fourth-degree polynomial and the divisor is a first-degree polynomial. Therefore, the quotient is a third-degree polynomial. The coefficients of the quotient are found below the line: 1, 2, -4, 6. The quotient is $x^3 + 2x^2 - 4x + 6$, and the remainder is 6.

$$\frac{x^4 + 4x^3 - 2x + 18}{x + 2} = x^3 + 2x^2 - 4x + 6 + \frac{6}{x + 2}$$

Skill Practice 5   Use synthetic division to divide.

$$(-3x + 7x^3 + 5 + 2x^4) \div (x + 1)$$

3. Apply the Remainder and Factor Theorems

Consider the special case of the division algorithm where $f(x)$ is the dividend and $(x - c)$ is the divisor.

$$f(x) = (x - c) \cdot q(x) + r$$

The remainder r is constant because its degree must be one less than the degree of $x - c$.

Now evaluate $f(c)$:

$$f(c) = (c - c) \cdot q(c) + r$$
$$f(c) = 0 \cdot q(c) + r$$
$$f(c) = r$$

This result is stated formally as the remainder theorem.

Remainder Theorem

If a polynomial $f(x)$ is divided by $x - c$, then the remainder is $f(c)$.

Note: The remainder theorem tells us that the value of $f(c)$ is the same as the remainder we get from dividing $f(x)$ by $x - c$.

The remainder theorem is demonstrated in Examples 6 and 7.

Answer

5. $2x^3 + 5x^2 - 5x + 2 + \dfrac{3}{x + 1}$

EXAMPLE 6   Using the Remainder Theorem to Evaluate a Polynomial

Given $f(x) = x^4 + 6x^3 - 12x^2 - 30x + 35$, use the remainder theorem to evaluate

a. $f(2)$ **b.** $f(-7)$

Solution:

a. If $f(x)$ is divided by $x - 2$, then the remainder is $f(2)$.

$$
\begin{array}{r|rrrrr}
2 & 1 & 6 & -12 & -30 & 35 \\
  &   & 2 & 16 & 8 & -44 \\
\hline
  & 1 & 8 & 4 & -22 & \underline{-9}
\end{array}
$$

By the remainder theorem, $f(2) = -9$.

b. If $f(x)$ is divided by $x - (-7)$ or equivalently $x + 7$, then the remainder is $f(-7)$.

$$
\begin{array}{r|rrrrr}
-7 & 1 & 6 & -12 & -30 & 35 \\
   &   & -7 & 7 & 35 & -35 \\
\hline
   & 1 & -1 & -5 & 5 & \underline{0}
\end{array}
$$

By the remainder theorem, $f(-7) = 0$.

The results can be checked by direct substitution:

$$f(2) = (2)^4 + 6(2)^3 - 12(2)^2 - 30(2) + 35 = -9 \checkmark$$
$$f(-7) = (-7)^4 + 6(-7)^3 - 12(-7)^2 - 30(-7) + 35 = 0 \checkmark$$

TIP From Example 6, the values $f(2) = -9$ and $f(-7) = 0$, imply that $(2, -9)$ and $(-7, 0)$ are on the graph of $y = f(x)$.

> **Skill Practice 6**   Given $f(x) = x^4 + x^3 - 6x^2 - 5x - 15$, use the remainder theorem to evaluate
>
> **a.** $f(5)$ **b.** $f(-3)$

The division algorithm and remainder theorem can be extended over the set of complex numbers. The definition of a polynomial was given in Section R.5.

$$f(x) = a_n x^n + a_{n-1} x^{n-1} + a_{n-2} x^{n-2} + \cdots + a_1 x + a_0$$

where $a_n \neq 0$ and the coefficients $a_n, a_{n-1}, a_{n-2}, \ldots, a_0$ are real numbers. We now extend our discussion to **complex polynomials.** These are polynomials with complex coefficients. This means that the coefficients can be real numbers or imaginary numbers.

We will also evaluate polynomials over the set of complex numbers rather than restricting x to the set of real numbers. A complex number $a + bi$ is a zero of a polynomial $f(x)$ if $f(a + bi) = 0$. For example, given $f(x) = x - (5 + 2i)$, we see that the imaginary number $5 + 2i$ is a zero of $f(x)$.

TIP Polynomials with complex coefficients include polynomials with real coefficients and with imaginary coefficients. The following are complex polynomials.

$$f(x) = (2 + 3i)x^2 + 4i$$
$$g(x) = \sqrt{2}x^2 + 3x + 4i$$
$$h(x) = 2x^2 + 3x + 4$$

EXAMPLE 7   Using the Remainder Theorem to Identify Zeros of a Polynomial

Use the remainder theorem to determine if the given number c is a zero of the polynomial.

a. $f(x) = 2x^3 - 4x^2 - 13x - 9;\ c = 4$
b. $f(x) = x^3 + x^2 - 3x - 3;\ c = \sqrt{3}$
c. $f(x) = x^3 + x + 10;\ c = 1 + 2i$

Answers

6. a. 560   **b.** 0

Solution:

In each case, divide $f(x)$ by $x - c$ to determine the remainder. If the remainder is 0, then the value c is a zero of the polynomial.

a. Divide $f(x)$ by $x - 4$.

$$
\begin{array}{r|rrrr}
4 & 2 & -4 & -13 & -9 \\
  &   & 8 & 16 & 12 \\
\hline
  & 2 & 4 & 3   & \boxed{3}
\end{array}
$$

By the remainder theorem, $f(4) = 3$. Since $f(4) \neq 0$, 4 is not a zero of $f(x)$.

b. Divide $f(x)$ by $x - \sqrt{3}$.

$$
\begin{array}{r|rrrr}
\sqrt{3} & 1 & 1 & -3 & -3 \\
  &   & \sqrt{3} & 3 + \sqrt{3} & 3 \\
\hline
  & 1 & 1 + \sqrt{3} & \sqrt{3}   & \boxed{0}
\end{array}
$$

By the remainder theorem, $f(\sqrt{3}) = 0$. Therefore, $\sqrt{3}$ is a zero of $f(x)$.

c. Divide $f(x)$ by $x - (1 + 2i)$.

$$
\begin{array}{r|rrrr}
1 + 2i & 1 & 0 & 1 & 10 \\
  &   & 1 + 2i & -3 + 4i & -10 \\
\hline
  & 1 & 1 + 2i & -2 + 4i   & \boxed{0}
\end{array}
$$

Note that $(1 + 2i)(1 + 2i)$
$= 1 + 2i + 2i + 4i^2$
$= 1 + 4i + 4(-1)$ Recall that $i^2 = -1$.
$= -3 + 4i$

Note that $(1 + 2i)(-2 + 4i)$
$= -2 + 4i - 4i + 8i^2$
$= -2 - 8$
$= -10$

By the remainder theorem, $f(1 + 2i) = 0$.
Therefore, $1 + 2i$ is a zero of $f(x)$.

> **Skill Practice 7** Use the remainder theorem to determine if the given number, c, is a zero of the function.
>
> **a.** $f(x) = 2x^4 - 3x^2 + 5x - 11; \ c = 2$
> **b.** $f(x) = 2x^3 + 5x^2 - 14x - 35; \ c = \sqrt{7}$
> **c.** $f(x) = x^3 - 7x^2 + 16x - 10; \ c = 3 + i$

Suppose that we again apply the division algorithm to a dividend of $f(x)$ and a divisor of $x - c$, where c is a complex number.

$$f(x) = (x - c) \cdot q(x) + r$$
$$f(x) = (x - c) \cdot q(x) + f(c)$$

If $f(c) = 0$, then $f(x) = (x - c) \cdot q(x)$

By the remainder theorem, $r = f(c)$.

This tells us that if $f(c)$ is a zero of $f(x)$, then $(x - c)$ is a factor of $f(x)$.

Now suppose that $x - c$ is a factor of $f(x)$. Then for some polynomial $q(x)$,

$$f(x) = (x - c) \cdot q(x)$$
$$f(c) = (c - c) \cdot q(x)$$
$$f(c) = 0$$

This tells us that if $(x - c)$ is a factor of $f(x)$, then c is a zero of $f(x)$.

These results can be summarized in the factor theorem.

> **Factor Theorem**
>
> Let $f(x)$ be a polynomial.
>
> **1.** If $f(c) = 0$, then $(x - c)$ is a factor of $f(x)$.
> **2.** If $(x - c)$ is a factor of $f(x)$, then $f(c) = 0$.

Answers

7. a. No **b.** Yes **c.** Yes

Identifying Factors of a Polynomial

Use the factor theorem to determine if the given polynomials are factors of
$f(x) = x^4 - x^3 - 11x^2 + 11x + 12$.

a. $x - 3$ **b.** $x + 2$

Solution:

a. If $f(3) = 0$, then $x - 3$ is a factor of $f(x)$. Using synthetic division we have

$$
\begin{array}{r|rrrrr}
3 & 1 & -1 & -11 & 11 & 12 \\
  &   & 3 & 6 & -15 & -12 \\
\hline
  & 1 & 2 & -5 & -4 & \boxed{0}
\end{array}
$$

By the factor theorem, since $f(3) = 0$, $x - 3$ is a factor of $f(x)$. $\boxed{f(3) = 0}$

b. If $f(-2) = 0$, then $x + 2$ is a factor of $f(x)$. Using synthetic division we have

$$
\begin{array}{r|rrrrr}
-2 & 1 & -1 & -11 & 11 & 12 \\
   &   & -2 & 6 & 10 & -42 \\
\hline
   & 1 & -3 & -5 & 21 & \boxed{-30}
\end{array}
$$

By the factor theorem, since $f(-2) \neq 0$, $x + 2$ is not a factor of $f(x)$. $\boxed{f(-2) = -30}$

Skill Practice 8   Use the factor theorem to determine if the given polynomials are factors of $f(x) = 2x^4 - 13x^3 + 10x^2 - 25x + 6$.

a. $x - 6$ **b.** $x + 3$

In Example 9, we illustrate the relationship between the zeros of a polynomial and the solutions (roots) of a polynomial equation.

Factoring a Polynomial Given a Known Zero

a. Factor $f(x) = 3x^3 + 25x^2 + 42x - 40$, given that -5 is a zero of $f(x)$.
b. Solve the equation. $3x^3 + 25x^2 + 42x - 40 = 0$

Solution:

a. The value -5 is a zero of $f(x)$, which means that $f(-5) = 0$. By the factor theorem, $x - (-5)$ or equivalently $x + 5$ is a factor of $f(x)$. Using synthetic division, we have

$$
\begin{array}{r|rrrr}
-5 & 3 & 25 & 42 & -40 \\
   &   & -15 & -50 & 40 \\
\hline
   & 3 & 10 & -8 & \boxed{0}
\end{array}
$$

divisor   quotient   remainder

This means that $3x^3 + 25x^2 + 42x - 40 = (x + 5)(3x^2 + 10x - 8) + 0$
Therefore, $f(x) = (x + 5)(3x - 2)(x + 4)$.

factors as $(3x - 2)(x + 4)$

b. $3x^3 + 25x^2 + 42x - 40 = 0$ To solve the equation, set one side equal to zero.

$(x + 5)(3x - 2)(x + 4) = 0$ Factor the left side.

$x = -5, \; x = \frac{2}{3}, \; x = -4$ Set each factor equal to zero and solve for x.

The solution set is $\left\{ -5, \frac{2}{3}, -4 \right\}$.

Skill Practice 9

a. Factor $f(x) = 2x^3 + 7x^2 - 14x - 40$, given that -4 is a zero of f.
b. Solve the equation. $2x^3 + 7x^2 - 14x - 40 = 0$

Answers

8. a. Yes   **b.** No
9. a. $f(x) = (x + 4)(x + 2)(2x - 5)$

b. $\left\{ -4, -2, \frac{5}{2} \right\}$

EXAMPLE 10   **Using the Factor Theorem to Build a Polynomial**

Write a polynomial $f(x)$ of degree 3 that has the zeros $\frac{1}{2}$, $\sqrt{6}$, and $-\sqrt{6}$.

Solution:

By the factor theorem, if $\frac{1}{2}$, $\sqrt{6}$, and $-\sqrt{6}$ are zeros of a polynomial $f(x)$, then $\left(x - \frac{1}{2}\right)$, $\left(x - \sqrt{6}\right)$, and $\left(x + \sqrt{6}\right)$ are factors of $f(x)$. Therefore, $f(x) = \left(x - \frac{1}{2}\right)\left(x - \sqrt{6}\right)\left(x + \sqrt{6}\right)$ is a third-degree polynomial with the given zeros.

$$f(x) = \left(x - \frac{1}{2}\right)(x^2 - 6) \qquad \text{Multiply conjugates.}$$

$$f(x) = x^3 - \frac{1}{2}x^2 - 6x + 3$$

Skill Practice 10   Write a polynomial $f(x)$ of degree 3 that has the zeros $\frac{1}{3}$, $\sqrt{3}$, and $-\sqrt{3}$.

In Example 10, the polynomial $f(x)$ is not unique. If we multiply $f(x)$ by any nonzero constant a, the polynomial will still have the desired factors and zeros.

$$g(x) = a\left(x - \frac{1}{2}\right)\left(x - \sqrt{6}\right)\left(x + \sqrt{6}\right) \qquad \text{The zeros are still } \frac{1}{2}, \sqrt{6}, \text{ and } -\sqrt{6}.$$

If a is any nonzero multiple of 2, then the polynomial will have integer coefficients.

$$g(x) = 2\left(x - \frac{1}{2}\right)\left(x - \sqrt{6}\right)\left(x + \sqrt{6}\right)$$

$$= 2\left(x^3 - \frac{1}{2}x^2 - 6x + 3\right)$$

$$= 2x^3 - x^2 - 12x + 6$$

The zeros of $f(x)$ and $g(x)$ are real numbers and correspond to the x-intercepts of the graphs of the related functions. The graphs of $y = f(x)$ and $y = g(x)$ are shown in Figure 3-14. Notice that the graphs have the same x-intercepts and differ only by a vertical stretch.

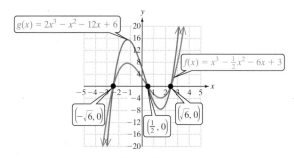

Figure 3-14

Answer

10. $f(x) = x^3 - \frac{1}{3}x^2 - 3x + 1$

SECTION 3.3   Practice Exercises

Review Exercises

For Exercises 1–2,

a. Determine whether the graph of the parabola opens upward or downward.

b. Determine the vertex.

c. Determine the axis of symmetry.

d. Determine the minimum or maximum value of the function.

e. Determine the x-intercept(s).

f. Determine the y-intercept.

g. Graph the function.

1. $g(x) = x^2 - 10x + 21$
2. $h(x) = -\dfrac{1}{2}x^2 - 6x - 16$

For Exercises 3–4, use long division to divide. Check the answer by using multiplication.

3. $25,019 \div 42$
4. $64,108 \div 23$

For Exercises 5–6, simplify the expression.

5. $\dfrac{-6x^5}{3x}$
6. $\dfrac{15x^3}{5x}$

Concept Connections

7. The polynomial $x^2 - x - 12$ factors as $(x - 4)(x + 3)$. What is the quotient of $(x^2 - x - 12) \div (x - 4)$? What is the remainder?

8. The polynomial $x^2 - x - 20$ factors as $(x - 5)(x + 4)$. What is the quotient of $(x^2 - x - 20) \div (x - 5)$? What is the remainder?

9. Given the division algorithm, identify the polynomials representing the dividend, divisor, quotient, and remainder.

$f(x) = d(x) \cdot q(x) + r(x)$

10. Given $\dfrac{2x^3 - 5x^2 - 6x + 1}{x - 3} = 2x^2 + x - 3 + \dfrac{-8}{x - 3}$, use the division algorithm to check the result.

11. The remainder theorem indicates that if a polynomial $f(x)$ is divided by $x - c$, then the remainder is _____.

12. A _____ polynomial is a polynomial with complex coefficients.

13. Answer true or false. The polynomial $p(x) = 6x^3 - 4x^2 + 3x + 5$ is a complex polynomial.

14. Given a polynomial $f(x)$, the factor theorem indicates that if $f(c) = 0$, then $x - c$ is a _____ of $f(x)$. Furthermore, if $x - c$ is a factor of $f(x)$, then $f(c) =$ _____.

15. Answer true or false. If $\sqrt{5}$ is a zero of a polynomial, then $\left(x - \sqrt{5}\right)$ is a factor of the polynomial.

16. Answer true or false. If $(x + 3)$ is a factor of a polynomial, then 3 is a zero of the polynomial.

Objective 1: Divide Polynomials Using Long Division

For Exercises 17–18, (See Example 1)

a. Use long division to divide.

b. Identify the dividend, divisor, quotient, and remainder.

c. Check the result from part (a) with the division algorithm.

17. $(6x^2 + 9x + 5) \div (2x - 5)$
18. $(12x^2 + 10x + 3) \div (3x + 4)$

For Exercises 19–30, use long division to divide. (See Examples 1–3)

19. $(3x^3 - 11x^2 - 10) \div (x - 4)$
20. $(2x^3 - 7x^2 - 65) \div (x - 5)$

21. $(8 + 30x - 27x^2 - 12x^3 + 4x^4) \div (x + 2)$
22. $(-48 - 28x + 20x^2 + 17x^3 + 3x^4) \div (x + 3)$

23. $(-20x^2 + 6x^4 - 16) \div (2x + 4)$

24. $(-60x^2 + 8x^4 - 108) \div (2x - 6)$

25. $(x^5 + 4x^4 + 18x^2 - 20x - 10) \div (x^2 + 5)$

26. $(x^5 - 2x^4 + x^3 - 8x + 18) \div (x^2 - 3)$

27. $\dfrac{6x^4 + 3x^3 - 7x^2 + 6x - 5}{2x^2 + x - 3}$

28. $\dfrac{12x^4 - 4x^3 + 13x^2 + 2x + 1}{3x^2 - x + 4}$

29. $\dfrac{x^3 - 27}{x - 3}$

30. $\dfrac{x^3 + 64}{x + 4}$

Objective 2: Divide Polynomials Using Synthetic Division

For Exercises 31–34, consider the division of two polynomials: $f(x) \div (x - c)$. The result of the synthetic division process is shown here. Write the polynomials representing the

a. Dividend.   **b.** Divisor.   **c.** Quotient.   **d.** Remainder.

31.
$$\begin{array}{r|rrrrr} 3 & 2 & -5 & -5 & -4 & 29 \\ & & 6 & 3 & -6 & -30 \\ \hline & 2 & 1 & -2 & -10 & \boxed{-1} \end{array}$$

32.
$$\begin{array}{r|rrrrr} 2 & 1 & -5 & 2 & -1 & 20 \\ & & 2 & -6 & -8 & -18 \\ \hline & 1 & -3 & -4 & -9 & \boxed{2} \end{array}$$

33.
$$\begin{array}{r|rrrr} -4 & 1 & -2 & -25 & -4 \\ & & -4 & 24 & 4 \\ \hline & 1 & -6 & -1 & \boxed{0} \end{array}$$

34.
$$\begin{array}{r|rrrr} -5 & 3 & 13 & -14 & -20 \\ & & -15 & 10 & 20 \\ \hline & 3 & -2 & -4 & \boxed{0} \end{array}$$

For Exercises 35–44, use synthetic division to divide the polynomials. (See Examples 4–5)

35. $(4x^2 + 15x + 1) \div (x + 6)$

36. $(6x^2 + 25x - 19) \div (x + 5)$

37. $(5x^2 - 17x - 12) \div (x - 4)$

38. $(2x^2 + x - 21) \div (x - 3)$

39. $(4 - 8x - 3x^2 - 5x^4) \div (x + 2)$

40. $(-5 + 2x + 5x^3 - 2x^4) \div (x + 1)$

41. $\dfrac{4x^5 - 25x^4 - 58x^3 + 232x^2 + 198x - 63}{x - 3}$

42. $\dfrac{2x^5 + 13x^4 - 3x^3 - 58x^2 - 20x + 24}{x - 2}$

43. $\dfrac{x^5 + 32}{x + 2}$

44. $\dfrac{x^4 - 81}{x + 3}$

Objective 3: Apply the Remainder and Factor Theorems

45. Given $f(x) = 2x^4 - 5x^3 + x^2 - 7$,

   a. Evaluate $f(4)$.

   b. Determine the remainder when $f(x)$ is divided by $(x - 4)$.

46. Given $g(x) = -3x^5 + 2x^4 + 6x^2 - x + 4$,

   a. Evaluate $g(2)$.

   b. Determine the remainder when $g(x)$ is divided by $(x - 2)$.

For Exercises 47–50, use the remainder theorem to evaluate the polynomial for the given values of x. (See Example 6)

47. $f(x) = 2x^4 + x^3 - 49x^2 + 79x + 15$

   a. $f(-1)$ **b.** $f(3)$ **c.** $f(4)$ **d.** $f\left(\dfrac{5}{2}\right)$

48. $g(x) = 3x^4 - 22x^3 + 51x^2 - 42x + 8$

   a. $g(-1)$ **b.** $g(2)$ **c.** $g(1)$ **d.** $g\left(\dfrac{4}{3}\right)$

49. $h(x) = 5x^3 - 4x^2 - 15x + 12$

   a. $h(1)$ **b.** $h\left(\dfrac{4}{5}\right)$ **c.** $h(\sqrt{3})$ **d.** $h(-1)$

50. $k(x) = 2x^3 - x^2 - 14x + 7$

   a. $k(2)$ **b.** $k\left(\dfrac{1}{2}\right)$ **c.** $k(\sqrt{7})$ **d.** $k(-2)$

For Exercises 51–58, use the remainder theorem to determine if the given number c is a zero of the polynomial. (See Example 7)

51. $f(x) = x^4 + 3x^3 - 7x^2 + 13x - 10$

   a. $c = 2$ **b.** $c = -5$

52. $g(x) = 2x^4 + 13x^3 - 10x^2 - 19x + 14$

   a. $c = -2$ **b.** $c = -7$

53. $p(x) = 2x^3 + 3x^2 - 22x - 33$

   a. $c = -2$ **b.** $c = -\sqrt{11}$

54. $q(x) = 3x^3 + x^2 - 30x - 10$

   a. $c = -3$ **b.** $c = -\sqrt{10}$

55. $m(x) = x^3 - 2x^2 + 25x - 50$

    a. $c = 5i$ **b.** $c = -5i$

57. $g(x) = x^3 - 11x^2 + 25x + 37$

    a. $c = 6 + i$ **b.** $c = 6 - i$

56. $n(x) = x^3 + 4x^2 + 9x + 36$

    a. $c = 3i$ **b.** $c = -3i$

58. $f(x) = 2x^3 - 5x^2 + 54x - 26$

    a. $c = 1 + 5i$ **b.** $c = 1 - 5i$

For Exercises 59–62, use the factor theorem to determine if the given binomial is a factor of $f(x)$. (See Example 8)

59. $f(x) = x^4 + 11x^3 + 41x^2 + 61x + 30$

    a. $x + 5$ **b.** $x - 2$

61. $f(x) = 2x^3 + x^2 - 16x - 8$

    a. $x - 1$ **b.** $x - 2\sqrt{2}$

60. $g(x) = x^4 - 10x^3 + 35x^2 - 50x + 24$

    a. $x - 4$ **b.** $x + 1$

62. $f(x) = 3x^3 - x^2 - 54x + 18$

    a. $x - 2$ **c.** $x - 3\sqrt{2}$

63. a. Use synthetic division and the factor theorem to determine if $[x - (2 + 5i)]$ is a factor of $f(x) = x^2 - 4x + 29$.

    b. Use synthetic division and the factor theorem to determine if $[x - (2 - 5i)]$ is a factor of $f(x) = x^2 - 4x + 29$.

    c. Use the quadratic formula to solve the equation. $x^2 - 4x + 29 = 0$

    d. Find the zeros of the polynomial $f(x) = x^2 - 4x + 29$.

64. a. Use synthetic division and the factor theorem to determine if $[x - (3 + 4i)]$ is a factor of $f(x) = x^2 - 6x + 25$.

    b. Use synthetic division and the factor theorem to determine if $[x - (3 - 4i)]$ is a factor of $f(x) = x^2 - 6x + 25$.

    c. Use the quadratic formula to solve the equation. $x^2 - 6x + 25 = 0$

    d. Find the zeros of the polynomial $f(x) = x^2 - 6x + 25$.

65. a. Factor $f(x) = 2x^3 + x^2 - 37x - 36$, given that -1 is a zero. **(See Example 9)**

    b. Solve. $2x^3 + x^2 - 37x - 36 = 0$

67. a. Factor $f(x) = 20x^3 + 39x^2 - 3x - 2$, given that $\frac{1}{4}$ is a zero.

    b. Solve. $20x^3 + 39x^2 - 3x - 2 = 0$

69. a. Factor $f(x) = 9x^3 - 33x^2 + 19x - 3$, given that 3 is a zero.

    b. Solve. $9x^3 - 33x^2 + 19x - 3 = 0$

66. a. Factor $f(x) = 3x^3 + 16x^2 - 5x - 50$, given that -2 is a zero.

    b. Solve. $3x^3 + 16x^2 - 5x - 50 = 0$

68. a. Factor $f(x) = 8x^3 - 18x^2 - 11x + 15$, given that $\frac{3}{4}$ is a zero.

    b. Solve. $8x^3 - 18x^2 - 11x + 15 = 0$

70. a. Factor $f(x) = 4x^3 - 20x^2 + 33x - 18$, given that 2 is a zero.

    b. Solve. $4x^3 - 20x^2 + 33x - 18 = 0$

For Exercises 71–82, write a polynomial $f(x)$ that meets the given conditions. Answers may vary. (See Example 10)

71. Degree 3 polynomial with zeros 2, 3, and -4.

73. Degree 4 polynomial with zeros 1, $\frac{3}{2}$ (each with multiplicity 1), and 0 (with multiplicity 2).

75. Degree 2 polynomial with zeros $2\sqrt{11}$ and $-2\sqrt{11}$.

77. Degree 3 polynomial with zeros -2, $3i$, and $-3i$.

79. Degree 3 polynomial with integer coefficients and zeros of $-\frac{2}{3}$, $\frac{1}{2}$, and 4.

81. Degree 2 polynomial with zeros of $7 + 8i$ and $7 - 8i$.

72. Degree 3 polynomial with zeros 1, -6, and 3.

74. Degree 5 polynomial with zeros 2, $\frac{5}{2}$ (each with multiplicity 1), and 0 (with multiplicity 3).

76. Degree 2 polynomial with zeros $5\sqrt{2}$ and $-5\sqrt{2}$.

78. Degree 3 polynomial with zeros 4, $2i$, and $-2i$.

80. Degree 3 polynomial with integer coefficients and zeros of $-\frac{2}{5}$, $\frac{3}{2}$, and 6.

82. Degree 2 polynomial with zeros of $5 + 6i$ and $5 - 6i$.

Mixed Exercises

83. Given $p(x) = 2x^{452} - 4x^{92}$, is it easier to evaluate $p(1)$ by using synthetic division or by direct substitution? Find the value of $p(1)$.

84. Given $q(x) = 5x^{721} - 2x^{450}$, is it easier to evaluate $q(-1)$ by using synthetic division or by direct substitution? Find the value of $q(-1)$.

85. a. Is $(x - 1)$ a factor of $x^{100} - 1$?

    c. Is $(x - 1)$ a factor of $x^{99} - 1$?

    e. If n is a positive even integer, is $(x - 1)$ a factor of $x^n - 1$?

    b. Is $(x + 1)$ a factor of $x^{100} - 1$?

    d. Is $(x + 1)$ a factor of $x^{99} - 1$?

    f. If n is a positive odd integer, is $(x + 1)$ a factor of $x^n - 1$?

86. If a fifth-degree polynomial is divided by a second-degree polynomial, the quotient is a _____ -degree polynomial.

87. Determine if the statement is true or false: Zero is a zero of the polynomial $3x^5 - 7x^4 - 2x^3 - 14$.

88. Determine if the statement is true or false: Zero is a zero of the polynomial $-2x^4 + 5x^3 + 6x$.

89. Find m so that $x + 4$ is a factor of $4x^3 + 13x^2 - 5x + m$.

90. Find m so that $x + 5$ is a factor of $-3x^4 - 10x^3 + 20x^2 - 22x + m$.

91. Find m so that $x + 2$ is a factor of $4x^3 + 5x^2 + mx + 2$.

92. Find m so that $x - 3$ is a factor of $2x^3 - 7x^2 + mx + 6$.

93. For what value of r is the statement an identity?
$$\frac{x^2 - x - 12}{x - 4} = x + 3 + \frac{r}{x - 4} \text{ provided that } x \neq 4$$

94. For what value of r is the statement an identity?
$$\frac{x^2 - 5x - 8}{x - 2} = x - 3 + \frac{r}{x - 2} \text{ provided that } x \neq 2$$

95. A metal block is formed from a rectangular solid with a rectangular piece cut out.

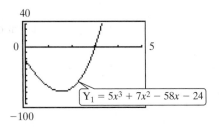

a. Write a polynomial $V(x)$ that represents the volume of the block. All distances in the figure are in centimeters.

b. Use synthetic division to evaluate the volume if x is 6 cm.

96. A wedge is cut from a rectangular solid.

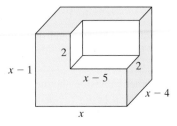

a. Write a polynomial $V(x)$ that represents the volume of the remaining part of the solid. All distances in the figure are in feet.

b. Use synthetic division to evaluate the volume if x is 10 ft.

Write About It

97. Under what circumstances can synthetic division be used to divide polynomials?

98. How can the division algorithm be used to check the result of polynomial division?

99. Given a polynomial $f(x)$ and a constant c, state two methods by which the value $f(c)$ can be computed.

100. Write an informal explanation of the factor theorem.

Expanding Your Skills

101. a. Factor $f(x) = x^3 - 5x^2 + x - 5$ into factors of the form $(x - c)$, given that 5 is a zero.

    b. Solve. $x^3 - 5x^2 + x - 5 = 0$

102. a. Factor $f(x) = x^3 - 3x^2 + 100x - 300$ into factors of the form $(x - c)$, given that 3 is a zero.

    b. Solve. $x^3 - 3x^2 + 100x - 300 = 0$

103. a. Factor $f(x) = x^4 + 2x^3 - 2x^2 - 6x - 3$ into factors of the form $(x - c)$, given that -1 is a zero.

    b. Solve. $x^4 + 2x^3 - 2x^2 - 6x - 3 = 0$

104. a. Factor $f(x) = x^4 + 4x^3 - x^2 - 20x - 20$ into factors of the form $(x - c)$, given that -2 is a zero.

    b. Solve. $x^4 + 4x^3 - x^2 - 20x - 20 = 0$

Technology Connections

For Exercises 105–106,

a. Use the graph to determine a solution to the given equation.

b. Verify your answer from part (a) using the remainder theorem.

c. Find the remaining solutions to the equation.

105. $5x^3 + 7x^2 - 58x - 24 = 0$

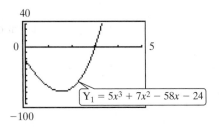

106. $2x^3 - x^2 - 41x + 70 = 0$

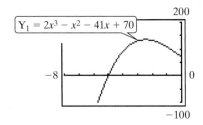

SECTION 3.4   **Zeros of Polynomials**

1. Apply the Rational Zero Theorem

The **zeros of a polynomial** $f(x)$ are the solutions (roots) to the corresponding polynomial equation $f(x) = 0$. For a polynomial function defined by $y = f(x)$, the real zeros of $f(x)$ are the x-intercepts of the graph of the function. Applications of polynomials and polynomial functions arise throughout mathematics. For this reason, it is important to learn techniques to find or approximate the zeros of a polynomial.

The zeros of a polynomial may be real numbers or imaginary numbers. The real zeros can be further categorized as rational or irrational numbers. For example, consider

$$f(x) = 2x^6 - 3x^5 - 7x^4 + 102x^3 - 88x^2 - 279x + 273$$

In factored form this is:

$$f(x) = (x - 1)(2x + 7)\left(x - \sqrt{3}\right)\left(x + \sqrt{3}\right)[x - (2 + 3i)][x - (2 - 3i)]$$

The zeros are:
$$\underbrace{1, -\frac{7}{2}}_{\text{rational zeros}}, \underbrace{\sqrt{3}, -\sqrt{3}}_{\text{irrational zeros}}, \underbrace{2 + 3i, 2 - 3i}_{\text{imaginary zeros}}$$

$$\underbrace{1, -\frac{7}{2}, \sqrt{3}, -\sqrt{3}}_{\text{real zeros}}, \underbrace{2 + 3i, 2 - 3i}_{\text{nonreal zeros}}$$

In this section, we develop tools to search for the zeros of polynomials. First we will consider polynomials with integer coefficients and use the following theorem to search for rational zeros.

TIP   Recall that a rational number is a number that can be expressed as a ratio of two integers.

> **Rational Zero Theorem**
>
> If $f(x) = a_n x^n + a_{n-1}x^{n-1} + a_{n-2}x^{n-2} + \cdots + a_1 x + a_0$ has integer coefficients and $a_n \neq 0$, and if $\frac{p}{q}$ (written in lowest terms) is a rational zero of f, then
>
> - p is a factor of the constant term a_0.
> - q is a factor of the leading coefficient a_n.

The rational zero theorem does not guarantee the existence of rational zeros. Rather, it indicates that *if* a rational zero exists for a polynomial, then it must be of the form

$$\frac{p}{q} = \frac{\text{Factors of } a_0 \, (\text{constant term})}{\text{Factors of } a_n \, (\text{leading coefficient})}$$

The rational zero theorem is important because it limits our search to find rational zeros (if they exist) to a finite number of choices.

EXAMPLE 1 Listing All Possible Rational Zeros

List all possible rational zeros. $f(x) = -2x^5 + 3x^2 - 2x^2 + 10$

Solution:

First note that the polynomial has integer coefficients.

$$f(x) = -2x^5 + 3x^2 - 2x^2 + 10$$

The constant term is 10. $\pm 1, \pm 2, \pm 5, \pm 10$ — Factors of 10

The leading coefficient is -2. $\pm 1, \pm 2$ — Factors of -2

$$\frac{\text{Factors of } 10}{\text{Factors of } -2} = \frac{\pm 1, \pm 2, \pm 5, \pm 10}{\pm 1, \pm 2} = \pm \frac{1}{1}, \pm \frac{2}{1}, \pm \frac{5}{1}, \pm \frac{10}{1}, \pm \frac{1}{2}, \pm \frac{2}{2}, \pm \frac{5}{2}, \pm \frac{10}{2}$$

The values $\pm \frac{2}{2}$ and $\pm \frac{10}{2}$ are redundant. They equal ± 1 and ± 5, respectively. The possible rational zeros are $\pm 1, \pm 2, \pm 5, \pm 10, \pm \frac{1}{2}$, and $\pm \frac{5}{2}$.

> **Skill Practice 1** List all possible rational zeros.
> $f(x) = -4x^4 + 5x^3 - 7x^2 + 8$

EXAMPLE 2 Finding the Zeros of a Polynomial

Find the zeros. $f(x) = x^3 - 4x^2 + 3x + 2$

Solution:

We begin by first looking for rational zeros. We can apply the rational zero theorem because the polynomial has integer coefficients.

$$f(x) = 1x^3 - 4x^2 + 3x + 2$$

Possible rational zeros: $\dfrac{\text{Factors of } 2}{\text{Factors of } 1} = \dfrac{\pm 1, \pm 2}{\pm 1} = \pm 1, \pm 2$

Next, use synthetic division and the remainder theorem to determine if any of the numbers in the list is a zero of f.

> **TIP** Since $f(1) = 2$ and $f(-1) = -6$, we know from the intermediate value theorem that $f(x)$ must have a zero between -1 and 1.

Test $x = 1$:

$$\begin{array}{r|rrrr} 1 & 1 & -4 & 3 & 2 \\ & & 1 & -3 & 0 \\ \hline & 1 & -3 & 0 & |2 \end{array}$$

The remainder is not zero. Therefore, 1 is not a zero of $f(x)$.

Test $x = -1$:

$$\begin{array}{r|rrrr} -1 & 1 & -4 & 3 & 2 \\ & & -1 & 5 & -8 \\ \hline & 1 & -5 & 8 & |-6 \end{array}$$

The remainder is not zero. Therefore, -1 is not a zero of $f(x)$.

Test $x = 2$:

$$\begin{array}{r|rrrr} 2 & 1 & -4 & 3 & 2 \\ & & 2 & -4 & -2 \\ \hline & 1 & -2 & -1 & |0 \end{array}$$

The remainder *is* zero. Therefore, 2 is a zero of $f(x)$.

By the factor theorem, since $f(2) = 0$, then $(x - 2)$ is a factor of $f(x)$. The quotient $(x^2 - 2x - 1)$ is also a factor of $f(x)$. We have

$$f(x) = x^3 - 4x^2 + 3x + 2 = (x - 2)(x^2 - 2x - 1)$$

We now have a third-degree polynomial written as the product of a first-degree polynomial and a quadratic polynomial. The quotient $x^2 - 2x - 1$ is called a **reduced polynomial** (or a **depressed polynomial**) of $f(x)$. It has degree 1 less than the degree of $f(x)$, and the remaining zeros of $f(x)$ are the zeros of the reduced polynomial.

Answer

1. $\pm 1, \pm 2, \pm 4, \pm 8, \pm \frac{1}{2}$, and $\pm \frac{1}{4}$

TIP The graph of $f(x) = x^3 - 4x^2 + 3x + 2$ is shown here. The zeros are $1 + \sqrt{2} \approx 2.41$, $1 - \sqrt{2} \approx -0.41$, and 2.

At this point, we no longer need to test for more rational zeros. The reason is that any remaining zeros (whether they be rational, irrational, or imaginary) are the solutions to the quadratic equation $x^2 - 2x - 1 = 0$. There is no guess work because the equation can be solved by using the quadratic formula.

$$x^2 - 2x - 1 = 0$$

$$x = \frac{-(-2) \pm \sqrt{(-2)^2 - 4(1)(-1)}}{2(1)} = \frac{2 \pm \sqrt{8}}{2} = \frac{2 \pm 2\sqrt{2}}{2}$$

$$= 1 \pm \sqrt{2}$$

The zeros of $f(x)$ are 2, $1 + \sqrt{2}$, and $1 - \sqrt{2}$.

Skill Practice 2   Find the zeros. $f(x) = x^3 - x^2 - 4x - 2$

The polynomial in Example 2 has one rational zero. If we had continued testing for more rational zeros, we would not have found others because the remaining two zeros are irrational numbers. In Example 3, we illustrate the case where a function has multiple rational zeros.

EXAMPLE 3   **Finding the Zeros of a Polynomial**

Find the zeros and their multiplicities. $f(x) = 2x^4 + 5x^3 - 2x^2 - 11x - 6$

Solution:

Begin by searching for rational zeros.

$$f(x) = 2x^4 + 5x^3 - 2x^2 - 11x - 6$$

Possible rational zeros:

$$\frac{\text{Factors of } -6}{\text{Factors of } 2} = \frac{\pm 1, \pm 2, \pm 3, \pm 6}{\pm 1, \pm 2} = \pm 1, \pm 2, \pm 3, \pm 6, \pm \frac{1}{2}, \pm \frac{3}{2}$$

TIP It does not matter in which order you test the potential rational zeros.

We can work methodically through the list of possible rational zeros to determine which if any are actual zeros of $f(x)$. After trying several possibilities, we find that -1 is a zero of $f(x)$.

$$\begin{array}{r|rrrr} -1 & 2 & 5 & -2 & -11 & -6 \\ & & -2 & -3 & 5 & 6 \\ \hline & 2 & 3 & -5 & -6 & \underline{|0} \end{array}$$ The quotient is $2x^3 + 3x^2 - 5x - 6$.

Since $f(-1) = 0$, then $x + 1$ is a factor of $f(x)$.

$$f(x) = 2x^4 + 5x^3 - 2x^2 - 11x - 6 = (x + 1)\underbrace{(2x^3 + 3x^2 - 5x - 6)}$$

Now find the zeros of the quotient.

The zeros of $f(x)$ are -1 along with the roots of the equation $2x^3 + 3x^2 - 5x - 6 = 0$. Therefore, we need to find the zeros of $g(x) = 2x^3 + 3x^2 - 5x - 6$.

The possible rational zeros are $\pm 1, \pm 2, \pm 3, \pm 6, \pm \frac{1}{2}, \pm \frac{3}{2}$.

TIP The zeros of the polynomial in Example 3 are rational numbers (and therefore real numbers). They correspond to x-intercepts on the graph of $y = f(x)$. Also notice that the graph has a touch point at $(-1, 0)$ because -1 has an even multiplicity.

We will test -1 again because it may have multiplicity greater than 1.

$$\begin{array}{r|rrr} -1 & 2 & 3 & -5 & -6 \\ & & -2 & -1 & 6 \\ \hline & 2 & 1 & -6 & \underline{|0} \end{array}$$ The quotient is $2x^2 + x - 6$.

Answer

2. $-1, 1 - \sqrt{3}$, and $1 + \sqrt{3}$

The value -1 is a repeated zero. We have:

$$f(x) = 2x^4 + 5x^3 - 2x^2 - 11x - 6 = (x + 1)(x + 1)(2x^2 + x - 6)$$
$$= (x + 1)^2(2x - 3)(x + 2)$$

> $2x^2 + x - 6$ factors as $(2x - 3)(x + 2)$.

The zeros of $f(x)$ are

-1 (multiplicity 2), $\frac{3}{2}$ (multiplicity 1), and -2 (multiplicity 1).

> **Skill Practice 3** Find the zeros and their multiplicities.
>
> $f(x) = 2x^4 + 3x^3 - 15x^2 - 32x - 12$

In Example 4, we have a polynomial with no rational zeros.

> ## EXAMPLE 4 Finding the Zeros of a Polynomial
>
> Find the zeros. $f(x) = x^4 - 2x^2 - 3$
>
> **Solution:**
>
> $f(x) = 1x^4 - 2x^2 - 3$ The possible rational zeros are $\dfrac{\pm 1, \pm 3}{\pm 1} = \pm 1, \pm 3$.
>
> If we apply the rational zero theorem, we see that $f(x)$ has no *rational* zeros.
>
> $$\begin{array}{c|ccccc} 1 & 1 & 0 & -2 & 0 & -3 \\ & & 1 & 1 & -1 & -1 \\ \hline & 1 & 1 & -1 & -1 & \underline{|-4} \end{array} \qquad \begin{array}{c|ccccc} -1 & 1 & 0 & -2 & 0 & -3 \\ & & -1 & 1 & 1 & -1 \\ \hline & 1 & -1 & -1 & 1 & \underline{|-4} \end{array}$$
>
> $$\begin{array}{c|ccccc} 3 & 1 & 0 & -2 & 0 & -3 \\ & & 3 & 9 & 21 & 63 \\ \hline & 1 & 3 & 7 & 21 & \underline{|60} \end{array} \qquad \begin{array}{c|ccccc} -3 & 1 & 0 & -2 & 0 & -3 \\ & & -3 & 9 & -21 & 63 \\ \hline & 1 & -3 & 7 & -21 & \underline{|60} \end{array}$$
>
> However, finding the zeros of $f(x)$ is equivalent to finding the roots of the equation $x^4 - 2x^2 - 3 = 0$.
>
> $$x^4 - 2x^2 - 3 = 0$$
> $$(x^2 - 3)(x^2 + 1) = 0 \qquad \text{Factor the trinomial.}$$
> $$x^2 - 3 = 0 \quad \text{or} \quad x^2 + 1 = 0 \qquad \text{Set each factor equal to zero.}$$
> $$x = \pm\sqrt{3} \quad \text{or} \quad x = \pm i \qquad \text{Apply the square root property.}$$
>
> > **TIP** From the factor theorem, $f(x) = (x - \sqrt{3})(x + \sqrt{3})(x - i)(x + i)$.
>
> The zeros are $\sqrt{3}$, $-\sqrt{3}$, i, and $-i$.

> **Skill Practice 4** Find the zeros. $f(x) = x^4 - x^2 - 20$

TIP The graph of the function defined by $f(x) = x^4 - 2x^2 - 3$ shows the real zeros of $f(x)$ as x-intercepts.

2. Apply the Fundamental Theorem of Algebra

From Examples 2–4, we see that the zeros of a polynomial may be real numbers (either rational or irrational) or imaginary numbers. In any case, the zeros are complex numbers (recall that complex numbers include both real numbers and imaginary numbers).

To find the zeros of a polynomial, it is important to know how many zeros to expect. This is answered by the following three theorems. The first is called the fundamental theorem of algebra because it is so basic to the foundation of algebra.

Answers

3. -2 (multiplicity 2);
$-\dfrac{1}{2}$ (multiplicity 1); and
3 (multiplicity 1)

4. $\sqrt{5}, -\sqrt{5}, 2i,$ and $-2i$

> ### Fundamental Theorem of Algebra
>
> If $f(x)$ is a polynomial of degree $n \geq 1$ with complex coefficients, then $f(x)$ has at least one complex zero.

The fundamental theorem of algebra, first proved by German mathematician Carl Friedrich Gauss (1777–1855), guarantees that every polynomial function of degree 1 or greater has at least one zero.

Now suppose that $f(x)$ is a polynomial of degree $n \geq 1$ with complex coefficients. The fundamental theorem of algebra guarantees the existence of at least one complex zero, call this c_1. By the factor theorem, we have

$$f(x) = (x - c_1) \cdot q_1(x) \qquad \text{where } q_1(x) \text{ is a polynomial of degree } n - 1.$$

If $q_1(x)$ is of degree 1 or more, then the fundamental theorem of algebra guarantees that $q_1(x)$ must have at least one complex zero, call this c_2. Then,

$$f(x) = (x - c_1) \cdot (x - c_2) \cdot q_2(x) \quad \text{where } q_2(x) \text{ is a polynomial of degree } n - 2.$$

We can continue with this reasoning until the quotient polynomial, $q_n(x)$, is a constant equal to the leading coefficient of $f(x)$.

TIP The set of complex numbers includes the set of real numbers. Therefore, theorems relating to polynomials with complex coefficients also apply to polynomials with real coefficients.

> ### Linear Factorization Theorem
>
> If $f(x) = a_n x^n + a_{n-1} x^{n-1} + a_{n-2} x^{n-2} + \cdots + a_1 x + a_0$, where $n \geq 1$ and $a_n \neq 0$, then
>
> $$f(x) = a_n(x - c_1)(x - c_2) \ldots (x - c_n), \text{ where } c_1, c_2, \ldots, c_n \text{ are complex numbers.}$$
>
> *Note*: The complex numbers $c_1, c_2, \ldots, c_n$ include real and imaginary numbers and are not necessarily unique.

The linear factorization theorem tells us that a polynomial of degree $n \geq 1$ with complex coefficients has exactly n linear factors of the form $(x - c)$, where some of the factors may be repeated. The value of c in each factor is a zero of the function, so the function must also have n zeros provided that the zeros are counted according to their multiplicities.

TIP Refer to Examples 2–4. In each case the number of zeros (including multiplicities) is the same as the degree of the polynomial.

> ### Number of Zeros of a Polynomial
>
> If $f(x)$ is a polynomial of degree $n \geq 1$ with complex coefficients, then $f(x)$ has exactly n complex zeros provided that each zero is counted by its multiplicity.

Now consider the polynomial from Example 4.

$$f(x) = x^4 - 2x^2 - 3 \quad \text{Zeros: } \sqrt{3}, -\sqrt{3}, i, -i$$

Notice that the polynomial has real coefficients. Furthermore, the zeros i and $-i$ appear as a pair. This is not a coincidence. For a polynomial with real coefficients, if $a + bi$ is a zero, then $a - bi$ is a zero.

> ### Conjugate Zeros Theorem
>
> If $f(x)$ is a polynomial with real coefficients and if $a + bi$ $(b \neq 0)$ is a zero of $f(x)$, then its conjugate $a - bi$ is also a zero of $f(x)$.

EXAMPLE 5 Finding Zeros and Factoring a Polynomial

Given $f(x) = x^4 - 6x^3 + 28x^2 - 18x + 75$, and that $3 - 4i$ is a zero of $f(x)$,

a. Find the remaining zeros.

b. Factor $f(x)$ as a product of linear factors.

c. Solve the equation. $x^4 - 6x^3 + 28x^2 - 18x + 75 = 0$

Solution:

$f(x)$ is a fourth-degree polynomial, so we expect to find four zeros (including multiplicities). Further note that because $f(x)$ has real coefficients and because $3 - 4i$ is a zero, then the conjugate $3 + 4i$ must also be a zero. This leaves only two remaining zeros to find.

$$
\begin{array}{r|rrrrr}
3 - 4i & 1 & -6 & 28 & -18 & 75 \\
 & & 3-4i & -25 & 9-12i & -75 \\
\hline
 & 1 & -3-4i & 3 & -9-12i & \underline{0}
\end{array}
$$

Divide by $[x - (3 - 4i)]$. coefficients of the quotient

One strategy is to use synthetic division twice using the two known zeros.

Note: $(3 - 4i)(-3 - 4i)$
$= -9 - 12i + 12i + 16i^2$
$= -25$

Note: $(3 - 4i)(-9 - 12i)$
$= -27 - 36i + 36i + 48i^2$
$= -75$

Since $3 + 4i$ is a zero of $f(x)$ it must also be a zero of the quotient.

$$
\begin{array}{r|rrrr}
3 + 4i & 1 & -3-4i & 3 & -9-12i \\
 & & 3+4i & 0 & 9+12i \\
\hline
 & 1 & 0 & 3 & \underline{0}
\end{array}
$$

Divide by $[x - (3 + 4i)]$.

Divide the quotient by $[x - (3 + 4i)]$.

The resulting quotient is quadratic: $x^2 + 3$.

Now we have $f(x) = [x - (3 - 4i)][x - (3 + 4i)](x^2 + 3)$.
The remaining two zeros are found by solving $x^2 + 3 = 0$.

$$
\begin{aligned}
x^2 + 3 &= 0 \\
x^2 &= -3 \\
x &= \pm i\sqrt{3}
\end{aligned}
$$

a. The zeros of $f(x)$ are: $3 - 4i$, $3 + 4i$, $i\sqrt{3}$, and $-i\sqrt{3}$.

b. $f(x)$ factors as four linear factors:

$$f(x) = [x - (3 - 4i)][x - (3 + 4i)](x - i\sqrt{3})(x + i\sqrt{3})$$

c. The solution set for $x^4 - 6x^3 + 28x^2 - 18x + 75 = 0$ is $\{3 \pm 4i, \pm i\sqrt{3}\}$.

Skill Practice 5   Given $f(x) = x^4 - 2x^3 + 28x^2 - 4x + 52$, and that $1 + 5i$ is a zero of $f(x)$,

a. Find the zeros.

b. Factor $f(x)$ as a product of linear factors.

c. Solve the equation. $x^4 - 2x^3 + 28x^2 - 4x + 52 = 0$

Answers

5. a. Zeros:
$1 + 5i, 1 - 5i, i\sqrt{2}, -i\sqrt{2}$

b. $f(x) = [x - (1 + 5i)][x - (1 - 5i)]$
$(x - i\sqrt{2})(x + i\sqrt{2})$

c. $\{1 \pm 5i, \pm i\sqrt{2}\}$

> ### EXAMPLE 6   Building a Polynomial with Specified Conditions

a. Find a third-degree polynomial $f(x)$ with integer coefficients and with zeros of $2i$ and $\frac{2}{3}$.

b. Find a polynomial $g(x)$ of lowest degree with zeros of -2 (multiplicity 1) and 4 (multiplicity 3), and satisfying the condition that $g(0) = 256$.

Solution:

a. $f(x)$ is to be a polynomial with integer coefficients (and therefore real coefficients). If $2i$ is a zero, then $-2i$ must also be a zero. By the linear factorization theorem we have:

$$f(x) = a(x - 2i)(x + 2i)\left(x - \frac{2}{3}\right) \qquad a \text{ is a nonzero number.}$$

$$= a(x^2 + 4)\left(x - \frac{2}{3}\right) \qquad \text{Multiply conjugates.}$$

$$= a\left(x^3 - \frac{2}{3}x^2 + 4x - \frac{8}{3}\right)$$

$$= 3\left(x^3 - \frac{2}{3}x^2 + 4x - \frac{8}{3}\right) \qquad \begin{array}{l}\text{To give } f(x) \text{ integer coefficients, choose } a \text{ to}\\ \text{be any multiple of 3. We have chosen 3 itself.}\end{array}$$

$$= 3x^3 - 2x^2 + 12x - 8$$

b. $g(x) = a(x + 2)^1(x - 4)^3$ $\quad$ -2 is a zero of multiplicity 1.

$$= a(x + 2)(x^3 - 12x^2 + 48x - 64) \qquad \text{4 is a zero of multiplicity 3.}$$

$$= a(x^4 - 10x^3 + 24x^2 + 32x - 128)$$

Note:
$(x - 4)^3 = (x - 4)^2(x - 4)$
$= (x^2 - 8x + 16)(x - 4)$
$= x^3 - 12x^2 + 48x - 64$

We also have the condition that $g(0) = 256$.

$$g(0) = a[(0)^4 - 10(0)^3 + 24(0)^2 + 32(0) - 128] = 256$$

$$-128a = 256$$

$$a = -2$$

Therefore, $g(x) = -2(x^4 - 10x^3 + 24x^2 + 32x - 128)$

$$g(x) = -2x^4 + 20x^3 - 48x^2 - 64x + 256$$

Skill Practice 6

a. Find a third-degree polynomial $f(x)$ with integer coefficients and with zeros of $5i$ and $\frac{4}{3}$.

b. Find a polynomial $g(x)$ with zeros of -3 (multiplicity 2) and 5 (multiplicity 2), and satisfying the condition that $g(0) = 450$.

3. Apply Descartes' Rule of Signs

Finding the zeros of a polynomial analytically can be a difficult (or impossible) task. For example, consider

$$f(x) = x^5 - 18x^4 + 128x^3 - 450x^2 + 783x - 540$$

Applying the rational zero theorem gives us the following possible rational zeros:

$$\pm 1, \pm 2, \pm 3, \pm 4, \pm 5, \pm 6, \pm 9, \pm 10, \pm 12, \pm 15, \pm 18, \pm 20,$$
$$\pm 27, \pm 30, \pm 36, \pm 45, \pm 54, \pm 60, \pm 90, \pm 108, \pm 135, \pm 180, \pm 270, \pm 540$$

Answers
6. a. $f(x) = 3x^3 - 4x^2 + 75x - 100$
   b. $g(x) = 2x^4 - 8x^3 - 52x^2 + 120x + 450$

However, we can use the upper and lower bound theorem to show that the real zeros of $f(x)$ are between -1 and 18. Furthermore, we can use a tool called Descartes' rule of signs to show that none of the zeros is negative. This eliminates all possible rational zeros except for 1, 2, 3, 4, 5, 6, 9, 10, 12, and 15.

To study Descartes' rule of signs, we need to establish what is meant by "sign changes" between consecutive terms in a polynomial. For example, the following polynomial is written in descending order and has three changes in sign between consecutive coefficients.

$$2x^6 - 3x^4 - x^3 + 5x^2 - 6x - 4 \qquad \text{(3 sign changes)}$$

| positive to negative | negative to positive | positive to negative |

Descartes' Rule of Signs

Let $f(x)$ be a polynomial with real coefficients and a nonzero constant term. Then,

1. The number of *positive* real zeros is either
   - the same as the number of sign changes in $f(x)$ or
   - less than the number of sign changes in $f(x)$ by a positive even integer.
2. The number of *negative* real zeros is either
   - the same as the number of sign changes in $f(-x)$ or
   - less than the number of sign changes in $f(-x)$ by a positive even integer.

Descartes' rule of signs is demonstrated in Examples 7 and 8.

EXAMPLE 7   Applying Descartes' Rule of Signs

Determine the number of possible positive and negative real zeros.

$$f(x) = x^5 - 6x^4 + 12x^3 - 12x^2 + 11x - 6$$

Solution:

$f(x)$ has real coefficients and the constant term is nonzero.

To determine the number of possible positive real zeros, determine the number of sign changes in $f(x)$.

$$f(x) = x^5 - 6x^4 + 12x^3 - 12x^2 + 11x - 6 \qquad \text{(5 sign changes)}$$

The number of possible positive real zeros is either 5, 3, or 1.

To determine the number of possible negative real zeros, determine the number of sign changes in $f(-x)$.

$$f(-x) = (-x)^5 - 6(-x)^4 + 12(-x)^3 - 12(-x)^2 + 11(-x) - 6$$
$$f(-x) = -x^5 - 6x^4 - 12x^3 - 12x^2 - 11x - 6 \qquad \text{(0 sign changes)}$$

There are no sign changes in $f(-x)$. Therefore, $f(x)$ has no negative real zeros.

Number of possible positive real zeros	5	3	1
Number of possible negative real zeros	0	0	0
Number of imaginary zeros	0	2	4
Total (including multiplicities)	5	5	5

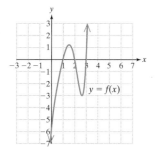

Figure 3-15

The graph of $f(x) = x^5 - 6x^4 + 12x^3 - 12x^2 + 11x - 6$ is shown in Figure 3-15. Notice that there are three positive x-intercepts and therefore, three positive real zeros. There are no negative x-intercepts as expected. The remaining zeros of the polynomial $x^5 - 6x^4 + 12x^3 - 12x^2 + 11x - 6$ are imaginary numbers.

Skill Practice 7   Determine the number of possible positive and negative real zeros. $f(x) = 4x^5 + 6x^3 + 2x^2 + 6$

EXAMPLE 8   **Applying Descartes' Rule of Signs**

Determine the number of possible positive and negative real zeros.

$$g(x) = 2x^6 - 5x^4 - 3x^3 + 7x^2 + 2x + 5$$

Solution:

$g(x)$ has real coefficients and the constant term is nonzero.

$$g(x) = 2x^6 - 5x^4 - 3x^3 + 7x^2 + 2x + 5 \qquad \text{2 sign changes in } g(x)$$

The number of possible positive real zeros is either 2 or 0.

$$g(-x) = 2(-x)^6 - 5(-x)^4 - 3(-x)^3 + 7(-x)^2 + 2(-x) + 5$$
$$g(-x) = 2x^6 - 5x^4 + 3x^3 + 7x^2 - 2x + 5 \qquad \text{4 sign changes in } g(-x)$$

The number of possible negative real zeros is either 4, 2, or 0.

Number of possible positive real zeros	2	2	2	0	0	0
Number of possible negative real zeros	4	2	0	4	2	0
Number of imaginary zeros	0	2	4	2	4	6
Total (including multiplicities)	6	6	6	6	6	6

Skill Practice 8   Determine the number of possible positive and negative real zeros. $g(x) = 8x^6 - 5x^7 + 3x^5 - x^2 - 3x + 1$

Descartes' rule of signs stipulates that the constant term of the polynomial $f(x)$ is nonzero. If the constant term is 0, we can factor out the lowest power of x and apply Descartes' rule of signs to the resulting factor.

$$f(x) = x^7 - 8x^6 + 15x^5$$
$$f(x) = x^5(x^2 - 8x + 15)$$

Descartes' rule of signs can be applied to $x^2 - 8x + 15$ to show that there may be 2 or 0 remaining positive real zeros.

The value 0 is a zero of $f(x)$ of multiplicity 5.

4. Find Upper and Lower Bounds

The next theorem helps us limit our search for the real zeros of a polynomial. First we define two key terms.

- A real number b is called an **upper bound** of the real zeros of a polynomial if all real zeros are less than or equal to b.
- A real number a is called a **lower bound** of the real zeros of a polynomial if all real zeros are greater than or equal to a.

Avoiding Mistakes

It is important to note that upper and lower bounds are not unique. Any number greater than b is also an upper bound for the zeros of the polynomial. Likewise any number less than a is also a lower bound.

Answers
7. Positive: 0; Negative: 1
8. Positive: 4, 2, or 0; Negative: 2 or 0

> ### Upper and Lower Bound Theorem for the Real Zeros of a Polynomial
>
> Let $f(x)$ be a polynomial of degree $n \geq 1$ with real coefficients and a positive leading coefficient. Further suppose that $f(x)$ is divided by $(x - c)$.
>
> 1. If $c > 0$ and if both the remainder and the coefficients of the quotient are nonnegative, then c is an upper bound for the real zeros of $f(x)$.
> 2. If $c < 0$ and the coefficients of the quotient and the remainder alternate in sign (with 0 being considered either positive or negative as needed), then c is a lower bound for the real zeros of $f(x)$.

The rules for finding upper and lower bounds are stated for polynomial functions having a positive leading coefficient. However, $f(x) = 0$ and $-f(x) = 0$ are equivalent equations. Therefore, if $f(x)$ has a negative leading coefficient, we can factor out -1 from $f(x)$ and apply the rule for upper and lower bounds accordingly.

EXAMPLE 9   Applying the Upper and Lower Bound Theorem

Given $f(x) = 2x^5 + x^4 + 9x^2 - 32x + 20$,

a. Determine if the upper bound theorem identifies 2 as an upper bound for the real zeros of $f(x)$.

b. Determine if the lower bound theorem identifies -2 as a lower bound for the real zeros of $f(x)$.

Solution:

a. Divide $f(x)$ by $(x - 2)$.

First note that $2 > 0$ and the leading coefficient of the polynomial is positive.

$$
\begin{array}{r|rrrrrr}
2 & 2 & 1 & 0 & 9 & -32 & 20 \\
  &   & 4 & 10 & 20 & 58 & 52 \\
\hline
  & 2 & 5 & 10 & 29 & 26 & \underline{|72} \\
\end{array}
$$

This row nonnegative

The remainder and all coefficients of the quotient are nonnegative.

2 is an upper bound for the real zeros of $f(x)$.

b. Divide $f(x)$ by $(x + 2)$.

$$
\begin{array}{r|rrrrrr}
-2 & 2 & 1 & 0 & 9 & -32 & 20 \\
   &   & -4 & 6 & -12 & 6 & 52 \\
\hline
   & 2 & -3 & 6 & -3 & -26 & \underline{|72} \\
   & + & - & + & - & - & + \\
\end{array}
$$

No sign change

The signs of the quotient do not alternate. Therefore, we cannot conclude that -2 is a lower bound for the real zeros of $f(x)$.

Skill Practice 9   Given $f(x) = x^4 - 2x^3 - 13x^2 - 4x - 30$,

a. Determine if the upper bound theorem identifies 4 as an upper bound for the real zeros of $f(x)$.

b. Determine if the lower bound theorem identifies -4 as a lower bound for the real zeros of $f(x)$.

Answers
9. a. No   **b.** Yes

TIP From Example 9, although we cannot conclude that -2 is a lower bound for the real zeros of $f(x)$, we can try other negative real numbers. For example, -3 is a lower bound for the real zeros of $f(x)$.

$$
\begin{array}{r|rrrrrr}
-3 & 2 & 1 & 0 & 9 & -32 & 20 \\
   &   & -6 & 15 & -45 & 108 & -228 \\
\hline
   & 2 & -5 & 15 & -36 & 76 & \boxed{-208}
\end{array}
\qquad \text{Therefore, } -3 \text{ is a lower bound.}
$$

signs all alternate

In Example 10, we will use the tools presented in Sections 3.2–3.4 to find all zeros of a polynomial.

EXAMPLE 10 | **Finding the Zeros of a Polynomial**

Find the zeros and their multiplicities. $f(x) = 2x^5 + x^4 + 9x^2 - 32x + 20$

Solution:

$f(x)$ is a fifth-degree polynomial and must have five zeros (including multiplicities). We begin by finding the rational zeros (if any exist). By the rational zero theorem, the possible rational zeros are

$$\pm 1,\ \pm 2,\ \pm 4,\ \pm 5,\ \pm 10,\ \pm 20,\ \pm \frac{1}{2},\ \pm \frac{5}{2}$$

However, we also know from Example 9 that 2 is not a zero of $f(x)$, but is an upper bound for the real zeros. From the Tip following Example 9, we know that -3 is not a zero of $f(x)$, but is a lower bound for the real zeros. Therefore, we can restrict the list of possible rational zeros to those on the interval $(-3, 2)$.

$$-\frac{5}{2},\ -2,\ \pm \frac{1}{2},\ \pm 1$$

After testing several possible rational zeros, we find that 1 is a zero.

$$
\begin{array}{r|rrrrrr}
1 & 2 & 1 & 0 & 9 & -32 & 20 \\
  &   & 2 & 3 & 3 & 12 & -20 \\
\hline
  & 2 & 3 & 3 & 12 & -20 & \boxed{0}
\end{array}
$$

We have $f(x) = (x - 1)(2x^4 + 3x^3 + 3x^2 + 12x - 20)$. Now look for the zeros of the reduced polynomial. We will try 1 again because it may be a repeated zero.

$$
\begin{array}{r|rrrrr}
1 & 2 & 3 & 3 & 12 & -20 \\
  &   & 2 & 5 & 8 & 20 \\
\hline
  & 2 & 5 & 8 & 20 & \boxed{0}
\end{array}
\qquad \text{The value 1 is a repeated zero.}
$$

We have $f(x) = (x - 1)^2 (2x^3 + 5x^2 + 8x + 20)$.

Because the polynomial $2x^3 + 5x^2 + 8x + 20$ has no sign changes, Descartes' rule of signs indicates that there are no other positive real zeros. Now the list of possible rational zeros is restricted to $-\frac{5}{2}$, -2, and -1. We find that $-\frac{5}{2}$ is a zero of $f(x)$.

$$
\begin{array}{r|rrrr}
-\frac{5}{2} & 2 & 5 & 8 & 20 \\
            &   & -5 & 0 & -20 \\
\hline
            & 2 & 0 & 8 & \boxed{0}
\end{array}
$$

Thus, $f(x) = (x - 1)^2(x + \frac{5}{2})(2x^2 + 8)$.

$$2x^2 + 8 = 0$$
$$x^2 = -4$$
$$x = \pm 2i$$

The remaining two zeros are found by solving the equation $2x^2 + 8 = 0$.

The zeros are: 1 (multiplicity of 2), $-\frac{5}{2}$, $2i$, and $-2i$ (each with multiplicity of 1).

> **Skill Practice 10** Find the zeros and their multiplicities.
> $f(x) = x^5 + 6x^3 - 2x^2 - 27x - 18$

The graph of $f(x) = 2x^5 + x^4 + 9x^2 - 32x + 20$ from Example 10 is shown in Figure 3-16. The end behavior is down to the left and up to the right as expected.

The real zeros of $f(x)$ correspond to the x-intercepts $\left(-\frac{5}{2}, 0\right)$ and $(1, 0)$. The point $(1, 0)$ is a touch point because 1 is a zero with an even multiplicity. The graph crosses the x-axis at $-\frac{5}{2}$ because $-\frac{5}{2}$ is a zero with an odd multiplicity.

Figure 3-16

TECHNOLOGY CONNECTIONS

Applications of Graphing Utilities to Polynomials

A graphing utility can help us analyze a polynomial. For example, given $f(x) = 2x^3 - 11x^2 - 5x + 50$, the possible rational zeros are: $\pm 1, \pm 2, \pm 5, \pm 10, \pm 25, \pm 50,$ $\pm\frac{1}{2}, \pm\frac{5}{2},$ and $\pm\frac{25}{2}$. By graphing the function f on a graphing utility, it appears that the function may cross the x-axis at -2, 2.5, and 5. So we might consider testing these values first.

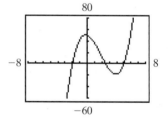

Our knowledge of algebra can also help us use a graphing device effectively. Consider $f(x) = 2x^5 + x^4 + 9x^2 - 32x + 20$ from Examples 9 and 10. We know that -3 is a lower bound for the real zeros of $f(x)$ and that 2 is an upper bound. Therefore, we can set a viewing window showing x between -3 and 2 and be guaranteed to see all the real zeros of $f(x)$.

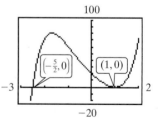

Finally, when analytical methods fail, we can use the **Zero** feature on a graphing utility to approximate the real zeros of a polynomial. Given $f(x) = x^3 - 7.14x^2 + 25.6x - 40.8$, the calculator approximates a zero of 3.1258745. The real zeros of a function can also be approximated by repeated use of the intermediate value theorem. (See the online group activity "Investigating the Bisection Method for Finding Zeros.")

Answer

10. -1 (multiplicity 2), 2, $3i$, $-3i$ (each with multiplicity 1)

SECTION 3.4   Practice Exercises

Review Exercises

1. For the elements in set A, determine which are

   a. Rational numbers.

   b. Irrational numbers.

   c. Real numbers.

   d. Imaginary numbers.

   e. Complex numbers.

$$A = \left\{ -4, \frac{2}{5}, \sqrt{10}, 6i, 3 + 8i, 4 - \sqrt{2} \right\}$$

2. a. Factor $x^2 - 25$ over the integers.

   b. Factor $x^2 + 25$ over the complex numbers.

For Exercises 3–4, determine the zeros and multiplicities for each polynomial.

3. $f(x) = -3x^4(x - 2)^3(4x - 7)^2$

4. $f(x) = 5x(x + 6)^2(5x - 1)^5$

5. Given $f(x) = 2x^3 - 7x^2 + 12x - 31$,

   a. Evaluate $f(3)$ by direct substitution

   b. Evaluate $f(3)$ by using synthetic division and the remainder theorem.

6. a. Solve the equation $x^4 - 13x^2 + 36 = 0$

   b. State the zeros of the polynomial $f(x) = x^4 - 13x^2 + 36$

Concept Connections

7. The _____ of a polynomial $f(x)$ are the solutions (or roots) of the equation $f(x) = 0$.

8. If $f(x)$ is a polynomial of degree $n \geq 1$ with complex coefficients, then $f(x)$ has at least one complex zero. This is the statement of what important theorem?

9. If $f(x)$ is a polynomial of degree $n \geq 1$ with complex coefficients, then $f(x)$ has exactly _____ complex zeros, provided that each zero is counted by its multiplicity.

10. The conjugate zeros theorem states that if $f(x)$ is a polynomial with real coefficients, and if $a + bi$ is a zero of $f(x)$, then _____ is also a zero of $f(x)$.

11. _____ rule of signs uses the number of variations in sign of $f(x)$ to determine the number of possible positive real zeros of $f(x)$. It uses the number of variations in sign of _____ to determine the number of possible negative real zeros of $f(x)$.

12. A real number b is called an _____ bound of the real zeros of a polynomial $f(x)$ if all real zeros of $f(x)$ are less than or equal to b.

13. A real number a is called a lower bound of the real zeros of a polynomial $f(x)$ if all real zeros of $f(x)$ are _____ or equal to a.

14. Explain why the number 7 cannot be a rational zero of the polynomial $f(x) = 2x^3 + 5x^2 - x + 6$.

Objective 1: Apply the Rational Zero Theorem

For Exercises 15–20, list the possible rational zeros. (See Example 1)

15. $f(x) = x^5 - 2x^3 + 7x^2 + 4$

16. $g(x) = x^3 - 5x^2 + 2x - 9$

17. $h(x) = 4x^4 + 9x^3 + 2x - 6$

18. $k(x) = 25x^7 + 22x^4 - 3x^2 + 10$

19. $m(x) = -12x^6 + 4x^3 - 3x^2 + 8$

20. $n(x) = -16x^4 - 7x^3 + 2x + 6$

21. Which of the following is *not* a possible zero of $f(x) = 2x^3 - 5x^2 + 12$?

$$1, 7, \frac{5}{3}, \frac{3}{2}$$

22. Which of the following is *not* a possible zero of $f(x) = 4x^5 - 2x^3 + 10$?

$$3, 5, \frac{5}{2}, \frac{3}{2}$$

For Exercises 23–24, find all the rational zeros.

23. $p(x) = 2x^4 - x^3 - 5x^2 + 2x + 2$

24. $q(x) = x^4 + x^3 - 7x^2 - 5x + 10$

For Exercises 25–34, find all the zeros. (See Examples 2–4)

25. $f(x) = x^3 - 7x^2 + 6x + 20$
26. $g(x) = x^3 - 7x^2 + 14x - 6$
27. $h(x) = 5x^3 - x^2 - 35x + 7$

28. $k(x) = 7x^3 - x^2 - 21x + 3$
29. $m(x) = 3x^4 - x^3 - 36x^2 + 60x - 16$
30. $n(x) = 2x^4 + 9x^3 - 5x^2 - 57x - 45$

31. $q(x) = x^3 - 4x^2 - 2x + 20$
32. $p(x) = x^3 - 8x^2 + 29x - 52$
33. $t(x) = x^4 - x^2 - 90$

34. $v(x) = x^4 - 12x^2 - 13$

Objective 2: Apply the Fundamental Theorem of Algebra

35. Given a polynomial $f(x)$ of degree $n \geq 1$, the fundamental theorem of algebra guarantees at least _____ complex zero.

36. The number of zeros of $f(x) = 4x^3 - 5x^2 + 6x - 3$ is _____, provided that each zero is counted according to its multiplicity.

37. If $f(x)$ is a polynomial with real coefficients and zeros of 5 (multiplicity 2), -1 (multiplicity 1), $2i$, and $3 + 4i$, what is the minimum degree of $f(x)$?

38. If $g(x)$ is a polynomial with real coefficients and zeros of -4 (multiplicity 3), 6 (multiplicity 2), $1 + i$, and $2 - 7i$, what is the minimum degree of $g(x)$?

For Exercises 39–44, a polynomial $f(x)$ and one or more of its zeros is given.

a. Find all the zeros.

b. Factor $f(x)$ as a product of linear factors.

c. Solve the equation $f(x) = 0$. (**See Example 5**)

39. $f(x) = x^4 - 4x^3 + 22x^2 + 28x - 203$; $2 - 5i$ is a zero
40. $f(x) = x^4 - 6x^3 + 5x^2 + 30x - 50$; $3 - i$ is a zero

41. $f(x) = 3x^3 - 28x^2 + 83x - 68$; $4 + i$ is a zero
42. $f(x) = 5x^3 - 54x^2 + 170x - 104$; $5 + i$ is a zero

43. $f(x) = 4x^5 + 37x^4 + 117x^3 + 87x^2 - 193x - 52$; $-3 + 2i$ and $-\dfrac{1}{4}$ are zeros

44. $f(x) = 2x^5 - 5x^4 - 4x^3 - 22x^2 + 50x + 75$; $-1 - 2i$ and $\dfrac{5}{2}$ are zeros

For Exercises 45–52, write a polynomial $f(x)$ that satisfies the given conditions. (See Example 6)

45. Degree 3 polynomial with integer coefficients with zeros $6i$ and $\frac{4}{5}$

46. Degree 3 polynomial with integer coefficients with zeros $-4i$ and $\frac{3}{2}$

47. Polynomial of lowest degree with zeros of -4 (multiplicity 1), 2 (multiplicity 3) and with $f(0) = 160$

48. Polynomial of lowest degree with zeros of 5 (multiplicity 2) and -3 (multiplicity 2) and with $f(0) = -450$

49. Polynomial of lowest degree with zeros of $-\frac{4}{3}$ (multiplicity 2) and $\frac{1}{2}$ (multiplicity 1) and with $f(0) = -16$

50. Polynomial of lowest degree with zeros of $-\frac{5}{6}$ (multiplicity 2) and $\frac{1}{3}$ (multiplicity 1) and with $f(0) = -25$

51. Polynomial of lowest degree with real coefficients and with zeros $7 - 4i$ (multiplicity 1) and 0 (multiplicity 4)

52. Polynomial of lowest degree with real coefficients and with zeros $5 - 10i$ (multiplicity 1) and 0 (multiplicity 3)

Objective 3: Apply Descartes' Rule of Signs

For Exercises 53–60, determine the number of possible positive and negative real zeros for the given function. (See Examples 7–8)

53. $f(x) = x^6 - 2x^4 + 4x^3 - 2x^2 - 5x - 6$
54. $g(x) = 3x^7 + 4x^4 - 6x^3 + 5x^2 - 6x + 1$

55. $k(x) = -8x^7 + 5x^6 - 3x^4 + 2x^3 - 11x^2 + 4x - 3$
56. $h(x) = -4x^9 + 6x^8 - 5x^5 - 2x^4 + 3x^2 - x + 8$

57. $p(x) = 0.11x^4 + 0.04x^3 + 0.31x^2 + 0.27x + 1.1$
58. $q(x) = -0.6x^4 + 0.8x^3 - 0.6x^2 + 0.1x - 0.4$

59. $v(x) = \dfrac{1}{8}x^6 + \dfrac{1}{6}x^4 + \dfrac{1}{3}x^2 + \dfrac{1}{10}$
60. $t(x) = \dfrac{1}{1000}x^6 + \dfrac{1}{100}x^4 + \dfrac{1}{10}x^2 + 1$

For Exercises 61–62, use Descartes' rule of signs to determine the total number of real zeros and the number of positive and negative real zeros. (*Hint*: First factor out x to its lowest power.)

61. $f(x) = x^8 + 5x^6 + 6x^4 - x^3$
62. $f(x) = -5x^8 - 3x^6 - 4x^2 + x$

Objective 4: Find Upper and Lower Bounds

For Exercises 63–68, (See Example 9)

a. Determine if the upper bound theorem identifies the given number as an upper bound for the real zeros of $f(x)$.

b. Determine if the lower bound theorem identifies the given number as a lower bound for the real zeros of $f(x)$.

63. $f(x) = x^5 + 6x^4 + 5x^2 + x - 3$
    a. 2   **b.** -5

64. $f(x) = x^4 + 8x^3 - 4x^2 + 7x - 3$
    a. 3   **b.** -4

65. $f(x) = 8x^3 - 42x^2 + 33x + 28$
    a. 6   **b.** -1

66. $f(x) = 6x^3 - x^2 - 57x + 70$
    a. 4   **b.** -4

67. $f(x) = 2x^5 + 11x^4 - 63x^2 - 50x + 40$
    a. 3   **b.** -6

68. $f(x) = 3x^5 - 16x^4 + 5x^3 + 90x^2 - 138x + 36$
    a. 6   **b.** -3

For Exercises 69–72, determine if the statement is true or false.

69. If 5 is an upper bound for the real zeros of $f(x)$, then 6 is also an upper bound.

70. If 5 is an upper bound for the real zeros of $f(x)$, then 4 is also an upper bound.

71. If -3 is a lower bound for the real zeros of $f(x)$, then -2 is also a lower bound.

72. If -3 is a lower bound for the real zeros of $f(x)$, then -4 is also a lower bound.

For Exercises 73–84, find the zeros and their multiplicities. Consider using Descartes' rule of signs and the upper and lower bound theorem to limit your search for rational zeros. (See Example 10)

73. $f(x) = 8x^3 - 42x^2 + 33x + 28$
    (*Hint*: See Exercise 65.)

74. $f(x) = 6x^3 - x^2 - 57x + 70$
    (*Hint*: See Exercise 66.)

75. $f(x) = 2x^5 + 11x^4 - 63x^2 - 50x + 40$
    (*Hint*: See Exercise 67.)

76. $f(x) = 3x^5 - 16x^4 + 5x^3 + 90x^2 - 138x + 36$
    (*Hint*: See Exercise 68.)

77. $f(x) = 4x^4 + 20x^3 + 13x^2 - 30x + 9$

78. $f(x) = 9x^4 + 30x^3 + 13x^2 - 20x + 4$

79. $f(x) = x^6 + 2x^5 + 11x^4 + 20x^3 + 10x^2$

80. $f(x) = x^6 + 6x^5 + 12x^4 + 18x^3 + 27x^2$

81. $f(x) = x^5 - 10x^4 + 34x^3$

82. $f(x) = x^6 - 12x^5 + 40x^4$

83. $f(x) = -x^3 + 3x^2 - 9x - 13$

84. $f(x) = -x^3 + 5x^2 - 11x + 15$

Mixed Exercises

For Exercises 85–90, determine if the statement is true or false.

85. A polynomial with real coefficients of degree 4 must have at least one real zero.

86. Given $f(x) = 2ix^4 - (3 + 6i)x^3 + 5x^2 + 7$, if $a + bi$ is a zero of $f(x)$, then $a - bi$ must also be a zero.

87. The graph of a 10th-degree polynomial must cross the x-axis exactly once.

88. Suppose that $f(x)$ is a polynomial, and that a and b are real numbers where $a < b$. If $f(a) < 0$ and $f(b) < 0$, then $f(x)$ has no real zeros on the interval $[a, b]$.

89. If c is a zero of a polynomial $f(x)$, with degree $n \geq 2$ then all other zeros of $f(x)$ are zeros of $\dfrac{f(x)}{x - c}$.

90. If b is an upper bound for the real zeros of a polynomial, then $-b$ is a lower bound for the real zeros of the polynomial.

91. Given that $x - c$ divides evenly into a polynomial $f(x)$, which statements are true?
    a. $x - c$ is a factor of $f(x)$.
    b. c is a zero of $f(x)$.
    c. The remainder of $f(x) \div (x - c)$ is 0.
    d. c is a solution (root) of the equation $f(x) = 0$.

92. a. Use the quadratic formula to solve
    $x^2 - 7x + 5 = 0$.
    b. Write $x^2 - 7x + 5$ as a product of linear factors.

93. a. Use the intermediate value theorem to show that $f(x) = 2x^2 - 7x + 4$ has a real zero on the interval $[2, 3]$.
    b. Find the zeros.

94. Show that $x - a$ is a factor of $x^n - a^n$ for any positive integer n and constant a.

Write About It

95. Explain why a polynomial with real coefficients of degree 3 must have at least one real zero.

96. Why is it not necessary to apply the rational zero theorem, Descartes' rule of signs, or the upper and lower bound theorem to find the zeros of a second-degree polynomial?

97. Explain why $f(x) = 5x^6 + 7x^4 + x^2 + 9$ has no real zeros.

98. Explain why the fundamental theorem of algebra does not apply to $f(x) = \sqrt{x} + 3$. That is, no complex number c exists such that $f(c) = 0$.

Expanding Your Skills

99. Let n be a positive even integer. Determine the greatest number of possible imaginary zeros of $f(x) = x^n - 1$.

100. Let n be a positive odd integer. Determine the greatest number of possible imaginary zeros of $f(x) = x^n - 1$.

101. The front face of a tent is triangular and the height of the triangle is two-thirds of the base. The length of the tent is 3 ft more than the base of the triangular face. If the tent holds a volume of 108 ft^3, determine its dimensions.

102. An underground storage tank for gasoline is in the shape of a right circular cylinder with hemispheres on each end. If the total volume of the tank is $\dfrac{104\pi}{3}$ ft^3, find the radius of the tank.

10 ft

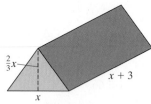

103. A food company originally sells cereal in boxes with dimensions 10 in. by 7 in. by 2.5 in. To make more profit, the company decreases each dimension of the box by x inches but keeps the price the same. If the new volume is 81 in.^{3} by how much was each dimension decreased?

104. A truck rental company rents a 12-ft by 8-ft by 6-ft truck for $69.95 per day plus mileage. A customer prefers to rent a less expensive smaller truck whose dimensions are x ft smaller on a side. If the volume of the smaller truck is 240 ft^3, determine the dimensions of the smaller truck.

105. A rectangle is bounded by the x-axis and a parabola defined by $y = 4 - x^2$. What are the dimensions of the rectangle if the area is 6 cm^2? Assume that all units of length are in centimeters.

106. A rectangle is bounded by the parabola defined by $y = x^2$, the x-axis, and the line $x = 5$ as shown in the figure. If the area of the rectangle is 12 in.^{2} determine the dimensions of the rectangle.

The linear factorization theorem tells us that a polynomial of degree $n \geq 1$ factors into n linear factors over the complex numbers. If we do not factor over the set of complex numbers, then a polynomial with real coefficients can be factored into linear factors and irreducible quadratic factors. An *irreducible quadratic factor* is a quadratic polynomial that does not factor further over the set of real numbers.

For example, consider the polynomial $f(x) = x^4 - 5x^3 + 5x^2 + 25x - 26$.

Factoring over the real numbers, we have two linear factors and one irreducible quadratic factor:

$$x^4 - 5x^3 + 5x^2 + 25x - 26 = \underbrace{(x + 2)(x - 1)}_{\text{2 linear factors}}\underbrace{(x^2 - 6x + 13)}_{\substack{\text{irreducible} \\ \text{quadratic factor}}}$$

Factoring over the complex numbers, we have four linear factors as guaranteed by the linear factor theorem.

$$x^4 - 5x^3 + 5x^2 + 25x - 26 = (x + 2)(x - 1)[x - (3 + 2i)][x - (3 - 2i)]$$

For Exercises 107–110,

   a. Factor the polynomial over the set of real numbers.   **b.** Factor the polynomial over the set of complex numbers.

107. $f(x) = x^4 + 2x^3 + x^2 + 8x - 12$ **108.** $f(x) = x^4 - 6x^3 + 9x^2 - 6x + 8$

109. $f(x) = x^4 + 2x^2 - 35$ **110.** $f(x) = x^4 + 8x^2 - 33$

111. Find all fourth roots of 1, by solving the equation $x^4 = 1$. (*Hint*: Find the zeros of the polynomial $f(x) = x^4 - 1$.)

112. Find all sixth roots of 1, by solving the equation $x^6 = 1$. [*Hint*: Find the zeros of the polynomial $f(x) = x^6 - 1$. Begin by factoring $x^6 - 1$ as $(x^3 - 1)(x^3 + 1)$.]

113. Use the rational zero theorem to show that $\sqrt{5}$ is an irrational number. (*Hint*: Show that $f(x) = x^2 - 5$ has no rational zeros.)

114. a. Given a linear equation $ax + b = 0$ $(a \neq 0)$, the solution is given by $x =$ _____.

     b. Given a quadratic equation $ax^2 + bx + c = 0$ $(a \neq 0)$, the solutions are given by $x =$ _____.

From Exercise 114, we see that linear and quadratic equations have generic formulas that can be used to find the solution sets. But what about a cubic polynomial equation? Mathematicians struggled for centuries to find such a formula. Finally, Italian mathematician Niccolo Tartaglia (1500–1557) developed a method to solve a cubic equation of the form

$$x^3 + mx = n$$

The result was later published in *Ars Magna*, by Gerolamo Cardano (1501–1576).

The formula to solve a cubic equation of the form $x^3 + mx = n$ is given by

$$x = \sqrt[3]{\sqrt{\left(\frac{n}{2}\right)^2 + \left(\frac{m}{3}\right)^3} + \frac{n}{2}} - \sqrt[3]{\sqrt{\left(\frac{n}{2}\right)^2 + \left(\frac{m}{3}\right)^3} - \frac{n}{2}}$$

In Exercises 115–116, the equation has one real solution. Use this formula to find the real solution.

115. $x^3 - 3x = -2$ **116.** $x^3 + 9x = 26$

> **Point of Interest**
>
> Early in the sixteenth century, Italian mathematicians Niccolo Tartaglia and Gerolamo Cardano solved a general cubic equation in terms of the constants appearing in the equation. Cardano's pupil, Ludovico Ferrari, then solved a general equation of fourth degree. Despite decades of work, no general solution to a fifth-degree equation was found. Finally, Norwegian mathematician Niels Abel and French mathematician Evariste Galois proved that no such solution exists.

SECTION 3.5   Rational Functions

OBJECTIVES

1. Apply Notation Describing Infinite Behavior of a Function
2. Identify Vertical Asymptotes
3. Identify Horizontal Asymptotes
4. Identify Slant Asymptotes
5. Graph Rational Functions
6. Use Rational Functions in Applications

1. Apply Notation Describing Infinite Behavior of a Function

In this chapter we have studied polynomials and polynomial functions. Now we look at functions that are defined as the ratio of two polynomials. These are called rational functions.

> **Definition of a Rational Function**
>
> Let $p(x)$ and $q(x)$ be polynomials where $q(x) \neq 0$. A function f defined by
>
> $$f(x) = \frac{p(x)}{q(x)} \text{ is called a } \textbf{rational function.}$$
>
> *Note*: The domain of a rational function is all real numbers excluding the real zeros of $q(x)$.

Function	Factored Form	Domain
$f(x) = \dfrac{1}{x}$	$f(x) = \dfrac{1}{x}$	$\{x \mid x \neq 0\}$ $(-\infty, 0) \cup (0, \infty)$
$g(x) = \dfrac{5x^2}{2x^2 + 5x - 12}$	$g(x) = \dfrac{5x^2}{(2x - 3)(x + 4)}$	$\left\{x \mid x \neq \frac{3}{2}, x \neq -4\right\}$ $(-\infty, -4) \cup \left(-4, \frac{3}{2}\right) \cup \left(\frac{3}{2}, \infty\right)$
$k(x) = \dfrac{x + 3}{x^2 + 4}$	$k(x) = \dfrac{x + 3}{x^2 + 4}$	$\mathbb{R}$ $(-\infty, \infty)$

We want to analyze the graphs and behavior of rational functions, but we first need to understand the following notation (Table 3-1).

Table 3-1

Notation	Meaning
$x \to c^+$	x approaches c from the right (but will not equal c).
$x \to c^-$	x approaches c from the left (but will not equal c).
$x \to \infty$	x approaches infinity (x increases without bound).
$x \to -\infty$	x approaches negative infinity (x decreases without bound).

For example, consider the reciprocal function $f(x) = \frac{1}{x}$ first introduced in Section 2.6 (Figure 3-17).

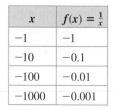

x	$f(x) = \frac{1}{x}$
-1	-1
-10	-0.1
-100	-0.01
-1000	-0.001

x	$f(x) = \frac{1}{x}$
-1	-1
-0.1	-10
-0.01	-100
-0.001	-1000

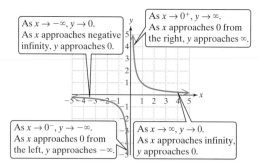

Figure 3-17

x	$f(x) = \frac{1}{x}$
1	1
0.1	10
0.01	100
0.001	1000

x	$f(x) = \frac{1}{x}$
1	1
10	0.1
100	0.01
1000	0.001

In Example 1, we study the graph of another basic rational function, $f(x) = \frac{1}{x^2}$. From the definition of the function, we make the following observations.

- The domain of $f(x) = \frac{1}{x^2}$ is all real numbers excluding zero.

- f is an even function and the graph is symmetric to the y-axis.
- The values of $f(x)$ are positive over the domain of f.

EXAMPLE 1 **Investigating the Behavior of a Rational Function**

The graph of $f(x) = \frac{1}{x^2}$ is given.

Complete the statements.

a. As $x \to -\infty, f(x) \to$ _____.

b. As $x \to 0^-$, $f(x) \to$ _____.

c. As $x \to 0^+$, $f(x) \to$ _____.

d. As $x \to \infty$, $f(x) \to$ _____.

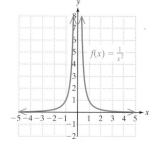

Solution:

a. As $x \to -\infty, f(x) \to 0$.

b. As $x \to 0^-$, $f(x) \to \infty$.

c. As $x \to 0^+$, $f(x) \to \infty$.

d. As $x \to \infty$, $f(x) \to 0$.

Skill Practice 1 The graph of $f(x) = \dfrac{1}{x-2}$ is given.

Complete the statements.

  a. As $x \to -\infty, f(x) \to$ _____.
  b. As $x \to 2^-$, $f(x) \to$ _____.
  c. As $x \to 2^+$, $f(x) \to$ _____.
  d. As $x \to \infty$, $f(x) \to$ _____.

2. Identify Vertical Asymptotes

The graphs of $f(x) = \dfrac{1}{x}$ and $f(x) = \dfrac{1}{x^2}$ both approach the y-axis, but do not touch the y-axis. The y-axis is called a vertical asymptote of the graphs of the functions.

Definition of a Vertical Asymptote

The line $x = c$ is a **vertical asymptote** of the graph of a function f if $f(x)$ approaches infinity or negative infinity as x approaches c from either side.

A function may have no vertical asymptotes, one vertical asymptote, or many vertical asymptotes. To locate the vertical asymptotes of a function, determine the real numbers x where the denominator is zero, but the numerator is nonzero.

Identifying Vertical Asymptotes of a Rational Function

Consider a rational function f defined by $f(x) = \dfrac{p(x)}{q(x)}$, where $p(x)$ and $q(x)$ have no common factors other than 1. If c is a real zero of $q(x)$, then $x = c$ is a vertical asymptote of the graph of f.

Answers

1. a. 0   **b.** $-\infty$ **c.** ∞ **d.** 0

EXAMPLE 2   Identifying Vertical Asymptotes

Identify the vertical asymptotes.

a. $f(x) = \dfrac{2}{x - 3}$ **b.** $g(x) = \dfrac{x - 4}{3x^2 + 5x - 2}$ **c.** $k(x) = \dfrac{4x^2}{x^2 + 4}$

Solution:

a. $f(x) = \dfrac{2}{x - 3}$

The expression $\frac{2}{x-3}$ is written in lowest terms. The denominator is zero for $x = 3$.

f has a vertical asymptote of $x = 3$.

Avoiding Mistakes

A vertical asymptote is a line and should be identified by an equation of the form $x = c$, where c is a constant.

b. $g(x) = \dfrac{x - 4}{3x^2 + 5x - 2}$

$g(x) = \dfrac{x - 4}{(3x - 1)(x + 2)}$

The vertical asymptotes are

$x = \dfrac{1}{3}$ and $x = -2$.

Factor the numerator and denominator.

The numerator and denominator share no common factors other than 1. The zeros of the denominator are $\frac{1}{3}$ and -2.

c. $k(x) = \dfrac{4x^2}{x^2 + 4}$

The denominator has no real zeros, so the graph of k has no vertical asymptotes.

The numerator and denominator are already factored over the real numbers and the rational expression is in lowest terms.

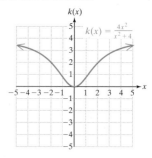

Skill Practice 2   Identify the vertical asymptotes.

a. $f(x) = \dfrac{3}{x + 1}$ **b.** $h(x) = \dfrac{x + 7}{2x^2 - x - 10}$ **c.** $m(x) = \dfrac{5x}{x^4 + 1}$

Answers

2. a. $x = -1$

  b. $x = \dfrac{5}{2}$ and $x = -2$

  c. No vertical asymptotes

Avoiding Mistakes

The procedure to find the vertical asymptotes of a rational function is given under the condition that the numerator and denominator share no common factors. This important observation can be illustrated by the graph of

$$f(x) = \frac{2x^2 + 5x + 3}{x + 1}$$ (Figure 3-18). The numerator and

denominator share a common factor of $(x + 1)$.

$$f(x) = \frac{2x^2 + 5x + 3}{x + 1} = \frac{(2x + 3)(x + 1)}{x + 1}$$

The value $x = -1$ is not in the domain of f, but the graph of f has a "hole" at $x = -1$ rather than a vertical asymptote.

Figure 3-18

3. Identify Horizontal Asymptotes

Refer back to the graph of $f(x) = \frac{1}{x}$ (Figure 3-19). Toward the far left and far right of the graph, $f(x)$ approaches the line $y = 0$ (the x-axis). The x-axis is called a horizontal asymptote of the graph of f.

Figure 3-19

TIP While the graph of a function may not cross a vertical asymptote, it may cross a horizontal asymptote.

Definition of a Horizontal Asymptote

The line $y = d$ is a **horizontal asymptote** of the graph of a function f if $f(x)$ approaches d as x approaches infinity or negative infinity.

Recall that the leading term determines the far left and far right behavior of the graph of a polynomial function. Since a rational function is the ratio of two polynomials, it seems reasonable that the leading terms of the numerator and denominator determine the end behavior of a rational function.

TIP A rational function may have many vertical asymptotes, but at most one horizontal asymptote.

Identifying Horizontal Asymptotes of a Rational Function

Let f be a rational function defined by

$$f(x) = \frac{a_n x^n + a_{n-1} x^{n-1} + a_{n-2} x^{n-2} + \cdots + a_1 x + a_0}{b_m x^m + b_{m-1} x^{m-1} + b_{m-2} x^{m-2} + \cdots + b_1 x + b_0}$$

The definition of $f(x)$ indicates that n is the degree of the numerator and m is the degree of the denominator.

1. If $n > m$, then f has no horizontal asymptote.
2. If $n < m$, then the line $y = 0$ (the x-axis) is the horizontal asymptote of f.
3. If $n = m$, then the line $y = \dfrac{a_n}{b_m}$ is the horizontal asymptote of f.

1. If the degree of the numerator is greater than the degree of the denominator ($n > m$), then the numerator will "dominate" the quotient. For example:

$$f(x) = \frac{x^4 + \cdots}{x^2 + \cdots}$$ will behave like $y = x^2$ as $|x|$ becomes large. Therefore, f has no horizontal asymptote.

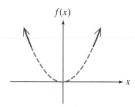

2. If the degree of the numerator is less than the degree of the denominator ($n < m$), then the denominator will "dominate" the quotient. For example:

$$f(x) = \frac{x^2 + \cdots}{x^4 + \cdots}$$ will behave like $y = \dfrac{1}{x^2}$. The ratio $\dfrac{1}{x^2}$ tends toward 0 as $|x|$ becomes large. Therefore, f has a horizontal asymptote of $y = 0$.

3. If the degree of the numerator is equal to the degree of the denominator ($n = m$), then the magnitude of the numerator and denominator somewhat "offset" each other. As a result, the function tends toward a constant value equal to the ratio of the leading coefficients. For example:

$$f(x) = \frac{4x^2 + \cdots}{3x^2 + \cdots}$$ will behave like $y = \frac{4}{3}$ as $|x|$ becomes large. Therefore, f has a horizontal asymptote of $y = \frac{4}{3}$.

EXAMPLE 3   Identifying Horizontal Asymptotes

Find the horizontal asymptotes (if any) for the given functions.

a. $f(x) = \dfrac{8x^2 + 1}{x^4 + 1}$ **b.** $g(x) = \dfrac{2x^3 - 6x}{x^2 + 4}$ **c.** $h(x) = \dfrac{8x^2 + 9x - 5}{2x^2 + 1}$

Solution:

a. $f(x) = \dfrac{8x^2 + 1}{x^4 + 1}$

The degree of the numerator is 2 ($n = 2$).
The degree of the denominator is 4 ($m = 4$).

Since $n < m$, then the line $y = 0$ (the x-axis) is a horizontal asymptote of f.

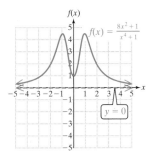

b. $g(x) = \dfrac{2x^3 - 6x}{x^2 + 4}$

The degree of the numerator is 3 ($n = 3$).
The degree of the denominator is 2 ($m = 2$).

Since $n > m$, then the function has no horizontal asymptotes.

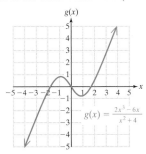

c. $h(x) = \dfrac{8x^2 + 9x - 5}{2x^2 + 1}$

The degree of the numerator is 2 ($n = 2$).
The degree of the denominator is 2 ($m = 2$).

Since $n = m$, then the line $y = \frac{8}{2}$ or equivalently $y = 4$ is a horizontal asymptote of the graph of f.

Skill Practice 3   Find the horizontal asymptotes (if any) for the given functions.

a. $f(x) = \dfrac{7x^2 + 2x}{4x^2 - 3}$ **b.** $m(x) = \dfrac{4x^3 + 2}{2x - 1}$ **c.** $n(x) = \dfrac{5}{4x^2 + 9}$

The graph of a rational function may not cross a vertical asymptote. However, as demonstrated in Example 3(c), the graph may cross a horizontal asymptote. For the purpose of graphing a rational function, it is helpful to determine where a graph crosses a horizontal asymptote.

Suppose that the line $y = d$ is a horizontal asymptote of a rational function $y = f(x)$. The solutions to the equation $f(x) = d$ are the values of x where the graph of f crosses its horizontal asymptote. If the equation has no real solution, then the graph does not cross its horizontal asymptote.

Answers

3. a. $y = \dfrac{7}{4}$

  b. No horizontal asymptotes

  c. $y = 0$

EXAMPLE 4   Determining Where a Graph Crosses a Horizontal Asymptote

Given $h(x) = \dfrac{8x^2 + 9x - 5}{2x^2 + 1}$, determine the point where the graph of h crosses its horizontal asymptote.

Solution:

$h(x) = \dfrac{8x^2 + 9x - 5}{2x^2 + 1}$ From Example 3(c), the horizontal asymptote is $y = 4$.

$\dfrac{8x^2 + 9x - 5}{2x^2 + 1} = 4$ Set $\dfrac{8x^2 + 9x - 5}{2x^2 + 1}$ equal to 4.

$\dfrac{8x^2 + 9x - 5}{2x^2 + 1} \cdot (2x^2 + 1) = 4 \cdot (2x^2 + 1)$ Clear fractions by multiplying by the LCD.

$$8x^2 + 9x - 5 = 8x^2 + 4$$
$$9x - 5 = 4$$
$$x = 1$$

The function crosses its horizontal asymptote at $(1, 4)$.

Skill Practice 4   Given $g(x) = \dfrac{3x^2 + 4x - 3}{x^2 + 3}$, determine the horizontal asymptote and the point where the graph crosses the horizontal asymptote.

4. Identify Slant Asymptotes

Consider the function defined by $f(x) = \dfrac{x^2 + 1}{x - 1}$. The graph has a vertical asymptote of $x = 1$, but no horizontal asymptote (the degree of the numerator is greater than the degree of the denominator). However, as x approaches infinity and negative infinity, the graph approaches the graph of $y = x + 1$ (shown in red in Figure 3-20). This line is called a **slant asymptote** because it is neither horizontal nor vertical.

Figure 3-20

Identifying a Slant Asymptote of a Rational Function

- A rational function will have a slant asymptote if the degree of the numerator is exactly one greater than the degree of the denominator.
- To find an equation of a slant asymptote, divide the numerator of the function by the denominator. The quotient will be linear and the slant asymptote will be of the form $y = $ quotient.

Answer

4. Horizontal asymptote $y = 3$; Crosses at $(3, 3)$

TIP Because the divisor is of the form $x - c$, we can also use synthetic division to determine the slant asymptote.

$$\begin{array}{r|rrr} 1 & 1 & 0 & 1 \\ & & 1 & 1 \\ \hline & 1 & 1 & \underline{|2} \end{array}$$

The quotient is $x + 1$. The slant asymptote is $y = x + 1$.

For $f(x) = \dfrac{x^2 + 1}{x - 1}$, divide $(x^2 + 1)$ by $(x - 1)$ using long division or synthetic division.

$$\begin{array}{r} x + 1 \\ x - 1 \overline{)x^2 + 0x + 1} \\ \underline{-(x^2 - x)} \\ x + 1 \\ \underline{-(x - 1)} \\ 2 \end{array}$$

The slant asymptote is $y = x + 1$.

Using the division algorithm, $f(x) = \dfrac{x^2 + 1}{x - 1} = x + 1 + \dfrac{2}{x - 1}$. The expression $\dfrac{2}{x - 1}$ will approach 0 as $|x|$ approaches infinity. Therefore, $f(x)$ will approach the line $y = x + 1$ as $|x|$ approaches infinity.

EXAMPLE 5   **Identifying the Asymptotes of a Rational Function**

Determine the asymptotes. $f(x) = \dfrac{2x^2 - 5x - 3}{x - 2}$

Solution:

$f(x) = \dfrac{2x^2 - 5x - 3}{x - 2}$

The expression $\dfrac{2x^2 - 5x - 3}{x - 2} = \dfrac{(2x + 1)(x - 3)}{x - 2}$ is in lowest terms, and the denominator is zero at $x = 2$.

f has a vertical asymptote of $x = 2$.

f has no horizontal asymptote.

The degree of the numerator is exactly one greater than the degree of the denominator. Therefore, f has no horizontal asymptote, but does have a slant asymptote.

To find the slant asymptote divide $(2x^2 - 5x - 3)$ by $(x - 2)$.

$$\begin{array}{r} 2x - 1 \\ x - 2 \overline{)2x^2 - 5x - 3} \\ \underline{-(2x^2 - 4x)} \\ -x - 3 \\ \underline{-(-x + 2)} \\ -5 \end{array}$$

The quotient is $2x - 1$. (The remainder of -5 does not affect the slant asymptote.)

The slant asymptote is given by $y = 2x - 1$.

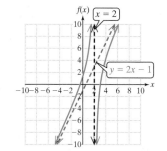

Skill Practice 5   Determine the asymptotes. $g(x) = \dfrac{2x^2 - 9}{x + 1}$

---

5. Graph Rational Functions

We now turn our attention to graphing rational functions. The transformations used in Section 2.6 can be applied to the basic rational functions $y = \dfrac{1}{x}$ and $y = \dfrac{1}{x^2}$.

Answer
5. Vertical asymptote: $x = -1$;
   No horizontal asymptote; Slant
   asymptote: $y = 2x - 2$

EXAMPLE 6   **Using Transformations to Graph a Rational Function**

Use transformations to graph $f(x) = \dfrac{1}{(x+2)^2} + 3$.

Solution:

$$f(x) = \frac{1}{(x+2)^2} + 3$$

The graph of f is the graph of $y = \dfrac{1}{x^2}$ with a shift to the left 2 units and a shift upward 3 units.

Shift 2 units left. New vertical asymptote is $x = -2$.

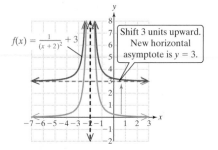

$f(x) = \frac{1}{(x+2)^2} + 3$

Shift 3 units upward. New horizontal asymptote is $y = 3$.

Skill Practice 6   Use transformations to graph $g(x) = \dfrac{1}{x-3} - 2$.

To graph a rational function that is not a simple transformation of $y = \dfrac{1}{x}$ or $y = \dfrac{1}{x^2}$, more steps must be employed. Our strategy is to find all asymptotes and key points (intercepts and points where the function crosses a horizontal asymptote). Then determine the behavior of the function on the intervals defined by these key points and the vertical asymptotes.

Graphing a Rational Function

Consider a rational function f defined by $f(x) = \dfrac{p(x)}{q(x)}$, where $p(x)$ and $q(x)$ are polynomials with no common factors.

1. Determine the y-intercept by evaluating $f(0)$.
2. Determine the x-intercept(s) by finding the real solutions of $f(x) = 0$.
3. Identify any vertical asymptotes and graph them as dashed lines.
4. Determine whether the function has a horizontal asymptote or a slant asymptote (or neither), and graph the asymptote as a dashed line.
5. Determine where the function crosses the horizontal or slant asymptote (if applicable).
6. Test for symmetry. Recall:
   - f is an even function (symmetric to the y-axis) if $f(-x) = f(x)$.
   - f is an odd function (symmetric to the origin) if $f(-x) = -f(x)$.
7. Plot at least one point on the intervals defined by the x-intercepts, vertical asymptotes, and points where the function crosses a horizontal or slant asymptote.
8. Sketch the function based on the information found in steps 1–7.

Answer

6.

$g(x) = \frac{1}{x-3} - 2$

EXAMPLE 7   **Graphing a Rational Function**

Graph $f(x) = \dfrac{4x}{x^2 - 4}$.

Solution:

1. Determine the y-intercept.

$$f(0) = \frac{4(0)}{(0)^2 - 4} = 0 \qquad \text{The } y\text{-intercept is } (0, 0).$$

2. Determine the x-intercept(s).

$$\frac{4x}{x^2 - 4} = 0 \quad \text{for } x = 0. \qquad \text{The } x\text{-intercept is } (0, 0).$$

3. Identify the vertical asymptotes.

The zeros of $x^2 - 4$ are 2 and -2. Vertical asymptotes: $x = 2$ and $x = -2$.

4. Determine whether f has a horizontal or slant asymptote.

The degree of the numerator is less than the degree of the denominator. The horizontal asymptote is $y = 0$.

5. Determine where f crosses its horizontal asymptote.

Set $f(x) = 0$. We have $\dfrac{4x}{x^2 - 4} = 0$ for $x = 0$.

Therefore, f crosses its horizontal asymptote at $(0, 0)$.

6. Test for symmetry.

f is an odd function because $f(-x) = \dfrac{4(-x)}{(-x)^2 - 4} = -\dfrac{4x}{x^2 - 4} = -f(x)$.

7. Determine the behavior of f on each interval.

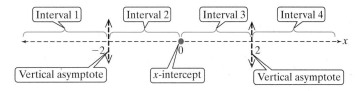

TIP The graph of f is symmetric to the origin because $f(-x) = -f(x)$. Therefore, if $\left(-3, -\frac{12}{5}\right)$ and $\left(-1, \frac{4}{3}\right)$ are points on the graph of f, then $\left(3, \frac{12}{5}\right)$ and $\left(1, -\frac{4}{3}\right)$ are also points on the graph.

Interval	Test Point	Comments
$(-\infty, -2)$	$\left(-3, -\dfrac{12}{5}\right)$	• Since $f(x)$ is negative on this interval, $f(x)$ must approach the horizontal asymptote $y = 0$ from below as $x \to -\infty$. • Since $f(x)$ is negative on this interval, as x approaches the vertical asymptote $x = -2$ from the left, $f(x) \to -\infty$.
$(-2, 0)$	$\left(-1, \dfrac{4}{3}\right)$	• Since $f(x)$ is positive on this interval, as x approaches the vertical asymptote $x = -2$ from the right, $f(x) \to \infty$.
$(0, 2)$	$\left(1, -\dfrac{4}{3}\right)$	• Since $f(x)$ is negative on this interval, as x approaches the vertical asymptote $x = 2$ from the left, $f(x) \to -\infty$.
$(2, \infty)$	$\left(3, \dfrac{12}{5}\right)$	• Since $f(x)$ is positive on this interval, $f(x)$ must approach the horizontal asymptote from above as $x \to \infty$. • Since $f(x)$ is positive on this interval, as x approaches the vertical asymptote $x = 2$ from the right, $f(x) \to \infty$.

8. Sketch the function.

Plot the x- and y-intercept $(0, 0)$.

Graph the asymptotes as dashed lines.

Plot the points:

$$\left(-3, -\frac{12}{5}\right), \left(-1, \frac{4}{3}\right), \left(1, -\frac{4}{3}\right), \text{and} \left(3, \frac{12}{5}\right)$$

Sketch the curve.

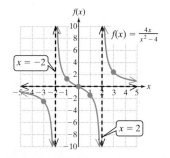

Skill Practice 7   Graph $g(x) = \dfrac{-5x}{x^2 - 9}$.

TECHNOLOGY CONNECTIONS

Graphing a Rational Function in Dot Mode

The graph of a rational function may be misleading on some graphing utilities. For example, $f(x) = \dfrac{4x}{x^2 - 4}$ has vertical asymptotes of $x = -2$ and $x = 2$, but the vertical asymptotes are *not* part of the graph (Figure 3-21). A graphing utility may try to "connect the dots" between two consecutive points to the left and right of a vertical asymptote. This creates a line segment that is nearly vertical and appears to be part of the graph.

Figure 3-21

To show that this line is not part of the graph, we can graph the function in dot mode. The graph of $f(x) = \dfrac{4x}{x^2 - 4}$ in dot mode indicates that the lines $x = -2$ and $x = 2$ are not part of the graph of the function (Figure 3-22).

Figure 3-22

EXAMPLE 8   **Graphing a Rational Function**

Graph $g(x) = \dfrac{2x^2 - 3x - 5}{x^2 + 1}$.

Solution:

1. Determine the y-intercept.

$$g(0) = \frac{2(0)^2 - 3(0) - 5}{(0)^2 + 1} = -5 \qquad \text{The } y\text{-intercept is } (0, -5).$$

2. Determine the x-intercept(s).

$$\frac{2x^2 - 3x - 5}{x^2 + 1} = 0$$

$$2x^2 - 3x - 5 = 0$$

$$(2x - 5)(x + 1) = 0$$

$$x = \frac{5}{2}, \ x = -1 \qquad \text{The } x\text{-intercepts are } \left(\tfrac{5}{2}, 0\right) \text{ and } (-1, 0).$$

Answer

7.

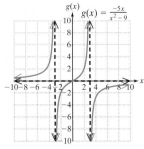

3. Identify the vertical asymptotes.

$x^2 + 1$ is nonzero for all real numbers. The graph of g has no vertical asymptotes.

4. Determine whether g has a horizontal or slant asymptote.

The degree of the numerator is equal to the degree of the denominator. The horizontal asymptote is $y = \frac{2}{1}$ or simply $y = 2$.

5. Determine where g crosses its horizontal asymptote.

Find the real solutions to the equation $\dfrac{2x^2 - 3x - 5}{x^2 + 1} = 2$.

$$2x^2 - 3x - 5 = 2(x^2 + 1)$$
$$2x^2 - 3x - 5 = 2x^2 + 2$$
$$-3x - 5 = 2$$
$$x = -\frac{7}{3} \qquad \text{g crosses its horizontal asymptote at } \left(-\frac{7}{3}, 2\right).$$

6. Test for symmetry.

g is neither even nor odd because $g(-x) \neq g(x)$ and $g(-x) \neq -g(x)$.

7. Determine the behavior of g on each interval.

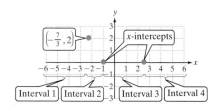

Interval	Test Point	Comments
$\left(-\infty, -\dfrac{7}{3}\right)$	$\left(-3, \dfrac{11}{5}\right)$	• Since $g(-3) = \frac{11}{5}$ is above the horizontal asymptote $y = 2$, $g(x)$ must approach the horizontal asymptote from above as $x \to -\infty$.
$\left(-\dfrac{7}{3}, -1\right)$	$\left(-2, \dfrac{9}{5}\right)$	• Plot the point $\left(-2, \frac{9}{5}\right)$ between the horizontal asymptote and the x-intercept of $(-1, 0)$.
$\left(-1, \dfrac{5}{2}\right)$	$(0, -5)$	• The point $(0, -5)$ is the y-intercept.
$\left(\dfrac{5}{2}, \infty\right)$	$\left(3, \dfrac{2}{5}\right)$	• Since $g(3) = \frac{2}{5}$ is below the horizontal asymptote $y = 2$, $g(x)$ must approach the horizontal asymptote from below as $x \to \infty$.

8. Sketch the function.

Answer

8.

Skill Practice 8   Graph $g(x) = \dfrac{4x^2 + 7x - 2}{x^2 + 4}$.

EXAMPLE 9   **Graphing a Rational Function**

Graph. $h(x) = \dfrac{2x^2 + 9x + 4}{x + 3}$

Solution:

1. Determine the y-intercept.

$$h(0) = \frac{2(0)^2 + 9(0) + 4}{(0) + 3} = \frac{4}{3}$$ The y-intercept is $\left(0, \frac{4}{3}\right)$.

2. Determine the x-intercept(s).

$$\frac{2x^2 + 9x + 4}{x + 3} = 0$$

$$2x^2 + 9x + 4 = 0$$

$$(2x + 1)(x + 4) = 0$$

$$x = -\frac{1}{2}, \; x = -4$$ The x-intercepts are $\left(-\frac{1}{2}, 0\right)$ and $(-4, 0)$.

3. Identify the vertical asymptotes.

$\dfrac{2x^2 + 9x + 4}{x + 3}$ is in lowest terms, and $x + 3$ is zero for $x = -3$.

4. Determine whether h has a horizontal or slant asymptote.

The degree of the numerator is one greater than the degree of the denominator. To find the slant asymptote, divide $(2x^2 + 9x + 4)$ by $(x + 3)$.

$$
\begin{array}{r|rrr}
-3 & 2 & 9 & 4 \\
   &   & -6 & -9 \\
\hline
   & 2 & 3 & \underline{-5}
\end{array}
$$

The quotient is $2x + 3$.
The slant asymptote is $y = 2x + 3$.

5. Determine where h will cross the slant asymptote.

Set $h(x) = 2x + 3$. We have $\dfrac{2x^2 + 9x + 4}{x + 3} = 2x + 3$.

> The equation has no solution. Therefore, the graph does not cross the slant asymptote.

$$2x^2 + 9x + 4 = (2x + 3)(x + 3)$$
$$2x^2 + 9x + 4 = 2x^2 + 9x + 9$$
$$4 = 9 \quad \text{(No solution)}$$

6. Test for symmetry.

h is neither even nor odd because $h(-x) \neq h(x)$ and $h(-x) \neq -h(x)$.

7. Plot test points. Pick values of x on the intervals defined by the x-intercepts and vertical asymptote.

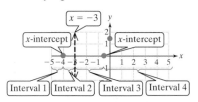

Select test points from each interval.
The graph of $y = h(x)$ passes through $(-5, -4.5)$, $(-3.5, 6)$, $(-2, -6)$, and $(2, 6)$.

8. Sketch the graph.

Plot the *x*-intercepts: $(-4, 0)$ and $\left(-\frac{1}{2}, 0\right)$.

Plot the *y*-intercept: $\left(0, \frac{4}{3}\right)$.

Graph the asymptotes as dashed lines.
Plot the points:

$(-5, -4.5)$, $(-3.5, 6)$, $(-2, -6)$, and $(2, 6)$.

Sketch the graph.

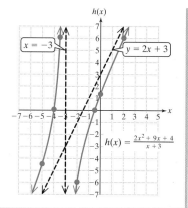

$x = -3$ $y = 2x + 3$

$h(x) = \dfrac{2x^2 + 9x + 4}{x + 3}$

Skill Practice 9 Graph $k(x) = \dfrac{2x^2 - 7x + 3}{x - 2}$.

6. Use Rational Functions in Applications

In Section 2.5, we presented a linear model for the cost for a business to manufacture *x* items. The model is $C(x) = mx + b$, where *m* is the variable cost to produce an individual item, and *b* is the fixed cost.

The average cost $\overline{C}(x)$ per item manufactured is the sum of all costs (variable and fixed) divided by the total number of items produced *x*. This is given by

$$\overline{C}(x) = \frac{C(x)}{x}$$

The average cost per item will decrease as more items are produced because the fixed cost will be distributed over a greater number of items. This is demonstrated in Example 10.

TIP Recall that variable costs include items such as materials and labor. Fixed costs include overhead costs such as rent and utilities.

EXAMPLE 10 Investigating Average Cost

A cleaning service cleans homes. For each house call, the cost to the company is approximately $40 for cleaning supplies, gasoline, and labor. The business also has fixed monthly costs of $300 from phone service, advertising, and depreciation on the vehicles.

a. Write a cost function to represent the cost $C(x)$ (in dollars) for *x* house calls per month.

b. Write the average cost function that represents the average cost $\overline{C}(x)$ (in $) for *x* house calls per month.

c. Evaluate $\overline{C}(5)$, $\overline{C}(20)$, $\overline{C}(30)$, and $\overline{C}(100)$.

d. The cleaning service can realistically make a maximum of 160 calls per month. However, if the number of calls were unlimited, what value would the average cost approach? What does this mean in the context of the problem?

Answer

9.

$k(x) = \dfrac{2x^2 - 7x + 3}{x - 2}$

Solution:

a. $C(x) = 40x + 300$ — The variable cost is $40 per call ($m = 40$), and the fixed cost is $300 ($b = 300$). $C(x) = mx + b$.

b. $\overline{C}(x) = \dfrac{40x + 300}{x}$ — The average cost per item is the total cost divided by the total number of items produced.

c. $\overline{C}(5) = 100$ The average cost per house call is $100 if 5 calls are made.

$\overline{C}(20) = 55$ The average cost per house call is $55 if 20 calls are made.

$\overline{C}(30) = 50$ The average cost per house call is $50 if 30 calls are made.

$\overline{C}(100) = 43$ The average cost per house call is $43 if 100 calls are made.

d. As x approaches infinity, $\overline{C}(x)$ will approach its horizontal asymptote $y = 40$. This is the cost per house call in the absence of other fixed costs.

$$\overline{C}(x) = \frac{40x + 300}{x}$$

Answers

10. a. $C(x) = 50x + 200$

b. $\overline{C}(x) = \dfrac{50x + 200}{x}$

c. $\overline{C}(5) = 90$; $\overline{C}(20) = 60$; $\overline{C}(30) = 56.67$; $\overline{C}(100) = 52$

d. The average cost $\overline{C}(x)$ will approach $50 per house call.

Skill Practice 10   Repeat Example 10 under the assumption that the company cuts its fixed costs to $200 per month and pays its employees more, leading to a variable cost per house call of $50.

Review Exercises

For Exercises 1–2, find the zeros of the polynomial function.

1. $f(x) = 4x^4 - 25x^2 + 36$

2. $g(x) = 9x^4 - 43x^2 + 50$

For Exercises 3–4, evaluate the function for the given values of x. Round to 4 decimal places if necessary.

3. $h(x) = \dfrac{6}{x - 2}$; $x = 1$, $x = 1.9$, $x = 1.99$

4. $k(x) = \dfrac{2x^2 + 3}{x^2 + 1}$; $x = 1$, $x = 10$, $x = 100$

Concept Connections

5. A _____ function is a function that can be written in the form $f(x) = \dfrac{p(x)}{q(x)}$, where $p(x)$ and $q(x)$ are polynomials, and $q(x) \neq 0$.

6. The domain of a rational function defined by $f(x) = \dfrac{p(x)}{q(x)}$ is all real numbers excluding the zeros of _____.

7. The notation $x \rightarrow \infty$ is read as _____.

8. The notation $x \rightarrow 5^-$ is read as _____.

9. The line $x = c$ is a _____ asymptote of the graph of a function f if $f(x)$ approaches infinity or negative infinity as x approaches _____ from either the left or right.

10. To locate the vertical asymptotes of a function, determine the real numbers x where the denominator is zero, but the numerator is _____.

11. Given $f(x) = \dfrac{2x^3 + 7}{5x^3}$, the graph of f will behave like the graph of which of the following functions for large values of $|x|$?

a. $y = \dfrac{2}{5x}$ **b.** $y = \dfrac{2x}{5}$ **c.** $y = \dfrac{2}{5}$ **d.** $y = \dfrac{2}{5}x^3$

12. Consider a rational function in which the degree of the numerator is n and the degree of the denominator is m. If n _____ m, then the x-axis is the horizontal asymptote. If n _____ m, then the function has no horizontal asymptote.

13. The graph of $f(x) = \dfrac{1}{x + 6} - 3$ is the graph of $y = \dfrac{1}{x}$ shifted (left/right) 6 units and (up/down) 3 units.

14. A rational function will have a slant asymptote if the degree of the numerator is exactly _____ greater than the degree of the denominator.

15. To find an equation for the slant asymptote of a rational function, begin by dividing the numerator by the _____.

16. If $C(x)$ represents the cost to manufacture x items, then $\overline{C}(x) =$ _____ represents the average cost per item.

Objective 1: Apply Notation Describing Infinite Behavior of a Function

For Exercises 17–22, write the domain of the function in interval notation.

17. $f(x) = \dfrac{x^2 - 25}{x - 5}$

18. $g(x) = \dfrac{x^2 - 9}{x - 3}$

19. $r(x) = \dfrac{2x - 3}{4x^2 + 3x - 1}$

20. $p(x) = \dfrac{3x - 5}{2x^2 + 5x - 7}$

21. $h(x) = \dfrac{18x}{x^2 + 100}$

22. $k(x) = \dfrac{14}{x^2 + 49}$

For Exercises 23–26, refer to the graph of the function and complete the statement. (See Example 1)

23. a. As $x \to -\infty, f(x) \to$ _____.
   c. As $x \to 4^+, f(x) \to$ _____.
   e. The graph is increasing over the interval(s) _____.
   g. The domain is _____.
   i. The vertical asymptote is the line _____.

b. As $x \to 4^-, f(x) \to$ _____.
d. As $x \to \infty, f(x) \to$ _____.
f. The graph is decreasing over the interval(s) _____.
h. The range is _____.
j. The horizontal asymptote is the line _____.

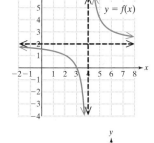

24. a. As $x \to -\infty, f(x) \to$ _____.
   c. As $x \to -3^+, f(x) \to$ _____.
   e. The graph is increasing over the interval(s) _____.
   g. The domain is _____.
   i. The vertical asymptote is the line _____.

b. As $x \to -3^-, f(x) \to$ _____.
d. As $x \to \infty, f(x) \to$ _____.
f. The graph is decreasing over the interval(s) _____.
h. The range is _____.
j. The horizontal asymptote is the line _____.

25. a. As $x \to -\infty, f(x) \to$ _____.
   c. As $x \to -3^+, f(x) \to$ _____.
   e. The graph is increasing over the interval(s) _____.
   g. The domain is _____.
   i. The vertical asymptote is the line _____.

b. As $x \to -3^-, f(x) \to$ _____.
d. As $x \to \infty, f(x) \to$ _____.
f. The graph is decreasing over the interval(s) _____.
h. The range is _____.
j. The horizontal asymptote is the line _____.

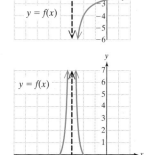

26. a. As $x \to -\infty, f(x) \to$ _____.
   c. As $x \to 1^+, f(x) \to$ _____.
   e. The graph is increasing over the interval(s) _____.
   g. The domain is _____.
   i. The vertical asymptote is the line _____.

b. As $x \to 1^-, f(x) \to$ _____.
d. As $x \to \infty, f(x) \to$ _____.
f. The graph is decreasing over the interval(s) _____.
h. The range is _____.
j. The horizontal asymptote is the line _____.

Objective 2: Identify Vertical Asymptotes

For Exercises 27–34, determine the vertical asymptotes of the graph of the function. (See Example 2)

27. $f(x) = \dfrac{8}{x - 4}$

28. $g(x) = \dfrac{2}{x + 7}$

29. $h(x) = \dfrac{x - 3}{2x^2 - 9x - 5}$

30. $k(x) = \dfrac{x + 2}{3x^2 + 8x - 3}$

31. $m(x) = \dfrac{x}{x^2 + 5}$

32. $n(x) = \dfrac{6}{x^4 + 1}$

33. $f(t) = \dfrac{t^2 + 2}{2t^2 + 4t - 3}$

34. $k(a) = \dfrac{5 + a^4}{3a^2 + 4a - 1}$

Objective 3: Identify Horizontal Asymptotes

For Exercises 35–42,

a. Identify the horizontal asymptotes (if any). (**See Example 3**)

b. If the graph of the function has a horizontal asymptote, determine the point where the graph crosses the horizontal asymptote. (**See Example 4**)

35. $p(x) = \dfrac{5}{x^2 + 2x + 1}$

36. $q(x) = \dfrac{8}{x^2 + 4x + 4}$

37. $h(x) = \dfrac{3x^2 + 8x - 5}{x^2 + 3}$

38. $r(x) = \dfrac{-4x^2 + 5x - 1}{x^2 + 2}$

39. $m(x) = \dfrac{x^4 + 2x + 1}{5x + 2}$

40. $n(x) = \dfrac{x^3 - x^2 + 1}{2x - 3}$

41. $t(x) = \dfrac{2x + 4}{x^2 + 7x - 4}$

42. $s(x) = \dfrac{x + 3}{2x^2 - 3x - 5}$

43. Consider the expression $\dfrac{x^2 + 3x + 1}{2x^2 + 5}$.

    a. Divide the numerator and denominator by the greatest power of x that appears in the denominator. That is, divide numerator and denominator by x^2.

    b. As $|x| \to \infty$ what value will $\dfrac{3}{x}, \dfrac{1}{x^2}$, and $\dfrac{5}{x^2}$ approach?

    (*Hint*: Substitute large values of x such as 100, 1000, 10,000, and so on to help you understand the behavior of each expression.)

    c. Use the results from parts (a) and (b) to identify the horizontal asymptote for the graph of

    $f(x) = \dfrac{x^2 + 3x + 1}{2x^2 + 5}$.

44. Consider the expression $\dfrac{3x^3 - 2x^2 + 7x}{5x^3 + 1}$.

    a. Divide the numerator and denominator by the greatest power of x that appears in the denominator.

    b. As $|x| \to \infty$ what value will $-\dfrac{2}{x}, \dfrac{7}{x^2}$, and $\dfrac{1}{x^3}$ approach?

    c. Use the results from parts (a) and (b) to identify the horizontal asymptote for the graph of

    $f(x) = \dfrac{3x^3 - 2x^2 + 7x}{5x^3 + 1}$.

Objective 4: Identify Slant Asymptotes

For Exercises 45–54, identify the asymptotes. (**See Example 5**)

45. $f(x) = \dfrac{2x^2 + 3}{x}$

46. $g(x) = \dfrac{3x^2 + 2}{x}$

47. $h(x) = \dfrac{-3x^2 + 4x - 5}{x + 6}$

48. $k(x) = \dfrac{-2x^2 - 3x + 7}{x + 3}$

49. $p(x) = \dfrac{x^3 + 5x^2 - 4x + 1}{x^2 - 5}$

50. $q(x) = \dfrac{x^3 + 3x^2 - 2x - 4}{x^2 - 7}$

51. $r(x) = \dfrac{2x + 1}{x^3 + x^2 - 4x - 4}$

52. $t(x) = \dfrac{3x - 4}{x^3 + 2x^2 - 9x - 18}$

53. $f(x) = \dfrac{4x^3 - 2x^2 + 7x - 3}{2x^2 + 4x + 3}$

54. $a(x) = \dfrac{9x^3 - 5x + 4}{3x^2 + 2x + 1}$

Objective 5: Graph Rational Functions

For Exercises 55–62, graph the functions by using transformations of the graphs of $y = \dfrac{1}{x}$ and $y = \dfrac{1}{x^2}$. (**See Example 6**)

55. $f(x) = \dfrac{1}{x - 3}$

56. $g(x) = \dfrac{1}{x + 4}$

57. $h(x) = \dfrac{1}{x^2} + 2$

58. $k(x) = \dfrac{1}{x^2} - 3$

59. $m(x) = \dfrac{1}{(x + 4)^2} - 3$

60. $n(x) = \dfrac{1}{(x - 1)^2} + 2$

61. $p(x) = -\dfrac{1}{x}$

62. $q(x) = -\dfrac{1}{x^2}$

For Exercises 63–68, for the graph of $y = f(x)$,

    a. Identify the x-intercepts.

    c. Identify the horizontal asymptote or slant asymptote if applicable.

    b. Identify any vertical asymptotes.

    d. Identify the y-intercept.

63. $f(x) = \dfrac{(x + 3)(2x - 7)}{(x + 2)(4x + 1)}$

64. $f(x) = \dfrac{(3x - 4)(x - 6)}{(2x - 3)(x + 5)}$

65. $f(x) = \dfrac{4x - 9}{x^2 - 9}$

66. $f(x) = \dfrac{5x - 8}{x^2 - 4}$

67. $f(x) = \dfrac{(5x - 1)(x + 3)}{x + 2}$

68. $f(x) = \dfrac{(4x + 3)(x + 2)}{x + 3}$

For Exercises 69–72, sketch a rational function subject to the given conditions. Answers may vary.

69. Horizontal asymptote: $y = 2$
Vertical asymptote: $x = 3$
y-intercept: $\left(0, \frac{8}{3}\right)$
x-intercept: $(4, 0)$

70. Horizontal asymptote: $y = 0$
Vertical asymptote: $x = -1$
y-intercept: $(0, 1)$
No x-intercepts
Range: $(0, \infty)$

71. Horizontal asymptote $y = 0$
Vertical asymptotes $x = -2$ and $x = 2$
y-intercept $(0, 1)$
No x-intercepts
Symmetric to the y-axis
Passes through the point $\left(3, -\frac{4}{5}\right)$

72. Horizontal asymptote: $y = 3$
Vertical asymptotes: $x = -1$ and $x = 1$
y-intercept: $(0, 0)$
x-intercept $(0, 0)$
Symmetric to the y-axis
Passes through the point $(2, 4)$

For Exercises 73–92, graph the function. (See Examples 7–9)

73. $n(x) = \dfrac{-3}{2x + 7}$

74. $m(x) = \dfrac{-4}{2x - 5}$

75. $p(x) = \dfrac{6}{x^2 - 9}$

76. $q(x) = \dfrac{4}{x^2 - 16}$

77. $r(x) = \dfrac{5x}{x^2 - x - 6}$

78. $t(x) = \dfrac{4x}{x^2 - 2x - 3}$

79. $k(x) = \dfrac{5x - 3}{2x - 7}$

80. $h(x) = \dfrac{4x + 3}{3x - 5}$

81. $g(x) = \dfrac{3x^2 - 5x - 2}{x^2 + 1}$

82. $c(x) = \dfrac{2x^2 - 5x - 3}{x^2 + 1}$

83. $n(x) = \dfrac{x^2 + 2x + 1}{x}$

84. $m(x) = \dfrac{x^2 - 4x + 4}{x}$

85. $f(x) = \dfrac{x^2 + 7x + 10}{x + 3}$

86. $d(x) = \dfrac{x^2 - x - 12}{x - 2}$

87. $w(x) = \dfrac{-4x^2}{x^2 + 4}$

88. $u(x) = \dfrac{-3x^2}{x^2 + 1}$

89. $f(x) = \dfrac{x^3 + x^2 - 4x - 4}{x^2 + 3x}$

90. $g(x) = \dfrac{x^3 + 3x^2 - x - 3}{x^2 - 2x}$

91. $v(x) = \dfrac{2x^4}{x^2 + 9}$

92. $g(x) = \dfrac{4x^4}{x^2 + 8}$

Objective 6: Use Rational Functions in Applications

93. A sports trainer has monthly costs of $69.95 for phone service and $39.99 for his website and advertising. In addition he pays a $20 fee to the gym for each session in which he trains a client. (**See Example 10**)

a. Write a cost function to represent the cost $C(x)$ for x training sessions per month.

b. Write a function representing the average cost $\overline{C}(x)$ for x sessions.

c. Evaluate $\overline{C}(5)$, $\overline{C}(30)$, and $\overline{C}(120)$.

d. The trainer can realistically have 120 sessions per month. However, if the number of sessions were unlimited, what value would the average cost approach? What does this mean in the context of the problem?

94. An on-demand printing company has monthly overhead costs of $1200 in rent, $420 in electricity, $100 for phone service, and $200 for advertising and marketing. The printing cost is $40 per thousand pages for paper and ink.

a. Write a cost function to represent the cost $C(x)$ for printing x thousand pages per month.

b. Write a function representing the average cost $\overline{C}(x)$ for printing x thousand pages.

c. Evaluate $\overline{C}(20)$, $\overline{C}(50)$, $\overline{C}(100)$, and $\overline{C}(200)$.

d. Interpret the meaning of $\overline{C}(200)$.

e. For a given month, if the printing company could print an unlimited number of pages, what value would the average cost per thousand pages approach? What does this mean in the context of the problem?

95. A monthly phone plan costs $59.95 for unlimited texts and 400 min. If more than 400 min are used the plan charges an addition $0.45 per minute. For x minutes used, the average cost per minute $\overline{C}_1(x)$ (in $) is given by

$$\overline{C}_1(x) = \begin{cases} \dfrac{59.95}{x} & \text{for } 0 < x \le 400 \\[2ex] \dfrac{59.95 + 0.45(x - 400)}{x} & \text{for } x > 400 \end{cases}$$

a. Find the average cost if a customer talks for 252 min, 366 min, and 400 min. Round to 2 decimal places.

b. Find the average cost if a customer talks for 436 min, 582 min, and 700 min. Round to 2 decimal places.

c. Suppose a second phone plan costs $79.95 per month for unlimited minutes and unlimited texts. Write an average cost function to represent the average cost $\overline{C}_2(x)$ (in $) for x minutes used.

d. Find the average cost $\overline{C}_2(x)$ for the second plan for 252 min, 400 min, and 700 min.

96. The yearly membership for a professional organization is $250 per year for the current year and increases by $25 per year. If a person joins for x consecutive years, the average cost per year $\overline{C}_1(x)$ (in $) is given by

$$\overline{C}_1(x) = \frac{475 + 25x}{2}$$

a. Find the average cost per year if a person joins for 5 yr, 10 yr, and 15 yr.

b. The professional organization also offers a one-time fee of $2000 for a lifetime membership. If a person purchases a lifetime membership, write an average cost function representing the average cost per year $\overline{C}_2(x)$ (in $) for x years of membership.

c. If a person purchases a lifetime membership, compute the average cost per year for 5 yr, 10 yr, and 15 yr.

d. Interpret the meaning of the horizontal asymptote for the graph of $y = \overline{C}_2(x)$.

97. A power company burns coal to generate electricity. The cost $C(x)$ (in $1000) to remove $x\%$ of the air pollutants is given by

$$C(x) = \frac{600x}{100 - x}$$

a. Compute the cost to remove 25% of the air pollutants. (*Hint*: $x = 25$.)

b. Determine the cost to remove 50%, 75%, and 90% of the air pollutants.

c. If the power company budgets $1.4 million for pollution control, what percentage of the air pollutants can be removed?

98. The cost $C(x)$ (in $1000) for a city to remove $x\%$ of the waste from a polluted river is given by

$$C(x) = \frac{80x}{100 - x}$$

a. Determine the cost to remove 20%, 40%, and 90% of the waste. Round to the nearest thousand dollars.

b. If the city has $320,000 budgeted for river cleanup, what percentage of the waste can be removed?

99. The number of adults in U.S. prisons and jails for the years 1980–2008 is shown in the graph. (*Source*: U.S. Department of Justice, www.justice.gov) The variable t represents the number of years since 1980.

The function defined by $P(t) = -0.091t^3 + 3.48t^2 + 15.4t + 335$ represents the number of adults in prison $P(t)$ (in thousands).

The function defined by $J(t) = 23.0t + 159$ represents the number of adults in jail $J(t)$ (in thousands).

a. Write the function defined by $N(t) = (P + J)(t)$ and interpret its meaning in context.

b. Write the function defined by $R(t) = \left(\dfrac{J}{N}\right)(t)$ and interpret its meaning in the context of this problem.

c. Evaluate $R(25)$ and interpret its meaning in context. Round to 3 decimal places.

Number of Adults in U.S. Prisons and Jails

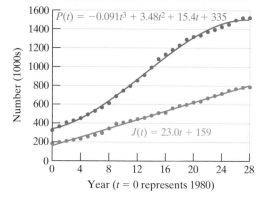

100. The number of U.S. citizens of voting age, $N(t)$ (in millions), can be modeled according to the number of years t since 1932.

$$N(t) = 0.0135t^2 + 1.09t + 73.2$$

The function defined by

$$V(t) = 1.08t + 36.9$$

represents the number of people who voted $V(t)$ (in millions) in U.S. presidential elections (t is the number of years since 1932 and t is a multiple of 4). (*Source*: U.S. Census Bureau, www.census.gov)

a. Write the function defined by $P(t) = \left(\dfrac{V}{N}\right)(t)$ and interpret its meaning in the context of this problem.

b. Evaluate $P(60)$ and interpret its meaning in the context of this problem. Round to 2 decimal places.

Number of Eligible Voters and Number Who Voted

Mixed Exercises

101. a. Write an equation for a rational function f whose graph is the same as the graph of $y = \dfrac{1}{x^2}$ shifted up 3 units and to the left 1 unit.

b. Write the domain and range of the function in interval notation.

102. a. Write an equation for a rational function f whose graph is the same as the graph of $y = \frac{1}{x}$ shifted to the right 4 units and down 3 units.

b. Write the domain and range of the function in interval notation.

For Exercises 103–104, given $y = f(x)$,

a. Divide the numerator by the denominator to write $f(x)$ in the form $f(x) = \text{quotient} + \dfrac{\text{remainder}}{\text{divisor}}$.

b. Use transformations of $y = \dfrac{1}{x}$ to graph the function.

103. $f(x) = \dfrac{2x + 7}{x + 3}$

104. $f(x) = \dfrac{5x + 11}{x + 2}$

Write About It

105. Explain why $x = -2$ is not a vertical asymptote of the graph of $f(x) = \dfrac{x^2 + 7x + 10}{x + 2}$.

106. Write an informal definition of a horizontal asymptote of a rational function.

Expanding Your Skills

For Exercises 107–110, write an equation of a function that meets the given conditions. Answers may vary.

107. x-intercepts: $(-3, 0)$ and $(-1, 0)$
vertical asymptote: $x = 2$
horizontal asymptote: $y = 1$
y-intercept: $\left(0, \frac{3}{4}\right)$

108. x-intercepts: $(4, 0)$ and $(2, 0)$
vertical asymptote: $x = 1$
horizontal asymptote: $y = 1$
y-intercept: $(0, 8)$

109. x-intercept: $\left(\frac{3}{2}, 0\right)$
vertical asymptotes: $x = -2$ and $x = 5$
horizontal asymptote: $y = 0$
y-intercept: $(0, 3)$

110. x-intercept: $\left(\frac{4}{3}, 0\right)$
vertical asymptotes: $x = -3$ and $x = -4$
horizontal asymptote: $y = 0$
y-intercept: $(0, -1)$

Technology Connections

111. Given $f(x) = \dfrac{4x^2 - 11x - 3}{5x^2 + 7x - 6}$,

     a. Make a table and evaluate f for $x = -1, -1.9, -1.99$, and -1.999.

     b. Make a table and evaluate f for $x = 1, 10, 100, 1000$, and $10,000$.

     c. Identify the vertical and horizontal asymptotes of the graph of f.

Sometimes it is necessary to use a "friendly" viewing window on a graphing calculator to see the key features of a graph. For example, for a calculator screen that is 96 pixels wide and 64 pixels high, the "decimal viewing window" defined by $[-4.7, 4.7, 1]$ by $[-3.1, 3.1, 1]$ creates a scaling where each pixel represents 0.1 unit. The window $[-9.4, 9.4, 1]$ by $[-6.2, 6.2, 1]$ defines each pixel as 0.2 unit, and so on. Exercises 112–113 compare the use of the standard viewing window to a "friendly" viewing window.

112. a. Identify any vertical asymptotes of the function defined by $f(x) = \dfrac{x^2 + 3x + 2}{x + 1}$.

     b. Compare the graph of $f(x) = \dfrac{x^2 + 3x + 2}{x + 1}$ on the standard viewing window $[-10, 10, 1]$ by $[-10, 10, 1]$ and on the window $[-4.7, 4.7, 1]$ by $[-3.1, 3.1, 1]$. Which graph shows the behavior at $x = -1$ more completely?

113. a. Identify any vertical asymptotes of the function defined by $f(x) = \dfrac{x^2 - 5x + 4}{x - 4}$.

     b. Compare the graph of $f(x) = \dfrac{x^2 - 5x + 4}{x - 4}$ on the standard viewing window $[-10, 10, 1]$ by $[-10, 10, 1]$ and on the window $[-9.4, 9.4, 1]$ by $[-6.2, 6.2, 1]$. Which graph shows the behavior at $x = 4$ more completely?

PROBLEM RECOGNITION EXERCISES

Polynomial and Rational Functions

For Exercises 1–8, refer to $p(x) = x^3 + 3x^2 - 6x - 8$ and $q(x) = x^3 - 2x^2 - 5x + 6$.

1. Find the zeros of $p(x)$.

2. Find the zeros of $q(x)$.

3. Find the x-intercept(s) of the graph of $y = q(x)$.

4. Find the x-intercept(s) of the graph of $y = p(x)$.

5. Find the x-intercepts of the graph of
$f(x) = \dfrac{p(x)}{q(x)} = \dfrac{x^3 + 3x^2 - 6x - 8}{x^3 - 2x^2 - 5x + 6}$.

6. Find the vertical asymptotes of the graph of
$f(x) = \dfrac{p(x)}{q(x)} = \dfrac{x^3 + 3x^2 - 6x - 8}{x^3 - 2x^2 - 5x + 6}$.

7. Find the horizontal asymptote or slant asymptote of the graph of $f(x) = \dfrac{p(x)}{q(x)} = \dfrac{x^3 + 3x^2 - 6x - 8}{x^3 - 2x^2 - 5x + 6}$.

8. Determine where the graph of $f(x) = \dfrac{x^3 + 3x^2 - 6x - 8}{x^3 - 2x^2 - 5x + 6}$ crosses its horizontal or slant asymptote.

For Exercises 9–16, refer to $c(x) = x^3 - 4x^2 - 2x + 8$ and $d(x) = x^3 + 3x^2 - 4$.

9. Find the zeros of $c(x)$.

10. Find the zeros of $d(x)$.

11. Find the x-intercept(s) of the graph of $y = d(x)$.

12. Find the x-intercept(s) of the graph of $y = c(x)$.

13. Find the x-intercepts of the graph of
$g(x) = \dfrac{c(x)}{d(x)} = \dfrac{x^3 - 4x^2 - 2x + 8}{x^3 + 3x^2 - 4}$.

14. Find the vertical asymptotes of the graph of
$g(x) = \dfrac{c(x)}{d(x)} = \dfrac{x^3 - 4x^2 - 2x + 8}{x^3 + 3x^2 - 4}$.

15. Find the horizontal asymptote or slant asymptote of the graph of $g(x) = \dfrac{c(x)}{d(x)} = \dfrac{x^3 - 4x^2 - 2x + 8}{x^3 + 3x^2 - 4}$.

16. Determine where the graph of $g(x) = \dfrac{x^3 - 4x^2 - 2x + 8}{x^3 + 3x^2 - 4}$ crosses its horizontal or slant asymptote.

For Exercises 17–18, use the results from Exercises 5–8 and 13–16 to match the function with its graph.

17. $f(x) = \dfrac{x^3 + 3x^2 - 6x - 8}{x^3 - 2x^2 - 5x + 6}$

18. $g(x) = \dfrac{x^3 - 4x^2 - 2x + 8}{x^3 + 3x^2 - 4}$

a.

b.

19. Divide $(2x^3 - 4x^2 - 10x + 12) \div (x^2 - 11)$ by using an appropriate method.

   a. Identify the quotient $q(x)$.   **b.** Idenitfy the remainder $r(x)$.

20. Identify the slant asymptote of $f(x) = \dfrac{2x^3 - 4x^2 - 10x + 12}{x^2 - 11}$.

21. Identify the point where the graph of $f(x) = \dfrac{2x^3 - 4x^2 - 10x + 12}{x^2 - 11}$ crosses its slant asymptote.

22. Refer back to Exercise 19. Solve the equation $r(x) = 0$. How does the solution to the equation $r(x) = 0$ relate to the point where the graph of f crosses its slant asymptote?

SECTION 3.6   Polynomial and Rational Inequalities

OBJECTIVES

1. Solve Polynomial Inequalities
2. Solve Rational Inequalities
3. Solve Applications Involving Polynomial and Rational Inequalities

1. Solve Polynomial Inequalities

An engineer for a food manufacturer must design an aluminum container for a hot drink mix. The container is to be a right circular cylinder 5.5 in. in height. The surface area represents the amount of aluminum used and is given by

$$S(r) = 2\pi r^2 + 11\pi r \qquad \text{where } r \text{ is the radius of the can.}$$

The engineer wants to limit the surface area so that at most 90 in.^{2} of aluminum is used. To determine the restrictions on the radius, the engineer must solve the inequality $2\pi r^2 + 11\pi r \leq 90$ (see Exercise 123). This inequality is a quadratic inequality in the variable r. It is also categorized as a polynomial inequality of degree 2.

> **TIP** If $f(x)$ is a quadratic polynomial, then the inequalities $f(x) < 0, f(x) > 0,$ $f(x) \leq 0,$ and $f(x) \geq 0$ are called quadratic inequalities.

Definition of a Polynomial Inequality

Let $f(x)$ be a polynomial. Then an inequality of the form

$f(x) < 0, f(x) > 0, f(x) \leq 0,$ or $f(x) \geq 0$ is called a **polynomial inequality.**

Note: A polynomial inequality is nonlinear if $f(x)$ is a polynomial of degree greater than 1.

Consider the polynomial inequalities $f(x) < 0$ and $f(x) > 0$. We need to determine the intervals over which $f(x)$ is negative or positive. For example, consider the graph of $f(x) = x^2 - 6x + 5$ (Figure 3-23).

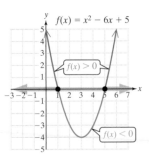

Figure 3-23

The graph shows the solution sets for the following equation and inequalities.

- $f(x) = 0$ for $\{1, 5\}$.
- $f(x) < 0$ on the interval $(1, 5)$. (shown in blue)
- $f(x) > 0$ on the interval $(-\infty, 1) \cup (5, \infty)$. (shown in red)

Notice that the x-intercepts define the endpoints (or "boundary" points) for the solution sets of the inequalities. We can solve a polynomial inequality if we can identify the *sign* of the polynomial for each interval defined by the boundary points. This is the basis on which we solve any nonlinear inequality.

> **Procedure to Solve a Nonlinear Inequality**
>
> 1. Express the inequality as $f(x) < 0$, $f(x) > 0$, $f(x) \le 0$, or $f(x) \ge 0$. That is, rearrange the terms of the inequality so that one side is set to zero.
> 2. Find the real solutions of the related equation $f(x) = 0$ and any values of x that make $f(x)$ undefined. These are the "boundary" points for the solution set to the inequality.
> 3. Determine the sign of $f(x)$ on the intervals defined by the boundary points.
>   - If $f(x)$ is positive, then the values of x on the interval are solutions to $f(x) > 0$.
>   - If $f(x)$ is negative, then the values of x on the interval are solutions to $f(x) < 0$.
> 4. Determine whether the boundary points are included in the solution set.
> 5. Write the solution set in interval notation or set-builder notation.

EXAMPLE 1   **Solving a Quadratic Inequality**

Solve the inequality. $3x(x - 1) > 10 - 2x$

Solution:

$3x(x - 1) > 10 - 2x$ **Step 1:** Write the inequality in the form $f(x) > 0$.

$3x^2 - 3x > 10 - 2x$

$\overbrace{3x^2 - x - 10}^{f(x)} > 0$

$3x^2 - x - 10 = 0$ **Step 2:** Find the real solutions to the related equation $f(x) = 0$.

$(3x + 5)(x - 2) = 0$

$x = -\dfrac{5}{3}$ and $x = 2$ The boundary points are $-\frac{5}{3}$ and 2.

Step 3: Divide the x-axis into intervals defined by the boundary points.

Determine the sign of $f(x) = 3x^2 - x - 10$ on each interval. One method is to evaluate $f(x)$ for a test value x on each interval.

Step 4: The solution set does not include the boundary points because the inequality is strict.

The solution set is $\left(-\infty, -\frac{5}{3}\right) \cup (2, \infty)$ or equivalently in set-builder notation $\left\{x \mid x < -\frac{5}{3} \text{ or } x > 2\right\}$.

Step 5: Write the solution set.

Skill Practice 1   Solve the inequality. $2x(x - 1) < 21 - x$

From Example 1, the key step is to determine the sign of $f(x)$ on the intervals $\left(-\infty, -\frac{5}{3}\right)$, $\left(-\frac{5}{3}, 2\right)$, and $(2, \infty)$. We can avoid the arithmetic from evaluating $f(x)$ at the test points by creating a sign chart. The inequality $3x^2 - x - 10 > 0$ is equivalent to $(3x + 5)(x - 2) > 0$. We have

Sign of $(3x + 5)$:	$-$	$+$	$+$
Sign of $(x - 2)$:	$-$	$-$	$+$
Sign of $(3x + 5)(x - 2)$:	$+$	$-$	$+$

$$-\frac{5}{3} \qquad 2$$

The sign chart organizes the signs of each factor on the given intervals. Then the sign of the product of factors is given in the bottom row. We see that $f(x) = (3x + 5)(x - 2) > 0$ for $\left(-\infty, -\frac{5}{3}\right) \cup (2, \infty)$.

The result of Example 1 can also be viewed graphically. From Section 3.1, the graph of $f(x) = 3x^2 - x - 10$ is a parabola opening upward (Figure 3-24).

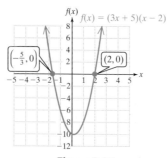

Figure 3-24

From the factored form $f(x) = (3x + 5)(x - 2)$, we see that the x-intercepts $\left(-\frac{5}{3}, 0\right)$ and $(2, 0)$ mark the points of transition between the intervals where $f(x)$ potentially changes sign.

Answer

1. Interval notation: $\left(-3, \frac{7}{2}\right)$;
    Set-builder notation:
    $\left\{x \mid -3 < x < \frac{7}{2}\right\}$

EXAMPLE 2 **Solving a Polynomial Inequality**

Solve the inequality. $x^4 - 12x \geq 8x^2 - x^3$

Solution:

$x^4 - 12x \geq 8x^2 - x^3$ **Step 1:** Write the inequality in the form $f(x) \geq 0$.

$$\overbrace{x^4 + x^3 - 8x^2 - 12x}^{f(x)} \geq 0$$

$x^4 + x^3 - 8x^2 - 12x = 0$ **Step 2:** Find the real solutions to the related equation $f(x) = 0$.

$x(x^3 + x^2 - 8x - 12) = 0$ Factor the left side of the equation.

The possible rational zeros of $x^3 + x^2 - 8x - 12$ are $\pm 1, \pm 2, \pm 3, \pm 4, \pm 6, \pm 12$.

$$\begin{array}{r|rrrr} 3 & 1 & 1 & -8 & -12 \\ & & 3 & 12 & 12 \\ \hline & 1 & 4 & 4 & \lfloor 0 \end{array}$$

After testing several potential rational zeros, we find that 3 is a zero of $f(x)$.

$x(x - 3)(x^2 + 4x + 4) = 0$ Now factor the quadratic polynomial.

$x(x - 3)(x + 2)^2 = 0$

$x = 0, x = 3, x = -2$ The boundary points are 0, 3, and -2.

Step 3: The inequality $x^4 + x^3 - 8x^2 - 12x \geq 0$ is equivalent to $x(x - 3)(x + 2)^2 \geq 0$. Divide the x-axis into intervals defined by the boundary points and determine the sign of $f(x)$ on each interval.

	Interval 1	Interval 2	Interval 3	Interval 4
Evaluate: $f(x) = x(x - 3)(x + 2)^2$	$f(-3) = 18$ $f(x) > 0$	$f(-1) = 4$ $f(x) > 0$	$f(1) = -18$ $f(x) < 0$	$f(4) = 144$ $f(x) > 0$
Sign of x	$-$	$-$	$+$	$+$
Sign of $(x - 3)$	$-$	$-$	$-$	$+$
Sign of $(x + 2)^2$	$+$	$+$	$+$	$+$
Sign of $x(x - 3)(x + 2)^2$	$+$	$+$	$-$	$+$

$$\xleftarrow{\qquad} \underset{-2}{\quad} \underset{0}{\quad} \underset{3}{\quad} \xrightarrow{\qquad}$$

The solution set is $(-\infty, 0] \cup [3, \infty)$.
In set-builder notation this is $\{x \mid x \leq 0 \text{ or } x \geq 3\}$.

Step 4: The solution set includes the boundary points because the inequality sign includes equality. Therefore, the union of intervals 1 and 2 becomes $(-\infty, 0]$.

Step 5: Write the solution set.

Skill Practice 2 Solve the inequality. $x^4 - 18x \geq 3x^2 - 4x^3$

The result of Example 2 can also be interpreted graphically. From Section 3.2, the graph of $f(x) = x^4 + x^3 - 8x^2 - 12x$ is up to the far left and up to the far right.

In factored form $f(x) = x(x - 3)(x + 2)^2$. The x-intercepts are $(0, 0)$, $(3, 0)$, and $(-2, 0)$. Furthermore, the factors x and $(x - 3)$ have odd exponents. This means

Answer

2. Interval notation: $(-\infty, 0] \cup [2, \infty)$;
Set-builder notation: $\{x \mid x \leq 0 \text{ or } x \geq 2\}$

that the corresponding zeros have odd multiplicities, and that the graph will cross the x-axis at $(0, 0)$ and $(3, 0)$ and change sign. The factor $(x + 2)$ has an even exponent meaning that the corresponding zero has an even multiplicity. The graph will touch the x-axis at $(-2, 0)$ but will *not* change sign. From the sketch in Figure 3-25, we see that $f(x) \geq 0$ on the intervals $(-\infty, 0]$ and $[3, \infty)$.

In some situations, the sign of a polynomial may be easily determined by inspection. In such a case, we can abbreviate the procedure to solve a polynomial inequality. This is demonstrated in Example 3.

Figure 3-25

EXAMPLE 3   **Solving Polynomial Inequalities**

Solve the inequalities.

a. $4x^2 - 12x + 9 < 0$ **b.** $4x^2 - 12x + 9 \leq 0$

c. $4x^2 - 12x + 9 > 0$ **d.** $4x^2 - 12x + 9 \geq 0$

Solution:

a. $4x^2 - 12x + 9 < 0$ Factor $4x^2 - 12x + 9$ as $(2x - 3)^2$.

    $(2x - 3)^2 < 0$ The square of any real number is nonnegative. Therefore, this inequality has no solution.

    The solution set is { }.

b. $4x^2 - 12x + 9 \leq 0$ The inequality in part (b) is the same as the inequality in part (a) except that equality is included.

    $(2x - 3)^2 \leq 0$

    The solution set is $\left\{\frac{3}{2}\right\}$.   The expression $(2x - 3)^2 = 0$ for $x = \frac{3}{2}$.

c. $4x^2 - 12x + 9 > 0$ The expression $(2x - 3)^2 > 0$ for all real numbers except where $(2x - 3)^2 = 0$. Therefore, the solution set is all real numbers except $\frac{3}{2}$.

    $(2x - 3)^2 > 0$

    The solution set is $\left(-\infty, \frac{3}{2}\right) \cup \left(\frac{3}{2}, \infty\right)$.

    In set-builder notation: $\left\{x \,\middle|\, x < \frac{3}{2} \text{ or } x > \frac{3}{2}\right\}$.

d. $4x^2 - 12x + 9 \geq 0$ The square of any real number is greater than or equal to zero. Therefore, the solution set is all real numbers.

    $(2x - 3)^2 \geq 0$

    The solution set is $(-\infty, \infty)$.

Skill Practice 3   Solve the inequalities.

    a. $25x^2 - 10x + 1 < 0$ **b.** $25x^2 - 10x + 1 \leq 0$

    c. $25x^2 - 10x + 1 > 0$ **d.** $25x^2 - 10x + 1 \geq 0$

2. Solve Rational Inequalities

We now turn our attention to solving rational inequalities.

Definition of a Rational Inequality

Let $f(x)$ be a rational expression. Then an inequality of the form $f(x) < 0$, $f(x) > 0$, $f(x) \leq 0$, or $f(x) \geq 0$ is called a **rational inequality.**

Answers

3. a. { }   **b.** $\left\{\frac{1}{5}\right\}$

   c. Interval notation: $\left(-\infty, \frac{1}{5}\right) \cup \left(\frac{1}{5}, \infty\right)$; Set-builder notation: $\left\{x \,\middle|\, x < \frac{1}{5} \text{ or } x > \frac{1}{5}\right\}$.

   d. $(-\infty, \infty)$

We solve polynomial and rational inequalities in the same way with one exception. With a rational inequality such as $f(x) < 0$, the list of boundary points must include the real solutions to the related equation $f(x) = 0$ along with the values of x that make $f(x)$ undefined.

The graph of a rational function will not always change sign to the left and right of a vertical asymptote or x-intercept. However, since the possibility exists, we must test each interval defined by these values of x.

The graph of $f(x) = \dfrac{2x - 5}{x + 2}$ is shown in Figure 3-26. Notice that the function changes sign to the left and right of the vertical asymptote $x = -2$ and to the left and right of the x-intercept $\left(\frac{5}{2}, 0\right)$.

From the graph of $f(x) = \dfrac{2x - 5}{x + 2}$ we can determine the solution sets for the following inequalities.

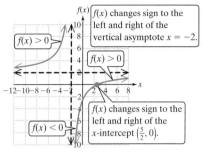

$f(x)$ changes sign to the left and right of the vertical asymptote $x = -2$.

$f(x) > 0$

$f(x) > 0$

$f(x) < 0$

$f(x)$ changes sign to the left and right of the x-intercept $\left(\frac{5}{2}, 0\right)$.

Figure 3-26

$$\frac{2x - 5}{x + 2} < 0 \qquad \text{on the interval } \left(-2, \tfrac{5}{2}\right)$$

$$\frac{2x - 5}{x + 2} > 0 \qquad \text{on the intervals } (-\infty, -2) \cup \left(\tfrac{5}{2}, \infty\right)$$

$$\frac{2x - 5}{x + 2} \leq 0 \qquad \text{on the interval } \left(-2, \tfrac{5}{2}\right]$$

$$\frac{2x - 5}{x + 2} \geq 0 \qquad \text{on the intervals } (-\infty, -2) \cup \left[\tfrac{5}{2}, \infty\right)$$

The value -2 is excluded from the solution set because -2 makes the expression $\dfrac{2x - 5}{x + 2}$ undefined.

EXAMPLE 4   Solving a Rational Inequality

Solve the inequality. $\dfrac{4x - 5}{x - 2} \leq 3$

Solution:

$$\frac{4x - 5}{x - 2} \leq 3$$

$$\overbrace{\frac{4x - 5}{x - 2} - 3}^{f(x)} \leq 0$$

Step 1: First write the inequality in the form $f(x) \leq 0$. That is, set one side to 0.

$$\frac{4x - 5}{x - 2} - 3 \cdot \frac{x - 2}{x - 2} \leq 0$$

Write each term with a common denominator.

$$\frac{4x - 5 - 3(x - 2)}{x - 2} \leq 0$$

Simplify.

$$\frac{4x - 5 - 3x + 6}{x - 2} \leq 0$$

We immediately see that the boundary point 2 must be excluded from the solution set because $\dfrac{x + 1}{x - 2}$ is undefined at 2.

$$\frac{x + 1}{x - 2} \leq 0$$

The expression $\dfrac{x + 1}{x - 2}$ is undefined for $x = 2$. Therefore, the value $x = 2$ is *not* part of the solution set. However, 2 *is* a boundary point for the solution set.

$$\frac{x + 1}{x - 2} = 0$$

Step 2: Solve for the real solutions to the equation $f(x) = 0$. The solution is -1, and this is another boundary point.

$$x = -1$$

The boundary points are $x = 2$ and $x = -1$.

Step 3: Divide the x-axis into intervals defined by the boundary points and determine the sign of $f(x)$ on each interval.

	Interval 1	Interval 2	Interval 3
Evaluate: $f(x) = \frac{x+1}{x-2}$	$f(-2) = \frac{1}{4}$ $f(x) > 0$	$f(1) = -2$ $f(x) < 0$	$f(3) = 4$ $f(x) > 0$
Sign of $(x + 1)$	$-$	$+$	$+$
Sign of $(x - 2)$	$-$	$-$	$+$
Sign of $\frac{(x+1)}{(x-2)}$	$+$	$-$	$+$

$$-1 \qquad\qquad 2$$

Step 4: The boundary point -1 is included in the solution set because equality is included.
The boundary point 2 is excluded because $\dfrac{x+1}{x-2}$ is undefined for $x = 2$.

Step 5: Write the solution set.
The solution set is $[-1, 2)$.
In set-builder notation this is $\{x \mid -1 \leq x < 2\}$.

> **TIP** A rational expression is equal to zero where the numerator is equal to zero.
> A rational expression is undefined where the denominator is equal to zero.

Skill Practice 4 Solve the inequality. $\dfrac{5 - x}{x - 1} \geq -2$

EXAMPLE 5   Solving Rational Inequalities

Solve the inequalities.

a. $\dfrac{x^2}{x^2 + 4} \geq 0$ **b.** $\dfrac{x^2}{x^2 + 4} > 0$

c. $\dfrac{x^2}{x^2 + 4} \leq 0$ **d.** $\dfrac{x^2}{x^2 + 4} < 0$

Solution:

The solution to the related equation $\dfrac{x^2}{x^2 + 4} = 0$ is $x = 0$.

The denominator is nonzero for all real numbers.

Therefore, the only boundary point is $x = 0$.

Sign of x^2	$+$	$+$
Sign of $x^2 + 4$	$+$	$+$
Sign of $\dfrac{x^2}{x^2 + 4}$	$+$	$+$

$$0$$

Therefore, $\dfrac{x^2}{x^2 + 4} = 0$ at $x = 0$ and is positive for all other real numbers.

a. $\dfrac{x^2}{x^2 + 4} \geq 0$ Solution set: $(-\infty, \infty)$

b. $\dfrac{x^2}{x^2 + 4} > 0$ Solution set: $(-\infty, 0) \cup (0, \infty)$

c. $\dfrac{x^2}{x^2 + 4} \leq 0$ Solution set: $\{0\}$

d. $\dfrac{x^2}{x^2 + 4} < 0$ Solution set: $\{\ \}$

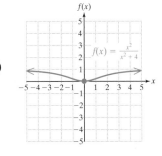

Answer
4. $(-\infty, -3] \cup (1, \infty)$

Skill Practice 5   Solve the inequalities.

a. $\dfrac{x^2}{x^4 + 1} \geq 0$ **b.** $\dfrac{x^2}{x^4 + 1} > 0$ **c.** $\dfrac{x^2}{x^4 + 1} \leq 0$ **d.** $\dfrac{x^2}{x^4 + 1} < 0$

3. Solve Applications Involving Polynomial and Rational Inequalities

In Section 1.5, we studied the vertical position $s(t)$ of an object moving upward or downward under the influence of gravity. We use this model to solve the application in Example 6.

$$s(t) = -\frac{1}{2}gt^2 + v_0t + s_0$$

where

g is the acceleration due to gravity (32 ft/sec^2 or 9.8 m/sec^2).

t is the time of travel.

v_0 is the initial velocity.

s_0 is the initial vertical position.

EXAMPLE 6   **Solving an Application of a Polynomial Inequality**

A toy rocket is shot straight upward from a launch pad 1 ft above ground level with an initial velocity of 64 ft/sec.

a. Write a model to express the vertical position $s(t)$ (in ft) of the rocket t seconds after launch.

b. Determine the times at which the rocket is above a height of 50 ft.

Solution:

TIP Choose $g = 32$ ft/sec^2 because the height is given in feet and velocity is given in feet per second.

a. $s(t) = -\dfrac{1}{2}gt^2 + v_0t + s_0$

$s(t) = -\dfrac{1}{2}(32)t^2 + (64)t + (1)$

$s(t) = -16t^2 + 64t + 1$

In this example,

$s_0 = 1$ ft
$v_0 = 64$ ft/sec
$g = 32$ ft/sec^2

b. $-16t^2 + 64t + 1 > 50$

$\overbrace{-16t^2 + 64t - 49}^{f(t)} > 0$

$-16t^2 + 64t - 49 = 0$

$t = \dfrac{-64 \pm \sqrt{(64)^2 - 4(-16)(-49)}}{2(-16)}$

$t = \dfrac{8 \pm \sqrt{15}}{4}$ ⟶ ≈ 2.97
                                ≈ 1.03

Write the inequality in the form $f(t) > 0$.

Use the quadratic formula to solve the related equation $f(t) = 0$.

Evaluate $f(t) = -16t^2 + 64t - 49$ for test points in each interval.

$f(1) = -1$ ┊ $f(2) = 15$ ┊ $f(3) = -1$
$f(t) < 0$ ┊ $f(t) > 0$ ┊ $f(t) < 0$

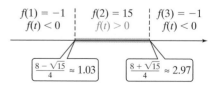

$\dfrac{8 - \sqrt{15}}{4} \approx 1.03$ $\dfrac{8 + \sqrt{15}}{4} \approx 2.97$

Answers

5. a. $(-\infty, \infty)$
   b. $(-\infty, 0) \cup (0, \infty)$
   c. $\{0\}$
   d. $\{\ \}$

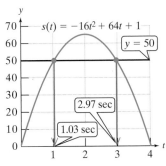

Figure 3-27

The solution set is $\left(\dfrac{8 - \sqrt{15}}{4}, \dfrac{8 + \sqrt{15}}{4}\right)$ or approximately $(1.03, 2.97)$. The rocket will be above 50 ft high between 1.03 sec and 2.97 sec after launch.

   The graph of $s(t) = -16t^2 + 64t + 1$ is a parabola opening downward (Figure 3-27). We see that $s(t) > 50$ for t between 1.03 and 2.97 as expected.

Skill Practice 6   Repeat Example 6 under the assumption that the rocket is launched with an initial velocity of 80 ft/sec from a height of 5 ft.

Answers

6. a. $s(t) = -16t^2 + 80t + 5$

   b. $\left(\dfrac{10 - \sqrt{55}}{4}, \dfrac{10 + \sqrt{55}}{4}\right)$

SECTION 3.6   Practice Exercises

Review Exercises

For Exercises 1–4, find the real solutions to the equation.

   1. $2x^3 + 5x^2 - 12x = 0$

   2. $-12x^3 + 32x^2 + 12x = 0$

   3. $\dfrac{2x + 1}{x - 5} = 0$

   4. $\dfrac{4x - 3}{x + 1} = 0$

For Exercises 5–6, determine the real values of x for which the expression is undefined.

   5. $\dfrac{2x + 1}{x - 5} = 0$

   6. $\dfrac{4x - 3}{x + 1} = 0$

Concept Connections

   7. Let $f(x)$ be a polynomial. An inequality of the form $f(x) < 0$, $f(x) > 0$, $f(x) \geq 0$, or $f(x) \leq 0$ is called a _____ inequality. If the polynomial is of degree _____, then the inequality is also called a quadratic inequality.

   8. Let $f(x)$ be a rational expression. An inequality of the form $f(x) < 0$, $f(x) > 0$, $f(x) \geq 0$, or $f(x) \leq 0$ is called a _____ inequality.

   9. The solutions to an inequality $f(x) < 0$ are the values of x on the intervals where $f(x)$ is (positive/negative).

   10. The solution set for the inequality $(x + 10)^2 \geq -4$ is _____, whereas the solution set for the inequality $(x + 10)^2 \leq -4$ is _____.

Objective 1: Solve Polynomial Inequalities

For Exercises 11–20, the graph of $y = f(x)$ is given. Solve the inequalities.

   a. $f(x) < 0$ **b.** $f(x) \leq 0$ **c.** $f(x) > 0$ **d.** $f(x) \geq 0$

11.

12.

13.

14.

15.

16.

17.

18.

19.

20.

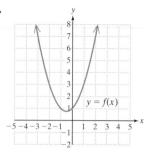

For Exercises 21–26, solve the equations and inequalities. (See Example 3)

21. **a.** $(5x - 3)(x - 5) = 0$

    b. $(5x - 3)(x - 5) < 0$

    c. $(5x - 3)(x - 5) \leq 0$

    d. $(5x - 3)(x - 5) > 0$

    e. $(5x - 3)(x - 5) \geq 0$

22. **a.** $(3x + 7)(x - 2) = 0$

    b. $(3x + 7)(x - 2) < 0$

    c. $(3x + 7)(x - 2) \leq 0$

    d. $(3x + 7)(x - 2) > 0$

    e. $(3x + 7)(x - 2) \geq 0$

23. **a.** $-x^2 + x + 12 = 0$

    b. $-x^2 + x + 12 < 0$

    c. $-x^2 + x + 12 \leq 0$

    d. $-x^2 + x + 12 > 0$

    e. $-x^2 + x + 12 \geq 0$

24. **a.** $-x^2 - 10x - 9 = 0$

    b. $-x^2 - 10x - 9 < 0$

    c. $-x^2 - 10x - 9 \leq 0$

    d. $-x^2 - 10x - 9 > 0$

    e. $-x^2 - 10x - 9 \geq 0$

25. **a.** $x^2 + 12x + 36 = 0$

    b. $x^2 + 12x + 36 < 0$

    c. $x^2 + 12x + 36 \leq 0$

    d. $x^2 + 12x + 36 > 0$

    e. $x^2 + 12x + 36 \geq 0$

26. **a.** $x^2 - 14x + 49 = 0$

    b. $x^2 - 14x + 49 < 0$

    c. $x^2 - 14x + 49 \leq 0$

    d. $x^2 - 14x + 49 > 0$

    e. $x^2 - 14x + 49 \geq 0$

For Exercises 27–54, solve the inequalities. (See Examples 1–2)

27. $3w^2 + w < 2(w + 2)$

28. $5y^2 + 7y < 3(y + 4)$

29. $a^2 \geq 3a$

30. $d^2 \geq 6d$

31. $10 - 6x > 5x^2$

32. $6 - 4x > 3x^2$

33. $(x + 4)(x - 1)(x - 3) \geq 0$

34. $(x + 2)(x + 5)(x - 4) \geq 0$

35. $-5c(c + 2)^2(4 - c) > 0$

36. $-6u(u + 1)^2(3 - u) > 0$

37. $t^4 - 10t^2 + 9 \leq 0$

38. $w^4 - 20w^2 + 64 \leq 0$

39. $2x^3 + 5x^2 < 8x + 20$

40. $3x^3 - 3x < 4x^2 - 4$

41. $-2x^4 + 10x^3 - 6x^2 - 18x \geq 0$

42. $-4x^4 + 4x^3 + 64x^2 + 80x \geq 0$

43. $-5u^6 + 28u^5 - 15u^4 \leq 0$

44. $-3w^6 + 8w^5 - 4w^4 \leq 0$

45. $6x(2x - 5)^4(3x + 1)^5(x - 4) < 0$ **46.** $5x(3x - 2)^2(4x + 1)^3(x - 3)^4 < 0$ **47.** $(5x - 3)^2 > -2$

48. $(4x + 1)^2 > -6$ **49.** $-4 \geq (x - 7)^2$ **50.** $-1 \geq (x + 2)^2$

51. $16y^2 > 24y - 9$ **52.** $4w^2 > 20w - 25$ **53.** $(x + 3)(x + 1) \leq -1$

54. $(x + 2)(x + 4) \leq -1$

Objective 2: Solve Rational Inequalities

For Exercises 55–58, the graph of $y = f(x)$ is given. Solve the inequalities.

   a. $f(x) < 0$ **b.** $f(x) \leq 0$ **c.** $f(x) > 0$ **d.** $f(x) \geq 0$

55.

56.

57.

58.

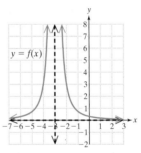

For Exercises 59–62, solve the inequalities. (See Example 5)

59. a. $\dfrac{x + 2}{x - 3} \leq 0$ **60. a.** $\dfrac{x + 4}{x - 1} \leq 0$ **61. a.** $\dfrac{x^4}{x^2 + 9} \leq 0$ **62. a.** $\dfrac{-x^2}{x^4 + 16} \leq 0$

   b. $\dfrac{x + 2}{x - 3} < 0$ **b.** $\dfrac{x + 4}{x - 1} < 0$ **b.** $\dfrac{x^4}{x^2 + 9} < 0$ **b.** $\dfrac{-x^2}{x^4 + 16} < 0$

   c. $\dfrac{x + 2}{x - 3} \geq 0$ **c.** $\dfrac{x + 4}{x - 1} \geq 0$ **c.** $\dfrac{x^4}{x^2 + 9} \geq 0$ **c.** $\dfrac{-x^2}{x^4 + 16} \geq 0$

   d. $\dfrac{x + 2}{x - 3} > 0$ **d.** $\dfrac{x + 4}{x - 1} > 0$ **d.** $\dfrac{x^4}{x^2 + 9} > 0$ **d.** $\dfrac{-x^2}{x^4 + 16} > 0$

For Exercises 63–84, solve the inequalities. (See Example 4)

63. $\dfrac{5 - x}{x + 1} \geq 0$ **64.** $\dfrac{2 - x}{x + 6} \geq 0$ **65.** $\dfrac{4 - 2x}{x^2} \leq 0$

66. $\dfrac{9 - 3x}{x^2} \leq 0$ **67.** $\dfrac{x^2 - x - 2}{x + 3} \geq 0$ **68.** $\dfrac{x^2 - 2x - 8}{x - 1} \geq 0$

69. $\dfrac{5}{2x - 7} > 1$ **70.** $\dfrac{4}{3x - 8} > 1$ **71.** $\dfrac{2x}{x - 2} \leq 2$

72. $\dfrac{3x}{3x - 7} \leq 1$ **73.** $\dfrac{4 - x}{x + 5} \geq 2$ **74.** $\dfrac{3 - x}{x + 2} \geq 4$

75. $\dfrac{x - 2}{x^2 + 4} \leq 0$ **76.** $\dfrac{x - 3}{x^2 + 1} \leq 0$ **77.** $\dfrac{10}{x + 2} \geq \dfrac{2}{x + 2}$

78. $\dfrac{4}{x-3} \geq \dfrac{1}{x-3}$

79. $\dfrac{4}{x+3} > -\dfrac{2}{x}$

80. $\dfrac{2}{x-1} > -\dfrac{4}{x}$

81. $\dfrac{3}{4-x} \leq \dfrac{6}{1-x}$

82. $\dfrac{5}{2-x} \leq \dfrac{3}{3-x}$

83. $\dfrac{(2-x)(2x+1)^2}{(x-4)^4} \leq 0$

84. $\dfrac{(3-x)(4x-1)^4}{(x+2)^2} \leq 0$

Objective 3: Solve Applications Involving Polynomial and Rational Inequalities

85. A professional fireworks team shoots an 8-in. mortar straight upwards from ground level with an initial velocity of 216 ft/sec. (**See Example 6**)

   a. Write a function modeling the vertical position $s(t)$ (in ft) of the shell at a time t seconds after launch.

   b. The mortar is designed to explode when the shell is at its maximum height. How long after launch will the shell explode? (*Hint*: Consider the vertex formula from Section 3.1.)

   c. The spectators can see the shell rising once it clears a 200-ft tree line. For what period of time after launch is the shell visible before it explodes?

86. Suppose that a basketball player jumps straight up for a rebound.

   a. If his initial velocity is 16 ft/sec, write a function modeling his vertical position $s(t)$ (in ft) at a time t seconds after leaving the ground.

   b. Find the times after leaving the ground when the player will be at a height of more than 3 ft in the air.

87. For a certain stretch of road, the distance d (in ft) required to stop a car that is traveling at speed v (in mph) before the brakes are applied can be approximated by $d(v) = 0.06v^2 + 2v$. Find the speeds for which the car can be stopped within 250 ft.

88. The population $P(t)$ of a bacteria culture is given by $P(t) = -1500t^2 + 60{,}000t + 10{,}000$, where t is the time in hours after the culture is started. Determine the time(s) at which the population will be greater than 460,000 organisms.

89. Suppose that an object that is originally at room temperature of 32°C is placed in a freezer. The temperature $T(x)$ (in °C) of the object can be approximated by the model $T(x) = \dfrac{320}{x^2 + 3x + 10}$, where x is the time in hours after the object is placed in the freezer.

   a. What is the horizontal asymptote of the graph of this function and what does it represent in the context of this problem?

   b. A chemist needs a compound cooled to less than 5°C. Determine the amount of time required for the compound to cool so that its temperature is less than 5°C.

90. The average round trip speed S (in mph) of a vehicle traveling a distance of d miles in each direction is given by

$$S = \dfrac{2d}{\dfrac{d}{r_1} + \dfrac{d}{r_2}}$$

where r_1 and r_2 are the rates of speed for the initial trip and the return trip, respectively.

   a. Suppose that a motorist travels 200 mi from her home to an athletic event and averages 50 mph for the trip to the event. Determine the speeds necessary if the motorist wants the average speed for the round trip to be at least 60 mph?

   b. Would the motorist be traveling within the speed limit of 70 mph?

91. A rectangular quilt is to be made so that the length is 1.2 times the width. The quilt must be between 72 ft² and 96 ft² to cover the bed. Determine the restrictions on the width so that the dimensions of the quilt will meet the required area. Give exact values and the approximated values to the nearest tenth of a foot.

92. A landscaping team plans to build a rectangular garden that is between 480 yd² and 720 yd² in area. For aesthetic reasons, they also want the length to be 1.5 times the width. Determine the restrictions on the width so that the dimensions of the garden will meet the required area. Give exact values and the approximated values to the nearest tenth of a yard.

Mixed Exercises

For Exercises 93–102, write the domain of the function in interval notation.

93. $f(x) = \sqrt{9 - x^2}$

94. $g(t) = \sqrt{1 - t^2}$

95. $h(a) = \sqrt{a^2 - 5}$

96. $f(u) = \sqrt{u^2 - 7}$

97. $p(x) = \sqrt{2x^2 + 9x - 18}$

98. $q(x) = \sqrt{4x^2 + 7x - 2}$

99. $r(x) = \dfrac{1}{\sqrt{2x^2 + 9x - 18}}$

100. $s(x) = \dfrac{1}{\sqrt{4x^2 + 7x - 2}}$

101. $h(x) = \sqrt{\dfrac{3x}{x + 2}}$

102. $k(x) = \sqrt{\dfrac{2x}{x + 1}}$

103. Let a, b, and c represent positive real numbers, where $a < b < c$, and let $f(x) = (x - a)^2(b - x)(x - c)^3$.

  a. Complete the sign chart.

Sign of $(x - a)^2$:			
Sign of $(b - x)$:			
Sign of $(x - c)^3$:			
Sign of $(x - a)^2(b - x)(x - c)^3$:			

                                       a b c

  b. Solve $f(x) > 0$.   **c.** Solve $f(x) < 0$.

104. Let a, b, and c represent positive real numbers, where $a < b < c$, and let $g(x) = \dfrac{(a - x)(x - b)^2}{(c - x)^5}$.

  a. Complete the sign chart.

Sign of $(a - x)$:			
Sign of $(x - b)^2$:			
Sign of $(c - x)^5$:			
Sign of $\dfrac{(a - x)(x - b)^2}{(c - x)^5}$:			

                                         a b c

  b. Solve $g(x) > 0$.   **c.** Solve $g(x) < 0$.

Write About It

105. Explain how the solution set to the inequality $f(x) < 0$ is related to the graph of $y = f(x)$.

106. Explain how the solution set to the inequality $f(x) \geq 0$ is related to the graph of $y = f(x)$.

107. Explain why $\dfrac{x^2 + 2}{x^2 + 1} < 0$ has no solution.

108. Given $\dfrac{x - 3}{x - 1} \leq 0$, explain why the solution set includes 3, but does not include 1.

Expanding Your Skills

The procedure to solve a polynomial or rational inequality may be applied to all inequalities of the form $f(x) > 0$, $f(x) < 0$, $f(x) \geq 0$, and $f(x) \leq 0$. That is, find the real solutions to the related equation and determine restricted values of x. Then determine the sign of $f(x)$ on each interval defined by the boundary points. Use this process to solve the inequalities in Exercises 109–120.

109. $\sqrt{2x - 6} - 2 < 0$

110. $\sqrt{3x - 5} - 4 < 0$

111. $\sqrt{4 - x} - 6 \geq 0$

112. $\sqrt{5 - x} - 7 \geq 0$

113. $\dfrac{1}{\sqrt{x - 2} - 4} \leq 0$

114. $\dfrac{1}{\sqrt{x - 3} - 5} \leq 0$

115. $-3 < x^2 - 6x + 5 \leq 5$

116. $8 \leq x^2 + 4x + 3 < 15$

117. $|x^2 - 4| < 5$

118. $|x^2 + 1| < 17$

119. $|x^2 - 18| > 2$

120. $|x^2 - 6| > 3$

Technology Connections

121. Given the inequality,
$0.552x^3 + 4.13x^2 - 1.84x - 3.5 < 6.7$,

  a. Write the inequality in the form $f(x) < 0$.

  b. Graph $y = f(x)$ on a suitable viewing window.

  c. Use the **Zero** feature to approximate the real zeros of $f(x)$. Round to 1 decimal place.

  d. Use the graph to approximate the solution set for the inequality $f(x) < 0$.

122. Given the inequality,
$0.24x^4 + 1.8x^3 + 3.3x^2 + 2.84x - 1.8 > 4.5$,

  a. Write the inequality in the form $f(x) > 0$.

  b. Graph $y = f(x)$ on a suitable viewing window.

  c. Use the **Zero** feature to approximate the real zeros of $f(x)$. Round to 1 decimal place.

  d. Use the graph to approximate the solution set for the inequality $f(x) > 0$.

123. An engineer for a food manufacturer designs an aluminum container for a hot drink mix. The container is to be a right circular cylinder 5.5 in. in height. The surface area represents the amount of aluminum used and is given by

$$S(r) = 2\pi r^2 + 11\pi r, \text{ where } r \text{ is the radius of the can.}$$

a. Graph the function $y = S(r)$ and the line $y = 90$ on the viewing window [0, 3, 1] by [0, 150, 10].

b. Use the Intersect feature to determine point of intersection of $y = S(r)$ and $y = 90$.

c. Determine the restrictions on r so that the amount of aluminum used is at most 90 in.^{2}. Round to 1 decimal place.

124. The concentration $C(t)$ (in ng/mL) of a drug in the bloodstream t hours after ingestion is modeled by

$$C(t) = \frac{500t}{t^3 + 100}$$

a. Graph the function $y = C(t)$ and the line $y = 4$ on the window [0, 32, 4] by [0, 15, 3].

b. Use the Intersect feature to determine the point(s) of intersection of $y = C(t)$ and $y = 4$.

c. To avoid toxicity, a physician may give a second dose of the medicine once the concentration falls below 4 ng/mL for increasing values of t. Determine the times at which it is safe to give a second dose. Round to 1 decimal place.

PROBLEM RECOGNITION EXERCISES

Solving Equations and Inequalities

At this point in the text, we have studied several categories of equations and related inequalities. These include

- linear equations and inequalities
- quadratic equations and inequalities
- polynomial equations and inequalities
- rational equations and inequalities
- radical equations and inequalities
- absolute value equations and inequalities
- compound inequalities

For Exercises 1–30, solve the equations and inequalities. Write the solution sets to the inequalities in interval notation if possible.

1. $-\dfrac{1}{2} \le -\dfrac{1}{4}x - 5 < 2$

2. $2x^2 - 6x = 5$

3. $50x^3 - 25x^2 - 2x + 1 = 0$

4. $\dfrac{-5x(x-3)^2}{2+x} \le 0$

5. $\sqrt[4]{m+4} - 5 = -2$

6. $-5 < y$ and $-3y + 4 \ge 7$

7. $|5t - 4| + 2 = 7$

8. $3 - 4\{x - 5[x + 2(3 - 2x)]\} = -2[4 - (x - 1)]$

9. $10x(2x - 14) = -29x^2 - 100$

10. $\dfrac{5}{y-4} = \dfrac{3y}{y+2} - \dfrac{2y^2 - 14y}{y^2 - 2y - 8}$

11. $x(x - 14) \le -40$

12. $\dfrac{1}{x^2 - 14x + 40} \le 0$

13. $|x - 0.15| = |x + 0.05|$

14. $\sqrt{t-1} - 5 \le 1$

15. $n^{1/2} + 7 = 10$

16. $-4x(3 - x)(x + 2)^2(x - 5)^3 \ge 0$

17. $-2x - 5(x + 3) = -4(x + 2) - 3x$

18. $\sqrt{7x + 29} - 3 = x$

19. $(x^2 - 9)^2 - 5(x^2 - 9) - 14 = 0$

20. $2 + 7x^{-1} - 15x^{-2} = 0$

21. $|8x - 3| + 10 \le 7$

22. $2(x - 1)^{3/4} = 16$

23. $x^3 - 3x^2 < 6x - 8$

24. $\dfrac{3 - x}{x + 5} \ge 1$

25. $15 - 3(x - 1) = -2x - (x - 18)$

26. $25x^2 + 70x > -49$

27. $2 < |3 - x| - 9$

28. $-4(x - 3) < 8$ or $-7 > x - 3$

29. $\dfrac{1}{3}x + \dfrac{2}{5} > \dfrac{5}{6}x - 1$

30. $2|2x + 1| - 2 \le 8$

SECTION 3.7 Variation

1. Write Models Involving Direct, Inverse, and Joint Variation

The familiar relationship $d = rt$ tells us that distance traveled equals the rate of speed times the time of travel. For a car traveling 60 mph, we have $d = 60t$. From Table 3-2, notice that as the time of travel increases, the distance increases proportionally. We say that d is directly proportional to t, or that d varies directly as t. This is shown graphically in Figure 3-28.

Table 3-2

t (hr)	d (mi)
1	60
2	120
3	180
4	240
5	300
6	360

$d = 60t$

Figure 3-28

Now suppose that a motorist travels a fixed distance of 240 mi. We have

$$d = rt$$
$$240 = rt \longrightarrow t = \frac{240}{r}$$

The time of travel t varies *inversely* as the rate of speed. As the rate r increases, the time of travel will decrease proportionally. Likewise, for slower rates, the time of travel is greater. See Table 3-3 and Figure 3-29.

Table 3-3

r (mph)	t (hr)
10	24
20	12
30	8
40	6
50	4.8
60	4

$t = \frac{240}{r}$

Figure 3-29

Direct and Inverse Variation

Let k be a nonzero constant real number. Then the following statements are equivalent:

1. y varies **directly** as x.
   y is **directly** proportional to x. $\left.\right\}$ $y = kx$

2. y varies **inversely** as x.
   y is **inversely** proportional to x. $\left.\right\}$ $y = \dfrac{k}{x}$

Note: The value of k is called the **constant of variation.**

The first step in using a variation model is to write an English statement as an equivalent mathematical equation.

EXAMPLE 1 Writing a Variation Model

Write a variation model using k as the constant of variation.

Solution:

a. The amount of medicine A prescribed by a physician varies directly as the weight of the patient w.

$$A = kw$$

Since the variables are directly related, set up the *product* of k and w.

b. The frequency f in a vibrating string is inversely proportional to its length L.

$$f = \frac{k}{L}$$

Since the variables are inversely related, set up the *quotient* of k and L.

c. The variable y varies directly as the square of x and inversely as the square root of z.

$$y = \frac{kx^2}{\sqrt{z}}$$

Since the square of the variable x is directly related to y, set up the *product* of k and x^2. And since the square root of z is inversely related to y, set up the *quotient* of k and $\sqrt{z}$.

> **TIP** Notice that in each variation model, the constant of variation, k, is always in the numerator.

Skill Practice 1 Write a variation model using k as the constant of variation.

a. The distance d that a spring stretches varies directly as the force F applied to the spring.

b. The force F required to keep a car from skidding on a curved road varies inversely as the radius r of the curve.

c. The variable a varies directly as b and inversely as the cube root of c.

Sometimes a variable varies directly as the product of two or more other variables. In such a case we have joint variation.

Joint Variation

Let k be a nonzero constant real number. Then the following statements are equivalent:

$$\left.\begin{array}{l} y \text{ varies } \textbf{jointly} \text{ as } w \text{ and } x. \\ y \text{ is } \textbf{jointly} \text{ proportional to } w \text{ and } x. \end{array}\right\} y = kwx$$

EXAMPLE 2 Writing a Joint Variation Model

Write a variation model using k as the constant of variation.

Solution:

a. y varies jointly as t and the cube root of u.

$$y = kt\sqrt[3]{u}$$

The variable t and the quantity $\sqrt[3]{u}$ are jointly related to y. Set up the product of k, t, and $\sqrt[3]{u}$.

b. The gravitational force of attraction between two planets varies jointly as the product of their masses and inversely as the square of the distance between them.

$$F = \frac{km_1 m_2}{d^2}$$

Let m_1 and m_2 represent the masses of the planets, let d represent the distance between the planets, and let F represent the gravitational force between the planets.

Answers

1. a. $d = kF$ **b.** $F = \dfrac{k}{r}$

c. $a = \dfrac{kb}{\sqrt[3]{c}}$

> **Skill Practice 2**   Write a variation model using k as the constant of variation.
>
> **a.** The kinetic energy of an object varies jointly as the object's mass and the square of its velocity.
> **b.** z varies jointly as x and y and inversely as the square root of w.

2. Solve Applications Involving Variation

Consider the variation models $y = kx$ and $y = \dfrac{k}{x}$. In either case, if values for x and y are known, we can solve for k. Once k is known, we can write a variation model and use it to find y if x is known, or to find x if y is known. This concept is the basis for solving many problems involving variation.

> ### Procedure to Solve an Application Involving Variation
>
> **Step 1** Write a general variation model that relates the variables given in the problem. Let k represent the constant of variation.
> **Step 2** Solve for k by substituting known values of the variables into the model from step 1.
> **Step 3** Substitute the value of k into the original variation model from step 1.
> **Step 4** Use the variation model from step 3 to solve the application.

EXAMPLE 3   **Solving an Application Involving Direct Variation**

The amount of an allergy medicine that a physician prescribes for a child varies directly as the weight of the child. Clinical research suggests that 13.5 mg of the drug should be given for a 30-lb child.

  a. How much should be prescribed for a 50-lb child?
  b. How much should be prescribed for a 60-lb child?
  c. A nurse wants to double check the dosage on a doctor's order of 18 mg. For a child of what weight is this dosage appropriate?

Solution:

Let A represent the amount of medicine.   Label the variables.
Let w represent the weight of the child.

$A = kw$	**Step 1:** Write a general variation model.
$13.5 = k(30)$	**Step 2:** Substitute known values of A and w into the variation model.
$\dfrac{13.5}{30} = k$	Solve for k by dividing both sides by 30.
$k = 0.45$	
$A = 0.45w$	**Step 3:** Substitute the value of k into the original variation model.

a. $A = 0.45(50)$ **Step 4:** Solve the application by substituting 50 for w.
  $A = 22.5$ A 50-lb child would require 22.5 mg of the drug.

Answers

2. a. $E = kmv^2$ **b.** $z = \dfrac{kxy}{\sqrt{w}}$

b. $A = 0.45(60)$ Substitute 60 for w.

   $A = 27$ A 60-lb child would require 27 mg of the drug.

c. $A = 0.45w$

   $18 = 0.45w$ Substitute 18 mg for the amount of medicine.

   $40 = w$ Solve for the weight w. A 40-lb child would receive 18 mg.

Skill Practice 3   The amount of the medicine ampicillin that a physician prescribes for a child varies directly as the weight of the child. A physician prescribes 420 mg for a 35-lb child.

  a. How much should be prescribed for a 30-lb child?

  b. How much should be prescribed for a 40-lb child?

EXAMPLE 4   **Solving an Application Involving Inverse Variation**

The loudness of sound measured in decibels (dB) varies inversely as the square of the distance between the listener and the source of the sound. If the loudness of sound is 17.92 dB at a distance of 10 ft from a stereo speaker, what is the decibel level 20 ft from the speaker?

Solution:

Let L represent the loudness of sound in decibels and d represent the distance in feet. The inverse relationship between decibel level and the square of the distance is modeled by

$$L = \frac{k}{d^2}$$

$$17.92 = \frac{k}{(10)^2}$$ Substitute $L = 17.92$ dB and $d = 10$ ft.

$$17.92 = \frac{k}{100}$$

$$(17.92)100 = \frac{k}{100} \cdot \cancel{100}$$ Solve for k (clear fractions).

$$k = 1792$$

$$L = \frac{1792}{d^2}$$ Substitute $k = 1792$ into the original model $L = \frac{k}{d^2}$.

With the value of k known, we can find L for any value of d.

$$L = \frac{1792}{(20)^2}$$ Find the loudness when $d = 20$ ft.

$$= 4.48 \text{ dB}$$

Notice that the loudness of sound is 17.92 dB at a distance 10 ft from the speaker. When the distance from the speaker is increased to 20 ft, the decibel level decreases to 4.48 dB. This is consistent with an inverse relationship. For $k > 0$, as one variable is increased, the other is decreased. It also seems reasonable that the farther one moves away from the source of a sound, the softer the sound becomes.

Answers

3. a. 360 mg   **b.** 480 mg

4. 5%

Skill Practice 4   The yield on a bond varies inversely as the price. The yield on a particular bond is 4% when the price is $100. Find the yield when the price is $80.

| EXAMPLE 5 | Solving an Application Involving Joint Variation |

In the early morning hours of August 29, 2005, Hurricane Katrina plowed into the Gulf Coast of the United States, bringing unprecedented destruction to southern Louisiana, Mississippi, and Alabama. The winds of a hurricane are strong enough to send a piece of plywood through a tree.

The kinetic energy of an object varies jointly as the weight of the object at sea level and as the square of its velocity. During a hurricane, a 0.5-lb stone traveling 60 mph has 81 joules (J) of kinetic energy. Suppose the wind speed doubles to 120 mph. Find the kinetic energy.

Solution:

Let E represent the kinetic energy, let w represent the weight, and let v represent the velocity of the stone. The variation model is

$$E = kwv^2$$
$$81 = k(0.5)(60)^2 \quad \text{Substitute } E = 81 \text{ J}, w = 0.5 \text{ lb}, \text{ and } v = 60 \text{ mph.}$$
$$81 = k(0.5)(3600) \quad \text{Simplify the exponent.}$$
$$81 = k(1800)$$
$$\frac{81}{1800} = \frac{k(\cancel{1800})}{\cancel{1800}} \quad \text{Divide by 1800.}$$
$$0.045 = k \quad \text{Solve for } k.$$

With the value of k known, the model $E = kwv^2$ can be written as $E = 0.045wv^2$. We now find the kinetic energy of a 0.5-lb stone traveling 120 mph.

$$E = 0.045(0.5)(120)^2$$
$$= 324$$

The kinetic energy of a 0.5-lb stone traveling 120 mph is 324 J.

Skill Practice 5   The amount of simple interest earned in an account varies jointly as the interest rate and time of the investment. An account earns $200 in 2 yr at 4% interest. How much interest would be earned in 3 yr at a rate of 5%?

Answer
5. $375

| SECTION 3.7 | Practice Exercises |

Review Exercises

For Exercises 1–4, solve the equations.

1. $\dfrac{9}{4} = \dfrac{3}{32}k$

2. $\dfrac{7}{10} = \dfrac{7}{5}k$

3. $0.24 = \dfrac{1.68}{\sqrt{x}}$

4. $0.32 = \dfrac{2.56}{\sqrt{y}}$

Concept Connections

5. If k is a nonzero constant real number, then the statement $y = kx$ implies that y varies _____ as x.

6. If k is a nonzero constant real number, then the statement $y = \frac{k}{x}$ implies that y varies _____ as x.

7. The value of k in the variation models $y = kx$ and $y = \frac{k}{x}$ is called the _____ of _____.

8. If y varies directly as two or more other variables such as x and w, then $y = kxw$, and we say that y varies _____ as x and w.

9. a. Given $y = 2x$, evaluate y for the given values of x: $x = 1, x = 2, x = 3, x = 4$, and $x = 5$.

    b. How does y change when x is doubled?

    c. How does y change when x is tripled?

    d. Complete the statement. Given $y = 2x$, when x increases, y (increases/decreases) proportionally.

    e. Complete the statement. Given $y = 2x$, when x decreases, y (increases/decreases) proportionally.

10. a. Given $y = \frac{24}{x}$, evaluate y for the given values of x: $x = 1, x = 2, x = 3, x = 4$, and $x = 6$.

    b. How does y change when x is doubled?

    c. How does y change when x is tripled?

    d. Complete the statement. Given $y = \frac{24}{x}$, when x increases, y (increases/decreases) proportionally.

    e. Complete the statement. Given $y = \frac{24}{x}$, when x decreases, y (increases/decreases) proportionally.

Objective 1: Write Models Involving Direct, Inverse, and Joint Variation

For Exercises 11–20, write a variation model using k as the constant of variation. (See Examples 1–2)

11. The circumference C of a circle varies directly as its radius r.

12. Simple interest I on a loan or investment varies directly as the amount A of the loan.

13. The average cost per minute $\overline{C}$ for a flat rate cell phone plan is inversely proportional to the number of minutes used n.

14. The time of travel t is inversely proportional to the rate of travel r.

15. The volume V of a right circular cylinder varies jointly as the height h of the cylinder and as the square of the radius r of the cylinder.

16. The volume V of a rectangular solid varies jointly as the length l and width w of the solid.

17. The variable E is directly proportional to s and inversely proportional to the square root of n.

18. The variable n is directly proportional to the square of σ and inversely proportional to the square of E.

19. The variable c varies jointly as m and n and inversely as the cube of t.

20. The variable d varies jointly as u and v and inversely as the cube root of T.

Objective 2: Solve Applications Involving Variation

For Exercises 21–26, find the constant of variation k.

21. y varies directly as x. When x is 8, y is 20.

22. m varies directly as x. When x is 10, m is 42.

23. p is inversely proportional to q. When q is 18, p is 54.

24. T is inversely proportional to x. When x is 50, T is 200.

25. y varies jointly as w and v. When w is 40 and v is 0.2, y is 40.

26. N varies jointly as t and p. When t is 2 and p is 2.5, N is 15.

27. The value of y equals 4 when $x = 10$. Find y when $x = 5$ if

    a. y varies directly as x.

    b. y varies inversely as x.

28. The value of y equals 24 when x is $\frac{1}{2}$. Find y when $x = 3$ if

    a. y varies directly as x.

    b. y varies inversely as x.

For Exercises 29–48, use a variation model to solve for the unknown value.

29. The amount of a pain reliever that a physician prescribes for a child varies directly as the weight of the child. A physician prescribes 180 mg of the medicine for a 40-lb child. (**See Example 3**)

    a. How much medicine would be prescribed for a 50-lb child?

    b. How much would be prescribed for a 60-lb child?

    c. How much would be prescribed for a 70-lb child?

    d. If 135 mg of medicine is prescribed, what is the weight of the child?

30. The number of people that a ham can serve varies directly as the weight of the ham. An 8-lb ham feeds 20 people.

    a. How many people will a 10-lb ham serve?

    b. How many people will a 15-lb ham serve?

    c. How many people will an 18-lb ham serve?

    d. If a ham feeds 30 people, what is the weight of the ham?

31. The average daily cost to rent a car is inversely proportional to the number of miles driven. If 100 mi is driven, the average daily cost is $0.80 per mile.

   a. Find the average daily cost if 200 mi is driven.

   b. Find the average daily cost if 300 mi is driven.

   c. Find the average daily cost if 400 mi is driven.

   d. If the average cost is $0.16, how many miles were driven?

33. The distance that a bicycle travels in 1 min varies directly as the number of revolutions per minute (rpm) that the wheels are turning. A bicycle with a 14-in. radius travels approximately 440 ft in 1 min if the wheels turn at 60 rpm. How far will the bicycle travel in 1 min if the wheels turn at 87 rpm?

35. The stopping distance of a car is directly proportional to the square of the speed of the car.

   a. If a car traveling 50 mph has a stopping distance of 170 ft, find the stopping distance of a car that is traveling 70 mph.

   b. If it takes 244.8 ft for a car to stop, how fast was it traveling before the brakes were applied?

37. The time required to complete a job varies inversely as the number of people working on the job. It takes 8 people 12 days to do a job. **(See Example 4)**

   a. How many days will it take if 15 people work on the job?

   b. If the contractor wants to complete the job in 8 days, how many people should work on the job?

39. The current in a wire varies directly as the voltage and inversely as the resistance. If the current is 9 amperes (A) when the voltage is 90 volts (V) and the resistance is 10 ohms (Ω), find the current when the voltage is 160 V and the resistance is 5 Ω.

41. The amount of simple interest owed on a loan varies jointly as the amount of principal borrowed and the amount of time the money is borrowed. If $4000 in principal results in $480 in interest in 2 yr, determine how much interest will be owed on $6000 in 4 yr.

32. A chef self-publishes a cookbook and finds that the number of books she can sell per month varies inversely as the price of the book. The chef can sell 1500 books per month when the price is set at $8 per book.

   a. How many books would she expect to sell per month if the price were $12?

   b. How many books would she expect to sell per month if the price were $15?

   c. How many books would she expect to sell per month if the price were $6?

   d. If the chef sells 1200 books, what price was set?

34. The amount of pollution entering the atmosphere varies directly as the number of people living in an area. If 100,000 people create 71,000 tons of pollutants, how many tons enter the atmosphere in a city with 750,000 people?

36. The area of a picture projected on a wall varies directly as the square of the distance from the projector to the wall.

   a. If a 15-ft distance produces a 36 ft^2 picture, what is the area of the picture when the projection unit is moved to a distance of 25 ft from the wall?

   b. If the projected image is 144 ft^2, how far is the projector from the wall?

38. The yield on a bond varies inversely as the price. The yield on a particular bond is 5% when the price is $120.

   a. Find the yield when the price is $100.

   b. What price is necessary for a yield of 7.5%?

40. The resistance of a wire varies directly as its length and inversely as the square of its diameter. A 50-ft wire with a 0.2-in. diameter has a resistance of 0.0125 Ω. Find the resistance of a 40-ft wire with a diameter of 0.1-in.

42. The amount of simple interest earned in an account varies jointly as the amount of principal invested and the amount of time the money is invested. If $5000 in principal earns $750 in 6 yr, determine how much interest will be earned on $8000 in 4 yr.

43. The body mass index (BMI) of an individual varies directly as the weight of the individual and inversely as the square of the height of the individual. The body mass index for a 150-lb person who is 70 in. tall is 21.52. Determine the BMI for an individual who is 68 in. tall and 180 lb. Round to 2 decimal places. **(See Example 5)**

44. The strength of a wooden beam varies jointly as the width of the beam and the square of the thickness of the beam, and inversely as the length of the beam. A beam that is 48 in. long, 6 in. wide, and 2 in. thick can support a load of 417 lb. Find the maximum load that can be safely supported by a board that is 12 in. wide, 72 in. long, and 4 in. thick.

L = length

T = thickness

W = width

45. The speed of a racing canoe in still water varies directly as the square root of the length of the canoe. A 16-ft canoe can travel 6.2 mph in still water. Find the speed of a 25-ft canoe.

46. The period of a pendulum is the length of time required to complete one swing back and forth. The period varies directly as the square root of the length of the pendulum. If it takes 1.8 sec for a 0.81-m pendulum to complete one period, what is the period of a 1-m pendulum?

47. The cost to carpet a rectangular room varies jointly as the length of the room and the width of the room. A 10-yd by 15-yd room costs \$3870 to carpet. What is the cost to carpet a room that is 18 yd by 24 yd?

48. The cost to tile a rectangular kitchen varies jointly as the length of the kitchen and the width of the kitchen. A 10-ft by 12-ft kitchen costs \$1104 to tile. How much will it cost to tile a kitchen that is 20 ft by 14 ft?

Mixed Exercises

For Exercises 49–52, use the given data to find a variation model relating y to x.

49.
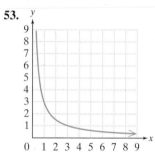

X	Y₁	
5	16	
10	32	
15	48	
20	64	
25	80	
30	96	
35	112	

X=5

50.
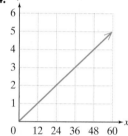

X	Y₁	
5	24	
15	72	
25	120	
35	168	
45	216	
55	264	
65	312	

X=5

51.

	A	B	C	D	E
1	**x**	2	4	12	48
2	**y**	6	3	1	0.25

52.

	A	B	C	D	E
1	**x**	4	8	32	100
2	**y**	2	1	0.25	0.08

For Exercises 53–54, use the graph to develop a variation model in the form $y = kx$ or $y = \dfrac{k}{x}$.

53.

54.

55. Which formula(s) can represent a variation model?

  a. $y = kxyz$ **b.** $y = kx + yz$

  c. $y = \dfrac{kx}{yz}$ **d.** $y = kx - yz$

56. Which formula(s) can represent a variation model?

  a. $y = k\sqrt{x} - z^2$ **b.** $y = \dfrac{k\sqrt{x}}{z^2}$

  c. $y = k\sqrt{x}z^2$ **d.** $y = k + \sqrt{x}z^2$

Write About It

For Exercises 57–58, write a statement in words that describes the variation model given. Use k as the constant of variation.

57. $P = \dfrac{kv^2}{t}$

58. $E = \dfrac{kc^2}{\sqrt{b}}$

Expanding Your Skills

59. The light from a lightbulb radiates outward in all directions.

  a. Consider the interior of an imaginary sphere on which the light shines. The surface area of the sphere is directly proportional to the square of the radius. If the surface area of a sphere with a 10-m radius is 400π m², determine the surface area of a sphere with a 20-m radius.

  b. Explain how the surface area changed when the radius of the sphere increased from 10 m to 20 m.

  c. Based on your answer from part (b) how would you expect the intensity of light to change from a point 10 m from the lightbulb to a point 20 m from the lightbulb?

  d. The intensity of light from a light source varies inversely as the square of the distance from the source. If the intensity of a lightbulb is 200 lumen/m² (lux) at a distance of 10 m, determine the intensity at 20 m.

60. Kepler's third law states that the square of the time T required for a planet to complete one orbit around the Sun is directly proportional to the cube of the average distance d of the planet to the Sun. For the Earth assume that $d = 9.3 \times 10^7$ mi and $T = 365$ days.

  a. Find the period of Mars, given that the distance between Mars and the Sun is 1.5 times the distance from the Earth to the Sun. Round to the nearest day.

  b. Find the average distance of Venus to the Sun, given that Venus revolves around the Sun in 223 days. Round to the nearest million miles.

61. The intensity of radiation varies inversely as the square of the distance from the source to the receiver. If the distance is increased to 10 times its original value, what is the effect on the intensity to the receiver?

62. Suppose that y varies inversely as the cube of x. If the value of x is decreased to $\frac{1}{4}$ of its original value, what is the effect on y?

63. Suppose that y varies directly as x^2 and inversely as w^4. If both x and w are doubled, what is the effect on y?

64. Suppose that y varies directly as x^5 and inversely as w^2. If both x and w are doubled, what is the effect on y?

65. Suppose that y varies jointly as x and w^3. If x is replaced by $\frac{1}{3}x$ and w is replaced by $3w$, what is the effect on y?

66. Suppose that y varies jointly as x^4 and w. If x is replaced by $\frac{1}{4}x$ and w is replaced by $4w$, what is the effect on y?

CHAPTER 3   KEY CONCEPTS

SECTION 3.1 Quadratic Functions and Applications	Reference
Quadratic function: The function defined by $f(x) = ax^2 + bx + c$ $(a \neq 0)$ is called a **quadratic function.** A quadratic function can be written in **vertex form:** $f(x) = a(x - h)^2 + k$ by completing the square.	p. 320
• The graph of a quadratic function is a parabola. • The vertex is (h, k). • If $a > 0$, the parabola opens upward, and the minimum value of the function is k. • If $a < 0$, the parabola opens downward, and the maximum value of the function is k. • The axis of symmetry is the line $x = h$. • The x-intercepts are determined by the real solutions to the equation $f(x) = 0$. • The y-intercept is determined by $f(0)$.	p. 320
Given $f(x) = ax^2 + bx + c$ $(a \neq 0)$, the vertex of the parabola is $\left(\dfrac{-b}{2a},\ f\left(\dfrac{-b}{2a} \right) \right)$.	p. 323

SECTION 3.2 Introduction to Polynomial Functions	Reference
Let n be a whole number and $a_n, a_{n-1}, a_{n-2}, \ldots , a_1, a_0$ be real numbers, where $a_n \neq 0$. Then a function defined by $$f(x) = a_n x^n + a_{n-1} x^{n-1} + a_{n-2} x^{n-2} + \cdots + a_1 x + a_0$$ is called a **polynomial function of degree n.**	p. 334
The far left and far right behavior of the graph of a polynomial function is determined by the leading term of the polynomial, $a_n x^n$. n is even and $a_n > 0$ n is even and $a_n < 0$ n is odd and $a_n > 0$ n is odd and $a_n < 0$	p. 335
The **zeros** of a polynomial function defined by $y = f(x)$ are the values of x in the domain of f for which $f(x) = 0$. These are the real solutions (or **roots**) of the equation $f(x) = 0$.	p. 336

If a polynomial function has a factor $(x - c)$ that appears exactly k times, then c is a **zero of multiplicity k.** • If c is a zero of odd multiplicity, then the graph *crosses* the x-axis at c. • If c is a zero of even multiplicity, then the graph *touches* the x-axis (but does not cross) at c.	p. 338
Intermediate value theorem: Let f be a polynomial function. For $a < b$, if $f(a)$ and $f(b)$ have opposite signs, then f has at least one zero on the interval $[a, b]$.	p. 339
The graph of a polynomial function of degree n will have at most $n - 1$ turning points.	p. 340

SECTION 3.3 Division of Polynomials and the Remainder and Factor Theorems	Reference
Long division can be used to divide two polynomials.	p. 348
Synthetic division can be used to divide polynomials if the divisor is of the form $x - c$.	p. 350
Remainder theorem: If a polynomial $f(x)$ is divided by $x - c$, then the remainder is $f(c)$.	p. 352
Factor theorem: Let $f(x)$ be a polynomial. 1. If $f(c) = 0$, then $(x - c)$ is a factor of $f(x)$. 2. If $(x - c)$ is a factor of $f(x)$, then $f(c) = 0$.	p. 354

SECTION 3.4 Zeros of Polynomials	Reference
Rational zero theorem: If $f(x) = a_n x^n + a_{n-1} x^{n-1} + \cdots + a_1 x + a_0$ has integer coefficients and $a_n \neq 0$, and if $\frac{p}{q}$ (written in lowest terms) is a rational zero of f, then • p is a factor of the constant term, a_0. • q is a factor of the leading coefficient a_n.	p. 361
Fundamental theorem of algebra: If $f(x)$ is a polynomial of degree $n \geq 1$ with complex coefficients, then $f(x)$ has at least one complex zero.	p. 365
Linear factorization theorem: If $f(x) = a_n x^n + a_{n-1} x^{n-1} + \cdots + a_1 x + a_0$ where $n \geq 1$ and $a_n \neq 0$, then $f(x) = a_n(x - c_1)(x - c_2) \ldots (x - c_n)$ where $c_1, c_2, \ldots, c_n$ are complex numbers.	p. 365
If $f(x)$ is a polynomial of degree $n \geq 1$ with complex coefficients, then $f(x)$ has exactly n complex zeros provided that each zero is counted by its multiplicity.	p. 365
Conjugate zeros theorem: If $f(x)$ is a polynomial with real coefficients and if $a + bi$ is a zero of $f(x)$, then its conjugate $a - bi$ is also a zero of $f(x)$.	p. 365

Descartes' rule of signs:
Let $f(x)$ be a polynomial with real coefficients and a nonzero constant term. Then,
   1. The number of *positive* real zeros is either the same as the number of sign changes in $f(x)$ or less than the number of sign changes in $f(x)$ by a positive even integer.
   2. The number of *negative* real zeros is either the same as the number of sign changes in $f(-x)$ or less than the number of sign changes in $f(-x)$ by a positive even integer.
	p. 368

Upper and lower bounds:
Let $f(x)$ be a polynomial of degree $n \geq 1$ with real coefficients and a positive leading coefficient. Further suppose that $f(x)$ is divided by $(x - c)$.
   1. If $c > 0$ and if both the remainder and the coefficients of the quotient are nonnegative, then c is an upper bound for the real zeros of $f(x)$.
   2. If $c < 0$ and the coefficients of the quotient and the remainder alternate in sign (with 0 being considered either positive or negative as needed), then c is a lower bound for the real zeros of $f(x)$.
	p. 370

SECTION 3.5 Rational Functions	Reference
Let $p(x)$ and $q(x)$ be polynomials where $q(x) \neq 0$. A function f defined by $f(x) = \dfrac{p(x)}{q(x)}$ is called a **rational function.**	p. 377
The line $x = c$ is a **vertical asymptote** of the graph of $y = f(x)$ if $f(x)$ approaches infinity or negative infinity as x approaches c from either side. To locate the vertical asymptotes of a function, determine the real numbers x where the denominator is zero, but the numerator is nonzero.	p. 379
The line $y = d$ is a **horizontal asymptote** of the graph of $y = f(x)$ if $f(x)$ approaches d as x approaches infinity or negative infinity.	p. 381
Let f be a rational function defined by $$f(x) = \frac{a_n x^n + a_{n-1}x^{n-1} + a_{n-2}x^{n-2} + \cdots + a_1 x + a_0}{b_m x^m + b_{m-1}x^{m-1} + b_{m-2}x^{m-2} + \cdots + b_1 x + b_0}$$ 1. If $n > m$, then f has no horizontal asymptote. 2. If $n < m$, then the line $y = 0$ (the x-axis) is the horizontal asymptote of f. 3. If $n = m$, then the line $y = \dfrac{a_n}{b_m}$ is the horizontal asymptote of f.	p. 382
A rational function will have a slant asymptote if the degree of the numerator is exactly one greater than the degree of the denominator. To find an equation of a slant asymptote of a rational function, divide the numerator by the denominator. The quotient will be linear and the slant asymptote will be of the form $y =$ quotient.	p. 384

SECTION 3.6 Polynomial and Rational Inequalities	Reference
Let $f(x)$ be a polynomial. Then an inequality of the form $f(x) < 0,\quad f(x) > 0,\quad f(x) \leq 0,\quad$ or $\quad f(x) \geq 0$ is called a **polynomial inequality.**	p. 399
Let $f(x)$ be a rational expression. Then an inequality of the form $f(x) < 0,\quad f(x) > 0,\quad f(x) \leq 0,\quad$ or $\quad f(x) \geq 0$ is called a **rational inequality.**	p. 403

Solving nonlinear inequalities:
 	
 1. Express the inequality as $f(x) < 0, f(x) > 0, f(x) \leq 0,$ or $f(x) \geq 0$.
 2. Find the real solutions of the related equation $f(x) = 0$ and the values of x where $f(x)$ is undefined. These are the "boundary" points for the solution set to the inequality.
 3. Determine the sign of $f(x)$ on the intervals defined by the boundary points.
   • If $f(x)$ is positive, then the values of x on the interval are solutions to $f(x) > 0$.
   • If $f(x)$ is negative, then the values of x on the interval are solutions to $f(x) < 0$.
 4. Determine whether the boundary points are included in the solution set.
 5. Write the solution set.
	p. 400

SECTION 3.7 Variation	Reference
Let k be a nonzero constant real number. Then the following statements are equivalent:	p. 413
1. y varies **directly** as x. y is **directly** proportional to x. $\Big\} y = kx$	
2. y varies **inversely** as x. y is **inversely** proportional to x. $\Big\} y = \dfrac{k}{x}$	
3. y varies **jointly** as w and x. y is **jointly** proportional to w and x. $\Big\} y = kwx$	p. 414
The value of k is called the **constant of variation.**	

Expanded Chapter Summary available at www.mhhe.com/millerca.

CHAPTER 3   Review Exercises

SECTION 3.1

1. Given $f(x) = -(x + 5)^2 + 2$, identify the vertex of the graph of the parabola.

For Exercises 2–3,

a. Write the equation in vertex form: $f(x) = a(x - h)^2 + k$.

b. Determine whether the parabola opens upward or downward.

c. Identify the vertex.

d. Identify the x-intercepts.

e. Identify the y-intercept.

f. Sketch the function.

g. Determine the axis of symmetry.

h. Determine the minimum or maximum value of the function.

i. State the domain and range.

2. $f(x) = x^2 - 8x + 15$

3. $f(x) = -2x^2 + 4x + 6$

4. a. Use the vertex formula to determine the vertex of $f(x) = 2x^2 + 12x + 19$.

   b. Based on the location of the vertex and the orientation of the parabola, how many x-intercepts will the graph of $f(x) = 2x^2 + 12x + 19$ have?

5. Suppose that a farmer encloses a corral for cattle adjacent to a river. No fencing is used by the river.

   a. If he has 180 yd of fencing, what dimensions should he use to maximize the area?

   b. What is the maximum area?

6. Suppose that p is the probability that a randomly selected person is left-handed. The value $(1 - p)$ is the probability that the person is not left-handed. In a sample of 100 people, the function $V(p) = 100p(1 - p)$ represents the variance of the number of left-handed people in a group of 100.

   a. What value of p maximizes the variance?

   b. What is the maximum variance?

7. The annual expenditure for cell phones and cellular service varies in part by the age of an individual. The average annual expenditure $E(a)$ (in \$) for individuals of age a (in yr) is given in the table.
(*Source*: U.S. Bureau of Labor Statistics, www.bls.gov)

a	20	30	40	50	60	70
$E(a)$	502	658	649	627	476	213

   a. Use regression to find a quadratic function to model the data.

   b. At what age is the yearly expenditure for cell phones and cellular service the greatest? Round to the nearest year.

   c. What is the maximum yearly expenditure? Round to the nearest dollar.

SECTION 3.2

For Exercises 8–11,

a. Determine the end behavior of the graph of the function.

b. Find all the zeros of the function and state their multiplicities.

c. Determine the x-intercepts.

d. Determine the y-intercept.

e. Is the function even, odd, or neither?

f. Graph the function.

8. $f(x) = -4x^3 + 16x^2 + 25x - 100$

9. $f(x) = x^4 - 10x^2 + 9$

10. $f(x) = x^4 + 3x^3 - 3x^2 - 11x - 6$

11. $f(x) = x^5 - 8x^4 + 13x^3$

12. Determine whether the intermediate value theorem guarantees that the function has a zero on the given interval.

$$f(x) = 2x^3 - 5x^2 - 6x + 2$$

   a. $[-2, -1]$ **b.** $[-1, 0]$ **c.** $[0, 1]$ **d.** $[1, 2]$

For Exercises 13–14, determine if the statement is true or false.

13. A fourth-degree polynomial has exactly three turning points.

14. A fourth-degree polynomial has at most three turning points.

15. There is exactly one polynomial with zeros of 2, 3, and 4.

16. If c is a real zero of an odd polynomial function, then $-c$ is also a zero.

SECTION 3.3

For Exercises 17–18,

a. Divide the polynomials.

b. Identify the dividend, divisor, quotient, and remainder.

17. $(-2x^4 + x^3 + 4x - 1) \div (x^2 + x - 3)$

18. $\dfrac{3x^4 - 2x^3 - 15x^2 + 22x - 8}{3x - 2}$

For Exercises 19–20, use synthetic division to divide the polynomials.

19. $(2x^5 + x^2 - 5x + 1) \div (x + 2)$

20. $\dfrac{x^4 + 3x^3 - x^2 + 7x + 2}{x - 3}$

For Exercises 21–22, use the remainder theorem to evaluate the polynomial for the given values of x.

21. $f(x) = 3x^4 + 2x^2 - 4x + 1; f(-2)$

22. $f(x) = x^4 + 2x^3 - 4x^2 - 10x - 5; f(\sqrt{5})$

For Exercises 23–24, use the remainder theorem to determine if the given number c is a zero of the polynomial.

23. $f(x) = 3x^4 + 13x^3 + 2x^2 + 52x - 40$

    a. $c = 2$ **b.** $c = \frac{2}{3}$

24. $f(x) = 3x^4 + 13x^3 + 2x^2 + 52x - 40$

    a. $c = -5$ **b.** $c = 2i$

For Exercises 25–26, use the factor theorem to determine if the given binomial is a factor of the polynomial.

25. $f(x) = x^3 + 4x^2 + 9x + 36$

    a. $(x + 4)$ **b.** $(x - 3i)$

26. $f(x) = x^2 - 4x - 46$

    a. $(x + 2)$ **b.** $\left[x - \left(2 - 5\sqrt{2}\right)\right]$

27. Factor $f(x) = 15x^3 - 67x^2 + 26x + 8$, given that $\frac{2}{3}$ is a zero of $f(x)$.

28. Write a third-degree polynomial $f(x)$ with zeros -1, $3\sqrt{2}$, and $-3\sqrt{2}$.

29. Write a third-degree polynomial $f(x)$ with integer coefficients and zeros of $\frac{1}{4}$, $-\frac{1}{2}$, and 3.

SECTION 3.4

30. Given $f(x) = 2x^5 - 7x^4 + 9x^3 - 18x^2 + 4x + 40$,

    a. How many zeros does $f(x)$ have (including multiplicities)?

    b. List the possible rational zeros of $f(x)$.

    c. Find all rational zeros of $f(x)$.

    d. Find all the zeros of $f(x)$.

31. Given $f(x) = x^4 + 4x^3 + 2x^2 - 8x - 8$,

    a. How many zeros does $f(x)$ have (including multiplicities)?

    b. List the possible rational zeros of $f(x)$.

    c. Find all rational zeros of $f(x)$.

    d. Find all the zeros of $f(x)$.

32. If $f(x)$ is a polynomial with real coefficients and zeros of 4 (multiplicity 3), -2 (multiplicity 1), and $2 + 7i$ (multiplicity 1), what is the minimum degree of $f(x)$?

33. Given $f(x) = x^4 - 6x^3 + 5x^2 + 30x - 50$ and that $3 - i$ is a zero of $f(x)$,

    a. Find all the zeros of $f(x)$.

    b. Factor $f(x)$ as a product of linear factors.

    c. Solve the equation $f(x) = 0$.

34. Write a polynomial $f(x)$ of lowest degree with real coefficients and with zeros $2 - 3i$ (multiplicity 1) and 0 (multiplicity 2).

35. Write a third-degree polynomial $f(x)$ with integer coefficients and with zeros of $-2i$ and $\frac{5}{3}$.

For Exercises 36–37, determine the number of possible positive and negative real zeros for the given function.

36. $g(x) = -3x^7 + 4x^6 - 2x^2 + 5x - 4$

37. $n(x) = x^6 + \frac{1}{3}x^4 + \frac{2}{7}x^3 + 4x^2 + 3$

For Exercises 38–39,

a. Determine if the upper bound theorem identifies the given number as an upper bound for the real zeros of $f(x)$.

b. Determine if the lower bound theorem identifies the given number as a lower bound for the real zeros of $f(x)$.

38. $f(x) = x^4 - 3x^3 + 2x - 3$

    a. 2   **b.** -2

39. $f(x) = x^3 - 4x^2 + 2x + 1$

    a. 5   **b.** -2

SECTION 3.5

40. Refer to the graph of $y = f(x)$ and complete the statements.

    a. As $x \to -\infty$, $f(x) \to$ _____.

    b. As $x \to -2^-$, $f(x) \to$ _____.

    c. As $x \to -2^+$, $f(x) \to$ _____.

    d. As $x \to \infty$, $f(x) \to$ _____.

    e. The graph is increasing over the interval(s) _____.

    f. The graph is decreasing over the interval(s) _____.

    g. The domain is _____.

    h. The range is _____.

    i. The vertical asymptote is the line _____.

    j. The horizontal asymptote is the line _____.

For Exercises 41–42, determine the vertical asymptotes of the graph of the function.

41. $f(x) = \dfrac{x + 4}{2x^2 + x - 15}$ **42.** $g(x) = \dfrac{5}{x^2 + 3}$

For Exercises 43–45,

a. Determine the horizontal asymptotes (if any).

b. If the graph of the function has a horizontal asymptote, determine the point where the graph crosses the horizontal asymptote.

43. $r(x) = \dfrac{3}{x^2 + 2x + 1}$ **44.** $q(x) = \dfrac{-2x^2 - 3x + 4}{x^2 + 1}$

45. $k(x) = \dfrac{x^3 + 4}{x + 1}$

For Exercises 46–47, identify all asymptotes (vertical, horizontal, and slant).

46. $m(x) = \dfrac{2x^3 - x^2 - 6x + 7}{x^2 - 3}$

47. $n(x) = \dfrac{-4x^2 + 5}{3x^2 - 14x - 5}$

For Exercises 48–51, graph the function.

48. $f(x) = \dfrac{1}{x - 4} + 2$

49. $k(x) = \dfrac{x^2}{x^2 - x - 12}$

50. $m(x) = \dfrac{x^2 + 6x + 9}{x}$

51. $q(x) = \dfrac{12}{x^2 + 6}$

52. After taking a certain class, the percentage of material retained $P(t)$ decreases with the number of months t after taking the class. $P(t)$ can be approximated by

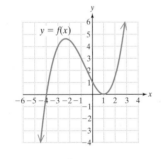

$$P(t) = \frac{t + 90}{0.16t + 1}$$

a. Determine the percentage retained after 1 month, 4 months, and 6 months. Round to the nearest percent.

b. As t becomes infinitely large, what percentage of material will be retained?

SECTION 3.6

53. The graph of $y = f(x)$ is given. Solve the inequalities.

a. $f(x) < 0$

b. $f(x) \le 0$

c. $f(x) > 0$

d. $f(x) \ge 0$

54. The graph of $y = f(x)$ is given. Solve the inequalities.

a. $f(x) < 0$

b. $f(x) \le 0$

c. $f(x) > 0$

d. $f(x) \ge 0$

55. Solve the equation and inequalities.

a. $x^2 + 7x + 10 = 0$

b. $x^2 + 7x + 10 < 0$

c. $x^2 + 7x + 10 \le 0$

d. $x^2 + 7x + 10 > 0$

e. $x^2 + 7x + 10 \ge 0$

56. Solve the inequalities.

a. $\dfrac{x + 1}{x - 5} \le 0$

b. $\dfrac{x + 1}{x - 5} < 0$

c. $\dfrac{x + 1}{x - 5} \ge 0$

d. $\dfrac{x + 1}{x - 5} > 0$

For Exercises 57–66, solve the inequalities.

57. $t(t - 3) \ge 18$

58. $w^3 + w^2 - 9w - 9 > 0$

59. $x^2 - 2x + 4 \le 3$

60. $-6x^4(3x - 4)^2(x + 2)^3 \le 0$

61. $z^3 - 3z^2 > 10z - 24$

62. $(4x - 5)^4 > 0$

63. $\dfrac{6 - 2x}{x^2} \ge 0$

64. $\dfrac{8}{3x - 4} \le 1$

65. $\dfrac{3}{x - 2} < -\dfrac{2}{x}$

66. $\dfrac{(1 - x)(3x + 5)^2}{(x - 3)^4} < 0$

67. A sports trainer has monthly costs of $80 for phone service and $40 for his website and advertising. In addition he pays a $15 fee to the gym for each session in which he works with a client.

a. Write a function representing the average cost $\overline{C}(x)$ (in $) for x training sessions.

b. Find the number of sessions the trainer needs if he wants the average cost to drop below $16 per session.

68. A child throws a ball straight upwards to his friend who is sitting in a tree 18 ft above ground level.

a. If the ball leaves the child's hand at a height of 2 ft with an initial velocity of 40 ft/sec, write a function representing the vertical position of the ball $s(t)$ (in ft) in terms of the time t after the ball leaves the child's hand. (*Hint:* Use the model $s(t) = -\frac{1}{2}gt^2 + v_0 t + s_0$.)

b. Determine the time interval for which the ball will be more than 18 ft high.

SECTION 3.7

For Exercises 69–71, write a variation model using k as the constant of variation.

69. The mass m of an animal varies directly as the weight w of the animal's heart.

70. The value of x varies inversely to the square of p.

71. The variable y is jointly proportional to x and the square root of z, and inversely proportional to the cube of t.

For Exercises 72–73, determine the constant of variation k.

72. The variable Q varies jointly as p and the square root of t. The value of Q is 132 when p is 11 and t is 9.

73. The variable d is directly proportional to c and inversely proportional to the square of x. The value of d is 1.8 when c is 3 and x is 2.

74. The weight of a ball varies directly as the cube of its radius. A weighted exercise ball of radius 3 in. weighs 3.24 lb. How much would a ball weigh if its radius were 5 in.?

75. In karate, the force F required to break a board varies inversely as the length L of the board. If it takes 6.25 lb of force to break a board 1.6 ft long, determine how much force is required to break a 2-ft board.

76. The power in an electric circuit varies jointly as the current and the square of the resistance. If the power is

144 watts (W) when the current is 4 A and the resistance is 6 Ω, find the power when the current is 3 A and the resistance is 10 Ω.

77. Coulomb's law states that the force F of attraction between two oppositely charged particles varies jointly as the magnitude of their electrical charges q_1 and q_2 and inversely as the square of the distance d between the particles. Find the effect on F of doubling q_1 and q_2 and halving the distance between them.

CHAPTER 3   Test

1. Given $f(x) = 2x^2 - 12x + 16$,

   a. Write the equation in vertex form: $f(x) = a(x - h)^2 + k$.

   b. Determine whether the parabola opens upward or downward.

   c. Identify the vertex.

   d. Identify the x-intercepts.

   e. Identify the y-intercept.

   f. Sketch the function.

   g. Determine the axis of symmetry.

   h. Determine the minimum or maximum value of the function.

   i. State the domain and range.

2. Given $f(x) = 2x^4 - 5x^3 - 17x^2 + 41x - 21$,

   a. Determine the end behavior of the graph of the function.

   b. List all possible rational zeros.

   c. Find all the zeros of the function and state their multiplicities.

   d. Determine the x-intercepts.

   e. Determine the y-intercept.

   f. Is the function even, odd, or neither?

   g. Graph the function.

3. Given $f(x) = -0.25x^3(x - 2)^2(x + 1)^4$,

   a. Identify the leading term.

   b. Determine the end behavior of the graph of the function.

   c. Find all the zeros of the function and state their multiplicities.

4. Given $f(x) = x^4 + 5x^2 - 36$,

   a. How many zeros does $f(x)$ have (including multiplicities)?

   b. Find the zeros of $f(x)$.

   c. Identify the x-intercepts of the graph of f.

   d. Is the function even, odd, or neither?

5. Determine whether the intermediate value theorem guarantees that the function has a zero on the given interval.

$$f(x) = x^3 - 5x^2 + 2x + 5$$

   a. $[-2, -1]$ **b.** $[-1, 0]$ **c.** $[0, 1]$ **d.** $[1, 2]$

6. a. Divide the polynomials. $\dfrac{2x^4 - 4x^3 + x - 5}{x^2 - 3x + 1}$

   b. Identify the dividend, divisor, quotient, and remainder.

7. Given $f(x) = 5x^4 + 47x^3 + 80x^2 - 51x - 9$,

   a. Is $\dfrac{3}{5}$ a zero of $f(x)$?

   b. Is -1 a zero of $f(x)$?

   c. Is $(x + 1)$ a factor of $f(x)$?

   d. Is $(x + 3)$ a factor of $f(x)$?

   e. Use the remainder theorem to evaluate $f(-2)$.

8. Given $f(x) = x^4 - 8x^3 + 21x^2 - 32x + 68$ and that $2i$ is a zero of $f(x)$,

   a. Find all zeros of $f(x)$.

   b. Factor $f(x)$ as a product of linear factors.

   c. Solve the equation $f(x) = 0$.

9. Given $f(x) = 3x^4 + 7x^3 - 12x^2 - 14x + 12$,

   a. How many zeros does $f(x)$ have (including multiplicities)?

   b. List the possible rational zeros.

   c. Determine if the upper bound theorem identifies 2 as an upper bound for the real zeros of $f(x)$.

   d. Determine if the lower bound theorem identifies -4 as a lower bound for the real zeros of $f(x)$.

   e. Revise the list of possible rational zeros based on the answers to parts (c) and (d).

   f. Find the rational zeros.

   g. Find all the zeros.

   h. Graph the function.

10. Write a third-degree polynomial $f(x)$ with integer coefficients and zeros of $\frac{1}{5}$, $-\frac{2}{3}$, and 4.

11. Determine the number of possible positive and negative real zeros for $f(x) = -6x^7 - 4x^5 + 2x^4 - 3x^2 + 1$.

For Exercises 12–14, determine the asymptotes (vertical, horizontal, and slant).

12. $r(x) = \dfrac{2x^2 - 3x + 5}{x - 7}$

13. $p(x) = \dfrac{-3x + 1}{4x^2 - 1}$

14. $n(x) = \dfrac{5x^2 - 2x + 1}{3x^2 + 4}$

For Exercises 15–17, graph the function.

15. $m(x) = -\dfrac{1}{x^2} + 3$

16. $h(x) = \dfrac{-4}{x^2 - 4}$

17. $k(x) = \dfrac{x^2 + 2x + 1}{x}$

For Exercises 18–24, solve the inequality.

18. $c^2 < c + 20$

19. $y^3 > 13y - 12$

20. $-2x(x - 4)^2(x + 1)^3 \le 0$

21. $9x^2 + 42x + 49 > 0$

22. $\dfrac{x + 3}{2 - x} \le 0$

23. $\dfrac{-4}{x^2 - 9} \ge 0$

24. $\dfrac{4}{x - 1} < -\dfrac{3}{x}$

25. Write a variation model using k as the constant of variation: Energy E varies directly as the square of the velocity v of the wind.

26. Solve for the constant of variation k: The variable w varies jointly as y and the square root of x, and inversely as z. The value of w is 7.2 when x is 4, y is 6, and z is 7.

27. The surface area of a cube varies directly as the square of the length of an edge. The surface area is 24 ft^2 when the length of an edge is 2 ft. Find the surface area of a cube with an edge that is 7 ft.

28. The weight of a body varies inversely as the square of its distance from the center of the Earth. The radius of the Earth is approximately 4000 mi. How much would a 180-lb man weigh 20 mi above the surface of the Earth? Round to the nearest pound.

29. The pressure of wind on a wall varies jointly as the area of the wall and the square of the velocity of the wind. If the velocity of the wind is tripled, what is the effect on the pressure on the wall?

30. The population $P(t)$ of rabbits in a wildlife area t years after being introduced to the area is given by

$$P(t) = \frac{2000t}{t + 1}$$

   a. Determine the number of rabbits after 1 yr, 5 yr, and 10 yr. Round to the nearest whole unit.

   b. What will the rabbit population approach as t approaches infinity?

31. An agricultural school wants to determine the number of corn plants per acre that will produce the maximum yield. The model $y(n) = -0.103n^2 + 8.32n + 15.1$ represents the yield $y(n)$ (in bushels per acre) based on n thousand plants per acre.

   a. Evaluate $y(20)$, $y(30)$, and $y(60)$ and interpret their meaning in the context of this problem.

   b. Determine the number of plants per acre that will maximize yield. Round to the nearest hundred plants.

   c. What is the maximum yield? Round to the nearest bushel per acre.

32. Suppose that a rocket is shot straight upward from ground level with an initial velocity of 98 m/sec.

   a. Write a model that represents the height of the rocket $s(t)$ (in meters) t seconds after launch. (*Hint*: Use the model $s(t) = -\dfrac{1}{2}gt^2 + v_0t + s_0$. See page 406.)

   b. When will the rocket reach its maximum height?

   c. What is the maximum height?

   d. Determine the time interval for which the rocket will be more than 200 m high. Round to the nearest tenth of a second.

33. The number of yearly visits to physicians' offices varies in part by the age of the patient. For the data shown in the table, a represents the age of patients (in yr) and $n(a)$ represents the corresponding number of visits to physicians' offices. (*Source*: Centers for Disease Control, www.cdc.gov)

a	8	20	35	55	65	85
$n(a)$	2.7	2.0	2.5	3.7	6.7	7.6

   a. Use regression to find a quadratic function to model the data.

   b. At what age is the number of yearly visits to physicians' offices the least? Round to the nearest year of age.

   c. What is the minimum number of yearly visits? Round to 1 decimal place.

CHAPTER 3   Cumulative Review Exercises

1. Given $r(x) = \dfrac{2x^2 - 3}{x^2 - 16}$,

   a. Find the vertical asymptotes.

   b. Find the horizontal asymptote or slant asymptote.

2. Find a polynomial $f(x)$ of lowest degree with real coefficients and with zeros of $3 + 2i$ and 2.

3. Given $f(x) = 2x^3 - x^2 - 8x - 5$,

   a. Determine the end behavior of the graph of f.

   b. Find the zeros and their multiplicities.

   c. Find the x-intercepts.

   d. Find the y-intercept.

   e. Graph the function.

4. Divide and write the answer in the form $a + bi$.

$$\frac{3 + 2i}{4 - i}$$

5. Determine the center and radius of the circle given by

$$x^2 + y^2 + 8x - 14y + 56 = 0$$

6. Write an equation of the line passing through the points $(4, -8)$ and $(2, -3)$. Write the answer in slope-intercept form.

7. Determine the x- and y-intercepts of the graph of $x = y^2 - 9$.

8. Graph $f(x) = \begin{cases} -x - 1 & \text{for } x < 1 \\ \sqrt{x - 1} & \text{for } x \geq 1 \end{cases}$

9. Solve the equation for m. $v_0 t = \sqrt{m - t}$

10. Given $f(x) = 2x^2 - 6x + 1$,

   a. Find the x-intercepts.

   b. Find the y-intercept.

   c. Find the vertex of the parabola.

11. Factor. $125x^6 - y^9$

For Exercises 12–14, simplify the expression.

12. $\left(\dfrac{4x^3 y^{-5}}{z^{-2}}\right)^{-3}\left(\dfrac{4y^{-6}}{x^{-12}}\right)^{1/2}$

13. $\sqrt[3]{250z^5 xy^{21}}$

14. $\dfrac{\dfrac{1}{3x} - \dfrac{1}{x^2}}{\dfrac{1}{3} - \dfrac{3}{x^2}}$

For Exercises 15–20, solve the equations and inequalities. Write the solutions to the inequalities in interval notation if possible.

15. $-5 \leq -\dfrac{1}{4}x + 3 < \dfrac{1}{2}$

16. $|x - 3| + 4 \leq 10$

17. $|2x + 1| = |x - 4|$

18. $c^2 - 5c + 9 < c(c + 3)$

19. $\dfrac{49x^2 + 14x + 1}{x} > 0$

20. $\sqrt{4x - 3} - \sqrt{x + 12} = 0$

4

Exponential and Logarithmic Functions

Chapter Outline

Psychologist and television talk show host Dr. Phil McGraw makes a statement that "when one member of a family gets cancer, the whole family gets cancer." (*Source*: www.drphil.com) Treatment for the disease is often debilitating and may include surgery, chemotherapy, and radiation therapy. Radiation therapy is considered the least invasive. Doctors use high-energy radiation to shrink and kill cancer cells, while trying to minimize damage to the healthy, surrounding cells. Several types of radiation may be used with a variety of delivery techniques. Radiation may be delivered by a machine external to the body, by intravenous fluid, or by tiny pellets containing radioactive material implanted into or near a tumor. In all cases, doctors want to monitor the radiation level in the patient. Fortunately, the amount of radiation left in the body after treatment follows a specific pattern called exponential decay.

In this chapter, we investigate exponential functions and a related category of functions called logarithmic functions. As you work through the chapter, you will see that applications of these functions are far-reaching and include applications to business, finance, geology, chemistry, physics, and of course, the treatment of cancer.

Inverse Functions

1. Identify One-to-One Functions

Throughout our study of algebra, we have made use of the fact that the operations of addition and subtraction are inverse operations. For example, adding 5 to a number and then subtracting 5 from the result gives us the original number. Likewise, multiplication and division are inverse operations. We now look at the concept of an inverse function.

Suppose that the lung capacity of a mammal of any size is proportional to the mass of the animal. The model:

$$f(x) = 0.063x$$

relates $f(x)$, the lung capacity of a mammal (in liters), to the mass of the animal x (in kg).

We can reverse this process to obtain the *inverse* function.

$$g(x) = \frac{x}{0.063}$$

where $g(x)$ is the mass of a mammal (in kg) and x is the lung capacity (in liters).

Table 4-1 shows the lung capacities $f(x)$ for several mammals of mass x. Table 4-2 shows the mass $g(x)$ of several mammals with lung capacity x.

Table 4-1

Animal	Mass (kg) x	Lung capacity (L) $f(x) = 0.063x$
Mouse	0.02	0.00126
Cat	6	0.378
Human	70	4.41
Horse	450	28.35
Elephant	4000	252

Table 4-2

Animal	Lung capacity (L) x	Mass (kg) $g(x) = \dfrac{x}{0.063}$
Mouse	0.00126	0.02
Cat	0.378	6
Human	4.41	70
Horse	28.35	450
Elephant	252	4000

We now look at several interesting characteristics of a function f and its inverse g.

- By listing the ordered pairs from Tables 4-1 and 4-2, we see that the x and y values are reversed between function f and its inverse g.

$$f: \quad \{(0.02, 0.00126), (6, 0.378), (70, 4.41), (450, 28.35), (4000, 252)\}$$

$$g: \quad \{(0.00126, 0.02), (0.378, 6), (4.41, 70), (28.35, 450), (252, 4000)\}$$

The reversal of the x and y values tells us that the domain of a function is the same as the range of its inverse. Likewise the range of the function is the same as the domain of the inverse.

- From the graph of the ordered pairs (Figure 4-1), we see that the corresponding points on function f and function g are symmetric with respect to the line $y = x$.

Figure 4-1

- When we compose functions f and g in both directions, the result is the input value x. In a sense, what function f does to x, function g "undoes" and vice versa.

$$(f \circ g)(x) = f(g(x)) = 0.063\left(\frac{x}{0.063}\right) = x$$

$$(g \circ f)(x) = g(f(x)) = \frac{(0.063x)}{0.063} = x$$

We have made several observations about the relationship between a function and its inverse. Before we give a formal definition of an inverse function, however, we must note that not every function has a function as its inverse. A function must be a *one-to-one* function to have an inverse function.

> **Avoiding Mistakes**
>
> It is also important to realize that a one-to-one function meets the criteria to be a function. That is, for each value of x in the domain, there corresponds exactly one y value in the range.

> **Definition of a One-to-One Function**
>
> A function f is a **one-to-one function,** if for a and b in the domain of f,
>
> if $a \neq b$, then $f(a) \neq f(b)$, or equivalently, if $f(a) = f(b)$, then $a = b$.

The definition of a one-to-one function given by $y = f(x)$, tells us that each y value in the range is associated with only one x value in the domain.

EXAMPLE 1   Determining Whether a Function Is One-to-One

Determine whether function f is a one-to-one function.

$$f = \{(1, 4), (2, 3), (-2, 4)\}$$

Solution:

                same y value
$$f = \{(1, 4), (2, 3), (-2, 4)\}$$
                different x value

The ordered pairs $(1, 4)$ and $(-2, 4)$ have the same y value but different x values. This means that the function f fails to be a one-to-one function.

We have that $f(1) = f(-2)$, but $1 \neq -2$.

Therefore, f fails the definition of a one-to-one function.

> **Skill Practice 1**   Determine whether function f is a one-to-one function.
> $f = \{(3, 5), (4, 5), (-2, 1)\}$

> **Avoiding Mistakes**
>
> The ordered pairs $(4, 1)$ and $(4, -2)$ have the same x value but different y values. This shows that the relation is not a function.

From Example 1, $f = \{(1, 4), (2, 3), (-2, 4)\}$ is not a one-to-one function. Notice that if we reverse the x and y values in the ordered pairs, the resulting relation is not a function.

f is not one-to-one. $f = \{(1, 4), (2, 3), (-2, 4)\}$

This relation is not a function. $\{(4, 1), (3, 2), (4, -2)\}$

Answer

1. No

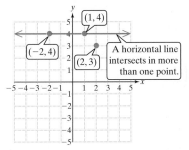

Figure 4-2

The graph of $f = \{(1, 4), (2, 3), (-2, 4)\}$ is shown in Figure 4-2. The points $(1, 4)$ and $(-2, 4)$ fail to make f a one-to-one function. On the graph, notice that these points are horizontally aligned because they have the same y-coordinates. Thus, no one-to-one function may have two or more points horizontally aligned.

Horizontal Line Test for a One-to-One Function

A function defined by $y = f(x)$ is a one-to-one function if no horizontal line intersects the graph in more than one point.

EXAMPLE 2   Using the Horizontal Line Test

Use the horizontal line test to determine if the graph in blue defines y as a one-to-one function of x.

Solution:

a.

The graph does not define y as a one-to-one function of x because a horizontal line intersects the graph in more than one point.

b.

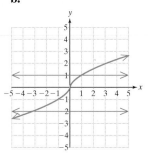

The graph does define y as a one-to-one function of x because no horizontal line intersects the graph in more than one point.

c.

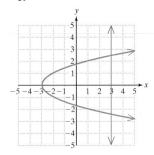

The relation does not define y as a function of x, because it fails the vertical line test. If the relation is not a function, it is not a one-to-one function.

Skill Practice 2   Use the horizontal line test to determine if the graph defines y as a one-to-one function of x.

a.

b.

c.

In Example 3, we use algebraic methods to determine whether a function is one-to-one.

EXAMPLE 3   **Determining Whether a Function Is One-to-One**

Use the definition of a one-to-one function to determine whether the function is one-to-one.

   a. $f(x) = 2x - 3$ **b.** $f(x) = x^2 + 1$

Solution:

a. We must show that if $f(a) = f(b)$, then $a = b$.

Assume that $f(a) = f(b)$. That is,

$$2a - 3 = 2b - 3$$
$$2a - 3 + 3 = 2b - 3 + 3$$
$$\frac{2a}{2} = \frac{2b}{2}$$
$$a = b$$

Since $f(a) = f(b)$ implies that $a = b$, then f is one-to-one.

> The logic of this algebraic proof begins with the assumption that $f(a) = f(b)$, that is, that two y values are equal. For a one-to-one function, this can happen only if the x values (in this case a and b) are the same.
>
> Otherwise, if $a \neq b$, we would have the same y value with two different x values and f would not be one-to-one.

b. Given $f(x) = x^2 + 1$, if we assume that $f(a) = f(b)$, it follows that $a^2 + 1 = b^2 + 1$. This implies that $a^2 = b^2$ and that $a = \pm b$. Thus, for nonzero values of b, $f(a) = f(b)$ does not necessarily imply that $a = b$.

From the graph of $f(x) = x^2 + 1$, we see that f is not one-to-one (Figure 4-3). To show this algebraically, we need to find two ordered pairs with the same y value but different x values. From the graph, we have arbitrarily selected $(-2, 5)$ and $(2, 5)$.

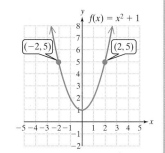

If $a = 2$ and $b = -2$, we have:

$$f(a) = f(2) = (2)^2 + 1 = 5$$
$$f(b) = f(-2) = (-2)^2 + 1 = 5$$

Same y value but different x values

We have that $f(a) = f(b)$, but $a \neq b$.

Therefore, f fails to be a one-to-one function.

Figure 4-3

Skill Practice 3   Determine whether the function is one-to-one.

   a. $f(x) = -4x + 1$ **b.** $f(x) = |x| - 3$

2. Determine Whether Two Functions Are Inverses

We now have enough background to define an inverse function.

Definition of an Inverse Function

Let f be a one-to-one function. Then g is the **inverse of f** if the following conditions are both true.

   1. $(f \circ g)(x) = x$ for all x in the domain of g.
   2. $(g \circ f)(x) = x$ for all x in the domain of f.

Answers
3. a. Yes   **b.** No

We should also note that if g is the inverse of f, then f is the inverse of g. Furthermore, given a function f, we often denote its inverse as f^{-1}. So given a function f and its inverse f^{-1}, the definition implies that

$$(f \circ f^{-1})(x) = x \text{ and } (f^{-1} \circ f)(x) = x$$

EXAMPLE 4   Determining Whether Two Functions Are Inverses

The cost for a speeding ticket is $100 plus $12 for each mile per hour over the speed limit. The cost of the ticket $f(x)$ (in $) is given by $f(x) = 100 + 12x$, where x is the number of miles per hour over the posted speed limit.

a. Determine if the function defined by $g(x) = \dfrac{x - 100}{12}$ is the inverse of f.

b. Interpret the meaning of $g(x)$ in the context of this problem.

Solution:

To verify that f and g are inverses, we must show that $(f \circ g)(x) = x$ and $(g \circ f)(x) = x$.

a. $(f \circ g)(x) = f(g(x))$ 　　　　　　 $(g \circ f)(x) = g(f(x))$

$$= f\left(\frac{x - 100}{12}\right) \qquad\qquad\qquad = g(100 + 12x)$$

$$= 100 + 12\left(\frac{x - 100}{12}\right) \qquad\quad = \frac{(100 + 12x) - 100}{12}$$

$$= 100 + (x - 100) \qquad\qquad\quad = \frac{12x}{12}$$

$$= x \checkmark \qquad\qquad\qquad\qquad\qquad = x \checkmark$$

Function g is the inverse of function f.

b. The value $g(x)$ represents the number of miles per hour over the speed limit that a motorist was traveling based on the cost of the speeding ticket, x.

Skill Practice 4   The cost to rent a kayak at a beach resort is a flat fee of $10 plus $5 per hour. The cost $f(x)$ (in $) is given by $f(x) = 10 + 5x$, where x is the number of hours that the kayak is rented.

a. Determine if the function defined by $g(x) = \dfrac{x - 10}{5}$ is the inverse of f.

b. Interpret the meaning of $g(x)$ in the context of this problem.

3. Find the Inverse of a Function

For a one-to-one function defined by $y = f(x)$, the inverse is a function $y = f^{-1}(x)$ that performs the inverse operations in the reverse order. The function given by $f(x) = 100 + 12x$ multiplies x by 12 first, and then adds 100 to the result. Therefore, the inverse function must *subtract* 100 from x first and then *divide* by 12.

$$f^{-1}(x) = \frac{x - 100}{12}$$

To facilitate the process of finding an equation of the inverse of a one-to-one function, we offer the following steps.

Answers

4. a. Yes

　b. The value $g(x)$ represents the number of hours for which a kayak was rented based on the total cost x for the rental.

Procedure to Find an Equation of an Inverse of a Function

For a one-to-one function defined by $y = f(x)$, the equation of the inverse can be found as follows:

Step 1 Replace $f(x)$ by y.
Step 2 Interchange x and y.
Step 3 Solve for y.
Step 4 Replace y by $f^{-1}(x)$.

EXAMPLE 5   **Finding an Equation of an Inverse Function**

Write an equation for the inverse function for $f(x) = 3x - 1$.

Solution:

Function f is a linear function, and its graph is a nonvertical line. Therefore, f is a one-to-one function.

$$f(x) = 3x - 1$$

$$y = 3x - 1 \qquad \textbf{Step 1: } \text{Replace } f(x) \text{ by } y.$$

$$x = 3y - 1 \qquad \textbf{Step 2: } \text{Interchange } x \text{ and } y.$$

$$x + 1 = 3y \qquad \textbf{Step 3: } \text{Solve for } y. \text{ Add 1 to both sides and divide by 3.}$$

$$\frac{x + 1}{3} = y$$

$$f^{-1}(x) = \frac{x + 1}{3} \qquad \textbf{Step 4: } \text{Replace } y \text{ by } f^{-1}(x).$$

> **TIP** We can sometimes find an equation of an inverse function by mentally reversing the operations given in the original function. In Example 5, the function f multiplies x by 3 and then subtracts 1. Therefore, f^{-1} must add 1 to x and then divide by 3.

To check the result, verify that $(f \circ f^{-1})(x) = x$ and $(f^{-1} \circ f)(x) = x$.

$$(f \circ f^{-1})(x) = 3\left(\frac{x + 1}{3}\right) - 1 = x \ \checkmark \quad \text{and} \quad (f^{-1} \circ f)(x) = \frac{(3x - 1) + 1}{3} = x \ \checkmark$$

Skill Practice 5   Write an equation for the inverse function for $f(x) = 4x + 3$.

The key step in determining the equation of the inverse of a function is to interchange x and y. By so doing, a point (a, b) on f corresponds to a point (b, a) on f^{-1}. This is why the graphs of f and f^{-1} are symmetric with respect to the line $y = x$. From Example 5, notice that the point $(2, 5)$ on the graph of f corresponds to the point $(5, 2)$ on the graph of f^{-1} (Figure 4-4).

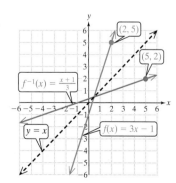

Figure 4-4

Answer

5. $f^{-1}(x) = \dfrac{x - 3}{4}$

EXAMPLE 6 **Finding an Equation of an Inverse Function**

Write an equation for the inverse function for the one-to-one function defined by $f(x) = \dfrac{3 - x}{x + 3}$.

Solution:

$$f(x) = \frac{3 - x}{x + 3}$$

$$y = \frac{3 - x}{x + 3} \qquad \textbf{Step 1:} \ \text{Replace } f(x) \text{ by } y.$$

$$x = \frac{3 - y}{y + 3} \qquad \textbf{Step 2:} \ \text{Interchange } x \text{ and } y.$$

$$x(y + 3) = 3 - y \qquad \textbf{Step 3:} \ \text{Solve for } y.$$
$$\qquad\qquad\qquad\qquad \text{Clear fractions (multiply both sides by } y + 3\text{).}$$

$$xy + 3x = 3 - y \qquad\qquad \text{Apply the distributive property.}$$

$$xy + y = 3 - 3x \qquad\qquad \text{Collect the } y \text{ terms on one side.}$$

$$y(x + 1) = 3 - 3x \qquad\qquad \text{Factor out } y \text{ as the greatest common factor.}$$

$$y = \frac{3 - 3x}{x + 1} \qquad\qquad \text{Divide both sides by } x + 1.$$

$$f^{-1}(x) = \frac{3 - 3x}{x + 1} \qquad \textbf{Step 4:} \ \text{Replace } y \text{ by } f^{-1}(x).$$

> **TIP** In Example 6, we can show that f is a one-to-one function by graphing the function (see Section 3.5). Or we can show that $f(a) = f(b)$ implies that $a = b$ by solving the equation $\dfrac{3 - a}{a + 3} = \dfrac{3 - b}{b + 3}$ for a or b to show that $a = b$.

Skill Practice 6 Write an equation for the inverse function for the one-to-one function defined by $f(x) = \dfrac{x - 2}{x + 2}$.

For a function that is not one-to-one, sometimes we restrict its domain to create a new function that is one-to-one. This is demonstrated in Example 7.

EXAMPLE 7 **Finding an Equation of an Inverse Function**

Given $m(x) = x^2 + 4$ for $x \geq 0$, write an equation of the inverse.

Solution:

The graph of $y = x^2 + 4$ is a parabola with vertex $(0, 4)$. See Figure 4-5. The function is not one-to-one. However, with the restriction on the domain that $x \geq 0$, the graph consists of only the right branch of the parabola (Figure 4-6). This *is* a one-to-one function.

Figure 4-5

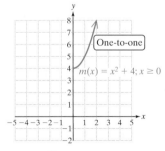

Figure 4-6

Answer

6. $f^{-1}(x) = -\dfrac{2x + 2}{x - 1}$

To find the inverse, we have

$$m(x) = x^2 + 4; \quad x \geq 0$$
$$y = x^2 + 4; \quad x \geq 0 \qquad \textbf{Step 1:} \text{ Replace } m(x) \text{ by } y.$$
$$x = y^2 + 4 \quad y \geq 0 \qquad \textbf{Step 2:} \text{ Interchange } x \text{ and } y. \text{ Notice that the restriction } x \geq 0 \text{ becomes } y \geq 0.$$
$$x - 4 = y^2 \qquad \textbf{Step 3:} \text{ Solve for } y \text{ by subtracting 4 from both sides.}$$
$$y = \pm\sqrt{x - 4} \qquad \qquad \text{Apply the square root property.}$$
$$y = +\sqrt{x - 4} \qquad \qquad \text{Choose the positive square root of } (x - 4) \text{ because of the restriction } y \geq 0.$$
$$m^{-1}(x) = \sqrt{x - 4} \qquad \textbf{Step 4:} \text{ Replace } y \text{ by } m^{-1}(x).$$

The graphs of m and m^{-1} are symmetric with respect to the line $y = x$ as expected.

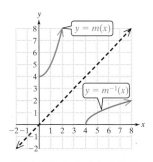

Skill Practice 7   Given $n(x) = x^2 + 1$ for $x \leq 0$, write an equation of the inverse.

EXAMPLE 8   Finding an Equation of an Inverse Function

Given $f(x) = \sqrt{x - 1}$, find an equation of the inverse.

Solution:

The function f is a one-to-one function and the graph is the same as the graph of $y = \sqrt{x}$ with a shift 1 unit to the right. The domain of f is $\{x \mid x \geq 1\}$ and the range is $\{y \mid y \geq 0\}$. When defining the inverse, we will have the conditions that $x \geq 0$ and $y \geq 1$.

$$f(x) = \sqrt{x - 1} \qquad \text{Note that } x \geq 1 \text{ and } y \geq 0.$$
$$y = \sqrt{x - 1}$$
$$x = \sqrt{y - 1} \qquad \text{Interchange } x \text{ and } y. \text{ Note that } y \geq 1 \text{ and } x \geq 0.$$
$$x^2 = y - 1 \qquad \text{Square both sides.}$$
$$y = x^2 + 1$$

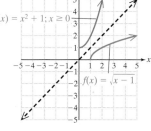

$$f^{-1}(x) = x^2 + 1 \quad x \geq 0 \qquad \text{The restriction } x \geq 0 \text{ on } f^{-1} \text{ is necessary because } f \text{ has the restriction that } y \geq 0. \text{ Furthermore, } y = x^2 + 1 \text{ is not a one-to-one function without a restricted domain.}$$

TIP When finding the inverse of a function, the key step of interchanging x and y has the effect of interchanging the domain and range between the function and its inverse.

Skill Practice 8   Given $g(x) = \sqrt{x + 2}$, find an equation of the inverse.

Answers
7. $n^{-1}(x) = -\sqrt{x - 1}$
8. $g^{-1}(x) = x^2 - 2; x \geq 0$

SECTION 4.1   Practice Exercises

Concept Connections

1. Given the function $f = \{(1, 2), (2, 3), (3, 4)\}$ write the set of ordered pairs representing f^{-1}.

2. A function f is a _____-_____-_____ function if for a and b in the domain of f, if $a \neq b$, then $f(a) \neq f(b)$.

3. The graph of a function and its inverse are symmetric with respect to the line _____.

4. The function $f = \{(1, 5), (-2, 3), (-4, 2), (2, 5)\}$ (is/is not) a one-to-one function.

5. A function defined by $y = f(x)$ (is/is not) a one-to-one function if no horizontal line intersects the graph of f in more than one point.

6. Given a one-to-one function defined by $y = f(x)$, if $f(a) = f(b)$, then a _____ b.

7. Let f be a one-to-one function and let g be the inverse of f. Then $(f \circ g)(x) = $ _____ and $(g \circ f)(x) = $ _____.

8. The notation _____ is often used to represent the inverse of a function f and not the reciprocal of f.

9. If (a, b) is a point on the graph of a one-to-one function f, then the corresponding ordered pair _____ is a point on the graph of f^{-1}.

10. The function defined by $f(x) = x^2 - 9$ (is/is not) a one-to-one function, whereas $g(x) = x^2 - 9$; $x \geq 0$ (is/is not) a one-to-one function.

Objective 1: Identify One-to-One Functions

For Exercises 11–18, a relation in x and y is given. Determine if the relation defines y as a one-to-one function of x. (See Example 1)

11. $\{(6, -5), (4, 2), (3, 1), (8, 4)\}$

12. $\{(-14, 1), (-2, 3), (7, 4), (-9, -2)\}$

13.

	A	B
1	**x**	**y**
2	0.6	1.8
3	1	-1.1
4	0.5	1.8
5	2.4	0.7

14.

	A	B
1	**x**	**y**
2	12.5	3.21
3	5.75	-4.5
4	2.34	7.25
5	-12.7	3.21

15.

x	y
California	Sacramento
Texas	Austin
New York	Albany
Florida	Tallahassee

16.

x	y
Green Bay	Packers
Miami	Dolphins
Atlanta	Falcons
Denver	Broncos

17.

18.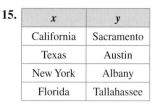

For Exercises 19–28, determine if the relation defines y as a one-to-one function of x. (See Example 2)

19.

20.

21.

22.

23.

24.

25.

26.

27.

28.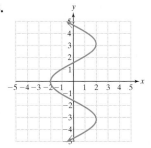

For Exercises 29–36, use the definition of a one-to-one function to determine if the function is one-to-one. (See Example 3)

29. $f(x) = 4x - 7$

30. $h(x) = -3x + 2$

31. $g(x) = x^3 + 8$

32. $k(x) = x^3 - 27$

33. $m(x) = x^2 - 4$

34. $n(x) = x^2 + 1$

35. $p(x) = |x + 1|$

36. $q(x) = |x - 3|$

Objective 2: Determine Whether Two Functions Are Inverses

For Exercises 37–42, determine whether the two functions are inverses. (See Example 4)

37. $f(x) = 5x + 4$ and $g(x) = \dfrac{x - 4}{5}$

38. $h(x) = 7x - 3$ and $k(x) = \dfrac{x + 3}{7}$

39. $m(x) = \dfrac{-2 + x}{6}$ and $n(x) = 6x - 2$

40. $p(x) = \dfrac{-3 + x}{4}$ and $q(x) = 4x - 3$

41. $t(x) = \dfrac{4}{x - 1}$ and $v(x) = \dfrac{x + 4}{x}$

42. $w(x) = \dfrac{6}{x + 2}$ and $z(x) = \dfrac{6 - 2x}{x}$

43. There were 2000 applicants for enrollment to the freshman class at a small college in the year 2010. The number of applications has risen linearly by roughly 150 per year. The number of applications $f(x)$ is given by $f(x) = 2000 + 150x$, where x is the number of years since 2010.

   a. Determine if the function $g(x) = \dfrac{x - 2000}{150}$ is the inverse of f.

   b. Interpret the meaning of function g in the context of this problem.

44. The monthly sales for January for a whole foods market was \$60,000 and has increased linearly by \$2500 per month. The amount in sales $f(x)$ (in \$) is given by $f(x) = 60,000 + 2500x$, where x is the number of months since January.

   a. Determine if the function $g(x) = \dfrac{x - 60,000}{2500}$ is the inverse of f.

   b. Interpret the meaning of function g in the context of this problem.

Objective 3: Find the Inverse of a Function

45. **a.** Show that $f(x) = 2x - 3$ defines a one-to-one function.

   b. Write an equation for $f^{-1}(x)$.

   c. Graph $y = f(x)$ and $y = f^{-1}(x)$ on the same coordinate system.

46. **a.** Show that $f(x) = 4x + 4$ defines a one-to-one function.

   b. Write an equation for $f^{-1}(x)$.

   c. Graph $y = f(x)$ and $y = f^{-1}(x)$ on the same coordinate system.

For Exercises 47–58, a one-to-one function is given. Write an equation for the inverse function. (See Examples 5–6)

47. $f(x) = \dfrac{4 - x}{9}$

48. $g(x) = \dfrac{8 - x}{3}$

49. $h(x) = \sqrt[3]{x - 5}$

50. $k(x) = \sqrt[3]{x + 8}$

51. $m(x) = 4x^3 + 2$

52. $n(x) = 2x^3 - 5$

53. $c(x) = \dfrac{5}{x + 2}$

54. $s(x) = \dfrac{2}{x - 3}$

55. $t(x) = \dfrac{x - 4}{x + 2}$

56. $v(x) = \dfrac{x - 5}{x + 1}$

57. $f(x) = \dfrac{(x - a)^3}{b} - c$

58. $g(x) = b(x + a)^3 + c$

59. a. Graph $f(x) = x^2 - 3;\ x \le 0$. **(See Example 7)**
   b. From the graph of f, is f a one-to-one function?
   c. Write the domain of f in interval notation.
   d. Write the range of f in interval notation.
   e. Write an equation for $f^{-1}(x)$.
   f. Graph $y = f(x)$ and $y = f^{-1}(x)$ on the same coordinate system.
   g. Write the domain of f^{-1} in interval notation.
   h. Write the range of f^{-1} in interval notation.

60. a. Graph $f(x) = x^2 + 1;\ x \le 0$.
   b. From the graph of f, is f a one-to-one function?
   c. Write the domain of f in interval notation.
   d. Write the range of f in interval notation.
   e. Write an equation for $f^{-1}(x)$.
   f. Graph $y = f(x)$ and $y = f^{-1}(x)$ on the same coordinate system.
   g. Write the domain of f^{-1} in interval notation.
   h. Write the range of f^{-1} in interval notation.

61. a. Graph $f(x) = \sqrt{x + 1}$. **(See Example 8)**
   b. From the graph of f, is f a one-to-one function?
   c. Write the domain of f in interval notation.
   d. Write the range of f in interval notation.
   e. Write an equation for $f^{-1}(x)$.
   f. Explain why the restriction $x \ge 0$ is placed on f^{-1}.
   g. Graph $y = f(x)$ and $y = f^{-1}(x)$ on the same coordinate system.
   h. Write the domain of f^{-1} in interval notation.
   i. Write the range of f^{-1} in interval notation.

62. a. Graph $f(x) = \sqrt{x - 2}$.
   b. From the graph of f, is f a one-to-one function?
   c. Write the domain of f in interval notation.
   d. Write the range of f in interval notation.
   e. Write an equation for $f^{-1}(x)$.
   f. Explain why the restriction $x \ge 0$ is placed on f^{-1}.
   g. Graph $y = f(x)$ and $y = f^{-1}(x)$ on the same coordinate system.
   h. Write the domain of f^{-1} in interval notation.
   i. Write the range of f^{-1} in interval notation.

63. Given that the domain of a one-to-one function f is $[0, \infty)$ and the range of f is $[0, 4)$, state the domain and range of f^{-1}.

64. Given that the domain of a one-to-one function f is $[-3, 5)$ and the range of f is $(-2, \infty)$, state the domain and range of f^{-1}.

65. Given $f(x) = |x| + 3;\ x \le 0$, write an equation for f^{-1}. (*Hint:* Sketch $f(x)$ and note the domain and range.)

66. Given $f(x) = |x| - 3;\ x \ge 0$, write an equation for f^{-1}. (*Hint:* Sketch $f(x)$ and note the domain and range.)

For Exercises 67–72, fill in the blanks and determine an equation for $f^{-1}(x)$ mentally.

67. If function f adds 6 to x, then f^{-1} _____ 6 from x. Function f is defined by $f(x) = x + 6$, and function f^{-1} is defined by $f^{-1}(x) = $ _____.

68. If function f multiplies x by 2, then f^{-1} _____ x by 2. Function f is defined by $f(x) = 2x$, and function f^{-1} is defined by $f^{-1}(x) = $ _____.

69. Suppose that function f multiplies x by 7 and subtracts 4. Write an equation for $f^{-1}(x)$.

70. Suppose that function f divides x by 3 and adds 11. Write an equation for $f^{-1}(x)$.

71. Suppose that function f cubes x and adds 20. Write an equation for $f^{-1}(x)$.

72. Suppose that function f takes the cube root of x and subtracts 10. Write an equation for $f^{-1}(x)$.

For Exercises 73–76, find the inverse mentally.

73. $f(x) = 8x + 1$

74. $p(x) = 2x - 10$

75. $q(x) = \sqrt[5]{x - 4} + 1$

76. $m(x) = \sqrt[3]{4x} + 3$

Mixed Exercises

For Exercises 77–80, the graph of a function is given. Graph the inverse function.

77.

78.

79.

80.

For Exercises 81–82, the table defines $Y_1 = f(x)$ as a one-to-one function of x. Find the values of f^{-1} for the selected values of x.

81. **a.** $f^{-1}(32)$

  b. $f^{-1}(-2.5)$

  c. $f^{-1}(26)$

X	Y₁
6	14
-2	-10
.5	-2.5
12	32
4.5	9.5
-8	-28
10	26

X=6

82. **a.** $f^{-1}(5)$

  b. $f^{-1}(9.45)$

  c. $f^{-1}(8)$

X	Y₁
-3	10.75
4	9
2.2	9.45
8	8
-12	13
20	5
4.6	8.85

X=-3

For Exercises 83–86, determine if the statement is true or false.

83. All linear functions with a nonzero slope have an inverse function.

84. The domain of any one-to-one function is the same as the domain of its inverse function.

85. The range of a one-to-one function is the same as the range of its inverse function.

86. No quadratic function defined by $f(x) = ax^2 + bx + c$ $(a \neq 0)$ is one-to-one.

87. Suppose that during normal respiration, the volume of air inhaled per breath (called "tidal volume") by a mammal of any size is 6.33 mL per kilogram of body mass.

  a. Write a function representing the tidal volume $T(x)$ (in mL) of a mammal of mass x (in kg).

  b. Write an equation for $T^{-1}(x)$.

  c. What does the inverse function represent in the context of this problem?

  d. Find $T^{-1}(170)$ and interpret its meaning in context. Round to the nearest whole unit.

88. At a cruising altitude of 35,000 ft, a certain airplane travels 555 mph.

  a. Write a function representing the distance $d(t)$ (in mi) for t hours at cruising altitude.

  b. Write an equation for $d^{-1}(t)$.

  c. What does the inverse function represent in the context of this problem?

  d. Evaluate $d^{-1}(2553)$ and interpret its meaning in context.

89. The millage rate is the amount of property tax per $1000 of the taxable value of a home. For a certain county the millage rate is 24 mil. A city within the county also imposes a flat fee of $108 per home.

  a. Write a function representing the total amount of property tax $T(x)$ (in $) for a home with a taxable value of x thousand dollars.

  b. Write an equation for $T^{-1}(x)$.

  c. What does the inverse function represent in the context of this problem?

  d. Evaluate $T^{-1}(2988)$ and interpret its meaning in context.

90. Beginning on January 1, park rangers in Everglades National Park began recording the water level for one particularly dry area of the park. The water level was initially 2.5 ft and decreased by approximately 0.015 ft/day.

  a. Write a function representing the water level $L(x)$ (in ft), x days after January 1.

  b. Write an equation for $L^{-1}(x)$.

  c. What does the inverse function represent in the context of this problem?

  d. Evaluate $L^{-1}(1.9)$ and interpret its meaning in context.

91. $V(r) = \dfrac{4}{3}\pi r^3$ gives the volume of a sphere as a function of its radius r. Find an equation for $r(V)$ and interpret its meaning in the context of this problem.

92. $F(C) = \dfrac{9}{5}C + 32$ gives the temperature in degrees Fahrenheit as a function of the temperature C in degrees Celsius. Find an equation for $C(F)$ and interpret its meaning in the context of this problem.

Write About It

93. Explain the relationship between the domain and range of a one-to-one function f and its inverse f^{-1}.

94. Write an informal definition of a one-to-one function.

95. Explain why if a horizontal line intersects the graph of a function in more than one point, then the function is not one-to-one.

96. Explain why the domain of $f(x) = x^2 + k$ must be restricted to find an inverse function.

Expanding Your Skills

97. Consider a function defined as follows. Given x, the value $f(x)$ is the exponent above the base of 2 that produces x. For example, $f(16) = 4$ because $2^4 = 16$. Evaluate

   a. $f(8)$ **b.** $f(32)$

   c. $f(2)$ **d.** $f\left(\frac{1}{8}\right)$

98. Consider a function defined as follows. Given x, the value $f(x)$ is the exponent above the base of 3 that produces x. For example, $f(9) = 2$ because $3^2 = 9$. Evaluate

   a. $f(27)$ **b.** $f(81)$

   c. $f(3)$ **d.** $f\left(\frac{1}{9}\right)$

99. Show that every increasing function is one-to-one.

100. A function is said to be periodic if there exists some nonzero real number p, called the period, such that $f(x + p) = f(x)$ for all real numbers x in the domain of f. Explain why no periodic function is one-to-one.

Technology Connections

101. Given the functions defined by $f(x) = 2x - 1$ and $g(x) = \dfrac{x + 1}{2}$,

   a. Graph $y = f(x)$, $y = g(x)$, and the line $y = x$. Does the graph suggest that f and g are inverses? Why?

   b. Enter the following functions into the graphing editor. (*Hint*: Use the **VARS** key to access the y-variables for functions.)

      $Y_1 = 2x - 1$

      $Y_2 = (x + 1)/2$

      $Y_3 = Y_1(Y_2)$

      $Y_4 = Y_2(Y_1)$

   c. Create a table of points showing Y_3 and Y_4 for several values of x. (*Hint*: Use the right and left arrows to scroll through the table editor to show functions Y_3 and Y_4.) Does the table suggest that f and g are inverses? Why?

SECTION 4.2   Exponential Functions

OBJECTIVES

1. Graph Exponential Functions

2. Evaluate the Exponential Function Base e

3. Use Exponential Functions to Compute Compound Interest

4. Use Exponential Functions in Applications

1. Graph Exponential Functions

The concept of a function was first introduced in Section 2.3. Since then we have learned to recognize several categories of functions. In this section and the next, we will define two new types of functions called exponential functions and logarithmic functions.

To introduce exponential functions, consider two salary plans for a new job. Plan A pays $1 million for 1 month's work. Plan B starts with 2¢ on the first day, and every day thereafter the salary is doubled. At first glance, the million-dollar plan appears to be more favorable. However, Table 4-3 shows otherwise. The daily payments for 30 days are listed for Plan B.

Table 4-3

Day	Payment	Day	Payment	Day	Payment
1	2¢	11	$20.48	21	$20,971.52
2	4¢	12	$40.96	22	$41,943.04
3	8¢	13	$81.92	23	$83,886.08
4	16¢	14	$163.84	24	$167,772.16
5	32¢	15	$327.68	25	$335,554.32
6	64¢	16	$655.36	26	$671,088.64
7	$1.28	17	$1310.72	27	$1,342,177.28
8	$2.56	18	$2621.44	28	$2,684,354.56
9	$5.12	19	$5242.88	29	$5,368,709.12
10	$10.24	20	$10,485.76	30	$10,737,418.24

The salary for the 30th day for Plan B is over $10 million. Taking the sum of the payments, we see that the total salary for the 30-day period is $21,474,836.46.

The daily salary $S(x)$ (in ¢) for Plan B can be represented by the function $S(x) = 2^x$, where x is the number of days on the job. An interesting characteristic of this function is that for every positive 1-unit change in x, the function value doubles. The function $S(x) = 2^x$ is called an exponential function.

Definition of an Exponential Function

Let b be a constant real number such that $b > 0$ and $b \neq 1$. Then for any real number x, a function of the form $f(x) = b^x$ is called an **exponential function.**

An exponential function is recognized as a function with a constant base (positive and not equal to 1) with a variable exponent, x.

Exponential Functions	Not Exponential Functions
$f(x) = 3^x$	$m(x) = x^2$ — base is not constant
$g(x) = \left(\dfrac{1}{3}\right)^x$	$n(x) = \left(-\dfrac{1}{3}\right)^x$ — base is negative
$h(x) = \left(\sqrt{2}\right)^x$	$p(x) = 1^x$ — base is 1

Avoiding Mistakes

- The base of an exponential function must not be negative to avoid situations where the function values are not real numbers. For example, $f(x) = (-4)^x$ is not defined for $x = \frac{1}{2}$ because $\sqrt{-4}$ is not a real number.
- The base of an exponential function must not equal 1 because $f(x) = 1^x = 1$ for all real numbers x. This is a constant function, not an exponential function.

At this point in the text, we have evaluated exponential expressions with integer exponents and with rational exponents. For example,

$$4^2 = 16 \qquad\qquad 4^{1/2} = \sqrt{4} = 2$$

$$4^{-1} = \frac{1}{4} \qquad\qquad 4^{10/23} = \sqrt[23]{4^{10}} \approx 1.827112184$$

However, how do we evaluate an exponential expression with an *irrational* exponent such as 4^{π}? In such a case, the exponent is a nonterminating, nonrepeating decimal. We define an exponential expression raised to an irrational exponent as a sequence of approximations using rational exponents. For example:

$$4^{3.14} \approx 77.7084726$$
$$4^{3.141} \approx 77.81627412$$
$$4^{3.1415} \approx 77.87023095$$
$$\cdots$$
$$4^{\pi} \approx 77.88023365$$

With this definition of a base raised to an irrational exponent, we can define an exponential function over the entire set of real numbers. In Example 1, we graph two exponential functions by plotting points.

EXAMPLE 1   **Graphing Exponential Functions**

Graph the functions.

a. $f(x) = 2^x$ **b.** $g(x) = \left(\dfrac{1}{2}\right)^x$

Solution:

Table 4-4 shows several function values $f(x)$ and $g(x)$ for both positive and negative values of x.

Table 4-4

x	$f(x) = 2^x$	$g(x) = \left(\frac{1}{2}\right)^x$
-3	$\frac{1}{8}$	8
-2	$\frac{1}{4}$	4
-1	$\frac{1}{2}$	2
0	1	1
1	2	$\frac{1}{2}$
2	4	$\frac{1}{4}$
3	8	$\frac{1}{8}$

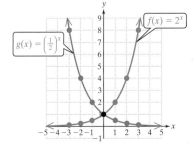

Figure 4-7

TIP The values of $f(x)$ become closer and closer to 0 as $x \to -\infty$. This means that the x-axis is a horizontal asymptote.

Likewise, the values of $g(x)$ become closer to 0 as $x \to \infty$. The x-axis is a horizontal asymptote.

Notice that $g(x) = \left(\frac{1}{2}\right)^x$ is equivalent to $g(x) = 2^{-x}$. Therefore, the graph of $g(x) = \left(\frac{1}{2}\right)^x = 2^{-x}$ is the same as the graph of $f(x) = 2^x$ with a reflection across the y-axis.

Skill Practice 1   Graph the functions.

a. $f(x) = 5^x$ **b.** $g(x) = \left(\dfrac{1}{5}\right)^x$

The graphs in Figure 4-7 illustrate several important features of exponential functions.

Answer

1.

Graphs of $f(x) = b^x$

The graph of an exponential function defined by $f(x) = b^x$ ($b > 0$ and $b \neq 1$) has the following properties.

1. If $b > 1$, f is an *increasing* exponential function, sometimes called an **exponential growth function.**

   If $0 < b < 1$, f is a *decreasing* exponential function, sometimes called an **exponential decay function.**

2. The domain is the set of all real numbers, $(-\infty, \infty)$.

3. The range is $(0, \infty)$.

4. The line $y = 0$ (x-axis) is a horizontal asymptote.

5. The function passes through the point $(0, 1)$ because $f(0) = b^0 = 1$.

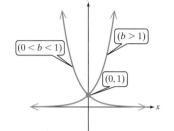

These properties indicate that the graph of an exponential function is an increasing function if the base is greater than 1. Furthermore, the base affects the rate of increase. Consider the graphs of $f(x) = 2^x$ and $k(x) = 5^x$ (Figure 4-8). For every positive 1-unit change in x, $f(x) = 2^x$ is 2 times as great and $k(x) = 5^x$ is 5 times as great (Table 4-5).

Table 4-5

x	$f(x) = 2^x$	$k(x) = 5^x$
-3	$\frac{1}{8}$	$\frac{1}{125}$
-2	$\frac{1}{4}$	$\frac{1}{25}$
-1	$\frac{1}{2}$	$\frac{1}{5}$
0	1	1
1	2	5
2	4	25
3	8	125

Figure 4-8

In Example 2, we use the transformations of functions learned in Section 2.6 to graph an exponential function.

If $h > 0$, shift to the right.
If $h < 0$, shift to the left.

$$f(x) = ab^{x-h} + k$$

If $a < 0$, reflect across the x-axis.
Shrink vertically if $0 < |a| < 1$.
Stretch vertically if $|a| > 1$.

If $k > 0$, shift upward.
If $k < 0$, shift downward.

EXAMPLE 2   **Graphing an Exponential Function**

Graph. $f(x) = 3^{x-2} + 4$

Solution:

The graph of f is the graph of the parent function $y = 3^x$ shifted 2 units to the right and 4 units upward.

The parent function $y = 3^x$ is an increasing exponential function. We can plot a few points on the graph of $y = 3^x$ and use these points and the horizontal asymptote to form the outline of the transformed graph.

x	$y = 3^x$
-2	$\frac{1}{9}$
-1	$\frac{1}{3}$
0	1
1	3
2	9

Shift 2 units to the right. For example, the point $(0, 1)$ on $y = 3^x$ corresponds to $(2, 1)$ on $y = 3^{x-2}$.

Shift the graph of $y = 3^{x-2}$ up 4 units. Notice that with the vertical shift, the new horizontal asymptote is $y = 4$.

Skill Practice 2   Graph. $g(x) = 2^{x+2} - 1$

2. Evaluate the Exponential Function Base e

We now introduce an important exponential function whose base is an irrational number called e. Consider the expression $\left(1 + \dfrac{1}{x}\right)^x$. The value of the expression for increasingly large values of x approaches a constant (Table 4-6).

As $x \to \infty$, the expression $\left(1 + \dfrac{1}{x}\right)^x$ approaches a constant value that we call e. From Table 4-6, this value is approximately 2.718281828.

$$e \approx 2.718281828$$

The value of e is an irrational number (a non-terminating, nonrepeating decimal) and like the number π, it is a universal constant. The function defined by $f(x) = e^x$ is called the exponential function base e or the **natural exponential function.**

Table 4-6

x	$\left(1 + \dfrac{1}{x}\right)^x$
100	2.70481382942
1000	2.71692393224
10,000	2.71814592683
100,000	2.71826823717
1,000,000	2.71828046932
1,000,000,000	2.71828182710

Answer

2.

EXAMPLE 3   Graphing $f(x) = e^x$

Graph the function. $f(x) = e^x$

Solution:

Because the base e is greater than 1 ($e \approx 2.718281828$), the graph is an increasing exponential function. We can use a calculator to evaluate $f(x) = e^x$ at several values of x. On many calculators, the exponential function, base e, is invoked by selecting **2ND** **LN** or by accessing e^x on the keyboard.

TIP In Section 4.3, we will see that the exponential function base e is the inverse of the natural logarithmic function, $y = \ln x$. This is why the exponential function base e is accessed with the **2ND** **LN** keys.

```
e^(1)
       2.718281828
e^(2)
       7.389056099
e^(3)
       20.08553692
```
```
e^(-3)
       .0497870684
e^(-2)
       .1353352832
e^(-1)
       .3678794412
```

x	$f(x) = e^x$
-3	0.050
-2	0.135
-1	0.368
0	1.000
1	2.718
2	7.389
3	20.086

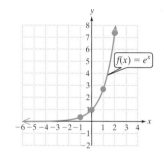

Figure 4-9

The graph of $f(x) = e^x$ is shown in Figure 4-9.

Skill Practice 3   Explain how the graph of $f(x) = -e^{x-1}$ is related to the graph of $y = e^x$.

3. Use Exponential Functions to Compute Compound Interest

Recall that simple interest is interest computed on the principal amount invested (or borrowed). Compound interest is interest computed on both the original principal and the interest already accrued.

Suppose that interest is compounded annually (one time per year) on an investment of P dollars at an annual interest rate r for t years. Then the amount A (in $) in the account after 1, 2, and 3 yr is computed as follows.

After 1 yr: $\begin{pmatrix} \text{Total} \\ \text{amount} \end{pmatrix} = \begin{pmatrix} \text{Initial} \\ \text{principal} \end{pmatrix} + (\text{Interest})$

$A = P + Pr$ ⟵ The interest is given by $I = Prt$, where $t = 1$ yr. So $I = Pr$.

$\qquad = P(1 + r)$ Factor out P.

After 2 yr: $\begin{pmatrix} \text{Total} \\ \text{amount} \end{pmatrix} = \begin{pmatrix} \text{Year 1} \\ \text{balance} \end{pmatrix} + \begin{pmatrix} \text{Interest on} \\ \text{Year 1 balance} \end{pmatrix}$

$A = P(1 + r) + [P(1 + r)]r$

$\qquad = P(1 + r)(1 + r)$ Factor out $P(1 + r)$.

$\qquad = P(1 + r)^2$

Answer

3. The graph of $f(x) = -e^{x-1}$ is the graph of $y = e^x$ with a shift to the right 1 unit and a reflection across the x-axis.

$$\text{After 3 yr:} \begin{pmatrix} \text{Total} \\ \text{amount} \end{pmatrix} = \begin{pmatrix} \text{Year 2} \\ \text{balance} \end{pmatrix} + \begin{pmatrix} \text{Interest on} \\ \text{Year 2 balance} \end{pmatrix}$$

$$\begin{aligned} A &= P(1 + r)^2 + [P(1 + r)^2]r \\ &= P(1 + r)^2(1 + r) \qquad \text{Factor out } P(1 + r)^2. \\ &= P(1 + r)^3 \end{aligned}$$

$\cdots$

After t years: $\quad A = P(1 + r)^t$ — Amount in an account with interest compounded annually.

Compound interest is often computed more frequently during the course of 1 yr. Let n represent the number of compounding periods per year. For example:

$\quad n = 1 \qquad$ for interest compounded annually
$\quad n = 4 \qquad$ for interest compounded quarterly
$\quad n = 12 \qquad$ for interest compounded monthly
$\quad n = 365 \qquad$ for interest compounded daily

Each compounding period represents a fraction of a year and the interest rate is scaled accordingly for each compounding period as $\frac{1}{n} \cdot r$ or $\frac{r}{n}$. The number of compounding periods over the course of the investment is nt. Therefore, to determine the amount in an account where interest is compounded n times per year we have

replace t by nt

$$A = P(1 + r)^t \qquad\qquad A = P\left(1 + \frac{r}{n}\right)^{nt}$$ — Amount in an account with interest compounded n times per year.

replace r by $\frac{r}{n}$

Now suppose it were possible to compute interest continuously, that is, for $n \to \infty$. If we use the substitution $x = \frac{n}{r}$ (which implies that $n = xr$) the formula for compound interest becomes

$$A = P\left(1 + \frac{r}{n}\right)^{nt} \xrightarrow{\text{Substitute } x = \frac{n}{r}} P\left(1 + \frac{1}{x}\right)^{xrt} = P\left[\left(1 + \frac{1}{x}\right)^x\right]^{rt}$$

For a fixed interest rate r, as n approaches infinity, x also approaches infinity. Since the expression $\left(1 + \frac{1}{x}\right)^x$ approaches e as $x \to \infty$, we have

$$A = Pe^{rt}$$ — Amount in an account with interest compounded continuously.

Summary of Formulas Relating to Simple and Compound Interest

Suppose that P dollars in principal is invested (or borrowed) at an annual interest rate r for t years. Then

- $I = Prt$ — Amount of simple interest I (in \$).
- $A = P\left(1 + \frac{r}{n}\right)^{nt}$ — The future value A (in \$) of the account after t years with n compounding periods per year.
- $A = Pe^{rt}$ — The future value A (in \$) of the account after t years under continuous compounding.

In Example 4, we compare the value of an investment after 10 yr under several different compounding options.

EXAMPLE 4 **Computing the Balance on an Account**

Suppose that $5000 is invested and pays 6.5% per year under the following compounding options.

a. Compounded annually   b. Compounded quarterly
c. Compounded monthly   d. Compounded daily
e. Compounded continuously

Determine the total amount in the account after 10 yr with each option.

Solution:

Using $A = P\left(1 + \dfrac{r}{n}\right)^{nt}$ and $A = Pe^{rt}$, we have

Compounding Option	n Value	Formula	Result
Annually	$n = 1$	$A = 5000\left(1 + \dfrac{0.065}{1}\right)^{(1\cdot 10)}$	$9385.69
Quarterly	$n = 4$	$A = 5000\left(1 + \dfrac{0.065}{4}\right)^{(4\cdot 10)}$	$9527.79
Monthly	$n = 12$	$A = 5000\left(1 + \dfrac{0.065}{12}\right)^{(12\cdot 10)}$	$9560.92
Daily	$n = 365$	$A = 5000\left(1 + \dfrac{0.065}{365}\right)^{(365\cdot 10)}$	$9577.15
Continuously	Not applicable	$A = 5000e^{(0.065\,\cdot\,10)}$	$9577.70

Notice that there is a $192.01 difference in the account balance between annual compounding and continuous compounding. The table also supports our finding that

$$A = P\left(1 + \frac{r}{n}\right)^{nt} \quad \text{converges to} \quad A = Pe^{rt} \quad \text{as } n \to \infty.$$

Skill Practice 4   Suppose that $8000 is invested and pays 4.5% per year under the following compounding options.

a. Compounded annually   b. Compounded quarterly
c. Compounded monthly   d. Compounded daily
e. Compounded continuously

Determine the total amount in the account after 5 yr with each option.

4. Use Exponential Functions in Applications

Increasing and decreasing exponential functions can be used in a variety of real-world applications. For example:

- Population growth can often be modeled by an exponential function.
- The growth of an investment under compound interest increases exponentially.
- The mass of a radioactive substance decreases exponentially with time.
- The temperature of a cup of coffee decreases exponentially as it approaches room temperature.

Answers
4. a. $9969.46   **b.** $10,006.00
c. $10,014.37   **d.** $10,018.44
e. $10,018.58

A substance that undergoes radioactive decay is said to be radioactive. The half-life of a radioactive substance is the amount of time it takes for one-half of the original amount of the substance to change into something else. That is, after each half-life, the amount of the original substance decreases by one-half.

| EXAMPLE 5 | Using an Exponential Function in an Application |

In a sample originally having 1 g of radium 226, the amount $A(t)$ (in grams) of radium 226 present after t years is given by $A(t) = \left(\frac{1}{2}\right)^{t/1620}$ where t is the time in years after the start of the experiment. How much radium will be present after

a. 1620 yr? **b.** 3240 yr? **c.** 4860 yr?

Solution:

a. $A(t) = \left(\frac{1}{2}\right)^{t/1620}$ **b.** $A(t) = \left(\frac{1}{2}\right)^{t/1620}$ **c.** $A(t) = \left(\frac{1}{2}\right)^{t/1620}$

$A(1620) = \left(\frac{1}{2}\right)^{1620/1620}$ $\quad A(3240) = \left(\frac{1}{2}\right)^{3240/1620}$ $\quad A(4860) = \left(\frac{1}{2}\right)^{4860/1620}$

$= \left(\frac{1}{2}\right)^{1}$ $\qquad\qquad = \left(\frac{1}{2}\right)^{2}$ $\qquad\qquad\quad = \left(\frac{1}{2}\right)^{3}$

$= 0.5$ $\qquad\qquad\quad = 0.25$ $\qquad\qquad\qquad = 0.125$

After 1620 yr (1 half-life), 0.5 g remains ($\frac{1}{2}$ of the original amount remains).

After 3240 yr (2 half-lives), 0.25 g remains ($\frac{1}{4}$ of the original amount remains).

After 4860 yr (3 half-lives), 0.125 g remains ($\frac{1}{8}$ of the original amount remains).

Skill Practice 5 Cesium-137 is a radioactive metal with a short half-life of 30 yr. In a sample originally having 2 g of cesium-137, the amount $A(t)$ (in grams) of cesium-137 present after t years is given by $A(t) = 2\left(\frac{1}{2}\right)^{t/30}$. How much cesium-137 will be present after

a. 30 yr? **b.** 60 yr? **c.** 90 yr?

Point of Interest

In 1898, Marie Curie discovered the highly radioactive element radium. She shared the 1903 Nobel Prize in physics for her research on radioactivity and was awarded the 1911 Nobel Prize in chemistry for her discovery of radium and polonium. Marie Curie died in 1934 from complications of excessive exposure to radiation.

Marie and Pierre Curie

TECHNOLOGY CONNECTIONS

Graphing an Exponential Function

A graphing utility can be used to graph and analyze exponential functions. The table shows several values of $A(x) = \left(\frac{1}{2}\right)^{x/1620}$ for selected values of x.

Plot1 Plot2 Plot3
\Y₁⊟(1/2)^(X/1620)
\Y₂=
\Y₃=
\Y₄=
\Y₅=
\Y₆=

$Y_1 = \left(\frac{1}{2}\right)^{x/1620}$

X	Y1
0	1
1620	.5
3240	.25
4860	.125
6480	.0625
8100	.03125
9720	.01563

X=0

The graph of $A(x) = \left(\frac{1}{2}\right)^{x/1620}$ is shown on the viewing window [0, 10,000, 1000] by [−0.2, 1.2, 0.1]. Notice that the graph is a decreasing exponential function because the base is between 0 and 1.

Y1=(1/2)^(X/1620)

X=1620   Y=.5

SECTION 4.2   Practice Exercises

Review Exercises

For Exercises 1–2, determine if the relation defines y as a one-to-one function of x.

1. $y = 3x - 5$

2. $y = x^2$

For Exercises 3–4, a one-to-one function is given. Write an equation for the inverse function.

3. $f(x) = \dfrac{6}{x + 2}$

4. $g(x) = \dfrac{-2}{x - 5}$

For Exercises 5–6, given the graph of f, graph f^{-1}.

5.

6.

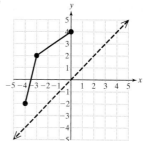

Concept Connections

7. Given a real number b, where $b > 0$ and $b \neq 1$, a function defined by $f(x) = $ _____ is called an exponential function.

8. The function defined by $y = x^3$ (is/is not) an exponential function, whereas the function defined by $y = 3^x$ (is/is not) an exponential function.

9. The graph of $f(x) = \left(\dfrac{5}{3}\right)^x$ is (increasing/decreasing) over its domain.

10. The graph of $f(x) = \left(\dfrac{3}{5}\right)^x$ is (increasing/decreasing) over its domain.

11. The domain of an exponential function $f(x) = b^x$ is _____.

12. The range of an exponential function $f(x) = b^x$ is _____.

13. All exponential functions $f(x) = b^x$ pass through the point _____.

14. The horizontal asymptote of an exponential function $f(x) = b^x$ is the line _____.

15. The function defined by $f(x) = 1^x$ (is/is not) an exponential function.

16. As $x \to \infty$, the value of $\left(1 + \dfrac{1}{x}\right)^x$ approaches _____.

17. The function $f(x) = e^x$ is the exponential function base _____ and is also called the _____ exponential function.

18. The formula $A = Pe^{rt}$ gives the amount A in an account after t years at an interest rate r under the assumption that interest is compounded _____.

Objective 1: Graph Exponential Functions

For Exercises 19–22, evaluate the functions at the given values of x. Round to 4 decimal places if necessary.

19. $f(x) = 5^x$
  a. $f(-1)$
  b. $f(4.8)$
  c. $f(\sqrt{2})$
  d. $f(\pi)$

20. $g(x) = 7^x$
  a. $g(-2)$
  b. $g(5.9)$
  c. $g(\sqrt{11})$
  d. $g(e)$

21. $h(x) = \left(\dfrac{1}{4}\right)^x$
  a. $h(-3)$
  b. $h(1.4)$
  c. $h(\sqrt{3})$
  d. $h(0.5e)$

22. $k(x) = \left(\dfrac{1}{6}\right)^x$
  a. $k(-3)$
  b. $k(1.4)$
  c. $k(\sqrt{0.5})$
  d. $h(0.5\pi)$

23. Which functions are exponential functions?

    a. $f(x) = 4.2^x$ **b.** $g(x) = x^{4.2}$ **c.** $h(x) = 4.2x$

    d. $k(x) = (\sqrt{4.2})^x$ **e.** $m(x) = (-4.2)^x$

24. Which functions are exponential functions?

    a. $v(x) = (-\pi)^x$ **b.** $t(x) = \pi^x$ **c.** $w(x) = \pi x$

    d. $n(x) = (\sqrt{\pi})^x$ **e.** $p(x) = x^\pi$

For Exercises 25–32, graph the functions and write the domain and range in interval notation. (See Example 1)

25. $f(x) = 3^x$

26. $g(x) = 4^x$

27. $h(x) = \left(\dfrac{1}{3}\right)^x$

28. $k(x) = \left(\dfrac{1}{4}\right)^x$

29. $m(x) = \left(\dfrac{3}{2}\right)^x$

30. $n(x) = \left(\dfrac{5}{4}\right)^x$

31. $b(x) = \left(\dfrac{2}{3}\right)^x$

32. $c(x) = \left(\dfrac{4}{5}\right)^x$

For Exercises 33–42, use the graphs of $y = 3^x$ (see Exercise 25) and $y = 4^x$ (see Exercise 26) to graph the given functions. Write the domain and range in interval notation. (See Example 2)

33. $f(x) = 3^x + 2$

34. $g(x) = 4^x - 3$

35. $m(x) = 3^{x+2}$

36. $n(x) = 4^{x-3}$

37. $p(x) = 3^{x-4} - 1$

38. $q(x) = 4^{x+1} + 2$

39. $k(x) = -3^x$

40. $h(x) = -4^x$

41. $t(x) = 3^{-x}$

42. $v(x) = 4^{-x}$

For Exercises 43–46, use the graphs of $y = \left(\frac{1}{3}\right)^x$ (see Exercise 27) and $y = \left(\frac{1}{4}\right)^x$ (see Exercise 28) to graph the given functions. Write the domain and range in interval notation.

43. $f(x) = \left(\dfrac{1}{3}\right)^{x+1} - 3$

44. $g(x) = \left(\dfrac{1}{4}\right)^{x-2} + 1$

45. $k(x) = -\left(\dfrac{1}{3}\right)^x + 2$

46. $h(x) = -\left(\dfrac{1}{4}\right)^x - 2$

Objective 2: Evaluate the Exponential Function Base e

For Exercises 47–48, evaluate the functions for the given values of x. Round to 4 decimal places.

47. $f(x) = e^x$

    a. $f(4)$ **b.** $f(-3.2)$

    c. $f(\sqrt{13})$ **d.** $f(\pi)$

48. $f(x) = e^x$

    a. $f(-3)$ **b.** $f(6.8)$

    c. $f(\sqrt{7})$ **d.** $f(e)$

For Exercises 49–54, use transformations of the graph of $y = e^x$ to graph the function. Write the domain and range in interval notation. (See Example 3)

49. $f(x) = e^{x-4}$

50. $g(x) = e^{x-2}$

51. $h(x) = e^x + 2$

52. $k(x) = e^x - 1$

53. $m(x) = -e^x - 3$

54. $n(x) = -e^x + 4$

Objective 3: Use Exponential Functions to Compute Compound Interest

For Exercises 55–56, complete the table to determine the effect of the number of compounding periods when computing interest. (See Example 4)

55. Suppose that $10,000 is invested with 4% interest for 5 yr under the following compounding options. Complete the table.

	Compounding Option	*n* Value	Result
a.	Annually		
b.	Quarterly		
c.	Monthly		
d.	Daily		
e.	Continuously		

56. Suppose that $8000 is invested with 3.5% interest for 20 yr under the following compounding options. Complete the table.

	Compounding Option	*n* Value	Result
a.	Annually		
b.	Quarterly		
c.	Monthly		
d.	Daily		
e.	Continuously		

For Exercises 57–58, suppose that P dollars in principal is invested for t years at the given interest rates with continuous compounding. Determine the amount that the investment is worth at the end of the given time period.

57. $P = \$20{,}000$, $t = 10$ yr

    a. 3% interest

    b. 4% interest

    c. 5.5% interest

58. $P = \$6000$, $t = 12$ yr

    a. 1% interest

    b. 2% interest

    c. 4.5% interest

59. Bethany needs to borrow $10,000. She can borrow the money at 5.5% simple interest for 4 yr or she can borrow at 5% with interest compounded continuously for 4 yr.

    a. How much total interest would Bethany pay at 5.5% simple interest?

    b. How much total interest would Bethany pay at 5% interest compounded continuously?

    c. Which option results in less total interest?

60. Al needs to borrow $15,000 to buy a car. He can borrow the money at 6.7% simple interest for 5 yr or he can borrow at 6.4% interest compounded continuously for 5 yr.

    a. How much total interest would Al pay at 6.7% simple interest?

    b. How much total interest would Al pay at 6.4% interest compounded continuously?

    c. Which option results in less total interest?

61. Jerome wants to invest $25,000 as part of his retirement plan. He can invest the money at 5.2% simple interest for 30 yr, or he can invest at 3.8% interest compounded continuously for 30 yr. Which option results in more total interest?

62. Heather wants to invest $35,000 of her retirement. She can invest at 4.8% simple interest for 20 yr, or she can choose an option with 3.6% interest compounded continuously for 20 yr. Which option results in more total interest?

Objective 4: Use Exponential Functions in Applications

63. Strontium-90 (^{90}Sr) is a by-product of nuclear fission with a half-life of approximately 28.9 yr. After the Chernobyl nuclear reactor accident in 1986, large areas surrounding the site were contaminated with ^{90}Sr. If 10 μg (micrograms) of ^{90}Sr is present in a sample, the function $A(t) = 10\left(\dfrac{1}{2}\right)^{t/28.9}$ gives the amount $A(t)$ (in μg) present after t years. Evaluate the function for the given values of t and interpret the meaning in context. Round to 3 decimal places. (**See Example 5**)

    a. $A(28.9)$ **b.** $A(57.8)$ **c.** $A(100)$

64. In 2006, the murder of Alexander Litvinenko, a Russian dissident, was thought to be by poisoning from the rare and highly radioactive element polonium-210 (^{210}Po). The half-life of ^{210}Po is 138.4 yr. If 0.1 mg of ^{210}Po is present in a sample then $A(t) = 0.1\left(\dfrac{1}{2}\right)^{t/138.4}$ gives the amount $A(t)$ (in mg) present after t years. Evaluate the function for the given values of t and interpret the meaning in context. Round to 3 decimal places.

    a. $A(138.4)$ **b.** $A(276.8)$ **c.** $A(500)$

65. According to the CIA's *World Fact Book*, in 2010, the population of the United States was approximately 310 million with a 0.97% annual growth rate. (*Source:* www.cia.gov) At this rate, the population $P(t)$ (in millions) can be approximated by $P(t) = 310(1.0097)^t$, where t is the time in years since 2010.

    a. Is the graph of P an increasing or decreasing exponential function?

    b. Evaluate $P(0)$ and interpret its meaning in the context of this problem.

    c. Evaluate $P(10)$ and interpret its meaning in the context of this problem. Round the population value to the nearest million.

    d. Evaluate $P(20)$ and $P(30)$.

    e. Evaluate $P(200)$ and use this result to determine if it is reasonable to expect this model to continue indefinitely.

66. The population of Canada in 2010 was approximately 34 million with an annual growth rate of 0.804%. At this rate, the population $P(t)$ (in millions) can be approximated by $P(t) = 34(1.00804)^t$, where t is the time in years since 2010. (*Source:* www.cia.gov)

    a. Is the graph of P an increasing or decreasing exponential function?

    b. Evaluate $P(0)$ and interpret its meaning in the context of this problem.

    c. Evaluate $P(5)$ and interpret its meaning in the context of this problem. Round the population value to the nearest million.

    d. Evaluate $P(15)$, $P(25)$, and $P(200)$.

67. The atmospheric pressure on an object decreases as altitude increases. If a is the height (in km) above sea level, then the pressure $P(a)$ (in mmHg) is approximated by $P(a) = 760e^{-0.13a}$.

a. Find the atmospheric pressure at sea level.

b. Determine the atmospheric pressure at 8.848 km (the altitude of Mt. Everest). Round to the nearest whole unit.

68. The function defined by $A(t) = 100e^{0.0318t}$ approximates the equivalent amount of money needed t years after the year 2010 to equal $100 of buying power in the year 2010. The value 0.0318 is related to the average rate of inflation.

a. Evaluate $A(15)$ and interpret its meaning in the context of this problem.

b. Verify that by the year 2032, more than $200 will be needed to have the same buying power as $100 in 2010.

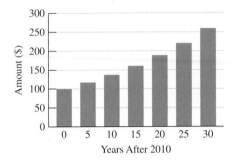

Newton's law of cooling indicates that the temperature of a warm object, such as a cake coming out of the oven, will decrease exponentially with time and will approach the temperature of the surrounding air. The temperature $T(t)$ is modeled by $T(t) = T_a + (T_0 - T_a)e^{-kt}$. In this model, T_a represents the temperature of the surrounding air, T_0 represents the initial temperature of the object, and t is the time after the object starts cooling. The value of k is the cooling rate and is a constant related to the physical properties of the object. Use this model for Exercises 69–70.

69. A cake comes out of the oven at 350°F and is placed on a cooling rack in a 78°F kitchen. After checking the temperature several minutes later, it is determined that the cooling rate k is 0.046.

a. Write a function that models the temperature $T(t)$ (in °F) of the cake t minutes after being removed from the oven.

b. What is the temperature of the cake 10 min after coming out of the oven? Round to the nearest degree.

c. It is recommended that the cake should not be frosted until it has cooled to under 100°F. If Jessica waits 1 hr to frost the cake, will the cake be cool enough to frost?

70. Water in a water heater is originally 122°F. The water heater is shut off and the water cools to the temperature of the surrounding air, which is 60°F. The water cools slowly because of the insulation inside the heater, and the rate of cooling is 0.00351.

a. Write a function that models the temperature $T(t)$ (in °F) of the water t hours after the water heater is shut off.

b. What is the temperature of the water 12 hr after the heater is shut off? Round to the nearest degree.

c. Dominic does not like to shower with water less than 115°F. If Dominic waits 24 hr, will the water still be warm enough for a shower?

71. A farmer depreciates a $120,000 tractor. He estimates that the resale value $V(t)$ (in $1000) of the tractor t years after purchase is 80% of its value from the previous year. Therefore, the resale value can be approximated by $V(t) = 120(0.8)^t$.

a. Find the resale value 5 yr after purchase. Round to the nearest $1000.

b. The farmer estimates that the cost to run the tractor is $18/hr in labor, $36/hr in fuel, and $22/hr in overhead costs (for maintenance and repair). Estimate the farmer's cost to run the tractor for the first year if he runs the tractor for a total of 800 hr. Include hourly costs and depreciation.

72. A veterinarian depreciates a $10,000 X-ray machine. He estimates that the resale value $V(t)$ (in $) after t years is 90% of its value from the previous year. Therefore, the resale value can be approximated by $V(t) = 10,000(0.9)^t$.

a. Find the resale value after 4 yr.

b. If the veterinarian wants to sell his practice 8 yr after the X-ray machine was purchased, how much is the machine worth? Round to the nearest $100.

73. A multiple-choice test has four choices for each question and only one correct answer. The probability that a student guesses correctly on an individual question is $\frac{1}{4}$. In practice, this means that over the long run, with repeated guesses on different questions, a student would guess correctly approximately 25% of the time. If a test has x questions, then the probability $P(x)$ that a student will guess correctly on all questions is given by $P(x) = \left(\frac{1}{4}\right)^x$.

a. Evaluate $P(2)$, $P(3)$, $P(4)$, and $P(5)$.

b. Does the probability of guessing correctly on all x questions increase or decrease as more questions are added to the test?

c. The probability of an event is a number between 0 and 1, inclusive. Values closer to 1 represent a greater likelihood that the event will occur, and values closer to 0 represent a lesser likelihood. Would it be likely or unlikely for a student to guess correctly on all questions if the test had 10 questions?

74. If a fair coin is tossed, the probability that the coin will land on "tails" is $\frac{1}{2}$. If a fair coin is flipped x times, then the probability $P(x)$ that it will land on "tails" x times in a row is given by $P(x) = \left(\frac{1}{2}\right)^x$.

a. Evaluate $P(2)$, $P(3)$, $P(4)$, and $P(10)$.

b. Based on the answer from part (a), is it likely or unlikely to flip a fair coin and get "tails" 10 times in a row?

Mixed Exercises

For Exercises 75–76, solve the equations in parts (a)–(c) by inspection. Then estimate the solutions to parts (d) and (e) between two consecutive integers.

75. a. $2^x = 4$

    b. $2^x = 8$

    c. $2^x = 16$

    d. $2^x = 7$

    e. $2^x = 10$

76. a. $3^x = 3$

    b. $3^x = 9$

    c. $3^x = 27$

    d. $3^x = 7$

    e. $3^x = 10$

77. a. Graph $f(x) = 2^x$. (**See Example 1**)

    b. Is f a one-to-one function?

    c. Write the domain and range of f in interval notation.

    d. Graph f^{-1} on the same coordinate system as f.

    e. Write the domain and range of f^{-1} in interval notation.

    f. From the graph evaluate $f^{-1}(1)$, $f^{-1}(2)$, and $f^{-1}(4)$.

78. a. Graph $g(x) = 3^x$ (see Exercise 25).

    b. Is g a one-to-one function?

    c. Write the domain and range of g in interval notation.

    d. Graph g^{-1} on the same coordinate system as g.

    e. Write the domain and range of g^{-1} in interval notation.

    f. From the graph evaluate $g^{-1}(1)$, $g^{-1}(3)$, and $g^{-1}\left(\frac{1}{3}\right)$.

79. Refer back to the graphs of $f(x) = 2^x$ and the inverse function, $y = f^{-1}(x)$ from Exercise 77. Fill in the blanks.

    a. As $x \to \infty$, $f(x) \to$ _____.

    b. As $x \to -\infty$, $f(x) \to$ _____.

    c. As $x \to \infty$, $f^{-1}(x) \to$ _____.

    d. As $x \to 0^+$, $f^{-1}(x) \to$ _____.

80. Refer back to the graphs of $g(x) = 3^x$ and the inverse function, $y = g^{-1}(x)$ from Exercise 78. Fill in the blanks.

    a. As $x \to \infty$, $g(x) \to$ _____.

    b. As $x \to -\infty$, $g(x) \to$ _____.

    c. As $x \to \infty$, $g^{-1}(x) \to$ _____.

    d. As $x \to 0^+$, $g^{-1}(x) \to$ _____.

Write About It

81. Explain why the equation $2^x = -2$ has no solution.

82. Explain why the $f(x) = x^2$ is not an exponential function.

Expanding Your Skills

An exponential function $y = b^x$ with base $b > 1$ increases over its domain. An exponential function with base $0 < b < 1$ decreases over its domain. However, in both cases, the rate of increase or decrease changes with increasing values of x. For Exercises 83–86, demonstrate this statement by finding the average rate of change on each interval $[a, b]$. Round to 4 decimal places where necessary. Recall that for $y = f(x)$, the average rate of change on $[a, b]$ is $\dfrac{f(b) - f(a)}{b - a}$.

83. $f(x) = 2^x$

    a. $[-2, 0]$

    b. $[0, 2]$

    c. $[2, 4]$

    d. $[4, 6]$

X	Y1
-4	.0625
-2	.25
0	1
2	4
4	16
6	64
8	256

X= -4

84. $f(x) = 3^x$

    a. $[-2, 0]$

    b. $[0, 2]$

    c. $[2, 4]$

    d. $[4, 6]$

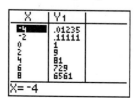

X	Y1
-4	.01235
-2	.11111
0	1
2	9
4	81
6	729
8	6561

X= -4

85. $f(x) = \left(\dfrac{1}{2}\right)^x$

X	Y1
-4	16
-2	4
0	1
2	.25
4	.0625
6	.01563
8	.00391

X= -4

  a. $[-2, 0]$
  b. $[0, 2]$
  c. $[2, 4]$
  d. $[4, 6]$

86. $f(x) = \left(\dfrac{1}{3}\right)^x$

X	Y1
-4	81
-2	9
0	1
2	.11111
4	.01235
6	.00137
8	1.5E-4

X= -4

  a. $[-2, 0]$
  b. $[0, 2]$
  c. $[2, 4]$
  d. $[4, 6]$

For Exercises 87–88, find the real solutions to the equation.

87. $3x^2 e^{-x} - 6xe^{-x} = 0$

88. $x^2 e^x - e^x = 0$

89. Use the properties of exponents to simplify.

  a. $e^x e^h$ b. $(e^x)^2$ c. $\dfrac{e^x}{e^h}$

  d. $e^x \cdot e^{-x}$ e. e^{-2x}

90. Factor.

  a. $e^{x+h} - e^x$
  b. $e^{4x} - e^{2x}$

91. Multiply. $(e^x + e^{-x})^2$

92. Multiply. $(e^x - e^{-x})^2$

93. Show that $\left(\dfrac{e^x + e^{-x}}{2}\right)^2 - \left(\dfrac{e^x - e^{-x}}{2}\right)^2 = 1$.

94. Show that $2\left(\dfrac{e^x - e^{-x}}{2}\right)\left(\dfrac{e^x + e^{-x}}{2}\right) = \dfrac{e^{2x} - e^{-2x}}{2}$.

For Exercises 95–96, find the difference quotient $\dfrac{f(x + h) - f(x)}{h}$. **Write the answers in factored form.**

95. $f(x) = e^x$

96. $f(x) = 2^x$

Technology Connections

97. Graph the following functions on the window $[-3, 3, 1]$ by $[-1, 8, 1]$ and comment on the behavior of the graphs near $x = 0$.

$Y_1 = e^x$

$Y_2 = 1 + x + \dfrac{x^2}{2}$

$Y_3 = 1 + x + \dfrac{x^2}{2} + \dfrac{x^3}{6}$

SECTION 4.3   Logarithmic Functions

OBJECTIVES

1. Convert Between Logarithmic and Exponential Forms
2. Evaluate Logarithmic Expressions
3. Apply Basic Properties of Logarithms
4. Graph Logarithmic Functions
5. Use Logarithmic Functions in Applications

1. Convert Between Logarithmic and Exponential Forms

Consider the following equations in which the variable is located in the exponent of an expression. In some cases, the solution can be found by inspection.

Equation	Solution
$5^x = 5$	$x = 1$
$5^x = 20$	$x = ?$
$5^x = 25$	$x = 2$
$5^x = 60$	$x = ?$
$5^x = 125$	$x = 3$

The equation $5^x = 20$ cannot be solved by inspection. However, we suspect that x is between 1 and 2 because $5^1 = 5$ and $5^2 = 25$. To solve for x explicitly, we must isolate x by performing the inverse operation of 5^x. Fortunately, all exponential functions $y = b^x$ ($b > 0$, $b \neq 1$) are one-to-one and have inverse functions. The inverse of an exponential function, base b, is the *logarithmic* function base b which we define here.

Definition of a Logarithmic Function

If x and b are positive real numbers such that $b \neq 1$, then $y = \log_b x$ is called the **logarithmic function base b** where

$$y = \log_b x \text{ is equivalent to } b^y = x$$

Notes:

- Given $y = \log_b x$, the value y is the exponent to which b must be raised to obtain x.
- The value of y is called the **logarithm**, b is called the **base**, and x is called the **argument.**
- The expressions $y = \log_b x$ and $b^y = x$ both define the same relationship between x and y. The expression $y = \log_b x$ is called the **logarithmic form,** and $b^y = x$ is called the **exponential form.**

The logarithmic function base b is defined as the inverse of the exponential function base b.

exponential function	$f(x) = b^x$	First replace $f(x)$ by y.
	$y = b^x$	Next, interchange x and y.
inverse of exponential function	$x = b^y$	$\longleftarrow$ This equation provides an implicit relationship between x and y. To solve for y explicitly (that is, to isolate y), we must use logarithmic notation.
	$y = \log_b x$	
logarithmic function		

To be able to solve equations involving logarithms, it is often advantageous to write a logarithmic expression in its exponential form.

EXAMPLE 1   Writing Logarithmic Form and Exponential Form

Write each equation in exponential form.

a. $\log_2 16 = 4$ **b.** $\log_{10}\left(\dfrac{1}{100}\right) = -2$ **c.** $\log_7 1 = 0$

Solution:

Logarithmic form $y = \log_b x$ **Exponential form $b^y = x$**

The logarithm is the exponent to which the base is raised to obtain x.

a. $\log_2 16 = 4$ $\Leftrightarrow$ $2^4 = 16$

b. $\log_{10}\left(\dfrac{1}{100}\right) = -2$ $\Leftrightarrow$ $10^{-2} = \dfrac{1}{100}$

c. $\log_7 1 = 0$ $\Leftrightarrow$ $7^0 = 1$

Skill Practice 1   Write each equation in exponential form.

a. $\log_3 9 = 2$ **b.** $\log_{10}\left(\dfrac{1}{1000}\right) = -3$ **c.** $\log_6 1 = 0$

In Example 2 we reverse this process and write an exponential equation in its logarithmic form.

Answers

1. a. $3^2 = 9$ **b.** $10^{-3} = \dfrac{1}{1000}$

c. $6^0 = 1$

| EXAMPLE 2 | Writing Exponential Form and Logarithmic Form |

Write each equation in logarithmic form.

a. $3^4 = 81$ **b.** $10^6 = 1,000,000$ **c.** $\left(\dfrac{1}{5}\right)^{-1} = 5$

Solution:

Exponential form $b^y = x$ **Logarithmic form** $y = \log_b x$

$\boxed{\text{logarithm}}$

a. $3^4 = 81$ $\Leftrightarrow$ $\log_3 81 = 4$

$\boxed{\text{base}}$ $\boxed{\text{argument}}$

b. $10^6 = 1,000,000$ $\Leftrightarrow$ $\log_{10} 1,000,000 = 6$

c. $\left(\dfrac{1}{5}\right)^{-1} = 5$ $\Leftrightarrow$ $\log_{1/5} 5 = -1$

Skill Practice 2   Write each equation in logarithmic form.

a. $2^5 = 32$ **b.** $10^4 = 10,000$ **c.** $\left(\dfrac{1}{8}\right)^{-2} = 64$

---

2. Evaluate Logarithmic Expressions

In Example 3, we evaluate several logarithmic expressions.

| EXAMPLE 3 | Evaluating a Logarithmic Expression |

Evaluate each expression.

a. $\log_4 16$ **b.** $\log_2 8$ **c.** $\log_{1/2} 8$

Solution:

a. $\log_4 16$ is the exponent to which 4 must be raised to equal 16. That is, $4^{\square} = 16$.

$\log_4 16 = y$ Let y represent the value of the logarithm.

    $4^y = 16$ or equivalently $4^y = 4^2$ Write the equivalent exponential form.

    $y = 2$

Therefore, $\log_4 16 = 2$.   Check: $4^2 = 16$ ✓

TIP Once you become comfortable with the concept of a logarithm, you can take fewer steps to evaluate a logarithm.

To evaluate the expression $\log_4 16$ we ask $4^{\square} = 16$. The exponent is 2, so $\log_4 16 = 2$.

Likewise, to evaluate $\log_2 8$ we ask $2^{\square} = 8$. So $\log_2 8 = 3$.

b. $\log_2 8$ is the exponent to which 2 must be raised to obtain 8. That is, $2^{\square} = 8$.

$\log_2 8 = y$ Let y represent the value of the logarithm.

    $2^y = 8$ or equivalently $2^y = 2^3$ Write the equivalent exponential form.

    $y = 3$

Therefore, $\log_2 8 = 3$.   Check: $2^3 = 8$ ✓

c. $\log_{1/2} 8 = y$ Let y represent the value of the logarithm. Then,

    $\left(\dfrac{1}{2}\right)^y = 8$ or equivalently $\left(\dfrac{1}{2}\right)^y = \left(\dfrac{1}{2}\right)^{-3}$ Write the equivalent exponential form.

    $y = -3$

Therefore, $\log_{1/2} 8 = -3$.   Check: $\left(\dfrac{1}{2}\right)^{-3} = 8$ ✓

Answers

2. a. $\log_2 32 = 5$
   b. $\log_{10} 10,000 = 4$
   c. $\log_{1/8} 64 = -2$

Skill Practice 3 Evaluate each expression.

a. $\log_5 125$ **b.** $\log_3 81$ **c.** $\log_4\left(\dfrac{1}{64}\right)$

The statement $y = \log_b x$ represents a family of logarithmic functions where the base is any positive real number except 1. Two specific logarithmic functions that come up often in applications are the logarithmic functions base 10 and base e.

> **TIP** To help you remember the notation $y = \ln x$, think of "ln" as "log natural."

Definition of Common and Natural Logarithmic Functions

- The logarithmic function base 10 is called the **common logarithmic function.** The common logarithmic function is denoted by $y = \log x$. Notice that the base 10 is not explicitly written; that is, $y = \log_{10} x$ is written simply as $y = \log x$.
- The logarithmic function base e is called the **natural logarithmic function.** The natural logarithmic function is denoted by $y = \ln x$; that is, $y = \log_e x$ is written as $y = \ln x$.

EXAMPLE 4 **Evaluating Common and Natural Logarithms**

Evaluate.

a. $\log 100{,}000$ **b.** $\log 0.001$ **c.** $\ln e^4$ **d.** $\ln\left(\dfrac{1}{e}\right)$

Solution:

Let y represent the value of the logarithm.

a. $\log 100{,}000 = y$

$10^y = 100{,}000$ or equivalently $10^y = 10^5$ Write the exponential form.

$y = 5$

Thus, $\log 100{,}000 = 5$ because $10^5 = 100{,}000$.

b. $\log 0.001 = y$

$10^y = 0.001$ or equivalently $10^y = 10^{-3}$ Write the exponential form.

$y = -3$

Thus, $\log 0.001 = -3$ because $10^{-3} = 0.001$.

> **TIP** In Example 4, to evaluate:
> **a.** $\log 100{,}000$ we ask $10^{\square} = 100{,}000$.
> **b.** $\log 0.001$ we ask $10^{\square} = 0.001$.
> **c.** $\ln e^4$ we ask $e^{\square} = e^4$.
> **d.** $\ln\left(\dfrac{1}{e}\right)$ we ask $e^{\square} = e^{-1}$

c. $\ln e^4 = y$

$e^y = e^4$ Write the equivalent exponential form.

$y = 4$

Therefore, $\ln e^4 = 4$.

d. $\ln\left(\dfrac{1}{e}\right) = y$

$e^y = \left(\dfrac{1}{e}\right)$ or equivalently $e^y = e^{-1}$ Write the equivalent exponential form.

$y = -1$

Therefore, $\ln\left(\dfrac{1}{e}\right) = -1$.

Answers

3. a. 3   **b.** 4   **c.** -3

4. a. 7   **b.** -1 **c.** 5   **d.** 1

Skill Practice 4 Evaluate.

a. $\log 10{,}000{,}000$ **b.** $\log 0.1$ **c.** $\ln e^5$ **d.** $\ln e$

Most scientific calculators have a key for the common logarithmic function **LOG** and a key for the natural logarithmic function **LN**. We demonstrate their use in Example 5.

EXAMPLE 5   **Approximating Common and Natural Logarithms**

Approximate the logarithms. Round to 4 decimal places.

a. $\log 5809$ **b.** $\log(4.6 \times 10^7)$ **c.** $\log 0.003$

d. $\ln 472$ **e.** $\ln 0.05$ **f.** $\ln \sqrt{87}$

Solution:

For parts (a)−(c), use the **LOG** key.   For parts (d)−(f), use the **LN** key.

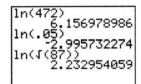

```
log(5809)
          3.764101376
log(4.6E7)
          7.662757832
log(.003)
         -2.522878745
```

```
ln(472)
          6.156978986
ln(.05)
         -2.995732274
ln(√(87))
          2.232954059
```

When using a calculator, there is always potential for user-input error. Therefore, it is good practice to estimate values when possible to confirm the reasonableness of an answer from a calculator. For example,

For part (a), $10^3 < 5809 < 10^4$. Therefore, $3 < \log 5809 < 4$.

For part (b), $10^7 < 4.6 \times 10^7 < 10^8$. Therefore, $7 < \log(4.6 \times 10^7) < 8$.

For part (c), $10^{-3} < 0.003 < 10^{-2}$. Therefore, $-3 < \log 0.003 < -2$.

Skill Practice 5   Approximate the logarithms. Round to 4 decimal places.

a. $\log 229$ **b.** $\log(3.76 \times 10^{12})$ **c.** $\log 0.0216$

d. $\ln 87$ **e.** $\ln 0.0032$ **f.** $\ln \pi$

---

3. Apply Basic Properties of Logarithms

From the definition of a logarithmic function, we have the following basic properties.

Basic Properties of Logarithms	
Property	**Example**
1. $\log_b 1 = 0$ because $b^0 = 1$	$\log_5 1 = 0$ because $5^0 = 1$
2. $\log_b b = 1$ because $b^1 = b$	$\log_3 3 = 1$ because $3^1 = 3$
3. $\log_b b^x = x$ because $b^x = b^x$	$\log_2 2^x = x$ because $2^x = 2^x$
4. $b^{\log_b x} = x$ because $\log_b x = \log_b x$	$7^{\log_7 x} = x$ because $\log_7 x = \log_7 x$

TIP There are an infinite number of logarithmic functions. The calculator has keys for the base 10 and base e logarithmic functions only.

To approximate a logarithm of different base, we need to use the change-of-base theorem presented in Section 4.4.

Properties 3 and 4 follow from the fact that a logarithmic function is the inverse of an exponential function of the same base. Given $f(x) = b^x$ and $f^{-1}(x) = \log_b x$,

$$(f \circ f^{-1})(x) = b^{(\log_b x)} = x \qquad \text{(Property 4)}$$
$$(f^{-1} \circ f)(x) = \log_b(b^x) = x \qquad \text{(Property 3)}$$

EXAMPLE 6   Applying the Properties of Logarithms

Simplify.

a. $\log_3 3^{10}$ **b.** $\ln e^2$ **c.** $\log_{11} 11$ **d.** $\log 10$

e. $\log_{\sqrt 7} 1$ **f.** $\ln 1$ **g.** $5^{\log_5(c^2+4)}$ **h.** $10^{\log(a^2+b^2)}$

Solution:

a. $\log_3 3^{10} = 10$ Property 3   **b.** $\ln e^2 = \log_e e^2 = 2$ Property 3

c. $\log_{11} 11 = 1$ Property 2   **d.** $\log 10 = \log_{10} 10 = 1$ Property 2

e. $\log_{\sqrt 7} 1 = 0$ Property 1   **f.** $\ln 1 = 0$ Property 1

g. $5^{\log_5(c^2+4)} = c^2 + 4$ Property 4   **h.** $10^{\log(a^2+b^2)} = a^2 + b^2$ Property 4

Skill Practice 6   Simplify.

a. $\log_{13} 13$ **b.** $\ln e$ **c.** $a^{\log_a 3}$ **d.** $e^{\ln 6}$

e. $\log_\pi 1$ **f.** $\log 1$ **g.** $\log_9 9^{\sqrt 2}$ **h.** $\log 10^e$

4. Graph Logarithmic Functions

Since a logarithmic function $y = \log_b x$ is the inverse of the corresponding exponential function $y = b^x$, their graphs must be symmetric with respect to the line $y = x$. See Figures 4-10 and 4-11.

Figure 4-10

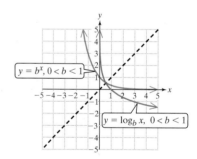

Figure 4-11

From Figures 4-10 and 4-11, the range of $y = b^x$ is the set of positive real numbers. As expected, the domain of its inverse function $y = \log_b x$ is the set of positive real numbers.

Answers

6. a. 1   **b.** 1   **c.** 3   **d.** 6

      e. 0   **f.** 0   **g.** $\sqrt 2$ **h.** e

EXAMPLE 7 **Graphing Logarithmic Functions**

Graph the functions.

a. $y = \log_2 x$ **b.** $y = \log_{1/4} x$

Solution:

To find points on a logarithmic function, we can interchange the x- and y-coordinates of the ordered pairs on the corresponding exponential function.

a. To graph $y = \log_2 x$, interchange the x- and y-coordinates of the ordered pairs from its inverse function $y = 2^x$. The graph of $y = \log_2 x$ is shown in Figure 4-12.

Exponential Function   **Logarithmic Function**

x	$y = 2^x$
-3	$\frac{1}{8}$
-2	$\frac{1}{4}$
-1	$\frac{1}{2}$
0	1
1	2
2	4
3	8

x	$y = \log_2 x$
$\frac{1}{8}$	-3
$\frac{1}{4}$	-2
$\frac{1}{2}$	-1
1	0
2	1
4	2
8	3

Switch x and y.

Figure 4-12

b. To graph $y = \log_{1/4} x$, interchange the x- and y-coordinates of the ordered pairs from its inverse function $y = \left(\frac{1}{4}\right)^x$. See Figure 4-13.

Exponential Function   **Logarithmic Function**

x	$y = \left(\dfrac{1}{4}\right)^x$
-3	64
-2	16
-1	4
0	1
1	$\frac{1}{4}$
2	$\frac{1}{16}$
3	$\frac{1}{64}$

x	$y = \log_{1/4} x$
64	-3
16	-2
4	-1
1	0
$\frac{1}{4}$	1
$\frac{1}{16}$	2
$\frac{1}{64}$	3

Switch x and y.

Figure 4-13

Answers

7. a.

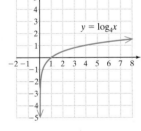

b.

Skill Practice 7 Graph the functions.

a. $y = \log_4 x$ **b.** $y = \log_{1/2} x$

Based on the graphs in Example 7 and our knowledge of exponential functions, we offer the following summary of the characteristics of logarithmic and exponential functions.

Graphs of Exponential and Logarithmic Functions

Exponential Functions	Logarithmic Functions

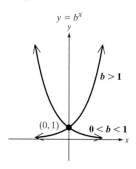

Exponential Functions

Domain: $(-\infty, \infty)$
Range: $(0, \infty)$
Horizontal asymptote: $y = 0$
Passes through $(0, 1)$
If $b > 1$, the function is increasing.
If $0 < b < 1$, the function is decreasing.

Logarithmic Functions

Domain: $(0, \infty)$
Range: $(-\infty, \infty)$
Vertical asymptote: $x = 0$
Passes through $(1, 0)$
If $b > 1$, the function is increasing.
If $0 < b < 1$, the function is decreasing.

The roles of x and y are reversed between a function and its inverse. Therefore, it is not surprising that the domain and range are reversed between exponential and logarithmic functions. Furthermore, an exponential function passes through $(0, 1)$, whereas a logarithmic function passes through $(1, 0)$. An exponential function has a horizontal asymptote of $y = 0$, whereas a logarithmic function has a vertical asymptote of $x = 0$.

In Example 8 we use the transformations of functions learned in Section 2.6 to graph a logarithmic function.

If $h > 0$, shift to the right.
If $h < 0$, shift to the left.

If $k > 0$, shift upward.
If $k < 0$, shift downward.

$$f(x) = a \log_b(x - h) + k$$

If $a < 0$, reflect across the x-axis.
Shrink vertically if $0 < |a| < 1$.
Stretch vertically if $|a| > 1$.

EXAMPLE 8   Using Transformations to Graph Logarithmic Functions

Graph the function. Identify the vertical asymptote and write the domain in interval notation.

$$f(x) = \log_2(x + 3) - 2$$

Solution:

The graph of the "parent" function $y = \log_2 x$ was presented in Example 7. The graph of $f(x) = \log_2(x + 3) - 2$ is the graph of $y = \log_2 x$ shifted to the left 3 units and down 2 units.

We can plot a few points on the graph of $y = \log_2 x$ and use these points and the vertical asymptote to form an outline of the transformed graph.

x	$y = \log_2 x$
$\frac{1}{4}$	-2
$\frac{1}{2}$	-1
1	0
2	1
4	2

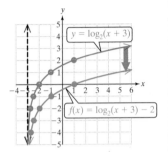

The graph of $f(x) = \log_2(x + 3) - 2$ is shown in blue.
The vertical asymptote is $x = -3$. The domain is $(-3, \infty)$.

Skill Practice 8 Graph the function. Identify the vertical asymptote and write the domain in interval notation. $g(x) = \log_3(x - 4) + 1$

The domain of $f(x) = \log_b x$ is restricted to $x > 0$. In Example 8, this graph was shifted to the left 3 units, restricting the domain of $f(x) = \log_2(x + 3) - 2$ to $x > -3$. The domain of a logarithmic function is the set of real numbers that make the argument positive.

EXAMPLE 9 Identifying the Domain of a Logarithmic Function

Write the domain in interval notation.

a. $f(x) = \log_2(2x + 4)$ **b.** $g(x) = \ln(5 - x)$

Solution:

a. $f(x) = \log_2(2x + 4)$

$\begin{aligned}
2x + 4 &> 0 &&\text{Set the argument greater than zero.}\\
2x &> -4 &&\text{Solve for } x.\\
x &> -2
\end{aligned}$

The domain is $(-2, \infty)$.
The graph of f is shown in Figure 4-14.

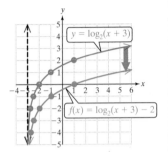

Figure 4-14

b. $g(x) = \ln(5 - x)$

$\begin{aligned}
5 - x &> 0 &&\text{Set the argument greater than zero.}\\
-x &> -5 &&\text{Subtract 5 and divide by } -1\\
x &< 5 &&\text{(reverse the inequality sign).}
\end{aligned}$

The domain is $(-\infty, 5)$.
The graph of g is shown in Figure 4-15.
The vertical asymptote is $x = 5$.

Figure 4-15

Skill Practice 9 Write the domain in interval notation.

a. $\log_4(1 - 3x)$ **b.** $\log(2 + x)$

Avoiding Mistakes

On a graphing utility, the graph of a logarithmic function may look like it terminates near the vertical asymptote. See Example 9(b). This is due to limited resolution. The graph actually approaches $-\infty$ as x approaches 5 from the left.

Answers
8. Vertical asymptote: $x = 4$
Domain: $(4, \infty)$

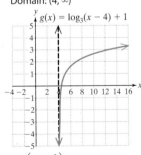

9. a. $\left(-\infty, \dfrac{1}{3}\right)$ **b.** $(-2, \infty)$

5. Use Logarithmic Functions in Applications

When physical quantities vary over a large range, it is often convenient to take a logarithm of the quantity to have a more manageable set of numbers. For example, suppose a set of data values consists of 10, 100, 1000, and 10,000. The corresponding common logarithms are 1, 2, 3, and 4. The latter list of numbers is easier to manipulate and to visualize on a graph.

For this reason, logarithmic scales are used in applications such as

- Measuring acidity on the pH scale.
- Measuring the wave energy from an earthquake.
- Measuring the loudness of sound on the decibel scale.
- Measuring the intensity of light or other electromagnetic radiation.

In 1935, American geologist Charles Richter developed the local magnitude (M_L) scale, or Richter scale, for moderate-sized earthquakes ($3 < M_L < 7$). In Example 10, we use the Richter scale to compare the magnitudes of two earthquakes.

EXAMPLE 10   **Using a Logarithmic Function in an Application**

The intensity I of an earthquake is measured by a seismograph—a device that measures amplitudes of shock waves. I_0 is a minimum reference intensity of a "zero-level" earthquake against which the intensities of other earthquakes may be compared. The local magnitude M_L (on the Richter scale) of an earthquake of intensity I is given by $M_L = \log\left(\dfrac{I}{I_0}\right)$.

a. Determine the local magnitude of the earthquake that devastated Haiti on January 12, 2010, if the intensity was approximately $10^{7.0}$ times I_0.

b. Determine the local magnitude of the earthquake that occurred near Washington, D.C., on August 23, 2011, if the intensity was approximately $10^{5.8}$ times I_0.

c. How many times more intense was the earthquake that hit Haiti than the earthquake that hit Washington, D.C.? Round to the nearest whole unit.

Solution:

a. $M = \log\left(\dfrac{I}{I_0}\right)$ **b.** $M = \log\left(\dfrac{I}{I_0}\right)$

$\quad M = \log\left(\dfrac{10^{7.0} \cdot I_0}{I_0}\right)$ $\quad M = \log\left(\dfrac{10^{5.8} \cdot I_0}{I_0}\right)$

$\qquad = \log 10^{7.0}$ $\qquad = \log 10^{5.8}$

$\qquad = 7.0$ $\qquad = 5.8$

c. Using the intensities given in parts (a) and (b) we have

$$\frac{10^{7.0} I_0}{10^{5.8} I_0} = 10^{7.0-5.8} = 10^{1.2} \approx 16$$

The earthquake in Haiti was approximately 16 times more intense.

Skill Practice 10

a. Determine the magnitude of an earthquake that is $10^{5.2}$ times I_0.

b. Determine the magnitude of an earthquake that is $10^{4.2}$ times I_0.

c. How many times more intense is a 5.2-magnitude earthquake than a 4.2-magnitude earthquake?

Point of Interest

The formal and methodical use of logarithms is attributed to Scottish mathematician John Napier (1550–1617). In addition, Napier is credited with the first systematic use of the decimal point and for the construction of "Napier's Bones," a set of rods (made of wood or bone) used to compute products and quotients based on principles of logarithms.

Answers

10. a. 5.2   **b.** 4.2

   c. 10 times more intense

The Richter scale is a logarithmic scale base 10. Therefore, a 1-unit increase in the magnitude of an earthquake results in an intensity 10^1 times as great. A 2-unit increase in magnitude results in an intensity 10^2 times as great. From Example 10, the earthquake in Haiti (magnitude 7.0) and the earthquake in Washington, D.C. (magnitude 5.8), differed in magnitude by 1.2 units. Therefore, the intensity differed by $10^{1.2}$ times.

SECTION 4.3   Practice Exercises

Review Exercises

For Exercises 1–2, write an equation for the inverse function.

1. $f(x) = \sqrt[3]{x - 4}$

2. $g(x) = 2x - 7$

For Exercises 3–6, fill in the blank to make a true statement.

3. $3^{\square} = 81$

4. $2^{\square} = 8$

5. $6^{\square} = \dfrac{1}{36}$

6. $4^{\square} = \dfrac{1}{64}$

Concept Connections

7. Given positive real numbers x and b such that $b \neq 1$, $y = \log_b x$ is the _____ function base b and is equivalent to $b^y = x$.

8. Given $y = \log_b x$, the value y is called the _____, b is called the _____, and x is called the _____.

9. $y = \log_b x$ is called the logarithmic form of a logarithmic equation and $b^y = x$ is called the _____ form.

10. The inverse of an exponential function base b is the _____ function base b.

11. The logarithmic function base 10 is called the _____ logarithmic function, and the logarithmic function base e is called the _____ logarithmic function.

12. Given $y = \log x$, the base is understood to be _____. Given $y = \ln x$, the base is understood to be _____.

13. $\log_b 1 = $ _____ because $b^{\square} = 1$.

14. $\log_b b = $ _____ because $b^{\square} = b$.

15. $f(x) = \log_b x$ and $g(x) = b^x$ are inverse functions. Therefore, $\log_b b^x = $ _____ and $b^{\log_b x} = $ _____.

16. Given $y = \log_b x$, if $b > 1$, then the graph of the function is a(n) (increasing/decreasing) logarithmic function. If $0 < b < 1$, then the graph is (increasing/decreasing).

17. The graph of $y = \log_b x$ passes through the point $(1, 0)$ and the line _____ is a (horizontal/vertical) asymptote.

18. The graph of $f(x) = \log_4(x + 6) - 8$ is the graph of $y = \log_4 x$ shifted 6 units (left/right/upward/downward) and shifted 8 units (left/right/upward/downward).

For the exercises in this set, assume that all variable expressions represent positive real numbers.

Objective 1: Convert Between Logarithmic and Exponential Forms

For Exercises 19–26, write the equation in exponential form. (See Example 1)

19. $\log_8 64 = 2$

20. $\log_9 81 = 2$

21. $\log\left(\dfrac{1}{10,000}\right) = -4$

22. $\log\left(\dfrac{1}{1,000,000}\right) = -6$

23. $\log_4 1 = 0$

24. $\log_8 1 = 0$

25. $\log_a b = c$

26. $\log_x M = N$

For Exercises 27–34, write the equation in logarithmic form. (See Example 2)

27. $5^3 = 125$

28. $2^5 = 32$

29. $\left(\dfrac{1}{5}\right)^{-3} = 125$

30. $\left(\dfrac{1}{2}\right)^{-5} = 32$

31. $10^9 = 1,000,000,000$

32. $10^1 = 10$

33. $a^7 = b$

34. $M^3 = N$

Objective 2: Evaluate Logarithmic Expressions

For Exercises 35–54, simplify the expression. (See Examples 3–4)

35. $\log_3 9$

36. $\log_2 16$

37. $\log_5 5$

38. $\log_6 6$

39. $\log 100,000,000$

40. $\log 10,000,000$

41. $\log_2\left(\dfrac{1}{16}\right)$

42. $\log_3\left(\dfrac{1}{9}\right)$

43. $\log\left(\dfrac{1}{10}\right)$

44. $\log\left(\dfrac{1}{10,000}\right)$

45. $\ln e^6$

46. $\ln e^{10}$

47. $\ln\left(\dfrac{1}{e^3}\right)$

48. $\ln\left(\dfrac{1}{e^8}\right)$

49. $\log_{1/7} 49$

50. $\log_{1/4} 16$

51. $\log_{1/2}\left(\dfrac{1}{32}\right)$

52. $\log_{1/6}\left(\dfrac{1}{36}\right)$

53. $\log 0.00001$

54. $\log 0.0001$

For Exercises 55–56, estimate the value of each logarithm between two consecutive integers. Then use a calculator to approximate the value to 4 decimal places. For example, log 8970 is between 3 and 4 because $10^3 < 8970 < 10^4$. (See Example 5)

55. a. $\log 46,832$

    b. $\log 1,247,310$

    c. $\log 0.24$

    d. $\log 0.0000032$

    e. $\log(5.6 \times 10^5)$

    f. $\log(5.1 \times 10^{-3})$

56. a. $\log 293,416$

    b. $\log 897$

    c. $\log 0.038$

    d. $\log 0.00061$

    e. $\log(9.1 \times 10^8)$

    f. $\log(8.2 \times 10^{-2})$

For Exercises 57–58, approximate $f(x) = \ln x$ for the given values of x. Round to 4 decimal places. (See Example 5)

57. a. $f(94)$

    b. $f(0.182)$

    c. $f(\sqrt{155})$

    d. $f(4\pi)$

    e. $f(3.9 \times 10^9)$

    f. $f(7.1 \times 10^{-4})$

58. a. $f(1860)$

    b. $f(0.0694)$

    c. $f(\sqrt{87})$

    d. $f(2\pi)$

    e. $f(1.3 \times 10^{12})$

    f. $f(8.5 \times 10^{-17})$

Objective 3: Apply Basic Properties of Logarithms

For Exercises 59–68, simplify the expression. (See Example 6)

59. $\log_4 4^{11}$

60. $\log_6 6^7$

61. $\log_c c$

62. $\log_d d$

63. $5^{\log_5(x+y)}$

64. $4^{\log_4(a-c)}$

65. $\ln e^{a+b}$

66. $\ln e^{x^2+1}$

67. $\log_{\sqrt{5}} 1$

68. $\log_\pi 1$

Objective 4: Graph Logarithmic Functions

For Exercises 69–74, graph the function. (See Example 7)

69. $y = \log_3 x$

70. $y = \log_5 x$

71. $y = \log_{1/3} x$

72. $y = \log_{1/5} x$

73. $y = \ln x$

74. $y = \log x$

For Exercises 75–82, (See Example 8)

a. Use transformations of the graphs of $y = \log_2 x$ (see Example 7) and $y = \log_3 x$ (see Exercise 69) to graph the given functions.

b. Write the domain and range in interval notation.

c. Determine the vertical asymptote.

75. $y = \log_3(x + 2)$

76. $y = \log_2(x + 3)$

77. $y = 2 + \log_3 x$

78. $y = 3 + \log_2 x$

79. $y = \log_3(x - 1) - 3$

80. $y = \log_2(x - 2) - 1$

81. $y = -\log_3 x$

82. $y = -\log_2 x$

For Exercises 83–92, write the domain in interval notation. (See Example 9)

83. $f(x) = \log(8 - x)$ **84.** $g(x) = \log(3 - x)$ **85.** $h(x) = \log_2(6x + 7)$ **86.** $k(x) = \log_3(5x + 6)$

87. $m(x) = \ln(x^2 + 14)$ **88.** $n(x) = \ln(x^2 + 11)$ **89.** $p(x) = \log(x^2 - x - 12)$ **90.** $q(x) = \log(x^2 + 10x + 9)$

91. $r(x) = \log_3(4 - x)^2$ **92.** $s(x) = \log_5(3 - x)^2$

Objective 5: Use Logarithmic Functions in Applications

93. In 1989, the Loma Prieta earthquake damaged the city of San Francisco with an intensity of approximately $10^{6.9}I_0$. Film footage of the 1989 earthquake was captured on a number of video cameras including a broadcast of Game 3 of the World Series played at Candlestick Park. (**See Example 10**)

   a. Determine the magnitude of the Loma Prieta earthquake.

   b. Smaller earthquakes occur daily in the San Francisco area and most are not detectable without a seismograph. Determine the magnitude of an earthquake with an intensity of $10^{3.2}\,I_0$.

   c. How many times more intense was the Loma Prieta earthquake than an earthquake with a magnitude of 3.2 on the Richter scale? Round to the nearest whole unit.

94. The intensities of earthquakes are measured with seismographs all over the world at different distances from the epicenter. Suppose that the intensity of a medium earthquake is originally reported as $10^{5.4}$ times I_0. Later this value is revised as $10^{5.8}$ times I_0.

   a. Determine the magnitude of the earthquake using the original estimate for intensity.

   b. Determine the magnitude using the revised estimate for intensity.

   c. How many times more intense was the earthquake than originally thought? Round to 1 decimal place.

Sounds are produced when vibrating objects create pressure waves in some medium such as air. When these variations in pressure reach the human eardrum, it causes the eardrum to vibrate in a similar manner and the ear detects sound. The intensity of sound is measured as power per unit area. The threshold for hearing (minimum sound detectable by a young, healthy ear) is defined to be $I_0 = 10^{-12}$ W/m² (watts per square meter). The sound level L, or "loudness" of sound, is measured in decibels (dB) as $L = 10 \log\left(\dfrac{I}{I_0}\right)$, where I is the intensity of the given sound. Use this formula for Exercises 95–96.

95. a. Find the sound level of a jet plane taking off if its intensity is 10^{15} times the intensity of I_0.

   b. Find the sound level of the noise from city traffic if its intensity is 10^9 times I_0.

   c. How many times more intense is the sound of a jet plane taking off than noise from city traffic?

96. a. Find the sound level of a motorcycle if its intensity is 10^{10} times I_0.

   b. Find the sound level of a vacuum cleaner if its intensity is 10^7 times I_0.

   c. How many times more intense is the sound of a motorcycle than a vacuum cleaner?

Scientists use the pH scale to represent the level of acidity or alkalinity of a liquid. This is based on the molar concentration of hydrogen ions, [H⁺]. Since the values of [H⁺] vary over a large range, 1×10^0 mole per liter to 1×10^{-14} mole per liter (mol/L), a logarithmic scale is used to compute pH. The formula

$$\text{pH} = -\log[\text{H}^+]$$

represents the pH of a liquid as a function of its concentration of hydrogen ions, [H⁺].

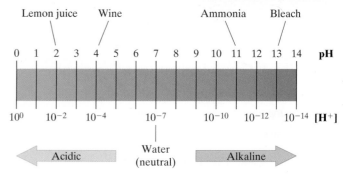

The pH scale ranges from 0 to 14. Pure water is taken as neutral having a pH of 7. A pH less than 7 is acidic. A pH greater than 7 is alkaline (or basic). For Exercises 97–98, use the formula for pH. Round pH values to 1 decimal place.

97. Vinegar and lemon juice are both acids. Their [H⁺] values are 5.0×10^{-3} mol/L and 1×10^{-2} mol/L, respectively.

   a. Find the pH for vinegar.

   b. Find the pH for lemon juice.

   c. Which substance is more acidic?

98. Bleach and milk of magnesia are both bases. Their [H⁺] values are 2.0×10^{-13} mol/L and 4.1×10^{-10} mol/L, respectively.

   a. Find the pH for bleach.

   b. Find the pH for milk of magnesia.

   c. Which substance is more basic?

99. Scientists categorize sediment size on a base-2 scale called the "Phi" scale. The Phi function is denoted by φ, where $\varphi(d)$ represents the Phi-scale value for a particle of diameter d (in mm). The value of $\varphi(d)$ is given by

$$\varphi(d) = -\log_2 d$$

Complete the table to determine the Phi-scale values for each category of sediment.

Sediment Class	Diameter d (in mm)	$\varphi(d)$
Cobble	128	
Gravel	8	
Fine gravel	4	
Course sand	1	
Medium sand	0.5	

100. Refer to Exercise 99.

    a. If a sample of sand in the Bahamas has a $\varphi(d)$ value of -1, what is the diameter of a particle of sand?

    b. If glacial sediments from Montana have a $\varphi(d)$ value of -5, what is the diameter of a particle?

Mixed Exercises

For Exercises 101–104,

a. Write the equation in exponential form.

b. Solve the equation from part (a).

c. Verify that the solution checks in the original equation.

101. $\log_3(x + 1) = 4$ **102.** $\log_2(x - 5) = 4$ **103.** $\log_4(7x - 6) = 3$ **104.** $\log_5(9x - 11) = 2$

For Exercises 105–108, evaluate the expressions.

105. $\log_3(\log_4 64)$ **106.** $\log_2\left[\log_{1/2}\left(\dfrac{1}{4}\right)\right]$ **107.** $\log_{16}(\log_{81} 3)$ **108.** $\log_4(\log_{16} 4)$

109. a. Evaluate $\log_2 2 + \log_2 4$

    b. Evaluate $\log_2(2 \cdot 4)$

    c. How do the values of the expressions in parts (a) and (b) compare?

110. a. Evaluate $\log_3 3 + \log_3 27$

    b. Evaluate $\log_3(3 \cdot 27)$

    c. How do the values of the expressions in parts (a) and (b) compare?

111. a. Evaluate $\log_4 64 - \log_4 4$

    b. Evaluate $\log_4\left(\dfrac{64}{4}\right)$

    c. How do the values of the expressions in parts (a) and (b) compare?

112. a. Evaluate $\log 100{,}000 - \log 100$

    b. Evaluate $\log\left(\dfrac{100{,}000}{100}\right)$

    c. How do the values of the expressions in parts (a) and (b) compare?

113. a. Evaluate $\log_2 2^5$

    b. Evaluate $5 \cdot \log_2 2$

    c. How do the values of the expressions in parts (a) and (b) compare?

114. a. Evaluate $\log_7 7^6$

    b. Evaluate $6 \cdot \log_7 7$

    c. How do the values of the expressions in parts (a) and (b) compare?

115. The time t (in years) required for an investment to double with interest compounded continuously depends on the interest rate r according to the function $t(r) = \dfrac{\ln 2}{r}$.

    a. If an interest rate of 3.5% is secured, determine the length of time needed for an initial investment to double. Round to 1 decimal place.

    b. Evaluate $t(0.04)$, $t(0.06)$, and $t(0.08)$.

116. The number n of monthly payments of P dollars each required to pay off a loan of A dollars in its entirety at interest rate r is given by

$$n = -\frac{\log\left(1 - \dfrac{Ar}{12P}\right)}{\log\left(1 + \dfrac{r}{12}\right)}$$

   a. A college student wants to buy a car and realizes that he can only afford payments of $200 per month. If he borrows $3000 and pays it off at 6% interest, how many months will it take him to retire the loan? Round to the nearest month.

   b. Determine the number of monthly payments of $611.09 that would be required to pay off a home loan of $128,000 at 4% interest.

Write About It

For Exercises 117–118, use a calculator to approximate the given logarithms to 4 decimal places.

117. a. Avogadro's number is 6.022×10^{23}. Approximate $\log(6.022 \times 10^{23})$.

   b. Planck's constant is 6.626×10^{-34} J $\cdot$ sec. Approximate $\log(6.626 \times 10^{-34})$.

   c. Compare the value of the common logarithm to the power of 10 used in scientific notation.

118. a. The speed of light is 2.9979×10^{8} m/sec. Approximate $\log(2.9979 \times 10^{8})$.

   b. An elementary charge is 1.602×10^{-19} C. Approximate $\log(1.602 \times 10^{-19})$.

   c. Compare the value of the common logarithm to the power of 10 used in scientific notation.

Expanding Your Skills

A logarithmic function $y = \log_b x$ with base $b > 1$ increases over its domain. However, the rate of increase decreases with larger and larger values of x. For Exercises 119–120, demonstrate this statement by finding the average rate of change on each interval $[a, b]$. Round to 4 decimal places where necessary.

119. $Y_1 = \log x$

   a. $[0.5, 1]$

   b. $[1, 10]$

   c. $[10, 20]$

   d. $[20, 30]$

$Y_1 = \log x$	
X	Y1
.5	-.301
1	0
10	1
20	1.301
30	1.4771
X=.5	

120. $Y_1 = \ln x$

   a. $[0.5, 1]$

   b. $[1, 10]$

   c. $[10, 20]$

   d. $[20, 30]$

$Y_1 = \ln x$	
X	Y1
.5	-.6931
1	0
10	2.3026
20	2.9957
30	3.4012
X=.5	

For Exercises 121–126, write the domain in interval notation.

121. $t(x) = \log_4\left(\dfrac{x-1}{x-3}\right)$

122. $r(x) = \log_5\left(\dfrac{x+2}{x-4}\right)$

123. $s(x) = \ln\left(\sqrt{x+5} - 1\right)$

124. $v(x) = \ln\left(\sqrt{x-8} - 1\right)$

125. $c(x) = \log\left(\dfrac{1}{\sqrt{x-6}}\right)$

126. $d(x) = \log\left(\dfrac{1}{\sqrt{x+8}}\right)$

Technology Connections

127. a. Graph $f(x) = \ln x$ and
$$g(x) = (x-1) - \frac{(x-1)^2}{2} + \frac{(x-1)^3}{3} - \frac{(x-1)^4}{4}$$
on the viewing window $[-2, 4, 1]$ by $[-5, 2, 1]$. How do the graphs compare on the interval $(0, 2)$?

   b. Use function g to approximate $\ln 1.5$. Round to 4 decimal places.

128. Compare the graphs of $Y_1 = \dfrac{e^x - e^{-x}}{2}$, $Y_2 = \ln(x + \sqrt{x^2 + 1})$, and $Y_3 = x$ on the viewing window $[-15.1, 15.1, 1]$ by $[-10, 10, 1]$. Based on the graphs, how do you suspect that the functions are related?

129. Compare the graphs of the functions.
$$Y_1 = \ln(2x) \quad \text{and} \quad Y_2 = \ln 2 + \ln x$$

130. Compare the graphs of the functions.
$$Y_1 = \ln\left(\frac{x}{2}\right) \quad \text{and} \quad Y_2 = \ln x - \ln 2$$

PROBLEM RECOGNITION EXERCISES

Analyzing Functions

For Exercises 1–14,

  a. Write the domain.   **b.** Write the range.   **c.** Find the x-intercept(s).   **d.** Find the y-intercept.

  e. Determine the asymptotes if applicable.   **f.** Determine the intervals over which the function is increasing.

  g. Determine the intervals over which the function is decreasing.   **h.** Match the function with its graph.

1. $f(x) = 3$ **2.** $g(x) = 2x - 3$ **3.** $d(x) = (x - 3)^2 - 4$ **4.** $h(x) = \sqrt[3]{x - 2}$

5. $k(x) = \dfrac{2}{x - 1}$ **6.** $z(x) = \dfrac{3x}{x + 2}$ **7.** $p(x) = \left(\dfrac{4}{3}\right)^x$ **8.** $q(x) = -x^2 - 6x - 9$

9. $m(x) = |x - 4| - 1$ **10.** $n(x) = -|x| + 3$ **11.** $r(x) = \sqrt{3 - x}$ **12.** $s(x) = \sqrt{x - 3}$

13. $t(x) = e^x + 2$ **14.** $v(x) = \ln(x + 2)$

A.

B.

C.

D.

E.

F.

G.

H.

I.

J.

K.

L.

M.

N.
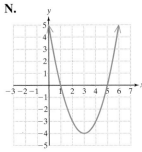

| SECTION 4.4 | Properties of Logarithms |

OBJECTIVES

1. Apply the Product, Quotient, and Power Properties of Logarithms
2. Write a Logarithmic Expression in Expanded Form
3. Write a Logarithmic Expression as a Single Logarithm
4. Apply the Change-of-Base Formula

1. Apply the Product, Quotient, and Power Properties of Logarithms

By definition, $y = \log_b x$ is equivalent to $b^y = x$. Because a logarithm is an exponent, the properties of exponents can be applied to logarithms. The first is called the product property of logarithms.

> **Product Property of Logarithms**
>
> Let b, x, and y be positive real numbers where $b \neq 1$. Then
> $$\log_b(xy) = \log_b x + \log_b y$$
> The logarithm of a product equals the sum of the logarithms of the factors.

TIP When two factors of the same base are multiplied, the base is unchanged and we add the exponents. This is the underlying principle for the product property of logarithms.

Proof:

Let $M = \log_b x$, which implies $b^M = x$.
Let $N = \log_b y$, which implies $b^N = y$.
Then $xy = b^M b^N = b^{M+N}$.

Writing the expression $xy = b^{M+N}$ in logarithmic form, we have,
$$\log_b(xy) = M + N$$
$$\log_b(xy) = \log_b x + \log_b y \checkmark$$

To demonstrate the product property of logarithms, simplify the following expressions by using the order of operations.

$$\log_3(3 \cdot 9) \overset{?}{=} \log_3 3 + \log_3 9$$
$$\log_3 27 \overset{?}{=} 1 + 2$$
$$3 \overset{?}{=} 3 \checkmark \text{ True}$$

EXAMPLE 1   **Applying the Product Property of Logarithms**

Write the logarithm as a sum and simplify if possible. Assume that x and y represent positive real numbers.

  a. $\log_2(8x)$ **b.** $\ln(5xy)$

Solution:

  a. $\log_2(8x) = \log_2 8 + \log_2 x$ Product property of logarithms
              $= 3 + \log_2 x$ Simplify. $\log_2 8 = \log_2 2^3 = 3$

  b. $\ln(5xy) = \ln 5 + \ln x + \ln y$

> **Skill Practice 1**   Write the logarithm as a sum and simplify if possible. Assume that a, c, and d represent positive real numbers.
>   **a.** $\log_4(16a)$ **b.** $\log(12cd)$

Answers
1. a. $2 + \log_4 a$
   b. $\log 12 + \log c + \log d$

The quotient rule of exponents tells us that $\dfrac{b^M}{b^N} = b^{M-N}$ for $b \neq 0$. This property can be applied to logarithms.

Quotient Property of Logarithms

Let b, x, and y be positive real numbers where $b \neq 1$. Then

$$\log_b\left(\frac{x}{y}\right) = \log_b x - \log_b y$$

The logarithm of a quotient equals the difference of the logarithm of the numerator and the logarithm of the denominator.

The proof of the quotient property for logarithms is similar to the proof of the product property (see Exercise 107). To demonstrate the quotient property for logarithms, simplify the following expressions by using the order of operations.

$$\log\left(\frac{1,000,000}{100}\right) \overset{?}{=} \log 1,000,000 - \log 100$$

$$\log 10,000 \overset{?}{=} 6 - 2$$

$$4 \overset{?}{=} 4 \; \checkmark \; \text{True}$$

EXAMPLE 2   Applying the Quotient Property of Logarithms

Write the logarithm as the difference of logarithms and simplify if possible. Assume that the variables represent positive real numbers.

a. $\log_3\left(\dfrac{c}{d}\right)$ **b.** $\log\left(\dfrac{x}{1000}\right)$

Solution:

a. $\log_3\left(\dfrac{c}{d}\right) = \log_3 c - \log_3 d$ Quotient property of logarithms.

b. $\log\left(\dfrac{x}{1000}\right) = \log x - \log 1000$ Quotient property of logarithms.

        $= \log x - 3$ Simplify. $\log 1000 = \log 10^3 = 3$

Skill Practice 2   Write the logarithm as the difference of logarithms and simplify if possible. Assume that t represents a positive real number.

a. $\log_6\left(\dfrac{8}{t}\right)$ **b.** $\ln\left(\dfrac{e}{12}\right)$

The last property we present here is the power property of logarithms. The power property of exponents tells us that $(b^M)^N = b^{MN}$. The same principle can be applied to logarithms.

Power Property of Logarithms

Let b and x be positive real numbers where $b \neq 1$. Let p be any real number. Then

$$\log_b x^p = p \log_b x$$

The power property of logarithms is proved in Exercise 108.

Answers
2. a. $\log_6 8 - \log_6 t$ **b.** $1 - \ln 12$

EXAMPLE 3 **Applying the Power Property of Logarithms**

Apply the power property of logarithms. **a.** $\ln \sqrt[5]{x^2}$ **b.** $\log x^2$

Solution:

a. $\ln \sqrt[5]{x^2} = \ln x^{2/5}$ Write $\sqrt[5]{x^2}$ using rational exponents.

                $= \dfrac{2}{5} \ln x$ provided that $x > 0$ Apply the power rule.

b. $\log x^2 = 2 \log x$ provided that $x > 0$ Apply the power rule.

In both parts (a) and (b), the condition that $x > 0$ is mandatory. The properties of logarithms hold true only for values of the variable for which the logarithms are defined. That is, the arguments must be positive.

From the graphs of $y = \log x^2$ and $y = 2 \log x$, we see that the domains are different. Therefore, the statement $\log x^2 = 2 \log x$ is true only for $x > 0$.

$y = \log x^2$ Domain: $(-\infty, 0) \cup (0, \infty)$ $y = 2 \log x$ Domain: $(0, \infty)$

Skill Practice 3 Apply the power property of logarithms.
    a. $\log_5 \sqrt[5]{x^4}$ **b.** $\ln x^4$

At this point, we have learned seven properties of logarithms. The properties hold true for values of the variable for which the logarithms are defined. **Therefore, in the examples and exercises, we will assume that the variable expressions within the logarithms represent positive real numbers.**

Properties of Logarithms

Let b, x, and y be positive real numbers where $b \neq 1$, and let p be a real number. Then the following properties of logarithms are true.

1. $\log_b 1 = 0$ **5.** $\log_b(xy) = \log_b x + \log_b y$ **Product property for logarithms**

2. $\log_b b = 1$ **6.** $\log_b\left(\dfrac{x}{y}\right) = \log_b x - \log_b y$ **Quotient property for logarithms**

3. $\log_b b^p = p$ **7.** $\log_b x^p = p \log_b x$ **Power property for logarithms**

4. $b^{\log_b x} = x$

---

2. Write a Logarithmic Expression in Expanded Form

The properties of logarithms tell us that the expression

$$\log\left(\frac{ab}{c}\right) \text{ can be written as } \log a + \log b - \log c.$$

In some applications of algebra and calculus, the "condensed" form of the logarithm is preferred. In other applications, the "expanded" form is preferred. In Examples 4–6, we practice manipulating logarithmic expressions in both forms.

Answers

3. a. $\dfrac{4}{5} \log_5 x$ provided that $x > 0$

    b. $4 \ln x$ provided that $x > 0$

| EXAMPLE 4 | Writing a Logarithmic Expression in Expanded Form |

Write the expression as the sum or difference of logarithms.

a. $\log_2\left(\dfrac{z^3}{xy^5}\right)$ **b.** $\log\sqrt[3]{\dfrac{(x+y)^2}{10}}$

Solution:

a. $\log_2\left(\dfrac{z^3}{xy^5}\right) = \log_2 z^3 - \log_2(xy^5)$ Apply the quotient property.

$\qquad = \log_2 z^3 - (\log_2 x + \log_2 y^5)$ Apply the product property.

$\qquad = \log_2 z^3 - \log_2 x - \log_2 y^5$ Apply the distributive property.

$\qquad = 3\log_2 z - \log_2 x - 5\log_2 y$ Apply the power property.

Avoiding Mistakes

In Example 4(b) do not try to simplify $\log(x+y)$. The argument contains a sum, not a product.

$\log(\underbrace{x+y}_{\text{sum}})$ cannot be simplified,

whereas

$\log(\underbrace{xy}_{\text{product}}) = \log x + \log y$

b. $\log\sqrt[3]{\dfrac{(x+y)^2}{10}} = \log\left[\dfrac{(x+y)^2}{10}\right]^{1/3}$ Write the radical expression with rational exponents.

$\qquad = \dfrac{1}{3}\log\left[\dfrac{(x+y)^2}{10}\right]$ Apply the power property.

$\qquad = \dfrac{1}{3}[\log(x+y)^2 - \log 10]$ Apply the quotient property.

$\qquad = \dfrac{1}{3}[2\log(x+y) - 1]$ Apply the power property and simplify: $\log 10 = 1$.

$\qquad = \dfrac{2}{3}\log(x+y) - \dfrac{1}{3}$ Apply the distributive property.

Skill Practice 4   Write the expression as the sum or difference of logarithms.

a. $\ln\left(\dfrac{a^4 b}{c^9}\right)$ **b.** $\log_5\sqrt[3]{\dfrac{25}{(a^2+b)^2}}$

3. Write a Logarithmic Expression as a Single Logarithm

In Examples 5 and 6, we demonstrate how to write a sum or difference of logarithms as a single logarithm. We apply Properties 5, 6, and 7 of logarithms in reverse.

| EXAMPLE 5 | Writing the Sum or Difference of Logarithms as a Single Logarithm |

Write the expression as a single logarithm and simplify the result if possible.

$$\log_2 560 - \log_2 7 - \log_2 5$$

Solution:

$\log_2 560 - \log_2 7 - \log_2 5$

$= \log_2 560 - (\log_2 7 + \log_2 5)$ Factor out -1 from the last two terms.

$= \log_2 560 - \log_2(7 \cdot 5)$ Apply the product property of logarithms.

$= \log_2\left(\dfrac{560}{7 \cdot 5}\right)$ Apply the quotient property.

$= \log_2 16$ Simplify within the argument.

$= 4$ Simplify. $\log_2 16 = \log_2 2^4 = 4$

Answers

4. a. $4\ln a + \ln b - 9\ln c$

  b. $\dfrac{2}{3} - \dfrac{2}{3}\log_5(a^2+b)$

Skill Practice 5 Write the expression as a single logarithm and simplify the result if possible. $\log_3 54 + \log_3 10 - \log_3 20$

EXAMPLE 6 Writing the Sum or Difference of Logarithms as a Single Logarithm

Write the expression as a single logarithm and simplify the result if possible.

a. $3 \log a - \dfrac{1}{2}\log b - \dfrac{1}{2}\log c$ **b.** $\dfrac{1}{2}\ln x + \ln(x^2 - 1) - \ln(x + 1)$

Solution:

a. $3 \log a - \dfrac{1}{2}\log b - \dfrac{1}{2}\log c$

$= 3 \log a - \dfrac{1}{2}(\log b + \log c)$ Factor out $-\frac{1}{2}$ from the last two terms.

$= 3 \log a - \dfrac{1}{2}\log(bc)$ Apply the product property of logarithms.

$= \log a^3 - \log\sqrt{bc}$ Apply the power property.

$= \log\left(\dfrac{a^3}{\sqrt{bc}}\right)$ Apply the quotient property.

Avoiding Mistakes

In all examples and exercises in which we manipulate logarithmic expressions, it is important to note that the equivalences are true only for the values of the variables that make the expressions defined. In Example 6(b) we have the restriction that $x > 1$.

b. $\dfrac{1}{2}\ln x + \ln(x^2 - 1) - \ln(x + 1)$

$= \ln x^{1/2} + \ln(x^2 - 1) - \ln(x + 1)$ Apply the power property of logarithms.

$= \ln[x^{1/2}(x^2 - 1)] - \ln(x + 1)$ Apply the product property.

$= \ln\left[\dfrac{\sqrt{x}(x^2 - 1)}{x + 1}\right]$ Apply the quotient property.

$= \ln\left[\dfrac{\sqrt{x}(x + 1)(x - 1)}{x + 1}\right]$ Factor the numerator of the argument.

$= \ln\left[\sqrt{x}(x - 1)\right]$ Simplify the argument.

Skill Practice 6 Write the expression as a single logarithm and simplify the result if possible.

a. $3 \log x - \dfrac{1}{3}\log y - \dfrac{2}{3}\log z$ **b.** $\dfrac{1}{3}\ln t + \ln(t^2 - 9) - \ln(t - 3)$

EXAMPLE 7 Applying Properties of Logarithms

Given that $\log_b 2 \approx 0.356$ and $\log_b 3 \approx 0.565$, approximate the value of $\log_b 36$.

Solution:

$\log_b 36 = \log_b(2 \cdot 3)^2$ Write the argument as a product of the factors 2 and 3.

$= 2 \log_b(2 \cdot 3)$ Apply the power property of logarithms.

$= 2(\log_b 2 + \log_b 3)$ Apply the product property of logarithms.

$\approx 2(0.356 + 0.565)$ Simplify.

≈ 1.842

Answers

5. 3

6. a. $\log\left(\dfrac{x^3}{\sqrt[3]{yz^2}}\right)$

    b. $\ln\left[\sqrt[3]{t}(t + 3)\right]$

> **Skill Practice 7**   Given that $\log_b 2 \approx 0.356$ and $\log_b 3 \approx 0.565$, approximate the value of $\log_b 24$.

4. Apply the Change-of-Base Formula

A calculator can be used to approximate the value of a logarithm base 10 or base e by using the **LOG** key or the **LN** key, respectively. However, to use a calculator to evaluate a logarithmic expression with a different base, we must use the change-of-base formula.

Change-of-Base Formula

Let a and b be positive real numbers such that $a \neq 1$ and $b \neq 1$. Then for any positive real number x,

$$\log_b x = \frac{\log_a x}{\log_a b}$$

Note: The change-of-base formula converts a logarithm of one base to a ratio of logarithms of a different base. For the purpose of using a calculator, we often apply the change-of-base formula with base 10 or base e.

$$\log_b x = \frac{\log x}{\log b} \quad \text{Ratio of base 10 logarithms}$$
Original base is b.

$$\log_b x = \frac{\ln x}{\ln b} \quad \text{Ratio of base } e \text{ logarithms}$$
Original base is b.

To derive the change-of-base formula, assume that a and b are positive real numbers with $a \neq 1$ and $b \neq 1$. Begin by letting $y = \log_b x$. If $y = \log_b x$, then

$$b^y = x \qquad \text{Write the original logarithm in exponential form.}$$
$$\log_a b^y = \log_a x \qquad \text{Take the logarithm base } a \text{ on both sides.}$$
$$y \cdot \log_a b = \log_a x \qquad \text{Apply the power property of logarithms.}$$
$$y = \frac{\log_a x}{\log_a b} \qquad \text{Solve for } y.$$
$$\log_b x = \frac{\log_a x}{\log_a b} \qquad \begin{array}{l}\text{Replace } y \text{ by } \log_b x.\\ \text{This is the change-of-base formula.}\end{array}$$

EXAMPLE 8   Applying the Change-of-Base Formula

a. Estimate $\log_4 153$ between two consecutive integers.

b. Use the change-of-base formula to approximate $\log_4 153$ by using base 10. Round to 4 decimal places.

c. Use the change-of-base formula to approximate $\log_4 153$ by using base e.

d. Check the result by using the related exponential form.

Solution:

a. $64 < 153 < 256$
$4^3 < 153 < 4^4$
$3 < \log_4 153 < 4 \qquad \log_4 153$ is between 3 and 4.

Answer

7. 1.633

TIP Although the numerators and denominators in parts (b) and (c) are different, their ratios are the same.

b. $\log_4 153 = \dfrac{\log 153}{\log 4} \approx \dfrac{2.184691431}{0.6020599913} \approx 3.6287$

c. $\log_4 153 = \dfrac{\ln 153}{\ln 4} \approx \dfrac{5.030437921}{1.386294361} \approx 3.6287$

d. Check: $4^{3.6287} \approx 153$ ✓

Skill Practice 8

a. Estimate $\log_6 23$ between two consecutive integers.

b. Use the change-of-base formula to evaluate $\log_6 23$ by using base 10. Round to 4 decimal places.

c. Use the change-of-base formula to evaluate $\log_6 23$ by using base e. Round to 4 decimal places.

d. Check the result by using the related exponential form.

TECHNOLOGY CONNECTIONS

Using the Change-of-Base Formula to Graph a Logarithmic Function

The change-of-base formula can be used to graph logarithmic functions using a graphing utility. For example, to graph $Y_1 = \log_2 x$, enter the function as

$$Y = \log(x)/\log(2) \quad \text{or} \quad Y = \ln(x)/\ln(2)$$

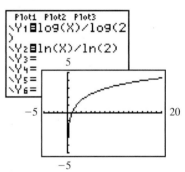

Point of Interest

The slide rule, first built in England in the early seventeenth century, is a mechanical computing device that uses logarithmic scales to perform operations involving multiplication, division, roots, logarithms, exponentials, and trigonometry. Amazingly, slide rules were used into the space age by engineers as late as the 1960s to help send astronauts to the moon. It was only with the invention of the pocket calculator that slide rules were replaced by modern computing devices.

Answers

8. a. Between 1 and 2
   b. 1.7500
   c. 1.7500
   d. $6^{1.7500} \approx 23$

SECTION 4.4 Practice Exercises

Review Exercises

For Exercises 1–6, evaluate the logarithms.

1. a. $\log_2 4 + \log_2 8$ **b.** $\log_2(4 \cdot 8)$

2. a. $\log_5 5 + \log_5 25$ **b.** $\log_5(5 \cdot 25)$

3. a. $\log_4 256 - \log_4 16$ **b.** $\log_4\left(\dfrac{256}{16}\right)$

4. a. $\log 1{,}000{,}000 - \log 10$ **b.** $\log\left(\dfrac{1{,}000{,}000}{10}\right)$

5. a. $\log_3 81$ **b.** $\log_3 3^4$

6. a. $\log_8 64$ **b.** $\log_8 8^2$

For Exercises 7–10, fill in the blank to make a true statement. Assume that b, x, and y are positive real numbers where $b \neq 1$.

7. $\log_b b =$ _____

8. $\log_b 1 =$ _____

9. $\log_b b^x =$ _____

10. $b^{\log_b x} =$ _____

Concept Connections

11. The product property of logarithms states that $\log_b(xy) =$ _____ for positive real numbers b, x, and y, where $b \neq 1$.

12. The _____ property of logarithms states that $\log_b\left(\dfrac{x}{y}\right) =$ _____ for positive real numbers b, x, and y, where $b \neq 1$.

13. The power property of logarithms states that for any real number p, $\log_b x^p =$ _____ for positive real numbers b, x, and y, where $b \neq 1$.

14. The change-of-base formula states that $\log_b x$ can be written as a ratio of logarithms with base a as

$$\log_b x = \dfrac{\square}{\square}$$

15. The change-of-base formula is often used to convert a logarithm to a ratio of logarithms with base _____ or base _____ so that a calculator can be used to approximate the logarithm.

16. To use a graphing utility to graph the function defined by $y = \log_5 x$, use the change-of-base formula to write the function as $y =$ _____ or $y =$ _____.

For the exercises in this set, assume that all variable expressions represent positive real numbers.

Objective 1: Apply the Product, Quotient, and Power Properties of Logarithms

For Exercises 17–22, use the product property of logarithms to write the logarithm as a sum of logarithms. Then simplify if possible. (See Example 1)

17. $\log_5(125z)$

18. $\log_7(49k)$

19. $\log(8cd)$

20. $\log(24vw)$

21. $\log_2[(x + y) \cdot z]$

22. $\log_3[(a + b) \cdot c]$

For Exercises 23–28, use the quotient property of logarithms to write the logarithm as a difference of logarithms. Then simplify if possible. (See Example 2)

23. $\log_{12}\left(\dfrac{p}{q}\right)$

24. $\log_9\left(\dfrac{m}{n}\right)$

25. $\ln\left(\dfrac{e}{5}\right)$

26. $\ln\left(\dfrac{x}{e}\right)$

27. $\log\left(\dfrac{m^2 + n}{100}\right)$

28. $\log\left(\dfrac{1000}{c^2 + 1}\right)$

For Exercises 29–34, apply the power property of logarithms. (See Example 3)

29. $\log(2x - 3)^4$

30. $\log(8t - 3)^2$

31. $\log_6 \sqrt[7]{x^3}$

32. $\log_8 \sqrt[4]{x^3}$

33. $\ln 2^{kt}$

34. $\ln(0.5)^{rt}$

Objective 2: Write a Logarithmic Expression in Expanded Form

For Exercises 35–48, write the logarithm as a sum or difference of logarithms. Simplify each term as much as possible. (See Example 4)

35. $\log_7\left(\dfrac{1}{7}mn^2\right)$

36. $\log_4\left(\dfrac{1}{16}t^3v\right)$

37. $\log_6\left(\dfrac{p^5}{qt^3}\right)$

38. $\log_8\left(\dfrac{a^4}{b^9c}\right)$

39. $\log\left(\dfrac{10}{\sqrt{a^2 + b^2}}\right)$

40. $\log\left(\dfrac{\sqrt{d^2 + 1}}{10,000}\right)$

41. $\ln\left(\dfrac{\sqrt[3]{xy}}{wz^2}\right)$

42. $\ln\left(\dfrac{\sqrt[4]{pq}}{t^3m}\right)$

43. $\ln\sqrt[4]{\dfrac{a^2 + 4}{e^3}}$

44. $\ln\sqrt[5]{\dfrac{e^2}{c^2 + 5}}$

45. $\log\left[\dfrac{2x(x^2 + 3)^8}{\sqrt{4 - 3x}}\right]$

46. $\log\left[\dfrac{5y(4x + 1)^7}{\sqrt[3]{2 - 7x}}\right]$

47. $\log_5 \sqrt[3]{x\sqrt{5}}$

48. $\log_2 \sqrt[4]{y\sqrt{2}}$

Objective 3: Write a Logarithmic Expression as a Single Logarithm

For Exercises 49–68, write the logarithmic expression as a single logarithm with coefficient 1, and simplify as much as possible. (See Examples 5–6)

49. $\log_{15} 3 + \log_{15} 5$

50. $\log_{12} 8 + \log_{12} 18$

51. $\log_7 98 - \log_7 2$

52. $\log_6 144 - \log_6 4$

53. $\log 150 - \log 3 - \log 5$

54. $\log_3 693 - \log_3 33 - \log_3 7$

55. $2 \log_2 x + \log_2 t$

56. $5 \log_4 y + \log_4 w$

57. $4 \log_8 m - 3 \log_8 n - 2 \log_8 p$

58. $8 \log_3 x - 2 \log_3 z - 7 \log_3 y$

59. $\frac{1}{2}\ln(x + 1) - \frac{1}{2}\ln(x - 1)$

60. $\frac{1}{3}\ln(x^2 + 1) - \frac{1}{3}\ln(x + 1)$

61. $6 \log x - \frac{1}{3}\log y - \frac{2}{3}\log z$

62. $15 \log c - \frac{1}{4}\log d - \frac{3}{4}\log k$

63. $\frac{1}{3}\log_4 p + \log_4(q^2 - 16) - \log_4(q - 4)$

64. $\frac{1}{4}\log_2 w + \log_2(w^2 - 100) - \log_2(w + 10)$

65. $\frac{1}{2}[6 \ln(x + 2) + \ln x - \ln x^2]$

66. $\frac{1}{3}[12 \ln(x - 5) + \ln x - \ln x^3]$

67. $\log(8y^2 - 7y) + \log y^{-1}$

68. $\log(9t^3 - 5t) + \log t^{-1}$

For Exercises 69–78, use $\log_b 2 \approx 0.356$, $\log_b 3 \approx 0.565$, and $\log_b 5 \approx 0.827$ to approximate the value of the given logarithms. (See Example 7)

69. $\log_b 15$

70. $\log_b 10$

71. $\log_b 81$

72. $\log_b 125$

73. $\log_b 50$

74. $\log_b 12$

75. $\log_b\left(\dfrac{15}{2}\right)$

76. $\log_b\left(\dfrac{6}{5}\right)$

77. $\log_b 100$

78. $\log_b 225$

Objective 4: Apply the Change-of-Base Formula

For Exercises 79–84, (See Example 8)

a. Estimate the value of the logarithm between two consecutive integers. For example, $\log_2 7$ is between 2 and 3 because $2^2 < 7 < 2^3$.

b. Use the change-of-base formula and a calculator to approximate the logarithm to 4 decimal places.

c. Check the result by using the related exponential form.

79. $\log_2 15$

80. $\log_3 15$

81. $\log_5 3$

82. $\log_8 5$

83. $\log_2 0.3$

84. $\log_2 0.2$

For Exercises 85–88, use the change-of-base formula and a calculator to approximate the given logarithms. Round to 4 decimal places. Then check the answer by using the related exponential form. (See Example 8)

85. $\log_2(4.68 \times 10^7)$

86. $\log_2(2.54 \times 10^{10})$

87. $\log_4(5.68 \times 10^{-6})$

88. $\log_4(9.84 \times 10^{-5})$

Mixed Exercises

For Exercises 89–98, determine if the statement is true or false. For each false statement, provide a counterexample. For example, $\log(x + y) \neq \log x + \log y$ because $\log(2 + 8) \neq \log 2 + \log 8$ (the left side is 1 and the right side is approximately 1.204).

89. $\log e = \dfrac{1}{\ln 10}$

90. $\ln 10 = \dfrac{1}{\log e}$

91. $\log_5\left(\dfrac{1}{x}\right) = \dfrac{1}{\log_5 x}$

92. $\log_6\left(\dfrac{1}{t}\right) = \dfrac{1}{\log_6 t}$

93. $\log_4\left(\dfrac{1}{p}\right) = -\log_4 p$

94. $\log_8\left(\dfrac{1}{w}\right) = -\log_8 w$

95. $\log(xy) = (\log x)(\log y)$

96. $\log\left(\dfrac{x}{y}\right) = \dfrac{\log x}{\log y}$

97. $\log_2(7y) + \log_2 1 = \log_2(7y)$

98. $\log_4(3d) + \log_4 1 = \log_4(3d)$

Write About It

99. Explain why the product property of logarithms does not apply to the following statement.

$$\log_5(-5) + \log_5(-25)$$
$$= \log_5[(-5)(-25)]$$
$$= \log_5 125 = 3$$

100. Explain how to use the change-of-base formula and explain why it is important.

Expanding Your Skills

101. a. Write the difference quotient for $f(x) = \ln x$.

   b. Show that the difference quotient from part (a) can be written as $\ln\left(\dfrac{x + h}{x}\right)^{1/h}$.

102. Show that
$$-\ln\left(x - \sqrt{x^2 - 1}\right) = \ln\left(x + \sqrt{x^2 - 1}\right)$$

103. Show that
$$\log\left(\frac{-b + \sqrt{b^2 - 4ac}}{2a}\right) + \log\left(\frac{-b - \sqrt{b^2 - 4ac}}{2a}\right)$$
$$= \log c - \log a$$

104. Show that
$$\ln\left(\frac{c + \sqrt{c^2 - x^2}}{c - \sqrt{c^2 - x^2}}\right) = 2\ln\left(c + \sqrt{c^2 - x^2}\right) - 2\ln x$$

105. Use the change-of-base formula to write $(\log_2 5)(\log_5 9)$ as a single logarithm.

106. Use the change-of-base formula to write $(\log_3 11)(\log_{11} 4)$ as a single logarithm.

107. Prove the quotient property of logarithms:

$$\log_b\left(\frac{x}{y}\right) = \log_b x - \log_b y.$$

(*Hint*: Modify the proof of the product property given on page 475.)

108. Prove the power property of logarithms:
$\log_b x^p = p \log_b x.$

Technology Connections

For Exercises 109–112, graph the function.

109. $f(x) = \log_5(x + 4)$ **110.** $g(x) = \log_7(x - 3)$

111. $k(x) = -3 + \log_{1/2} x$ **112.** $h(x) = 4 + \log_{1/3} x$

113. a. Graph $Y_1 = \log |x|$ and $Y_2 = \dfrac{1}{2}\log x^2$. How are the graphs related?

   b. Show algebraically that $\dfrac{1}{2}\log x^2 = \log |x|$.

114. Graph $Y_1 = \ln(0.1x)$, $Y_2 = \ln(0.5x)$, $Y_3 = \ln x$, and $Y_4 = \ln(2x)$. How are the graphs related? Support your answer algebraically.

SECTION 4.5   Exponential and Logarithmic Equations

OBJECTIVES

1. Solve Exponential Equations

2. Solve Logarithmic Equations

3. Use Exponential and Logarithmic Equations in Applications

1. Solve Exponential Equations

A couple invests $8000 in a bond fund. The expected yield is 4.5% and the earnings are reinvested monthly. The growth of the investment is modeled by

$$A = 8000\left(1 + \frac{0.045}{12}\right)^{12t}$$ where A is the amount in the account after t years.

If the couple wants to know how long it will take for the investment to double, they would solve the equation:

$$16,000 = 8000\left(1 + \frac{0.045}{12}\right)^{12t}$$ (See Example 11.)

This equation is called an **exponential equation** because the equation contains a variable in the exponent. To solve an exponential equation first note that all exponential functions are one-to-one. Therefore, $b^x = b^y$ implies that $x = y$. This is called the equivalence property of exponential expressions.

> **TIP** The equivalence property tells us that if two exponential expressions with the same base are equal, then their exponents must be equal.

Equivalence Property of Exponential Expressions

Let b, x, and y be real numbers with $b > 0$ and $b \neq 1$. Then,

$$b^x = b^y \quad \text{implies that} \quad x = y.$$

EXAMPLE 1 Solving Exponential Equations Using the Equivalence Property

Solve. **a.** $3^{2x-6} = 81$ **b.** $25^{4-t} = \left(\dfrac{1}{5}\right)^{3t+1}$

Solution:

a.
$$3^{2x-6} = 81$$
$$3^{2x-6} = 3^4 \qquad \text{Write 81 as an exponential expression with a base of 3.}$$
$$2x - 6 = 4 \qquad \text{Equate the exponents.}$$
$$x = 5$$

The solution set is $\{5\}$.

Check: $3^{2x-6} = 81$
$$3^{2(5)-6} \stackrel{?}{=} 81$$
$$3^4 \stackrel{?}{=} 81 \checkmark$$

b.
$$25^{4-t} = \left(\frac{1}{5}\right)^{3t+1}$$
$$(5^2)^{4-t} = (5^{-1})^{3t+1} \qquad \text{Express both 25 and } \tfrac{1}{5} \text{ as integer powers of 5.}$$
$$5^{2(4-t)} = 5^{-1(3t+1)} \qquad \text{Apply the power property of exponents: } (b^m)^n = b^{m \cdot n}.$$
$$5^{8-2t} = 5^{-3t-1} \qquad \text{Apply the distributive property within the exponents.}$$
$$8 - 2t = -3t - 1 \qquad \text{Equate the exponents.}$$
$$t = -9 \qquad \text{The solution checks in the original equation.}$$

The solution set is $\{-9\}$.

Skill Practice 1 Solve. **a.** $4^{2x-3} = 64$ **b.** $27^{2w+5} = \left(\dfrac{1}{3}\right)^{2-5w}$

In Example 1, we were able to write the left and right sides of the equation with a common base. However, most exponential equations cannot be written in this form by inspection. For example:

$$7^x = 60 \qquad \text{60 is not a recognizable}$$
$$7^x = 7^? \qquad \text{power of 7.}$$

To solve such an equation, we can take a logarithm of the same base on each side of the equation, and then apply the power property of logarithms. This is demonstrated in Example 2.

EXAMPLE 2   Solving an Exponential Equation Using Logarithms

Solve. $7^x = 60$

Solution:

$$7^x = 60$$

$$\log 7^x = \log 60$$ Take a logarithm of the same base on both sides of the equation. In this case, we have chosen base 10.

$$x \log 7 = \log 60$$ Apply the power property of logarithms.

This equation is now linear. $$x = \frac{\log 60}{\log 7} \approx 2.1041$$ Divide both sides by log 7.

It is important to note that the exact solution to this equation is $\dfrac{\log 60}{\log 7}$ or equivalently by the change-of-base formula, $\log_7 60$. The value 2.1041 is merely an approximation.

The solution set is $\left\{ \dfrac{\log 60}{\log 7} \right\}$ or $\{\log_7 60\}$.

Avoiding Mistakes

While 2.1041 is only an approximation, it is useful to check the result.

$$7^{2.1041} \approx 60$$

Skill Practice 2   Solve. $5^x = 83$

To solve the equation from Example 2, we can take a logarithm of any base. For example:

$$7^x = 60$$ Take the natural logarithm on both sides. $$7^x = 60$$

$$\log_7 7^x = \log_7 60$$ $$\ln 7^x = \ln 60$$

Take the logarithm base 7 on both sides. $$x = \log_7 60 \text{ (solution)}$$ $$x \ln 7 = \ln 60$$

$$x = \frac{\ln 60}{\ln 7} \text{ (solution)}$$

The values $\log_7 60$, $\dfrac{\log 60}{\log 7}$, and $\dfrac{\ln 60}{\ln 7}$ are all equivalent. However, common logarithms and natural logarithms are often used to express the solution to an exponential equation so that the solution can be approximated on a calculator.

EXAMPLE 3   Solving Exponential Equations Using Logarithms

Solve.   **a.** $10^{5+2x} + 820 = 49{,}600$ **b.** $2000 = 18{,}000e^{-0.4t}$

Solution:

a. $10^{5+2x} + 820 = 49{,}600$ Isolate the exponential expression on the left by subtracting 820 on both sides.

$$10^{5+2x} = 48{,}780$$

$$\log 10^{5+2x} = \log 48{,}780$$ Since the exponential expression on the left has a base of 10, take the log base 10 on both sides. On the left, $\log 10^{5+2x} = 5 + 2x$.

$$5 + 2x = \log 48{,}780$$

$$2x = \log 48{,}780 - 5$$ Solve the linear equation by subtracting 5 and dividing by 2.

$$x = \frac{\log 48{,}780 - 5}{2} \approx -0.1559$$ The solution checks in the original equation.

The solution set is $\left\{ \dfrac{\log 48{,}780 - 5}{2} \right\}$.

Answer

2. $\left\{ \dfrac{\log 83}{\log 5} \right\}$ or $\{\log_5 83\}$

b. $2000 = 18{,}000e^{-0.4t}$ Isolate the exponential expression on the left by dividing both sides by 18,000.

$$\frac{1}{9} = e^{-0.4t}$$

Since the exponential expression on the left has a base of e, take the log base e on both sides.

$$\ln\left(\frac{1}{9}\right) = \ln e^{-0.4t}$$

On the right, $\ln e^{-0.4t} = -0.4t$.

$$\ln\left(\frac{1}{9}\right) = -0.4t$$

(linear equation)

Solve the linear equation by dividing by -0.4.

$$\frac{\ln\left(\dfrac{1}{9}\right)}{-0.4} = t$$

The exact solution to the equation can be written in a variety of forms by applying the properties of logarithms:

$$\frac{\ln\left(\dfrac{1}{9}\right)}{-0.4} = \frac{\ln 1 - \ln 9}{-0.4} = \frac{0 - \ln 9}{-0.4} = \frac{\ln 9}{0.4} \approx 5.4931$$

Alternatively, $\dfrac{\ln 9}{0.4} = \dfrac{\ln 9}{\frac{2}{5}} = \dfrac{5\ln 9}{2} \approx 5.4931$

The solution set is $\left\{\dfrac{\ln 9}{0.4}\right\}$ or $\left\{\dfrac{5 \ln 9}{2}\right\}$.

Skill Practice 3 Solve.

   a. $400 + 10^{4x-1} = 63{,}000$ **b.** $100 = 700e^{-0.2k}$

In Example 4, we have an equation with two exponential expressions involving different bases.

EXAMPLE 4   **Solving an Exponential Equation**

Solve. $4^{2x-7} = 5^{3x+1}$

Solution:

$$4^{2x-7} = 5^{3x+1}$$

$$\ln 4^{2x-7} = \ln 5^{3x+1}$$

Take a logarithm of the same base on both sides.

$$(2x - 7)\ln 4 = (3x + 1)\ln 5$$

Apply the power property of logarithms.

$$2x \ln 4 - 7 \ln 4 = 3x \ln 5 + \ln 5$$

Apply the distributive property.

$$2x \ln 4 - 3x \ln 5 = \ln 5 + 7 \ln 4$$

Collect x terms on one side of the equation.

$$x(2 \ln 4 - 3 \ln 5) = \ln 5 + 7 \ln 4$$

Factor out x on the left.

$$x = \frac{\ln 5 + 7 \ln 4}{2 \ln 4 - 3 \ln 5} \approx -5.5034$$

Divide by $(2 \ln 4 - 3 \ln 5)$.

The solution set is $\left\{\dfrac{\ln 5 + 7 \ln 4}{2 \ln 4 - 3 \ln 5}\right\}$.

The solution checks in the original equation.

Skill Practice 4   Solve. $3^{5x-6} = 2^{4x+1}$

In Example 5, we look at an exponential equation in quadratic form.

Answers

3. a. $\left\{\dfrac{\log 62{,}600 + 1}{4}\right\}$

  b. $\left\{\dfrac{\ln 7}{0.2}\right\}$ or $\{5 \ln 7\}$

4. $\left\{\dfrac{\ln 2 + 6 \ln 3}{5 \ln 3 - 4 \ln 2}\right\}$

> **EXAMPLE 5**   **Solving an Exponential Equation in Quadratic Form**

Solve. $e^{2x} + 5e^x - 36 = 0$

Solution:

$$e^{2x} + 5e^x - 36 = 0$$

$$(e^x)^2 + 5(e^x) - 36 = 0 \qquad \text{Note that } e^{2x} = (e^x)^2.$$

$$u^2 + 5u - 36 = 0 \qquad \text{The equation is in quadratic form. Let } u = e^x.$$

$$(u - 4)(u + 9) = 0 \qquad \text{Factor.}$$

$$u = 4 \quad \text{or} \quad u = -9$$

$$e^x = 4 \quad \text{or} \quad e^x = -9 \qquad \text{Back substitute. The second equation } e^x = -9 \text{ has no}$$

$$\ln e^x = \ln 4 \qquad\qquad\qquad \text{solution.}$$

$$x = \ln 4 \approx 1.3863 \qquad \boxed{\text{No solution to this equation because } \ln(-9) \text{ is undefined.}}$$

The solution set is $\{\ln 4\}$.   The solution checks in the original equation.

Avoiding Mistakes

Recall that the range of $f(x) = e^x$ is the set of positive real numbers. Therefore, $e^x \neq -9$.

> **Skill Practice 5**   Solve. $e^{2x} - 5e^x - 14 = 0$

2. Solve Logarithmic Equations

An equation containing a variable within a logarithmic expression is called a **logarithmic equation.** For example:

$$\log_2(3x - 4) = \log_2(x + 2) \quad \text{and} \quad \ln(x + 4) = 7 \quad \text{are logarithmic equations.}$$

Given an equation in which two logarithms of the same base are equated, we can apply the equivalence property of logarithms. Since all logarithmic functions are one-to-one, $\log_b x = \log_b y$ implies that $x = y$.

TIP The equivalence property tells us that if two logarithmic expressions with the same base are equal, then their arguments must be equal.

> **Equivalence Property of Logarithmic Expressions**
>
> Let b, x, and y be positive real numbers with $b \neq 1$. Then,
>
> $$\log_b x = \log_b y \quad \text{implies that} \quad x = y.$$

> **EXAMPLE 6**   **Solving a Logarithmic Equation Using the Equivalence Property**

Solve. $\log_2(3x - 4) = \log_2(x + 2)$

Solution:

$$\log_2(3x - 4) = \log_2(x + 2) \qquad \text{Two logarithms of the same base are equated.}$$

$$3x - 4 = x + 2 \qquad \text{Equate the arguments.}$$

$$2x = 6 \qquad \text{Solve for } x.$$

$$x = 3 \qquad \text{Because the domain of a logarithm function is restricted, it is mandatory that we check all potential solutions to a logarithmic equation.}$$

$$\text{Check: } \log_2(3x - 4) = \log_2(x + 2)$$

$$\log_2[3(3) - 4] \overset{?}{=} \log_2[(3) + 2]$$

The solution set is $\{3\}$. $\log_2 5 \overset{?}{=} \log_2 5 \ \checkmark$

> **Skill Practice 6**   Solve. $\log_2(7x - 4) = \log_2(2x + 1)$

TECHNOLOGY CONNECTIONS

Using a Calculator to View the Potential Solutions to a Logarithmic Equation

The solution to the equation in Example 6 is the x-coordinate of the point of intersection of $Y_1 = \log_2(3x - 4)$ and $Y_2 = \log_2(x + 2)$. The domain of $Y_1 = \log_2(3x - 4)$ is $\{x \mid x > \frac{4}{3}\}$ and the domain of $Y_2 = \log_2(x + 2)$ is $\{x \mid x > -2\}$. The solution to the equation $Y_1 = Y_2$ may not lie outside the domain of either function. This is why it is mandatory to check all potential solutions to a logarithmic equation.

Many logarithmic equations involve logarithmic terms and constant terms. In such a case, we can apply the properties of logarithms to write the equation in the form $\log_b x = k$, where k is a constant. At this point, we can solve for x by writing the equation in its equivalent exponential form $x = b^k$.

Solving Logarithmic Equations by Using Exponential Form

Step 1 Given a logarithmic equation, isolate the logarithms on one side of the equation.

Step 2 Use the properties of logarithms to write the equation in the form $\log_b x = k$ where k is a constant.

Step 3 Write the equation in exponential form.

Step 4 Solve the equation from step 3.

Step 5 Check the potential solution(s) in the original equation.

EXAMPLE 7   Solving a Logarithmic Equation

Solve. $4 \log_3(2t - 7) = 8$

Solution:

$$4 \log_3(2t - 7) = 8$$

$$\log_3(2t - 7) = 2 \qquad \text{Isolate the logarithm by dividing both sides by 4.}$$

$$\text{The equation is in the form } \log_b x = k \text{ where } x = 2t - 7.$$

$$2t - 7 = 3^2 \qquad \text{Write the equation in exponential form.}$$

$$2t - 7 = 9 \qquad \underline{\text{Check:}} \quad 4 \log_3(2t - 7) = 8$$

$$t = 8 \qquad\qquad\qquad 4 \log_3[2(8) - 7] \overset{?}{=} 8$$

$$\qquad\qquad\qquad\qquad 4 \log_3 9 \overset{?}{=} 8$$

$$\qquad\qquad\qquad\qquad 4 \cdot 2 \overset{?}{=} 8 \checkmark$$

The solution set is $\{8\}$.

Skill Practice 7   Solve. $8 \log_4(w + 6) = 24$

> **EXAMPLE 8**   **Solving a Logarithmic Equation**
>
> Solve. $\log(w + 47) = 2.6$
>
> **Solution:**
>
> $\log(w + 47) = 2.6$ The equation is in the form $\log_b x = k$ where $x = w + 47$ and $b = 10$.
>
> $w + 47 = 10^{2.6}$ Write the equation in exponential form.
>
> $w = 10^{2.6} - 47 \approx 351.1072$ Solve the resulting linear equation.
>
>   Check: $\log(w + 47) = 2.6$
>
> The solution set is $\{10^{2.6} - 47\}$. $\log[(10^{2.6} - 47) + 47] \overset{?}{=} 2.6$
>
> $\log 10^{2.6} \overset{?}{=} 2.6 \checkmark$
>
> ---
>
> **Skill Practice 8**   Solve. $\log(t - 18) = 1.4$

Examples 9 and 10 contain equations with multiple logarithmic terms.

> **EXAMPLE 9**   **Solving a Logarithmic Equation**
>
> Solve. $\log_2 x = 3 - \log_2(x - 2)$
>
> **Solution:**
>
> $\log_2 x = 3 - \log_2(x - 2)$
>
> $\log_2 x + \log_2(x - 2) = 3$ Isolate the logarithms on one side of the equation.
>
> $\log_2[x(x - 2)] = 3$ Use the multiplication property of logarithms to write a single logarithm.
>
> $x(x - 2) = 2^3$ Write the equation in exponential form.
>
> $x^2 - 2x = 8$
>
> $x^2 - 2x - 8 = 0$ Set one side equal to zero.
>
> $(x - 4)(x + 2) = 0$
>
> $x = 4$ $x = -2$ Check: $\log_2 x = 3 - \log_2(x - 2)$ $\log_2 x = 3 - \log_2(x - 2)$
>
> $\log_2 4 \overset{?}{=} 3 - \log_2(4 - 2)$ $\log_2(-2) \overset{?}{=} 3 - \log_2(-2 - 2)$
>
> $\log_2 4 \overset{?}{=} 3 - \log_2 2$ $\log_2(-2) \overset{?}{=} 3 - \log_2(-4)$
>
> $2 \overset{?}{=} 3 - 1 \checkmark$ undefined   undefined
>
> The only solution that checks is $x = 4$.
>
> The solution set is $\{4\}$.
>
> ---
>
> **Skill Practice 9**   Solve. $2 - \log_7 x = \log_7(x - 48)$

Answers

8. $\{10^{1.4} + 18\}$

9. $\{49\}$; The value -1 does not check.

EXAMPLE 10   Solving a Logarithmic Equation

Solve. $\ln(x - 4) = \ln(x + 6) - \ln x$

Solution:

$\ln(x - 4) = \ln(x + 6) - \ln x$	The equation has multiple logarithms.
$\ln(x - 4) + \ln x - \ln(x + 6) = 0$	Isolate the logarithms on one side.
$\ln[x(x - 4)] - \ln(x + 6) = 0$	Apply the product property of logarithms.
$\ln\left[\dfrac{x(x - 4)}{x + 6}\right] = 0$	Apply the quotient property of logarithms.
$\dfrac{x(x - 4)}{x + 6} = e^0$	Write the equation in exponential form.
$\dfrac{x^2 - 4x}{x + 6} = 1$	Simplify. $e^0 = 1$
$x^2 - 4x = x + 6$	Clear fractions by multiplying both sides by $(x + 6)$.
$x^2 - 5x - 6 = 0$	The resulting equation is quadratic.
$(x - 6)(x + 1) = 0$	
$x = 6$ or $x = -1$	The potential solutions are 6 and -1.

> **TIP** The equivalence property of logarithms can also be used to solve the equation in Example 10.
>
> $\ln(x - 4) = \ln(x + 6) - \ln x$
>
> $\ln(x - 4) = \ln\left(\dfrac{x + 6}{x}\right)$
>
> $x - 4 = \dfrac{x + 6}{x}$

Check:

The only solution that checks is 6.

$\ln(x - 4) = \ln(x + 6) - \ln x$

$\ln(6 - 4) \overset{?}{=} \ln(6 + 6) - \ln 6$

$\ln 2 \overset{?}{=} \ln 12 - \ln 6$

The solution set is $\{6\}$.

$\ln 2 \overset{?}{=} \ln\left(\dfrac{12}{6}\right)$ ✓

$\ln(x - 4) = \ln(x + 6) - \ln x$

$\ln(-1 - 4) \overset{?}{=} \ln(-1 + 6) - \ln(-1)$

$\ln(-5) \overset{?}{=} \ln 5 - \ln(-1)$

undefined   undefined

> **Skill Practice 10**   Solve. $\ln x + \ln(x - 8) = \ln(x - 20)$

3. Use Exponential and Logarithmic Equations in Applications

In Examples 11 and 12, we solve applications involving exponential and logarithmic equations.

EXAMPLE 11   Using an Exponential Equation in a Finance Application

A couple invests \$8000 in a bond fund. The expected yield is 4.5% and the earnings are reinvested monthly.

a. Use $A = P\left(1 + \dfrac{r}{n}\right)^{nt}$ to write a model representing the amount A (in \$) in the account after t years. The value r is the interest rate and n is the number of times interest is compounded per year.

b. Determine how long it will take the initial investment to double. Round to 1 decimal place.

> **TIP** Recall that monthly compounding indicates that interest is computed $n = 12$ times per year.

Solution:

a. $A = P\left(1 + \dfrac{r}{n}\right)^{nt}$

$A = 8000\left(1 + \dfrac{0.045}{12}\right)^{12t}$ Substitute $P = 8000$, $r = 0.045$, and $n = 12$.

Answer

10. $\{\ \}$; The values 4 and 5 do not check.

b. $16{,}000 = 8000\left(1 + \dfrac{0.045}{12}\right)^{12t}$ The couple wants to double their money from $8000 to $16,000. Substitute $A = 16{,}000$ and solve for t.

$2 = \left(1 + \dfrac{0.045}{12}\right)^{12t}$ Isolate the exponential expression by dividing both sides by 8000.

$\ln 2 = \ln\left(1 + \dfrac{0.045}{12}\right)^{12t}$ Take a logarithm of the same base on both sides. We have chosen to use the natural logarithm.

$\ln 2 = 12t \ln\left(1 + \dfrac{0.045}{12}\right)$ The equation is now linear in the variable t.

$\dfrac{\ln 2}{12 \ln\left(1 + \dfrac{0.045}{12}\right)} = t$ Divide both sides by $12 \ln\left(1 + \frac{0.045}{12}\right)$.

$t \approx 15.4$

It will take approximately 15.4 yr for the investment to double.

Skill Practice 11   Determine how long it will take $8000 compounded monthly at 6% to double. Round to 1 decimal place.

In Example 12, we use a logarithmic equation in an application.

EXAMPLE 12   Using a Logarithmic Equation in a Medical Application

Suppose that the sound at a rock concert measures 124 dB (decibels).

a. Use the formula $L = 10 \log\left(\frac{I}{I_0}\right)$ to find the intensity of sound I (in W/m^2). The variable L represents the loudness of sound (in dB) and $I_0 = 10^{-12}$ W/m^2.

b. If the threshold at which sounds become painful is 1 W/m^2, will the music at this concert be physically painful? (Ignore the quality of the music.)

Solution:

a. $L = 10 \log\left(\dfrac{I}{I_0}\right)$

$124 = 10 \log\left(\dfrac{I}{10^{-12}}\right)$ Substitute 124 for L and 10^{-12} for I_0.

$12.4 = \log\left(\dfrac{I}{10^{-12}}\right)$ Divide both sides by 10. The logarithm is now isolated.

$10^{12.4} = \dfrac{I}{10^{-12}}$ Write the equation in exponential form.

$10^{12.4} \cdot 10^{-12} = I$ Multiply both sides by 10^{-12}.

$I = 10^{0.4} \approx 2.5$ W/m^2 Simplify.

b. The intensity of sound at the rock concert is approximately 2.5 W/m^2. This is above the threshold for pain.

Skill Practice 12

a. Find the intensity of sound from a leaf blower if the decibel level is 115 dB.

b. Is the intensity of sound from a leaf blower above the threshold for pain?

Answers
11. 11.6 yr
12. a. $10^{-0.5}$ W/m$^2 \approx 0.3$ W/m^2
    b. No

TECHNOLOGY CONNECTIONS

Using a Calculator to Approximate the Solutions to Exponential and Logarithmic Equations

There are many situations in which analytical methods fail to give a solution to a logarithmic or exponential equation. We can find solutions graphically as follows.

Enter the left side of the equation as Y_1.

Enter the right side of the equation as Y_2.

Then determine the point(s) of intersection of their graphs.

<u>Example</u>: $e^x + 2x - 7 = 0$
$Y_1 = e^x + 2x - 7$
$Y_2 = 0$ Solution: $x \approx 1.4237$

<u>Example</u>: $4 \ln x - 3x = -8$
$Y_1 = 4 \ln x - 3x$
$Y_2 = -8$ Solutions: $x \approx 0.1516$ and $x \approx 4.7419$

SECTION 4.5   Practice Exercises

Review Exercises

For Exercises 1–2, write the logarithmic form for the given equation.

1. $400 = e^{-0.2t}$

2. $8721 = 10^{-0.003k}$

For Exercises 3–4, write the exponential form for the given equation.

3. $\log 11{,}000 = 4w + 6$

4. $\ln 850 = 3z + 2$

For Exercises 5–6, solve the equation.

5. $14x \ln 7 = 2 \ln 3 + 7 \ln 2$

6. $7x \log 3 = 2 \log 5 - 3 \log 11$

Concept Connections

7. An equation such as $4^x = 9$ is called an _____ equation because the equation contains a variable in the exponent.

8. The equivalence property of exponential expressions states that if $b^x = b^y$, then _____ = _____.

9. The equivalence property of logarithmic expressions states that if $\log_b x = \log_b y$, then _____ = _____.

10. An equation containing a variable within a logarithmic expression is called a _____ equation.

Objective 1: Solve Exponential Equations

For Exercises 11–22, solve the equation. (See Example 1)

11. $3^x = 81$　　　　**12.** $2^x = 32$　　　　**13.** $\sqrt[3]{5} = 5^t$　　　　**14.** $\sqrt{3} = 3^w$

15. $2^{-3y+1} = 16$　　**16.** $5^{2z+2} = 625$　　**17.** $11^{3c+1} = \left(\dfrac{1}{11}\right)^{c-5}$　　**18.** $7^{2x-3} = \left(\dfrac{1}{49}\right)^{x+1}$

19. $8^{2x-5} = 32^{x-6}$　　**20.** $27^{x-4} = 9^{2x+1}$　　**21.** $100^{3t-5} = 1000^{3-t}$　　**22.** $100,000^{2w+1} = 10,000^{4-w}$

For Exercises 23–38, solve the equation. Write the solution set with the exact values given in terms of common or natural logarithms. Also give approximate solutions to 4 decimal places. (See Examples 2–5)

23. $6^t = 87$ 　　　　　　　　　**24.** $2^z = 70$ 　　　　　　　　　**25.** $1024 = 19^x + 4$

26. $801 = 23^y + 6$ 　　　　　　**27.** $10^{3+4x} - 8100 = 120,000$ 　　**28.** $10^{5+8x} + 4200 = 84,000$

29. $21,000 = 63,000e^{-0.2t}$ 　　**30.** $80 = 320e^{-0.5t}$ 　　　　　　**31.** $3^{6x+5} = 5^{2x}$

32. $7^{4x-1} = 3^{5x}$ 　　　　　　**33.** $2^{1-6x} = 7^{3x+4}$ 　　　　　　**34.** $11^{1-8x} = 9^{2x+3}$

35. $e^{2x} - 9e^x - 22 = 0$ 　　　**36.** $e^{2x} - 6e^x - 16 = 0$ 　　　　**37.** $e^{2x} = -9e^x$

38. $e^{2x} = -7e^x$

Objective 2: Solve Logarithmic Equations

For Exercises 39–40, determine if the given value of x is a solution to the logarithmic equation.

39. $\log_2(x - 31) = 5 - \log_2 x$ 　　　　　　**40.** $\log_4 x = 3 - \log_4(x - 63)$

　　a. $x = 16$ 　　　　　　　　　　　　　　　　**a.** $x = 64$

　　b. $x = 32$ 　　　　　　　　　　　　　　　　**b.** $x = -1$

　　c. $x = -1$ 　　　　　　　　　　　　　　　　**c.** $x = 32$

For Exercises 41–62, solve the equation. Write the solution set with the exact solutions. Also give approximate solutions to 4 decimal places if necessary. (See Examples 6–10)

41. $\log_4(3w + 11) = \log_4(3 - w)$ 　　**42.** $\log_7(12 - t) = \log_7(t + 6)$ 　　**43.** $\log(x^2 + 7x) = \log 18$

44. $\log(p^2 + 6p) = \log 7$ 　　　　　**45.** $6 \log_5(4p - 3) = 18$ 　　　　　**46.** $5 \log_6(7w + 1) = 10$

47. $\log_8(3y - 5) + 10 = 12$ 　　　**48.** $\log_3(7 - 5z) + 14 = 17$ 　　　**49.** $\log(p + 17) = 4.1$

50. $\log(q - 6) = 3.5$ 　　　　　　　**51.** $2 \ln(4 - 3t) + 1 = 7$ 　　　　　**52.** $4 \ln(6 - 5t) + 2 = 22$

53. $\log_2 w - 3 = -\log_2(w + 2)$ 　　**54.** $\log_3 y + \log_3(y + 6) = 3$ 　　**55.** $\log_6(7x - 2) = 1 + \log_6(x + 5)$

56. $\log_4(5x - 13) = 1 + \log_4(x - 2)$ 　**57.** $\log_5 z = 3 - \log_5(z - 20)$ 　　**58.** $\log_2 x = 4 - \log_2(x - 6)$

59. $\ln x + \ln(x - 4) = \ln(3x - 10)$ 　**60.** $\ln x + \ln(x - 3) = \ln(5x - 7)$ 　**61.** $\log x + \log(x - 7) = \log(x - 15)$

62. $\log x + \log(x - 10) = \log(x - 18)$

Objective 3: Use Exponential and Logarithmic Equations in Applications

For Exercises 63–64, use the model $A = Pe^{rt}$. The variable A represents the future value of P dollars invested at an interest rate r compounded continuously for t years.

63. If $10,000 is invested in an account earning 5.5% interest compounded continuously, determine how long it will take the money to triple. Round to the nearest year.

64. If a couple has $80,000 in a retirement account, how long will it take the money to grow to $1,000,000 if it grows by 6% compounded continuously? Round to the nearest year.

For Exercises 65–66, use the model $A = P\left(1 + \dfrac{r}{n}\right)^{nt}$. The variable A represents the future value of P dollars invested at an interest rate r compounded n times per year for t years. (See Example 11)

65. If $4000 is put aside in a money market account with interest reinvested monthly at 2.2%, find the time required for the account to *earn* $1000. Round to the nearest month.

66. Barb puts aside $10,000 in an account with interest reinvested monthly at 2.5%. How long will it take for her to *earn* $2000? Round to the nearest month.

67. Physicians often treat thyroid cancer with a radioactive form of iodine called iodine-131 (^{131}I). The radiological half-life of ^{131}I is approximately 8 days, but the biological half-life for most individuals is 4.2 days. The biological half-life is shorter because in addition to ^{131}I being lost to decay, the iodine is also excreted from the body in urine, sweat, and saliva.

For a patient treated with 100 mCi (millicuries) of ^{131}I, the radioactivity level R (in mCi) after t days is given by $R = 100(2)^{-t/4.2}$.

a. State law mandates that the patient stay in an isolated hospital room for 2 days after treatment with ^{131}I. Determine the radioactivity level at the end of 2 days. Round to the nearest whole unit.

b. After the patient is released from the hospital, the patient is directed to avoid direct human contact until the radioactivity level drops below 30 mCi. For how many days *after* leaving the hospital will the patient need to stay in isolation? Round to the nearest tenth of a day.

68. Caffeine occurs naturally in a variety of food products such as coffee, tea, and chocolate. The kidneys filter the blood and remove caffeine and other drugs through urine. The biological half-life of caffeine is approximately 6 hr. If one cup of coffee has 80 mg of caffeine, then the amount of caffeine C (in mg) remaining after t hours is given by $C = 80(2)^{-t/6}$.

a. How long will it take for the amount of caffeine to drop below 60 mg? Round to 1 decimal place.

b. Laura has trouble sleeping if she has more than 30 mg of caffeine in her bloodstream. How many hours before going to bed should she stop drinking coffee? Round to 1 decimal place.

Sunlight is absorbed in water, and as a result the light intensity in oceans, lakes, and ponds decreases exponentially with depth. The percentage of visible light P (in decimal form) at a depth of x meters is given by $P = e^{-kx}$, where k is a constant related to the clarity and other physical properties of the water. The graph shows models for the open ocean, Lake Tahoe, and Lake Erie for data taken under similar conditions. Use these models for Exercises 69–72.

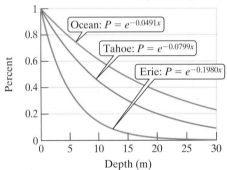

Percent of Surface Light vs. Depth

Ocean: $P = e^{-0.0491x}$
Tahoe: $P = e^{-0.0799x}$
Erie: $P = e^{-0.1980x}$

69. Determine the depth at which the light intensity is half the value from the surface for each body of water given. Round to the nearest tenth of a meter.

70. Determine the depth at which the light intensity is 20% of the value from the surface for each body of water given. Round to the nearest tenth of a meter.

71. The *euphotic* depth is the depth at which light intensity falls to 1% of the value at the surface. This depth is of interest to scientists because no appreciable photosynthesis takes place. Find the euphotic depth for the open ocean. Round to the nearest tenth of a meter.

72. Refer back to Exercise 71, and find the euphotic depth for Lake Tahoe and for Lake Erie. Round to the nearest tenth of a meter.

73. Forge welding is a process in which two pieces of steel are joined together by heating the pieces of steel and hammering them together. A welder takes a piece of steel from a forge at 1600°F and places it on an anvil where the outdoor temperature is 50°F. The temperature of the steel T (in °F) can be modeled by $T = 50 + 1550e^{-0.05t}$, where t is the time in minutes after the steel is removed from the forge. How long will it take for the steel to reach a temperature of 100°F so that it can be handled without heat protection? Round to the nearest minute.

74. A pie comes out of the oven at 325°F and is placed to cool in a 70°F kitchen. The temperature of the pie T (in °F) after t minutes is given by $T = 70 + 255e^{-0.017t}$. The pie is cool enough to cut when the temperature reaches 110°F. How long will this take? Round to the nearest minute.

For Exercises 75–76, the formula $L = 10 \log\left(\frac{I}{I_0}\right)$ gives the loudness of sound L (in dB) based on the intensity of sound I (in W/m^2). The value $I_0 = 10^{-12}$ W/m^2 is the minimal threshold for hearing for midfrequency sounds. Hearing impairment is often measured according to the minimal sound level (in dB) detected by an individual for sounds at various frequencies. For one frequency, the table depicts the level of hearing impairment.

Category	Loudness (dB)
Mild	$26 \le L \le 40$
Moderate	$41 \le L \le 55$
Moderately severe	$56 \le L \le 70$
Severe	$71 \le L \le 90$
Profound	$L > 90$

75. a. If the minimum intensity heard by an individual is 3.4×10^{-8} W/m^2, determine if the individual has a hearing impairment.

   b. If the minimum loudness of sound detected by an individual is 30 dB, determine the corresponding intensity of sound. (**See Example 12**)

76. Determine the range that represents the intensity of sound that can be heard by an individual with severe hearing impairment.

The apparent magnitude of a star refers to the brightness of the star. Objects with lower magnitude appear brighter to the eye than objects with higher magnitude. For example, the full moon has a magnitude of -12.6, whereas the naked eye can barely see an object of magnitude 6. For higher magnitudes, a telescope is required. However, even a telescope has its limitations. The limiting magnitude L of an optical telescope with lens diameter D (in inches) is given by $L(D) = 8.8 + 5.1 \log D$. Use this function for Exercises 77–78.

77. a. Find the limiting magnitude for a telescope with lens 6 in. in diameter. Round to 1 decimal place.

   b. Find the lens-diameter of a telescope whose limiting magnitude is 15.5. Round to the nearest inch.

78. a. Find the limiting magnitude for a telescope with a lens 4 in. in diameter. Round to 1 decimal place.

   b. How large a telescope is needed to see a galaxy with magnitude 17? Round to the nearest inch.

For Exercises 79–80, use the formula pH $= -\log[\text{H}^+]$. The variable pH represents the level of acidity or alkalinity of a liquid on the pH scale, and H$^+$ is the concentration of hydronium ions in the solution. Determine the value of H$^+$ (in mol/L) for the following liquids, given their pH values.

79. a. Seawater pH $= 8.5$

   b. Acid rain pH $= 2.3$

80. a. Milk pH $= 6.2$

   b. Sodium bicarbonate pH $= 8.4$

81. A new teaching method to teach vocabulary to sixth-graders involves having students work in groups on an assignment to learn new words. After the lesson was completed, the students were tested at 1-month intervals. The average score for the class $S(t)$ can be modeled by

$$S(t) = 94 - 18 \ln(t + 1)$$

where t is the time in months after completing the assignment. If the average score is 65, how many months had passed since the students completed the assignment?

82. A company spends x hundred dollars on an advertising campaign. The amount of money in sales $S(x)$ (in $1000) for the 4-month period after the advertising campaign can be modeled by

$$S(x) = 5 + 7 \ln(x + 1)$$

If the sales total $19,100, how much was spent on advertising?

83. A certain chemotherapy drug is sometimes given to patients undergoing bone marrow transplantation. The concentration $C(t)$ (in μmol/L) of the drug in the bloodstream t minutes after ingestion can be approximated by

$$C(t) = \begin{cases} -0.088 + 0.89 \ln(t + 2) & \text{for } 0 < t < 72 \\ 4.64e^{-0.003t} & \text{for } t \ge 72 \end{cases}$$

The prime efficacy of the drug takes place when the concentration is above 1.5 μmol/L. Determine the time interval for which the drug is most effective. Round to the nearest minute.

84. On August 31, 1854, an epidemic of cholera was discovered in London, England, resulting from a contaminated community water pump. By the end of September, more than 600 citizens who drank water from the pump had died. The cumulative number of deaths $D(t)$ at a time t days after August 31 is given by $D(t) = 91 + 160 \ln(t + 1)$.

   a. Determine the cumulative number of deaths by September 15. Round to the nearest whole unit.

   b. Approximately how many days after August 31 did the cumulative number of deaths reach 600?

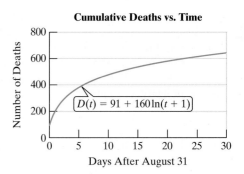

Cumulative Deaths vs. Time

$D(t) = 91 + 160 \ln(t + 1)$

Number of Deaths — Days After August 31

Mixed Exercises

For Exercises 85–92, find an equation for the inverse function.

85. $f(x) = 2^x - 7$ **86.** $f(x) = 5^x + 6$ **87.** $f(x) = \ln(x + 5)$

88. $f(x) = \ln(x - 7)$ **89.** $f(x) = 10^{x-3} + 1$ **90.** $f(x) = 10^{x+2} - 4$

91. $f(x) = \log(x + 7) - 9$ **92.** $f(x) = \log(x - 11) + 8$

For Exercises 93–110, solve the equation. Write the solution set with exact solutions. Also give approximate solutions to 4 decimal places if necessary.

93. $5^{|x|} - 3 = 122$ **94.** $11^{|x|} + 9 = 130$ **95.** $\log x - 2 \log 3 = 2$

96. $\log y - 3 \log 5 = 3$ **97.** $6^{x^2-2} = 36$ **98.** $8^{y^2-7} = 64$

99. $\log_9 |x + 4| = \log_9 6$ **100.** $\log_8 |3 - x| = \log_8 5$ **101.** $x^2 e^x = 9e^x$

102. $x^2 6^x = 6^x$ **103.** $\log_3(\log_3 x) = 0$ **104.** $\log_5(\log_5 x) = 1$

105. $3|\ln x| - 12 = 0$ **106.** $7|\ln x| - 14 = 0$ **107.** $\log_3 x - \log_3(2x + 6) = \dfrac{1}{2}\log_3 4$

108. $\log_5 x - \log_5(x + 1) = \dfrac{1}{3}\log_5 8$ **109.** $2e^x(e^x - 3) = 3e^x - 4$ **110.** $3e^x(e^x - 6) = 4e^x - 7$

Write About It

111. Explain the equivalence property of exponential expressions.

112. Explain the equivalence property of logarithmic expressions.

113. Explain the process to solve the equation $4^x = 11$.

114. Explain the process to solve the equation $\log_b 5 + \log_b(x - 3) = 4$.

Expanding Your Skills

For Exercises 115–126, solve the equation.

115. $\dfrac{10^x - 13 \cdot 10^{-x}}{3} = 4$ **116.** $\dfrac{e^x - 9e^{-x}}{2} = 4$ **117.** $(\ln x)^2 - \ln x^5 = -4$

118. $(\ln x)^2 + \ln x^3 = -2$ **119.** $(\log x)^2 = \log x^2$ **120.** $(\log x)^2 = \log x^3$

121. $\log w + 4\sqrt{\log w} - 12 = 0$ **122.** $\ln x + 3\sqrt{\ln x} - 10 = 0$ **123.** $e^{2x} - 8e^x + 6 = 0$

124. $e^{2x} - 6e^x + 4 = 0$ **125.** $\log_5\sqrt{6c + 5} + \log_5\sqrt{c} = 1$ **126.** $\log_3\sqrt{x - 8} + \log_3\sqrt{x} = 1$

Technology Connections

For Exercises 127–130, an equation is given in the form $Y_1(x) = Y_2(x)$. Graph Y_1 and Y_2 on a graphing utility on the window [10, 10, 1] by [10, 10, 1]. Then approximate the point(s) of intersection to approximate the solution(s) to the equation. Round to 4 decimal places.

127. $4x - e^x + 6 = 0$ **128.** $x^3 - e^{2x} + 4 = 0$ **129.** $x^2 + 5 \log x = 6$ **130.** $x^2 - 0.05 \ln x = 4$

SECTION 4.6   # Modeling with Exponential and Logarithmic Functions

1. Solve Literal Equations for a Specified Variable

A short-term model to predict the U.S. population P is $P = 310e^{0.00965t}$, where t is the number of years since 2010. If we solve this equation for t, we have

$$t = \frac{\ln\left(\dfrac{P}{310}\right)}{0.00965}$$

This is a model that predicts the time required for the U.S. population to reach a value P. Manipulating an equation for a specified variable was first introduced in Section 1.1. In Example 1, we revisit this skill using exponential and logarithmic equations.

EXAMPLE 1   **Solving an Equation for a Specified Variable**

a. Given $P = 100e^{kx} - 100$, solve for x. (Used in geology)
b. Given $L = 8.8 + 5.1 \log D$, solve for D. (Used in astronomy)

Solution:

a. $P = 100e^{kx} - 100$

$\qquad P + 100 = 100e^{kx}$ Add 100 to both sides to isolate the x term.

$\qquad \dfrac{P + 100}{100} = e^{kx}$ Divide by 100.

$\qquad \ln\left(\dfrac{P + 100}{100}\right) = \ln e^{kx}$ Take the natural logarithm of both sides.

$\qquad \ln\left(\dfrac{P + 100}{100}\right) = kx$ Simplify: $\ln e^{kx} = kx$

$\qquad x = \dfrac{\ln\left(\dfrac{P + 100}{100}\right)}{k}$ Divide by k.

b. $L = 8.8 + 5.1 \log D$

$\qquad \dfrac{L - 8.8}{5.1} = \log D$ Subtract 8.8 from both sides and divide by 5.1.

$\qquad D = 10^{(L-8.8)/5.1}$ Write the equation in exponential form.

Skill Practice 1

a. Given $T = 78 + 272e^{-kt}$, solve for k.
b. Given $S = 90 - 20 \ln(t + 1)$, solve for t.

2. Create Models for Exponential Growth and Decay

In Section 4.2, we defined an exponential function as $y = b^x$, where $b > 0$ and $b \neq 1$. Throughout the chapter, we have used transformations of basic exponential functions to solve a variety of applications. The following variation of the general exponential form is used to solve applications involving exponential growth and decay.

Answers

1. a. $k = -\dfrac{\ln\left(\dfrac{T - 78}{272}\right)}{t}$

$\quad$ **b.** $e^{(90-S)/20} - 1$

Exponential Growth and Decay Models

Let y be a variable changing exponentially with respect to t, and let y_0 represent the initial value of y when $t = 0$. Then for a constant k:

If $k > 0$, then $y = y_0 e^{kt}$ is a model for exponential growth.	If $k < 0$, then $y = y_0 e^{kt}$ is a model for exponential decay.

Example:

$y = 2000e^{0.06t}$ represents the value of a \$2000 investment after t years with interest compounded continuously.

(*Note:* $k = 0.06 > 0$)

Example:

$y = 100e^{-0.165t}$ represents the radioactivity level t hours after a patient is treated for thyroid cancer with 100 mCi of radioactive iodine.

(*Note:* $k = -0.165 < 0$)

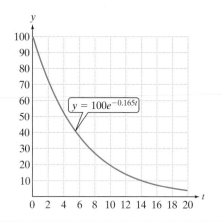

The model $y = y_0 e^{kt}$ is often presented with different letters or symbols in place of y, y_0, k, and t to convey their meaning in the context of the application. For example, to compute the value of an investment under continuous compounding, we have

$$A = Pe^{rt}$$

P (for principal) is used in place of y_0.
r (for the annual interest rate) is used in place of k.
A (for the future value of the investment) is used in place of y.

We can also use function notation when expressing a model for exponential growth or decay. For example, consider the model for population growth.

$$P(t) = P_0 e^{kt}$$

P_0 (for initial population) is used in place of y_0.
$P(t)$ represents the population as a function of time and is used in place of y.

EXAMPLE 2   Creating a Model for Growth of an Investment

Suppose that \$15,000 is initially invested in a mutual fund. At the end of 3 yr, the value of the account is \$19,356.92. Use the model $A = Pe^{rt}$ to determine the average rate of return r under continuous compounding.

Solution:

$$A = Pe^{rt} \qquad \text{Begin with an appropriate model.}$$

$$A = 15,000e^{rt} \qquad \begin{array}{l}\text{P represents the initial value of the account (initial} \\ \text{principal). Substitute 15,000 for P.}\end{array}$$

$$19,356.92 = 15,000e^{r(3)} \qquad \begin{array}{l}\text{We have a known data point where $A = 19,356.92$ when} \\ \text{$t = 3$. Substituting these values into the formula enables} \\ \text{us to solve for r.}\end{array}$$

$$\frac{19,356.92}{15,000} = e^{3r} \qquad \text{Divide both sides by 15,000.}$$

$$\ln\left(\frac{19,356.92}{15,000}\right) = \ln(e^{3r}) \qquad \text{Take the natural logarithm of both sides.}$$

$$\ln\left(\frac{19,356.92}{15,000}\right) = 3r \qquad \text{Simplify: } \ln e^{3r} = 3r$$

$$r = \frac{\ln\left(\dfrac{19,356.92}{15,000}\right)}{3} \qquad \text{Divide by 3 to isolate } r.$$

$$r \approx 0.085$$

The average rate of return is approximately 8.5%.

Skill Practice 2   Suppose that $10,000 is initially invested in a stock. At the end of 5 yr, the value of the account is $13,771.28. Use the model $A = Pe^{rt}$ to determine the average rate of return r under continuous compounding.

In Example 3, we build a model to predict short-term population growth.

EXAMPLE 3   Creating a Model for Population Growth

On January 1, 2000, the population of California was approximately 34 million. On January 1, 2010, the population was 37.3 million.

a. Write a function of the form $P(t) = P_0e^{kt}$ to represent the population of California $P(t)$ (in millions), t years after January 1, 2000. Round k to 5 decimal places.

b. Use the function in part (a) to predict the population on January 1, 2018. Round to 1 decimal place.

c. Use the function from part (a) to determine the year during which the population of California will be twice the value from the year 2000.

Solution:

a.

$$P(t) = P_0e^{kt} \qquad \text{Begin with an appropriate model.}$$

$$P(t) = 34e^{kt} \qquad \text{The initial population is } P_0 = 34 \text{ million.}$$

$$37.3 = 34e^{k(10)} \qquad \begin{array}{l}\text{We have a known data point $P(10) = 37.3$.} \\ \text{Substituting these values into the function enables us} \\ \text{to solve for k.}\end{array}$$

$$\frac{37.3}{34} = e^{k(10)} \qquad \text{Divide both sides by 34.}$$

$$\ln\left(\frac{37.3}{34}\right) = 10k \qquad \text{Take the natural logarithm of both sides.}$$

$$k = \frac{\ln\left(\dfrac{37.3}{34}\right)}{10} \approx 0.00926 \qquad \text{Divide by 10 to isolate } k.$$

$$P(t) = 34e^{0.00926t} \qquad \text{This model gives the population as a function of time.}$$

TIP The value of k in the model $P(t) = P_0e^{kt}$ is called a parameter and is related to the growth rate of the population being studied. The value of k will be different for different populations.

Answer

2. 6.4%

b. $P(t) = 34e^{0.00926t}$

$P(18) = 34e^{0.00926(18)}$ Substitute 18 for t.

$= 40.2$

The population in California on January 1, 2018, will be approximately 40.2 million if this trend continues.

c. $P(t) = 34e^{0.00926t}$

$68 = 34e^{0.00926t}$ Substitute 68 for $P(t)$.

$\dfrac{68}{34} = e^{0.00926t}$ Divide both sides by 34.

$\ln 2 = 0.00926t$ Take the natural logarithm of both sides.

$t = \dfrac{\ln 2}{0.00926} \approx 74.85$ Divide by 0.00926 to isolate t.

The population of California will reach 68 million toward the end of the year 2074 if this trend continues.

Skill Practice 3   On January 1, 2000, the population of Texas was approximately 21 million. On January 1, 2010, the population was 25.2 million.

a. Write a function of the form $P(t) = P_0 e^{kt}$ to represent the population $P(t)$ of Texas t years after January 1, 2000. Round k to 5 decimal places.

b. Use the function in part (a) to predict the population on January 1, 2020. Round to 1 decimal place.

c. Use the function in part (a) to determine the year during which the population of Texas will reach 40 million if this trend continues.

An exponential model can be presented with a base other than base e. For example, suppose that a culture of bacteria begins with 5000 organisms and the population doubles every 4 hr. Then the population $P(t)$ can be modeled by

$P(t) = 5000(2)^{t/4}$, where t is the time in hours after the culture was started.

Notice that this function is defined using base 2. It is important to realize that any exponential function of one base can be rewritten in terms of an exponential function of another base. In particular we are interested in expressing the function with base e.

Writing an Exponential Expression Using Base e

Let t and b be real numbers, where $b > 0$ and $b \neq 1$. Then,

$$b^t \text{ is equivalent to } e^{(\ln b)t}.$$

To show that $e^{(\ln b)t} = b^t$, use the power property of exponents; that is,

$$e^{(\ln b)t} = (e^{\ln b})^t = b^t$$

EXAMPLE 4   **Writing an Exponential Function with Base e**

a. The population $P(t)$ of a culture of bacteria is given by $P(t) = 5000(2)^{t/4}$, where t is the time in hours after the culture was started. Write the rule for this function using base e.

b. Find the population after 12 hr using both forms of the function from part (a).

Answers

3. a. $P(t) = 21e^{0.01823t}$

 b. 30.2 million

 c. 2035

Solution:

a. $P(t) = 5000(2)^{t/4}$

Note that $2^{t/4} = (2^t)^{1/4}$

$\qquad = \left[e^{(\ln 2)t}\right]^{1/4}$ Apply the property that $e^{(\ln b)t} = b^t$.

$\qquad = e^{[(\ln 2)/4]t}$ Apply the power rule of exponents.

Therefore, $P(t) = 5000(2)^{t/4}$

$\qquad\qquad\quad = 5000e^{[(\ln 2)/4]t}$

$\qquad\qquad\quad \approx 5000e^{0.17329t}$

b. $P(t) = 5000(2)^{t/4}$ $P(t) \approx 5000e^{0.17329t}$

$\quad P(12) = 5000(2)^{(12)/4}$ $P(12) \approx 5000e^{0.17329(12)}$

$\qquad\qquad = 40{,}000$ $\approx 40{,}000$

Skill Practice 4

a. Given $P(t) = 10{,}000(2)^{-0.4t}$, write the rule for this function using base e.

b. Find the function value for $t = 10$ for both forms of the function from part (a).

In Example 5, we apply an exponential decay function to determine the age of a bone through radiocarbon dating. Animals ingest carbon through respiration and through the food they eat. Most of the carbon is carbon-12 (^{12}C), an abundant and stable form of carbon. However, a small percentage of carbon is the radioactive isotope, carbon-14 (^{14}C). The ratio of carbon-12 to carbon-14 is constant for all living things. When an organism dies, it no longer takes in carbon from the environment. Therefore, as the carbon-14 decays, the ratio of carbon-12 to carbon-14 changes. Scientists know that the half-life of ^{14}C is 5730 years and from this, they can build a model to represent the amount of ^{14}C remaining t years after death. This is illustrated in Example 5.

EXAMPLE 5 **Creating a Model for Exponential Decay**

a. Carbon-14 has a half-life of 5730 yr. Write a model of the form $Q(t) = Q_0 e^{-kt}$ to represent the amount $Q(t)$ of carbon-14 remaining after t years if no additional carbon is ingested.

b. An archeologist uncovers human remains at an ancient Roman burial site and finds that 76.6% of the carbon-14 still remains in the bone. How old is the bone? Round to the nearest hundred years.

TIP Given the half-life of a radioactive substance, we can also write an exponential model using base $\frac{1}{2}$. The format is

$$Q(t) = Q_0\left(\frac{1}{2}\right)^{t/h}$$

where h is the half-life of the substance.

In Example 5, we have:

$$Q(t) = Q_0\left(\frac{1}{2}\right)^{t/5730}$$

Solution:

a. $Q(t) = Q_0 e^{-kt}$ Begin with a general exponential decay model.

$\quad 0.5Q_0 = Q_0 e^{-k(5730)}$ Substitute the known data value. One-half of the original quantity Q_0 is present after 5730 yr.

$\qquad 0.5 = e^{-k(5730)}$ Divide by Q_0 on both sides.

$\quad \ln 0.5 = -5730k$ Take the natural logarithm of both sides.

$\qquad\quad k = \dfrac{\ln 0.5}{-5730}$ Divide by -5730.

$\qquad\qquad \approx 0.000121$

$\quad Q(t) = Q_0 e^{-0.000121t}$

Answers

4. a. $P(t) = 10{,}000e^{-0.27726t}$

    b. 625

b. $0.766Q_0 = Q_0 e^{-0.000121t}$ The quantity $Q(t)$ of carbon-14 in the bone is 76.6% of Q_0.

$0.766 = e^{-0.000121t}$ Divide by Q_0 on both sides.

$\ln 0.766 = -0.000121t$ Take the natural logarithm of both sides.

$t = \dfrac{\ln 0.766}{-0.000121} \approx 2200$ Divide by -0.000121 to isolate t.

The bone is approximately 2200 years old.

Skill Practice 5   Use the function $Q(t) = Q_0 e^{-0.000121t}$ to determine the age of a piece of wood that has 42% of its carbon-14 remaining. Round to the nearest 10 yr.

---

3. Apply Logistic Growth Models

In Examples 3 and 4, we used a model of the form $P(t) = P_0 e^{kt}$ to predict population as an exponential function of time. However, unbounded population growth is not possible due to limited resources. A growth model that addresses this problem is called logistic growth. In particular, a logistic growth model imposes a limiting value on the dependent variable.

Logistic Growth Model

A logistic growth model is a function written in the form

$$y = \frac{c}{1 + ae^{-bt}}$$

where a, b, and c are positive constants.

The general logistic growth equation can be written with a complex fraction.

$$y = \frac{c}{1 + \dfrac{a}{e^{bt}}}$$ This term approaches 0 as t approaches ∞.

In this form, we can see that for large values of t, the term $\dfrac{a}{e^{bt}}$ approaches 0, and the function value y approaches $\frac{c}{1}$.

The line $y = c$ is a horizontal asymptote of the graph, and c represents the limiting value of the function (see Figure 4-16).

Notice that the graph of a logistic curve is increasing over its entire domain. However, the *rate* of increase begins to decrease as the function levels off and approaches the horizontal asymptote $y = c$.

In Example 3 we created a function to approximate the population of California assuming unlimited growth. In Example 6, we use a logistic growth model.

TIP The rate of increase of a logistic curve changes from increasing to decreasing to the left and right of a point called the *point of inflection*.

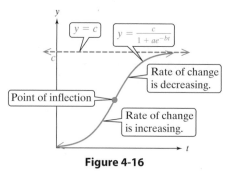

Figure 4-16

EXAMPLE 6   **Using Logistic Growth to Model Population**

The population of California $P(t)$ (in millions) can be approximated by the logistic growth function

$$P(t) = \frac{95.2}{1 + 1.8e^{-0.018t}}, \text{ where } t \text{ is the number of years since the year 2000.}$$

a. Determine the population in the year 2000.

b. Use this function to determine the time required for the population of California to double from its value in 2000. Compare this with the result from Example 3(c).

c. What is the limiting value of the population of California under this model?

Solution:

a. $P(t) = \dfrac{95.2}{1 + 1.8e^{-0.018t}}$

$P(0) = \dfrac{95.2}{1 + 1.8e^{-0.018(0)}} = \dfrac{95.2}{1 + 1.8(1)} = 34$ Substitute 0 for t. Recall that $e^0 = 1$.

The population was approximately 34 million in the year 2000.

b. $68 = \dfrac{95.2}{1 + 1.8e^{-0.018t}}$ Substitute 68 for $P(t)$.

$68(1 + 1.8e^{-0.018t}) = 95.2$ Multiply both sides by $(1 + 1.8e^{-0.018t})$.

$1 + 1.8e^{-0.018t} = 1.4$ Divide by 68 on both sides.

$1.8e^{-0.018t} = 1.4 - 1$ Subtract 1 from both sides.

$e^{-0.018t} = \dfrac{0.4}{1.8}$ Divide by 1.8 on both sides.

$-0.018t = \ln\left(\dfrac{0.4}{1.8}\right)$ Take the natural logarithm of both sides.

$t = \dfrac{\ln\left(\dfrac{0.4}{1.8}\right)}{-0.018} \approx 83.6$ Divide by -0.018 on both sides.

The population will double in approximately 83.6 yr. This is 9 yr later than the predicted value from Example 3(c).

The graphs of $P(t) = \dfrac{95.2}{1 + 1.8e^{-0.018t}}$ and $P(t) = 34e^{0.00926t}$ are shown in Figure 4-17. Notice that the two models agree relatively closely for short-term population growth (out to about 2060). However, in the long term, the unbounded exponential model breaks down. The logistic growth model approaches a limiting population, which is reasonable due to the limited resources to sustain a large human population.

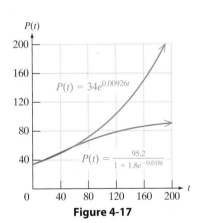

Figure 4-17

c. $P(t) = \dfrac{95.2}{1 + 1.8e^{-0.018t}} = \dfrac{95.2}{1 + \dfrac{1.18}{e^{0.018t}}}$ As $t \to \infty$, the term $\dfrac{1.18}{e^{0.018t}} \to 0$.

As t becomes large, the denominator of $\dfrac{1.18}{e^{0.018t}}$ also becomes large. This causes the quotient to approach zero. Therefore, as t approaches infinity, $P(t)$ approaches 95.2. Under this model, the limiting value for the population of California is 95.2 million.

Skill Practice 6   The score on a test of dexterity is given by

$$P(t) = \frac{100}{1 + 19e^{-0.354x}},$$ where x is the number of times the test is taken.

a. Determine the initial score.

b. Use the function to determine the minimum number of times required for the score to exceed 90.

c. What is the limiting value of the scores?

4. Create Exponential and Logarithmic Models Using Regression

In Examples 7 and 8, we use a graphing utility and regression techniques to find an exponential model or logarithmic model based on observed data.

EXAMPLE 7   Creating an Exponential Model from Observed Data

The amount of sunlight y [in langleys (Ly)—a unit used to measure solar energy in calories/cm^2] is measured for six different depths x (in meters) in Lake Lyndon B. Johnson in Texas.

x (m)	1	3	5	7	9	11
y (Ly)	300	161	89	50	27	15

a. Graph the data.

b. From visual inspection of the graph, which model would best represent the data? Choose from $y = mx + b$ (linear), $y = ab^x$ (exponential), or $y = a + b \ln x$ (logarithmic).

c. Use a graphing utility to find a regression equation that fits the data.

Solution:

a. Enter the data in two lists.

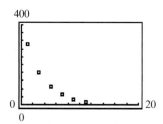

b. Note that for large depths, the amount of sunlight approaches 0. Therefore, the curve is asymptotic to the x-axis. This is consistent with a decreasing exponential model. The exponential model $y = ab^x$ appears to fit.

c. Under the STAT menu, choose CALC, ExpReg, and then Calculate.

The equation is $y = 400(0.742)^x$.

Skill Practice 7   For the given data,

x	1	3	5	7	9	11
y	2.9	5.6	11.1	22.4	43.0	85.0

a. Graph the data points.

b. Use a graphing utility to find a model of the form $y = ab^x$ to fit the data.

EXAMPLE 8   **Creating a Logarithmic Model from Observed Data**

The diameter x (in mm) of a sugar maple tree, along with the corresponding age y (in yr) of the tree is given for six different trees.

x (mm)	1	50	100	200	300	400
y (yr)	4	60	72	82	89	94

a. Graph the data.

b. From visual inspection of the graph, which model would best represent the data? Choose from $y = mx + b$ (linear), $y = ab^x$ (exponential), or $y = a + b \ln x$ (logarithmic).

c. Use a graphing utility to find a regression equation that fits the data.

Solution:

a. Enter the data into two lists.

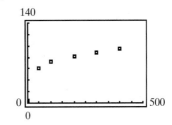

b. From an inspection of the graph, the logarithmic model $y = a + b \ln x$ appears to fit.

c. Under the STAT menu, choose CALC, and then LnReg.

Skill Practice 8   For the given data,

x	1	5	9	13	17	21
y	11.9	19.3	21.9	23.5	24.7	25.7

a. Graph the data points.

b. Use a graphing utility to find a model of the form $y = a + b \ln x$ to fit the data.

Answers

7. a–b.

$y = 2.05(1.4)^x$

8. a–b.

$y = 11.9 + 4.52 \ln x$

SECTION 4.6   Practice Exercises

Review Exercises

1. Which functions are exponential?

a. $f(x) = \left(\dfrac{1}{\sqrt{3}}\right)^x$ **b.** $f(x) = 1^x$ **c.** $f(x) = x^{\sqrt{3}}$ **d.** $f(x) = (-2)^x$ **e.** $f(x) = \pi^x$

2. Given $f(x) = b^x$, then $f^{-1}(x) = $ _____ for $b > 0$ and $b \neq 1$.

3. Write $10^{2x-4} = 80{,}600$ in logarithmic form.   **4.** Write $\ln(x + 4) = 6$ in exponential form.

For Exercises 5–6, write an equation for the inverse of the function.

5. $f(x) = e^{x-2}$ **6.** $g(x) = 4 \ln x$

For Exercises 7–8, write the domain in interval notation.

7. $f(x) = \log_5(5 - 3x)$ **8.** $p(x) = \log x^2$

Concept Connections

9. If $k > 0$, the equation $y = y_0 e^{kt}$ is a model for exponential (growth/decay), whereas if $k < 0$, the equation is a model for exponential (growth/decay).

10. A function defined by $y = ab^x$ can be written in terms of an exponential function base e as _____.

11. A function defined by $y = \dfrac{c}{1 + ae^{-bt}}$ is called a _____ growth model and imposes a limiting value on y.

12. Given a logistic growth function $y = \dfrac{c}{1 + ae^{-bt}}$, the limiting value of y is _____.

Objective 1: Solve Literal Equations for a Specified Variable

For Exercises 13–22, solve for the indicated variable. (See Example 1)

13. $Q = Q_0 e^{-kt}$ for k (used in chemistry)   **14.** $N = N_0 e^{-0.025t}$ for t (used in chemistry)

15. $M = 8.8 + 5.1 \log D$ for D (used in astronomy)   **16.** $\log E - 12.2 = 1.44M$ for E (used in geology)

17. $\text{pH} = -\log[\text{H}^+]$ for H^+ (used in chemistry)   **18.** $L = 10 \log\left(\dfrac{I}{I_0}\right)$ for I (used in medicine)

19. $A = P(1 + r)^t$ for t (used in finance)   **20.** $A = Pe^{rt}$ for r (used in finance)

21. $\ln\left(\dfrac{k}{A}\right) = \dfrac{-E}{RT}$ for k (used in chemistry)   **22.** $-\dfrac{1}{k}\ln\left(\dfrac{P}{14.7}\right) = A$ for P (used in meteorology)

Objective 2: Create Models for Exponential Growth and Decay

23. Suppose that \$12,000 is invested in a bond fund and the account grows to \$14,309.26 in 4 yr. **(See Example 2)**

a. Use the model $A = Pe^{rt}$ to determine the average rate of return under continuous compounding.

b. How long will it take the investment to reach \$20,000 if the rate of return continues? Round to 1 decimal place.

24. Suppose that \$50,000 from a retirement account is invested in a large cap stock fund. After 20 yr, the value is \$194,809.67.

a. Use the model $A = Pe^{rt}$ to determine the average rate of return under continuous compounding.

b. How long will it take the investment to reach one-quarter million dollars? Round to 1 decimal place.

25. Suppose that P dollars in principal is invested in an account earning 3.2% interest compounded continuously. At the end of 3 yr, the amount in the account has earned \$806.07 in interest.

a. Find the original principal. Round to the nearest dollar. (*Hint:* Use the model $A = Pe^{rt}$ and substitute $P + 806.07$ for A.)

b. Using the original principal from part (a) and the model $A = Pe^{rt}$, determine the time required for the investment to reach \$10,000.

26. Suppose that P dollars in principal is invested in an account earning 2.1% interest compounded continuously. At the end of 2 yr, the amount in the account has earned \$193.03 in interest.

a. Find the original principal. Round to the nearest dollar. (*Hint:* Use the model $A = Pe^{rt}$ and substitute $P + 193.03$ for A.)

b. Using the original principal from part (a) and the model $A = Pe^{rt}$, determine the time required for the investment to reach \$6000.

27. a. The populations of two countries are given for January 1, 2000, and for January 1, 2010. Write a function of the form $P(t) = P_0 e^{kt}$ to model each population $P(t)$ (in millions) t years after January 1, 2000. (**See Example 3**)

Country	Population in 2000 (millions)	Population in 2010 (millions)	$P(t) = P_0 e^{kt}$
Australia	19.0	22.6	
Taiwan	22.9	23.7	

b. Use the models from part (a) to predict the population on January 1, 2020, for each country. Round to the nearest hundred thousand.

c. Australia had fewer people than Taiwan in the year 2000, yet from the result of part (b), Australia will have more people in the year 2020? Why?

d. Use the models from part (a) to predict the year during which each population will reach 30 million if this trend continues.

29. A function of the form $P(t) = ab^t$ represents the population of the given country t years after January 1, 2000. (**See Example 4**)

a. Write an equivalent function using base e; that is, write a function of the form $P(t) = P_0 e^{kt}$. Also, determine the population of each country for the year 2000.

Country	$P(t) = ab^t$	$P(t) = P_0 e^{kt}$	Population in 2000
Costa Rica	$P(t) = 4.3(1.0135)^t$		
Norway	$P(t) = 4.6(1.0062)^t$		

b. The population of the two given countries is very close for the year 2000, but their growth rates are different. Determine the year during which the population of each country will reach 5 million.

c. Costa Rica had fewer people in the year 2000 than Norway. Why will Costa Rica reach a population of 5 million sooner than Norway?

28. a. The populations of two countries are given for January 1, 2000, and for January 1, 2010. Write a function of the form $P(t) = P_0 e^{kt}$ to model each population $P(t)$ (in millions) t years after January 1, 2000.

Country	Population in 2000 (millions)	Population in 2010 (millions)	$P(t) = P_0 e^{kt}$
Switzerland	7.3	7.8	
Israel	6.7	7.7	

b. Use the models from part (a) to predict the population on January 1, 2020, for each country. Round to the nearest hundred thousand.

c. Israel had fewer people than Switzerland in the year 2000, yet from the result of part (b), Israel will have more people in the year 2020? Why?

d. Use the models from part (a) to predict the year during which each population will reach 10 million if this trend continues.

30. A function of the form $P(t) = ab^t$ represents the population of the given country t years after January 1, 2000.

a. Write an equivalent function using base e; that is, write a function of the form $P(t) = P_0 e^{kt}$. Also, determine the population of each country for the year 2000.

Country	$P(t) = ab^t$	$P(t) = P_0 e^{kt}$	Population in 2000
Haiti	$P(t) = 8.5(1.0158)^t$		
Sweden	$P(t) = 9.0(1.0048)^t$		

b. The population of the two given countries is very close for the year 2000, but their growth rates are different. Determine the year during which the population of each country will reach 10.5 million.

c. Haiti had fewer people in the year 2000 than Sweden. Why did Haiti reach a population of 10.5 million sooner?

For Exercises 31–32, refer to the model $Q(t) = Q_0 e^{-0.000121t}$ used in Example 5 for radiocarbon dating.

31. A sample from a mummified bull was taken from a pyramid in Dashur, Egypt. The sample shows that 78% of the carbon-14 still remains. How old is the sample? Round to the nearest year. (**See Example 5**)

32. At the "Marmes Man" archeological site in southeastern Washington State, scientists uncovered the oldest human remains yet to be found in Washington State. A sample from a human bone taken from the site showed that 29.4% of the carbon-14 still remained. How old is the sample? Round to the nearest year.

33. The isotope of plutonium ^{238}Pu is used to make thermoelectric power sources for spacecraft. Suppose that a space probe is launched in 2012 with 2.0 kg of ^{238}Pu.

  a. If the half-life of ^{238}Pu is 87.7 yr, write a function of the form $Q(t) = Q_0e^{-kt}$ to model the quantity $Q(t)$ of ^{238}Pu left after t years.

  b. If 1.6 kg of ^{238}Pu is required to power the spacecraft's data transmitter, for how long will scientists be able to receive data? Round to the nearest year.

34. Technetium-99 (^{99m}Tc) is a radionuclide used widely in nuclear medicine. ^{99m}Tc is combined with another substance that is readily absorbed by a targeted body organ. Then, special cameras sensitive to the gamma rays emitted by the technetium are used to record pictures of the organ. Suppose that a technician prepares a sample of ^{99m}Tc-pyrophosphate to image the heart of a patient suspected of having had a mild heart attack.

  a. At noon, the patient is given 10 mCi (millicuries) of ^{99m}Tc. If the half-life of ^{99m}Tc is 6 hr, write a function of the form $Q(t) = Q_0e^{-kt}$ to model the radioactivity level $Q(t)$ after t hours.

  b. At what time will the level of radioactivity reach 3 mCi? Round to 1 decimal place.

35. Fluorodeoxyglucose is a derivative of glucose that contains the radionuclide fluorine-18 (^{18}F). A patient is given a sample of this material containing 300 MBq of ^{18}F (a megabecquerel is a unit of radioactivity). The patient then undergoes a PET scan (positron emission tomography) to detect areas of metabolic activity indicative of cancer. After 174 min, one-third of the original dose remains in the body.

  a. Write a function of the form $Q(t) = Q_0e^{-kt}$ to model the radioactivity level $Q(t)$ of fluorine-18 at a time t minutes after the initial dose.

  b. What is the half-life of ^{18}F?

36. Painful bone metastases are common in advanced prostate cancer. Physicians often order treatment with strontium-89 (^{89}Sr), a radionuclide with a strong affinity for bone tissue. A patient is given a sample containing 4 mCi of ^{89}Sr.

  a. If 20% of the ^{89}Sr remains in the body after 90 days, write a function of the form $Q(t) = Q_0e^{-kt}$ to model the amount $Q(t)$ of radioactivity in the body t days after the initial dose.

  b. What is the biological half-life of ^{89}Sr under this treatment?

37. Two million *E. coli* bacteria are present in a laboratory culture. An antibacterial agent is introduced and the population of bacteria $P(t)$ decreases by half every 6 hr. The population can be represented by $P(t) = 2{,}000{,}000(\frac{1}{2})^{t/6}$.

  a. Convert this to an exponential function using base e.

  b. Verify that the original function and the result from part (a) yield the same result for $P(0)$, $P(6)$, $P(12)$, and $P(60)$. (*Note:* There may be round-off error.)

38. The half-life of radium-226 is 1620 yr. Given a sample of 1 g of radium-226, the quantity left $Q(t)$ (in g) after t years is given by $Q(t) = (\frac{1}{2})^{t/1620}$.

  a. Convert this to an exponential function using base e.

  b. Verify that the original function and the result from part (a) yield the same result for $Q(0)$, $Q(1620)$, and $Q(3240)$. (*Note:* There may be round-off error.)

Objective 3: Apply Logistic Growth Models

39. The population of the United States $P(t)$ (in millions) since January 1, 1900, can be approximated by

$$P(t) = \frac{725}{1 + 8.295e^{-0.0165t}}$$

where t is the number of years since January 1, 1900. (**See Example 6**)

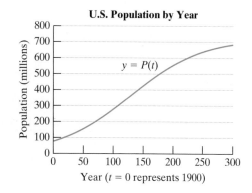

U.S. Population by Year

Year ($t = 0$ represents 1900)

  a. Evaluate $P(0)$ and interpret its meaning in the context of this problem.

  b. Use the function to predict the U.S. population on January 1, 2020. Round to the nearest million.

  c. Use the function to predict the U.S. population on January 1, 2050.

  d. Determine the year during which the U.S. population will reach 500 million.

  e. What value will the term $\dfrac{8.295}{e^{0.0165t}}$ approach as $t \to \infty$?

  f. Determine the limiting value of $P(t)$.

40. The population of Canada $P(t)$ (in millions) since January 1, 1900, can be approximated by

$$P(t) = \frac{55.1}{1 + 9.6e^{-0.02515t}}$$

where t is the number of years since January 1, 1900.

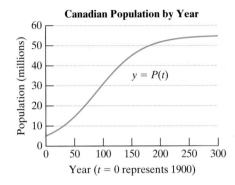

Canadian Population by Year

Population (millions)

$y = P(t)$

Year ($t = 0$ represents 1900)

a. Evaluate $P(0)$ and interpret its meaning in the context of this problem.

b. Use the function to predict the Canadian population on January 1, 2015. Round to the nearest million.

c. Use the function to predict the Canadian population on January 1, 2040.

d. Determine the year during which the Canadian population will reach 45 million.

e. What value will the term $\dfrac{9.6}{e^{0.02515t}}$ approach as $t \to \infty$?

f. Determine the limiting value of $P(t)$.

41. The number of computers $N(t)$ (in millions) infected by a computer virus can be approximated by

$$N(t) = \frac{2.4}{1 + 15e^{-0.72t}}$$

where t is the time in months after the virus was first detected.

a. Determine the number of computers initially infected when the virus was first detected.

b. How many computers were infected after 6 months? Round to the nearest hundred thousand.

c. Determine the amount of time required after initial detection for the virus to affect 1 million computers. Round to 1 decimal place.

d. What is the limiting value of the number of computers infected according to this model?

42. After a new product is launched the cumulative sales $S(t)$ (in \$1000) t weeks after launch is given by:

$$S(t) = \frac{72}{1 + 9e^{-0.36t}}$$

a. Determine the cumulative amount in sales 3 weeks after launch. Round to the nearest thousand.

b. Determine the amount of time required for the cumulative sales to reach \$70,000.

c. What is the limiting value in sales?

Objective 4: Create Exponential and Logarithmic Models Using Regression

For Exercises, 43–46, a graph of data is given. From visual inspection, which model would best fit the data? Choose from

$y = mx + b$ (linear) $y = ab^x$ (exponential)

$y = a + b \ln x$ (logarithmic) $y = \dfrac{c}{1 + ae^{-bx}}$ (logistic)

43.

44.

45.
46.

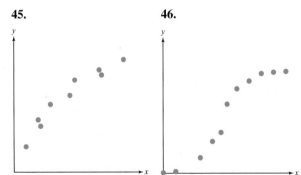

For Exercises 47–54, a table of data is given.

a. Graph the points and from visual inspection, select the model that would best fit the data. Choose from

$$y = mx + b \text{ (linear)} \qquad y = ab^x \text{ (exponential)}$$

$$y = a + b \ln x \text{ (logarithmic)} \qquad y = \frac{c}{1 + ae^{-bx}} \text{ (logistic)}$$

b. Use a graphing utility to find a function that fits the data. (*Hint:* For a logistic model, go to **STAT**, **CALC**, **Logistic**.)

47.

x	y
0	2.3
4	3.6
8	5.7
12	9.1
16	14
20	22

48.

x	y
0	52
1	67
2	87
3	114
4	147
5	195

49.

x	y
3	2.7
7	12.2
13	25.7
15	30
17	34
21	44.4

50.

x	y
0	640
20	530
40	430
50	360
80	210
100	90

51.

x	y
10	43.3
20	50
30	53
40	56.8
50	58.8
60	60.8

52.

x	y
5	29
10	40
15	45.6
20	50
25	53.3
30	56

53.

x	y
2	0.326
4	2.57
6	10.8
8	16.8
10	17.9
5	6
7	14.8

54.

x	y
0	0.05
2	0.45
4	2.94
5	5.8
6	8.8
7	10.6
8	11.5
10	11.9

55. The number of Facebook users is given based on the number of months since December 2004. (*Source:* www.facebook.com) (**See Example 7**)

Months After Dec. 2004 (t)	Number of Users (millions) (y)
0	1
12	5.5
24	12
34	50
44	100
60	350
67	500

Number of Facebook Users vs. Time

Time in Months
($t = 0$ represents December 2004)

a. Use a graphing utility to find a model of the form $y = ab^t$.

b. Write the function from part (a) as an exponential function with base e.

c. Use the model to predict the number of Facebook users in December 2013 if this trend continues. Does it seem reasonable that this trend can continue in the long term?

d. Use a graphing utility to find a logistic model $y = \dfrac{c}{1 + ae^{-bt}}$.

e. Use the logistic model from part (d) to predict the number of Facebook users in December 2013.

56. The monthly costs for a small company to do business has been increasing over time due in part to inflation. The table gives the monthly cost y (in $) for the month of January for selected years. The variable t represents the number of years since 2008.

Year (t = 0 is 2008)	Monthly Costs ($) y
0	12,000
1	12,400
2	12,800
3	13,300

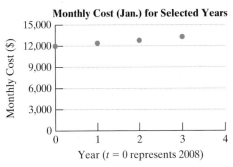

Monthly Cost (Jan.) for Selected Years

a. Use a graphing utility to find a model of the form $y = ab^t$.

b. Write the function from part (a) as an exponential function with base e.

c. Use the model to predict the monthly cost for January in the year 2015 if this trend continues. Round to the nearest hundred dollars.

57. The age of a tree t (in yr) and its corresponding height $H(t)$ is given in the table. (**See Example 8**)

Height of Tree vs. Age

Age of Tree (yr) t	Height (ft) H(t)
1	5
2	8.3
3	11.6
4	14.6
5	15.4
6	16.5
7	17.5
8	18.3
9	19
10	19.4
11	19.7
12	20

a. Write a model of the form $H(t) = a + b \ln t$.

b. Use the model to predict the age of a tree if it is 25 ft high. Round to the nearest year.

c. Is it reasonable to assume that this logarithmic trend will continue indefinitely? Why or why not?

58. The sales of a book tend to increase over the short-term as word-of-mouth makes the book "catch on." The number of books sold $N(t)$ for a new novel t weeks after release at a certain book store is given in the table for the first 6 weeks.

Weeks t	Number Sold N(t)
1	20
2	27
3	31
4	35
5	38
6	39

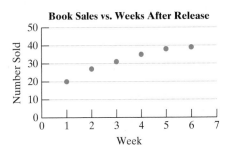

Book Sales vs. Weeks After Release

a. Find a model of the form $N(t) = a + b \ln t$.

b. Use the model to predict the sales in week 7. Round to the nearest whole unit.

c. Is it reasonable to assume that this logarithmic trend will continue? Why or why not?

Mixed Exercises

59. A van is purchased new for $29,200.

   a. Write a linear function of the form $y = mt + b$ to represent the value y of the vehicle t years after purchase. Assume that the vehicle is depreciated by $2920 per year.

   b. Suppose that the vehicle is depreciated so that it holds only 80% of its value from the previous year. Write an exponential function of the form $y = V_0 b^t$, where V_0 is the initial value and t is the number of years after purchase.

   c. To the nearest dollar, determine the value of the vehicle after 5 yr and after 10 yr using the linear model.

   d. To the nearest dollar, determine the value of the vehicle after 5 yr and after 10 yr using the exponential model.

60. A delivery truck is purchased new for $54,000.

   a. Write a linear function of the form $y = mt + b$ to represent the value y of the vehicle t years after purchase. Assume that the vehicle is depreciated by $6750 per year.

   b. Suppose that the vehicle is depreciated so that it holds 70% of its value from the previous year. Write an exponential function of the form $y = V_0 b^t$, where V_0 is the initial value and t is the number of years after purchase.

   c. To the nearest dollar, determine the value of the vehicle after 4 yr and after 8 yr using the linear model.

   d. To the nearest dollar, determine the value of the vehicle after 4 yr and after 8 yr using the exponential model.

Write About It

61. Why is it important to graph a set of data before trying to find an equation or function to model the data.

62. How does the average rate of change differ for a linear function versus an increasing exponential function?

63. Explain the difference between an exponential growth model and a logistic growth model.

64. Explain how to convert an exponential expression b^t to an exponential expression base e.

Expanding Your Skills

65. The monthly payment P (in $) to pay off a loan of amount A (in $) at an interest rate r in t years is given by

$$P = \frac{\dfrac{Ar}{12}}{1 - \left(1 + \dfrac{r}{12}\right)^{-12t}}$$

   a. Solve for t (note that there are numerous equivalent algebraic forms for the result).

   b. Interpret the meaning of the resulting relationship.

66. Suppose that a population follows a logistic growth pattern, with a limiting population N. If the initial population is denoted by P_0, and t is the amount of time elapsed, then the population P can be represented by

$$P = \frac{P_0 N}{P_0 + (N - P_0)e^{-kt}}$$

   where k is a constant related to the growth rate.

   a. Solve for t (note that there are numerous equivalent algebraic forms for the result).

   b. Interpret the meaning of the resulting relationship.

67. From Exercise 41, the number of computers $N(t)$ (in millions) infected by a computer virus can be approximated by

$$N(t) = \frac{2.4}{1 + 15e^{-0.72t}}$$

where t is the time in months after the virus was first detected. Determine the average rate of change over the given interval $[a, b]$. Recall that average rate of change is given by $\dfrac{N(b) - N(a)}{b - a}$.

   a. $[1, 2]$

   b. $[2, 3]$

   c. $[3, 4]$

   d. $[4, 5]$

   e. $[5, 6]$

   f. $[6, 7]$

X	Y1	
1	.28911	
2	.52702	
3	.87916	
4	1.3029	
5	1.7023	
6	2.0008	
7	2.1876	
X=1		

   g. Interpret the meaning of the rate of change on the interval $[1, 2]$.

   h. Comment on the how the rate of change differs from month 1 through month 7.

CHAPTER 4 KEY CONCEPTS

SECTION 4.1 Inverse Functions	Reference
A function f is **one-to-one** if for a and b in the domain of f, if $a \neq b$, then $f(a) \neq f(b)$, or equivalently, if $f(a) = f(b)$, then $a = b$.	p. 433
Horizontal line test: A function defined by $y = f(x)$ is one-to-one if no horizontal line intersects the graph in more than one point.	p. 434
Function **g is the inverse of f** if $(f \circ g)(x) = x$ for all x in the domain of g and $(g \circ f)(x) = x$ for all x in the domain of f.	p. 435
Procedure to find $f^{-1}(x)$: 1. Replace $f(x)$ by y. 2. Interchange x and y. 3. Solve for y. 4. Replace y by $f^{-1}(x)$.	p. 437

SECTION 4.2 Exponential Functions	Reference
Let b be a real number with $b > 0$ and $b \neq 1$. Then for any real number x, a function of the form $f(x) = b^x$ is an **exponential function.**	p. 445
The graph of an exponential function $f(x) = b^x$: • If $b > 1$, f is an increasing function. • If $0 < b < 1$, f is a decreasing function. • The domain is $(-\infty, \infty)$. • The range is $(0, \infty)$. • The line $y = 0$ is a horizontal asymptote. • The function passes through $(0, 1)$.	p. 447
The irrational number e is the limiting value of the expression $\left(1 + \frac{1}{x}\right)^x$ as x approaches ∞. $e \approx 2.71828$	p. 448
If P dollars in principal is invested or borrowed at an annual interest rate r for t years, then $I = Prt$ Simple interest $A = P\left(1 + \dfrac{r}{n}\right)^{nt}$ Future value A with interest compounded n times per year. $A = Pe^{rt}$ Future value A with interest compounded continuously.	p. 450

SECTION 4.3 Logarithmic Functions	Reference
If x and b are positive real numbers such that $b \neq 1$, then $y = \log_b x$ is called the **logarithmic function** base b, where <div align="center">$y = \log_b x$ is equivalent to $b^y = x$.</div> <div align="center">logarithmic form exponential form</div>	p. 459
The functions $f(x) = \log_b x$ and $g(x) = b^x$ are inverses.	p. 459
Basic properties of logarithms: 1. $\log_b 1 = 0$ 2. $\log_b b = 1$ 3. $\log_b b^x = x$ 4. $b^{\log_b x} = x$	p. 462
$y = \log_{10} x$ is written as $y = \log x$ and is called the **common logarithmic function.**	p. 461
$y = \log_e x$ is written as $y = \ln x$ and is called the **natural logarithmic function.**	

Given $f(x) = \log_b x$, • If $b > 1$, f is an increasing function. • If $0 < b < 1$, f is a decreasing function. • The domain is $(0, \infty)$. • The range is $(-\infty, \infty)$. • The line $x = 0$ is a vertical asymptote. • The function passes through $(1, 0)$.	p. 465
The domain of $f(x) = \log_b x$ is $\{x \mid x > 0\}$.	p. 466

SECTION 4.4 Properties of Logarithms — Reference

Let b, x, and y be positive real numbers with $b \neq 1$. Then, $\log_b(xy) = \log_b x + \log_b y$ (Product property) $\log_b\left(\dfrac{x}{y}\right) = \log_b x - \log_b y$ (Quotient property) $\log_b x^p = p \log_b x$ (Power property)	p. 476

Change-of-base formula: p. 479

For positive real numbers a and b, where $a \neq 1$ and $b \neq 1$, $\log_b x = \dfrac{\log_a x}{\log_a b}$.

SECTION 4.5 Exponential and Logarithmic Equations — Reference

Equivalence property of exponential expressions: Let b, x, and y be real numbers with $b > 0$ and $b \neq 1$. Then, $b^x = b^y$ implies that $x = y$.	p. 484
Equivalence property of logarithmic expressions: Let b, x, and y be positive real numbers and $b \neq 1$. Then, $\log_b x = \log_b y$ implies that $x = y$.	p. 487
Guidelines to solve a logarithmic equation: 1. Isolate the logarithms on one side of the equation. 2. Use the properties of logarithms to write the equation in the form $\log_b x = k$, where k is a constant. 3. Write the equation in exponential form. 4. Solve the equation from step 3. 5. Check the potential solution(s) in the original equation.	p. 488

SECTION 4.6 Modeling with Exponential and Logarithmic Functions — Reference

The function defined by $y = y_0 e^{kt}$ represents exponential growth if $k > 0$ and exponential decay if $k < 0$.	p. 498
An exponential expression can be rewritten as an expression of a different base. In particular, to convert to base e, we have: b^t is equivalent to $e^{(\ln b)t}$	p. 500
A **logistic growth function** is a function of the form: $$y = \dfrac{c}{1 + ae^{-bt}}$$ A logistic growth function imposes a limiting value on the dependent variable.	p. 502

Expanded Chapter Summary available at www.mhhe.com/millerca.

CHAPTER 4 Review Exercises

SECTION 4.1

For Exercises 1–2, determine if the relation defines y as a one-to-one function of x.

1.

2.

	A	B
1	**x**	**y**
2	5	7
3	-3	1
4	-4	-2
5	6	0

For Exercises 3–4, use the definition of a one-to-one function to determine if the function is one-to-one. Recall that f is one-to-one if $a \neq b$ implies that $f(a) \neq f(b)$, or equivalently, if $f(a) = f(b)$, then $a = b$.

3. $f(x) = x^3 - 1$ **4.** $f(x) = x^2 - 1$

For Exercises 5–6, determine if the functions are inverses.

5. $f(x) = 4x - 3$ and $g(x) = \dfrac{x + 3}{4}$

6. $m(x) = \sqrt[3]{x + 1}$ and $n(x) = (x - 1)^3$

For Exercises 7–8, a one-to-one function is given. Write an equation for the inverse function.

7. $f(x) = 2x^3 - 5$ **8.** $f(x) = \dfrac{2}{x + 7}$

9. a. Graph $f(x) = x^2 - 3, x \leq 0$.

  b. Is f a one-to-one function?

  c. Write the domain of f in interval notation.

  d. Write the range of f in interval notation.

  e. Find an equation for f^{-1}.

  f. Graph $y = f(x)$ and $y = f^{-1}(x)$ on the same coordinate system.

  g. Write the domain of f^{-1} in interval notation.

  h. Write the range of f^{-1} in interval notation.

10. a. Graph $g(x) = \sqrt{x + 1}$.

  b. Is g a one-to-one function?

  c. Write the domain of g in interval notation.

  d. Write the range of g in interval notation.

  e. Find an equation for g^{-1}.

  f. Graph $y = g(x)$ and $y = g^{-1}(x)$ on the same coordinate system.

  g. Write the domain of g^{-1} in interval notation.

  h. Write the range of g^{-1} in interval notation.

11. The function $f(x) = 5280x$ provides the conversion from x miles to $f(x)$ feet.

  a. Write an equation for f^{-1}.

  b. What does the inverse function represent in the context of this problem?

  c. Determine the number of miles represented by 22,176 ft.

SECTION 4.2

12. Which of the following functions is an exponential function?

  a. $f(x) = x^4$ **b.** $h(x) = 4^{-x}$ **c.** $g(x) = \left(\dfrac{4}{3}\right)^x$

  d. $k(x) = \dfrac{4x}{3}$ **e.** $n(x) = \dfrac{4}{3x}$ **f.** $r(x) = \left(-\dfrac{4}{3}\right)^x$

For Exercises 13–16,

  a. Graph the function.

  b. Write the domain in interval notation.

  c. Write the range in interval notation.

  d. Write an equation of the asymptote.

13. $f(x) = \left(\dfrac{5}{2}\right)^x$ **14.** $g(x) = \left(\dfrac{5}{2}\right)^{-x}$

15. $k(x) = -3^x + 1$ **16.** $h(x) = 2^{x-3} - 4$

17. Is the graph of $y = e^x$ an increasing or decreasing exponential function?

For Exercises 18–19, use the formulas on page 450.

18. Suppose that $24,000 is invested at the given interest rates and compounding options. Determine the amount that the investment is worth at the end of t years.

  a. 5% interest compounded monthly for 10 yr

  b. 4.5% interest compounded continuously for 30 yr

19. Jorge needs to borrow $12,000 to buy a car. He can borrow the money at 7.2% simple interest for 4 yr or he can borrow at 6.5% interest compounded continuously for 4 yr.

  a. How much total interest would Jorge pay at 7.2% simple interest?

  b. How much total interest would Jorge pay at 6.5% interest compounded continuously?

  c. Which option results in less total interest?

20. A patient is treated with 128 mCi (millicuries) of iodine-131 (^{131}I). The radioactivity level $R(t)$ (in mCi) after t days is given by $R(t) = 128(2)^{-t/4.2}$. (In this model, the value 4.2 is related to the biological half-life of radioactive iodine in the body.)

  a. Determine the radioactivity level of ^{131}I in the body after 6 days. Round to the nearest whole unit.

b. Evaluate $R(4.2)$ and interpret its meaning in the context of this problem.

c. After how many half-lives will the radioactivity level be 16 mCi?

SECTION 4.3

For Exercises 21–22, write the equation in exponential form.

21. $\log_b(x^2 + y^2) = 4$ **22.** $\ln x = (c + d)$

For Exercises 23–24, write the equation in logarithmic form.

23. $10^6 = 1,000,000$ **24.** $8^{-1/3} = \dfrac{1}{2}$

For Exercises 25–32, evaluate the logarithmic expression without using a calculator.

25. $\log_3 81$ **26.** $\log 100,000$

27. $\log_2\left(\dfrac{1}{64}\right)$ **28.** $\log_{1/4}(16)$

29. $\log_{11} 1$ **30.** $\log_5 5$

31. $4^{\log_4 7}$ **32.** $\ln e^{11}$

For Exercises 33–37, write the domain of the function in interval notation.

33. $f(x) = \log(x - 4)$ **34.** $g(x) = \ln(3 - 2x)$

35. $h(x) = \log_2(x^2 + 4)$ **36.** $k(x) = \log_2(x^2 - 4)$

37. $m(x) = \log_2(x - 4)^2$

For Exercises 38–39,

a. Graph the function.

b. Write the domain in interval notation.

c. Write the range in interval notation.

d. Write an equation of the asymptote.

38. $f(x) = \log_2(x - 3)$ **39.** $g(x) = 2 + \ln x$

For Exercise 40–41, use the formula $pH = -\log[H^+]$ to compute the pH of a liquid as a function of its concentration of hydronium ions, $[H^+]$ in mol/L. If the pH is less than 7, then the substance is acidic. If the pH is greater than 7, then the substance is alkaline (or basic).

a. Find the pH.

b. Determine whether the substance is acidic or alkaline.

40. Baking soda: $H^+ = 5.0 \times 10^{-9}$ mol/L

41. Tomatoes: $H^+ = 3.16 \times 10^{-5}$ mol/L

SECTION 4.4

For Exercises 42–48, fill in the blanks to state the basic properties of logarithms. Assume that x, y, and b are positive real numbers with $b \neq 1$.

42. $\log_b 1 =$ _____   **43.** $\log_b b =$ _____

44. $\log_b b^p =$ _____   **45.** $b^{\log_b x} =$ _____

46. $\log_b(xy) =$ _____   **47.** $\log_b\left(\dfrac{x}{y}\right) =$ _____

48. $\log_b x^p =$ _____

For Exercises 49–52, write the logarithm as a sum or difference of logarithms. Simplify each term as much as possible.

49. $\log\left(\dfrac{100}{\sqrt{c^2 + 10}}\right)$ **50.** $\log_2\left(\dfrac{1}{8}a^2 b\right)$

51. $\ln\left(\dfrac{\sqrt[3]{ab^2}}{cd^5}\right)$ **52.** $\log\left(\dfrac{x^2(2x + 1)^5}{\sqrt{1 - x}}\right)$

For Exercises 53–55, write the logarithmic expression as a single logarithm with coefficient 1, and simplify as much as possible.

53. $4 \log_5 y - 3 \log_5 x + \dfrac{1}{2}\log_5 z$

54. $\log 250 + \log 2 - \log 5$

55. $\dfrac{1}{4}\ln(x^2 - 9) - \dfrac{1}{4}\ln(x - 3)$

For Exercises 56–58, use $\log_b 2 \approx 0.289$, $\log_b 3 \approx 0.458$, and $\log_b 5 \approx 0.671$ to approximate the value of the given logarithms.

56. $\log_b 8$ **57.** $\log_b 45$ **58.** $\log_b\left(\dfrac{1}{9}\right)$

For Exercises 59–60, use the change-of-base formula and a calculator to approximate the given logarithms. Round to 4 decimal places. Then check the answer by using the related exponential form.

59. $\log_7 596$ **60.** $\log_4 0.982$

SECTION 4.5

For Exercises 61–80, solve the equation. Write the solution set with exact values and give approximate solutions to 4 decimal places.

61. $4^{2y-7} = 64$ **62.** $1000^{2x+1} = \left(\dfrac{1}{100}\right)^{x-4}$

63. $7^x = 51$ **64.** $516 = 11^w - 21$

65. $3^{2x+1} = 4^{3x}$ **66.** $2^{c+3} = 7^{2c+5}$

67. $400e^{-2t} = 2.989$ **68.** $2 \cdot 10^{1.2t} = 58$

69. $e^{2x} - 3e^x - 40 = 0$ **70.** $e^{2x} = -10e^x$

71. $\log_5(4p + 7) = \log_5(2 - p)$

72. $\log_2(m^2 + 10m) = \log_2 11$

73. $2 \log_6(4 - 8y) + 6 = 10$

74. $5 = -4 \log_3(2 - 5x) + 1$

75. $3 \ln(n - 8) = 6.3$

76. $-4 + \log_2 x = -\log_2(x + 6)$

77. $\log_6(3x + 2) = \log_6(x + 4) + 1$

78. $\ln x + \ln(x + 2) = \ln(x + 6)$

79. $\log_5(\log_2 x) = 1$

80. $(\log x)^2 - \log x^2 = 35$

For Exercises 81–82, find the inverse of the function.

81. $f(x) = 4^x$

82. $g(x) = \log(x - 5) - 1$

83. The percentage of visible light P (in decimal form) at a depth of x meters for Long Island Sound can be approximated by $P = e^{-0.5x}$.

    a. Determine the depth at which the light intensity is half the value from the surface. Round to the nearest hundredth of a meter. Based on your answer, would you say that Long Island Sound is murky or clear water?

    b. Determine the euphotic depth for Long Island Sound. That is, find the depth at which the light intensity falls below 1%.

SECTION 4.6

For Exercises 84–85, solve for the indicated variable.

84. $\log B - 1.7 = 2.3M$ for B

85. $T = T_f + T_0 e^{-kt}$ for t

86. Suppose that $18,000 is invested in a bond fund and the account grows to $23,344.74 in 5 yr.

    a. Use the model $A = Pe^{rt}$ to determine the average rate of return under continuous compounding.

    b. How long will it take the investment to reach $30,000 if the rate of return continues? Round to 1 decimal place.

87. The population of Germany in 2011 was approximately 85.5 million. The model $P = 85.5e^{-0.00208t}$ represents a short-term model for the population, t years after 2011.

    a. Based on this model, is the population of Germany increasing or decreasing?

    b. Determine the number of years after 2011 at which the population of Germany decreases to 80 million if this trend continues.

88. The population of Chile was approximately 16.9 million in the year 2011, with an annual growth rate of 0.836%. The population $P(t)$ (in millions) can be modeled by $P(t) = 16.9(1.00836)^t$, where t is the number of years since 2011.

    a. Write a function of the form $P(t) = P_0 e^{kt}$ to model the population.

    b. Determine the amount of time required for the population to grow to 20 million if this trend continues. Round to the nearest year.

89. A sample from human remains found near Stonehenge in England shows that 71.2% of the carbon-14 still remains. Use the model $Q(t) = Q_0 e^{-0.000121t}$ to determine the age of the sample. In this model, $Q(t)$ represents the amount of carbon-14 remaining t years after death, and Q_0 represents the initial amount of carbon-14 at the time of death. Round to the nearest 100 yr.

90. A lake is stocked with bass by the U.S. Park Service. The population of bass is given by $P(t) = \dfrac{3000}{1 + 2e^{-0.37t}}$, where t is the time in years after the lake was stocked.

    a. Evaluate $P(0)$ and interpret its meaning in the context of this problem.

    b. Use the function to predict the bass population 2 yr after being stocked. Round to the nearest whole unit.

    c. Use the function to predict the bass population 4 yr after being stocked.

    d. Determine the number of years required for the bass population to reach 2800. Round to the nearest year.

    e. What value will the term $\dfrac{2}{e^{0.37t}}$ approach as $t \to \infty$.

    f. Determine the limiting value of $P(t)$.

91. For the given data,

    a. Use a graphing utility to find an exponential function $Y_1 = ab^x$ that fits the data.

    b. Graph the data and the function from part (a) on the same coordinate system.

x	y
0	2.4
1	3.5
2	5.5
3	8.1
4	12.0
5	18.4

92. The number of hospitals in the United States has been decreasing since 1990. The data in the table give the number of hospitals y according to the number of years x since 1990. (*Source*: American Hospital Association, www.ahadata.com)

Year ($x = 0$ is 1990)	Number of Hospitals (y)
1	6649
5	6291
10	5810
13	5764
14	5759
15	5756
16	5747
17	5708
21	5631

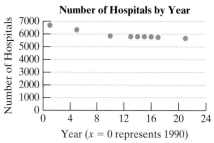

Number of Hospitals by Year

    a. Use a graphing utility to find a model of the form $y = a + b \ln x$.

    b. Predict the number of hospitals in the year 2016.

CHAPTER 4   Test

1. Given $f(x) = 4x^3 - 1$,

    a. Write an equation for $f^{-1}(x)$.

    b. Verify that $(f \circ f^{-1})(x) = (f^{-1} \circ f)(x) = x$.

2. The graph of f is given.

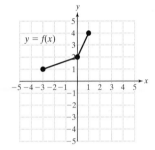

    a. Is f a one-to-one function?

    b. If f is a one-to-one function, graph f^{-1} on the same coordinate system as f.

3. Given $f(x) = \dfrac{x + 3}{x - 4}$,

    write an equation for the inverse function.

For Exercises 4–6,

    a. Write the domain and range of f in interval notation.

    b. Write an equation of the inverse function.

    c. Write the domain and range of f^{-1} in interval notation.

    4. $f(x) = -x^2 + 1, x \le 0$ **5.** $f(x) = \log x$

    6. $f(x) = 3^x + 1$

For Exercises 7–10,

    a. Graph the function.

    b. Write the domain in interval notation.

    c. Write the range in interval notation.

    d. Write an equation of the asymptote.

    7. $f(x) = \left(\dfrac{1}{3}\right)^x + 2$ **8.** $g(x) = 2^{x-4}$

    9. $h(x) = -\ln x$ **10.** $k(x) = \log_2(x + 1) - 3$

11. Write the statement in exponential form. $\ln(x + y) = a$

12. Write the statement in logarithmic form. $10^{4x+3} = y$

For Exercises 13–18, evaluate the logarithmic expression without using a calculator.

    13. $\log_9 \dfrac{1}{81}$ **14.** $\log_6 216$ **15.** $\ln e^8$

    16. $\log 10^{-4}$ **17.** $10^{\log(a^2 + b^2)}$ **18.** $\log_{1/2} 1$

For Exercises 19–20, write the domain of the function in interval notation.

    19. $f(x) = \log(7 - 2x)$ **20.** $g(x) = \log_4(x^2 - 25)$

For Exercises 21–22, write the logarithm as a sum or difference of logarithms. Simplify each term as much as possible.

    21. $\ln\left(\dfrac{x^5 y^2}{w\sqrt[3]{z}}\right)$ **22.** $\log\left(\dfrac{\sqrt{a^2 + b^2}}{10^4}\right)$

For Exercises 23–24, write the logarithmic expression as a single logarithm with coefficient 1, and simplify as much as possible.

    23. $6 \log_2 a - 4 \log_2 b + \dfrac{2}{3}\log_2 c$

    24. $\dfrac{1}{2}\ln(x^2 - x - 12) - \dfrac{1}{2}\ln(x - 4)$

For Exercises 25–26, use $\log_b 2 \approx 0.289$, $\log_b 3 \approx 0.458$, and $\log_b 5 \approx 0.671$ to approximate the value of the given logarithms.

    25. $\log_b 72$ **26.** $\log_b\left(\dfrac{1}{125}\right)$

For Exercises 27–36, solve the equation. Write the solution set with exact values and give approximate solutions to 4 decimal places.

    27. $2^{5y+1} = 4^{y-3}$ **28.** $5^{x+3} = 53$

    29. $2^{c+7} = 3^{2c+3}$ **30.** $7e^{4x} = 14$

    31. $e^{2x} + 7e^x - 8 = 0$

    32. $\log_5(3 - x) = \log_5(x + 1)$

    33. $5 \ln(x + 2) + 1 = 16$

    34. $\log x + \log(x - 1) = \log 12$

    35. $-3 + \log_4 x = -\log_4(x + 30)$

    36. $\log 3 + \log(x + 3) = \log(4x + 5)$

For Exercises 37–38, solve for the indicated variable.

    37. $S = 92 - k \ln(t + 1)$ for t

    38. $A = P\left(1 + \dfrac{r}{n}\right)^{nt}$ for t

39. Suppose that $10,000 is invested and the account grows to $13,566.25 in 5 yr.

    a. Use the model $A = Pe^{rt}$ to determine the average rate of return under continuous compounding.

    b. How long will it take the investment to reach $50,000 if the rate of return continues? Round to 1 decimal place.

40. The number of bacteria in a culture begins with approximately 10,000 organisms at the start of an experiment. If the bacteria doubles every 5 hr, the model $P(t) = 10{,}000(2)^{t/5}$ represents the population $P(t)$ after t hours.

  a. Write a function of the form $P(t) = P_0 e^{kt}$ to model the population.

  b. Determine the amount of time required for the population to grow to 5 million. Round to the nearest hour.

41. The population $P(t)$ of a herd of deer on an island can be modeled by $P(t) = \dfrac{1200}{1 + 2e^{-0.12t}}$, where t represents the number of years since the park service has been tracking the herd.

  a. Evaluate $P(0)$ and interpret its meaning in the context of this problem.

  b. Use the function to predict the deer population after 4 yr. Round to the nearest whole unit.

  c. Use the function to predict the deer population after 8 yr.

  d. Determine the number of years required for the deer population to reach 900. Round to the nearest year.

  e. What value will the term $\dfrac{2}{e^{0.12t}}$ approach as $t \to \infty$.

  f. Determine the limiting value of $P(t)$.

42. A junior in high school takes a vocabulary course to help him study for college entrance exams. After the student completes the course, the instructor gives the student a test on the vocabulary at 1-week intervals. The purpose is to determine the student's retention of material as a function of time. These data may be helpful to the school in scheduling the class.

Week (x)	Score (y)
1	88
2	83.4
3	81
4	79
5	77
6	74.7
7	74.2
8	73.1
9	71.8
10	71

Score on Test vs. Weeks After Course

  a. The student's score y is shown x weeks after taking the course. Use a graphing utility to find a model of the form $y = a + b \ln x$.

  b. Predict the student's score on a test of the vocabulary 12 weeks after completing the course. Round to the nearest whole unit.

CHAPTER 4   Cumulative Review Exercises

For Exercises 1–2, simplify the expression.

1. $\dfrac{3x^{-1} - 6x^{-2}}{2x^{-2} - x^{-1}}$

2. $\dfrac{5}{\sqrt[3]{2x^2}}$

3. Factor. $a^3 - b^3 - a + b$

4. Perform the operations and write the answer in scientific notation. $\dfrac{(3.0 \times 10^7)(8.2 \times 10^{-3})}{1.23 \times 10^{-5}}$

For Exercises 5–13, solve the equations and inequalities. Write the solution sets to the inequalities in interval notation.

5. $5 \le 3 + |2x - 7|$

6. $3x(x - 1) = x + 6$

7. $\sqrt{t + 3} + 4 = t + 1$

8. $9^{2m-3} = 27^{m+1}$

9. $-x^3 - 5x^2 + 4x + 20 < 0$

10. $|5x - 1| = |3 - 4x|$

11. $(x^2 - 9)^2 - 2(x^2 - 9) - 35 = 0$

12. $\log_2(3x - 1) = \log_2(x + 1) + 3$

13. $\dfrac{x - 4}{x + 2} \le 0$

14. Find all the zeros of $f(x) = x^4 + 10x^3 + 10x^2 + 10x + 9$

15. Given $f(x) = x^2 - 16x + 55$,

    a. Does the graph of the parabola open upward or downward?

    b. Find the vertex of the parabola.

    c. Identify the maximum or minimum point.

    d. Identify the maximum or minimum value of the function.

    e. Identify the x-intercept(s).

    f. Identify the y-intercept.

    g. Graph the function.

    h. Write an equation for the axis of symmetry.

    i. Write the domain in interval notation.

    j. Write the range in interval notation.

16. Graph. $f(x) = -1.5x^2(x - 2)^3(x + 1)$

17. Given $f(x) = \dfrac{3x + 6}{x - 2}$,

    a. Identify the vertical asymptote(s).

    b. Identify the horizontal or slant asymptote.

    c. Graph the function.

18. Given $f(x) = 2^{x+2} - 3$,

    a. Graph the function.

    b. Identify the asymptote.

    c. Write the domain in interval notation.

    d. Write the range in interval notation.

19. Write the expression as a single logarithm and simplify.
$\log 40 + \log 50 - \log 2$

20. Given the one-to-one function defined by
$f(x) = \sqrt[3]{x - 4} + 1$, write an equation for $f^{-1}(x)$.

5

Systems of Equations and Inequalities

Chapter Outline

The economy influences how people spend their money, but it also impacts how people save. When comparing options for investments such as stocks, bonds, and mutual funds, an individual can easily become overwhelmed by the possible scenarios. Collecting data on the rates of return on different investments is helpful in making an informed decision. In some scenarios, we turn to systems of linear equations to analyze such data.

In this chapter, we will solve systems involving both linear and nonlinear equations. In addition, we will use systems of linear inequalities in manufacturing applications. In such applications, the goal is to determine constraints on the production process (such as limits on the amount of material, labor, and equipment) and then maximize profit or minimize cost subject to these constraints.

SECTION 5.1   Systems of Linear Equations in Two Variables and Applications

1. Identify Solutions to Systems of Linear Equations in Two Variables

The amount of money spent per consumer unit on cellular service has increased since the year 2000, while the amount spent on residential lines has decreased (Figure 5-1). (*Source*: Bureau of Labor Statistics, www.bls.gov) The amount y (in $) spent on cellular service can be approximated by $y = 64.0x + 144$, where x is the number of years since the year 2000. The amount y (in $) spent on residential service is approximated by $y = -30.7x + 712.2$.

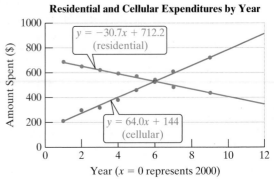

Residential and Cellular Expenditures by Year

$y = -30.7x + 712.2$ (residential)

$y = 64.0x + 144$ (cellular)

Year ($x = 0$ represents 2000)

Amount Spent ($)

Figure 5-1

Two or more linear equations taken together form a **system of linear equations.**

$$\left. \begin{array}{l} y = 64.0x + 144 \\ y = -30.7x + 712.2 \end{array} \right\} \quad \text{system of linear equations}$$

A **solution** to a system of equations in two variables is an ordered pair that is a solution to each individual equation. Graphically, this is the point of intersection of the graphs of the equations. For the system given here, the solution is (6, 528). This means that in the year 2006, the amount that consumers spent on cellular service and on residential phone service was approximately equal at $528 per year. The **solution set** to a system of equations is the set of all solutions to the system. In this case, the solution set is $\{(6, 528)\}$.

EXAMPLE 1   Determining if an Ordered Pair Is a Solution to a System of Equations

Determine if the ordered pair is a solution to the system.

$$\begin{array}{l} 6x + y = -2 \\ 4x - 3y = 17 \end{array}$$

a. $\left(\dfrac{1}{2}, -5 \right)$ **b.** $(0, -2)$

Solution:

a. <u>First equation</u>

$6x + y = -2$

$6\left(\frac{1}{2}\right) + (-5) \overset{?}{=} -2$

$-2 \overset{?}{=} -2$ ✓ true

<u>Second equation</u>

$4x - 3y = 17$

$4\left(\frac{1}{2}\right) - 3(-5) \overset{?}{=} 17$

$17 \overset{?}{=} 17$ ✓ true

Test the ordered pair $\left(\frac{1}{2}, -5\right)$ in each equation.

The ordered pair is a solution to both equations.

The ordered pair $\left(\frac{1}{2}, -5\right)$ is a solution to the system.

b. <u>First equation</u>

$6x + y = -2$

$6(0) + (-2) \overset{?}{=} -2$

$0 + (-2) \overset{?}{=} -2$

$-2 \overset{?}{=} -2$ ✓ true

<u>Second equation</u>

$4x - 3y = 17$

$4(0) - 3(-2) \overset{?}{=} 17$

$0 + 6 \overset{?}{=} 17$

$6 \overset{?}{=} 17$ false

Test the ordered pair $(0, -2)$ in each equation.

The ordered pair is *not* a solution to the second equation.

The ordered pair $(0, -2)$ is *not* a solution to the system.

Avoiding Mistakes

For an ordered pair to be a solution to a system of equations, it must satisfy *both* equations. If it fails in either equation, it is *not* a solution.

Figure 5-2

The lines from Example 1 are shown in Figure 5-2. From the graph, we can verify that $\left(\frac{1}{2}, -5\right)$ is the only solution to the system of equations.

There are three different possibilities regarding the number of solutions to a system of linear equations.

Solutions to Systems of Linear Equations in Two Variables

One Unique Solution	**No Solution**	**Infinitely Many Solutions**
		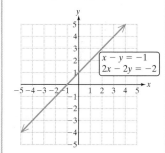
If a system of linear equations represents intersecting lines, then it has exactly one solution.	If a system of linear equations represents parallel lines, then the lines do not intersect, and the system has no solution. In such a case, we say that the system is **inconsistent.**	If a system of linear equations represents the same line, then all points on the common line satisfy each equation. Therefore, the system has infinitely many solutions. In such a case, we say that the equations are **dependent.**

---

2. Solve Systems of Linear Equations in Two Variables

Graphing a system of equations is one method to find the solution(s) to the system. However, sometimes it is difficult to determine the solution(s) using this method because of limitations in the accuracy of the graph. Instead we often use algebraic methods to solve a system of equations. The first method we present is called the **substitution method.**

Solving a System of Equations by Using the Substitution Method

Step 1   Isolate one of the variables from one equation.

Step 2   Substitute the quantity found in step 1 into the *other* equation.

Step 3   Solve the resulting equation.

Step 4   Substitute the value found in step 3 back into the equation in step 1 to find the value of the remaining variable.

Step 5   Check the ordered pair in each equation and write the solution as an ordered pair in set notation.

Answers

1. a. Yes   **b.** No

EXAMPLE 2   **Solving a System of Equations by the Substitution Method**

Solve the system by using the substitution method. $-5x - 4y = 2$
$4x + y = 5$

Solution:

$-5x - 4y = 2$

$4x + y = 5 \longrightarrow y = \underbrace{-4x + 5}$ **Step 1:** Isolate one of the variables from one of the equations. A variable with coefficient 1 or −1 is easily isolated.

$-5x - 4(-4x + 5) = 2$ **Step 2:** Substitute the expression from step 1 into the other equation.

$-5x + 16x - 20 = 2$ **Step 3:** Solve for the remaining variable.

$11x = 22$

$x = 2$

$y = -4x + 5$ **Step 4:** Substitute the known value of x into the equation where y is isolated. From step 1, this is $y = -4x + 5$.

$y = -4(2) + 5$

$y = -3$

Step 5: Check the ordered pair $(2, -3)$ in each original equation.

Check $(2, -3)$.

$-5x - 4y = 2$	$4x + y = 5$
$-5(2) - 4(-3) \overset{?}{=} 2$	$4(2) + (-3) \overset{?}{=} 5$
$-10 + 12 \overset{?}{=} 2$ ✓ true	$8 - 3 \overset{?}{=} 5$ ✓ true

The solution set is $\{(2, -3)\}$.

TIP The lines from Example 2 are shown here. The graph shows the point of intersection at $(2, -3)$.

Skill Practice 2   Solve the system by using the substitution method.

$3x + 4y = 5$

$x - 3y = 6$

Now consider the following system of equations.

$$5x - 4y = 6$$
$$-3x + 7y = 1$$

None of the variable terms has a coefficient of 1 or −1. Therefore, if we isolate x or y from either equation, the resulting equation will have one or more terms with fractional coefficients. To avoid this scenario, we can use another method called the **addition method** (also called the elimination method).

Solving a System of Equations by Using the Addition Method

Step 1 Write both equations in standard form: $Ax + By = C$.

Step 2 Clear fractions or decimals (optional).

Step 3 Multiply one or both equations by nonzero constants to create opposite coefficients for one of the variables.

Step 4 Add the equations from step 3 to eliminate one variable.

Step 5 Solve for the remaining variable.

Step 6 Substitute the known value found in step 5 into one of the original equations to solve for the other variable.

Step 7 Check the ordered pair in each equation and write the solution set.

Answer

2. $\{(3, -1)\}$

| EXAMPLE 3 | Solving a System of Equations by the Addition Method |

Solve the system by using the addition method. $5x = 4y + 6$
$-3x + 7y = 1$

Solution:

$$5x = 4y + 6 \xrightarrow{\text{Subtract } 4y.} 5x - 4y = 6$$
$$-3x + 7y = 1 \qquad\qquad\qquad -3x + 7y = 1$$

Step 1: Write each equation in standard form: $Ax + By = C$.

Step 2: There are no decimals or fractions.

$$5x - 4y = 6 \xrightarrow{\text{Multiply by 3.}} 15x - 12y = 18$$
$$-3x + 7y = 1 \xrightarrow[\text{Multiply by 5.}]{} \underline{-15x + 35y = 5}$$

Step 3: Multiply the first equation by 3. Multiply the second equation by 5.

$$23y = 23$$

Step 4: Add the equations to eliminate x.

$$y = 1$$

Step 5: Solve for y.

$5x = 4y + 6$

$5x = 4(1) + 6$

$5x = 10$

$x = 2$

Step 6: Substitute $y = 1$ into one of the original equations to solve for x.

Step 7: Check the ordered pair $(2, 1)$ in each original equation.

$$5x = 4y + 6 \qquad\qquad -3x + 7y = 1$$
$$5(2) \overset{?}{=} 4(1) + 6 \qquad -3(2) + 7(1) \overset{?}{=} 1$$
$$10 \overset{?}{=} 4 + 6 \checkmark \text{ true} \qquad -6 + 7 \overset{?}{=} 1 \checkmark \text{ true}$$

The solution set is $\{(2, 1)\}$.

> **TIP** In Example 3, the variable x was eliminated.
>
> Alternatively, we could have eliminated y by multiplying the first equation by 7 and the second equation by 4. This would create new equations with coefficients of -28 and 28 on the y terms.

Skill Practice 3   Solve the system by using the addition method.

$2x - 9y = 1$
$3x = 17 - 2y$

TECHNOLOGY CONNECTIONS

Solving a System of Linear Equations in Two Variables Using Intersect

The solution to a system of linear equations can be checked on a graphing calculator by first writing the equations in slope-intercept form. From Example 3 we have

$$5x = 4y + 6 \longrightarrow y = \frac{5}{4}x - \frac{3}{2}$$

$$-3x + 7y = 1 \longrightarrow y = \frac{3}{7}x + \frac{1}{7}$$

Then graph the equations and use the Intersect feature to approximate the point of intersection. In this case, the Intersect feature gives the exact solution $(2, 1)$.

It is important to write the individual equations in a system of equations in standard form so that the variables line up. Also consider clearing decimals or fractions within an equation to make integer coefficients.

Answer

3. $\{(5, 1)\}$

EXAMPLE 4 Solving a System of Equations by the Addition Method

Solve the system by using the addition method.

$$\frac{2}{5}x - y = \frac{19}{10}$$

$$5(x + y) = -7y - 41$$

Solution:

$$\frac{2}{5}x - y = \frac{19}{10} \xrightarrow{\text{Multiply by 10.}} 4x - 10y = 19$$

$$5(x + y) = -7y - 41 \xrightarrow{\text{Simplify.}} 5x + 12y = -41$$

Clear the fractions in the first equation. Write the second equation in standard form.

$$4x - 10y = 19 \xrightarrow{\text{Multiply by } -5.} -20x + 50y = -95$$

$$5x + 12y = -41 \xrightarrow{\text{Multiply by 4.}} \underline{20x + 48y = -164}$$

$$98y = -259$$

The LCM of the x coefficients, 4 and 5, is 20. Create opposite coefficients on x of 20 and -20.

$$y = \frac{-259}{98}$$

Solve for y.

$$y = -\frac{37}{14}$$

Simplify to lowest terms.

Substituting $y = -\frac{37}{14}$ back into one of the original equations to solve for x would be cumbersome. Alternatively, we can solve for x by repeating the addition method. This time we will eliminate y by creating opposite coefficients on the y terms and then solving for x.

$$4x - 10y = 19 \xrightarrow{\text{Multiply by 6.}} 24x - 60y = 114$$

$$5x + 12y = -41 \xrightarrow{\text{Multiply by 5.}} \underline{25x + 60y = -205}$$

$$49x = -91$$

The LCM of 10 and 12 is 60. Create opposite coefficients of -60 and 60 on the y terms.

$$x = \frac{-91}{49}$$

Solve for y.

$$x = -\frac{13}{7}$$

Simplify.

The ordered pair $\left(-\frac{13}{7}, -\frac{37}{14}\right)$ checks in both original equations.

The solution set is $\left\{\left(-\frac{13}{7}, -\frac{37}{14}\right)\right\}$.

Skill Practice 4 Solve the system by using the addition method.

$$2(x - 2y) = y + 14$$

$$\frac{1}{2}x + \frac{7}{6}y = -\frac{13}{3}$$

The systems in Examples 1–4 each have one unique solution. That is, the lines represented by the two equations intersect in exactly one point. In Examples 5 and 6, we investigate systems with no solution or infinitely many solutions.

Answer

4. $\left\{\left(-\frac{32}{29}, -\frac{94}{29}\right)\right\}$

EXAMPLE 5   Identifying a System of Equations with No Solution

Solve the system.
$$2x + y = 4$$
$$6x + 3y = 6$$

Solution:

$$2x + y = 4 \xrightarrow{\text{Multiply by } -3} -6x - 3y = -12$$
$$6x + 3y = 6 \xrightarrow{} \underline{6x + 3y = 6}$$
$$0 = -6$$

We can eliminate either the x terms or y terms by multiplying the first equation by -3.

Both the x and y terms are eliminated, leading to the contradiction $0 = -6$.

The system of equations reduces to a contradiction. This indicates that there is no solution and the system is inconsistent. The equations represent parallel lines and two parallel lines do not intersect.

The solution set is { }.

> **Avoiding Mistakes**
>
> To verify that the system in Example 5 has no solution, write the equations in slope-intercept form.
>
> $2x + y = 4 \Rightarrow y = -2x + 4$
> $6x + 3y = 6 \Rightarrow y = -2x + 2$
>
> The equations have the same slope, but different y-intercepts. Therefore, the lines are parallel and do not intersect.

> **Skill Practice 5**   Solve the system.
> $$3x - y = 2$$
> $$-9x + 3y = 4$$

EXAMPLE 6   Solving a System of Dependent Equations

Solve the system.
$$y = 2x - 1$$
$$8x - 4y = 4$$

Solution:

$$y = 2x - 1$$
$$8x - 4y = 4 \qquad 8x - 4(2x - 1) = 4$$
$$8x - 8x + 4 = 4$$
$$4 = 4$$

With y already isolated in the first equation, apply the substitution method.

Solve the resulting equation.

Identity.

Notice that both the variable terms and the constant terms were eliminated. The system of equations is reduced to the identity $4 = 4$. Therefore, the two original equations are dependent and represent the same line. The solution set consists of an infinite number of ordered pairs (x, y) that fall on the common line of intersection. The solution set can be written in either of the two equivalent forms:

$$\{(x, y) \mid y = 2x - 1\} \quad \text{or} \quad \{(x, y) \mid 8x - 4y = 4\}$$

> **Avoiding Mistakes**
>
> To verify the solution to Example 6, write the two equations in slope-intercept form.
>
> $y = 2x - 1 \Rightarrow y = 2x - 1$
> $8x - 4y = 4 \Rightarrow y = 2x - 1$
>
> The equations have the same slope-intercept form and define the same line.

> **Skill Practice 6**   Solve the system.
> $$x = 5 - 3y$$
> $$2x + 6y = 10$$

Answers

5. { }
6. $\{(x, y) \mid x = 5 - 3y\}$ or
   $\{(x, y) \mid 2x + 6y = 10\}$

The solution set to Example 6 is read as the set of all ordered pairs (x, y) such that the ordered pair satisfies the relationship $y = 2x - 1$ (or equivalently $8x - 4y = 4$). The set $\{(x, y) \mid y = 2x - 1\}$ is called the **general solution** and consists of an infinite number of points. To find several *individual* solutions to the system of equations, substitute arbitrary values of x or y into either equation. For example:

Figure 5-3

	$y = 2x - 1$	**Solution**
If $x = 1$,	$y = 2(1) - 1 = 1$	$(1, 1)$
If $x = 2$,	$y = 2(2) - 1 = 3$	$(2, 3)$
If $x = 3$,	$y = 2(3) - 1 = 5$	$(3, 5)$
If $x = -1$,	$y = 2(-1) - 1 = -3$	$(-1, -3)$

These points are all on the line defined by $y = 2x - 1$. See Figure 5-3.

It is also common to write the general solution to a system of dependent equations using an arbitrary variable called a **parameter.** For example, letting t represent any real number, then the solution set can be expressed as

$$\{(t, 2t - 1) \mid t \text{ is any real number})\}$$

> **TIP** The equations $y = 2x - 1$ and $8x - 4y = 4$ represent the same relationship between x and y. Therefore, we have only one unique equation, but two variables. As a result, y *depends* on the choice of x and vice versa.

3. Use Systems of Linear Equations in Applications

When solving an application involving two unknowns, sometimes it is convenient to use a system of two independent equations as demonstrated in Examples 7 and 8.

EXAMPLE 7   **Solving an Application Involving Mixtures**

A hospital uses a 15% bleach solution to disinfect a quarantine area. How much 6% bleach solution must be mixed with an 18% bleach solution to make 50 L of a 15% bleach solution?

Solution:

Let x represent the amount of 6% bleach solution.

Let y represent the amount of 18% bleach solution.

The amount of pure bleach in each mixture is found by multiplying the amount of solution by the concentration rate. This information can be organized in a table.

	6% Solution	**18% Solution**	**15% Solution**
Amount of mixture	x	y	50
Amount of pure bleach	$0.06x$	$0.18y$	$0.15(50)$

There are two unknown quantities. We will set up a system of two independent equations relating x and y.

$$\begin{pmatrix} \text{Amount of} \\ \text{6\% mixture} \end{pmatrix} + \begin{pmatrix} \text{Amount of} \\ \text{18\% mixture} \end{pmatrix} = \begin{pmatrix} \text{Amount of} \\ \text{15\% mixture} \end{pmatrix}$$

$$\begin{pmatrix} \text{Amount of} \\ \text{pure bleach in} \\ \text{6\% mixture} \end{pmatrix} + \begin{pmatrix} \text{Amount of} \\ \text{pure bleach in} \\ \text{18\% mixture} \end{pmatrix} = \begin{pmatrix} \text{Amount of} \\ \text{pure bleach in} \\ \text{15\% mixture} \end{pmatrix}$$

$x + y = 50$

$0.06x + 0.18y = 0.15(50)$

$$x + y = 50 \qquad\qquad x + y = 50 \longrightarrow x + y = 50$$

$$0.06x + 0.18y = 7.5 \xrightarrow{\text{Multiply by 100.}} 6x + 18y = 750 \xrightarrow{\text{Divide by } -6.} \underline{-x - 3y = -125}$$

$$-2y = -75$$
$$y = 37.5$$

Substitute $y = 37.5$ back into the equation $x + y = 50$.

$$x + y = 50$$
$$x + 37.5 = 50$$
$$x = 12.5$$

Therefore, 12.5 L of the 6% bleach solution should be mixed with 37.5 L of the 18% bleach solution to make 50 L of 15% bleach solution.

Avoiding Mistakes

Check that the answer is reasonable. The total amount of the resulting solution is 12.5 L + 37.5 L, which is 50 L.

Amount of pure bleach:
0.06(12.5 L) = 0.75 L
0.18(37.5 L) = 6.75 L
0.15(50 L) = 7.5 L ✓

> **Skill Practice 7**   How many ounces of 20% and 35% acid solution should be mixed to produce 15 oz of 30% acid solution?

EXAMPLE 8   **Solving an Application Involving Uniform Motion**

A riverboat traveling upstream against the current on the Mississippi River takes 3 hr to travel 24 mi. The return trip downstream with the current takes only 2 hr. Find the speed of the boat in still water and the speed of the current.

Solution:

Let b represent the speed of the boat in still water.
Let c represent the speed of the current.

The given information can be organized in a table.

	Distance (mi)	Rate (mph)	Time (hr)
Upstream	24	$b - c$	3
Downstream	24	$b + c$	2

Use the relationship $d = rt$, that is distance = (rate)(time).

$$\left(\begin{array}{c}\text{Distance}\\\text{upstream}\end{array}\right) = \left(\begin{array}{c}\text{Rate}\\\text{upstream}\end{array}\right)\left(\begin{array}{c}\text{Time}\\\text{upstream}\end{array}\right) \longrightarrow 24 = (b - c) \cdot 3$$

$$\left(\begin{array}{c}\text{Distance}\\\text{downstream}\end{array}\right) = \left(\begin{array}{c}\text{Rate}\\\text{downstream}\end{array}\right)\left(\begin{array}{c}\text{Time}\\\text{downstream}\end{array}\right) \longrightarrow 24 = (b + c) \cdot 2$$

$$24 = 3b - 3c \xrightarrow{\text{Divide by 3.}} 8 = b - c$$
$$24 = 2b + 2c \xrightarrow{\text{Divide by 2.}} \underline{12 = b + c}$$
$$20 = 2b$$
$$10 = b$$

Avoiding Mistakes

Check that the answer is reasonable.

Speed upstream
$(10 - 2)$ mph is 8 mph

Speed downstream
$(10 + 2)$ mph is 12 mph

Distance upstream
24 mi = (8 mph)(3 hr) ✓

Distance downstream
24 mi = (12 mph)(2 hr) ✓

Substitute $b = 10$ into the equation $12 = b + c$, which gives $c = 2$.
The boat's speed in still water is 10 mph and the speed of the current is 2 mph.

> **Skill Practice 8**   A boat takes 3 hr to go 24 mi upstream against the current. It can go downstream with the current a distance of 48 mi in the same amount of time. Determine the speed of the boat in still water and the speed of the current.

Answers

7. Mix 5 oz of 20% acid solution with 10 oz of 35% acid solution to make 15 oz of 30% acid solution.

8. The boat's speed in still water is 12 mph and the speed of the current is 4 mph.

SECTION 5.1   Practice Exercises

Concept Connections

1. Two or more linear equations taken together are called a _____ of linear equations.

2. A _____ to a system of equations in two variables is an ordered pair that is a solution to each individual equation in the system.

3. Two algebraic methods to solve a system of linear equations in two variables are the _____ method and the _____ method.

4. A system of linear equations in two variables may have no solution. In such a case, the equations represent _____ lines.

5. A system of equations that has no solution is called an _____ system.

6. A system of linear equations in two variables may have infinitely many solutions. In such a case, the equations are said to be _____.

Objective 1: Identify Solutions to Systems of Linear Equations in Two Variables

For Exercises 7–10, determine if the ordered pair is a solution to the system of equations. (See Example 1)

7. $3x - 5y = -7$
  $x - 4y = -7$

  a. $(1, 2)$

  b. $\left(-\dfrac{2}{3}, 1\right)$

8. $-11x + 6y = -4$
  $7x + 3y = 23$

  a. $\left(1, \dfrac{7}{6}\right)$

  b. $(2, 3)$

9. $y = \dfrac{3}{2}x - 5$
  $6x - 4y = 20$

  a. $(2, -2)$

  b. $(-4, -11)$

10. $y = -\dfrac{1}{5}x + 2$
  $2x + 10y = 10$

  a. $(5, 1)$

  b. $(-10, 4)$

For Exercises 11–14, a system of equations is given in which each equation is written in slope-intercept form. Determine the number of solutions. If the system does not have one unique solution, state whether the system is inconsistent or whether the equations are dependent.

11. $y = \dfrac{2}{5}x - 7$

  $y = \dfrac{1}{4}x + 7$

12. $y = 6x - \dfrac{2}{3}$

  $y = 6x + 4$

13. $y = 8x - \dfrac{1}{2}$

  $y = 8x - \dfrac{1}{2}$

14. $y = \dfrac{1}{2}x + 3$

  $y = 2x + \dfrac{1}{3}$

Objective 2: Solve Systems of Linear Equations in Two Variables

For Exercises 15–20, solve the system of equations by using the substitution method. (See Example 2)

15. $x + 3y = 5$
  $3x - 2y = -18$

16. $2x + y = 2$
  $5x + 3y = 9$

17. $2x + 7y = 1$
  $3y - 7 = 2$

18. $3x = 2y - 11$
  $6 + 5x = 1$

19. $2(x + y) = 2 - y$
  $4x - 1 = 2 - 5y$

20. $5(x + y) = 9 + 2y$
  $6y - 2 = 10 - 7x$

For Exercises 21–28, solve the system of equations by using the addition method. (See Examples 3–4)

21. $3x - 7y = 1$
  $6x + 5y = -17$

22. $5x - 2y = -2$
  $3x + 4y = 30$

23. $11x = -5 - 4y$
  $2(x - 2y) = 22 + y$

24. $-3(x - y) = y - 14$
  $2x + 2 = 7y$

25. $0.6x + 0.1y = 0.4$
  $2x - 0.7y = 0.3$

26. $0.25x - 0.04y = 0.24$
  $0.15x - 0.12y = 0.12$

27. $2x + 11y = 4$
  $3x - 6y = 5$

28. $3x - 4y = 9$
  $2x + 9y = 2$

For Exercises 29–34, solve the system by using any method. If a system does not have one unique solution, state whether the system is inconsistent or whether the equations are dependent. (See Examples 5–6)

29. $3x - 4y = 6$
$9x = 12y + 4$

30. $-4x - 8y = 2$
$2x = 8 - 4y$

31. $3x + y = 6$
$x + \dfrac{1}{3}y = 2$

32. $2x - y = 8$
$x - \dfrac{1}{2}y = 4$

33. $2x + 4 = 4 - 5y$
$2 + 4(x + y) = 7y + 2$

34. $3(x - 3y) = 2y$
$2x + 5 = 5 - 7y$

Mixed Exercises

For Exercises 35–48, solve the system using any method.

35. $3x - 10y = 1900$
$5y + 800 = x$

36. $2x - 7y = 2400$
$-4x + 1800 = y$

37. $5(2x + y) = y - x - 8$
$x - \dfrac{3}{2}y = \dfrac{5}{2}$

38. $3(2x - y) = 2 - x$
$x + \dfrac{5}{4}y = \dfrac{3}{2}$

39. $y = \dfrac{2}{3}x - 1$
$y = \dfrac{1}{6}x + 2$

40. $y = -\dfrac{1}{4}x + 7$
$y = -\dfrac{3}{2}x + 17$

41. $4(x - 2) = 6y + 3$
$\dfrac{1}{4}x - \dfrac{3}{8}y = -\dfrac{1}{2}$

42. $\dfrac{1}{14}x - \dfrac{1}{7}y = \dfrac{1}{2}$
$2(x - 2y) + 3 = 20$

43. $2x = \dfrac{y}{2} + 1$
$0.04x - 0.01y = 0.02$

44. $0.05x + 0.01y = 0.03$
$x + \dfrac{y}{5} = \dfrac{3}{5}$

45. $y = 2.4x - 1.54$
$y = -3.5x + 7.9$

46. $y = -0.18x + 0.129$
$y = -0.15x + 0.1275$

47. $\dfrac{x - 2}{8} + \dfrac{y + 1}{2} = -6$
$\dfrac{x - 2}{2} - \dfrac{y + 1}{4} = 12$

48. $\dfrac{x + 1}{2} - \dfrac{y - 2}{10} = -1$
$\dfrac{x + 1}{6} + \dfrac{y - 2}{2} = 21$

Objective 3: Use Systems of Linear Equations in Applications

49. One antifreeze solution is 36% alcohol and another is 20% alcohol. How much of each mixture should be added to make 40 L of a solution that is 30% alcohol? **(See Example 7)**

50. A pharmacist wants to mix a 30% saline solution with a 10% saline solution to get 200 mL of a 12% saline solution. How much of each solution should she use?

51. A radiator has 16 L of a 36% antifreeze solution. How much must be drained and replaced by pure antifreeze to bring the concentration level up to 50%?

52. Jonas performed an experiment for his science fair project. He learned that rinsing lettuce in vinegar kills more bacteria than rinsing with water or with a popular commercial product. As a follow-up to his project, he wants to determine the percentage of bacteria killed by rinsing with a diluted solution of vinegar.

  a. How much water and how much vinegar should be mixed to produce 10 cups of a mixture that is 40% vinegar?

  b. How much pure vinegar and how much 40% vinegar solution should be mixed to produce 10 cups of a mixture that is 60% vinegar?

53. Monique and Tara each make an ice cream sundae. Monique gets 2 scoops of Cherry ice cream and 1 scoop of Mint Chocolate Chunk ice cream for a total of 43 g of fat. Tara has 1 scoop of Cherry and 2 scoops of Mint Chocolate Chunk for a total of 47 g of fat. How many grams of fat does 1 scoop of each type of ice cream have?

54. Bryan and Jadyn had barbeque potato chips and soda at a football party. Bryan ate 3 oz of chips and drank 2 cups of soda for a total of 700 mg of sodium. Jadyn ate 1 oz of chips and drank 3 cups of soda for a total of 350 mg of sodium. How much sodium is in 1 oz of chips and how much is in 1 cup of soda?

55. Michelle borrows a total of $5000 in student loans from two lenders. One charges 4.6% simple interest and the other charges 6.2% simple interest. She is not required to pay off the principal or interest for 3 yr. However, at the end of 3 yr, she will owe a total of $762 for the interest from both loans. How much did she borrow from each lender?

56. Juan borrows $100,000 to pay for medical school. He borrows part of the money from the school whereby he will pay 4.5% simple interest. He borrows the rest of the money through a government loan that will charge him 6% interest. In both cases, he is not required to pay off the principal or interest during his 4 yr of medical school. However, at the end of 4 yr, he will owe a total of $19,200 for the interest from both loans. How much did he borrow from each source?

57. The average weekly salary of two employees is $1350. One makes $300 more than the other. Find their salaries

58. The average of an electrician's hourly wage and a plumber's hourly wage is $33. One day a contractor hires the electrician for 8 hr of work and the plumber for 5 hr of work and pays a total of $438 in wages. Find the hourly wage for the electrician and for the plumber.

59. A moving sidewalk in an airport moves people between gates. It takes Jason's 9-year-old daughter Josie 40 sec to travel 200 ft walking with the sidewalk. It takes her 30 sec to walk 90 ft against the moving sidewalk (in the opposite direction). Find the speed of the sidewalk and find Josie's speed walking on non-moving ground. **(See Example 8)**

60. A fishing boat travels along the east coast of the United States and encounters the Gulf Stream current. It travels 44 mi north with the current in 2 hr. It travels 56 mi south against the current in 4 hr. Find the speed of the current and the speed of the boat in still water.

61. Two runners begin at the same point on a 390-m circular track and run at different speeds. If they run in opposite directions, they pass each other in 30 sec. If they run in the same direction, they meet each other in 130 sec. Find the speed of each runner.

62. Two particles begin at the same point and move at different speeds along a circular path of circumference 280 ft. Moving in opposite directions, they pass in 10 sec. Moving in the same direction, they pass in 70 sec. Find the speed of each particle.

63. The points shown in the graph represent the per capita consumption of chicken and beef for the United States x years after the year 2000. (*Source*: U.S. Department of Agriculture, www.ers.usda.gov)

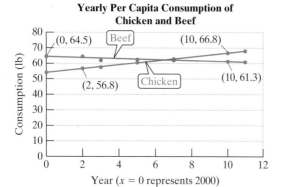

a. Use the given data points to write a linear function that approximates per capita consumption of chicken $C(x)$ (in lb) at a time x years since the year 2000.

b. Use the given data points to write a linear function that approximates per capita consumption of beef $B(x)$ (in lb) at a time x years since the year 2000.

c. Approximate the solution to the system of linear equations defined by the functions from parts (a) and (b). Round to 1 decimal place. Interpret the meaning of the solution to the system.

64. The points shown in the graph represent the number of travelers (in 1000s) to the United States from Brazil (shown in blue) and from Australia (shown in red) x years since the year 2000. (*Source*: U.S. Department of Commerce, International Trade Administration, http://tinet.ita.doc.gov)

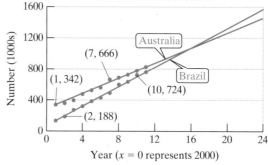

a. Use the given data points to write a linear function that predicts the number of travelers $A(x)$ (in 1000s) to the United States from Australia x years since the year 2000.

b. Use the given data points to write a linear function that predicts the number of travelers $B(x)$ (in 1000s) to the United States from Brazil x years since the year 2000.

c. Solve the system of linear equations using the functions from parts (a) and (b). Interpret the meaning of the solution to the system.

For Exercises 65–66, refer to Section 2.5 for a review of linear cost functions and linear revenue functions.

65. A cleaning company charges $100 for each office it cleans. The fixed monthly cost of $480 for the company includes telephone service and the depreciation on cleaning equipment and a van. The variable cost is $52 per office and includes labor, gasoline, and cleaning supplies.

   a. Write a linear cost function representing the cost $C(x)$ (in $) to clean x offices per month.

   b. Write a linear revenue function representing the revenue $R(x)$ (in $) for cleaning x offices per month.

   c. Determine the number of offices to be cleaned per month for the company to break even.

   d. If 28 offices are cleaned, will the company make money or lose money?

66. A vendor at a carnival sells cotton candy and caramel apples for $2.00 each. The vendor is charged $100 to set up his booth. Furthermore, the vendor's average cost for each product he produces is approximately $0.75.

   a. Write a linear cost function representing the cost $C(x)$ (in $) to produce x products.

   b. Write a linear revenue function representing the revenue $R(x)$ (in $) for selling x products.

   c. Determine the number of products to be produced and sold for the vendor to break even.

   d. If 60 products are sold, will the vendor make money or lose money?

67. a. Sketch the lines defined by $y = 2x$ and $y = -\frac{1}{2}x + 5$.

   b. Find the area of the triangle bounded by the lines in part (a) and the x-axis.

68. a. Sketch the lines defined by $y = x + 2$ and $y = -\frac{1}{2}x + 2$.

   b. Find the area of the triangle bounded by the lines in part (a) and the x-axis.

69. The **centroid** of a region is the geometric center. For the region shown, the centroid is the point of intersection of the diagonals of the parallelogram.

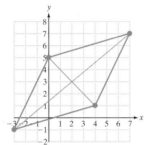

   a. Find an equation of the line through the points $(-3, -1)$ and $(7, 7)$.

   b. Find an equation of the line through the points $(0, 5)$ and $(4, 1)$.

   c. Find the centroid of the region.

70. The centroid of the region shown is the point of intersection of the diagonals of the parallelogram.

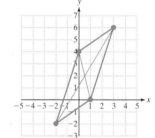

   a. Find an equation of the line through the points $(-2, -2)$ and $(3, 6)$.

   b. Find an equation of the line through the points $(1, 0)$ and $(0, 4)$.

   c. Find the centroid of the region.

71. Two angles are complementary. The measure of one angle is 6° less than twice the measure of the other angle. Find the measure of each angle.

72. Two angles are supplementary. The measure of one angle is 12° more than 5 times the measure of the other angle. Find the measure of each angle.

For Exercises 73–74, find the measure of angles x and y.

73.

74.

Mixed Exercises

75. Write a system of linear equations with solution set $\{(-3, 5)\}$.

76. Write a system of linear equations with solution set $\{(4, -3)\}$.

77. Find C and D so that the solution set to the system is $\{(4, 1)\}$.

$$Cx + 5y = 13$$
$$-2x + Dy = -5$$

78. Find A and B so that the solution set to the system is $\{(-5, 2)\}$.

$$3x + Ay = -3$$
$$Bx - y = -12$$

79. Given $f(x) = mx + b$, find m and b if $f(3) = -3$ and $f(-12) = -8$.

80. Given $g(x) = mx + b$, find m and b if $g(2) = 1$ and $g(-4) = 10$.

For Exercises 81–82, use the substitution $u = \frac{1}{x}$ and $v = \frac{1}{y}$ to rewrite the equations in the system in terms of the variables u and v. Solve the system in terms of u and v. Then back substitute to determine the solution set to the original system in terms of x and y.

81. $\dfrac{1}{x} + \dfrac{2}{y} = 1$

$-\dfrac{1}{x} + \dfrac{4}{y} = -7$

82. $-\dfrac{3}{x} + \dfrac{4}{y} = 11$

$\dfrac{1}{x} - \dfrac{2}{y} = -5$

83. During a race, Marta bicycled 12 mi and ran 4 mi in a total of 1 hr 20 min ($\frac{4}{3}$ hr). In another race, she bicycled 21 mi and ran 3 mi in 1 hr 40 min ($\frac{5}{3}$ hr). Determine the speed at which she bicycles and the speed at which she runs. Assume that her bicycling speed was the same in each race and that her running speed was the same in each race.

84. Shelia swam 1 mi and ran 6 mi in a total of 1 hr 15 min ($\frac{5}{4}$ hr). In another training session she swam 2 mi and ran 8 mi in a total of 2 hr. Determine the speed at which she swims and the speed at which she runs. Assume that her swimming speed was the same each day and that her running speed was the same each day.

85. A certain pickup truck gets 16 mpg in the city and 22 mpg on the highway. If a driver drives 254 mi on 14 gal of gas, determine the number of city miles and highway miles that the truck was driven.

86. A sedan gets 12 mpg in the city and 18 mpg on the highway. If a driver drives a total of 420 mi on 26 gal of gas, how many miles in the city and how many miles on the highway did he drive?

Systems of equations play an important role in the analysis of supply and demand. For example, suppose that a theater company wants to set an optimal price for tickets to a show. If the theater sells tickets for $1 each, there would be a high demand and many people would buy tickets. However, the revenue brought in would not cover the expense of the show. Therefore, the theater is not willing to offer (supply) tickets at this low price. If the theater sells tickets for $10,000 each, chances are that no one would buy a ticket (demand would be low).

In an open market, the price of an item is dependent on the demand by consumers and the supply offered by producers. Competition between buyers and sellers steers the price toward an equilibrium price—that is, the price where supply equals demand. The number of items offered and sold at the equilibrium price is the equilibrium quantity. Use this information for Exercises 87–88.

87. Suppose that the price p (in $) of theater tickets is influenced by the number of tickets x offered by the theater and demanded by consumers.

Supply: $p = 0.025x$

Demand: $p = -0.04x + 104$

a. Solve the system of equations defined by the supply and demand models.

b. What is the equilibrium price?

c. What is the equilibrium quantity?

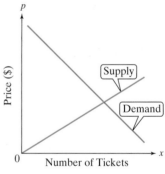

88. The price p (in $) of a cookbook is determined by the number of cookbooks x demanded by consumers and supplied by the publisher.

Supply: $p = 0.002x$

Demand: $p = -0.005x + 70$

a. Solve the system of equations defined by the supply and demand models.

b. What is the equilibrium price?

c. What is the equilibrium quantity?

Write About It

89. A system of linear equations in x and y can represent two intersecting lines, two parallel lines, or a single line. Describe the solution set to the system in each case.

90. When solving a system of linear equations in two variables using the substitution or addition method, explain how you can detect whether the equations are dependent.

91. When solving a system of linear equations in two variables using the substitution or addition method, explain how you can detect whether the system is inconsistent.

92. Consider a system of linear equations in two variables in which the solution set is $\{(x, y) \mid y = x + 2\}$. Why do we say that the equations in the system are dependent?

Expanding Your Skills

Pythagorean triples, denoted by (a, b, c), represent three positive integers a, b, and c that satisfy the relationship $a^2 + b^2 = c^2$. Suppose that $a = 4$. To find all values of b and c that would form Pythagorean triples with $a = 4$ we can use the following technique:

Substituting $a = 4$, we have $4^2 + b^2 = c^2$. Therefore, $c^2 - b^2 = 16$. In factored form this is $(c - b)(c + b) = 16$. Setting $c - b$ and $c + b$ equal to the positive factors of 16 and solving the resulting system of equations, we have

$$c - b = 1 \quad c - b = 2 \quad c - b = 4 \quad c - b = 8 \quad c - b = 16$$
$$c + b = 16 \quad c + b = 8 \quad c + b = 4 \quad c + b = 2 \quad c + b = 1$$

The only system that returns positive integer values for b and c is the second system. It gives $c = 5$ and $b = 3$ resulting in a Pythagorean triple of $(4, 3, 5)$. Use this technique for Exercises 93–94.

93. Find all Pythagorean triples (a, b, c) such that $a = 9$.

94. Find all Pythagorean triples (a, b, c) such that $b = 12$.

95. A 50-lb weight is supported from two cables and the system is in equilibrium. The magnitudes of the forces on the cables are denoted by $|F_1|$ and $|F_2|$, respectively. An engineering student knows that the horizontal components of the two forces (shown in red) must be equal in magnitude. Furthermore, the sum of the magnitudes of the vertical components of the forces (shown in blue) must be equal to 50 lb to offset the downward force of the weight. Find the values of $|F_1|$ and $|F_2|$. Write the answers in exact form with no radical in the denominator. Also give approximations to 1 decimal place.

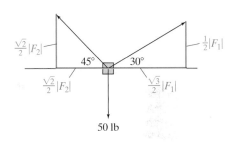

Technology Connections

For Exercises 96–99, use a graphing utility to approximate the solution to the system of equations. Round the x and y values to 3 decimal places.

96. $y = -3.729x + 6.958$
$y = 2.615x - 8.713$

97. $y = -0.041x + 0.068$
$y = 0.019x - 0.053$

98. $-0.25x + 0.04y = -0.42$
$6.775x + 2.5y = -38.1$

99. $0.36x - 0.075y = -0.813$
$0.066x + 0.008y = 0.194$

SECTION 5.2   Systems of Linear Equations in Three Variables and Applications

OBJECTIVES

1. Identify Solutions to a System of Linear Equations in Three Variables
2. Solve Systems of Linear Equations in Three Variables
3. Use Systems of Linear Equations in Applications
4. Modeling with Linear Equations in Three Variables

1. Identify Solutions to a System of Linear Equations in Three Variables

In Section 5.1 we solved systems of linear equations in two variables. In this section, we expand the discussion to solving systems involving three variables. A **linear equation in three variables** is an equation that can be written in the form

$$Ax + By + Cz = D, \text{ where } A, B, \text{ and } C \text{ are not all zero.}$$

For example, $x + 2y + z = 4$ is a linear equation in three variables. A solution to a linear equation in three variables is an ordered triple (x, y, z) that satisfies the equation. For example, several solutions to $x + 2y + z = 4$ are given here.

Solution	Check: $x + 2y + z = 4$
$(1, 1, 1)$	$(1) + 2(1) + (1) \overset{?}{=} 4$ ✓ true
$(4, 0, 0)$	$(4) + 2(0) + (0) \overset{?}{=} 4$ ✓ true
$(0, 2, 0)$	$(0) + 2(2) + (0) \overset{?}{=} 4$ ✓ true
$(0, 0, 4)$	$(0) + 2(0) + (4) \overset{?}{=} 4$ ✓ true

There are infinitely many solutions to the equation $x + 2y + z = 4$. The set of all solutions to a linear equation in three variables can be represented graphically by a plane in space. Figure 5-4 shows a portion of the plane defined by $x + 2y + z = 4$.

In many applications, we are interested in determining the point or points of intersection of two or more planes. This is given by the solutions to a system of linear equations in three variables. For example:

$$\begin{aligned} 2x + y - 3z &= -2 \\ x - 4y + z &= 24 \\ -3x - y + 4z &= 0 \end{aligned}$$

A solution to a system of linear equations in three variables is an **ordered triple** (x, y, z) that satisfies each equation in the system. Geometrically, a solution is a point of intersection of the planes represented by the equations in the system (Figure 5-5).

Figure 5-4

Figure 5-5

EXAMPLE 1 **Determining if an Ordered Triple Is a Solution to a System of Equations**

Determine if the ordered triple is a solution to the system.

$$\begin{aligned} 2x + y - 3z &= -2 \\ x - 4y + z &= 24 \\ -3x - y + 4z &= 0 \end{aligned}$$

a. $(3, -5, 1)$ **b.** $(2, -3, 1)$

Solution:

Test the ordered triple in each equation.

a. First equation

$2x + y - 3z = -2$
$2(3) + (-5) - 3(1) \stackrel{?}{=} -2$
$-2 \stackrel{?}{=} -2$ ✓ true

Second equation

$x - 4y + z = 24$
$(3) - 4(-5) + (1) \stackrel{?}{=} 24$
$24 \stackrel{?}{=} 24$ ✓ true

Third equation

$-3x - y + 4z = 0$
$-3(3) - (-5) + 4(1) \stackrel{?}{=} 0$
$0 \stackrel{?}{=} 0$ ✓ true

The ordered triple $(3, -5, 1)$ is a solution to the system of equations.

b. First equation

$2x + y - 3z = -2$
$2(2) + (-3) - 3(1) \stackrel{?}{=} -2$
$-2 \stackrel{?}{=} -2$ ✓ true

Second equation

$x - 4y + z = 24$
$(2) - 4(-3) + (1) \stackrel{?}{=} 24$
$15 \stackrel{?}{=} 24$ false

Third equation

$-3x - y + 4z = 0$
$-3(2) - (-3) + 4(1) \stackrel{?}{=} 0$
$1 \stackrel{?}{=} 0$ false

If an ordered triple fails to be a solution to any of the equations in the system, then it is not a solution to the system. The ordered triple $(2, -3, 1)$ is *not* a solution to the second or third equation. Therefore, $(2, -3, 1)$ is *not* a solution to the system of equations.

Skill Practice 1 Determine if the ordered triple is a solution to the system.

$$\begin{aligned} 5x - y + 3z &= -7 \\ 3x + 4y - z &= 5 \\ 9x + 5y + 7z &= 1 \end{aligned}$$

a. $(-2, -6, 3)$ **b.** $(-1, 2, 0)$

Answers

1. a. No   **b.** Yes

2. Solve Systems of Linear Equations in Three Variables

To solve a system of three linear equations in three variables, we first eliminate one variable. The system is then reduced to a two-variable system that can be solved by the techniques learned in Section 5.1.

Solving a System of Three Linear Equations in Three Variables

Step 1 Write each equation in standard form $Ax + By + Cz = D$.

Step 2 Choose a pair of equations and eliminate one of the variables by using the addition method.

Step 3 Choose a different pair of equations and eliminate the *same* variable.

Step 4 Once steps 2 and 3 are complete, you should have two equations in two variables. Solve this system by using the substitution or addition method.

Step 5 Substitute the values of the variables found in step 4 into any of the three original equations that contain the third variable. Solve for the third variable.

Step 6 Check the ordered triple in each original equation. Then write the solution as an ordered triple in set notation.

EXAMPLE 2 **Solving a System of Equations in Three Variables**

Solve the system.
$$3x - 2y + z = 2$$
$$5x + y - 2z = 1$$
$$4x - 3y + 3z = 7$$

TIP In Example 2, the y terms can also be eliminated easily because the coefficient on y in equation $\boxed{B}$ is 1. Therefore, y can be eliminated from equations $\boxed{A}$ and $\boxed{B}$ by multiplying equation $\boxed{B}$ by 2. Likewise y can be eliminated from equations $\boxed{B}$ and $\boxed{C}$ by multiplying equation $\boxed{B}$ by 3.

Solution:

$\boxed{A}$ $3x - 2y + z = 2$
$\boxed{B}$ $5x + y - 2z = 1$
$\boxed{C}$ $4x - 3y + 3z = 7$

Step 1: The equations are already in standard form.
- It is helpful to label the equations $\boxed{A}$, $\boxed{B}$, and $\boxed{C}$.
- The z variable can easily be eliminated from equations $\boxed{A}$ and $\boxed{B}$ and from equations $\boxed{A}$ and $\boxed{C}$. This is accomplished by creating opposite coefficients for the z terms and then adding the equations.

Step 2: Eliminate z from equations $\boxed{A}$ and $\boxed{B}$.

$\boxed{A}$ $3x - 2y + z = 2$ $\xrightarrow{\text{Multiply by 2.}}$ $6x - 4y + 2z = 4$
$\boxed{B}$ $5x + y - 2z = 1$ $\underline{5x + y - 2z = 1}$
$ 11x - 3y = 5$ $\boxed{D}$

Step 3: Eliminate z from equations $\boxed{A}$ and $\boxed{C}$.

$\boxed{A}$ $3x - 2y + z = 2$ $\xrightarrow{\text{Multiply by } -3.}$ $-9x + 6y - 3z = -6$
$\boxed{C}$ $4x - 3y + 3z = 7$ $\underline{4x - 3y + 3z = 7}$ $\boxed{E}$
$ -5x + 3y = 1$

Step 4: $\boxed{D}$ $11x - 3y = 5$ $\longrightarrow$ $\boxed{D}$ $11(1) - 3y = 5$ Solve the system
 $\boxed{E}$ $\underline{-5x + 3y = 1}$ $11 - 3y = 5$ of equations $\boxed{D}$
$ 6x = 6$ $-3y = -6$ and $\boxed{E}$.
$ x = 1$ $y = 2$

$\boxed{A}$ $3x - 2y + z = 2$
 $3(1) - 2(2) + z = 2$
 $3 - 4 + z = 2$
 $-1 + z = 2$
 $z = 3$

Step 5: Substitute the values of the known variables x and y back into one of the original equations. We have chosen equation $\boxed{A}$.

Step 6: Check the ordered triple (1, 2, 3) in the three original equations.

$\boxed{A}$ $3x - 2y + z = 2$	$\boxed{B}$ $5x + y - 2z = 1$	$\boxed{C}$ $4x - 3y + 3z = 7$
$3(1) - 2(2) + (3) \stackrel{?}{=} 2$	$5(1) + (2) - 2(3) \stackrel{?}{=} 1$	$4(1) - 3(2) + 3(3) \stackrel{?}{=} 7$
$2 \stackrel{?}{=} 2$ ✓ true	$1 \stackrel{?}{=} 1$ ✓ true	$7 \stackrel{?}{=} 7$ ✓ true

The solution set is {(1, 2, 3)}.

Skill Practice 2   Solve the system.
$$2x - y + 5z = -7$$
$$x + 4y - 2z = 1$$
$$3x + 2y + z = -7$$

In Example 3, we solve a system of linear equations in which one or more equations has a missing term.

EXAMPLE 3   **Solving a System of Equations in Three Variables**

Solve the system.
$$2x + y = -2$$
$$3y = 5z - 12$$
$$5(x + z) = 2z + 5$$

Solution:

Step 1: Write the equations in standard form.

$\boxed{A}$	$2x + y = -2$	$\longrightarrow$	$2x + y \quad\quad = -2$	Notice that the equations
$\boxed{B}$	$3y = 5z - 12$	$\longrightarrow$	$3y - 5z = -12$	already have missing
$\boxed{C}$	$5(x + z) = 2z + 5$	$\longrightarrow$	$5x \quad\quad + 3z = 5$	variable terms.

Steps 2 and 3: This system of equations has several missing terms. For example, equation $\boxed{C}$ is missing the variable y. If we eliminate y from equations $\boxed{A}$ and $\boxed{B}$, then we will have a second equation with variable y missing.

$\boxed{A}$	$2x + y \quad\quad = -2$	$\xrightarrow{\text{Multiply by } -3.}$	$-6x - 3y \quad\quad = 6$
$\boxed{B}$	$3y - 5z = -12$		$\underline{\quad\quad 3y - 5z = -12}$
			$-6x \quad\quad - 5z = -6$ $\boxed{D}$

Step 4: Pair up equations $\boxed{C}$ and $\boxed{D}$. These equations form a system of linear equations in two variables. To solve the system with equations $\boxed{C}$ and $\boxed{D}$ we have chosen to eliminate the z variable.

$\boxed{C}$	$5x + 3z = 5$	$\xrightarrow{\text{Multiply by 5.}}$	$25x + 15z = 25$
$\boxed{D}$	$-6x - 5z = -6$	$\xrightarrow[\text{Multiply by 3.}]{}$	$\underline{-18x - 15z = -18}$
			$7x \quad\quad = 7$
			$x = 1$

$\boxed{C}$ $5x + 3z = 5$
$\quad\quad 5(1) + 3z = 5$
$\quad\quad\quad\quad z = 0$

$\boxed{B}$ $3y = 5z - 12$ **Step 5:** Substitute the values of the known variables x
$\quad\quad 3y = 5(0) - 12$ and z back into one of the original equations containing
$\quad\quad 3y = -12$ y. We have chosen equation $\boxed{B}$.
$\quad\quad\quad y = -4$

Step 6: The ordered triple (1, −4, 0) checks in each original equation.

Answer
2. {(−3, 1, 0)}

The solution set is {(1, −4, 0)}.

Skill Practice 3   Solve the system.

$$a \quad\quad + 3c = 4$$
$$b + 2c = -1$$
$$2a - 4b \quad\quad = 14$$

A system of linear equations in three variables may have no solution. This occurs if the equations represent planes that do not all intersect (Figure 5-6). In such a case, we say that the system is **inconsistent.**

Figure 5-6

A system of linear equations in three variables may also have infinitely many solutions. This occurs if the equations represent planes that intersect in a common line or common plane (Figure 5-7). In such a case, we say that the equations are **dependent.**

Figure 5-7

EXAMPLE 4   **Determining the Number of Solutions to a System**

Determine the number of solutions to the system.

$$-x + 6y - 3z = -8$$
$$x - 2y + 2z = 3$$
$$3x + 2y + 4z = -6$$

Solution:

$$
\begin{array}{ll}
\boxed{A} & -x + 6y - 3z = -8 \\
\boxed{B} & x - 2y + 2z = 3 \\
\boxed{C} & 3x + 2y + 4z = -6
\end{array}
\longrightarrow
\begin{array}{l}
-x + 6y - 3z = -8 \\
\underline{x - 2y + 2z = \quad 3} \\
\quad\quad 4y - \ z = -5 \quad \boxed{D}
\end{array}
$$

Add equations $\boxed{A}$ and $\boxed{B}$ to eliminate x.

$$
\begin{array}{ll}
\boxed{A} & -x + 6y - 3z = -8 \\
\boxed{C} & 3x + 2y + 4z = -6
\end{array}
\xrightarrow{\text{Multiply by 3.}}
\begin{array}{l}
-3x + 18y - 9z = -24 \\
\underline{3x + \ 2y + 4z = -6} \\
\quad\quad 20y - 5z = -30 \quad \boxed{E}
\end{array}
$$

Multiply equation $\boxed{A}$ by 3 and add the result to $\boxed{C}$.

$$
\begin{array}{ll}
\boxed{D} & 4y - \ z = -5 \\
\boxed{E} & 20y - 5z = -30
\end{array}
\xrightarrow{\text{Multiply by } -5.}
\begin{array}{l}
-20y + 5z = 25 \\
\underline{20y - 5z = -30} \\
\quad\quad\quad 0 = -5
\end{array}
$$

Solving the system of equations $\boxed{D}$ and $\boxed{E}$ results in a contradiction.

The system of equations reduces to a contradiction.

The system is inconsistent.

Therefore, the system has no solution.

Answer

3. $\{(1, -3, 1)\}$

Skill Practice 4   Determine the number of solutions to the system.

$$x + y + 4z = -1$$
$$3x + y - 4z = 3$$
$$-4x - y + 8z = -2$$

In Example 5, we investigate the case in which a system of equations has infinitely many solutions.

EXAMPLE 5   **Determining the Number of Solutions to a System**

Determine the number of solutions to the system.

$$2x + y \quad\quad = -3$$
$$2y + 16z = -10$$
$$-7x - 3y + 4z = 8$$

Solution:

Eliminate variable z from equations $\boxed{B}$ and $\boxed{C}$.

$\boxed{A}$ $\quad 2x + y \quad\quad\quad = -3$

$\boxed{B}$ $\quad\quad\quad 2y + 16z = -10$ $\quad\longrightarrow\quad$ $\quad 2y + 16z = -10$

$\boxed{C}$ $\quad -7x - 3y + 4z = 8$ $\quad\underset{\text{by } -4.}{\overset{\text{Multiply}}{\longrightarrow}}$ $\quad \dfrac{28x + 12y - 16z = -32}{28x + 14y \quad\quad = -42}$ $\boxed{D}$

Pair up equations $\boxed{A}$ and $\boxed{D}$ to solve for x and y.

$\boxed{A}$ $\quad 2x + y = -3$ $\quad\longrightarrow\quad$ $\quad 2x + y = -3$

$\boxed{D}$ $\quad 28x + 14y = -42$ $\quad\underset{\text{Divide by } -14.}{\longrightarrow}$ $\quad \dfrac{-2x - y = 3}{0 = 0}$

The system reduces to the identity $0 = 0$. This implies that the equations are dependent and that the system has infinitely many solutions.

Skill Practice 5   Determine the number of solutions to the system.

$$5x + y \quad\quad = 0$$
$$4y - z = 0$$
$$5x + 5y - z = 0$$

In Example 5, we determined that the system has infinitely many solutions, but we did not actually find any solutions or offer a general solution to the system. This is discussed more fully when we learn matrix methods to solve systems of linear equations. With additional tools available, we can investigate whether dependent equations in a system represent planes that intersect in a line (called linear dependence) or whether the equations represent coincident planes (called coincident dependence).

3. Use Systems of Linear Equations in Applications

When solving an application involving three unknowns, sometimes it is convenient to use a system of three independent equations as demonstrated in Examples 6 and 7.

Answers

4. No solution

5. Infinitely many solutions

EXAMPLE 6   **Solving an Application Involving Finance**

Janette invested a total of $18,000 in three different mutual funds. She invested in a bond fund that returned 4% the first year. An aggressive growth fund lost 8% for the year, and an international fund returned 2%. Janette invested $2000 more in the growth fund than in the other two funds combined. If she had a net loss of −$540 for the year, how much did she invest in each fund?

Solution:

Let x represent the amount invested in the bond fund.

Let y represent the amount invested in the growth fund.

Let z represent the amount invested in the international fund.

Label the variables. With three unknowns, we need three independent equations.

$x + y + z = 18{,}000$ ⟶ The total amount invested was $18,000.

$y = (x + z) + 2000$ ⟶ The amount invested in the growth fund was $2000 more than the combined amount in the other two funds.

$0.04x - 0.08y + 0.02z = -540$ ⟶ The sum of the gain and loss from each fund equals −$540.

$$\boxed{A}\quad x + y + z = 18{,}000$$
$$\boxed{B}\quad y = (x + z) + 2000$$
$$\boxed{C}\quad 0.04x - 0.08y + 0.02z = -540$$

Standard form
Multiply by 100.

$$\boxed{A}\quad x + y + z = 18{,}000$$
$$\boxed{B}\quad -x + y - z = 2000$$
$$\boxed{C}\quad 4x - 8y + 2z = -54{,}000$$

Eliminate x from equations $\boxed{A}$ and $\boxed{B}$ and equations $\boxed{B}$ and $\boxed{C}$.

$$\boxed{A}\quad x + y + z = 18{,}000$$
$$\boxed{B}\quad \underline{-x + y - z = 2000}$$
$$\qquad\qquad 2y = 20{,}000$$
$$\qquad\qquad\ \ y = 10{,}000$$

$$4 \cdot \boxed{B}\quad -4x + 4y - 4z = 8000$$
$$\boxed{C}\quad \underline{\ 4x - 8y + 2z = -54{,}000}$$
$$\qquad\qquad -4y - 2z = -46{,}000 \quad \boxed{D}$$

Back substitute.

$$\boxed{D}\quad -4y - 2z = -46{,}000$$
$$-4(10{,}000) - 2z = -46{,}000$$
$$-2z = -6000$$
$$z = 3000$$

$$\boxed{A}\quad x + y + z = 18{,}000$$
$$x + (10{,}000) + (3000) = 18{,}000$$
$$x + 13{,}000 = 18{,}000$$
$$x = 5000$$

Janette invested $5000 in the bond fund, $10,000 in the aggressive growth fund, and $3000 in the international fund.

Avoiding Mistakes

For Example 6, verify that the conditions of the problem have been met.

Principal:
$5000 + $10,000 + $3000
   = $18,000 ✓

Return:
   0.04($5000)
−0.08($10,000)
+0.02($3000)
−$540 ✓

More invested in growth:
($5000 + $3000) + $2000
   = $10,000 ✓

Skill Practice 6   Nicolas mixes three solutions of acid with concentrations of 10%, 15%, and 5%. He wants to make 30 L of a mixture that is 12% acid and he uses four times as much of the 15% solution as the 5% solution. How much of each of the three solutions must he use?

4. Modeling with Linear Equations in Three Variables

In Section 3.1, we used regression to find a quadratic model $y = ax^2 + bx + c$ from observed data points. We will now learn how to find a quadratic model by using a system of linear equations in three variables. The premise is that any three noncollinear points (points that do not all fall on the same line) define a unique parabola given by $y = ax^2 + bx + c$ $(a \neq 0)$.

Answer

6. Nicolas mixes 10 L of the 10% solution, 16 L of the 15% solution, and 4 L of the 5% solution.

EXAMPLE 7   Using a System of Linear Equations to Create a Quadratic Model

Given the noncollinear points $(4, 2)$, $(1, -1)$, and $(-1, 7)$, find an equation of the form $y = ax^2 + bx + c$ that defines the parabola through the points.

Solution:

$$y = ax^2 + bx + c$$

Substitute $(4, 2)$: $2 = a(4)^2 + b(4) + c$ ⟶ $\boxed{A}$ $16a + 4b + c = 2$

Substitute $(1, -1)$: $-1 = a(1)^2 + b(1) + c$ ⟶ $\boxed{B}$ $a + b + c = -1$

Substitute $(-1, 7)$: $7 = a(-1)^2 + b(-1) + c$ ⟶ $\boxed{C}$ $a - b + c = 7$

Eliminate variable b from equations $\boxed{A}$ and $\boxed{C}$ and from equations $\boxed{B}$ and $\boxed{C}$.

$\boxed{A}$ $16a + 4b + c = 2$ $\boxed{B}$ $a + b + c = -1$

$4 \cdot \boxed{C}$ $\underline{4a - 4b + 4c = 28}$ $\boxed{C}$ $\underline{a - b + c = 7}$

$20a \quad\;\; + 5c = 30$ $\boxed{D}$ $2a \quad\; + 2c = 6$ $\boxed{E}$

$\boxed{D}$ $20a + 5c = 30$ —Divide by 5.→ $4a + c = 6$ $\boxed{E}$ $2a + 2c = 6$

$\boxed{E}$ $2a + 2c = 6$ —Divide by -2.→ $\dfrac{-a - c = -3}{3a \quad\;\; = 3}$ $2(1) + 2c = 6$

$a = 1$ Back substitute. $c = 2$

$\boxed{B}$ $a + b + c = -1$

$(1) + b + (2) = -1$

$b = -4$

Substituting $a = 1$, $b = -4$, and $c = 2$ into the equation $y = ax^2 + bx + c$ gives

$$y = x^2 - 4x + 2$$

The graph of $y = x^2 - 4x + 2$ passes through the points $(4, 2)$, $(1, -1)$, and $(-1, 7)$ as shown in Figure 5-8.

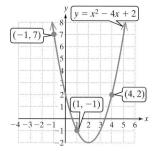

Figure 5-8

The results can also be verified by using the **Table** feature of a graphing utility. Enter $Y_1 = x^2 - 4x + 2$.

TIP We can verify that the three points given in Example 7 are *not* collinear by showing that the slopes between two pairs of points are different.

For $(4, 2)$ and $(1, -1)$,
$$m = \frac{-1 - 2}{1 - 4} = 1$$
For $(4, 2)$ and $(-1, 7)$,
$$m = \frac{7 - 2}{-1 - 4} = -1$$

Skill Practice 7   Given the noncollinear points $(-3, 2)$, $(-4, 1)$, and $(-6, -7)$, find an equation of the form $y = ax^2 + bx + c$ that defines the parabola through the points.

Answer

7. $y = -x^2 - 6x - 7$

SECTION 5.2   Practice Exercises

Review Exercises

For Exercises 1–4, solve the system of equations. If the system does not have one unique solution, state whether the system is inconsistent or the equations are dependent.

1. $x = 5y + 12$

$\frac{1}{2}x = \frac{1}{3} - \frac{1}{3}y$

2. $0.03x + 0.07y = 0.02$

$y = -2x - 6$

3. $y = -\frac{3}{4}x + 1$

$3x + 4y = 4$

4. $y = 2x - 5$

$\frac{1}{5}x - \frac{1}{10}y = 1$

Concept Connections

5. An equation of the form $Ax + By + Cz = D$ (where A, B, and C are not all zero) is called a _____ equation in three variables.

6. A solution to a linear equation in three variables is an ordered _____ (x, y, z) that satisfies the equation.

7. The graph of a linear equation in two variables is a line in a two-dimensional coordinate system. The graph of a linear equation in three variables is a _____ in a three-dimensional coordinate system.

8. A solution to a system of linear equations in three variables is an ordered _____ that satisfies each equation in the system. Graphically, this is a point of _____ of three planes.

Objective 1: Identify Solutions to a System of Linear Equations in Three Variables

For Exercises 9–10, find three ordered triples that are solutions to the linear equation in three variables.

9. $2x + 4y - 6z = 12$

10. $3x - 5y + z = 15$

For Exercises 11–14, determine if the ordered triple is a solution to the system of equations. (See Example 1)

11. $-x + 3y - 7z = 7$
$2x + 4y + z = 16$
$3x - 5y + 6z = -9$

  a. $(2, 3, 0)$
  b. $(-2, 4, 1)$

12. $2x - 3y + z = -12$
$x + y - 2z = 9$
$-3x + 2y - z = 7$

  a. $(2, 5, -1)$
  b. $(1, 4, -2)$

13. $x + y + z = 2$
$x + 2y - z = 2$
$3x + 5y - z = 6$

  a. $(2, 0, 0)$
  b. $(-1, 2, 1)$

14. $-x - y + z = 3$
$3x + 4y - z = 1$
$5x + 7y - z = -1$

  a. $(1, 2, 6)$
  b. $(3, -1, 5)$

Objective 2: Solve Systems of Linear Equations in Three Variables

For Exercises 15–36, solve the system of equations. If a system does not have one unique solution, determine the number of solutions to the system. (See Examples 2–5)

15. $x - 2y + z = -9$
$3x + 4y + 5z = 9$
$-2x + 3y - z = 12$

16. $2x - y + z = 6$
$-x + 5y - z = 10$
$3x + y - 3z = 12$

17. $4x = 3y - 2z - 5$
$2(x + y) = y + z - 6$
$6(x - y) + z = x - 5y - 8$

18. $3x = 5y - z + 13$
$-(x - y) - z = x - 3$
$5(x + y) = 3y - 3z - 4$

19. $2x + 5z = 2$
$3y - 7z = 9$
$-5x + 9y = 22$

20. $3x - 2y = -8$
$5y + 6z = 2$
$7x + 11z = -33$

21. $-4x - 3y = 0$
$3y + z = -1$
$4x - z = 12$

22. $4x - y + 2z = 1$
$3x + 5y - z = -2$
$-9x - 15y + 3z = 0$

23. $2x = 3y - 6z - 1$
$6y = 12z - 10x + 9$
$3z = 6y - 3x - 1$

24. $5x = 2y - 3z - 3$
$4y = -1 - 10x - 5z$
$2z = 5x - 6y$

25. $x + 2y + 4z = 3$
$y + 3z = 5$
$x - 2z = -7$

26. $3x + 2y + 5z = 6$
$3y - z = 4$
$3x + 17y = 26$

27. $0.2x = 0.1y - 0.6z$
$0.004x + 0.005y - 0.001z = 0$
$30x = 50z - 20y$

28. $0.3x = 0.5y - 1.2z$
$0.05x + 0.1y = 0.04z$
$100x = 300y - 700z$

29. $\frac{1}{12}x + \frac{1}{4}y + \frac{1}{3}z = \frac{7}{12}$
$-\frac{1}{10}x + \frac{1}{2}y - \frac{1}{5}z = -\frac{17}{10}$
$\frac{1}{2}x + \frac{1}{4}y + z = 3$

30. $x + \frac{7}{2}y + \frac{1}{2}z = 4$

$\frac{3}{4}x + y + \frac{1}{2}z = -1$

$\frac{1}{10}x - \frac{2}{5}y - \frac{3}{10}z = 1$

31. $3x + 2y + 5z = 12$

$3y + 8z = -8$

$10z = 20$

32. $-4x + 6y + z = -4$

$-2y - 4z = -24$

$6z = 48$

33. $\frac{x+2}{3} + \frac{y-4}{2} + \frac{z+1}{6} = 8$

$-\frac{x+2}{3} \quad + \frac{z+1}{2} = 8$

$\frac{y-4}{4} - \frac{z+1}{6} = -1$

34. $\frac{x-1}{7} + \frac{y-2}{3} + \frac{z+2}{4} = 13$

$\frac{y-2}{9} - \frac{z+2}{8} = 3$

$\frac{x-1}{7} \quad + \frac{z+2}{2} = 3$

35. $3(x + y) = 6 - 4z + y$

$4 = 6y + 5z$

$-3x + 4y + z = 0$

36. $4(x - y) = 8 - z - y$

$3 = 3x + 4z$

$-x + 3y + 3z = 1$

Objective 3: Use Systems of Linear Equations in Applications

37. Devon invested $8000 in three different mutual funds. A fund containing large cap stocks made 6.2% return in 1 yr. A real estate fund lost 13.5% in 1 yr, and a bond fund made 4.4% in 1 yr. The amount invested in the large cap stock fund was twice the amount invested in the real estate fund. If Devon had a net return of $66 across all investments, how much did he invest in each fund? (**See Example 6**)

38. Pierre inherited $120,000 from his uncle and decided to invest the money. He put part of the money in a money market account that earns 2.2% simple interest. The remaining money was invested in a stock that returned 6% in the first year and a mutual fund that lost 2% in the first year. He invested $10,000 more in the stock than in the mutual fund, and his net gain for 1 yr was $2820. Determine the amount invested in each account.

39. A basketball player scored 26 points in one game. In basketball, some baskets are worth 3 points, some are worth 2 points, and free-throws are worth 1 point. He scored four more 2-point baskets than he did 3-point baskets. The number of free-throws equaled the sum of the number of 2-point and 3-point shots made. How many free-throws, 2-point shots, and 3-point shots did he make?

40. A sawmill cuts boards for a lumber supplier. When saws A, B, and C all work for 6 hr, they cut 7200 linear board-ft of lumber. It would take saws A and B working together 9.6 hr to cut 7200 ft of lumber. Saws B and C can cut 7200 ft of lumber in 9 hr. Find the rate (in ft/hr) that each saw can cut lumber.

41. Plant fertilizers are categorized by the percentage of nitrogen (N), phosphorous (P), and potassium (K) they contain, by weight. For example, a fertilizer that has N-P-K numbers of 8-5-5 has 8% nitrogen, 5% phosphorous, and 5% potassium by weight. Suppose that a fertilizer has twice as much potassium by weight as phosphorous. The percentage of nitrogen equals the sum of the percentages of phosphorous and potassium. If nitrogen, phosphorous, and potassium make up 42% of the fertilizer, determine the proper N-P-K label on the fertilizer.

    a. 14-7-14   **b.** 21-7-14   **c.** 14-7-21   **d.** 14-21-21

42. A theater charges $50 per ticket for seats in section A, $30 per ticket for seats in section B, and $20 per ticket for seats in section C. For one play, 4000 tickets were sold for a total of $120,000 in revenue. If 1000 more tickets in section B were sold than the other two sections combined, how many tickets in each section were sold?

43. The perimeter of a triangle is 55 in. The shortest side is 7 in. less than the longest side. The middle side is 19 in. less than the combined lengths of the shortest and longest sides. Find the lengths of the three sides.

44. A package in the shape of a rectangular solid is to be mailed. The combination of the girth (perimeter of a cross section defined by w and h) and the length of the package is 48 in. The width is 2 in. greater than the height, and the length is 12 in. greater than the width. Find the dimensions of the package.

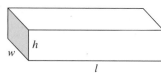

45. The measure of the largest angle in a triangle is 100° larger than the sum of the measures of the other two angles. The measure of the smallest angle is two-thirds the measure of the middle angle. Find the measure of each angle.

46. The measure of the largest angle in a triangle is 18° more than the sum of the measures of the other two angles. The measure of the smallest angle is one-half the measure of the middle angle. Find the measure of each angle.

Objective 4: Modeling with Linear Equations in Three Variables

47. a. Show that the points $(1, 0)$, $(3, 10)$, and $(-2, 15)$ are not collinear by finding the slope between $(1, 0)$ and $(3, 10)$, and the slope between $(3, 10)$ and $(-2, 15)$. (**See Example 7**)

   b. Find an equation of the form $y = ax^2 + bx + c$ that defines the parabola through the points.

   c. Use a graphing utility to verify that the graph of the equation in part (b) passes through the given points.

48. a. Show that the points $(2, 9)$, $(-1, -6)$, and $(-4, -3)$ are not collinear by finding the slope between $(2, 9)$ and $(-1, -6)$, and the slope between $(2, 9)$ and $(-4, -3)$.

   b. Find an equation of the form $y = ax^2 + bx + c$ that defines the parabola through the points.

   c. Use a graphing utility to verify that the graph of the equation in part (b) passes through the given points.

For Exercises 49–50, find an equation of the form $y = ax^2 + bx + c$ that defines the parabola through the three noncollinear points given.

49. $(0, 6)$, $(2, -6)$, $(-1, 9)$

50. $(0, -4)$, $(2, -6)$, $(-3, -31)$

51. The percentage of the adult population in the United States with diabetes has been rising since the year 2000. Let x represent the number of years since the year 2000, and let y represent the percentage of the adult population with diabetes for year x. The following data have been reported from the Centers for Disease Control. (*Source*: www.cdc.gov)

Number of Years Since 2000 (x)	Percentage of Adults with Diabetes (y)
0	6
4	7
9	9

   a. Use the data to create a model of the form $y = ax^2 + bx + c$.

   b. Use the model to approximate the percentage of adults with diabetes for the year 2012.

52. The amount of carbon dioxide released into the atmosphere from fossil fuels for China is given in the table. The variable x represents the number of years since the year 2000, and y represents the CO_2 emissions (in billions of metric tons) for year x. (*Source*: United Nations, http://mdgs.un.org)

Number of Years Since 2000 (x)	Billions of Metric Tons of CO_2 Emitted (y)
0	3
3	4
10	8

   a. Use the data to create a model of the form $y = ax^2 + bx + c$.

   b. Use the model to approximate the amount of CO_2 emitted from fossil fuels for China for the year 2015 if the trend continues. Round to the nearest billion metric tons.

The motion of an object traveling along a straight path is given by $s(t) = \frac{1}{2}at^2 + v_0 t + s_0$, where $s(t)$ is the position relative to the origin at time t. For Exercises 53–54, three observed data points are given. Find the values of a, v_0, and s_0.

53. $s(1) = 30$, $s(2) = 54$, $s(3) = 82$

54. $s(1) = -7$, $s(2) = 12$, $s(3) = 37$

Many statistics courses cover a topic called *multiple regression*. This provides a means to predict the value of a dependent variable y based on two or more independent variables $x_1, x_2, \ldots, x_n$. The model $y = ax_1 + bx_2 + c$ is a linear model that predicts y based on two independent variables x_1 and x_2. While statistical techniques may be used to find the values of a, b, and c based on a large number of data points, we can form a crude model given three data values (x_1, x_2, y). Use the information given in Exercises 55–56 to form a system of three equations and three variables to solve for a, b, and c.

55. The selling price of a home y (in $1000) is given based on the living area x_1 (in 100 ft^2) and on the lot size x_2 (in acres).

Living Area (100 ft^2) x_1	Lot Size (acres) x_2	Selling Price ($1000) y
28	0.5	225
25	0.8	207
18	0.4	154

   a. Use the data to create a model of the form $y = ax_1 + bx_2 + c$.

   b. Use the model from part (a) to predict the selling price of a home that is 2000 ft^2 on a 0.4-acre lot.

56. The gas mileage y (in mpg) for city driving is given based on the weight of the vehicle x_1 (in lb) and on the number of cylinders.

Weight (lb) x_1	Cylinders x_2	Mileage (mpg) y
3500	6	20
3200	4	26
4100	8	18

   a. Use the data to create a model of the form $y = ax_1 + bx_2 + c$.

   b. Use the model from part (a) to predict the gas mileage of a vehicle that is 3800 lb and has 6 cylinders.

Write About It

57. Give a geometric description of the solution set to a linear equation in three variables.

58. If a system of linear equations in three variables has no solution, then what can be said about the three planes represented by the equations in the system?

59. Explain the procedure presented in this section to solve a system of linear equations in three variables.

60. Explain how to check a solution to a system of linear equations in three variables.

Expanding Your Skills

For Exercises 61–62, find all solutions of the form (a, b, c, d).

61. $\begin{aligned} 2a + b - c + d &= 7 \\ 3b + 2c - 2d &= -11 \\ a + 3c + 3d &= 14 \\ 4a + 2b - 5c &= 6 \end{aligned}$

62. $\begin{aligned} 3a - 4b + 2c + d &= 8 \\ 2a + 3b + 2d &= 7 \\ 5b - 3c + 4d &= -4 \\ -a + b - 2c &= -7 \end{aligned}$

For Exercises 63–64, find all solutions of the form (u, v, w).

63. $\begin{aligned} \dfrac{u-3}{4} + \dfrac{v+1}{3} + \dfrac{w-2}{8} &= 1 \\[2mm] \dfrac{u-3}{2} + \dfrac{v+1}{2} + \dfrac{w-2}{4} &= 0 \\[2mm] \dfrac{u-3}{4} - \dfrac{v+1}{2} + \dfrac{w-2}{2} &= -6 \end{aligned}$

64. $\begin{aligned} \dfrac{u+1}{6} + \dfrac{v-1}{6} + \dfrac{w+3}{4} &= 11 \\[2mm] \dfrac{u+1}{3} - \dfrac{v-1}{2} + \dfrac{w+3}{4} &= 7 \\[2mm] \dfrac{u+1}{2} - \dfrac{v-1}{6} + \dfrac{w+3}{2} &= 20 \end{aligned}$

Recall that an equation of a circle can be written in the form $(x - h)^2 + (y - k)^2 = r^2$, where (h, k) is the center and r is the radius. Expanding terms, the equation can also be written in the form $x^2 + y^2 + Ax + By + C = 0$. For Exercises 65–66,

a. Find an equation of the form $x^2 + y^2 + Ax + By + C = 0$ that represents the circle that passes through the given points.

b. Find the center and radius of the circle.

65. $(2, 2), (6, 0), (7, -3)$

66. $(-1, 12), (5, 10), (9, 2)$

A plane in space can be represented by $Ax + By + Cz = D$. Dividing both sides by D produces an equivalent equation $\dfrac{A}{D}x + \dfrac{B}{D}y + \dfrac{C}{D}z = 1$. Letting $c_1 = \dfrac{A}{D}$, $c_2 = \dfrac{B}{D}$, and $c_3 = \dfrac{C}{D}$ we have the simplified form $c_1x + c_2y + c_3z = 1$. For Exercises 67–68, find an equation of the form $c_1x + c_2y + c_3z = 1$ that defines the plane through the three noncollinear points.

67. $(3, 1, 2), (-1, 1, 0), (1, -3, -2)$

68. $(5, 3, 4), (-1, 0, 1), (-1, 2, 5)$

For Exercises 69–70, find the constants A and B so that the two polynomials are equal. (*Hint*: Create a system of linear equations by equating the constant terms and by equating the coefficients on the x terms and x^2 terms.)

69. $11x^2 + 26x - 5 = 2Ax^2 + 5Ax + 3A + Bx^2 - 2Bx - 8B + 2Cx^2 - 7Cx - 4C$

70. $3x^2 + 37x - 82 = Ax^2 + Ax - 12A + 3Bx^2 - 10Bx + 3B + 3Cx^2 + 11Cx - 4C$

SECTION 5.3   Partial Fraction Decomposition

OBJECTIVES

1. Set Up a Partial Fraction Decomposition
2. Decompose $\dfrac{f(x)}{g(x)}$, Where $g(x)$ Is a Product of Linear Factors
3. Decompose $\dfrac{f(x)}{g(x)}$, Where $g(x)$ Has Irreducible Quadratic Factors

1. Set Up a Partial Fraction Decomposition

In Section R.7 we learned how to add and subtract rational expressions. For example,

$$\frac{5}{x+2} + \frac{3}{x-5} = \frac{5(x-5)}{(x+2)(x-5)} + \frac{3(x+2)}{(x-5)(x+2)}$$

$$= \frac{5(x-5) + 3(x+2)}{(x+2)(x-5)}$$

$$= \frac{8x - 19}{(x+2)(x-5)}$$

The fraction $\dfrac{8x - 19}{(x + 2)(x - 5)}$ is the result of adding two simpler fractions, $\dfrac{5}{x + 2}$ and $\dfrac{3}{x - 5}$. The sum $\dfrac{5}{x + 2} + \dfrac{3}{x - 5}$ is called the **partial fraction decomposition** of $\dfrac{8x - 19}{(x + 2)(x - 5)}$. In some applications in higher mathematics, it is more convenient to work with the partial fraction decomposition than the more complicated single fraction. Therefore, in this section, we will learn the technique of partial fraction decomposition to write a rational expression as a sum of simpler fractions. That is, we will reverse the process of adding two or more fractions. There are two parts to this process.

I. First we set up the "form" or "structure" for the partial fraction decomposition into simpler fractions. For example, the denominator of $\dfrac{8x - 19}{(x + 2)(x - 5)}$ consists of the distinct linear factors $(x + 2)$ and $(x - 5)$. From the preceding discussion, the partial fraction decomposition must be of the form:

$$\frac{8x - 19}{(x + 2)(x - 5)} = \frac{A}{x + 2} + \frac{B}{x - 5}$$

> The expression on the right is the "form" or "structure" for the partial fraction decomposition of $\dfrac{8x - 19}{(x + 2)(x - 5)}$.

II. Next, we solve for the constants A and B. To do so, multiply both sides of the equation by the LCD, and set up a system of linear equations.

$$(x + 2)(x - 5) \cdot \left[\frac{8x - 19}{(x + 2)(x - 5)} \right] = (x + 2)(x - 5) \cdot \left[\frac{A}{x + 2} + \frac{B}{x - 5} \right]$$

Multiply by the LCD to clear fractions.

$8x - 19 = A(x - 5) + B(x + 2)$

$8x - 19 = Ax - 5A + Bx + 2B$ Apply the distributive property.

$8x - 19 = (A + B)x + (-5A + 2B)$ Simplify and combine like terms.

x coefficients are equal.

$8x - 19 = (A + B)x + (-5A + 2B)$ Two polynomials are equal if and only if the coefficients on like terms are equal.

Constants are equal.

$A + B = 8$ Equate the coefficients on x.

$-5A + 2B = -19$ Equate the constant terms.

Solve the system of linear equations. Then substitute the values of A and B into the partial fraction decomposition.

		Multiply by 5.	
$\boxed{1}$	$A + B = 8$	$\longrightarrow$	$5A + 5B = 40$
$\boxed{2}$	$-5A + 2B = -19$		$-5A + 2B = -19$
			$7B = 21$
			$B = 3$

$\boxed{1}$ $A + B = 8$

$A + 3 = 8$

$A = 5$

$A = 5$ and $B = 3$

$$\frac{8x - 19}{(x + 2)(x - 5)} = \frac{A}{x + 2} + \frac{B}{x - 5} = \frac{5}{x + 2} + \frac{3}{x - 5}$$

We begin partial fraction decomposition by factoring the denominator into linear factors $(ax + b)$ and quadratic factors $(ax^2 + bx + c)$ that are irreducible over the integers. A quadratic factor that is irreducible over the integers cannot be factored as a product of binomials with integer coefficients. From the factorization of the denominator, we then determine the proper form for the partial fraction decomposition using the following guidelines.

Decomposition of $\dfrac{f(x)}{g(x)}$ into Partial Fractions

Consider a rational expression $\dfrac{f(x)}{g(x)}$, where $f(x)$ and $g(x)$ are polynomials with real coefficients, $g(x) \neq 0$, and the degree of $f(x)$ is less than the degree of $g(x)$.

PART I:

Step 1 Factor the denominator $g(x)$ completely into linear factors of the form $(ax + b)^m$ and quadratic factors of the form $(ax^2 + bx + c)^n$ that are not further factorible over the integers (irreducible over the integers).

Step 2 Set up the form for the decomposition. That is, write the original rational expression $\dfrac{f(x)}{g(x)}$ as a sum of simpler fractions using these guidelines. Note that $A_1, A_2, \ldots, A_m, B_1, B_2, \ldots, B_n$, and $C_1, C_2, \ldots, C_n$ are constants

- **Linear factors of $g(x)$:** For each linear factor of $g(x)$, the partial fraction decomposition must include the sum:

$$\frac{A_1}{(ax + b)^1} + \frac{A_2}{(ax + b)^2} + \cdots + \frac{A_m}{(ax + b)^m}$$

- **Quadratic factors of $g(x)$:** For each quadratic factor of $g(x)$, the partial fraction decomposition must include the sum:

$$\frac{B_1 x + C_1}{(ax^2 + bx + c)^1} + \frac{B_2 x + C_2}{(ax^2 + bx + c)^2} + \cdots + \frac{B_n x + C_n}{(ax^2 + bx + c)^n}$$

PART II:

Step 3 With the form of the partial fraction decomposition set up, multiply both sides of the equation by the LCD to clear fractions.

Step 4 Using the equation from step 3, set up a system of linear equations by equating the constant terms and equating the coefficients of like powers of x.

Step 5 Solve the system of equations from step 4 and substitute the solutions to the system into the partial fraction decomposition.

Avoiding Mistakes

It is important to note that to perform partial fraction decomposition on a rational expression, the degree of the numerator must be less than the degree of the denominator.

TIP The constants $A_1, A_2, \ldots, A_m$ are often replaced by A, B, C, and so on to avoid confusion with subscript notation.

TIP The constants $B_1, B_2, \ldots, B_n$ and $C_1, C_2, \ldots, C_n$ are often replaced by A, B, C, D, E, and so on to avoid confusion with subscript notation.

In Examples 1 and 2, we focus on setting up the proper form for a partial fraction decomposition (Part I). In each example, note that the factors of the denominator will fall into one of the following categories:

Linear factors: $ax + b$

Repeated linear factors: $(ax + b)^m$ ($m \geq 2$, an integer)

Quadratic factors (irreducible over the integers): $ax^2 + bx + c$

Repeated quadratic factors (irreducible over the integers): $(ax^2 + bx + c)^n$ ($n \geq 2$, an integer)

EXAMPLE 1   Setting Up the Form for a Partial Fraction Decomposition

Set up the form for the partial fraction decomposition for the given rational expressions.

a. $\dfrac{4x - 15}{(2x + 3)(x - 2)}$ **b.** $\dfrac{4x^2 + 10x + 9}{x^3 + 6x^2 + 9x}$

Solution:

a. $\dfrac{4x - 15}{(2x + 3)^1(x - 2)^1} = \dfrac{A}{(2x + 3)^1} + \dfrac{B}{(x - 2)^1}$

The denominator has distinct linear factors of the form $(2x + 3)^1$ and $(x - 2)^1$. Since each linear factor is raised to the first power, only one fraction is needed for each factor.

b. $\dfrac{4x^2 + 10x + 9}{x^3 + 6x^2 + 9x} = \dfrac{4x^2 + 10x + 9}{x(x^2 + 6x + 9)}$

Factor the denominator completely.

The denominator has a linear factor of x^1 and a *repeated* linear factor $(x + 3)^2$.

$= \dfrac{4x^2 + 10x + 9}{x^1(x + 3)^2} = \dfrac{A}{x^1} + \dfrac{B}{(x + 3)^1} + \dfrac{C}{(x + 3)^2}$

For a repeated factor that occurs m times, one fraction must be given for each power less than or equal to m.

> Include one fraction with $(x + 3)$ raised to each positive integer up to and including 2.

Skill Practice 1   Set up the form for the partial fraction decomposition for the given rational expressions.

a. $\dfrac{-x + 18}{(3x + 1)(x + 4)}$ **b.** $\dfrac{-x^2 + 3x + 8}{x^3 + 4x^2 + 4x}$

In Example 2, we practice setting up the form for the partial decomposition of a rational expression that contains irreducible quadratic factors in the denominator.

EXAMPLE 2   Setting Up the Form for a Partial Fraction Decomposition

Set up the form for the partial fraction decomposition for the given rational expressions.

a. $\dfrac{2x^2 - 3x + 4}{x^3 + 4x}$ **b.** $\dfrac{3x^2 + 8x + 14}{(x^2 + 2x + 5)^2}$

Solution:

a. $\dfrac{2x^2 - 3x + 4}{x^3 + 4x} = \dfrac{2x^2 - 3x + 4}{x(x^2 + 4)}$

Factor the denominator completely. The denominator has one linear factor x^1 and one irreducible quadratic factor $(x^2 + 4)^1$.

$= \dfrac{2x^2 - 3x + 4}{x^1(x^2 + 4)^1} = \dfrac{A}{x^1} + \dfrac{Bx + C}{(x^2 + 4)^1}$

Since each factor is raised to the first power, only one fraction is needed for each factor.

$= \dfrac{2x^2 - 3x + 4}{x(x^2 + 4)} = \dfrac{A}{x} + \dfrac{Bx + C}{(x^2 + 4)}$

TIP   For a first-degree (linear) denominator, the numerator is constant (degree 0). For a second-degree (quadratic) denominator, the numerator is linear (degree 1).

Answers

1. a. $\dfrac{A}{3x + 1} + \dfrac{B}{x + 4}$

b. $\dfrac{A}{x} + \dfrac{B}{x + 2} + \dfrac{C}{(x + 2)^2}$

b. $\dfrac{3x^2 + 8x + 14}{(x^2 + 2x + 5)^2}$

The quadratic factor $x^2 + 2x + 5$ does not factor further over the integers.

$$= \dfrac{Ax + B}{(x^2 + 2x + 5)^1} + \dfrac{Cx + D}{(x^2 + 2x + 5)^2}$$

The factor $(x^2 + 2x + 5)$ appears to the *second* power in the denominator. Therefore, in the partial fraction composition, one fraction must have $(x^2 + 2x + 5)^1$ in the denominator, and one fraction must have $(x^2 + 2x + 5)^2$ in the denominator.

Skill Practice 2 Set up the form for the partial fraction decomposition for the given rational expressions.

a. $\dfrac{7x^2 + 2x + 12}{x^3 + 3x}$ **b.** $\dfrac{-3x^2 - 5x - 19}{(x^2 + 3x + 6)^2}$

---

2. Decompose $\dfrac{f(x)}{g(x)}$, Where $g(x)$ Is a Product of Linear Factors

In Example 3, we find the partial fraction decomposition of a rational expression in which the denominator is a product of distinct linear factors.

EXAMPLE 3 Decomposing $\dfrac{f(x)}{g(x)}$, Where $g(x)$ Has Distinct Linear Factors

Find the partial fraction decomposition. $\dfrac{4x - 15}{(2x + 3)(x - 2)}$

Solution:

$$\dfrac{4x - 15}{(2x + 3)(x - 2)} = \dfrac{A}{2x + 3} + \dfrac{B}{x - 2}$$

From Example 1(a), we have the form for the partial fraction decomposition.

$$(2x + 3)(x - 2) \cdot \left[\dfrac{4x - 15}{(2x + 3)(x - 2)} \right] = (2x + 3)(x - 2) \cdot \left[\dfrac{A}{2x + 3} + \dfrac{B}{x - 2} \right]$$

To solve for A and B, first multiply both sides by the LCD to clear fractions.

$4x - 15 = A(x - 2) + B(2x + 3)$ Apply the distributive property.

$4x - 15 = Ax - 2A + 2Bx + 3B$

$4x - 15 = (A + 2B)x + (-2A + 3B)$ Combine like terms.

$\boxed{1}\quad 4 = A + 2B$ Equate the x term coefficients.

$\boxed{2}\ -15 = -2A + 3B$ Equate the constant terms.

Solve the system of linear equations by using the substitution method or addition method.

$\boxed{1}\quad 4 = A + 2B \xrightarrow{\text{Multiply by 2.}} \quad 2A + 4B = 8$

$\boxed{2}\ -15 = -2A + 3B \qquad\qquad\qquad \underline{-2A + 3B = -15}$

$$7B = -7$$
$$B = -1$$

$\boxed{1}\quad 4 = A + 2B$

$4 = A + 2(-1)$

$A = 6$

$A = 6$ and $B = -1$.

$$\frac{4x - 15}{(2x + 3)(x - 2)} = \frac{A}{2x + 3} + \frac{B}{x - 2}$$

Substitute $A = 6$ and $B = -1$ into the partial fraction decomposition.

$$\frac{4x - 15}{(2x + 3)(x - 2)} = \frac{6}{2x + 3} + \frac{-1}{x - 2} \quad \text{or equivalently} \quad \frac{6}{2x + 3} - \frac{1}{x - 2}$$

Skill Practice 3   Find the partial fraction decomposition. $\dfrac{-x + 18}{(3x + 1)(x + 4)}$

TIP   Always remember that the result of a partial fraction decomposition can be checked by adding the partial fractions and verifying that the sum equals the original rational expression.

To verify the result of Example 3, we can add the rational expressions.

$$\frac{6}{2x + 3} + \frac{-1}{x - 2} = \frac{6(x - 2)}{(2x + 3)(x - 2)} + \frac{-1(2x + 3)}{(x - 2)(2x + 3)}$$

$$= \frac{6(x - 2) - 1(2x + 3)}{(2x + 3)(x - 2)}$$

$$= \frac{4x - 15}{(2x + 3)(x - 2)} \checkmark$$

In Example 4, we perform partial fraction decomposition with a rational expression that has repeated linear factors in the denominator.

EXAMPLE 4   Decomposing $\dfrac{f(x)}{g(x)}$, Where $g(x)$ Has Repeated Linear Factors

Find the partial fraction decomposition. $\dfrac{4x^2 + 10x + 9}{x^3 + 6x^2 + 9x}$

Solution:

$$\frac{4x^2 + 10x + 9}{x(x + 3)^2} = \frac{A}{x} + \frac{B}{(x + 3)^1} + \frac{C}{(x + 3)^2}$$

From Example 1(b), we have the form for the partial fraction decomposition.

$$x(x + 3)^2 \cdot \left[\frac{4x^2 + 10x + 9}{x(x + 3)^2}\right] = x(x + 3)^2 \cdot \left[\frac{A}{x} + \frac{B}{(x + 3)^1} + \frac{C}{(x + 3)^2}\right]$$

$$4x^2 + 10x + 9 = A(x + 3)^2 + Bx(x + 3) + Cx$$
$$4x^2 + 10x + 9 = A(x^2 + 6x + 9) + Bx^2 + 3Bx + Cx$$
$$4x^2 + 10x + 9 = Ax^2 + 6Ax + 9A + Bx^2 + 3Bx + Cx$$
$$4x^2 + 10x + 9 = (A + B)x^2 + (6A + 3B + C)x + 9A$$

$$4 = A + B \qquad \text{Equate the } x^2 \text{ term coefficients.}$$
$$10 = 6A + 3B + C \qquad \text{Equate the } x \text{ term coefficients.}$$
$$9 = 9A \qquad \text{Equate the constant terms.}$$

$A = 1, B = 3, \text{ and } C = -5$ Solve the system of linear equations.

$$\frac{4x^2 + 10x + 9}{x(x + 3)^2} = \frac{A}{x} + \frac{B}{(x + 3)^1} + \frac{C}{(x + 3)^2}$$

Substitute $A = 1, B = 3,$ and $C = -5$ into the partial fraction decomposition.

$$\frac{4x^2 + 10x + 9}{x(x + 3)^2} = \frac{1}{x} + \frac{3}{(x + 3)^1} + \frac{-5}{(x + 3)^2} = \frac{1}{x} + \frac{3}{x + 3} - \frac{5}{(x + 3)^2}$$

Skill Practice 4   Find the partial fraction decomposition. $\dfrac{-x^2 + 3x + 8}{x^3 + 4x^2 + 4x}$

Answers

3. $\dfrac{5}{3x + 1} + \dfrac{-2}{x + 4}$

4. $\dfrac{2}{x} + \dfrac{-3}{x + 2} + \dfrac{1}{(x + 2)^2}$

3. Decompose $\dfrac{f(x)}{g(x)}$, Where $g(x)$ Has Irreducible Quadratic Factors

We now turn our attention to performing partial fraction decomposition where the denominator of a rational expression contains quadratic factors irreducible over the integers. In Example 5, we also address the situation in which the given rational expression is an **improper rational expression**; that is, the degree of the numerator is greater than or equal to the degree of the denominator. In such a case, we use long division to write the expression in the form:

$$\text{(polynomial)} + \text{(proper rational expression)}$$

where a **proper rational expression** is one in which the numerator is less than the degree of the denominator.

EXAMPLE 5 Decomposing $\dfrac{f(x)}{g(x)}$, Where $g(x)$ Has an Irreducible Quadratic Factor

Find the partial fraction decomposition. $\dfrac{x^4 + 3x^3 + 6x^2 + 9x + 4}{x^3 + 4x}$

Solution:

First note that the degree of the numerator is not less than the degree of the denominator. Therefore, perform long division first.

$$\dfrac{x^4 + 3x^3 + 6x^2 + 9x + 4}{x^3 + 4x} \xrightarrow{\text{Long division}}$$

$$\begin{array}{r}
x + 3 \\
x^3 + 4x \overline{\smash{)}\, x^4 + 3x^3 + 6x^2 + 9x + 4} \\
\underline{-(x^4 \qquad\quad + 4x^2)} \\
3x^3 + 2x^2 + 9x \\
\underline{-(3x^3 \qquad\quad + 12x)} \\
2x^2 - 3x + 4
\end{array}$$

$$= x + 3 + \dfrac{2x^2 - 3x + 4}{x^3 + 4x} \xleftarrow{\text{Equivalent form}}$$

$$= \underbrace{x + 3}_{\text{polynomial}} + \underbrace{\dfrac{2x^2 - 3x + 4}{x(x^2 + 4)}}_{\substack{\text{proper rational}\\ \text{expression}}} \qquad \text{Factor the denominator.}$$

$$\dfrac{2x^2 - 3x + 4}{x(x^2 + 4)} = \dfrac{A}{x} + \dfrac{Bx + C}{(x^2 + 4)} \qquad$$

Perform partial fraction decomposition on the proper fraction. From Example 2(a), we have the form for the partial fraction decomposition.

$$x(x^2 + 4)\left[\dfrac{2x^2 - 3x + 4}{x(x^2 + 4)}\right] = x(x^2 + 4)\left[\dfrac{A}{x} + \dfrac{Bx + C}{(x^2 + 4)}\right] \qquad$$

To solve for A, B, and C, multiply both sides by the LCD to clear fractions.

$$2x^2 - 3x + 4 = A(x^2 + 4) + (Bx + C)x \qquad \text{Apply the distributive property.}$$

$$2x^2 - 3x + 4 = Ax^2 + 4A + Bx^2 + Cx$$

$$2x^2 - 3x + 4 = (A + B)x^2 + Cx + 4A \qquad \text{Combine like terms.}$$

$$\left.\begin{array}{l} 2 = A + B \\ -3 = C \\ 4 = 4A \end{array}\right\} \quad \begin{array}{l} A = 1,\ B = 1, \\ \text{and } C = -3 \end{array}$$

Equate the x^2 term coefficients.

Equate the x term coefficients.

Equate the constant terms.

Solve the system of linear equations.

$$\dfrac{2x^2 - 3x + 4}{x(x^2 + 4)} = \dfrac{A}{x} + \dfrac{Bx + C}{(x^2 + 4)} \qquad \text{Substitute } A = 1,\ B = 1,\ \text{and } C = -3.$$

$$\frac{2x^2 - 3x + 4}{x(x^2 + 4)} = \frac{1}{x} + \frac{1x + (-3)}{x^2 + 4} \quad \text{or} \quad \frac{1}{x} + \frac{x - 3}{x^2 + 4}$$

Therefore, $\dfrac{x^4 + 3x^3 + 6x^2 + 9x + 4}{x^3 + 4x} = x + 3 + \dfrac{1}{x} + \dfrac{x - 3}{x^2 + 4}$.

> **Skill Practice 5** Find the partial fraction decomposition.
>
> $$\frac{x^4 + 2x^3 + 10x^2 + 8x + 12}{x^3 + 3x}$$

In Example 6, we demonstrate the case in which a rational expression contains a repeated quadratic factor.

EXAMPLE 6 Decomposing $\dfrac{f(x)}{g(x)}$, Where $g(x)$ Has a Repeated Irreducible Quadratic Factor

Find the partial fraction decomposition. $\qquad \dfrac{3x^2 + 8x + 14}{(x^2 + 2x + 5)^2}$

Solution:

$\dfrac{3x^2 + 8x + 14}{(x^2 + 2x + 5)^2} = \dfrac{Ax + B}{(x^2 + 2x + 5)^1} + \dfrac{Cx + D}{(x^2 + 2x + 5)^2}$ 　From Example 2(b), we have the form for the partial fraction decomposition.

To solve for A, B, C, and D, multiply both sides by the LCD to clear fractions.

$(x^2 + 2x + 5)^2 \left[\dfrac{3x^2 + 8x + 14}{(x^2 + 2x + 5)^2} \right] = (x^2 + 2x + 5)^2 \left[\dfrac{Ax + B}{x^2 + 2x + 5} + \dfrac{Cx + D}{(x^2 + 2x + 5)^2} \right]$

$3x^2 + 8x + 14 = (Ax + B)(x^2 + 2x + 5) + (Cx + D)$

$3x^2 + 8x + 14 = Ax^3 + 2Ax^2 + 5Ax + Bx^2 + 2Bx + 5B + Cx + D$

$3x^2 + 8x + 14 = Ax^3 + (2A + B)x^2 + (5A + 2B + C)x + 5B + D$ 　Combine like terms.

$\begin{aligned} 0 &= A & &\text{Equate the } x^3 \text{ term coefficients.} \\ 3 &= 2A + B & &\text{Equate the } x^2 \text{ term coefficients.} \\ 8 &= 5A + 2B + C & &\text{Equate the } x \text{ term coefficients.} \\ 14 &= 5B + D & &\text{Equate the constant terms.} \end{aligned}$

$A = 0$, $B = 3$, $C = 2$, and $D = -1$ 　Solve the system of linear equations.

$\dfrac{3x^2 + 8x + 14}{(x^2 + 2x + 5)^2} = \dfrac{Ax + B}{x^2 + 2x + 5} + \dfrac{Cx + D}{(x^2 + 2x + 5)^2}$ 　Substitute $A = 0$, $B = 3$, $C = 2$, and $D = -1$ into the partial fraction decomposition.

$\dfrac{3x^2 + 8x + 14}{(x^2 + 2x + 5)^2} = \dfrac{(0)x + (3)}{x^2 + 2x + 5} + \dfrac{(2)x + (-1)}{(x^2 + 2x + 5)^2}$ 　or　 $\dfrac{3}{x^2 + 2x + 5} + \dfrac{2x - 1}{(x^2 + 2x + 5)^2}$

> **Skill Practice 6** Find the partial fraction decomposition.
>
> $$\frac{-3x^2 - 5x - 19}{(x^2 + 3x + 6)^2}$$

Answers

5. $x + 2 + \dfrac{4}{x} + \dfrac{3x + 2}{x^2 + 3}$

6. $\dfrac{-3}{x^2 + 3x + 6} + \dfrac{4x - 1}{(x^2 + 3x + 6)^2}$

SECTION 5.3   Practice Exercises

Review Exercises

For Exercises 1–2,

a. Write each linear equation in slope-intercept form.

b. From the slope-intercept form, determine the number of solutions to the system.

c. Solve the system.

1. $3x - 2y = 6$
$4y = 6x - 12$

2. $2y - 7 = -4x$
$6x + 3y = 10$

For Exercises 3–4, solve the system.

3. $3A = 5B - C - 19$
$B = 5C - 2A - 1$
$7A + 3B + C = 13$

4. $3A + 7C = 18$
$B - 5C = -15$
$A - 4B = -1$

For Exercises 5–6, divide the polynomials using long division.

5. $\dfrac{3x^3 + 2x^2 - x - 5}{x^2 + 2x + 1}$

6. $\dfrac{2x^3 - 17x^2 + 54x - 68}{x^2 - 6x + 9}$

Concept Connections

7. The process of decomposing a rational expression into two or more simpler fractions is called partial _____.

8. When setting up a partial fraction decomposition, if a fraction has a linear denominator, then the numerator should be (constant/linear). That is, should the numerator be set up as A or $Ax + B$?

9. When setting up a partial fraction decomposition, if the denominator of a fraction is a quadratic polynomial irreducible over the integers, then the numerator should be (constant/linear). That is, should the numerator be set up as A or $Ax + B$?

10. In what situation should long division be used before attempting to decompose a rational expression into partial fractions?

Objective 1: Set Up a Partial Fraction Decomposition

For Exercises 11–26, set up the form for the partial fraction decomposition. Do not solve for A, B, C, and so on. (See Examples 1–2)

11. $\dfrac{-x - 37}{(x + 4)(2x - 3)}$

12. $\dfrac{20x - 4}{(x - 5)(3x + 1)}$

13. $\dfrac{8x - 10}{x^2 - 2x}$

14. $\dfrac{y - 12}{y^2 + 3y}$

15. $\dfrac{6w - 7}{w^2 + w - 6}$

16. $\dfrac{-10t - 11}{t^2 + 5t - 6}$

17. $\dfrac{x^2 + 26x + 100}{x^3 + 10x^2 + 25x}$

18. $\dfrac{-3x^2 + 2x + 8}{x^3 + 4x^2 + 4x}$

19. $\dfrac{13x^2 + 2x + 45}{2x^3 + 18x}$

20. $\dfrac{17x^2 - 7x + 18}{7x^3 + 42x}$

21. $\dfrac{2x^3 - x^2 + 13x - 5}{x^4 + 10x^2 + 25}$

22. $\dfrac{3x^3 - 4x^2 + 11x - 12}{x^4 + 6x^2 + 9}$

23. $\dfrac{5x^2 - 4x + 8}{(x - 4)(x^2 + x + 4)}$

24. $\dfrac{x^2 + 15x - 6}{(x + 6)(x^2 + 2x + 6)}$

25. $\dfrac{2x^5 + 3x^3 + 4x^2 + 5}{x(x + 2)^3(x^2 + 2x + 7)^2}$

26. $\dfrac{6x^4 - 5x^3 + 2x^2 - 5}{(x - 3)(2x + 9)^2(x^2 + 1)^2}$

Objectives 2 and 3: Decompose $\dfrac{f(x)}{g(x)}$ into Partial Fractions

For Exercises 27–48, find the partial fraction decomposition. (See Examples 3–6)

27. $\dfrac{-x - 37}{(x + 4)(2x - 3)}$

28. $\dfrac{20x - 4}{(x - 5)(3x + 1)}$

29. $\dfrac{8x - 10}{x^2 - 2x}$

30. $\dfrac{y - 12}{y^2 + 3y}$

31. $\dfrac{6w - 7}{w^2 + w - 6}$

32. $\dfrac{-10t - 11}{t^2 + 5t - 6}$

33. $\dfrac{x^2 + 26x + 100}{x^3 + 10x^2 + 25x}$

34. $\dfrac{-3x^2 + 2x + 8}{x^3 + 4x^2 + 4x}$

35. $\dfrac{13x^2 + 2x + 45}{2x^3 + 18x}$

36. $\dfrac{17x^2 - 7x + 18}{7x^3 + 42x}$

37. $\dfrac{x^4 - 3x^3 + 13x^2 - 28x + 28}{x^3 + 7x}$

38. $\dfrac{x^4 - 4x^3 + 11x^2 - 13x + 12}{x^3 + 2x}$

39. $\dfrac{2x^3 - x^2 + 13x - 5}{x^4 + 10x^2 + 25}$

40. $\dfrac{3x^3 - 4x^2 + 11x - 12}{x^4 + 6x^2 + 9}$

41. $\dfrac{5x^2 - 4x + 8}{(x - 4)(x^2 + x + 4)}$

42. $\dfrac{x^2 + 15x - 6}{(x + 6)(x^2 + 2x + 6)}$

43. $\dfrac{4x^3 - 4x^2 + 11x - 7}{x^4 + 5x^2 + 6}$

44. $\dfrac{3x^3 - 4x^2 + 6x - 7}{x^4 + 5x^2 + 4}$

45. $\dfrac{2x^3 - 11x^2 - 4x + 24}{x^2 - 3x - 10}$

46. $\dfrac{3x^3 + 11x^2 + x + 10}{x^2 + 3x - 4}$

47. $\dfrac{3x^3 + 2x^2 - x - 5}{x^2 + 2x + 1}$

48. $\dfrac{2x^3 - 17x^2 + 54x - 68}{x^2 - 6x + 9}$

49. a. Factor. $x^3 - x^2 - 21x + 45$
(*Hint*: Use the rational zero theorem.)
   b. Find the partial fraction decomposition for
   $\dfrac{-3x^2 + 35x - 70}{x^3 - x^2 - 21x + 45}$.

50. a. Factor. $x^3 + 2x^2 - 7x + 4$
   b. Find the partial fraction decomposition for
   $\dfrac{10x^2 + 17x - 17}{x^3 + 2x^2 - 7x + 4}$.

51. a. Factor. $x^3 + 6x^2 + 12x + 8$
   b. Find the partial fraction decomposition for
   $\dfrac{3x^2 + 8x + 5}{x^3 + 6x^2 + 12x + 8}$.

52. a. Factor. $x^3 - 9x^2 + 27x - 27$
   b. Find the partial fraction decomposition for
   $\dfrac{2x^2 - 17x + 37}{x^3 - 9x^2 + 27x - 27}$.

Write About It

53. Write an informal explanation of partial fraction decomposition.

55. What is meant by a *proper* rational expression?

54. Suppose that a proper rational expression has a single repeated linear factor $(ax + b)^3$ in the denominator. Explain how to set up the partial fraction decomposition.

56. Given an improper rational expression, what must be done first before the technique of partial fraction decomposition may be performed?

Expanding Your Skills

57. a. Determine the partial fraction decomposition
   for $\dfrac{2}{n(n + 2)}$.
   b. Use the partial fraction decomposition for $\dfrac{2}{n(n + 2)}$
   to rewrite the infinite sum
   $$\dfrac{2}{1(3)} + \dfrac{2}{2(4)} + \dfrac{2}{3(5)} + \dfrac{2}{4(6)} + \dfrac{2}{5(7)} \cdots$$
   c. Determine the value of $\dfrac{1}{n + 2}$ as $n \to \infty$.
   d. Find the value of the sum from part (b).

58. a. Determine the partial fraction decomposition
   for $\dfrac{3}{n(n + 3)}$.
   b. Use the partial fraction decomposition for $\dfrac{3}{n(n + 3)}$
   to rewrite the infinite sum
   $$\dfrac{3}{1(4)} + \dfrac{3}{2(5)} + \dfrac{3}{3(6)} + \dfrac{3}{4(7)} + \dfrac{3}{5(8)} \cdots$$
   c. Determine the value of $\dfrac{1}{n + 3}$ as $n \to \infty$.
   d. Find the value of the sum from part (b).

For Exercises 59–60, find the partial fraction decomposition. Assume that a and b are nonzero constants.

59. $\dfrac{1}{x(a + bx)}$

60. $\dfrac{1}{a^2 - x^2}$

For Exercises 61–62, find the partial fraction decomposition for the given expression. [*Hint*: Use the substitution $u = e^x$ and recall that $e^{2x} = (e^x)^2$.]

61. $\dfrac{5e^x + 7}{e^{2x} + 3e^x + 2}$

62. $\dfrac{-3e^x - 22}{e^{2x} + 3e^x - 4}$

SECTION 5.4   Systems of Nonlinear Equations in Two Variables

OBJECTIVES

1. Solve Nonlinear Systems of Equations by the Substitution Method
2. Solve Nonlinear Systems of Equations by the Addition Method
3. Use Nonlinear Systems of Equations to Solve Applications

1. Solve Nonlinear Systems of Equations by the Substitution Method

The attending physician in an emergency room treats an unconscious patient suspected of a drug overdose. The physician needs to know the concentration of the drug in the bloodstream at the time the drug was taken to determine the extent of damage to the kidneys. The patient's family does not know the original amount of the drug taken, but believes that he took the drug by injection 3 hr before arriving at the hospital. Blood work at the time of arrival ($t = 3$ hr after the patient had taken the drug) showed that the drug concentration in the bloodstream was 0.69 μg/dL. One hour later ($t = 4$ hr), the level had dropped to 0.655 μg/dL.

The physician can solve the following system of nonlinear equations to determine the concentration of the drug in the bloodstream at the time of injection. The value A_0 represents the initial concentration of the drug, and the value k is related to the rate at which the kidneys can remove the drug.

$$0.69 = A_0 e^{-3k}$$
$$0.655 = A_0 e^{-4k} \qquad \text{The solution to this problem is discussed in Exercise 59.}$$

A **nonlinear system of equations** is a system in which one or more equations is nonlinear. For example:

$$\begin{aligned} -x + 7y &= 50 \\ x^2 + y^2 &= 100 \end{aligned}$$ Second equation nonlinear

$$\left.\begin{aligned} 2x^2 + y^2 &= 17 \\ x^2 + 2y^2 &= 22 \end{aligned}\right\}$$ Both equations nonlinear

TIP A nonlinear system of equations may also have infinitely many solutions. In the graph shown, the "wave" pattern extends infinitely far in both directions.

A **solution** to a nonlinear system of equations in two variables is an ordered pair with real-valued coordinates that satisfies each equation in the system. Graphically, these are the points of intersection of the graphs of the equations. A nonlinear system of equations may have no solution or one or more solutions. See Figure 5-9 through Figure 5-11.

Two solutions

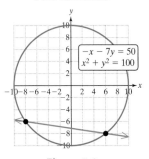

$-x - 7y = 50$
$x^2 + y^2 = 100$

Figure 5-9

Four solutions

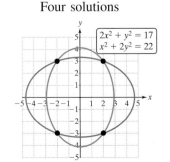

$2x^2 + y^2 = 17$
$x^2 + 2y^2 = 22$

Figure 5-10

No solution

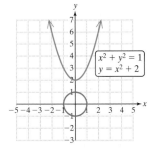

$x^2 + y^2 = 1$
$y = x^2 + 2$

Figure 5-11

We will solve nonlinear systems of equations by the substitution method and by the addition method. In Example 1, we begin with the substitution method.

EXAMPLE 1   **Solving a System of Nonlinear Equations by Using the Substitution Method**

Solve the system by using the substitution method. $-x - 7y = 50$
                                                                              $x^2 + y^2 = 100$

Solution:

$\boxed{A}$ $-x - 7y = 50$ Label the equations.

$\boxed{B}$ $x^2 + y^2 = 100$ Equation $\boxed{A}$ is a line and can be written in slope-intercept form as $y = -\frac{1}{7}x - \frac{50}{7}$.

Equation $\boxed{B}$ represents a circle centered at $(0, 0)$ with radius 10.

A sketch of the two equations suggests that the curves intersect at $(-8, -6)$ and $(6, -8)$. See Figure 5-12.

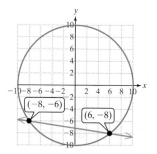

Figure 5-12

$\boxed{A}$ $-x - 7y = 50 \longrightarrow x = -7y - 50$ To solve the system algebraically by the substitution method, first solve for x or y from either equation.

$\boxed{B}$ $x^2 + y^2 = 100$

$\boxed{B}$ $(-7y - 50)^2 + y^2 = 100$ Substitute $x = -7y - 50$ from equation $\boxed{A}$ into equation $\boxed{B}$.

$49y^2 + 700y + 2500 + y^2 = 100$

$50y^2 + 700y + 2400 = 0$ Solve the resulting equation for y.

$50(y^2 + 14y + 48) = 0$ Factor out the GCF of 50.

$50(y + 6)(y + 8) = 0$

$y = -6 \quad \text{or} \quad y = -8$

For each value of y, find the corresponding x value by substituting y into the equation in which x is isolated. $x = -7y - 50$

$y = -6: \quad x = -7(-6) - 50 = -8$ The solution is $(-8, -6)$.

$y = -8: \quad x = -7(-8) - 50 = 6$ The solution is $(6, -8)$.

Check: $(-8, -6)$ Check: $(6, -8)$ The solutions both check in each equation.

$\boxed{A}$ $-(-8) - 7(-6) = 50$ ✓ $\boxed{A}$ $-(6) - 7(-8) = 50$ ✓

$\boxed{B}$ $(-8)^2 + (-6)^2 = 100$ ✓ $\boxed{B}$ $(6)^2 + (-8)^2 = 100$ ✓

The solution set is $\{(-8, -6), (6, -8)\}$.

Skill Practice 1   Solve the system by using the substitution method.

$2x + y = 5$
$x^2 + y^2 = 50$

As we solve systems of equations, we will consider only solutions with real coordinates. In Example 2, we have a system of equations in which one equation is $y = 3\sqrt{x - 8}$. The expression $\sqrt{x - 8}$ is a real number for values of x on the interval $[8, \infty)$. Therefore, any ordered pair with an x-coordinate less than 8 must be rejected as a potential solution.

Answer

1. $\{(5, -5), (-1, 7)\}$

**EXAMPLE 2   Solving a System of Nonlinear Equations
by Using the Substitution Method**

Solve the system by using the substitution method. $(x - 5)^2 + y^2 = 25$
$$y = 3\sqrt{x - 8}$$

Solution:

|A| $(x - 5)^2 + y^2 = 25$ Label the equations. The graphs of the equations
|B| $y = 3\sqrt{x - 8}$ are shown in Figure 5-13. The graph suggests that
there is only one solution: (9, 3).

|A| $(x - 5)^2 + \left(3\sqrt{x - 8}\right)^2 = 25$ Substitute $3\sqrt{x - 8}$
for y in equation |A|.

$x^2 - 10x + 25 + 9(x - 8) = 25$ Square each term.

$x^2 - x - 72 = 0$

$(x - 9)(x + 8) = 0$

$x = 9$ or $x = -8$ Reject $x = -8$
because $3\sqrt{x - 8}$
is not a real number
for $x = -8$.

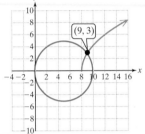

Figure 5-13

Given $x = 9$, solve for y:

|B| $y = 3\sqrt{x - 8}$

$y = 3\sqrt{9 - 8} = 3$ The solution is (9, 3) and checks in each original
equation.

The solution set is $\{(9, 3)\}$.

Skill Practice 2   Solve the system by using the substitution method.

$x^2 + y^2 = 90$
$$y = \sqrt{x}$$

---

2. Solve Nonlinear Systems of Equations by the Addition Method

The substitution method is used most often to solve a system of nonlinear equations.
In some situations, however, the addition method is an efficient way to find a solution. Examples 3 and 4 demonstrate that we can eliminate a variable from both
equations in a system provided the terms containing the corresponding variables are
like terms.

**EXAMPLE 3   Solving a System of Nonlinear Equations
by Using the Addition Method**

Solve the system by using the addition method. $2x^2 + y^2 = 17$
$$x^2 + 2y^2 = 22$$

Solution:

Using the addition method, the goal is to create opposite coefficients on either the x^2 terms or the y^2 terms. In this case, we have chosen to eliminate the x^2 terms.

$$\boxed{A}\quad 2x^2 + y^2 = 17 \qquad\qquad\qquad 2x^2 + y^2 = 17$$
$$\boxed{B}\quad x^2 + 2y^2 = 22 \xrightarrow[\text{Multiply by } -2.]{} \underline{-2x^2 - 4y^2 = -44}$$
$$-3y^2 = -27$$
$$y^2 = 9$$
$$y = \pm 3$$

$y = 3$: $\boxed{B}$ $x^2 + 2(3)^2 = 22$

$\qquad\qquad\quad x^2 = 4$

$\qquad\qquad\quad x = \pm 2$ The solutions are $(2, 3)$, $(-2, 3)$.

Substitute $y = \pm 3$ into either equation $\boxed{A}$ or $\boxed{B}$ to solve for the corresponding values of x.

$y = -3$: $\boxed{B}$ $x^2 + 2(-3)^2 = 22$

$\qquad\qquad\quad x^2 = 4$

$\qquad\qquad\quad x = \pm 2$ The solutions are $(2, -3)$, $(-2, -3)$.

The solutions all check in the original equations.

The solution set is $\{(2, 3), (-2, 3), (2, -3), (-2, -3)\}$.

Skill Practice 3   Solve the system by using the addition method.

$$x^2 + y^2 = 17$$
$$x^2 - 2y^2 = -31$$

TECHNOLOGY CONNECTIONS

Solving a System of Nonlinear Equations Using Intersect

The equations in Example 3 each represent a curve called an ellipse. We do not yet know how to graph an ellipse; however, we can graph the curves on a graphing calculator. First solve each equation for y. Enter the resulting functions in the calculator and use the Intersect feature to approximate the points of intersection (Figure 5-14).

Plot1 Plot2 Plot3
\Y1◻√(17−2X²)
\Y2◻−√(17−2X²)
\Y3◻√((22−X²)/2)

\Y4◻−√((22−X²)/2
)
\Y5=

$$2x^2 + y^2 = 17 \xrightarrow{\text{Solve for } y.} y = \pm\sqrt{17 - 2x^2}$$

$$x^2 + 2y^2 = 22 \longrightarrow y = \pm\sqrt{\frac{22 - x^2}{2}}$$

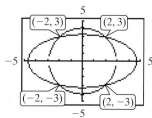

Figure 5-14

TIP The image produced by a graphing calculator in Figure 5-14 does not show the curves touching the x-axis, when indeed they do. This is a result of limited resolution on the calculator.

Answer

3. $\{(1, 4), (-1, 4), (1, -4), (-1, -4)\}$

Example 4 illustrates that a nonlinear system of equations may have no solution.

EXAMPLE 4   Solving an Inconsistent System by Using the Addition Method

Solve the system by using the addition method.
$$x^2 + 4y^2 = 4$$
$$x^2 - y^2 = 9$$

Solution:

$$
\begin{aligned}
x^2 + 4y^2 &= 4 \\
x^2 - y^2 &= 9
\end{aligned}
\xrightarrow{\text{Multiply by } -1.}
\begin{aligned}
x^2 + 4y^2 &= 4 \\
-x^2 + y^2 &= -9 \\
\hline
5y^2 &= -5 \\
y^2 &= -1 \\
y &= \pm i
\end{aligned}
$$

We use the addition method because like terms are aligned vertically.

The values for y are all imaginary numbers. Therefore, there is no solution to the system of equations.

The solution set is { }.

Skill Practice 4   Solve the system by using the addition method.
$$x^2 + y^2 = 16$$
$$4x^2 + 9y^2 = 36$$

TECHNOLOGY CONNECTIONS

Solving a Nonlinear System of Equations

The equations in Example 4 represent two curves that have not yet been studied: an ellipse and a hyperbola. However, we can graph the curves on a graphing calculator by solving for y and entering the functions into the calculator.

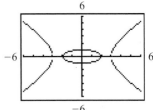

$$x^2 + 4y^2 = 4 \xrightarrow{\text{Solve for } y.} y = \pm\sqrt{\dfrac{4 - x^2}{4}}$$

$$x^2 - y^2 = 9 \longrightarrow y = \pm\sqrt{x^2 - 9}$$

From the graph, we see that the curves do not intersect.

---

3. Use Nonlinear Systems of Equations to Solve Applications

In Example 5, we set up a system of nonlinear equations to model an application involving two independent relationships between two variables.

> ### EXAMPLE 5   Solving an Application of a Nonlinear System
>
> The perimeter of a television screen is 140 in. The area is 1200 in.^{2}.
>
> **a.** Find the length and width of the screen.
>
> **b.** Find the length of the diagonal.
>
> **Solution:**
>
> Let x represent the length of the screen.
> Let y represent the width of the screen.
>
> The statement of the problem gives two independent relationships between the length and width of the screen.
>
>
>
> The perimeter of a television screen is 140 in. $\longrightarrow$ $2x + 2y = 140$
> The area is 1200 in.^{2}. $\longrightarrow$ $xy = 1200$
>
> **a.** Solve the nonlinear system of equations for x and y.
>
> $\boxed{A}$ $2x + 2y = 140$
>
> $\boxed{B}$ $xy = 1200$ $\xrightarrow{\text{Solve for } y.}$ $y = \dfrac{1200}{x}$ Using the substitution method, solve for x or y in either equation.
>
> $\boxed{A}$ $2x + 2\left(\dfrac{1200}{x}\right) = 140$ Substitute $y = \frac{1200}{x}$ from equation $\boxed{B}$ into equation $\boxed{A}$.
>
> $\qquad 2x + \dfrac{2400}{x} = 140$
>
> $\qquad x \cdot \left(2x + \dfrac{2400}{x}\right) = x \cdot (140)$ Multiply both sides by the LCD to clear fractions.
>
> $\qquad 2x^2 + 2400 = 140x$ The resulting equation is quadratic.
>
> $2x^2 - 140x + 2400 = 0$
>
> $2(x^2 - 70x + 1200) = 0$ Factor the left side.
>
> $2(x - 40)(x - 30) = 0$
>
> $x = 40 \quad \text{or} \quad x = 30$ There are two possible values for the length x.
>
> Substitute $x = 40$ and $x = 30$ into the equation $y = \dfrac{1200}{x}$.
>
> $x = 40$: $y = \dfrac{1200}{40} = 30$ If the length x is 40 in., then the width y is 30 in.
>
> $x = 30$: $y = \dfrac{1200}{30} = 40$ If the length x is 30 in., then the width y is 40 in.
>
> Taking the length to be the longer side, we have that the length is 40 in. and the width is 30 in.
>
> **b.** $x^2 + y^2 = d^2$ Use the Pythagorean theorem to determine the measure of the diagonal of the screen.
>
> $(40)^2 + (30)^2 = d^2$
>
> $1600 + 900 = d^2$
>
> $2500 = d^2$
>
> $d = \pm 50$
>
> Excluding the negative solution for d, the diagonal is 50 in.

Avoiding Mistakes

Check the solution to Example 5(a) by computing the perimeter and area.

Perimeter:
2(40 in.) + 2(30 in.)
= 140 in. ✓

Area:
(40 in.)(30 in.)
= 1200 in.^{2} ✓

Answer

5. The length of the rug is 12 ft and the width is 8 ft.

Skill Practice 5   The perimeter of a rectangular rug is 40 ft and the area is 96 ft^2. Find the dimensions of the rug.

SECTION 5.4   Practice Exercises

Review Exercises

For Exercises 1–4, graph the equation.

1. $y = (x - 2)^2 - 1$ **2.** $y = -3x - 2$ **3.** $(x - 3)^2 + (y + 2)^2 = 16$ **4.** $y = -x^2 + 3$

For Exercises 5–6, solve the system of linear equations in two variables.

5. $x = 4y + 7$
   $2x + 3y = 3$

6. $5x - 4y = -3$
   $3x + 7y = 17$

Concept Connections

7. A _____ system of equations in two variables is a system in which one or more equations in the system is nonlinear.

8. A solution to a nonlinear system of equations in two variables is an _____ pair with real-valued coordinates that satisfies each equation in the system. Graphically, a solution is a point of _____ of the graphs of the equations.

Objective 1: Solve Nonlinear Systems of Equations by the Substitution Method

For Exercises 9–18,

a. Graph the equations in the system.

b. Solve the system by using the substitution method. (**See Examples 1–2**)

9. $y = x^2 - 2$
   $2x - y = 2$

10. $y = -x^2 + 3$
   $y - 2x = 0$

11. $x^2 + y^2 = 25$
   $x + y = 1$

12. $x^2 + y^2 = 25$
   $3y = 4x$

13. $y = \sqrt{x}$
   $x^2 + y^2 = 20$

14. $x^2 + y^2 = 10$
   $y = \sqrt{x - 2}$

15. $(x + 2)^2 + y^2 = 9$
   $y = 2x - 4$

16. $x^2 + (y - 3)^2 = 4$
   $y = -x - 4$

17. $y = x^3$
   $y = x$

18. $y = \sqrt[3]{x}$
   $y = x$

Objective 2: Solve Nonlinear Systems of Equations by the Addition Method

For Exercises 19–26, solve the system by using the addition method. (**See Examples 3–4**)

19. $2x^2 + 3y^2 = 11$
   $x^2 + 4y^2 = 8$

20. $3x^2 + y^2 = 21$
   $4x^2 - 2y^2 = -2$

21. $x^2 - xy = 20$
   $-2x^2 + 3xy = -44$

22. $4xy + 3y^2 = -9$
   $2xy + y^2 = -5$

23. $5x^2 - 2y^2 = 1$
   $2x^2 - 3y^2 = -4$

24. $6x^2 + 5y^2 = 38$
   $7x^2 - 3y^2 = 9$

25. $x^2 = 1 - y^2$
   $9x^2 - 4y^2 = 36$

26. $4x^2 = 4 - y^2$
   $16y^2 = 144 + 9x^2$

Mixed Exercises

For Exercises 27–34, solve the system by using any method.

27. $x^2 - 4xy + 4y^2 = 1$
   $x + y = 4$

28. $x^2 - 6xy + 9y^2 = 0$
   $x - y = 2$

29. $y = x^2 + 4x + 5$
   $y = 4x + 5$

30. $y = x^2 - 6x + 9$
   $y = -2x + 5$

31. $y = x^2$
   $y = \dfrac{1}{x}$

32. $y = \dfrac{1}{x}$
   $y = \sqrt{x}$

33. $x^2 + (y - 4)^2 = 25$
   $y = -x^2 + 9$

34. $(x - 10)^2 + y^2 = 100$
   $x = y^2$

For Exercises 35–36, use the substitutions $u = \dfrac{1}{x^2}$ and $v = \dfrac{1}{y^2}$ to solve the system of equations.

35. $\dfrac{4}{x^2} - \dfrac{3}{y^2} = -23$
   $\dfrac{5}{x^2} + \dfrac{1}{y^2} = 14$

36. $-\dfrac{3}{x^2} + \dfrac{1}{y^2} = 13$
   $\dfrac{5}{x^2} - \dfrac{1}{y^2} = -5$

Objective 3: Use Nonlinear Systems of Equations to Solve Applications

37. Find two numbers whose sum is 12 and whose product is 35.

38. Find two numbers whose sum is 9 and whose product is -36.

39. The sum of the squares of two positive numbers is 29 and the difference of the squares of the numbers is 21. Find the numbers.

40. The sum of the squares of two negative numbers is 145 and the difference of the squares of the numbers is 17. Find the numbers.

41. The difference of two positive numbers is 2 and the difference of their squares is 44. Find the numbers.

42. The sum of two numbers is 4 and the difference of their squares is 64. Find the numbers.

43. The ratio of two numbers is 3 to 4 and the sum of their squares is 225. Find the numbers.

44. The ratio of two numbers is 5 to 12 and the sum of their squares is 676. Find the numbers.

45. Find the dimensions of a rectangle whose perimeter is 36 m and whose area is 80 m^2.

46. Find the dimensions of a rectangle whose perimeter is 56 cm and whose area is 192 cm^2.

47. The floor of a rectangular bedroom requires 240 ft^2 of carpeting. Molding is placed around the base of the floor except at two 3-ft doorways. If 58 ft of molding is required around the base of the floor, determine the dimensions of the floor. (**See Example 5**)

48. An electronic sign for a grocery store is in the shape of a rectangle. The perimeter of the sign is 72 ft and the area is 320 ft^2. Find the length and width of the sign.

49. A rental truck has a cargo capacity of 288 ft^3. A 10-ft pipe just fits resting diagonally on the floor of the truck. If the cargo space is 6 ft high, find the dimensions of the truck.

50. A rectangular window has a 15-yd diagonal and an area of 108 yd^2. Find the dimensions of the window.

51. An aquarium is 16 in. high with volume of 4608 in.^{3} (approximately 20 gal). If the amount of glass used for the bottom and four sides is 1440 in.^{2}, determine the dimensions of the aquarium.

52. A closed box is in the shape of a rectangular solid with height 3 m. Its surface area is 268 m^2. If the volume is 240 m^3, find the dimensions of the box.

53. The hypotenuse of a right triangle is $\sqrt{65}$ ft. The sum of the lengths of the legs is 11 ft. Find the lengths of the legs.

54. The hypotenuse of a right triangle is $\sqrt{73}$ in. The sum of the lengths of the legs is 11 in. Find the lengths of the legs.

55. A ball is kicked off the side of a hill at an angle of elevation of 30°. The hill slopes downward 30° from the horizontal. Consider a coordinate system in which the origin is the point on the edge of the hill from which the ball is kicked. The path of the ball and the line of declination of the hill can be approximated by

$$y = -\frac{x^2}{192} + \frac{\sqrt{3}}{3}x \quad \text{Path of the ball}$$

$$y = -\frac{\sqrt{3}}{3}x \quad \text{Line of declination of the hill}$$

Solve the system to determine where the ball will hit the ground.

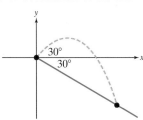

56. A child kicks a rock off the side of a hill at an angle of elevation of 60°. The hill slopes downward 30° from the horizontal. Consider a coordinate system in which the origin is the point on the edge of the hill from which the rock is kicked. The path of the ball and the line of declination of the hill can be approximated by

$$y = -\frac{x^2}{36} + \sqrt{3}x \quad \text{Path of the rock}$$

$$y = -\frac{\sqrt{3}}{3}x \quad \text{Line of declination of the hill}$$

Solve the system to determine where the rock will hit the ground.

Write About It

57. What is the difference between a system of linear equations and a system of nonlinear equations?

58. Describe a situation in which the addition method is an efficient technique to solve a system of nonlinear equations.

Expanding Your Skills

59. The attending physician in an emergency room treats an unconscious patient suspected of a drug overdose. The physician does not know the initial concentration A_0 of the drug in the bloodstream at the time of injection. However, the physician knows that after 3 hr, the drug concentration in the blood is 0.69 μg/dL and after 4 hr, the concentration is 0.655 μg/dL. The model $A(t) = A_0 e^{-kt}$ represents the drug concentration $A(t)$ (in μg/dL) in the bloodstream t hours after injection. The value of k is a constant related to the rate at which the drug is removed by the body.

  a. Substitute 0.69 for $A(t)$ and 3 for t in the model and write the resulting equation.

  b. Substitute 0.655 for $A(t)$ and 4 for t in the model and write the resulting equation.

  c. Use the system of equations from parts (a) and (b) to solve for k. Round to 3 decimal places.

  d. Use the system of equations from parts (a) and (b) to approximate the initial concentration A_0 (in μg/dL) at the time of injection. Round to 2 decimal places.

  e. Determine the concentration of the drug after 12 hr. Round to 2 decimal places.

60. A patient undergoing a heart scan is given a sample of fluorine-18 (^{18}F). After 4 hr, the radioactivity level in the patient is 44.1 MBq (megabecquerel). After 5 hr, the radioactivity level drops to 30.2 MBq. The radioactivity level $Q(t)$ can be approximated by $Q(t) = Q_0 e^{-kt}$, where t is the time in hours after the initial dose Q_0 is administered.

  a. Determine the value of k. Round to 4 decimal places.

  b. Determine the initial dose, Q_0. Round to the nearest whole unit.

  c. Determine the radioactivity level after 12 hr. Round to 1 decimal place.

61. The population $P(t)$ of a culture of bacteria grows exponentially for the first 72 hr according to the model $P(t) = P_0 e^{kt}$. The variable t is the time in hours since the culture is started. The population of bacteria is 60,000 after 7 hr. The population grows to 80,000 after 12 hr.

  a. Determine the constant k to 3 decimal places.

  b. Determine the original population P_0. Round to the nearest thousand.

  c. Determine the time required for the population to reach 300,000. Round to the nearest hour.

62. An investment grows exponentially under continuous compounding. After 2 yr, the amount in the account is $7328.70. After 5 yr, the amount in the account is $8774.10. Use the model $A(t) = Pe^{rt}$ to

  a. Find the interest rate r. Round to the nearest percent.

  b. Find the original principal P. Round to the nearest dollar.

  c. Determine the amount of time required for the account to reach a value of $15,000. Round to the nearest year.

For Exercises 63–64, determine the number of solutions to the system of equations.

63.
$$y = 2^{x+1}$$
$$-1 + \log_2 y = x$$

64. $x^2 - y^2 = 0$
$$|x| = |y|$$

For Exercises 65–70, solve the system.

65. $\log x + 2 \log y = 5$
$$2 \log x - \log y = 0$$

66. $\log_2 x + 3 \log_2 y = 6$
$$\log_2 x - \log_2 y = 2$$

67. $2^x + 2^y = 6$
$$4^x - 2^y = 14$$

68. $3^x - 9^y = 18$
$$3^x + 3^y = 30$$

69. $(x - 1)^2 + (y + 1)^2 = 5$
$$x^2 + (y + 4)^2 = 29$$

70. $(x + 3)^2 + (y - 2)^2 = 4$
$$(x - 1)^2 + y^2 = 8$$

For Exercises 71–72, use substitution to solve the system for the set of ordered triples (x, y, λ) that satisfy the system.

71. $2 = 2\lambda x$
$$6 = 2\lambda y$$
$$x^2 + y^2 = 10$$

72. $8 = 4\lambda x$
$$2 = 2\lambda y$$
$$2x^2 + y^2 = 9$$

73. Two circles intersect as shown.

    a. Find the points of intersection.

$$x^2 + y^2 = 25$$
$$(x - 4)^2 + (y + 2)^2 = 25$$

    b. Find an equation of the chord common to both circles (shown in black). (*Hint*: A chord is a line segment on the interior of a circle with both endpoints on the circle.)

74. The minimum and maximum distances from a point P to a circle are found using the line determined by the given point and the center of the circle. Given the circle defined by $x^2 + y^2 = 9$ and the point $P(4, 5)$,

    a. Find the point on the circle closest to the point $(4, 5)$.

    b. Find the point on the circle furthest from the point $(4, 5)$.

Technology Connections

For Exercises 75–80, use a graphing utility to approximate the solution(s) to the system of equations. Round the coordinates to 3 decimal places.

75. $y = -0.6x + 7$
    $y = e^x - 5$

76. $y = -0.7x + 4$
    $y = \ln x$

77. $x^2 + y^2 = 40$
    $y = -x^2 + 8.5$

78. $x^2 + y^2 = 32$
    $y = 0.8x^2 - 9.2$

79. $y = x^2 - 8x + 20$
    $y = 4 \log x$

80. $y = 0.2e^x$
    $y = -0.6x^2 - 2x - 3$

SECTION 5.5 | # Inequalities and Systems of Inequalities in Two Variables

OBJECTIVES

1. Solve Linear Inequalities in Two Variables
2. Solve Nonlinear Inequalities in Two Variables
3. Solve Systems of Inequalities in Two Variables

1. Solve Linear Inequalities in Two Variables

Adriana estimates that she has 12 hr of available study time before she takes tests in algebra and biology in back-to-back classes. Suppose that x represents the time she spends studying algebra and y represents the time she spends studying biology. Then the inequality $x + y \leq 12$, where $x \geq 0$ and $y \geq 0$ represents the distribution of time she can allocate studying for each subject.

    An inequality of the form $Ax + By < C$, where A and B are not both zero, is called a **linear inequality in two variables.** (Note that the symbols $>$, $\leq$, and $\geq$ can be used in place of $<$ in the definition.) A **solution** to an inequality in two variables is an ordered pair that satisfies the inequality. The set of all such ordered pairs is called the **solution set** to the inequality. Graphically, the solution set is a region in the xy-plane.

    To graph the solution set to a linear inequality in two variables, follow these guidelines.

TIP To graph the line in step 1, we can
- Use the slope-intercept form of the equation of the line.
- Graph the *x*- and *y*-intercepts.
- Create a table of points.

Graphing a Linear Inequality in Two Variables

Step 1 Graph the related equation. That is, replace the inequality sign with an $=$ sign and graph the line represented by the equation.
- If the inequality is strict (stated with the symbols $<$ or $>$), then draw the line as a dashed line to indicate that the line *is not* part of the solution set.
- If the inequality is stated with the symbols $\leq$ or $\geq$, then draw the line as a solid line to indicate that the line *is* part of the solution set.

Step 2 Choose a test point from either side of the line (not a point on the line itself) and substitute the ordered pair into the inequality.
- If a true statement results, then shade the region (half-plane) from which the test point was taken.
- If a false statement results, then shade the region (half-plane) on the opposite side of the line from which the test point was taken.

EXAMPLE 1 Graphing a Linear Inequality in Two Variables

Graph the solution set. $3x - 2y < 6$

Solution:

$3x - 2y < 6 \xrightarrow[\text{equation}]{\text{related}} 3x - 2y = 6$ **Step 1:** Graph the related equation $3x - 2y = 6$ using any technique for graphing. In this case, we have chosen to find the *x*- and *y*-intercepts.

x-intercept: *y*-intercept:

$3x - 2(0) = 6$ $3(0) - 2y = 6$

$x = 2$ $y = -3$

The *x*- and *y*-intercepts are (2, 0) and (0, −3). Graph the line through the intercepts (Figure 5-15). Because the inequality is strict, draw the line as a dashed line.

Figure 5-15

TIP We can also graph the inequality from Example 1 by solving the inequality for *y*.

$3x - 2y < 6$

$-2y < -3x + 6$

$y > \frac{3}{2}x - 3$

Then shade the half-plane *above* the bounding line because this region contains points with *y*-coordinates greater than those on the bounding line.

Test (0, 0):

$3x - 2y < 6$

$3(0) - 2(0) \stackrel{?}{<} 6$

$0 \stackrel{?}{<} 6$ ✔ true

Step 2: Select a test point either above or below the line and test the ordered pair in the original inequality. In Figure 5-16, we have chosen (0, 0) as a test point.

The test point (0, 0) is a representative point above the line. Since (0, 0) satisfies the original inequality, then it and all other points above the line are solutions.

The solution set is the set of ordered pairs in the region (half-plane) above the line (Figure 5-16).

Figure 5-16

Answer

1.

Skill Practice 1 Graph the solution set. $4x - y > 3$

TECHNOLOGY CONNECTIONS

Graphing a System of Inequalities in Two Variables

A graphing utility can be used to graph an inequality in two variables. In most cases, we solve for y first and enter the related equation in the graphing editor. Place the cursor to the left of Y_1 and press ENTER two times. This will set the graph style to shade the region above the line ◥. Notice that the calculator image does not differentiate between a solid and dashed bounding line (Figure 5-17).

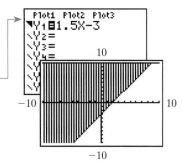

Figure 5-17

Note: With the cursor placed to the left of Y_1,

- Select the upper right triangle ◥ for inequalities of the form $Y_1 > f(x)$ and $Y_1 \geq f(x)$.
- Select the lower left triangle ◣ for inequalities of the form $Y_1 < f(x)$ and $Y_1 \leq f(x)$.

In Example 2, we graph the solutions to an inequality in which the bounding line passes through the origin.

EXAMPLE 2   Graphing a Linear Inequality

Graph the solution set. $4y \leq 3x$

Solution:

$4y \leq 3x \xrightarrow[\substack{related \\ equation}]{} 4y = 3x$

$y = \dfrac{3}{4}x + 0$

Step 1: Graph the related equation $4y = 3x$. In this case, we have chosen to find the slope-intercept form of the equation and then graph the line using the slope and y-intercept.

Graph the line having y-intercept $(0, 0)$ and slope $\frac{3}{4}$ (Figure 5-18). Because the inequality symbol $\leq$ allows for equality, draw the line as a solid line.

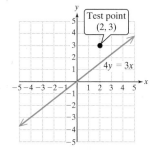

Figure 5-18

> **TIP** As a check, we can select a test point *below* the line, such as $(1, -1)$ and verify that it does indeed satisfy the original inequality.
>
> Test $(1, -1)$:
> $4(-1) \overset{?}{\leq} 3(1)$
> $-4 \overset{?}{\leq} 3$ ✓ true

Test $(2, 3)$:

$4y \leq 3x$

$4(3) \overset{?}{\leq} 3(2)$

$12 \overset{?}{\leq} 6$ false

Step 2: Select a test point. We have chosen $(2, 3)$.

The test point $(2, 3)$ is a representative point above the line. Since $(2, 3)$ does *not* satisfy the original inequality, then points on the other side of the line are solutions. Shade below the line.

The solution set is the set of ordered pairs on and below the line (Figure 5-19).

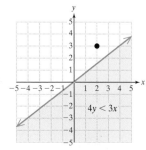

Figure 5-19

> **Skill Practice 2**   Graph the solution set. $2y \geq 5x$

Recall that for a constant k, the equation $x = k$ represents a vertical line in the xy-plane. The inequalities $x < k$ and $x > k$ represent half-planes to the left or right of the vertical line $x = k$ (Figure 5-20). Likewise, $y = k$ represents a horizontal line in the xy-plane. The inequalities $y < k$ and $y > k$ represent half-planes below or above the line $y = k$ (Figure 5-21).

Figure 5-20   **Figure 5-21**

EXAMPLE 3   **Graphing Linear Inequalities with a Horizontal or Vertical Bounding Line**

Graph the solution set.

a. $x \leq -1$ **b.** $3y > 5$

Solution:

a. $x \leq -1$

- The related equation $x = -1$ is a vertical line.

- The inequality $x \leq -1$ represents all points to the *left* of or on the line $x = -1$.

b. $3y > 5$

- The inequality is equivalent to $y > \frac{5}{3}$. The related equation $y = \frac{5}{3}$ is a horizontal line.

- The inequality $y > \frac{5}{3}$ represents all points strictly above the line $y = \frac{5}{3}$.

> **Skill Practice 3**   Graph the solution set.
>
>   **a.** $2y < 6$ **b.** $x \geq \frac{9}{4}$

Answers

2.

3. a.

b.

2. Solve Nonlinear Inequalities in Two Variables

The same approach used to graph a linear inequality in two variables is used to graph a *nonlinear* inequality in two variables. This is demonstrated in Example 4.

EXAMPLE 4   Graphing a Nonlinear Inequality

Graph the solution set. $(x - 2)^2 + y^2 > 9$

Solution:

$(x - 2)^2 + y^2 > 9 \xrightarrow[\text{equation}]{\text{related}} (x - 2)^2 + y^2 = 9$

Step 1: Graph the related equation. The equation represents a circle centered at (2, 0) with radius 3. Because the inequality is strict, draw the circle as a dashed curve (Figure 5-22).

Center: (2, 0)
Radius: 3

Figure 5-22

Test (2, 0):

$(x - 2)^2 + y^2 > 9$
$(2 - 2)^2 + (0)^2 \overset{?}{>} 9$
$0 \overset{?}{>} 9$ false

Step 2: Select a test point. We have chosen the center (2, 0).

The test point inside the circle does not satisfy the original inequality. Therefore, the solution set consists of the points strictly outside the circle (Figure 5-23).

Figure 5-23

Skill Practice 4   Graph the solution set. $x^2 + (y + 1)^2 < 16$

---

3. Solve Systems of Inequalities in Two Variables

Two or more inequalities in two variables make up a system of inequalities in two variables. The solution set is the set of ordered pairs that satisfy each inequality in the system. To graph the solution set to a system of inequalities, graph the solution sets to the individual inequalities first. The solution to the system of inequalities is the intersection of the graphs. This is demonstrated in Example 5.

Answer

4.

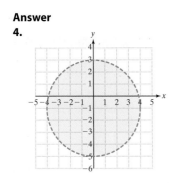

EXAMPLE 5 Graphing the Solution Set to a System of Linear Inequalities

Graph the solution set to the system of inequalities.

$$y \leq \tfrac{1}{2}x + 2$$
$$3x - y < 3$$

Solution:

$$y \leq \tfrac{1}{2}x + 2$$
$$3x - y < 3$$

First graph the solutions to the individual inequalities (Figures 5-24 and 5-25). Next, find the intersection (area of overlap) of the solution sets shown in purple in Figure 5-26.

Figure 5-24   Figure 5-25   Figure 5-26

Notice that the point of intersection between the two bounding lines is graphed as an open dot (Figure 5-27). This indicates that it is *not* part of the solution set. The reason is that it is not a solution to the strict inequality $3x - y < 3$.

The point of intersection can be found by solving the system of related equations. We have used the substitution method.

Figure 5-27

$$y = \tfrac{1}{2}x + 2$$
$$3x - y = 3 \qquad 3x - \left(\tfrac{1}{2}x + 2\right) = 3$$
$$3x - \tfrac{1}{2}x - 2 = 3$$
$$\tfrac{5}{2}x = 5$$
$$x = 2 \longrightarrow y = \tfrac{1}{2}(2) + 2$$
$$y = 3$$

The point of intersection is (2, 3) and is excluded from the solution set.

Answer
5.

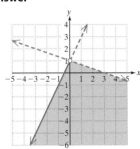

Skill Practice 5 Graph the solution set to the system of inequalities.

$$y < -\tfrac{1}{3}x + 1$$
$$-2x + y \leq 1$$

TECHNOLOGY CONNECTIONS

Graphing a System of Inequalities in Two Variables

To graph the system of inequalities from Example 5 on a graphing calculator, solve each inequality for y.

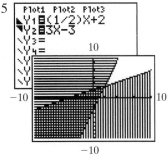

$$y \le \tfrac{1}{2}x + 2$$
$$3x - y < 3 \rightarrow -y < -3x + 3 \rightarrow y > 3x - 3$$

Then enter the related equations in the graphing editor. Choose the appropriate graphing style ◥ or ◣. For $Y_1 \le \tfrac{1}{2}x + 2$, choose ◣. For $Y_2 > 3x - 3$, choose ◥.

In Example 6, we graph a system of nonlinear inequalities in two variables. This is a system of inequalities in which one or more of the individual inequalities is nonlinear.

EXAMPLE 6   Solving a System of Nonlinear Inequalities

Graph the solution set to the system of inequalities.

$$y \le -x^2 + 4$$
$$x - y \ge -2$$
$$y > -5$$

Solution:

To graph the solution set to the given system, first graph each individual inequality.

$$y \le -x^2 + 4 \qquad\qquad x - y \ge -2 \qquad\qquad y > -5$$

The solution set to the system is the intersection of the three shaded regions (Figure 5-28). The points of intersection are found by pairing up the related equations and solving the system of equations. The inequalities $y \le -x^2 + 4$ and $x - y \ge -2$ include equality. Therefore, the intersection points between the parabola and slanted line are solutions to the system. These points are plotted as closed dots.

On the other hand, because the inequality $y > -5$ is strict, the intersection points between the parabola and horizontal line are *not* solutions to the system. These points are plotted as open dots.

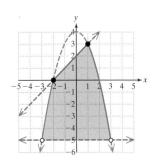

Figure 5-28

To find the points of intersection between the parabola $y = -x^2 + 4$ and the line $x - y = -2$, solve the system:

$$y = -x^2 + 4$$
$$x - y = -2 \qquad \text{The solutions are } (-2, 0) \text{ and } (1, 3).$$

To find the points of intersection between the parabola $y = -x^2 + 4$ and the line $y = -5$, solve the system:

$$y = -x^2 + 4$$
$$y = -5 \qquad \text{The solutions are } (-3, -5) \text{ and } (3, -5).$$

Skill Practice 6 Graph the solution set to the system of inequalities.

$$x^2 + y^2 \le 25$$
$$-x + y < 1$$
$$y \ge -4$$

In Example 7, we refer back to the problem addressed at the beginning of this section and set up a system of linear inequalities to model the allocation of time studying algebra and biology.

EXAMPLE 7 **Solving a System of Inequalities in an Application**

Adriana has 12 available study hours for algebra and biology.

- Let x represent the number of hours she spends studying algebra.
- Let y represent the number of hours that she studies biology.

a. Set up an inequality that indicates that the number of hours spent studying algebra cannot be negative.

b. Set up an inequality that indicates that the number of hours spent studying biology cannot be negative.

c. Set up an inequality that indicates that the combined number of hours she spends studying for these two classes is at most 12 hr.

d. Graph the solution set to the system of inequalities from parts (a)–(c).

Solution:

a. $x \ge 0$ — The number of hours spent studying algebra is 0 or more.

b. $y \ge 0$ — The number of hours spent studying biology is 0 or more.

c. $x + y \le 12$ — The sum of time spent studying algebra and the time spent studying biology cannot exceed the maximum number of study hours available. Therefore, the sum is less than or equal to 12 hr.

d. $x \ge 0$
$y \ge 0$
$x + y \le 12$

The inequalities $x \ge 0$ and $y \ge 0$ together represent the set of points in the first quadrant, including the bounding axes.

To graph the inequality $x + y \le 12$, we graph the related equation $x + y = 12$. A test point $(0, 0)$ taken below the line results in a true statement. Therefore, the inequality $x + y \le 12$ represents the set of points on and below the line $x + y = 12$.

The solution to the system of inequalities is shown in Figure 5-29.

TIP The points of intersection of the bounding lines are closed dots because they are part of the solution set.

Answer

6.

Figure 5-29

Answers

7. a. $x \geq 0; y \geq 0$

   b. $x + y \leq 16$

   c.

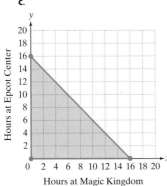

Hours at Magic Kingdom

Skill Practice 7   A family plans to spend two 8-hr days at Disney World and will split time between the Magic Kingdom and Epcot Center. Let x represent the number of hours spent at the Magic Kingdom and let y represent the number of hours spent at Epcot Center.

a. Set up two inequalities that indicate that the number of hours spent at the Magic Kingdom and the number of hours spent at Epcot cannot be negative.

b. Set up an inequality that indicates that the combined number of hours spent at the two parks is at most 16 hr.

c. Graph the solution set to the system of inequalities.

SECTION 5.5   Practice Exercises

Review Exercises

For Exercises 1–4, graph the equations.

1. $3x + y = -4$ **2.** $x + 2y = 2$ **3.** $y = x^2 - 4$ **4.** $y = -x^2 + 4$

For Exercises 5–6, solve the system.

5. $3x + \ y = -4$
   $\quad x + 2y = 2$

6. $y = \ x^2 - 4$
   $\quad y = -x^2 + 4$

Concept Connections

7. An inequality that can be written in the form $Ax + By < C$ (where A and B are not both zero) is called a _____ inequality in two variables.

8. For a constant real number k, the inequality $x < k$ represents the half-plane to the (left/right) of the (horizontal/vertical) line $x = k$.

9. For a constant real number k, the inequality $y > k$ represents the half-plane (above/below) the (horizontal/vertical) line $y = k$.

10. Given the inequality $y \leq 2x + 1$, the bounding line $y = 2x + 1$ is drawn as a (dashed/solid) line.

11. The solution set to the system of inequalities $x < 0$, $y > 0$ represents the points in quadrant (I, II, III, IV).

12. The equation $x^2 + y^2 = 4$ is a circle centered at _____ with radius _____. The solution set to the inequality $x^2 + y^2 < 4$ represents the set of points (inside/outside) the circle $x^2 + y^2 = 4$.

Objective 1: Solve Linear Inequalities in Two Variables

For Exercises 13–16, determine whether the ordered pair is a solution to the inequality.

13. $3x + 4y < 12$
   a. $(-1, 3)$
   b. $(5, 1)$
   c. $(4, 0)$

14. $2x + 3y > 6$
   a. $(-3, 3)$
   b. $(5, -1)$
   c. $(0, 2)$

15. $y \geq (x - 3)^2$
   a. $(-3, 30)$
   b. $(1, 4)$
   c. $(5, 5)$

16. $y \leq x^3 - 1$
   a. $(-1, -2)$
   b. $(2, 6)$
   c. $(-4, -50)$

17. a. Graph the solution set. $4x - 5y \leq 20$
      (See Example 1)
   b. Explain how the graph would differ for the inequality $4x - 5y < 20$.
   c. Explain how the graph would differ for the inequality $4x - 5y > 20$.

18. a. Graph the solution set. $2x + 5y > 10$
   b. Explain how the graph would differ for the inequality $2x + 5y \geq 10$.
   c. Explain how the graph would differ for the inequality $2x + 5y < 10$.

For Exercises 19–30, graph the solution set. (See Examples 1–3)

19. $2x + 5y > 5$

20. $-5x + 4y \leq 8$

21. $-30x \geq 20y + 600$

22. $-400x < 100y + 8000$

23. $5x \leq 6y$

24. $3x > 2y$

25. $3 + 2(x + y) > y + 3$

26. $-4 - 3(x - y) < 2y - 4$

27. $x < 6$

28. $y \leq 5$

29. $-\dfrac{1}{2}y + 4 \leq 5$

30. $-\dfrac{1}{3}x + 2 < 4$

Objective 2: Solve Nonlinear Inequalities in Two Variables

31. a. Graph the solution set. $x^2 + y^2 < 4$ (**See Example 4**)

    b. Explain how the graph would differ for the inequality $x^2 + y^2 > 4$.

    c. Explain how the graph would differ for the inequality $x^2 + y^2 \geq 4$.

32. a. Graph the solution set. $y \geq x^2 - 1$

    b. Explain how the graph would differ for the inequality $y \leq x^2 - 1$.

    c. Explain how the graph would differ for the inequality $y > x^2 - 1$.

For Exercises 33–42, graph the solution set. (See Example 4)

33. $y < -x^2$

34. $x^2 + y^2 \geq 16$

35. $y \leq (x - 2)^2 + 1$

36. $y \geq -(x + 1)^2 - 2$

37. $|x| \leq 3$

38. $|y| \leq 2$

39. $2|y| > 2$

40. $|x| + 1 > 3$

41. $y \geq \sqrt{x}$

42. $y < \sqrt{x - 1}$

Objective 3: Solve Systems of Inequalities in Two Variables

43. a. Is the point $(2, 1)$ a solution to the inequality $y < 2x + 3$?

    b. Is the point $(2, 1)$ a solution to the inequality $x + y \leq 1$?

    c. Is the point $(2, 1)$ a solution to the system of inequalities?

$$y < 2x + 3$$
$$x + y \leq 1$$

44. a. Is the point $(3, 2)$ a solution to the inequality $y < -x + 5$?

    b. Is the point $(3, 2)$ a solution to the inequality $3x + y \geq 11$?

    c. Is the point $(3, 2)$ a solution to the system of inequalities?

$$y < -x + 5$$
$$3x + y \geq 11$$

For Exercises 45–46, determine whether the ordered pair is a solution to the system of inequalities.

45. $x + y < 4$
$\quad y \leq 2x + 1$

    a. $(0, 1)$ **b.** $(3, 1)$ **c.** $(2, 0)$ **d.** $(1, 4)$

46. $y < -x^2 + 3$
$\quad x + 2y \leq 2$

    a. $(-2, -1)$ **b.** $(0, -2)$ **c.** $(0, 1)$ **d.** $(3, -6)$

For Exercises 47–64, graph the solution set. If there is no solution, indicate that the solution set is the empty set. (See Examples 5–6)

47. $y < \dfrac{1}{2}x - 4$
$\quad y > -2x + 1$

48. $y \geq \dfrac{1}{3}x - 2$
$\quad y \leq x - 4$

49. $2x + 5y \leq 5$
$\quad -3x + 4y \geq 4$

50. $4x - 3y > 3$
$\quad x + 4y < -4$

51. $x^2 + y^2 \geq 9$
$\quad x^2 + y^2 \leq 16$

52. $x^2 + y^2 \geq 1$
$\quad x^2 + y^2 < 25$

53. $y \geq 3x + 3$
$\quad -3x + y < 1$

54. $y < 2x - 4$
$\quad -2x + y \geq 2$

55. $|x| < 3$
$\quad |y| < 3$

56. $|x| \geq 2$
$\quad |y| \geq 2$

57. $y \geq x^2 - 2$
$\quad y > x$
$\quad y \leq 4$

58. $y \leq -x^2 + 7$
$\quad y \leq -x + 5$
$\quad y > 1$

59. $x^2 + y^2 \leq 100$
$\quad y < \dfrac{4}{3}x$
$\quad x \leq 8$

60. $x^2 + y^2 < 100$
$\quad y \geq x$
$\quad y \geq 1$

61. $y < e^x$
$\quad y > 1$
$\quad x < 2$

62. $y \leq \dfrac{2}{x}$
$\quad y > 0$
$\quad y < x$

63. $(x + 2)^2 + (y - 3)^2 \leq 9$
$\quad x - y > 2$

64. $(x - 4)^2 + (y + 1)^2 < 25$
$\quad 2x - y < -4$

Mixed Exercises

For Exercises 65–70, write an inequality to represent the statement.

65. x is at most 6.

66. y is no more than 7.

67. y is at least -2.

68. x is no less than $\frac{1}{2}$.

69. The sum of x and y does not exceed 18.

70. The difference of x and y is not less than 4.

71. Let x represent the number of hours that Trenton spends studying algebra, and let y represent the number of hours he spends studying history. For parts (a)–(e), write an inequality to represent the given statement. (**See Example 7**)

   a. Trenton has a total of at most 9 hr to study for both algebra and history combined.

   b. Trenton will spend at least 3 hr studying algebra.

   c. Trenton will spend no more than 4 hr studying history.

   d. The number of hours spent studying algebra cannot be negative.

   e. The number of hours spent studying history cannot be negative.

   f. Graph the solution set to the system of inequalities from parts (a)–(e).

72. Let x represent the number of country songs that Sierra puts on a playlist on her portable media player. Let y represent the number of rock songs that she puts on the playlist. For parts (a)–(e), write an inequality to represent the given statement.

   a. Sierra will put at least 6 country songs on the playlist.

   b. Sierra will put no more than 10 rock songs on the playlist.

   c. Sierra wants to limit the length of the playlist to at most 20 songs.

   d. The number of country songs cannot be negative.

   e. The number of rock songs cannot be negative.

   f. Graph the solution set to the system of inequalities from parts (a)–(e).

73. A couple has $60,000 to invest for retirement. They plan to put x dollars in stocks and y dollars in bonds. For parts (a)–(d), write an inequality to represent the given statement.

   a. The total amount invested is at most $60,000.

   b. The couple considers stocks a riskier investment, so they want to invest at least twice as much in bonds as in stocks.

   c. The amount invested in stocks cannot be negative.

   d. The amount invested in bonds cannot be negative.

   e. Graph the solution set to the system of inequalities from parts (a)–(d).

74. A college theater has a seating capacity of 2000. It reserves x tickets for students and y tickets for general admission. For parts (a)–(d) write an inequality to represent the given statement.

   a. The total number of seats available is at most 2000.

   b. The college wants to reserve at least 3 times as many student tickets as general admission tickets.

   c. The number of student tickets cannot be negative.

   d. The number of general admission tickets cannot be negative.

   e. Graph the solution set to the system of inequalities from parts (a)–(d).

75. Write a system of inequalities that represents the points in the first quadrant less than 3 units from the origin.

76. Write a system of inequalities that represents the points in the second quadrant more than 4 units from the origin

77. Write a system of inequalities that represents the points inside the triangle with vertices $(-3, -4)$, $(3, 2)$, and $(-5, 4)$.

78. Write a system of inequalities that represents the points inside the triangle with vertices $(-4, -4)$, $(1, 1)$, and $(5, -1)$.

79. A weak earthquake occurred roughly 9 km south and 12 km west of the center of Hawthorne, Nevada. The quake could be felt 16 km away. Suppose that the origin of a map is placed at the center of Hawthorne with the positive x-axis pointing east and the positive y-axis pointing north.

   a. Find an inequality that describes the points on the map for which the earthquake could be felt.

   b. Could the earthquake be felt at the center of Hawthorne?

80. A coordinate system is placed at the center of a town with the positive x-axis pointing east, and the positive y-axis pointing north. A cell tower is located 4 mi west and 5 mi north of the origin.

   a. If the tower has a 8-mi range, write an inequality that represents the points on the map serviced by this tower.

   b. Can a resident 5 mi east of the center of town get a signal from this tower?

Write About It

81. Under what circumstances should a dashed line or curve be used when graphing the solution set to an inequality in two variables?

82. Explain how test points are used to determine the region of the plane that represents the solution to an inequality in two variables.

83. Explain how to find the solution set to a system of inequalities in two variables.

84. Describe the solution set to the system of inequalities. $x \geq 0, y \geq 0, x \leq 1, y \leq 1$

Expanding Your Skills

For Exercises 85–86, graph the solution set.

85. $|x| \geq |y|$

86. $|x| + |y| \leq 1$

Technology Connections

For Exercises 87–88, use a graphing utility to graph the solution set to the system of inequalities.

87. $y \geq 0.4e^x$
$y \leq 0.25x^3 - 4x$

88. $y < \dfrac{4}{x^2 + 1}$

$y > \dfrac{-2}{x^2 + 0.5}$

PROBLEM RECOGNITION EXERCISES

Equations and Inequalities in Two Variables

For Exercises 1–2, for parts (a) and (b), graph the equation. For part (c), solve the system of equations. For parts (d) and (e) graph the solution set to the system of inequalities. If there is no solution, indicate that the solution set is the empty set.

1. **a.** $y = -3x + 5$ **b.** $-2x + y = 0$
   c. $y = -3x + 5$ **d.** $y > -3x + 5$ **e.** $y < -3x + 5$
   $-2x + y = 0$ $-2x + y < 0$ $-2x + y > 0$

2. **a.** $y = 2x - 3$ **b.** $4x - 2y = -2$
   c. $y = 2x - 3$ **d.** $y \geq 2x - 3$ **e.** $y \leq 2x - 3$
   $4x - 2y = -2$ $4x - 2y \geq -2$ $4x - 2y \leq -2$

For Exercises 3–4, for part (a), graph the equations in the system and determine the solution set. For parts (b) and (c), graph the solution set to the inequality.

3. **a.** $y = x^2$ **b.** $y \leq x^2$ **4.** **a.** $x - y = 1$ **b.** $x - y \geq 1$
   $y = \frac{1}{2}x^2$ $y \geq \frac{1}{2}x^2$ $y = (x - 3)^2$ $y \geq (x - 3)^2$
   c. $y \geq x^2$ **c.** $x - y \leq 1$
   $y \leq \frac{1}{2}x^2$ $y \leq (x - 3)^2$

SECTION 5.6   Linear Programming

OBJECTIVES

1. Write an Objective Function
2. Solve a Linear Programming Application

TIP The notation $z = f(x, y)$ is read as "z is a function of x and y."

1. Write an Objective Function

When a company manufactures a product, the goal is to obtain maximum profit at minimum cost. However, the production process is often limited by certain constraints such as the amount of labor available, the capacity of machinery, and the amount of money available for the company to invest in the process. In this section, we will study a process called **linear programming** that enables us to maximize or minimize a function under specified constraints.

The function to be optimized (maximized or minimized) in a linear programming application is called the **objective function.** The objective function often has two independent variables. For example, given $z = f(x, y)$, the variable z is dependent on the two independent variables x and y.

EXAMPLE 1   **Writing an Objective Function**

Suppose that a college wants to rent several buses to transport students to a championship college football game. A large bus costs $1200 to rent and a small bus costs $800 to rent.

Let x represent the number of large buses.

Let y represent the number of small buses.

Write an objective function that represents the total cost z (in $) to rent x large buses and y small buses.

Solution:

$$\begin{pmatrix} \text{Total} \\ \text{cost} \end{pmatrix} = \begin{pmatrix} \text{Cost to rent} \\ x \text{ large buses} \end{pmatrix} + \begin{pmatrix} \text{Cost to rent} \\ y \text{ small buses} \end{pmatrix}$$

$$\text{Cost:} \quad z \quad = \quad 1200x \quad + \quad 800y$$

The objective function is defined by $z = 1200x + 800y$.

TIP An objective function represents a quantity that is to be maximized or minimized. In Example 1, the school will want to minimize the cost to transport the students.

Skill Practice 1   An office manager needs to staff the office. She hires full-time employees at $18 per hour and part-time employees at $12 per hour. Write an objective function that represents the total cost (in $) to staff the office with x full-time employees and y part-time employees for 1 hr.

2. Solve a Linear Programming Application

In Example 2, we identify constraints imposed on the resources that affect the number of buses that the college can rent.

Answer

1. $z = 18x + 12y$

EXAMPLE 2   Writing a System of Constraints

Refer to the scenario from Example 1. We now set several constraints that affect the number of buses that can be rented.

> Let x represent the number of large buses.
> Let y represent the number of small buses.

For parts (a)–(d), write an inequality that represents the given statement.

a. The number of large buses cannot be negative.
b. The number of small buses cannot be negative.
c. Large buses can carry 60 people and small buses can carry 45 people. The college must transport at least 3600 students.
d. The number of available bus drivers is at most 75.

Solution:

a. $x \geq 0$ The number of large buses cannot be negative.
b. $y \geq 0$ The number of small buses cannot be negative.

c. $\left(\begin{array}{c}\text{Number of students}\\\text{carried by large buses}\end{array}\right) + \left(\begin{array}{c}\text{Number of students}\\\text{carried by small buses}\end{array}\right) \overset{\boxed{\text{is at least}}}{\geq} 3600$ Large buses hold 60 people and

$\qquad\quad 60x \qquad\qquad + \qquad\qquad 45y \qquad\qquad \geq 3600$ small buses hold 45 people.

d. $\left(\begin{array}{c}\text{Number of drivers}\\\text{for large buses}\end{array}\right) + \left(\begin{array}{c}\text{Number of drivers}\\\text{for small buses}\end{array}\right) \overset{\boxed{\text{is at most}}}{\leq} 75$ Because each bus has only one driver, the total number

$\qquad\qquad x \qquad\qquad + \qquad\qquad y \qquad\qquad \leq 75$ of buses is the same as the total number of drivers.

Skill Practice 2   Refer to Skill Practice 1. Suppose that the office manager needs at least 20 employees, but not more than 24 full-time employees. Furthermore, to make the office run smoothly, the manager knows that the number of full-time employees must always be greater than or equal to the number of part-time employees. Write a system of inequalities that represents the constraints on the number of full-time employees x and the number of part-time employees y.

The constraints in Example 2 make up a system of linear inequalities.

The number of large buses is nonnegative.	$x \geq 0$
The number of small buses is nonnegative.	$y \geq 0$
The school must transport at least 3600 students.	$60x + 45y \geq 3600$
The number of drivers (and therefore buses) is at most 75.	$x + y \leq 75$

Answer
2. $x \geq 0, y \geq 0, x \leq 24,$
$\quad x + y \geq 20, x \geq y$

The region in the plane that represents the solution set to the system of constraints is called the **feasible region** (Figure 5-30). The points of intersection of the bounding lines in the feasible region are called the **vertices** of the feasible region.

The vertices in Figure 5-30 are (60, 0), (75, 0), and (15, 60).

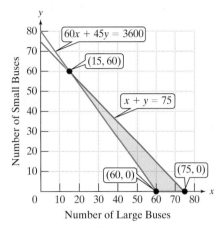

Figure 5-30

Points within the shaded region meet all the constraints in the problem. For example, the ordered pair (65, 5) represents 65 large buses and 5 small buses.

65 large buses and 5 small buses ⟶ 70 buses (≤ 75 drivers) ✓
65 large buses and 5 small buses ⟶ transports 4125 students (≥ 3600) ✓

However, points such as (65, 15) and (40, 20) are *outside* the feasible region and do not satisfy all constraints.

65 large buses and 15 small buses ⟶ 80 buses (exceeds the number of drivers)
40 large buses and 20 small buses ⟶ transports only 3300 students

The goal of a linear programming application is to find the maximum or minimum value of the objective function $z = f(x, y)$ when x and y are restricted to the ordered pairs in the feasible region. Fortunately, it has been proven mathematically that if a maximum or minimum value of a function exists, it occurs at one or more of the vertices of the feasible region. This is the basis for the following procedure to solve a linear programming application.

Solving an Application Involving Linear Programming

Step 1 Write an objective function $z = f(x, y)$.

Step 2 Write a system of inequalities defining the constraints on x and y.

Step 3 Graph the feasible region and identify the vertices.

Step 4 Evaluate the objective function at each vertex of the feasible region. Use the results to identify the values of x and y that optimize the objective function. Identify the optimal value of z.

In Example 3, we optimize the objective function found in Example 1 subject to the constraints defined in Example 2.

EXAMPLE 3 Solving a Linear Programming Application

A college wants to rent buses to transport at least 3600 students to a championship college football game. Large buses hold 60 people and small buses hold 45 people. Furthermore, the number of available bus drivers is at most 75. Each large bus costs $1200 to rent and each small bus costs $800 to rent. Find the optimal number of large and small buses that will minimize cost.

Solution:

Let x represent the number of large buses.   Define the relevant variables.
Let y represent the number of small buses.

Cost: $z = 1200x + 800y$ **Step 1:** Write an objective function. Since cost is to be minimized, write a cost function. (See Example 1.)

Constraints: **Step 2:** Write a system of constraints on the relevant variables. (See Example 2.)

$x \geq 0$

$y \geq 0$

$60x + 45y \geq 3600$

$x + y \leq 75$

Step 3: Graph the feasible region and identify the vertices.

The vertices are found by identifying the points of intersection between the bounding lines.

Bounding lines:

$60x + 45y = 3600$
$x + \quad y = 75$ Point of intersection $(15, 60)$

$60x + 45y = 3600$
$\qquad\quad y = 0$ Point of intersection $(60, 0)$

$x + y = 75$
$\quad\ \ y = 0$ Point of intersection $(75, 0)$

Cost function: $z = 1200x + 800y$

at $(15, 60)$ $z = 1200(15) + 800(60) = \boxed{\$66{,}000}$ **Step 4:** Evaluate the objective function $z = 1200x + 800y$ at each vertex.
at $(60, 0)$ $z = 1200(60) + 800(0)\ = \$72{,}000$
at $(75, 0)$ $z = 1200(75) + 800(0)\ = \$90{,}000$

The cost would be minimized if the college rents 15 large buses and 60 small buses. The minimum cost is $66,000.

Skill Practice 3   Refer to Skill Practices 1 and 2. The office manager needs at least 20 employees, but no more than 24 full-time employees. Furthermore, to make the office run smoothly, the manager knows that the number of full-time employees must always be greater than or equal to the number of part-time employees. If she pays full-time employees $18 per hour and part-time employees $12 per hour, determine the number of full-time and part-time employees she should hire to minimize total labor cost per hour.

Answer

3. The cost would be minimized at $300/hr if she hires 10 full-time employees and 10 part-time employees.

In Example 4, we investigate a situation in which we maximize profit.

EXAMPLE 4   **Solving a Linear Programming Application**

A baker produces whole wheat bread and cheese bread to sell at the farmer's market. The whole wheat bread is denser and requires more baking time, whereas the cheese bread requires more labor. The baking times and average amount of labor per loaf are given in the table along with the profit for each loaf.

	Time to Bake	**Labor**	**Profit**
Wheat bread	1.5 hr	$\frac{1}{3}$ hr	$1.20
Cheese bread	1 hr	$\frac{1}{2}$ hr	$1.00

The oven space restricts the baker from baking more than 120 loaves. Furthermore, the amount of oven time for baking is no more than 165 hr and the amount of available labor is at most 55 hr. Determine the number of loaves of each type of bread that the baker should bake to maximize his profit. Assume that all loaves of bread produced are sold.

Solution:

Let x represent the number of loaves of wheat bread.

Let y represent the number of loaves of cheese bread.

$\text{Profit} = \left(\begin{array}{c}\text{Profit from}\\\text{wheat bread}\end{array}\right) + \left(\begin{array}{c}\text{Profit from}\\\text{cheese bread}\end{array}\right)$ **Step 1:** Write an objective function. In this example, we need to maximize profit.

$z = 1.20x + 1.00y$

Step 2: Write a system of constraints on the independent variables.

$x \geq 0$	Number of loaves of wheat bread cannot be negative.
$y \geq 0$	Number of loaves of cheese bread cannot be negative.
$x + y \leq 120$	Total number of loaves is no more than 120.
$1.5x + y \leq 165$	The total amount of baking time is no more than 165 hr.
$\frac{1}{3}x + \frac{1}{2}y \leq 55$	The total amount of available labor is at most 55 hr.

Step 3: Graph the feasible region and identify the vertices. Find the points of intersection between pairs of bounding lines:

$x + y = 120$
$\frac{1}{3}x + \frac{1}{2}y = 55$ Point of intersection (30, 90)

$x + y = 120$
$1.5x + y = 165$ Point of intersection (90, 30)

$1.5x + y = 165$
$y = 0$ Point of intersection (110, 0)

$\frac{1}{3}x + \frac{1}{2}y = 55$
$x = 0$ Point of intersection (0, 110)

$x = 0$
$y = 0$ Point of intersection (0, 0)

Point of Interest

Linear programming was first introduced by Russian mathematician Leonid Kantorovich. The technique was used in World War II to minimize costs to the army. Later in 1975, Kantorovich won the Nobel Prize in economics for his contributions to the theory of optimum allocation of resources.

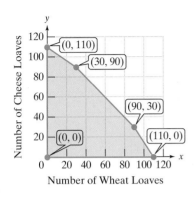

Number of Cheese Loaves vs Number of Wheat Loaves

Step 4: Evaluate the objective function at each vertex.

Profit: $z = 1.2x + y$

at $(0, 0)$ $z = 1.2(0) + (0) = \$0$

at $(0, 110)$ $z = 1.2(0) + (110) = \$110$

at $(30, 90)$ $z = 1.2(30) + (90) = \$126$

at $(90, 30)$ $z = 1.2(90) + (30) = \boxed{\$138}$

at $(110, 0)$ $z = 1.2(110) + (0) = \$132$

The profit will be maximized if the baker bakes 90 whole wheat loaves and 30 cheese loaves. The maximum profit is \$138.

Skill Practice 4   A manufacturer produces two sizes of leather handbags. It takes longer to cut and dye the leather for the smaller bag, but it takes more time sewing the larger bag. The production constraints and profit for each type of bag are given in the table.

	Cutting and Dying	Sewing	Profit
Large bag	0.6 hr	2 hr	\$30
Small bag	1 hr	1.5 hr	\$25

The machinery limits the number of bags produced to at most 1000 per week. If the company has 900 hr per week available for cutting and dying and 1800 hr available per week for sewing, determine the number of each type of bag that should be produced weekly to maximize profit. Assume that all bags produced are also sold.

Figure 5-31

To find the maximum or minimum value of an objective function, we evaluate the function at the vertices of the feasible region. It seems reasonable that the profit would be maximized at a point on the upper edge of the feasible region. These are the points in the feasible region where the combined values of x and y are the greatest.

The goal of Example 4 was to find the values of x and y that maximized the profit function $z = 1.2x + y$. To see why the profit z was maximized at a vertex of the feasible region, write the equation in slope-intercept form:

$$y = -1.2x + z$$

In this form, the objective function represents a family of parallel lines with slope -1.2 and y-intercept $(0, z)$. To maximize z, we want the line with the greatest y-intercept that still remains in contact with the feasible region. In Figure 5-31, we see that this occurs for the line passing through the point $(90, 30)$ as expected.

Answer

4. The maximum profit of \$28,000 is realized when the company produces 600 large bags and 400 small bags.

SECTION 5.6   Practice Exercises

Review Exercises

For Exercises 1–8, write an inequality to represent the given statement.

1. The sum of x and y is at most 70.

2. The sum of x and y is no more than 10.

3. The sum of three times x and 4 times y is no less than 60.

4. The sum of five times x and twice y is at least 54.

5. The value of y does not exceed three times the value of x.

6. The value of x is at least $\frac{2}{3}$ the value of y.

7. The value of x is more than 60 but not more than 80.

8. The value of y is at least 10, but less than 20.

Concept Connections

9. The process that maximizes or minimizes a function subject to linear constraints is called _____ programming.

10. The function to be optimized in a linear programming application is called the _____ function.

11. The region in the plane that represents the solution set to a system of constraints is called the _____ region.

12. The points of intersection of a feasible region are called the _____ of the region.

Objective 1: Write an Objective Function

13. A diner makes a profit of $0.80 for a cup of coffee and $1.10 for a cup of tea. Write an objective function $z = f(x, y)$ that represents the total profit for selling x cups of coffee and y cups of tea. (**See Example 1**)

14. An athlete burns 10 calories per minute running and 8 calories per minute lifting weights. Write an objective function $z = f(x, y)$ that represents the total number of calories burned by running for x minutes and lifting weights for y minutes.

15. A courier company makes deliveries with two different trucks. Truck A costs $0.62/mi to operate and truck B costs $0.50/mi to operate. Write an objective function $z = f(x, y)$ that represents the total cost for driving truck A for x miles and driving truck B for y miles.

16. The cost for an animal shelter to spay a female cat is $82 and the cost to neuter a male cat is $55. Write an objective function $z = f(x, y)$ that represents the total cost for spaying x female cats and neutering y male cats.

Objective 2: Solve a Linear Programming Application

For Exercises 17–20,

a. Determine the values of x and y that produce the maximum or minimum value of the objective function on the given feasible region.

b. Determine the maximum or minimum value of the objective function on the given feasible region.

17. Maximize: $z = 3x + 2y$

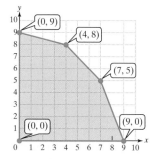

18. Maximize: $z = 1.8x + 2.2y$

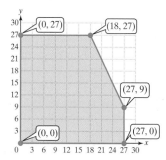

19. Minimize: $z = 1000x + 900y$

20. Minimize: $z = 6x + 9y$

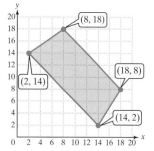

For Exercises 21–26,

a. For the given constraints, graph the feasible region and identify the vertices.

b. Determine the values of x and y that produce the maximum or minimum value of the objective function on the feasible region.

c. Determine the maximum or minimum value of the objective function on the feasible region.

21. $x \geq 0,\ y \geq 0$

$x + y \leq 60$

$y \leq 2x$

Maximize: $z = 250x + 150y$

22. $x \geq 0,\ y \geq 0$

$2x + y \leq 40$

$x + 2y \leq 50$

Maximize: $z = 9.2x + 8.1y$

23. $x \geq 0,\ y \geq 0$

$3x + y \geq 50$

$2x + y \geq 40$

Minimize: $z = 3x + 2y$

24. $x \geq 0,\ y \geq 0$

$4x + 3y \geq 60$

$2x + 3y \geq 36$

Minimize: $z = 4.5x + 6y$

25. $x \geq 0,\ y \geq 0$

$x \leq 36$

$y \leq 40$

$x + y \leq 48$

Maximize: $z = 150x + 90y$

26. $x \geq 0,\ y \geq 0$

$x \leq 10$

$y \leq 8$

$x + y \leq 12$

Maximize: $z = 50x + 70y$

For Exercises 27–28, use the given constraints to find the maximum value of the objective function and the ordered pair (x, y) that produces the maximum value.

27. $x \geq 0,\ y \geq 0$

$3x + 4y \leq 48$

$2x + y \leq 22$

$y \leq 9$

a. Maximize: $z = 100x + 120y$

b. Maximize: $z = 100x + 140y$

28. $x \geq 0,\ y \geq 0$

$x + y \leq 20$

$x + 2y \leq 36$

$x \leq 14$

a. Maximize: $z = 12x + 15y$

b. Maximize: $z = 15x + 12y$

29. A furniture manufacturer builds tables. The cost for materials and labor to build a kitchen table is $240 and the profit is $160. The cost to build a dining room table is $320 and the profit is $240. (**See Examples 2–3**)

Let x represent the number of kitchen tables produced per month. Let y represent the number of dining room tables produced per month.

a. Write an objective function representing the monthly profit for producing and selling x kitchen tables and y dining room tables.

b. The manufacturing process is subject to the following constraints. Write a system of inequalities representing the constraints.

- The number of each type of table cannot be negative.
- Due to labor and equipment restrictions, the company can build at most 120 kitchen tables.
- The company can build at most 90 dining room tables.
- The company does not want to exceed a monthly cost of $48,000.

c. Graph the system of inequalities represented by the constraints.

d. Find the vertices of the feasible region.

e. Test the objective function at each vertex.

f. How many kitchen tables and how many dining room tables should be produced to maximize profit? (Assume that all tables produced will be sold.)

g. What is the maximum profit?

30. Josh makes $24/hr tutoring chemistry and $20/hr tutoring math.

Let x represent the number of hours per week he spends tutoring chemistry. Let y represent the number of hours per week he spends tutoring math.

a. Write an objective function representing his weekly income for tutoring x hours of chemistry and y hours of math.

b. The time that Josh devotes to tutoring is limited by the following constraints. Write a system of inequalities representing the constraints.

- The number of hours spent tutoring each subject cannot be negative.
- Due to the academic demands of his own classes he tutors at most 18 hr per week.
- The tutoring center requires that he tutors math at least 4 hr per week.
- The demand for math tutors is greater than the demand for chemistry tutors. Therefore, the number of hours he spends tutoring math must be at least twice the number of hours he spends tutoring chemistry.

c. Graph the system of inequalities represented by the constraints.

d. Find the vertices of the feasible region.

e. Test the objective function at each vertex.

f. How many hours tutoring math and how many hours tutoring chemistry should Josh work to maximize his income?

g. What is the maximum income?

h. Explain why Josh's maximum income is found at a point on the line $x + y = 18$.

31. A plant nursery sells two sizes of oak trees to landscapers. Large trees cost the nursery $120 from the grower. Small trees cost the nursery $80. The profit for each large tree sold is $35 and the profit for each small tree sold is $30. The monthly demand is at most 400 oak trees. Furthermore, the nursery does not want to allocate more than $43,200 each month on inventory for oak trees.

   a. Determine the number of large oak trees and the number of small oak trees that the nursery should have in its inventory each month to maximize profit. (Assume that all trees in inventory are sold.)

   b. What is the maximum profit?

   c. If the profit on large trees were $50, and the profit on small trees remained the same, then how many of each should the nursery have to maximize profit?

33. A paving company delivers gravel for a road construction project. The company has a large truck and a small truck. The large truck has a greater capacity, but costs more for fuel to operate. The load capacity and cost to operate each truck per load are given in the table.

	Load Capacity	Cost per Load
Small truck	18 yd^3	$120
Large truck	24 yd^3	$150

The company must deliver at least 288 yd^3 of gravel to stay on schedule. Furthermore, the large truck takes longer to load and cannot make as many trips as the small truck. As a result, the number of trips made by the large truck is at most $\frac{3}{4}$ times the number of trips made by the small truck.

   a. Determine the number of trips that should be made by the large truck and the number of trips that should be made by the small truck to minimize cost.

   b. What is the minimum cost to deliver gravel under these constraints?

35. A manufacturer produces two models of a gas grill. Grill A requires 1 hr for assembly and 0.4 hr for packaging. Grill B requires 1.2 hr for assembly and 0.6 hr for packaging. The production information and profit for each grill are given in the table. (**See Example 4**)

	Assembly	Packaging	Profit
Grill A	1 hr	0.4 hr	$90
Grill B	1.2 hr	0.6 hr	$120

The manufacturer has 1200 hr of labor available for assembly and 540 hr of labor available for packaging.

   a. Determine the number of grill A units and the number of grill B units that should be produced to maximize profit assuming that all grills will be sold.

   b. What is the maximum profit under these constraints?

   c. If the profit on grill A units is $110 and the profit on grill B units is unchanged, how many of each type of grill unit should the manufacturer produce to maximize profit?

32. A sporting goods store sells two types of exercise bikes. The deluxe model costs the store $540 from the manufacturer and the standard model costs the store $420 from the manufacturer. The profit that the store makes on the deluxe model is $180 and the profit on the standard model is $120. The monthly demand for exercise bikes is at most 30. Furthermore, the store manager does not want to spend more than $14,040 on inventory for exercise bikes.

   a. Determine the number of deluxe models and the number of standard models that the store should have in its inventory each month to maximize profit. (Assume that all exercise bikes in inventory are sold.)

   b. What is the maximum profit?

   c. If the profit on the deluxe bikes were $150 and the profit on the standard bikes remained the same, how many of each should the store have to maximize profit?

34. A large department store needs at least 3600 labor hours covered per week. It employs full-time staff 40 hr/wk and part-time staff 25 hr/wk. The cost to employ a full-time staff member is more because the company pays benefits such as health care and life insurance.

	Hours per Week	Cost per Hour
Full time	40 hr	$20
Part time	25 hr	$12

The store manager also knows that to make the store run efficiently, the number of full-time employees must be at least 1.25 times the number of part-time employees.

   a. Determine the number of full-time employees and the number of part-time employees that should be used to minimize the weekly labor cost.

   b. What is the minimum weekly cost to staff the store under these constraints?

36. A manufacturer produces two models of patio furniture. Model A requires 2 hr for assembly and 1.2 hr for painting. Model B requires 3 hr for assembly and 1.5 hr for painting. The production information and profit for selling each model are given in the table.

	Assembly	Painting	Profit
Model A	2 hr	1.2 hr	$150
Model B	3 hr	1.5 hr	$200

The manufacturer has 1200 hr of labor available for assembly and 660 hr of labor available for painting.

   a. Determine the number of model A units and the number of model B units that should be produced to maximize profit assuming that all furniture will be sold.

   b. What is the maximum profit under these constraints?

   c. If the profit on model A units is $180 and the profit on model B units remains the same, how many of each type should the manufacturer produce to maximize profit?

37. A farmer has 1200 acres of land and plans to plant corn and soybeans. The input cost (cost of seed, fertilizer, herbicide, and insecticide) for 1 acre for each crop is given in the table along with the cost of machinery and labor. The profit for 1 acre of each crop is given in the last column.

	Input Cost per Acre	Labor/Machinery Cost per Acre	Profit per Acre
Corn	$180	$80	$120
Soybeans	$120	$100	$100

Suppose the farmer has budgeted a maximum of $198,000 for input costs and a maximum of $110,000 for labor and machinery.

a. Determine the number of acres of each crop that the farmer should plant to maximize profit. (Assume that all crops will be sold.)

b. What is the maximum profit?

c. If the profit per acre were reversed between the two crops (that is, $100 per acre for corn and $120 per acre for soybeans), how many acres of each crop should be planted to maximize profit?

38. To protect soil from erosion, some farmers plant winter cover crops such as winter wheat and rye. In addition to conserving soil, cover crops often increase crop yields in the row crops that follow in spring and summer. Suppose that a farmer has 800 acres of land and plans to plant winter wheat and rye. The input cost for 1 acre for each crop is given in the table along with the cost for machinery and labor. The profit for 1 acre of each crop is given in the last column.

	Input Cost per Acre	Labor/Machinery Cost per Acre	Profit per Acre
Wheat	$90	$50	$42
Rye	$120	$40	$35

Suppose the farmer has budgeted a maximum of $90,000 for input costs and a maximum of $36,000 for labor and machinery.

a. Determine the number of acres of each crop that the farmer should plant to maximize profit. (Assume that all crops will be sold.)

b. What is the maximum profit?

c. If the profit per acre for wheat were $40 and the profit per acre for rye were $45, how many acres of each crop should be planted to maximize profit?

Write About It

39. What is the purpose of linear programming?

41. How is the feasible region determined?

40. What is an objective function?

42. If an optimal value exists for an objective function, it exists at one of the vertices of the feasible region. Explain how to find the vertices.

CHAPTER 5   KEY CONCEPTS

SECTION 5.1 Systems of Linear Equations in Two Variables and Applications	Reference
Two or more linear equations taken together form a **system of linear equations.** A **solution** to a system of equations in two variables is an ordered pair that is a solution to each individual equation. Graphically, this is a point of intersection of the graphs of the equations.	p. 522
The substitution method and the addition method are often used to solve a system of linear equations in two variables.	pp. 523, 524
A system of linear equations will have no solution if the equations in the system represent parallel lines. In such a case, we say that the system is **inconsistent.**	p. 523
A system of linear equations will have infinitely many solutions if the equations represent the same line. In such a case, we say that the equations are **dependent.**	p. 523
SECTION 5.2 Systems of Linear Equations in Three Variables and Applications	Reference
A **linear equation in three variables** is an equation that can be written in the form $$Ax + By + Cz = D$$ where A, B, and C are not all zero.	p. 535
A solution to a system of linear equations in three variables is an **ordered triple** (x, y, z) that satisfies each equation in the system. Geometrically, a solution is a point of intersection of the planes represented by the equations in the system.	p. 536

SECTION 5.3 Partial Fraction Decomposition	Reference
Partial fraction decomposition is used to write a rational expression as a sum of simpler fractions.	p. 547
There are two basic parts to find the partial fraction decomposition of a rational expression.	p. 548
I. Factor the denominator of the expression into linear factors and quadratic factors that are not further factorable over the integers. Then set up the "form" or "structure" for the partial fraction decomposition into simpler fractions.	
II. Next, multiply both sides of the equation by the LCD. Then set up a system of linear equations to find the coefficients of the terms in the numerator of each fraction.	
Note: The numerator of the original rational expression must be of lesser degree than the denominator. If this is not the case, first use long division.	

SECTION 5.4 Systems of Nonlinear Equations in Two Variables	Reference
A **nonlinear system of equations** is a system in which one or more equations is nonlinear.	p. 556
The substitution method is often used to solve a nonlinear system of equations.	p. 557
In some cases, the addition method can be used provided that the terms containing the corresponding variables are like terms.	p. 558

SECTION 5.5 Inequalities and Systems of Inequalities in Two Variables	Reference
An inequality of the form $Ax + By < C$, where A and B are not both zero, is called a **linear inequality in two variables.** (The symbols $>$, $\leq$, and $\geq$ can be used in place of $<$ in the definition.)	p. 565
The basic steps to solve a linear inequality in two variables are as follows.	p. 566
1. Graph the related equation. The resulting line is drawn as a dashed line if the inequality is strict, and is otherwise drawn as a solid line.	
2. Select a test point from either side of the line. If the ordered pair makes the original inequality true, then shade the half-plane from which the point was taken. Otherwise, shade the other half-plane.	
A nonlinear inequality in two variables is solved using the same basic procedure.	p. 569
Two or more inequalities in two variables make up a system of inequalities in two variables. The solution set to the system is the region of overlap (intersection) of the solution sets of the individual inequalities.	p. 569

SECTION 5.6 Linear Programming	Reference
A process called **linear programming** enables us to maximize or minimize a function under specified constraints. The function to be maximized or minimized is called the **objective function.**	p. 577
The steps to solve a linear programming application are outlined here.	p. 579
Step 1 Write an objective function, $z = f(x, y)$.	
Step 2 Write a system of inequalities defining the constraints on x and y.	
Step 3 Graph the feasible region and identify the vertices.	
Step 4 Evaluate the objective function at each vertex of the feasible region. Use the results to identify the values of x and y that optimize the objective function and identify the optimal value of z.	

Expanded Chapter Summary available at www.mhhe.com/millerca.

CHAPTER 5   Review Exercises

SECTION 5.1

1. Determine if the ordered pair is a solution to the system.

$$2x - 3y = 0$$
$$-5x + 6y = -1$$

a. $\left(1, \dfrac{2}{3}\right)$ **b.** $(6, 4)$

For Exercises 2–3, based on the slope-intercept form of the equations, determine the number of solutions to the system.

2. $y = -\dfrac{3}{5}x - 4$

$y = -\dfrac{3}{5}x + 1$

3. $y = 2x + 6$

$y = \dfrac{1}{2}x - 6$

For Exercises 4–8, solve the system by using any method. If the system does not have one unique solution, state whether the system is inconsistent, or whether the equations are dependent.

4. $4x - y = 7$
$-2x + 5y = 19$

5. $5(x - y) = 19 - 2y$
$0.2x + 0.7y = -1.7$

6. $9x - 2y = 4$
$2x + 4y = 7$

7. $\frac{1}{10}x - \frac{1}{2}y = 1$
$2x = 10y + 6$

8. $y = \frac{3}{4}x$
$4(y - x) = -x$

9. Shenika wants to monitor her daily calcium intake. One day she had 3 cups of milk and 1 cup of cooked spinach for a total of 1140 mg of calcium. The next day, she had 2 cups of milk and $1\frac{1}{2}$ cups of cooked spinach for a total of 960 mg of calcium. How much calcium is in 1 cup of milk and how much is in 1 cup of cooked spinach?

10. How many liters of a 40% acid mixture and how many liters of a 10% acid mixture should be mixed to obtain 20 L of a 22% acid mixture?

11. A plane can travel 960 mi in 2 hr with a tail wind. The return trip against the wind takes 2 hr and 40 min. Find the speed of the plane in still air and the speed of the wind.

12. A fishing boat captain charges $250 per day for an excursion. His fixed monthly expenses are $1200 for insurance, rent for the dock, and minor office expenses. He also has variable costs of $100 per excursion to cover gasoline, bait, and other equipment.

   a. Write a linear cost function representing the cost $C(x)$ (in $) for the fishing boat captain to run x excursions per month.

b. Write a linear revenue function representing the revenue $R(x)$ (in $) for x excursions per month.

c. Determine the number of excursions per month for the captain to break even.

d. If 18 excursions are run in a given month, how much money will the fishing boat captain earn or lose?

SECTION 5.2

For Exercises 13–16, solve the system of equations. If a system does not have one unique solution, determine the number of solutions to the system.

13. $3a - 4b + 2c = -17$
$2a + 3b + c = 1$
$4a + b - 3c = 7$

14. $6x = 24 - 5y$
$14 = 7z - 3y$
$4x - 3z = 10$

15. $x + 2y + z = 5$
$x + y - z = 1$
$4x + 7y + 2z = 16$

16. $u + v + 2w = 1$
$2v - 5w = 2$
$3u + 5v + w = 1$

17. An arena that hosts sporting events and concerts has three sections for three levels of seating. For a basketball game, seats in Section A cost $90, seats in Section B cost $65, and seats in Section C cost $40. The number of seats in Section C equals the number of seats in Sections A and B combined. The arena holds 12,000 seats and the game is sold out. If the total revenue from ticket sales is $655,000, determine the number of seats in each section.

18. Emily receives an inheritance of $20,000 and decides to invest the money. She puts some money in her savings account that earns 1.5% simple interest per year. The remaining money is invested in a bond fund that returns 4.5% and a stock fund that returns 6.2%. She makes a total of $942 at the end of 1 yr. If she invested twice as much in the bond fund as the stock fund, determine the amount that she invested in each fund.

For Exercises 19–20, use a system of linear equations in three variables to find an equation of the form $y = ax^2 + bx + c$ that defines the parabola through the points.

19. $(-1, -4), (1, 6), (3, 8)$ 20. $(1, -2), (2, 1), (3, 10)$

SECTION 5.3

For Exercises 21–26, set up the form for the partial fraction decomposition. Do not solve for A, B, C, and so on.

21. $\dfrac{-x - 11}{(x + 2)(x - 1)}$

22. $\dfrac{5x + 22}{x^2 + 8x + 16}$

23. $\dfrac{7x^2 + 19x + 15}{2x^3 + 3x^2}$

24. $\dfrac{2x^2 + x - 10}{x^3 + 5x}$

25. $\dfrac{2x^3 - x^2 + 8x - 16}{x^4 + 5x^2 + 4}$

26. $\dfrac{4x^4 - 3x^2 + 2x + 5}{x(2x + 5)^3(x^2 + 2)^2}$

27. If the numerator of a rational expression has degree greater than or equal to the degree of the denominator, what must be done first to perform the partial fraction decomposition?

For Exercises 28–32, perform the partial fraction decomposition.

28. $\dfrac{-x - 11}{(x + 2)(x - 1)}$ **29.** $\dfrac{5x + 22}{x^2 + 8x + 16}$

30. $\dfrac{2x^4 + 7x^3 + 13x^2 + 19x + 15}{2x^3 + 3x^2}$

31. $\dfrac{2x^2 + x - 10}{x^3 + 5x}$ **32.** $\dfrac{2x^3 - x^2 + 8x - 16}{x^4 + 5x^2 + 4}$

SECTION 5.4

For Exercises 33–34,

a. Graph the equations.

b. Solve the system.

33. $y - x^2 = 1$ **34.** $y = \sqrt{x - 1}$
$\quad\ x - y = -3$ $\quad\ x^2 + y^2 = 5$

For Exercises 35–37, solve the system.

35. $3x^2 - y^2 = -4$ **36.** $2x^2 - xy = 24$
$\quad\ \ x^2 + 2y^2 = 36$ $\quad\ \ x^2 + 3xy = -9$

37. $y = \dfrac{8}{x}$
$\quad\ y = \sqrt{x}$

38. The sum of the squares of two negative numbers is 97 and the difference of their squares is 65. Find the numbers.

39. The ratio of two numbers is 4 to 3. The sum of the squares of the numbers is 100. Find the numbers.

40. The hypotenuse of a right triangle is $\sqrt{74}$ ft and the sum of the lengths of the legs is 12 ft. Find the lengths of the legs.

41. A rectangular billboard has a perimeter of 72 ft and an area of 288 ft². Find the dimensions of the billboard.

SECTION 5.5

42. Graph the solution set to the inequality.

   a. $3x + 4y \le 8$

   b. $3x + 4y > 8$

43. Graph the solution set to the inequality.

   a. $y < (x - 4)^2$

   b. $y \ge (x - 4)^2$

For Exercises 44–48, graph the solution set.

44. $5(x + y) \ge 8x + 15$ **45.** $x \le 3.5$

46. $-\dfrac{3}{2}y + 1 < 4$ **47.** $x^2 + (y + 2)^2 < 4$

48. $|y| > 2$

49. Determine if the given ordered pair is a solution to the system of inequalities.

$$x + 2y < 4$$
$$3x - 4y \ge 6$$

   a. $(0, 1)$ **b.** $(1, -4)$

For Exercises 50–53, graph the solution set. If there is no solution, indicate that the solution set is the empty set.

50. $y > \dfrac{1}{2}x + 1$ **51.** $x^2 + y^2 \le 9$
$\quad\ 3x + 2y < 4$ $\quad\ (x - 1)^2 + y^2 \ge 4$

52. $y \ge x^2 - 3$ **53.** $y > e^x$
$\quad\ y > 1$ $\quad\ y < -x^2 - 1$
$\quad\ x + y \le 3$

54. Let x represent the number of hours that Gordon spends tutoring math, and let y represent the number of hours that he spends tutoring English. For parts (a)–(d), write an inequality to represent the given statement.

   a. Gordon has at most 12 hr to tutor per week.

   b. The amount of time that Gordon spends tutoring English is at least twice the amount of time he spends tutoring math.

   c. The number of hours spent tutoring math cannot be negative.

   d. The number of hours spent tutoring English cannot be negative.

   e. Graph the solution set to the system of inequalities from parts (a)–(d).

SECTION 5.6

55. At a home store, one sheet of $\frac{3}{8}$-in. sanded pine plywood costs \$24. One sheet of $\frac{1}{4}$-in. sanded pine plywood costs \$20. Write an objective function $z = f(x, y)$ that represents the total cost for x $\frac{3}{8}$-in. sheets and y $\frac{1}{4}$-in. sheets.

56. For the feasible region given and the objective function $z = 36x + 50y$,

   a. Determine the values of x and y that produce the maximum value of the objective function.

   b. Determine the maximum value of the objective function.

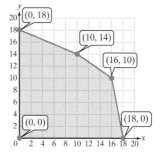

57. For the given constraints and the objective function, $z = 55x + 40y$,

    a. Graph the feasible region and identify the vertices.

$$x \geq 0, y \geq 0$$
$$2x + y \geq 18$$
$$5x + 4y \geq 60$$

    b. Determine the values of x and y that produce the minimum value of the objective function on the feasible region.

    c. Determine the minimum value of the objective function on the feasible region.

58. A fitness instructor wants to mix two brands of protein powder to form a blend that limits the amount of fat and carbohydrate but maximizes the amount of fiber.

The nutritional information is given in the table for a single scoop of protein powder.

	Fat	Carbohydrates	Fiber
Brand A	3 g	3 g	10 g
Brand B	2 g	4 g	8 g

Suppose that the fitness instructor wants to make at most 180 scoops of the mixture. She also wants to limit the amount of fat to 480 g and she wants to limit the amount of carbohydrate to 696 g.

    a. Determine the number of scoops of each type of powder that will maximum the amount of fiber.

    b. What is the maximum amount of fiber?

    c. If the fiber content were reversed between the two brands (that is, 8 g for brand A and 10 g for brand B), then how much of each type of protein powder should be used to maximize the amount of fiber?

CHAPTER 5 Test

For Exercises 1–3, determine if the ordered pair or ordered triple is a solution to the system.

1. $x - 5y = -3$
    $y = 2x - 12$
    a. $(7, 2)$
    b. $(-3, 0)$

2. $2x - 3y + z = -5$
    $5x + y - 3z = -18$
    $-x + 2y + 5z = 8$
    a. $(0, 1, -2)$
    b. $(-3, 0, 1)$

3. $2x - 4y < 9$
    $-3x + y \geq 4$
    a. $(-6, 1)$
    b. $(1, 4)$

For Exercises 4–14, solve the system.

4. $x = 5 - 4y$
    $-3x + 7y = 4$

5. $0.2x = 0.35y - 2.5$
    $0.16x + 0.5y = 5.8$

6. $x - \dfrac{2}{5}y = \dfrac{3}{10}$
    $5x = 2y + \dfrac{3}{2}$

7. $7(x - y) = 3 - 5y$
    $4(3x - y) = -2x$

8. $a + 6b + 3c = -14$
    $2a + b - 2c = -8$
    $-3a + 2b + c = -8$

9. $x + 4z = 10$
    $3y - 2z = 9$
    $2x + 5y = 21$

10. $2x - y + z = -3$
    $x - 3y = 2$
    $x + 2y + z = -7$

11. $(x - 4)^2 + y^2 = 25$
    $x - y = 3$

12. $5x^2 + y^2 = 14$
    $x^2 - 2y^2 = -17$

13. $2xy - y^2 = -24$
    $-3xy + 2y^2 = 38$

14. $\dfrac{1}{x + 3} - \dfrac{2}{y - 1} = -7$

$\dfrac{3}{x + 3} + \dfrac{1}{y - 1} = 7$

15. At a candy and nut shop, the manager wants to make a nut mixture that is 56% peanuts. How many pounds of peanuts must be added to an existing mixture of 45% peanuts to make 20 lb of a mixture that is 56% peanuts?

16. Two runners begin at the same point on a 400-m track. If they run in opposite directions they pass each other in 40 sec. If they run in the same direction, they will meet again in 200 sec. Find the speed of each runner.

17. Dylan invests $15,000 in three different stocks. One stock is very risky and after 1 yr loses 8%. The second stock returns 3.2%, and a third stock returns 5.8%. At the end of 1 yr, the total return is $274. If he invested $2000 more in the second stock than in the third stock, determine the amount he invested in each stock.

18. The difference of two positive numbers is 3 and the difference of their squares is 33. Find the numbers.

19. A rectangular television screen has a perimeter of 154 in. and an area of 1452 in.^{2}. Find the dimensions of the screen.

20. Use a system of linear equations in three variables to find an equation of the form $y = ax^2 + bx + c$ that defines the parabola through the points $(1, -1)$, $(2, 1)$, and $(-1, 7)$.

For Exercises 21–22, set up the form for the partial fraction decomposition. Do not solve for A, B, C, and so on.

21. $\dfrac{-15x + 15}{3x^2 + x - 2}$

22. $\dfrac{5x^6 + 3x^5 - 4x^3 + x - 3}{x^3(x - 3)(x^2 + 5x + 1)^2}$

For Exercises 23–27, perform the partial fraction decomposition.

23. $\dfrac{-12x - 29}{2x^2 + 11x + 15}$

24. $\dfrac{6x + 8}{x^2 + 4x + 4}$

25. $\dfrac{x^4 - 6x^3 + 4x^2 + 20x - 32}{x^3 - 4x^2}$

26. $\dfrac{x^2 - 2x - 21}{x^3 + 7x}$

27. $\dfrac{7x^3 + 4x^2 + 63x + 15}{x^4 + 11x^2 + 18}$

For Exercises 28–32, graph the solution set.

28. $2(x + y) > 6 - y$

29. $(x + 3)^2 + y^2 \geq 9$

30. $|x| < 4$

31. $x + y \leq 4$
$2x - y > -2$

32. $y \leq -x^2 + 5$
$y > 1$
$x + y \leq 3$

33. A donut shop makes a profit of $2.40 on a dozen donuts and $0.55 per muffin. Write an objective function $z = f(x, y)$ that represents the total profit for selling x dozen donuts and y muffins.

34. For the feasible region given and the objective function $z = 4x + 5y$,

   a. Determine the values of x and y that produce the minimum value of the objective function on the feasible region.

   b. Determine the minimum value of the objective function on the feasible region.

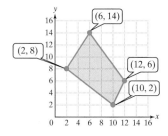

35. For the given constraints and objective function, $z = 600x + 850y$,

   a. Graph the feasible region and identify the vertices.

   $x \geq 0,\ y \geq 0$
   $x + y \leq 48$
   $y \leq 3x$

   b. Determine the values of x and y that produce the maximum value of the objective function on the feasible region.

   c. Determine the maximum value of the objective function on the feasible region.

36. A weight lifter wants to mix two types of protein powder. One is a whey protein and one is a soy protein. The fat, carbohydrate, and protein content (in grams) for 1 scoop of each powder is given in the table.

	Fat	Carbohydrates	Protein
Whey	3 g	3 g	20 g
Soy	2 g	4 g	18 g

Suppose that the weight lifter wants to make at most 60 scoops of a protein powder mixture. Furthermore, he wants to limit the total fat content to at most 150 g and the total carbohydrate content to at most 216 g.

   a. Determine the number of scoops of each type of powder that will maximize the total protein content under these constraints.

   b. What is the maximum total protein content?

   c. If the protein content were reversed between the two brands (that is, 18 g for the whey protein and 20 g for the soy protein), then how much of each type of protein powder should be used to maximize the amount of protein?

CHAPTER 5 Cumulative Review Exercises

For Exercises 1–5, solve the equation.

1. $2x(x + 2) = 5x + 7$

2. $\sqrt{2t + 8} - t = 4$

3. $(x^2 - 4)^2 - 7(x^2 - 4) - 60 = 0$

4. $\log_2(x - 4) = \log_2(x + 1) + 3$

5. $50e^{2x+1} = 2000$

For Exercises 6–7, solve the inequality. Write the solution set in interval notation.

6. $\dfrac{x + 4}{x - 2} \leq 1$

7. $3|x + 2| - 1 > 8$

8. Find the partial fraction decomposition. $\dfrac{-5x + 17}{x^2 - 6x + 9}$

9. Given $f(x) = 2x^2 - 3x$ and $g(x) = 5x + 1$,

    a. Find $(f \circ g)(x)$.

    b. Find $(g \circ f)(x)$.

10. Given $f(x) = \sqrt[3]{x - 2}$, write an equation for $f^{-1}(x)$.

11. Use a calculator to approximate the value of $\log_5 256$. Round to 4 decimal places.

12. Given $f(x) = -\frac{1}{2}x^3 + 4x^2 + 2$, find the average rate of change on the interval $[1, 3]$.

13. Write an equation of the line perpendicular to the line $x + 3y = 6$ and passing through the point $(2, -1)$.

14. Find all zeros of $f(x) = x^4 - 2x^3 + 10x^2 - 18x + 9$ and state the multiplicity of each zero.

For Exercises 15–17,

a. Graph the function.

b. Write the domain in interval notation.

c. Write the range in interval notation.

15. $f(x) = 2|x - 1| - 3$

16. $f(x) = \ln(x - 3)$

17. $f(x) = -x^2(x - 1)(x + 2)^2$

For Exercises 18–20, solve the system.

18. $3x = 5y + 1$

    $y = \frac{3}{5}x + 4$

19. $5a - 2b + 3c = 10$

    $-3a + b - 2c = -7$

    $a + 4b - 4c = -3$

20. $-2x^2 + 3y^2 = 10$

    $5x^2 + 2y^2 = 13$

21. Graph the solution set to the system of inequalities.

$$3x - y \leq 1$$
$$x + 2y < 4$$

22. Given $f(x) = -x^2 + 5x + 1$, find the difference quotient.

23. Simplify. $\dfrac{10}{\sqrt{5x}} + \dfrac{4\sqrt{5x}}{x}$

24. Shen invested $8000 and after 5 yr, the account is worth $10,907.40.

    a. Write a model of the form $A(t) = Pe^{rt}$, where $A(t)$ represents the amount (in $) in the account if P dollars in principal is invested at interest rate r for t years.

    b. How long will it take for the investment to double? Round to 1 decimal place.

25. The variable y varies jointly as x and the square of z. If y is 36 when x is 10 and z is 3, find the value of y when $x = 12$ and z is 4.

Matrices and Determinants and Applications

Chapter Outline

For matters of security, e-mail messages, websites, and other electronic media often use encryption techniques to encode data into an obscure form. This prevents those who do not know the code from understanding what has been transmitted. A computer program can encrypt words by using a matrix (a two-dimensional array) to encode the message, and then use the inverse of that matrix to decode it.

In this chapter, we will use matrices in a variety of ways. Matrices can be used to model systems of linear equations. Furthermore, a variety of techniques involving the algebra and manipulation of matrices can be used to solve the systems. The first two techniques are called Gaussian elimination and Gauss-Jordan elimination. These methods reduce a system of equations to a simpler system of equations so that the solution can be found by inspection. Next, we use the inverse of a matrix to solve a related matrix equation. Finally, we present Cramer's rule. This method provides convenient formulas to solve a system of linear equations based on the coefficients of the system.

OBJECTIVES

1. Write an Augmented Matrix
2. Use Elementary Row Operations
3. Use Gaussian Elimination and Gauss-Jordan Elimination

1. Write an Augmented Matrix

The data in Table 6-1 represent the body mass index (BMI) for people of selected heights and weights. The National Institutes of Health suggests that a BMI should ideally be between 18.5 and 24.9. A table of data values such as Table 6-1 can be represented as a rectangular array of elements called a **matrix.**

Table 6-1 Body Mass Index

Weight / Height	140 lb	160 lb	180 lb	200 lb
5′7″	21.9	25.1	28.2	31.3
5′10″	20.1	23.0	25.8	28.7
6′1″	18.5	21.1	23.7	26.4

$$\xrightarrow{\text{matrix}} \begin{bmatrix} 21.9 & 25.1 & 28.2 & 31.3 \\ 20.1 & 23.0 & 25.8 & 28.7 \\ 18.5 & 21.1 & 23.7 & 26.4 \end{bmatrix}$$

(*Source*: National Institutes of Health, www.nih.gov)

A matrix can be used to represent a system of linear equations written in standard form. To do so, we extract the coefficients of each term in the equation to form an **augmented matrix.** For example:

System of Equations

$$\begin{aligned} 3x + 2y &= 5 \\ x - y + 3z &= 1 \\ 2x + y + z &= 4 \end{aligned}$$

Augmented Matrix

$$\begin{bmatrix} 3 & 2 & 0 & | & 5 \\ 1 & -1 & 3 & | & 1 \\ 2 & 1 & 1 & | & 4 \end{bmatrix}$$

The vertical bar within the augmented matrix separates the coefficients of the variable terms in the equations from the constant terms.

EXAMPLE 1 Writing and Interpreting an Augmented Matrix

a. Write the augmented matrix for the system.
$$\begin{aligned} 2x &= 5y + 5 \\ 3(x + y) &= 17 + y \end{aligned}$$

b. Write a system of linear equations represented by the augmented matrix.
$$\begin{bmatrix} 1 & 0 & 0 & | & 6 \\ 0 & 1 & 0 & | & -10 \\ 0 & 0 & 1 & | & 4 \end{bmatrix}$$

Solution:

a. Write each equation in standard form.
$$\begin{aligned} 2x &= 5y + 5 &\longrightarrow\quad 2x - 5y &= 5 \\ 3(x + y) &= 17 + y &\longrightarrow\quad 3x + 2y &= 17 \end{aligned} \left.\right\} \xrightarrow[\text{matrix}]{\text{augmented}} \begin{bmatrix} 2 & -5 & | & 5 \\ 3 & 2 & | & 17 \end{bmatrix}$$

b. $\begin{bmatrix} 1 & 0 & 0 & | & 6 \\ 0 & 1 & 0 & | & -10 \\ 0 & 0 & 1 & | & 4 \end{bmatrix}$ $\begin{aligned} &\longrightarrow x + 0y + 0z = 6 \\ &\longrightarrow 0x + y + 0z = -10 \\ &\longrightarrow 0x + 0y + z = 4 \end{aligned}$ or simply $\begin{aligned} x &= 6 \\ y &= -10 \\ z &= 4 \end{aligned}$

Skill Practice 1

a. Write the augmented matrix.
$$\begin{aligned} 7x &= 9 + 2y \\ 2(x - y) &= 4 \end{aligned}$$

b. Write a system of linear equations represented $\begin{bmatrix} 1 & 0 & | & -8 \\ 0 & 1 & | & 3 \end{bmatrix}$ by the augmented matrix.

Answers

1. a. $\begin{bmatrix} 7 & -2 & | & 9 \\ 2 & -2 & | & 4 \end{bmatrix}$

b. $x = -8, y = 3$

2. Use Elementary Row Operations

We can use an augmented matrix to solve a system of linear equations in much the same way as we use the addition method. When using the addition method, notice that the following operations produce an equivalent system of equations.

- Interchange two equations.

  Example: $\begin{aligned} -3x - 5y &= -13 \\ x + 2y &= 5 \end{aligned} \quad \xrightarrow[\text{equations.}]{\text{Interchange}} \quad \begin{aligned} x + 2y &= 5 \\ -3x - 5y &= -13 \end{aligned}$

- Multiply an equation by a nonzero constant.

  Example: $\begin{aligned} x + 2y &= 5 \\ -3x - 5y &= -13 \end{aligned} \quad \xrightarrow{\text{Multiply by 3.}} \quad \begin{aligned} 3x + 6y &= 15 \\ -3x - 5y &= -13 \end{aligned}$

- Add a multiple of one equation to another equation.

  Example: $\begin{aligned} x + 2y &= 5 \\ -3x - 5y &= -13 \end{aligned} \quad \xrightarrow{\text{Multiply by 3.}} \quad \left.\begin{aligned} 3x + 6y &= 15 \\ -3x - 5y &= -13 \end{aligned}\right\} \begin{aligned}\text{Add the}\\\text{equations.}\end{aligned}$
  $$y = 2$$

These same operations performed on a matrix are called **elementary row operations.**

Elementary Row Operations

1. Interchange two rows.

  Example: $\begin{bmatrix} -3 & -5 & | & -13 \\ 1 & 2 & | & 5 \end{bmatrix} \xrightarrow[\substack{\text{Interchange rows} \\ \text{1 and 2.}}]{R_1 \Leftrightarrow R_2} \begin{bmatrix} 1 & 2 & | & 5 \\ -3 & -5 & | & -13 \end{bmatrix}$

2. Multiply a row by a nonzero constant.

  Example: $\begin{bmatrix} 1 & 2 & | & 5 \\ -3 & -5 & | & -13 \end{bmatrix} \xrightarrow[\substack{\text{Multiply} \\ \text{row 1 by 3.}}]{3R_1 \to R_1} \begin{bmatrix} 3 & 6 & | & 15 \\ -3 & -5 & | & -13 \end{bmatrix}$

3. Add a multiple of one row to another row.

  Example: $\begin{bmatrix} 1 & 2 & | & 5 \\ -3 & -5 & | & -13 \end{bmatrix} \xrightarrow[\substack{\text{Add 3 times} \\ \text{row 1 to row 2.}}]{3R_1 + R_2 \to R_2} \begin{bmatrix} 1 & 2 & | & 5 \\ 0 & 1 & | & 2 \end{bmatrix}$

Two matrices are said to be **row equivalent** if one matrix can be transformed into the other matrix through a series of elementary row operations.

EXAMPLE 2   **Performing Elementary Row Operations**

Given $\begin{bmatrix} 4 & 3 & 0 & | & 5 \\ 1 & 4 & -1 & | & 9 \\ 2 & 0 & -3 & | & -8 \end{bmatrix}$, perform the following elementary row operations.

a. $R_1 \Leftrightarrow R_2$ **b.** $\dfrac{1}{4} R_1 \to R_1$ **c.** $-2R_2 + R_3 \to R_3$

Solution:

a. $\begin{bmatrix} 4 & 3 & 0 & | & 5 \\ 1 & 4 & -1 & | & 9 \\ 2 & 0 & -3 & | & -8 \end{bmatrix} \xrightarrow[\substack{\text{Interchange rows} \\ \text{1 and 2.}}]{R_1 \Leftrightarrow R_2} \begin{bmatrix} 1 & 4 & -1 & | & 9 \\ 4 & 3 & 0 & | & 5 \\ 2 & 0 & -3 & | & -8 \end{bmatrix}$

b. $\begin{bmatrix} 4 & 3 & 0 & | & 5 \\ 1 & 4 & -1 & | & 9 \\ 2 & 0 & -3 & | & -8 \end{bmatrix} \xrightarrow[\text{Multiply row 1 by } \frac{1}{4}.]{\frac{1}{4}R_1 \rightarrow R_1} \begin{bmatrix} 1 & \frac{3}{4} & 0 & | & \frac{5}{4} \\ 1 & 4 & -1 & | & 9 \\ 2 & 0 & -3 & | & -8 \end{bmatrix}$

c. $\begin{bmatrix} 4 & 3 & 0 & | & 5 \\ 1 & 4 & -1 & | & 9 \\ 2 & 0 & -3 & | & -8 \end{bmatrix}$

$\begin{array}{ccc} -2R_2 & -2 & -8 & 2 & | -18 \\ + \quad R_3 & 2 & 0 & -3 & | -8 \\ \hline \rightarrow R_3 & 0 & -8 & -1 & | -26 \end{array}$

This now replaces row 3.

$\begin{bmatrix} 4 & 3 & 0 & | & 5 \\ 1 & 4 & -1 & | & 9 \\ 2 & 0 & -3 & | & -8 \end{bmatrix} \xrightarrow[\substack{\text{Add } -2 \text{ times row 2 to row 3.} \\ \text{The result replaces row 3.}}]{-2R_2 + R_3 \rightarrow R_3} \begin{bmatrix} 4 & 3 & 0 & | & 5 \\ 1 & 4 & -1 & | & 9 \\ 0 & -8 & -1 & | & -26 \end{bmatrix}$

Skill Practice 2 Use the matrix from Example 2 to perform the given row operations.

    a. $R_2 \Leftrightarrow R_3$ **b.** $-\frac{1}{2}R_3$ **c.** $-4R_2 + R_1 \rightarrow R_1$

3. Use Gaussian Elimination and Gauss-Jordan Elimination

When an elementary row operation is performed on an augmented matrix, a new row-equivalent augmented matrix is obtained that represents an equivalent system of equations. If we perform repeated row operations, we can form an augmented matrix that represents a system of equations that is easier to solve than the original system. In particular, it is easy to solve a system whose augmented matrix is in *row-echelon form* or *reduced row-echelon form*.

> **Row-Echelon Form and Reduced Row-Echelon Form**
>
> A matrix is in **row-echelon form** if it satisfies the following conditions.
>
>   **1.** Any rows consisting entirely of zeros are at the bottom of the matrix.
>   **2.** For all other rows, the first nonzero entry is 1. This is called the leading 1.
>   **3.** The leading 1 in each nonzero row is to the right of the leading 1 in the row immediately above.
>
> *Note*: A matrix is in **reduced row-echelon form** if it is in row-echelon form with the added condition that each row with a leading entry of 1 has zeros above the leading 1.

The following matrices illustrate row-echelon form and reduced row-echelon form.

    Row-Echelon Form

$\begin{bmatrix} 1 & 5 & | & 3 \\ 0 & 1 & | & 6 \end{bmatrix}$ $\begin{bmatrix} 1 & -4 & -\frac{1}{2} & | & 6 \\ 0 & 1 & 9 & | & -\frac{1}{3} \\ 0 & 0 & 1 & | & 2 \end{bmatrix}$ $\begin{bmatrix} 1 & 4.1 & 1.2 & | & 3.1 \\ 0 & 1 & 0.6 & | & 4.7 \\ 0 & 0 & 0 & | & 0 \end{bmatrix}$

    Reduced Row-Echelon Form

$\begin{bmatrix} 1 & 0 & | & -27 \\ 0 & 1 & | & 6 \end{bmatrix}$ $\begin{bmatrix} 1 & 0 & 0 & | & 150 \\ 0 & 1 & 0 & | & -85 \\ 0 & 0 & 1 & | & 12 \end{bmatrix}$ $\begin{bmatrix} 1 & 0 & 2 & | & 25 \\ 0 & 1 & -3 & | & -4 \\ 0 & 0 & 0 & | & 0 \end{bmatrix}$

After writing an augmented matrix in row-echelon form, the corresponding system of linear equations can be solved using back substitution. This method is called Gaussian elimination.

Answers

2. a. $\begin{bmatrix} 4 & 3 & 0 & | & 5 \\ 2 & 0 & -3 & | & -8 \\ 1 & 4 & -1 & | & 9 \end{bmatrix}$

b. $\begin{bmatrix} 4 & 3 & 0 & | & 5 \\ 1 & 4 & -1 & | & 9 \\ -1 & 0 & \frac{3}{2} & | & 4 \end{bmatrix}$

c. $\begin{bmatrix} 0 & -13 & 4 & | & -31 \\ 1 & 4 & -1 & | & 9 \\ 2 & 0 & -3 & | & -8 \end{bmatrix}$

> ### Solving a System of Linear Equations Using Gaussian Elimination
>
> 1. Write the augmented matrix for the system.
> 2. Use elementary row operations to write the augmented matrix in row-echelon form.
> 3. Use back substitution to solve the resulting system of equations.

When writing an augmented matrix in row-echelon form, the goal is to make the elements along the main diagonal 1 and the entries below the main diagonal 0. The **main diagonal** refers to the elements on the diagonal from the upper left to the lower right all to the left of the vertical bar.

The main diagonal stretches from the upper left to the lower right.

To write an augmented matrix in row-echelon form, work one column at a time from left to right. This is demonstrated in Example 3.

EXAMPLE 3   Solving a System Using Gaussian Elimination

Solve the system by using Gaussian elimination.

$$\begin{aligned} 3x + 7y - 15z &= -12 \\ x + 2y - 4z &= -3 \\ -4x - 6y + 15z &= 16 \end{aligned}$$

Solution:

$$\begin{aligned} 3x + 7y - 15z &= -12 \\ x + 2y - 4z &= -3 \\ -4x - 6y + 15z &= 16 \end{aligned} \qquad \left[\begin{array}{ccc|c} 3 & 7 & -15 & -12 \\ 1 & 2 & -4 & -3 \\ -4 & -6 & 15 & 16 \end{array}\right]$$

Set up the augmented matrix.

Use elementary row operations to write the augmented matrix in row-echelon form.

$$R_1 \Leftrightarrow R_2 \qquad \left[\begin{array}{ccc|c} 1 & 2 & -4 & -3 \\ 3 & 7 & -15 & -12 \\ -4 & -6 & 15 & 16 \end{array}\right]$$

Begin working with column 1.

To obtain a leading 1 in the first row, interchange rows 1 and 2.

$$\begin{aligned} -3R_1 + R_2 &\to R_2 \\ 4R_1 + R_3 &\to R_3 \end{aligned} \qquad \left[\begin{array}{ccc|c} 1 & 2 & -4 & -3 \\ 0 & 1 & -3 & -3 \\ 0 & 2 & -1 & 4 \end{array}\right]$$

Multiply row 1 by -3 and add the result to row 2. Multiply row 1 by 4 and add the result to row 3.

We now have zeros below the leading 1 in the first row with zeros below.

$$-2R_2 + R_3 \to R_3 \qquad \left[\begin{array}{ccc|c} 1 & 2 & -4 & -3 \\ 0 & 1 & -3 & -3 \\ 0 & 0 & 5 & 10 \end{array}\right]$$

The leading element in row 2 is already 1.

Next, obtain a 0 below the leading 1 in row 2. Multiply row 2 by -2 and add the result to row 3.

$$\tfrac{1}{5}R_3 \to R_3 \qquad \left[\begin{array}{ccc|c} 1 & 2 & -4 & -3 \\ 0 & 1 & -3 & -3 \\ 0 & 0 & 1 & 2 \end{array}\right]$$

Multiply row 3 by $\tfrac{1}{5}$ to obtain a leading 1 in row 3.

$$\left[\begin{array}{ccc|c} 1 & 2 & -4 & -3 \\ 0 & 1 & -3 & -3 \\ 0 & 0 & 1 & 2 \end{array}\right] \begin{array}{l} \longrightarrow x + 2y - 4z = -3 \\ \longrightarrow y - 3z = -3 \\ \longrightarrow z = 2 \end{array}$$

We now have row-echelon form. The corresponding system of equations has z isolated.

Use back substitution to find x and y.

$$\begin{aligned} y - 3z &= -3 \\ y - 3(2) &= -3 \\ y &= 3 \end{aligned}$$

Substitute $z = 2$ in the second equation.

$$\begin{aligned} x + 2y - 4z &= -3 \\ x + 2(3) - 4(2) &= -3 \\ x + 6 - 8 &= -3 \\ x &= -1 \end{aligned}$$

Substitute $z = 2$ and $y = 3$ into the first equation.

The solution set is $\{(-1, 3, 2)\}$.

The solution $(-1, 3, 2)$ checks in each original equation.

TIP In Example 3, the original augmented matrix has the value 3 as the leading entry in the first row. To obtain a leading entry of 1, we have the option of multiplying the first row by $\frac{1}{3}$. However, this would present fractions in the first row. It was "cleaner" to interchange rows 1 and 2.

Skill Practice 3   Solve the system by using Gaussian elimination.

$$2x + 7y + z = 14$$
$$x + 3y - z = 2$$
$$x + 7y + 12z = 45$$

Example 3 illustrates that a system of equations represented by an augmented matrix in row-echelon form is easily solved by using back substitution. If we write an augmented matrix in *reduced* row-echelon form, we can solve the corresponding system of equations by inspection. This is called the Gauss-Jordan elimination method [named after Carl Friedrich Gauss (1777–1855) and German scientist Wilhelm Jordan (1842–1899)].

When writing an augmented matrix in *reduced* row-echelon form, the goal is to make the elements along the main diagonal 1 and the entries above and below the main diagonal 0. This is demonstrated in Examples 4 and 5.

$$\left[\begin{array}{cc|c} 1 & 0 & \square \\ 0 & 1 & \square \end{array}\right] \qquad \left[\begin{array}{ccc|c} 1 & 0 & 0 & \square \\ 0 & 1 & 0 & \square \\ 0 & 0 & 1 & \square \end{array}\right]$$

EXAMPLE 4   **Solving a System Using Gauss-Jordan Elimination**

Solve the system by using Gauss-Jordan elimination.

$$x = 17 - 2y$$
$$3(x + 2y) = 47 - y$$

Solution:

$x = 17 - 2y \longrightarrow x + 2y = 17$
$3(x + 2y) = 47 - y \longrightarrow 3x + 7y = 47$

To use Gaussian elimination or Gauss-Jordan elimination, always begin by writing each equation in standard form.

$$\begin{array}{l} x + 2y = 17 \\ 3x + 7y = 47 \end{array} \qquad \left[\begin{array}{cc|c} 1 & 2 & 17 \\ 3 & 7 & 47 \end{array}\right]$$

Set up the augmented matrix.

$$-3R_1 + R_2 \rightarrow R_2 \longrightarrow \left[\begin{array}{cc|c} 1 & 2 & 17 \\ 0 & 1 & -4 \end{array}\right]$$

The leading entry in the first row is already 1. Multiply row 1 by -3 and add the result to row 2. This results in 0 below the leading 1 in the first row.

$$-2R_2 + R_1 \rightarrow R_1 \longrightarrow \left[\begin{array}{cc|c} 1 & 0 & 25 \\ 0 & 1 & -4 \end{array}\right]$$

Multiply row 2 by -2 and add the result to row 1. This results in 0 above the leading 1 in the second row.

$$\left[\begin{array}{cc|c} 1 & 0 & 25 \\ 0 & 1 & -4 \end{array}\right] \begin{array}{l} \longrightarrow x = 25 \\ \longrightarrow y = -4 \end{array}$$

From the corresponding system of equations, we can determine the solution $(25, -4)$ by inspection.

The solution set is $\{(25, -4)\}$.

The solution checks in each original equation.

Skill Practice 4   Solve the system by using Gauss-Jordan elimination.

$$x - 2y = -1$$
$$4x - 7y = 1$$

Answers
3. $\{(2, 1, 3)\}$ **4.** $\{(9, 5)\}$

In Example 5, we use the Gauss-Jordan elimination method to solve a three-variable system of linear equations.

EXAMPLE 5   Solving a System Using Gauss-Jordan Elimination

Solve the system by using Gauss-Jordan elimination.

$$2x - 5y - 21z = 39$$
$$x - 3y - 10z = 22$$
$$x + 3y + 2z = -8$$

Solution:

$$
\begin{aligned}
2x - 5y - 21z &= 39 \\
x - 3y - 10z &= 22 \\
x + 3y + 2z &= -8
\end{aligned}
\qquad
\left[\begin{array}{rrr|r}
2 & -5 & -21 & 39 \\
1 & -3 & -10 & 22 \\
1 & 3 & 2 & -8
\end{array}\right]
$$

Set up the augmented matrix.

$$
R_1 \Leftrightarrow R_2 \longrightarrow
\left[\begin{array}{rrr|r}
1 & -3 & -10 & 22 \\
2 & -5 & -21 & 39 \\
1 & 3 & 2 & -8
\end{array}\right]
$$

Use elementary row operations to write the augmented matrix in reduced row-echelon form.

To obtain a leading 1 in the first row, interchange rows 1 and 2.

$$
\begin{array}{l}
-2R_1 + R_2 \to R_2 \\
-R_1 + R_3 \to R_3
\end{array}
\longrightarrow
\left[\begin{array}{rrr|r}
1 & -3 & -10 & 22 \\
0 & 1 & -1 & -5 \\
0 & 6 & 12 & -30
\end{array}\right]
$$

Multiply row 1 by -2 and add the result to row 2. Multiply row 1 by -1 and add the result to row 3.

We now have zeros below the leading 1 in the first row.

$$
\begin{array}{l}
3R_2 + R_1 \to R_1 \\
\\
-6R_2 + R_3 \to R_3
\end{array}
\longrightarrow
\left[\begin{array}{rrr|r}
1 & 0 & -13 & 7 \\
0 & 1 & -1 & -5 \\
0 & 0 & 18 & 0
\end{array}\right]
$$

Row 2 already has a leading 1. Multiply row 2 by 3 and add the result to row 1. Multiply row 2 by -6 and add the result to row 3.

$$
\tfrac{1}{18}R_3 \to R_3 \longrightarrow
\left[\begin{array}{rrr|r}
1 & 0 & -13 & 7 \\
0 & 1 & -1 & -5 \\
0 & 0 & 1 & 0
\end{array}\right]
$$

Multiply row 3 by $\frac{1}{18}$ to obtain a leading 1 in row 3.

$$
\begin{array}{l}
13R_3 + R_1 \to R_1 \\
R_3 + R_2 \to R_2
\end{array}
\longrightarrow
\left[\begin{array}{rrr|r}
1 & 0 & 0 & 7 \\
0 & 1 & 0 & -5 \\
0 & 0 & 1 & 0
\end{array}\right]
$$

Multiply row 3 by 13 and add the result to row 1.
Multiply row 3 by 1 and add the result to row 2.

$$
\left[\begin{array}{rrr|r}
1 & 0 & 0 & 7 \\
0 & 1 & 0 & -5 \\
0 & 0 & 1 & 0
\end{array}\right]
\begin{array}{l}
\longrightarrow x = 7 \\
\longrightarrow y = -5 \\
\longrightarrow z = 0
\end{array}
$$

The augmented matrix is in reduced row-echelon form.

From the corresponding system of equations, we can determine the solution $(7, -5, 0)$ by inspection.

The solution set is $\{(7, -5, 0)\}$.   The solution checks in each original equation.

Skill Practice 5   Solve the system by using Gauss-Jordan elimination.

$$2x + 7y + 11z = 11$$
$$x + 2y + 8z = 14$$
$$x + 3y + 6z = 8$$

Answer

5. $\{(14, -4, 1)\}$

TECHNOLOGY CONNECTIONS

Finding the Row-Echelon Form and Reduced Row-Echelon Form of a Matrix

Many graphing utilities have the capability to enter and manipulate matrices. To enter the augmented matrix from Example 5, select the MATRIX menu and then the EDIT menu. Select a name for the matrix such as A. Then enter the dimensions of the matrix (in this case 3×4) followed by the individual elements.

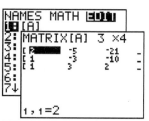

To access the commands for row-echelon form and reduced row-echelon form, select the MATH menu from within the MATRIX menu. Select either *ref* for row-echelon form or *rref* for reduced row-echelon form.

In the home screen, insert the matrix name within the parentheses for the *ref* and *rref* functions.

Alternatively, we can find the row-echelon form or reduced row-echelon form of a matrix if the calculator is in "MATHPRINT" mode. Select MODE, and using the arrow keys to navigate through the menu, highlight "MATHPRINT."

In the home screen, select the MATRIX menu, followed by MATH. Then select either *ref* or *rref*. Next, press the ALPHA key followed by F3. Enter the dimensions of the matrix (in this case 3×4). Then enter the elements of the matrix using the arrow keys to navigate through the matrix. Hit ENTER to complete the calculation.

SECTION 6.1   Practice Exercises

Review Exercises

For Exercises 1–4, solve the system.

1. $x - 5y = 21$
$\quad\ y = -4$

2. $x + 6y = 20$
$\quad\ y = 3$

3. $x + 2y - 3z = 4$
$\quad\quad\ y + 4z = 11$
$\quad\quad\quad\quad z = 2$

4. $x - 3y + z = -3$
$\quad\quad\ y - 4z = 15$
$\quad\quad\quad\quad z = -2$

Concept Connections

5. A rectangular array of elements is called a _____.

6. An _____ matrix is used to represent a system of linear equations written in standard form.

7. _____ row operations performed on an augmented matrix results in a new augmented matrix that represents an equivalent system of equations.

8. Identify the elements on the main diagonal.
$$\begin{bmatrix} -4 & -1 & 1 & | & 8 \\ 2 & 0 & 5 & | & 11 \\ 0 & 1 & -7 & | & -6 \end{bmatrix}$$

9. Explain the meaning of the notation $R_2 \Leftrightarrow R_3$.

10. Explain the meaning of the notation $-R_2 \rightarrow R_2$.

11. Explain the meaning of the notation $3R_1 \rightarrow R_1$.

12. Explain the meaning of $R_1 \Leftrightarrow R_3$.

13. Explain the meaning of the notation $3R_1 + R_2 \rightarrow R_2$.

14. Explain the meaning of the notation $4R_2 + R_3 \rightarrow R_3$.

Objective 1: Write an Augmented Matrix

For Exercises 15–20, write the augmented matrix for the given system. (See Example 1)

15.
$$-3x + 2y - z = 4$$
$$8x + 4z = 12$$
$$2y - 5z = 1$$

16.
$$-4x - y + z = 8$$
$$2x + 5z = 11$$
$$y - 7z = -6$$

17.
$$4(x - 2y) = 6y + 2$$
$$3x = 5y + 7$$

18.
$$2(y - x) = 4 - 8x$$
$$5y = 6 - x$$

19.
$$x = 2$$
$$y = \frac{6}{7}$$
$$z = 12$$

20.
$$x = 4$$
$$y = 2$$
$$z = -\frac{1}{2}$$

For Exercises 21–26, write a system of linear equations represented by the augmented matrix. (See Example 1)

21. $\begin{bmatrix} -4 & 6 & | & 11 \\ -3 & 9 & | & 1 \end{bmatrix}$

22. $\begin{bmatrix} -3 & 7 & | & -2 \\ -1 & 1 & | & 4 \end{bmatrix}$

23. $\begin{bmatrix} 1 & 4 & 3 & | & 8 \\ 0 & 1 & 2 & | & 12 \\ 0 & 0 & 1 & | & 6 \end{bmatrix}$

24. $\begin{bmatrix} 1 & 1 & -2 & | & -4 \\ 0 & 1 & 3 & | & 8 \\ 0 & 0 & 1 & | & 2 \end{bmatrix}$

25. $\begin{bmatrix} 1 & 0 & 0 & | & 8 \\ 0 & 1 & 0 & | & -9 \\ 0 & 0 & 1 & | & \frac{3}{2} \end{bmatrix}$

26. $\begin{bmatrix} 1 & 0 & 0 & | & 2 \\ 0 & 1 & 0 & | & 6 \\ 0 & 0 & 1 & | & -\frac{1}{2} \end{bmatrix}$

Objective 2: Use Elementary Row Operations

For Exercises 27–32, perform the elementary row operations on $\begin{bmatrix} 1 & 4 & | & 2 \\ -3 & 6 & | & 6 \end{bmatrix}$. (See Example 2)

27. $R_1 \Leftrightarrow R_2$

28. $-\frac{1}{3}R_2 \rightarrow R_2$

29. $3R_1 \rightarrow R_1$

30. $-3R_1 \rightarrow R_1$

31. $\frac{1}{3}R_2 + R_1 \rightarrow R_1$

32. $3R_1 + R_2 \rightarrow R_2$

For Exercises 33–38, perform the elementary row operations on $\begin{bmatrix} 1 & 5 & 6 & | & 2 \\ 2 & 1 & 5 & | & 1 \\ 4 & -2 & -3 & | & 10 \end{bmatrix}$. (See Example 2)

33. $R_2 \Leftrightarrow R_3$

34. $R_1 \Leftrightarrow R_2$

35. $\frac{1}{4}R_3 \rightarrow R_3$

36. $\frac{1}{2}R_2 \rightarrow R_2$

37. $-2R_1 + R_2 \rightarrow R_2$

38. $-4R_1 + R_3 \rightarrow R_3$

Objective 3: Use Gaussian Elimination and Gauss-Jordan Elimination

For Exercises 39–42, determine if the matrix is in row-echelon form. If not, explain why.

39. $\begin{bmatrix} 1 & 5 & | & 4 \\ 0 & 2 & | & 6 \end{bmatrix}$

40. $\begin{bmatrix} 1 & 6 & 4 & | & 2 \\ 0 & 1 & 0 & | & -1 \\ 0 & 3 & 1 & | & 3 \end{bmatrix}$

41. $\begin{bmatrix} 1 & 3 & 2 & | & 6 \\ 0 & 1 & 5 & | & 9 \\ 0 & 0 & 0 & | & 0 \end{bmatrix}$

42. $\begin{bmatrix} 1 & 4 & 2 & | & -6 \\ 0 & 1 & -3 & | & 2 \\ 0 & 0 & 1 & | & 0 \end{bmatrix}$

For Exercises 43–46, determine if the matrix is in reduced row-echelon form. If not, explain why.

43. $\begin{bmatrix} 1 & 0 & 0 & | & 3 \\ 1 & 0 & 0 & | & 4 \\ 1 & 0 & 0 & | & 5 \end{bmatrix}$ **44.** $\begin{bmatrix} 1 & 0 & 2 & | & 3 \\ 0 & 1 & 0 & | & 4 \\ 0 & 0 & 1 & | & 5 \end{bmatrix}$ **45.** $\begin{bmatrix} 1 & 0 & 0 & 0 & | & 1 \\ 0 & 1 & 0 & 0 & | & 2 \\ 0 & 0 & 1 & 0 & | & -7 \\ 0 & 0 & 0 & 1 & | & 4 \end{bmatrix}$ **46.** $\begin{bmatrix} 1 & 0 & 0 & -1 & | & 5 \\ 0 & 1 & 0 & 0 & | & 20 \\ 0 & 0 & 1 & 4 & | & -1 \\ 0 & 0 & 0 & 0 & | & 0 \end{bmatrix}$

For Exercises 47–66, solve the system by using Gaussian elimination or Gauss-Jordan elimination. (See Examples 3–5)

47. $2x + 3y = -13$
$x + 4y = -14$

48. $-3x + 11y = 58$
$x - 3y = -16$

49. $2x - 7y = -41$
$3x - 9y = -51$

50. $-2x + 15y = 6$
$3x - 12y = -9$

51. $-3(x - 6y) = -167 - y$
$14y = 2x - 122$

52. $2(x - y) = 4x + y - 40$
$9y = 105 - 3x$

53. $3x + 7y + 22z = 83$
$x + 3y + 10z = 37$
$-2x - 5y - 18z = -66$

54. $3x + 5y + 9z = 3$
$x + 3y + 7z = 5$
$-2x - 8y - 15z = -11$

55. $-2x + 4y + z = 7$
$4x - 13y + 10z = 17$
$3x - 9y + 6z = 9$

56. $2x - 8y + 54z = -4$
$x - 2y + 14z = -1$
$x - 3y + 19z = -3$

57. $-3x + 4y - 15z = -44$
$x - y + 4z = 13$
$x - 3y + 14z = 27$

58. $-2x + 5y - 4z = -4$
$x - 2y + z = 3$
$x - 5y + 9z = -5$

59. $2x + 8z = 7y - 46$
$x = 3y - 3z - 18$
$6z = 5y - x - 34$

60. $2x = 7 - y - 3z$
$x + y = z + 5$
$16z = 2y - x - 4$

61. $11y + 65 = 3x + 13z$
$x + 3z = 3y + 15$
$-2x + 4y - 7z = -25$

62. $2(x - 6z) = 3y + x + 17$
$2x - 19 = 3y + 18z$
$-3x + 7y + 36z = -41$

63. $w + 3x - 3z = -5$
$x - 2z = -6$
$-2w - 4x + y + 2z = 1$
$x + y = 5$

64. $w - 2x + 5y = 20$
$-x + 2y = 9$
$x - y = -5$
$2w - x + 7y + z = 25$

65. $x_1 + x_2 + 5x_4 = -4$
$x_2 + 2x_4 = 3$
$-2x_2 + x_3 - 3x_4 = -5$
$3x_1 + 3x_2 + 17x_4 = -10$

66. $x_1 + x_3 - 5x_4 = 1$
$-2x_1 + x_2 - 2x_3 + 16x_4 = -3$
$x_1 + 2x_3 - 10x_4 = 5$
$x_1 - x_3 + 7x_4 = -7$

Mixed Exercises

67. Andre borrowed $20,000 to buy a truck for his business. He borrowed from his parents who charge him 2% simple interest. He borrowed from a credit union that charges 4% simple interest, and he borrowed from a bank that charges 5% simple interest. He borrowed five times as much from his parents as from the bank, and the amount of interest he paid at the end of 1 yr was $620. How much did he borrow from each source?

68. Sylvia invested a total of $40,000. She invested part of the money in a certificate of deposit (CD) that earns 2% simple interest per year. She invested in a stock that returns the equivalent of 8% simple interest, and she invested in a bond fund that returns 5%. She invested twice as much in the stock as she did in the CD, and earned a total of $2300 at the end of 1 yr. How much principal did she put in each investment?

69. Danielle stayed in three different cities (Washington, D.C., Atlanta, Georgia, and Dallas, Texas) for a total of 14 nights. She spent twice as many nights in Dallas as she did in Washington. The total cost for 14 nights (excluding tax) was $2200. Determine the number of nights that she spent in each city.

City	Cost per Night
Washington	$200
Atlanta	$100
Dallas	$150

70. Three pumps (A, B, and C) work to drain water from a retention pond. Working together the pumps can pump 1500 gal/hr of water. Pump C works at a rate of 100 gal/hr faster than pump B. In 3 hr, pump C can pump as much water as pumps A and B working together in 2 hr. Find the rate at which each pump works.

For Exercises 71–72, find the partial fraction decomposition for the given rational expression. Use the technique of Gaussian elimination to find A, B, and C.

71. $\dfrac{5x^2 - 6x - 13}{(x + 3)(x - 2)^2} = \dfrac{A}{x + 3} + \dfrac{B}{x - 2} + \dfrac{C}{(x - 2)^2}$

72. $\dfrac{2x^2 + 17x + 3}{(x + 5)(x + 1)^2} = \dfrac{A}{x + 5} + \dfrac{B}{x + 1} + \dfrac{C}{(x + 1)^2}$

Write About It

73. Explain why interchanging two rows of an augmented matrix results in an augmented matrix that represents an equivalent system of equations.

74. Explain why multiplying a row of an augmented matrix by a nonzero constant results in an augmented matrix that represents an equivalent system of equations.

75. Explain the difference between a matrix in row-echelon form and reduced row-echelon form.

76. Consider the matrix $\begin{bmatrix} 5 & -9 & -57 \\ 1 & -2 & -12 \end{bmatrix}$. Identify two row operations that could be used to obtain a leading entry of 1 in the first row. Also indicate which operation would be less cumbersome as a first step toward writing the matrix in reduced row-echelon form.

Technology Connections

For Exercises 77–78, use a calculator to approximate the reduced row-echelon form of the augmented matrix representing the given system. Give the solution set where x, y, and z are rounded to 2 decimal places.

77. $\begin{aligned} 0.52x - 3.71y - 4.68z &= 9.18 \\ 0.02x + 0.06y + 0.11z &= 0.56 \\ 0.972x + 0.816y + 0.417z &= 0.184 \end{aligned}$

78. $\begin{aligned} -3.61x + 8.17y - 5.62z &= 30.2 \\ 8.04x - 3.16y + 9.18z &= 28.4 \\ -0.16x + 0.09y + 0.55z &= 4.6 \end{aligned}$

79. A small grocer finds that the monthly sales y (in \$) can be approximated as a function of the amount spent advertising on the radio x_1 (in \$) and the amount spent advertising in the newspaper x_2 (in \$) according to $y = ax_1 + bx_2 + c$.

The table gives the amounts spent in advertising and the corresponding monthly sales for 3 months.

Radio Advertising, x_1	Newspaper Advertising, x_2	Monthly sales, y
\$2400	\$800	\$36,000
\$2000	\$500	\$30,000
\$3000	\$1000	\$44,000

a. Use the data to write a system of linear equations to solve for a, b, and c.

b. Use a graphing utility to find the reduced row-echelon form of the augmented matrix.

c. Write the model $y = ax_1 + bx_2 + c$.

d. Predict the monthly sales if the grocer spends \$2500 advertising on the radio and \$500 advertising in the newspaper for a given month.

80. The purchase price of a home y (in \$1000) can be approximated based on the annual income of the buyer x_1 (in \$1000) and on the square footage of the home x_2 (in 100 ft^2) according to $y = ax_1 + bx_2 + c$.

The table gives the incomes of three buyers, the square footages of the home purchased, and the corresponding purchase prices of the home.

Income (\$1000) x_1	Square Footage (100 ft^2) x_2	Price (\$1000) y
80	21	180
150	28	250
75	18	160

a. Use the data to write a system of linear equations to solve for a, b, and c.

b. Use a graphing utility to find the reduced row-echelon form of the augmented matrix.

c. Write the model $y = ax_1 + bx_2 + c$.

d. Predict the purchase price for a buyer who makes \$100,000 per year and wants a 2500 ft^2 home.

For Exercises 81–82, the given function values satisfy a function defined by $f(x) = ax^2 + bx + c$.

a. Set up a system of equations to solve for a, b, and c.

b. Use a graphing utility to find the reduced row-echelon form of the augmented matrix.

c. Write a function of the form $f(x) = ax^2 + bx + c$ that fits the data.

81. $f(-3) = -7.28$
$f(-1) = 3.68$
$f(10) = 18.2$

82. $f(3) = 6.95$
$f(-2) = 20.2$
$f(12) = 39.8$

OBJECTIVES

1. **Identify Inconsistent Systems**
2. **Solve Systems with Dependent Equations**
3. **Solve Applications of Systems of Equations**

1. Identify Inconsistent Systems

When we studied systems of linear equations in two and three variables in Chapter 5, we learned that a system may have no solution. Such a system is said to be **inconsistent,** and we recognize an inconsistent system if the system reduces to a contradiction.

EXAMPLE 1   **Identifying an Inconsistent System**

Solve the system.
$$\begin{aligned} x - 3y - 17z &= -59 \\ x - 2y - 12z &= -41 \\ -2y - 10z &= 20 \end{aligned}$$

Solution:

$$\begin{aligned} x - 3y - 17z &= -59 \\ x - 2y - 12z &= -41 \\ -2y - 10z &= 20 \end{aligned} \qquad \left[\begin{array}{ccc|c} 1 & -3 & -17 & -59 \\ 1 & -2 & -12 & -41 \\ 0 & -2 & -10 & 20 \end{array}\right]$$

Write the augmented matrix.
The leading entry in row 1 is already 1.

$$-R_1 + R_2 \rightarrow R_2 \longrightarrow \left[\begin{array}{ccc|c} 1 & -3 & -17 & -59 \\ 0 & 1 & 5 & 18 \\ 0 & -2 & -10 & 20 \end{array}\right]$$

Multiply row 1 by -1 and add the result to row 2.

$$\begin{aligned} 3R_2 + R_1 \rightarrow R_1 \longrightarrow \\ 2R_2 + R_3 \rightarrow R_3 \longrightarrow \end{aligned} \left[\begin{array}{ccc|c} 1 & 0 & -2 & -5 \\ 0 & 1 & 5 & 18 \\ 0 & 0 & 0 & 56 \end{array}\right]$$

Multiply row 2 by 3 and add the result to row 1.
Multiply row 2 by 2 and add the result to row 3.

The last row of the matrix cannot be written with a leading 1 along the main diagonal. The last row represents a contradiction, $0 = 56$.

$$\left[\begin{array}{ccc|c} 1 & 0 & -2 & -5 \\ 0 & 1 & 5 & 18 \\ 0 & 0 & 0 & 56 \end{array}\right] \xrightarrow[\text{system}]{\text{equivalent}} \begin{cases} x - 2z = -5 \\ y + 5z = 18 \\ \qquad\quad 0 = 56 \end{cases}$$

The contradiction indicates that the system is inconsistent and that there is no solution. The solution set is { }.

Skill Practice 1   Solve the system.
$$\begin{aligned} 5x - 9y - 33z &= 3 \\ x - 2y - 7z &= 0 \\ -2x + y + 8z &= -12 \end{aligned}$$

Answer

1. { }

TECHNOLOGY CONNECTIONS

Recognizing an Inconsistent System on a Calculator

We can verify that the system of equations in Example 1 has no solution by using a calculator to find the reduced row-echelon form of the augmented matrix. Notice that the calculator also displays a contradiction in the third row, $0 = 1$.

In Example 1, once we reached the contradiction $0 = 56$, we stopped manipulating the augmented matrix. However, we have the option of simplifying the augmented matrix to reduced row-echelon form. To match the result given in the calculator, we would multiply row 3 by $\frac{1}{56}$. Then add -18 times row 3 to row 2, and add 5 times row 3 to row 1.

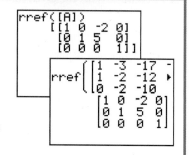

2. Solve Systems with Dependent Equations

A linear equation in three variables represents a plane in space. A solution to a system of equations in three variables is a common point of intersection among all the planes in the system. From Example 1, we have a system with no solution. This means that the planes do not all intersect (Figure 6-1).

Figure 6-1

A system of linear equations may have infinitely many solutions. In such a case, the equations are said to be **dependent.** For a system of three equations in three variables, this means that the planes intersect in a common line in space (Figure 6-2 and Figure 6-3), or the three planes all coincide (Figure 6-4).

Figure 6-2   **Figure 6-3**   **Figure 6-4**

EXAMPLE 2   **Solving a Dependent System**

Solve the system.
$$\begin{aligned} x - 4y + 7z &= 14 \\ -2x + 9y - 16z &= -31 \\ x - 7y + 13z &= 23 \end{aligned}$$

Solution:

$$\begin{aligned} x - 4y + 7z &= 14 \\ -2x + 9y - 16z &= -31 \\ x - 7y + 13z &= 23 \end{aligned} \qquad \left[\begin{array}{ccc|c} 1 & -4 & 7 & 14 \\ -2 & 9 & -16 & -31 \\ 1 & -7 & 13 & 23 \end{array}\right] \quad \text{Set up the augmented matrix.}$$

$$\xrightarrow[{-R_1 + R_3 \to R_3}]{2R_1 + R_2 \to R_2} \left[\begin{array}{ccc|c} 1 & -4 & 7 & 14 \\ 0 & 1 & -2 & -3 \\ 0 & -3 & 6 & 9 \end{array}\right] \xrightarrow[{3R_2 + R_3 \to R_3}]{4R_2 + R_1 \to R_1} \left[\begin{array}{ccc|c} 1 & 0 & -1 & 2 \\ 0 & 1 & -2 & -3 \\ 0 & 0 & 0 & 0 \end{array}\right]$$

The last row of the matrix cannot be written with a leading 1 along the main diagonal. The last row represents an identity, $0 = 0$.

$$\left[\begin{array}{ccc|c} 1 & 0 & -1 & 2 \\ 0 & 1 & -2 & -3 \\ 0 & 0 & 0 & 0 \end{array}\right] \xrightarrow[\text{system}]{\text{equivalent}} \begin{cases} x - z = 2 \\ y - 2z = -3 \\ \quad 0 = 0 \end{cases}$$

TIP A graphing utility can also be used to find the reduced row-echelon form of a system of dependent equations.

```
rref([A])
     [1  0  -1   2]
     [0  1  -2  -3]
     [0  0   0   0]
```

The system of three equations and three variables reduces to a system of two equations and three variables. The third equation, $0 = 0$, is true regardless of the values of x, y, and z. The top two equations each represent a plane in space. Furthermore, two nonparallel planes intersect in a line. All points on the line are solutions to the system, indicating that there are infinitely many solutions.

TIP In Example 2, we can also write the solution set by using a parameter. By choosing any real number t for z, we have:
$$\{(t + 2, 2t - 3, t)\}$$

We can write the solution set in different ways. Since the top two equations both contain the variable z, we can express x and y in terms of z.

$$x - z = 2 \xrightarrow{\text{Express } x \text{ in terms of } z.} x = z + 2$$
$$y - 2z = -3 \xrightarrow{\text{Express } y \text{ in terms of } z.} y = 2z - 3$$

The solution set can be written as

$$\{(x, y, z)\,|\,x = z + 2, y = 2z - 3, z \text{ is any real number}\}$$

or simply $\quad \{(z + 2, 2z - 3, z)\,|\,z \text{ is any real number}\}$

Skill Practice 2 Solve the system. $\quad \begin{aligned} -4x - 11y + 3z &= -24 \\ x + 3y - z &= 7 \\ 3x + 11y - 5z &= 29 \end{aligned}$

We can verify the solution to Example 2, by substituting $(z + 2, 2z - 3, z)$ back into each original equation.

$$x - 4y + 7z = 14 \longrightarrow (z + 2) - 4(2z - 3) + 7z \overset{?}{=} 14 \longrightarrow 14 = 14 \checkmark$$
$$-2x + 9y - 16z = -31 \longrightarrow -2(z + 2) + 9(2z - 3) - 16z \overset{?}{=} -31 \longrightarrow -31 = -31 \checkmark$$
$$x - 7y + 13z = 23 \longrightarrow (z + 2) - 7(2z - 3) + 13z \overset{?}{=} 23 \longrightarrow 23 = 23 \checkmark$$

In Example 2, the solution set $\{(z + 2, 2z - 3, z) \,|\, z \text{ is any real number}\}$ is the general solution representing an infinite number of ordered triples. To find individual solutions, substitute arbitrary real numbers for z, and construct the corresponding ordered triple. For example:

Choose z Arbitrarily	$(z + 2, 2z - 3, z)$	**Solution**
If $z = 1 \longrightarrow$	$(1 + 2, 2(1) - 3, 1)$	$(3, -1, 1)$
If $z = 2 \longrightarrow$	$(2 + 2, 2(2) - 3, 2)$	$(4, 1, 2)$
If $z = 3 \longrightarrow$	$(3 + 2, 2(3) - 3, 3)$	$(5, 3, 3)$
If $z = -1 \longrightarrow$	$(-1 + 2, 2(-1) - 3, -1)$	$(1, -5, -1)$

A system of linear equations that has the same number of equations as variables is called a **square system.** In Example 2, we were presented with three equations and three variables in the original system. However, after writing the augmented matrix in row-echelon form, we see that the system reduces to a system of two equations and three variables. A system of linear equations cannot have a unique solution unless there are at least the same number of equations as variables.

In Example 3, we investigate a nonsquare system that has fewer equations than variables.

EXAMPLE 3 **Solving a System with Fewer Equations than Variables**

Solve the system. $\quad \begin{aligned} 3x - 8y + 18z &= 15 \\ x - 3y + 4z &= 6 \end{aligned}$

Solution:

The two given equations each represent a plane in space. By finding the row-echelon form of the augmented matrix, we can determine the geometrical relationship between the planes.

- If we encounter a contradiction, then the system has no solution and the planes are parallel.
- If we encounter an identity, such as $0 = 0$, then the two equations must represent the same plane.
- Otherwise, the planes must meet in a line.

Answer

2. $\{(-2z - 5, z + 4, z)\,|\,z \text{ is any real number}\}$

$$3x - 8y + 18z = 15 \longrightarrow \begin{bmatrix} 3 & -8 & 18 & | & 15 \\ 1 & -3 & 4 & | & 6 \end{bmatrix} \quad R_1 \Leftrightarrow R_2 \begin{bmatrix} 1 & -3 & 4 & | & 6 \\ 3 & -8 & 18 & | & 15 \end{bmatrix}$$
$$x - 3y + 4z = 6 \longrightarrow$$

$$\xrightarrow{-3R_1 + R_2 \rightarrow R_2} \begin{bmatrix} 1 & -3 & 4 & | & 6 \\ 0 & 1 & 6 & | & -3 \end{bmatrix} \xrightarrow{3R_2 + R_1 \rightarrow R_1} \begin{bmatrix} 1 & 0 & 22 & | & -3 \\ 0 & 1 & 6 & | & -3 \end{bmatrix}$$

The augmented matrix is in reduced row-echelon form. $\begin{bmatrix} 1 & 0 & 22 & | & -3 \\ 0 & 1 & 6 & | & -3 \end{bmatrix} \longrightarrow \begin{cases} x + 22z = -3 \\ y + 6z = -3 \end{cases}$

The system did not reduce to a contradiction or an identity. Therefore, the two planes must intersect in a line and there must be infinitely many solutions.

To write the general solution, write x and y in terms of z.

$$x + 22z = -3 \xrightarrow{\text{Express } x \text{ in terms of } z.} x = -22z - 3$$
$$y + 6z = -3 \xrightarrow{\text{Express } y \text{ in terms of } z.} y = -6z - 3$$

The solution set is $\{(-22z - 3, -6z - 3, z) \mid z \text{ is any real number}\}$.

> **TIP** In parametric form, the solution to Example 3 is given by:
> $\{(-22t - 3, -6t - 3, t)\}$

> **Skill Practice 3**   Solve the system. $x - 3y - 17z = -17$
> $-2x + 7y + 38z = 40$

In Example 4, we investigate a situation in which the solution set to a system of three variables and three equations consists of all points on a common plane in space.

EXAMPLE 4   Solving a Dependent System

Solve the system. $x + 2y + 3z = 6$
$-x - 2y - 3z = -6$
$2x + 4y + 6z = 12$

Solution:

$\boxed{A}$ $x + 2y + 3z = 6$ Upon inspection, you might notice that each equation is a
$\boxed{B}$ $-x - 2y - 3z = -6$ constant multiple of the others. That is, equation $\boxed{B}$ is -1
$\boxed{C}$ $2x + 4y + 6z = 12$ times equation $\boxed{A}$. Equation $\boxed{C}$ is 2 times equation $\boxed{A}$. This
means that equations $\boxed{A}$, $\boxed{B}$, and $\boxed{C}$ represent the same
plane in space.

> **TIP** The solution to Example 4 tells us that $x = 6 - 2y - 3z$. That is, x depends on both y and z. If we write the solution set in parametric form, we would need two parameters.
> $\{(6 - 2s - 3t, s, t)\}$

$$\begin{bmatrix} 1 & 2 & 3 & | & 6 \\ -1 & -2 & -3 & | & -6 \\ 2 & 4 & 6 & | & 12 \end{bmatrix} \xrightarrow[\;-2R_1 + R_3 \rightarrow R_3\;]{R_1 + R_2 \rightarrow R_2} \begin{bmatrix} 1 & 2 & 3 & | & 6 \\ 0 & 0 & 0 & | & 0 \\ 0 & 0 & 0 & | & 0 \end{bmatrix}$$

The reduced row-echelon form tells us that the system reduces to an equivalent system of one equation with three variables.

The system is equivalent to the single equation $x + 2y + 3z = 6$. The solution set is the set of all ordered triples that satisfy this equation.

The solution set is: $\{(x, y, z) \mid x + 2y + 3z = 6\}$.

> **Skill Practice 4**   Solve the system. $2x - 3y + 5z = 3$
> $4x - 6y + 10z = 6$
> $20x - 30y + 50z = 30$

Answers

3. $\{(5z + 1, -4z + 6, z) \mid z \text{ is any real number}\}$

4. $\{(x, y, z) \mid 2x - 3y + 5z = 3\}$

3. Solve Applications of Systems of Equations

A city planner can study the flow of traffic through a network of streets by measuring the flow rates (number of vehicles per unit time) at various points. For traffic to flow freely, we use the principle that the flow rate into an intersection is equal to the flow rate out of the intersection. This must be true for all intersections in the network.

> **EXAMPLE 5** **Solving an Application Involving Dependent Equations**
>
> Consider the network of four one-way streets shown in Figure 6-5. In the figure, x_1, x_2, x_3, and x_4 indicate flow rates (in vehicles per hour) along the stretches of roads AB, BC, CD, and DA, respectively. The other numbers in the figure indicate other flow rates moving into and out of intersections A, B, C, and D.

a. Set up a system of equations that represents traffic flowing freely.

b. Write the augmented matrix for the system of equations in reduced row-echelon form.

c. If the traffic between intersections D and A is 260 vehicles per hour, determine the flow rates x_1, x_2, and x_3.

d. If the traffic between intersections D and A is between 250 and 300 vehicles per hour, inclusive, determine the flow rates x_1, x_2, and x_3.

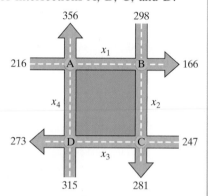

Figure 6-5

Solution:

a.

Intersection	Flow in	=	Flow out
A	$216 + x_4$	=	$356 + x_1$
B	$298 + x_1$	=	$166 + x_2$
C	$x_2 + 247$	=	$281 + x_3$
D	$x_3 + 315$	=	$273 + x_4$

The number of cars flowing into each intersection must equal the number of cars leaving the intersection for traffic to flow freely.

b.
$$\begin{aligned} -x_1 \qquad\qquad + x_4 &= 140 \\ x_1 - x_2 \qquad\qquad &= -132 \\ x_2 - x_3 \qquad &= 34 \\ x_3 - x_4 &= -42 \end{aligned}$$

$$\left[\begin{array}{cccc|c} -1 & 0 & 0 & 1 & 140 \\ 1 & -1 & 0 & 0 & -132 \\ 0 & 1 & -1 & 0 & 34 \\ 0 & 0 & 1 & -1 & -42 \end{array}\right]$$

Write the equations in standard form. Set up the augmented matrix.

$$\xrightarrow{-1R_1 \to R_1} \left[\begin{array}{cccc|c} 1 & 0 & 0 & -1 & -140 \\ 1 & -1 & 0 & 0 & -132 \\ 0 & 1 & -1 & 0 & 34 \\ 0 & 0 & 1 & -1 & -42 \end{array}\right] \xrightarrow{-1R_1 + R_2 \to R_2} \left[\begin{array}{cccc|c} 1 & 0 & 0 & -1 & -140 \\ 0 & -1 & 0 & 1 & 8 \\ 0 & 1 & -1 & 0 & 34 \\ 0 & 0 & 1 & -1 & -42 \end{array}\right]$$

$$\xrightarrow{-1R_2 \to R_2} \left[\begin{array}{cccc|c} 1 & 0 & 0 & -1 & -140 \\ 0 & 1 & 0 & -1 & -8 \\ 0 & 1 & -1 & 0 & 34 \\ 0 & 0 & 1 & -1 & -42 \end{array}\right] \xrightarrow{-1R_2 + R_3 \to R_3} \left[\begin{array}{cccc|c} 1 & 0 & 0 & -1 & -140 \\ 0 & 1 & 0 & -1 & -8 \\ 0 & 0 & -1 & 1 & 42 \\ 0 & 0 & 1 & -1 & -42 \end{array}\right]$$

$$\xrightarrow{-1R_3 \to R_3} \left[\begin{array}{cccc|c} 1 & 0 & 0 & -1 & -140 \\ 0 & 1 & 0 & -1 & -8 \\ 0 & 0 & 1 & -1 & -42 \\ 0 & 0 & 1 & -1 & -42 \end{array}\right] \xrightarrow{-1R_3 + R_4 \to R_4} \left[\begin{array}{cccc|c} 1 & 0 & 0 & -1 & -140 \\ 0 & 1 & 0 & -1 & -8 \\ 0 & 0 & 1 & -1 & -42 \\ 0 & 0 & 0 & 0 & 0 \end{array}\right]$$

c. From the reduced row-echelon form, we see that the flow rates x_1, x_2, and x_3 can all be expressed in terms of the flow rate x_4.

$$\begin{bmatrix} 1 & 0 & 0 & -1 & | & -140 \\ 0 & 1 & 0 & -1 & | & -8 \\ 0 & 0 & 1 & -1 & | & -42 \\ 0 & 0 & 0 & 0 & | & 0 \end{bmatrix}$$

$\longrightarrow x_1 - x_4 = -140 \longrightarrow x_1 = x_4 - 140$

$\longrightarrow x_2 - x_4 = -8 \longrightarrow x_2 = x_4 - 8$

$\longrightarrow x_3 - x_4 = -42 \longrightarrow x_3 = x_4 - 42$

If x_4 is 260 vehicles per hour, we have the following values for x_1, x_2, and x_3.

Flow rate between A and B: $x_1 = 260 - 140 \longrightarrow x_1 = 120$ vehicles per hour
Flow rate between B and C: $x_2 = 260 - 8 \longrightarrow x_2 = 252$ vehicles per hour
Flow rate between C and D: $x_3 = 260 - 42 \longrightarrow x_3 = 218$ vehicles per hour

d. If the traffic flow between intersections D and A is given by $250 \leq x_4 \leq 300$, we can solve the following inequalities to determine the flow rates x_1, x_2, and x_3.

$$250 \leq x_1 + 140 \leq 300 \longrightarrow 110 \leq x_1 \leq 160$$
$$250 \leq x_2 + 8 \leq 300 \longrightarrow 242 \leq x_2 \leq 292$$
$$250 \leq x_3 + 42 \leq 300 \longrightarrow 208 \leq x_3 \leq 258$$

Skill Practice 5   Refer to the figure. Assume that traffic flows freely with flow rates given in vehicles per hour.

a. If the traffic between intersections D and A is 400 vehicles per hour, determine the flow rates x_1, x_2, and x_3.

b. If the traffic between intersections D and A is between 380 and 420 vehicles per hour, determine the flow rates x_1, x_2, and x_3.

Answers
5. a. $x_1 = 140$, $x_2 = 384$, and $x_3 = 320$
b. $120 \leq x_1 \leq 160$, $364 \leq x_2 \leq 404$, $300 \leq x_3 \leq 340$

SECTION 6.2   Practice Exercises

Review Exercises

For Exercises 1–2, determine if the matrix is in reduced row-echelon form.

1. $\begin{bmatrix} 1 & 0 & 0 & | & 7 \\ 0 & 1 & -3 & | & 6 \\ 0 & 0 & 0 & | & 0 \end{bmatrix}$

2. $\begin{bmatrix} 1 & 0 & 0 & | & 0 \\ 0 & 1 & 0 & | & 0 \\ 0 & 0 & 1 & | & 0 \end{bmatrix}$

For Exercises 3–6, solve the system by using the substitution method or the addition method.

3. $3(x - 2y) = 10 - y$
$\frac{3}{10}x = \frac{1}{2}y + 1$

4. $y = 0.25x - 1.5$
$x - 4y = 6$

5. $0.03x + 0.02y = 0.6$
$y = -1.5x + 10$

6. $\frac{2}{5}x = 2 - \frac{1}{2}y$
$4x + 5y = 10$

Concept Connections

7. True or false? A system of linear equations in three variables may have no solution.

8. True or false? A system of linear equations in three variables may have exactly one solution.

9. True or false? A system of linear equations in three variables may have exactly two solutions.

10. True or false? A system of linear equations in three variables may have infinitely many solutions.

11. If a system of linear equations has no solution, then the system is said to be _____.

12. If a system of linear equations has infinitely many solutions, then the equations are said to be _____.

Objectives 1–2: Identify Inconsistent Systems and Solve Systems with Dependent Equations

For Exercises 13–20, an augmented matrix is given. Determine the number of solutions to the corresponding system of equations.

13. $\begin{bmatrix} 1 & 2 & | & 4 \\ 0 & 0 & | & 5 \end{bmatrix}$

14. $\begin{bmatrix} 1 & 0 & 2 & | & 5 \\ 0 & 1 & 4 & | & -2 \\ 0 & 0 & 0 & | & -1 \end{bmatrix}$

15. $\begin{bmatrix} 1 & 0 & 4 & | & 3 \\ 0 & 1 & -1 & | & 6 \\ 0 & 0 & 0 & | & 0 \end{bmatrix}$

16. $\begin{bmatrix} 1 & 3 & | & 5 \\ 0 & 0 & | & 0 \end{bmatrix}$

17. $\begin{bmatrix} 1 & 0 & 0 & | & -3 \\ 0 & 1 & 0 & | & 4 \\ 0 & 0 & 1 & | & 0 \end{bmatrix}$

18. $\begin{bmatrix} 1 & 0 & | & 3 \\ 0 & 1 & | & 0 \end{bmatrix}$

19. $\begin{bmatrix} 1 & 2 & 5 & | & -1 \\ 0 & 0 & 0 & | & 0 \\ 0 & 0 & 0 & | & 0 \end{bmatrix}$

20. $\begin{bmatrix} 1 & 0 & 6 & | & 7 \\ 0 & 0 & 0 & | & 0 \\ 0 & 0 & 0 & | & 0 \end{bmatrix}$

For Exercises 21–24, determine the solution set for the system represented by each augmented matrix.

21. a. $\begin{bmatrix} 1 & 2 & | & 5 \\ 0 & 1 & | & 0 \end{bmatrix}$ **b.** $\begin{bmatrix} 1 & 2 & | & 5 \\ 0 & 0 & | & 0 \end{bmatrix}$ **c.** $\begin{bmatrix} 1 & 2 & | & 5 \\ 0 & 0 & | & 1 \end{bmatrix}$

22. a. $\begin{bmatrix} 1 & 3 & | & -4 \\ 0 & 1 & | & 1 \end{bmatrix}$ **b.** $\begin{bmatrix} 1 & 3 & | & -4 \\ 0 & 0 & | & 1 \end{bmatrix}$ **c.** $\begin{bmatrix} 1 & 3 & | & -4 \\ 0 & 0 & | & 0 \end{bmatrix}$

23. a. $\begin{bmatrix} 1 & 0 & 6 & | & 3 \\ 0 & 1 & 4 & | & 5 \\ 0 & 0 & 1 & | & 0 \end{bmatrix}$ **b.** $\begin{bmatrix} 1 & 0 & 6 & | & 3 \\ 0 & 1 & 4 & | & 5 \\ 0 & 0 & 0 & | & 1 \end{bmatrix}$ **c.** $\begin{bmatrix} 1 & 0 & 6 & | & 3 \\ 0 & 1 & 4 & | & 5 \\ 0 & 0 & 0 & | & 0 \end{bmatrix}$

24. a. $\begin{bmatrix} 1 & 0 & -2 & | & 3 \\ 0 & 1 & 3 & | & 5 \\ 0 & 0 & 1 & | & 1 \end{bmatrix}$ **b.** $\begin{bmatrix} 1 & 0 & -2 & | & 3 \\ 0 & 1 & 3 & | & 5 \\ 0 & 0 & 0 & | & 0 \end{bmatrix}$ **c.** $\begin{bmatrix} 1 & 0 & -2 & | & 3 \\ 0 & 1 & 3 & | & 5 \\ 0 & 0 & 0 & | & 1 \end{bmatrix}$

For Exercises 25–44, solve the system by using Gaussian elimination or Gauss-Jordan elimination. (See Exercises 1–4)

25. $2x + 4y = 5$
$x + 2y = 4$

26. $4x + 16y = 21$
$x + 4y = -1$

27. $2x + 7y = 10$
$\frac{1}{5}x = 1 - \frac{7}{10}y$

28. $4x - 3y = 6$
$y = \frac{4}{3}x - 2$

29. $x - 3y + 14z = -9$
$-2x + 7y - 31z = 21$
$x - 5y + 20z = -14$

30. $x - 3y + 17z = 1$
$x - y + 7z = 2$
$2x - 5y + 29z = 5$

31. $5x + 7y - 11z = 45$
$3x + 5y - 9z = 23$
$x + y - z = 11$

32. $x + 3y + 9z = 12$
$2x + 7y + 22z = 26$
$-5x - 17y - 53z = -64$

33. $2x = 5y - 16z + 40$
$2(x + y) = 4z$
$x - 2y + 7z = 18$

34. $x = 2y + 4z + 5$
$y - 4 = -3z$
$5(x - y) - 9z = 4x - 7$

35. $2x - 5y - 20z = -24$
$x - 3y - 11z = -15$

36. $2x - y - 5z = -3$
$x - 2y - 7z = -12$

37. $2x + 3y + 4z = 12$
$-4x - 6y - 8z = -24$
$x + 1.5y + 2z = 6$

38. $-x + 2y + 7z = 14$
$10x - 20y - 70z = -140$
$-\frac{1}{7}x + \frac{2}{7}y + z = 2$

39. $2x - 3y + 9z = -2$
$x = 5y - 8z - 15$
$3(x - y) + 6z = 2x - 7$

40. $3x + 11y - 3z = -13$
$x + y = z - 15$
$3(x + y) = z + 2x - 7$

41. $-5x + 12y - 20z = -11$
$x + 4z = 3y + 1$

42. $x = 4y + 20z - 1$
$-2x + 5y + 25z = -1$

43. $x_1 - 3x_2 + 9x_3 - 14x_4 = 32$
$x_2 - 3x_3 + 6x_4 = -10$
$x_2 - x_3 + 2x_4 = -4$
$x_1 - 2x_2 + 8x_3 - 12x_4 = 24$

44. $x_1 - 3x_3 - 12x_4 = -15$
$x_2 + x_3 + 6x_4 = 8$
$x_2 - 2x_3 - 6x_4 = -7$
$-2x_1 + 4x_3 + 16x_4 = 22$

For Exercises 45–46, the solution set to a system of dependent equations is given. Write the specific solutions corresponding to the given values of z.

45. $\{(2z + 1, z - 4, z) \mid z$ is any real number$\}$

    a. $z = 1$ **b.** $z = 4$ **c.** $z = -2$

46. $\{(z + 5, 3z - 2, z) \mid z$ is any real number$\}$

    a. $z = -3$ **b.** $z = 1$ **c.** $z = 0$

For Exercises 47–50, the solution set to a system of dependent equations is given. Write three ordered triples that are solutions to the system. Answers may vary.

47. $\{(4z, 6 - z, z) \mid z$ is any real number$\}$

48. $\{(2z, z - 3, z) \mid z$ is any real number$\}$

49. $\{(x, y, z) \mid 2x + 3y + 6z = 6\}$

50. $\{(x, y, z) \mid -x + 4y + 2z = 20\}$

Objective 3: Solve Applications of Systems of Equations

For Exercises 51–54, assume that traffic flows freely through the intersections A, B, C, and D. The values x_1, x_2, x_3, and x_4 and the other numbers in the figures represent flow rates in vehicles per hour. (See Example 5)

51.

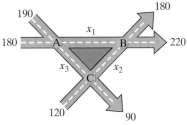

    a. Write an equation representing equal flow into and out of intersection A.

    b. Write an equation representing equal flow into and out of intersection B.

    c. Write an equation representing equal flow into and out of intersection C.

    d. Write the system of equations from parts (a)–(c) in standard form.

    e. Write the reduced row-echelon form of the augmented matrix representing the system of equations from part (d).

    f. If the flow rate between intersections A and C is 120 vehicles per hour, determine the flow rates x_1 and x_2.

    g. If the flow rate between intersections A and C is between 100 and 150 vehicles per hour, inclusive, determine the flow rates x_1 and x_2.

52.

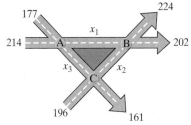

    a. Write an equation representing equal flow into and out of intersection A.

    b. Write an equation representing equal flow into and out of intersection B.

    c. Write an equation representing equal flow into and out of intersection C.

    d. Write the system of equations from parts (a)–(c) in standard form.

    e. Write the reduced row-echelon form of the augmented matrix representing the system of equations in part (d).

    f. If the flow rate between intersections A and C is 156 vehicles per hour, determine the flow rates x_1 and x_2.

    g. If the flow rate between intersections A and C is between 100 and 200 vehicles per hour, inclusive, determine the flow rates x_1 and x_2.

53.

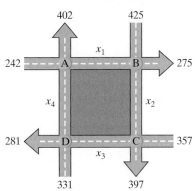

    a. Assume that traffic flows at a rate of 220 vehicles per hour on the stretch of road between intersections D and A. Find the flow rates x_1, x_2, and x_3.

    b. If traffic flows at a rate of between 200 and 250 vehicles per hour inclusive between intersections D and A, find the flow rates x_1, x_2, and x_3.

54.

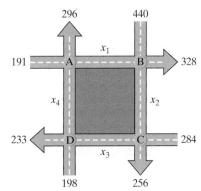

    a. Assume that traffic flows at a rate of 180 vehicles per hour on the stretch of road between intersections D and A. Find the flow rates x_1, x_2, and x_3.

    b. If traffic flows at a rate of between 150 and 200 vehicles per hour inclusive between intersections D and A, find the flow rates x_1, x_2, and x_3.

55. An accountant checks the reported earnings for a theater for three nightly performances against the number of tickets sold.

Night	Children Tickets	Student Tickets	General Admission	Total Revenue
1	80	400	480	$9280
2	50	350	400	$7800
3	75	525	600	$10,500

a. Let x, y, and z represent the cost for children tickets, student tickets, and general admission tickets, respectively. Set up a system of equations to solve for x, y, and z.

b. Set up the augmented matrix for the system and solve the system. (*Hint*: To make the augmented matrix simpler to work with, consider dividing each linear equation by an appropriate constant.)

c. Explain why the auditor knows that there was an error in the record keeping.

56. A concession stand at a city park sells hamburgers, hot dogs, and drinks. Three patrons buy the following food and drink combinations for the following prices.

Patron	Hamburgers	Hot Dogs	Drinks	Total Revenue
1	1	1	5	$11
2	0	1	2	$5
3	3	1	11	$22

a. Let x, y, and z represent the cost for a hamburger, a hot dog, and a drink, respectively. Set up a system of equations to solve for x, y, and z.

b. Set up the augmented matrix for the system and solve the system.

c. Explain why the concession stand manager knows that there was an error in the record keeping.

Mixed Exercises

57. The solution set to Exercise 31 is $\{(-2z + 16, 3z - 5, z) \mid z$ is any real number$\}$. Verify the solution by substituting the ordered triple into each individual equation.

58. The solution set to Exercise 32 is $\{(3z + 6, -4z + 2, z) \mid z$ is any real number$\}$. Verify the solution by substituting the ordered triple into each individual equation.

The systems in Exercises 59–62 are called **homogeneous** systems because each has $(0, 0, 0)$ as a solution. However, if a system is made up of dependent equations, it will have infinitely many more solutions. For each system, determine whether $(0, 0, 0)$ is the only solution or if the system has infinitely many solutions. If the system has infinitely many solutions, give the solution set.

59.
$$x + 2y - 8z = 0$$
$$-5x - 11y + 43z = 0$$
$$x + 5y - 12z = 0$$

60.
$$x - 2y - 7z = 0$$
$$-3x + 8y + 31z = 0$$
$$-2x + 5y + 22z = 0$$

61.
$$x - 5y + 13z = 0$$
$$-3x + 17y - 45z = 0$$
$$x - 4y + 10z = 0$$

62.
$$-2x + 15y - 83z = 0$$
$$x - 7y + 39z = 0$$
$$x - 5y + 29z = 0$$

Write About It

63. Explain how you can determine from the reduced row-echelon form of a matrix whether the corresponding system of equations is inconsistent.

64. What can you conclude about a system of equations if the corresponding reduced row-echelon form consists of a row entirely of zeros?

65. Consider the following system. By inspection describe the geometrical relationship among the planes representing the three equations.

$$x + y + z = 1$$
$$2x + 2y + 2z = 2$$
$$3x + 3y + 3z = 3$$

66. Explain why a system of two equations with three variables cannot have exactly one ordered triple as its solution.

Technology Connections

For Exercises 67–72, use a graphing utility to find the reduced row-echelon form of the augmented matrix for the system in the given exercise. Use the result to verify the answer to the given exercise.

67. Exercise 29

68. Exercise 30

69. Exercise 31

70. Exercise 32

71. Exercise 37

72. Exercise 38

SECTION 6.3 Operations on Matrices

1. Determine the Order of a Matrix

We have seen how the manipulation of an augmented matrix can be used to solve a system of linear equations. Matrices have many other useful mathematical applications, particularly when manipulating tables or databases. In particular, matrices play a useful role in digital photography, film, and computer animation.

The **order of a matrix** is determined by the number of rows and number of columns. A matrix with m rows and n columns is an $m \times n$ matrix (read as "m by n" matrix).

EXAMPLE 1   Determining the Order of a Matrix

Determine the order of each matrix.

a. $\begin{bmatrix} 3 & \pi & 1.7 \\ -1 & 6 & 10 \end{bmatrix}$ **b.** $\begin{bmatrix} -7 \\ 2 \\ 4 \\ \sqrt{2} \end{bmatrix}$ **c.** $\begin{bmatrix} 1 & 0 & 0 \\ 0 & 1 & 0 \\ 0 & 0 & 1 \end{bmatrix}$ **d.** $[x \quad y \quad z]$

Solution:

a. The matrix has 2 rows and 3 columns. Therefore, it is a 2×3 matrix.

b. The matrix has 4 rows and 1 column. Therefore, it is a 4×1 matrix. A matrix with only 1 column is called a **column matrix.**

c. The matrix has 3 rows and 3 columns. Therefore, it is a 3×3 matrix. A matrix with the same number of rows and columns is called a **square matrix.**

d. The matrix has 1 row and 3 columns. Therefore, it is a 1×3 matrix. A matrix with only 1 row is called a **row matrix.**

Skill Practice 1   Determine the order of each matrix.

a. $\begin{bmatrix} -9 & 2 \\ 4.1 & -3 \\ \sqrt{3} & 4 \end{bmatrix}$ **b.** $\begin{bmatrix} -4 \\ 11 \end{bmatrix}$ **c.** $\begin{bmatrix} -0.1 & 0.4 \\ 0.5 & 0.2 \end{bmatrix}$ **d.** $[105 \quad 311]$

A matrix can be represented generically as follows:

$$[a_{ij}] = \begin{bmatrix} a_{11} & a_{12} & \cdots & a_{1n} \\ a_{21} & a_{22} & \cdots & a_{2n} \\ \vdots & & & \\ a_{m1} & a_{m2} & \cdots & a_{mn} \end{bmatrix}$$

TIP The notation $[a_{ij}]$ is a generic way to denote a matrix with elements of the form a_{ij}, where i and j represent generic row and column numbers.

Using the double subscript notation, a_{43} represents the element in the 4th row, 3rd column. The notation a_{ij} represents the element in the ith row, jth column.

Answers
1. a. 3×2 **b.** 2×1
   c. 2×2 **d.** 1×2

EXAMPLE 2 Using Matrix Notation

Consider $A = \begin{bmatrix} -4 & 5 & \sqrt{2} & -\pi \\ 10 & \frac{1}{2} & 0 & 6 \\ -\frac{7}{6} & 8 & 12 & -9 \end{bmatrix}$, where $A = [a_{ij}]$. Determine the value of

a. a_{32} **b.** a_{23} **c.** a_{14}

Solution:

a. a_{32} represents the element in the 3rd row, 2nd column: 8
b. a_{23} represents the element in the 2nd row, 3rd column: 0
c. a_{14} represents the element in the 1st row, 4th column: $-\pi$

Skill Practice 2 Given matrix A from Example 2, find

a. a_{13} **b.** a_{31} **c.** a_{34}

2. Add and Subtract Matrices

We now consider the conditions under which two matrices are equal.

Equality of Matrices

Two matrices are equal if and only if they have the same order and if their corresponding elements are equal.

Example:

- The statement $\begin{bmatrix} 3 & -4 \\ x & z \end{bmatrix} = \begin{bmatrix} 3 & y \\ 9 & 7 \end{bmatrix}$ implies that $x = 9$, $y = -4$, and $z = 7$.

- Conversely, if $x = 9$, $y = -4$, and $z = 7$, then $\begin{bmatrix} 3 & -4 \\ x & z \end{bmatrix} = \begin{bmatrix} 3 & y \\ 9 & 7 \end{bmatrix}$.

Next, we define addition and subtraction of matrices.

Addition and Subtraction of Matrices

Let $A = [a_{ij}]$ and $B = [b_{ij}]$ be m by n matrices. Then,

$$A + B = [a_{ij} + b_{ij}] \text{ for } i = 1, 2, \ldots, m \text{ and } j = 1, 2, \ldots, n$$
$$A - B = [a_{ij} - b_{ij}] \text{ for } i = 1, 2, \ldots, m \text{ and } j = 1, 2, \ldots, n$$

That is, to add or subtract two matrices, the matrices must have the same order, and the sum or difference is found by adding or subtracting the corresponding elements.

Answers

2. a. $\sqrt{2}$ **b.** $-\dfrac{7}{6}$ **c.** -9

EXAMPLE 3   **Adding and Subtracting Matrices**

Given $A = \begin{bmatrix} 3 & -7 & 0 \\ 1 & \frac{4}{3} & -6 \end{bmatrix}$, $B = \begin{bmatrix} 8 & -3 & 4 \\ 0 & 1 & -9 \end{bmatrix}$, and $C = \begin{bmatrix} 3 & -5 \\ 4 & 18 \end{bmatrix}$,

find the sum or difference if possible.

a. $A + B$ **b.** $B - A$ **c.** $A + C$

Solution:

a. $A + B = \begin{bmatrix} 3 & -7 & 0 \\ 1 & \frac{4}{3} & -6 \end{bmatrix} + \begin{bmatrix} 8 & -3 & 4 \\ 0 & 1 & -9 \end{bmatrix}$ Matrix A and matrix B both have the same order (2×3), so the sum is well defined.

$= \begin{bmatrix} 3+8 & -7+(-3) & 0+4 \\ 1+0 & \frac{4}{3}+1 & -6+(-9) \end{bmatrix}$ Add the elements in the corresponding positions.

$= \begin{bmatrix} 11 & -10 & 4 \\ 1 & \frac{7}{3} & -15 \end{bmatrix}$ Simplify.

b. $B - A = \begin{bmatrix} 8 & -3 & 4 \\ 0 & 1 & -9 \end{bmatrix} - \begin{bmatrix} 3 & -7 & 0 \\ 1 & \frac{4}{3} & -6 \end{bmatrix}$ Matrix A and matrix B both have the same order (2×3), so the difference is well defined.

$= \begin{bmatrix} 8-3 & -3-(-7) & 4-0 \\ 0-1 & 1-\frac{4}{3} & -9-(-6) \end{bmatrix}$ Subtract the elements in the corresponding positions.

$= \begin{bmatrix} 5 & 4 & 4 \\ -1 & -\frac{1}{3} & -3 \end{bmatrix}$ Simplify.

c. Matrix A is a 2×3 matrix, whereas matrix C is a 2×2 matrix. The matrices are of different orders and therefore cannot be added or subtracted.

Skill Practice 3   Given $A = \begin{bmatrix} 3 & 4 & -7 \\ 9 & 2 & 0 \end{bmatrix}$, $B = \begin{bmatrix} -8 & 0 \\ 1 & 5 \\ -4 & \frac{1}{2} \end{bmatrix}$, and

$C = \begin{bmatrix} 4 & -5 \\ 12 & 3 \\ -2 & 2 \end{bmatrix}$, find the sum or difference if possible.

a. $A + B$ **b.** $B + C$ **c.** $C - B$

The opposite of a real number a is $-a$. The value $-a$ is also called the additive inverse of a. A matrix A also has an additive inverse, denoted by $-A$.

Additive Inverse of a Matrix

Given $A = [a_{ij}]$, the **additive inverse of A,** denoted by $-A$, is $-A = [-a_{ij}]$.

Verbal Interpretation	Example
The additive inverse of a matrix is found by taking the opposite of each element in the matrix.	Given $A = \begin{bmatrix} -4 & 5 & -1 \\ 0 & -3 & 2 \end{bmatrix}$, $-A = \begin{bmatrix} 4 & -5 & 1 \\ 0 & 3 & -2 \end{bmatrix}$.

Answers

3. a. Not possible

b. $\begin{bmatrix} -4 & -5 \\ 13 & 8 \\ -6 & \frac{5}{2} \end{bmatrix}$

c. $\begin{bmatrix} 12 & -5 \\ 11 & -2 \\ 2 & \frac{3}{2} \end{bmatrix}$

The number 0 is the identity element under the addition of real numbers because $a + (-a) = 0$. A matrix in which all elements are zero is called a **zero matrix** and is denoted by 0. The sum of a matrix A and its additive inverse $-A$ is the zero matrix of the same order. For example,

$$\begin{array}{cccc} A & + & (-A) & = & 0 \end{array}$$

$$\begin{bmatrix} -4 & 5 & -1 \\ 0 & -3 & 2 \end{bmatrix} + \begin{bmatrix} 4 & -5 & 1 \\ 0 & 3 & -2 \end{bmatrix} = \begin{bmatrix} 0 & 0 & 0 \\ 0 & 0 & 0 \end{bmatrix}$$

2×3 zero matrix

Properties of Matrix Addition

Let A, B, and C be matrices of order $m \times n$, and let 0 be the zero matrix of order $m \times n$. Then,

1. $A + B = B + A$ Commutative property of matrix addition
2. $A + (B + C) = (A + B) + C$ Associative property of matrix addition
3. $A + (-A) = 0$ Inverse property of matrix addition
4. $A + 0 = 0 + A = A$ Identity property of matrix addition

3. Multiply a Matrix by a Scalar

Next we look at the product of a real number k and a matrix. This is called **scalar multiplication.** The real number k is called a **scalar** to distinguish it from a matrix.

Scalar Multiplication

Let $A = [a_{ij}]$ be an $m \times n$ matrix and let k be a real number. Then, $kA = [ka_{ij}]$.

Verbal Interpretation	Example
To multiply a matrix A by a scalar k, multiply each element in the matrix by k.	Given $A = \begin{bmatrix} -4 & 5 & -1 \\ 0 & -3 & 2 \end{bmatrix}$, $5A = \begin{bmatrix} -20 & 25 & -5 \\ 0 & -15 & 10 \end{bmatrix}$.

The following properties of scalar multiplication are similar to those of the multiplication of real numbers.

Properties of Scalar Multiplication

Let A and B be $m \times n$ matrices and let c and d be real numbers. Then,

1. $c(A + B) = cA + cB$ Distributive property of scalar multiplication
2. $(c + d)A = cA + dA$ Distributive property of scalar multiplication
3. $c(dA) = (cd)A$ Associative property of scalar multiplication

EXAMPLE 4   Multiplying a Matrix by a Scalar

Given $A = \begin{bmatrix} 3 & -5 \\ 0 & 1 \\ -4 & 2 \end{bmatrix}$ and $B = \begin{bmatrix} -8 & 9 \\ 4 & -1 \\ 0 & 3 \end{bmatrix}$, find $2A + 4(A + B)$.

Solution:

$$2A + 4(A + B) = 2A + 4A + 4B \qquad \text{Apply the distributive property of scalar multiplication.}$$
$$= 6A + 4B$$

$$6A + 4B = 6\begin{bmatrix} 3 & -5 \\ 0 & 1 \\ -4 & 2 \end{bmatrix} + 4\begin{bmatrix} -8 & 9 \\ 4 & -1 \\ 0 & 3 \end{bmatrix} = \begin{bmatrix} 18 & -30 \\ 0 & 6 \\ -24 & 12 \end{bmatrix} + \begin{bmatrix} -32 & 36 \\ 16 & -4 \\ 0 & 12 \end{bmatrix}$$

$$= \begin{bmatrix} -14 & 6 \\ 16 & 2 \\ -24 & 24 \end{bmatrix}$$

Skill Practice 4   Given $A = \begin{bmatrix} 4 & -3 & 9 \end{bmatrix}$ and $B = \begin{bmatrix} -2 & 0 & 3 \end{bmatrix}$, find $-5A - 2(A + B)$.

TECHNOLOGY CONNECTIONS

Adding Matrices and Multiplying a Scalar by a Matrix

Many graphing utilities have the capability to perform operations on matrices. From Example 4, we can enter matrix A and matrix B into the calculator using the **EDIT** feature under the **MATRIX** menu. Then on the home screen enter 6[A] + 4[B] and press **ENTER**.

Alternatively, in "MATHPRINT" mode, enter the matrices on the home screen using **ALPHA F3**.

As seen, many of the same properties that are true for addition and multiplication of real numbers are true for the addition of matrices and for scalar multiplication. As a result, we can solve a matrix equation involving these operations in the same way as we solve a linear equation.

EXAMPLE 5   Solving a Matrix Equation

Solve the matrix equation for X, given that $A = \begin{bmatrix} 2 & 5 \\ 1 & -4 \end{bmatrix}$ and $B = \begin{bmatrix} 6 & -1 \\ -3 & -8 \end{bmatrix}$.

$4X - A = B$

Solution:

$$4X - A = B$$
$$4X = A + B \qquad \text{Add matrix } A \text{ to both sides.}$$
$$X = \frac{1}{4}(A + B) \qquad \text{Perform scalar multiplication by } \tfrac{1}{4} \text{ on both sides.}$$
$$X = \frac{1}{4}\left(\begin{bmatrix} 2 & 5 \\ 1 & -4 \end{bmatrix} + \begin{bmatrix} 6 & -1 \\ -3 & -8 \end{bmatrix}\right) \qquad \text{Add the matrices within parentheses.}$$
$$X = \frac{1}{4}\begin{bmatrix} 8 & 4 \\ -2 & -12 \end{bmatrix} \qquad \text{Multiply the matrix by the scalar } \tfrac{1}{4}.$$
$$X = \begin{bmatrix} 2 & 1 \\ -\frac{1}{2} & -3 \end{bmatrix} \qquad \text{Simplify.}$$

TIP We can substitute matrix X back into the equation $4X - A = B$ to verify that it is a solution to the equation.

Answer
4. $\begin{bmatrix} -24 & 21 & -69 \end{bmatrix}$

Skill Practice 5 Given $A = \begin{bmatrix} 4 & -3 \\ 1 & 11 \end{bmatrix}$ and $B = \begin{bmatrix} 2 & -1 \\ 6 & 5 \end{bmatrix}$, solve $2X + A = B$ for X.

4. Multiply Matrices

Finding the product of two matrices is more complicated than finding the product of a scalar and a matrix. We will demonstrate the process to multiply two matrices and then offer a formal definition.

Consider $A = \begin{bmatrix} 2 & -3 & 1 \\ -4 & 7 & 0 \end{bmatrix}$ and $B = \begin{bmatrix} -1 & -6 \\ 10 & 5 \\ 8 & -2 \end{bmatrix}$.

> **Avoiding Mistakes**
>
> For matrix multiplication, the number of rows of the first matrix does not need to be equal to the number of columns of the second matrix. For example, the product of a 3×4 and a 4×2 matrix results in a 3×2 matrix.
>
>

- To multiply AB, we require that the number of columns in A be equal to the number of rows in B.

- The resulting matrix will have dimensions equal to the number of rows of A by the number of columns of B.

The product AB will be a 2×2 matrix.

The product will be a 2×2 matrix.

$$\begin{bmatrix} 2 & -3 & 1 \\ -4 & 7 & 0 \end{bmatrix} \cdot \begin{bmatrix} -1 & -6 \\ 10 & 5 \\ 8 & -2 \end{bmatrix} = \begin{bmatrix} \square & \square \\ \square & \square \end{bmatrix}$$

To find the entry in the first row, first column of the product, multiply the corresponding elements in the first row of A by the elements in the first column of B, and take the sum.

$$\begin{bmatrix} 2 & -3 & 1 \\ -4 & 7 & 0 \end{bmatrix} \cdot \begin{bmatrix} -1 & -6 \\ 10 & 5 \\ 8 & -2 \end{bmatrix} = \begin{bmatrix} 2(-1) + (-3)(10) + 1(8) & \square \\ \square & \square \end{bmatrix}$$

To find the entry in the first row, second column of the product, take the sum of the products of the corresponding elements in the first row of A and second column of B.

$$\begin{bmatrix} 2 & -3 & 1 \\ -4 & 7 & 0 \end{bmatrix} \cdot \begin{bmatrix} -1 & -6 \\ 10 & 5 \\ 8 & -2 \end{bmatrix} = \begin{bmatrix} 2(-1) + (-3)(10) + 1(8) & 2(-6) + (-3)(5) + 1(-2) \\ \square & \square \end{bmatrix}$$

To find the entry in the second row, first column of the product, take the sum of the products of the corresponding elements in the second row of A and first column of B.

$$\begin{bmatrix} 2 & -3 & 1 \\ -4 & 7 & 0 \end{bmatrix} \cdot \begin{bmatrix} -1 & -6 \\ 10 & 5 \\ 8 & -2 \end{bmatrix} = \begin{bmatrix} 2(-1) + (-3)(10) + 1(8) & 2(-6) + (-3)(5) + 1(-2) \\ -4(-1) + 7(10) + 0(8) & \square \end{bmatrix}$$

Answer

5. $X = \begin{bmatrix} -1 & 1 \\ \frac{5}{2} & -3 \end{bmatrix}$

To find the entry in the second row, second column of the product, take the sum of the products of the corresponding elements in the second row of A and second column of B.

$$\begin{bmatrix} 2 & -3 & 1 \\ -4 & 7 & 0 \end{bmatrix} \cdot \begin{bmatrix} -1 & -6 \\ 10 & 5 \\ 8 & -2 \end{bmatrix} = \begin{bmatrix} 2(-1)+(-3)(10)+1(8) & 2(-6)+(-3)(5)+1(-2) \\ -4(-1)+7(10)+0(8) & -4(-6)+7(5)+0(-2) \end{bmatrix}$$

Simplifying, we have

$$AB = \begin{bmatrix} 2 & -3 & 1 \\ -4 & 7 & 0 \end{bmatrix} \cdot \begin{bmatrix} -1 & -6 \\ 10 & 5 \\ 8 & -2 \end{bmatrix} = \begin{bmatrix} -24 & -29 \\ 74 & 59 \end{bmatrix}$$

Matrix Multiplication

Let A be an $m \times p$ matrix and let B be a $p \times n$ matrix, then the product AB is an $m \times n$ matrix. For the matrix AB, the element in the ith row and jth column is the sum of the products of the corresponding elements in the ith row of A and the jth column of B.

Formally, if

$$A = \begin{bmatrix} a_{11} & a_{12} & \cdots & a_{1p} \\ a_{21} & a_{22} & \cdots & a_{2p} \\ \vdots & & & \\ a_{m1} & a_{m2} & \cdots & a_{mp} \end{bmatrix} \text{ and } B = \begin{bmatrix} b_{11} & b_{12} & \cdots & b_{1n} \\ b_{21} & b_{22} & \cdots & b_{2n} \\ \vdots & & & \\ b_{p1} & b_{p2} & \cdots & b_{pn} \end{bmatrix}$$

then the elements in the matrix $C = AB$ are given by

$$c_{ij} = a_{i1} \cdot b_{1j} + a_{i2} \cdot b_{2j} + \cdots + a_{ip} \cdot b_{pj}$$

Note: If the number of columns in A does not equal the number of rows in B, then the product AB is not defined.

EXAMPLE 6   Multiplying Matrices

Given $A = \begin{bmatrix} 2 & 5 & 6 \\ -3 & 0 & 1 \end{bmatrix}$, $B = \begin{bmatrix} 1 \\ 3 \\ -4 \end{bmatrix}$, and $C = \begin{bmatrix} -2 & 10 & 1 \end{bmatrix}$,

find the following products if possible.

a. AB **b.** BC **c.** AC

Solution:

a. $\underset{2 \times 3}{A} \cdot \underset{3 \times 1}{B}$

equal

The product is a 2×1 matrix.

Matrix A is a 2×3 matrix and matrix B is a 3×1 matrix. The number of columns in A is equal to the number of rows in B. The resulting matrix will be a 2×1 matrix.

$$= \begin{bmatrix} 2 & 5 & 6 \\ -3 & 0 & 1 \end{bmatrix} \cdot \begin{bmatrix} 1 \\ 3 \\ -4 \end{bmatrix} = \begin{bmatrix} 2(1)+5(3)+6(-4) \\ -3(1)+0(3)+1(-4) \end{bmatrix}$$

Multiply the elements in the first row of A by the elements in the first column of B.

$$= \begin{bmatrix} -7 \\ -7 \end{bmatrix}$$

Multiply the elements in the second row of A by the elements in the first column of B.

b. $\quad B \quad \cdot \quad C$

$\quad 3 \times 1 \qquad 1 \times 3$

equal

The product is a
3×3 matrix.

Matrix B is a 3×1 matrix and matrix C is a 1×3 matrix. The number of columns in B is equal to the number of rows in C. The resulting matrix will be a 3×3 matrix.

$$B \cdot C = \begin{bmatrix} 1 \\ 3 \\ -4 \end{bmatrix} \cdot \begin{bmatrix} -2 & 10 & 1 \end{bmatrix} = \begin{bmatrix} 1(-2) & 1(10) & 1(1) \\ 3(-2) & 3(10) & 3(1) \\ -4(-2) & -4(10) & -4(1) \end{bmatrix}$$

$$= \begin{bmatrix} -2 & 10 & 1 \\ -6 & 30 & 3 \\ 8 & -40 & -4 \end{bmatrix}$$

c. $\quad A \quad \cdot \quad C$

$\quad 2 \times 3 \qquad 1 \times 3$

not equal

The number of columns of A does not equal the number of rows of C. Therefore, the product AC is undefined.

Skill Practice 6 Given $A = \begin{bmatrix} 2 & -5 \\ 1 & 0 \end{bmatrix}$, $B = \begin{bmatrix} 3 & 5 & 4 \\ 6 & 0 & -8 \end{bmatrix}$, and $C = \begin{bmatrix} 1 \\ 0 \\ 6 \end{bmatrix}$,

find the products if possible. **a.** AB **b.** BC **c.** AC

In Example 7, we multiply two matrices to demonstrate that matrix multiplication is not a commutative operation.

EXAMPLE 7 **Multiplying Matrices**

Given $A = \begin{bmatrix} 3 & -4 \\ 1 & 5 \end{bmatrix}$ and $B = \begin{bmatrix} 1 & 0 \\ -3 & 6 \end{bmatrix}$, find the following products if possible.

a. AB **b.** BA

Solution:

a. $\quad A \quad \cdot \quad B$

$\quad 2 \times 2 \qquad 2 \times 2$

equal

The product is a
2×2 matrix.

$$AB = \begin{bmatrix} 3 & -4 \\ 1 & 5 \end{bmatrix} \cdot \begin{bmatrix} 1 & 0 \\ -3 & 6 \end{bmatrix}$$

$$= \begin{bmatrix} 3(1) + (-4)(-3) & 3(0) + (-4)(6) \\ 1(1) + 5(-3) & 1(0) + 5(6) \end{bmatrix}$$

$$= \begin{bmatrix} 15 & -24 \\ -14 & 30 \end{bmatrix}$$

b. $\quad B \quad \cdot \quad A$

$\quad 2 \times 2 \qquad 2 \times 2$

equal

The product is a
2×2 matrix.

$$BA = \begin{bmatrix} 1 & 0 \\ -3 & 6 \end{bmatrix} \cdot \begin{bmatrix} 3 & -4 \\ 1 & 5 \end{bmatrix}$$

$$= \begin{bmatrix} 1(3) + 0(1) & 1(-4) + 0(5) \\ -3(3) + 6(1) & -3(-4) + 6(5) \end{bmatrix}$$

$$= \begin{bmatrix} 3 & -4 \\ -3 & 42 \end{bmatrix}$$

Answers

6. a. $AB = \begin{bmatrix} -24 & 10 & 48 \\ 3 & 5 & 4 \end{bmatrix}$

b. $BC = \begin{bmatrix} 27 \\ -42 \end{bmatrix}$

c. Not possible

7. a. $AB = \begin{bmatrix} -16 & 1 \\ 30 & 5 \end{bmatrix}$

b. $BA = \begin{bmatrix} 2 & 14 \\ 6 & -13 \end{bmatrix}$

Skill Practice 7 Given $A = \begin{bmatrix} 1 & -3 \\ 0 & 5 \end{bmatrix}$ and $B = \begin{bmatrix} 2 & 4 \\ 6 & 1 \end{bmatrix}$, find the

following products if possible. **a.** AB **b.** BA

Example 7 shows us that for two matrices A and B, the product AB does not necessarily equal BA. That is, matrix multiplication is not commutative.

TECHNOLOGY CONNECTIONS

Multiplying Matrices

To multiply two matrices on a graphing utility, first enter the matrices into the calculator using the EDIT feature under the MATRIX menu. Then on the home screen, enter the product. The products AB and BA from Example 7 are shown here.

Alternatively, in "MATHPRINT" mode, enter the matrices on the home screen using ALPHA F3. The product AB is shown here.

---

5. Apply Operations on Matrices

In Examples 8–10, we look at three applications of matrices. Example 8 demonstrates how scalar multiplication can be used to multiply all elements in a database by a constant multiple.

EXAMPLE 8   Applying Scalar Multiplication

A surf shop buys four different models of long boards and short boards from the manufacturer at the following prices.

	Model A	Model B	Model C	Model D
Long board	$1020	$830	$610	$570
Short board	$890	$780	$540	$490

If the shop applies a 20% markup to the manufacturer price, use scalar multiplication to obtain a matrix representing the retail prices.

Solution:

To mark up each item 20%, the retail price will be 120% of the manufacturer price. Therefore, we need to multiply the manufacturer price for each item by 1.20.

$$1.20\begin{bmatrix} 1020 & 830 & 610 & 570 \\ 890 & 780 & 540 & 490 \end{bmatrix} = \begin{bmatrix} 1.2(1020) & 1.2(830) & 1.2(610) & 1.2(570) \\ 1.2(890) & 1.2(780) & 1.2(540) & 1.2(490) \end{bmatrix}$$

$$= \begin{bmatrix} 1224 & 996 & 732 & 684 \\ 1068 & 936 & 648 & 588 \end{bmatrix}$$

> **Skill Practice 8**   Suppose that the surf shop goes out of business and sells off its inventory at 80% of the manufacturer's price. Use scalar multiplication to obtain a matrix representing the sale prices.

In Chapter 2 we learned how to apply transformations to the graphs of functions. In Example 9 we see how matrices can also be used to transform images in a rectangular coordinate system.

Answer

8. $\begin{bmatrix} 816 & 664 & 488 & 456 \\ 712 & 624 & 432 & 392 \end{bmatrix}$

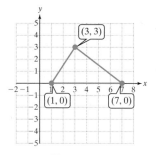

EXAMPLE 9   **Using Matrix Operations to Transform a Graph**

Consider the triangle shown in Figure 6-6. The vertices of the triangle can be represented in a matrix where the first row represents the x-coordinates and the second row represents the corresponding y-coordinates.

$$A = \begin{bmatrix} 1 & 3 & 7 \\ 0 & 3 & 0 \end{bmatrix} \longleftarrow x\text{-coordinates} \\ \longleftarrow y\text{-coordinates}$$

Figure 6-6

a. Use addition of matrices to shift the triangle 3 units to the left and 2 units upward.

b. Find the product $\begin{bmatrix} -1 & 0 \\ 0 & 1 \end{bmatrix} \cdot A$ and determine the effect on the graph.

c. Find the product $\begin{bmatrix} 1 & 0 \\ 0 & -1 \end{bmatrix} \cdot A$ and determine the effect on the graph.

Solution:

a. To shift the graph to the left, subtract 3 from each x-coordinate.
To shift the graph upward, add 2 to each y-coordinate.

$$\begin{bmatrix} 1 & 3 & 7 \\ 0 & 3 & 0 \end{bmatrix} + \begin{bmatrix} -3 & -3 & -3 \\ 2 & 2 & 2 \end{bmatrix} \begin{array}{l} \longleftarrow \text{This row subtracts 3 from each } x\text{-coordinate.} \\ \longleftarrow \text{This row adds 2 to each } y\text{-coordinate.} \end{array}$$

$$= \begin{bmatrix} -2 & 0 & 4 \\ 2 & 5 & 2 \end{bmatrix}$$

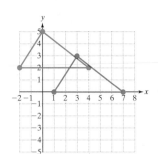

Figure 6-7

The vertices of the new triangle are $(-2, 2)$, $(0, 5)$, and $(4, 2)$. See Figure 6-7.

b. $\begin{bmatrix} -1 & 0 \\ 0 & 1 \end{bmatrix} \cdot A = \begin{bmatrix} -1 & 0 \\ 0 & 1 \end{bmatrix} \begin{bmatrix} 1 & 3 & 7 \\ 0 & 3 & 0 \end{bmatrix}$

$= \begin{bmatrix} -1(1) + 0(0) & -1(3) + 0(3) & -1(7) + 0(0) \\ 0(1) + 1(0) & 0(3) + 1(3) & 0(7) + 1(0) \end{bmatrix}$

$= \begin{bmatrix} -1 & -3 & -7 \\ 0 & 3 & 0 \end{bmatrix}$ The corresponding points are $(-1, 0)$, $(-3, 3)$, and $(-7, 0)$.

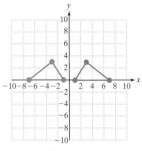

Figure 6-8

The triangle has been reflected across the y-axis. See Figure 6-8.

c. $\begin{bmatrix} 1 & 0 \\ 0 & -1 \end{bmatrix} \cdot A = \begin{bmatrix} 1 & 0 \\ 0 & -1 \end{bmatrix} \begin{bmatrix} 1 & 3 & 7 \\ 0 & 3 & 0 \end{bmatrix}$

$= \begin{bmatrix} 1(1) + 0(0) & 1(3) + 0(3) & 1(7) + 0(0) \\ 0(1) + -1(0) & 0(3) + -1(3) & 0(7) + -1(0) \end{bmatrix}$

$= \begin{bmatrix} 1 & 3 & 7 \\ 0 & -3 & 0 \end{bmatrix}$ The corresponding points are $(1, 0)$, $(3, -3)$, and $(7, 0)$.

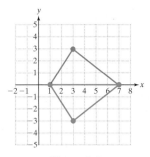

Figure 6-9

The triangle has been reflected across the x-axis. See Figure 6-9.

Answer

9. $\begin{bmatrix} -1 & -3 & -7 \\ 0 & -3 & 0 \end{bmatrix}$; The triangle is reflected across both the x- and y-axes.

Skill Practice 9   Use matrix A from Example 9. Find the product $\begin{bmatrix} -1 & 0 \\ 0 & -1 \end{bmatrix} \cdot A$ and determine the effect on the graph of the triangle in Figure 6-6.

The colors you see in a digital photograph or on the screen of your computer are the result of a color code assigned to each pixel. For a black-and-white image, each pixel is assigned a number usually between 0 and 255, where each value represents a different shade of gray. This is called a gray scale. A picture can be manipulated by adjusting the grayscale values for any given pixel in the image. We illustrate this concept in Example 10.

EXAMPLE 10   **Applying Matrix Addition to Adjust a Digital Image**

Consider a gray scale with eight shades of gray numbered 0 to 7.

| 0 | 1 | 2 | 3 | 4 | 5 | 6 | 7 |
| white | light gray | medium light | gray | medium gray | medium dark | dark gray | black |

The digit 4 shown in Figure 6-10 is dark gray on a gray background and can be represented by the matrix:

$$\begin{bmatrix} 6 & 3 & 6 \\ 6 & 3 & 6 \\ 6 & 6 & 6 \\ 3 & 3 & 6 \\ 3 & 3 & 6 \end{bmatrix}$$

Figure 6-10

Use matrix addition to change the pixels representing the digit 4 to black on a light gray background.

Solution:

$$\begin{bmatrix} 6 & 3 & 6 \\ 6 & 3 & 6 \\ 6 & 6 & 6 \\ 3 & 3 & 6 \\ 3 & 3 & 6 \end{bmatrix} + \begin{bmatrix} 1 & -2 & 1 \\ 1 & -2 & 1 \\ 1 & 1 & 1 \\ -2 & -2 & 1 \\ -2 & -2 & 1 \end{bmatrix} = \begin{bmatrix} 7 & 1 & 7 \\ 7 & 1 & 7 \\ 7 & 7 & 7 \\ 1 & 1 & 7 \\ 1 & 1 & 7 \end{bmatrix}$$

To adjust the contrast, we want to darken the pixels that form the digit 4 to black. To do so, add 1 to each pixel that forms the number 4.

To lighten the background to light gray, subtract 2 from the pixels that form the background.

The new image is shown in Figure 6-11.

Figure 6-11

Point of Interest

A computer font is a data file containing a set of individual writing elements called glyphs. A raster font consists of a matrix (also called a bitmap) whose individual elements represent each pixel in the image.

Skill Practice 10   Use matrix addition to transform the image from Figure 6-10 to an image in which the digit 4 is medium dark and the background is white.

Answer

10. $$\begin{bmatrix} 6 & 3 & 6 \\ 6 & 3 & 6 \\ 6 & 6 & 6 \\ 3 & 3 & 6 \\ 3 & 3 & 6 \end{bmatrix} + \begin{bmatrix} -1 & -3 & -1 \\ -1 & -3 & -1 \\ -1 & -1 & -1 \\ -3 & -3 & -1 \\ -3 & -3 & -1 \end{bmatrix}$$
$$= \begin{bmatrix} 5 & 0 & 5 \\ 5 & 0 & 5 \\ 5 & 5 & 5 \\ 0 & 0 & 5 \\ 0 & 0 & 5 \end{bmatrix}$$

SECTION 6.3   Practice Exercises

Review Exercises

1. Given a real number a, the additive inverse of a is _____ because $a + (\quad) = 0$.

2. What is the additive inverse of 7?

3. What is the additive inverse of $-\frac{2}{3}$?

4. Using the real numbers a, b, and c, state the
   a. commutative property of addition.
   b. associative property of addition.

5. Given the point $(5, -2)$, what is the corresponding point reflected across the x-axis?

6. Given the point $(-3, -1)$, what is the corresponding point reflected across the y-axis?

Concept Connections

7. If the _____ of a matrix is $p \times q$, then p represents the number of _____ and q represents the number of _____.

8. A matrix with only one column is called a _____ matrix.

9. A matrix with the same number of rows and columns is called a _____ matrix.

10. A matrix with only one row is called a _____ matrix.

11. What are the requirements for two matrices to be equal?

12. An $m \times n$ matrix whose elements are all zero is called a _____ matrix.

13. If $A = [a_{ij}]$ then the additive inverse of A is denoted by $-A$ and $-A =$ _____.

14. Given $A = [a_{ij}]$, then for a real number k, the product $kA =$ _____.

15. To multiply two matrices A and B, the number of _____ of A must equal the number of _____ of B.

16. If A is a 5×3 matrix and B is a 3×7 matrix, then the product AB will be a matrix of order _____. The product BA (is/is not) defined.

17. True or false: Matrix multiplication is a commutative operation.

18. True or false: If a row matrix A and a column matrix B have the same number of elements, then the product AB is well defined.

Objective 1: Determine the Order of a Matrix

For Exercises 19–24,

a. Give the order of the matrix.

b. Classify the matrix as a square matrix, row matrix, column matrix, or none of these. (**See Example 1**)

19. $\begin{bmatrix} 3 & 5 & -1 \\ \frac{1}{2} & \sqrt{3} & 1.7 \end{bmatrix}$

20. $\begin{bmatrix} 1 & 5 & 6 & 2 \\ -1 & 3 & -\frac{2}{3} & \pi \\ 0 & 1 & -6.1 & 12 \end{bmatrix}$

21. $\begin{bmatrix} 3 \\ 1 \\ 7 \end{bmatrix}$

22. $\begin{bmatrix} 2.4 & 6.9 \end{bmatrix}$

23. $\begin{bmatrix} 4 & 2 \\ 8 & 4 \end{bmatrix}$

24. $\begin{bmatrix} -4 & 10 & 3 & 0 \\ 0 & 1 & 0 & 0 \\ 7 & 0 & 9 & -1 \\ 0 & 2 & 0 & 1 \end{bmatrix}$

For Exercises 25–30, determine the value of the given element of the matrix $A = [a_{ij}]$. (See Example 2)

$$A = \begin{bmatrix} 3 & -6 & \frac{1}{3} \\ 2 & 4 & 0 \\ \sqrt{5} & 11 & 8.6 \\ \frac{1}{2} & 4 & 2 \end{bmatrix}$$

25. a_{31} **26.** a_{32} **27.** a_{13}

28. a_{23} **29.** a_{43} **30.** a_{42}

Objective 2: Add and Subtract Matrices

31. Given $A = \begin{bmatrix} 2 & x \\ z & -5 \end{bmatrix}$ and $B = \begin{bmatrix} y & 4 \\ 10 & -5 \end{bmatrix}$, for what values of x, y, and z will $A = B$?

32. Given $A = \begin{bmatrix} 4 & a \\ b & 7 \end{bmatrix}$ and $B = \begin{bmatrix} c & 12 \\ -1 & 6 \end{bmatrix}$, is it possible that $A = B$? Explain.

33. Given $B = \begin{bmatrix} -4 & 6 & 9 \\ \frac{3}{5} & 1 & 7 \end{bmatrix}$, find the additive inverse of B.

34. Given $C = \begin{bmatrix} -1 & 6 \\ \sqrt{3} & 9 \end{bmatrix}$, find the additive inverse of C.

For Exercises 35–40, add or subtract the given matrices if possible. (See Example 3)

$$A = \begin{bmatrix} 6 & -1 \\ 7 & \frac{1}{2} \\ 2 & \sqrt{2} \end{bmatrix} \quad B = \begin{bmatrix} -9 & 2 \\ 6.2 & 2 \\ \frac{1}{3} & \sqrt{8} \end{bmatrix} \quad C = \begin{bmatrix} 11 & 4 \\ 1 & -\frac{1}{3} \\ 1 & 6 \end{bmatrix} \quad D = \begin{bmatrix} 2 & 3 & 8 \\ -1 & 6 & \frac{1}{6} \end{bmatrix}$$

35. $A + B$ **36.** $A + C$ **37.** $C - A + B$

38. $B - A - C$ **39.** $B + D$ **40.** $C + D$

Objective 3: Multiply a Matrix by a Scalar

For Exercises 41–48, perform the indicated operations. (See Example 4)

$$A = \begin{bmatrix} 2 & 4 & -9 \\ 1 & \sqrt{3} & \frac{1}{2} \end{bmatrix} \quad B = \begin{bmatrix} -1 & 0 & 4 \\ 2 & 9 & \frac{2}{3} \end{bmatrix}$$

41. $3A$ **42.** $-6B$ **43.** $-2A - 7B$

44. $4A - 3B$ **45.** $-4(A + B)$ **46.** $2(A - B)$

47. $-3A + 5(A - B)$ **48.** $-8A - 2(A + B)$

For Exercises 49–54, given the matrices A and B, solve for X. (See Example 5)

$$A = \begin{bmatrix} 1 & 6 \\ 4 & -2 \end{bmatrix} \quad B = \begin{bmatrix} 2 & -4 \\ 6 & 9 \end{bmatrix}$$

49. $2X - B = A$ **50.** $3X + A = B$ **51.** $A + 5X = B$

52. $B - 4X = A$ **53.** $2A - B = 10X$ **54.** $3B - A = -2X$

Objective 4: Multiply Matrices

55. Given that A is a 4×2 matrix and B is a 2×1 matrix,
   a. Is AB defined? If so, what is the order of AB?
   b. Is BA defined? If so, what is the order of BA?

56. Given that C is a 3×7 matrix and D is a 7×2 matrix,
   a. Is CD defined? If so, what is the order of CD?
   b. Is DC defined? If so, what is the order of DC?

57. Given that E is a 5×1 matrix and F is a 1×5 matrix,
   a. Is EF defined? If so, what is the order of EF?
   b. Is FE defined? If so, what is the order of FE?

58. Given that G is a 1×6 matrix and H is a 6×1 matrix,
   a. Is GH defined? If so, what is the order of GH?
   b. Is HG defined? If so, what is the order of HG?

For Exercises 59–70, (See Examples 6–7)

a. Find AB if possible.

b. Find BA if possible

c. Find A^2 if possible. (*Hint*: $A^2 = A \cdot A$.)

59. $A = \begin{bmatrix} 2 & 3 \\ 5 & 7 \end{bmatrix}$ and $B = \begin{bmatrix} 1 & 4 \\ -1 & 3 \end{bmatrix}$

60. $A = \begin{bmatrix} 1 & -6 \\ 5 & 10 \end{bmatrix}$ and $B = \begin{bmatrix} -2 & 3 \\ 7 & -1 \end{bmatrix}$

61. $A = \begin{bmatrix} 2 & 4 \\ -6 & 3 \\ 1 & 7 \end{bmatrix}$ and $B = \begin{bmatrix} 1 & 4 & -1 \\ -2 & 0 & 10 \end{bmatrix}$

62. $A = \begin{bmatrix} 1 & 3 & 4 \\ -2 & 5 & 6 \end{bmatrix}$ and $B = \begin{bmatrix} 1 & 3 \\ 9 & 2 \\ 0 & 4 \end{bmatrix}$

63. $A = \begin{bmatrix} -9 & 2 & 3 \\ -1 & 5 & 4 \\ 0 & 1 & 7 \end{bmatrix}$ and $B = \begin{bmatrix} -1 \\ 5 \\ 0 \end{bmatrix}$

64. $A = \begin{bmatrix} 2 \\ -1 \\ 3 \end{bmatrix}$ and $B = \begin{bmatrix} 2 & 7 & -1 \\ 0 & 4 & 1 \\ 0 & 3 & -6 \end{bmatrix}$

65. $A = \begin{bmatrix} 1 & \frac{1}{2} \end{bmatrix}$ and $B = \begin{bmatrix} -\frac{1}{3} \\ 2 \end{bmatrix}$

66. $A = \begin{bmatrix} 4 \\ \frac{3}{4} \\ 1 \end{bmatrix}$ and $B = \begin{bmatrix} -5 & \frac{1}{2} & \frac{1}{3} \end{bmatrix}$

67. $A = \begin{bmatrix} 4 \\ -6 \end{bmatrix}$ and $B = \begin{bmatrix} 1 & 2 & 5 & 6 \end{bmatrix}$

68. $A = \begin{bmatrix} 4 \end{bmatrix}$ and $B = \begin{bmatrix} -3 & 4 & 1 \end{bmatrix}$

69. $A = \begin{bmatrix} -5 \end{bmatrix}$ and $B = \begin{bmatrix} 5 \end{bmatrix}$

70. $A = \begin{bmatrix} 6 \end{bmatrix}$ and $B = \begin{bmatrix} -2 \end{bmatrix}$

For Exercises 71–74, find AB and BA.

71. $A = \begin{bmatrix} 3.1 & -2.3 \\ 1.1 & 6.5 \end{bmatrix}$ and $B = \begin{bmatrix} 1 & 0 \\ 0 & 1 \end{bmatrix}$

72. $A = \begin{bmatrix} 1 & 0 \\ 0 & 1 \end{bmatrix}$ and $B = \begin{bmatrix} 0.05 & -0.07 \\ 0.16 & 0.09 \end{bmatrix}$

73. $A = \begin{bmatrix} 1 & 0 & 0 \\ 0 & 1 & 0 \\ 0 & 0 & 1 \end{bmatrix}$ and $B = \begin{bmatrix} \frac{9}{5} & -3 & \sqrt{6} \\ 5 & \frac{1}{2} & 2 \\ 3 & 0 & 1 \end{bmatrix}$

74. $A = \begin{bmatrix} \frac{2}{3} & 5 & \sqrt{2} \\ 1 & 0 & 3 \\ -\frac{1}{4} & 0 & 8 \end{bmatrix}$ and $B = \begin{bmatrix} 1 & 0 & 0 \\ 0 & 1 & 0 \\ 0 & 0 & 1 \end{bmatrix}$

Objective 5: Apply Operations on Matrices

75. According to Kelly Blue Book, matrix D gives the dealer invoice prices for four models of Honda 2011 cars. Matrix M gives the MSRP (manufacturer's suggested retail price) for the cars. (*Source*: www.kbb.com) **(See Example 8)**

$$D = \begin{matrix} & \textbf{Accord} & \textbf{Civic} \\ & \textbf{LX Sedan} & \textbf{LX Sedan} \\ & \begin{bmatrix} \$19,963 & \$17,109 \\ \$20,686 & \$17,843 \end{bmatrix} & \begin{matrix} \textbf{Manual} \\ \textbf{Automatic} \end{matrix} \end{matrix}$$

$$M = \begin{matrix} & \textbf{Accord} & \textbf{Civic} \\ & \textbf{LX Sedan} & \textbf{LX Sedan} \\ & \begin{bmatrix} \$21,930 & \$18,505 \\ \$22,730 & \$19,305 \end{bmatrix} & \begin{matrix} \textbf{Manual} \\ \textbf{Automatic} \end{matrix} \end{matrix}$$

a. Compute $M - D$ and interpret its meaning.

b. A buyer thinks that a fair price is 6% above dealer invoice. Use scalar multiplication to determine a matrix F that gives the fair price for these four cars. Round each entry to the nearest dollar.

76. In matrix C, a coffee shop records the cost to produce a cup of standard Columbian coffee and the cost to produce a cup of hot chocolate. Matrix P contains the selling prices to the customer.

$$C = \begin{matrix} & \textbf{Coffee} & \textbf{Chocolate} \\ & \begin{bmatrix} \$0.90 & \$0.84 \\ \$1.26 & \$1.15 \\ \$1.64 & \$1.50 \end{bmatrix} & \begin{matrix} \textbf{Small} \\ \textbf{Medium} \\ \textbf{Large} \end{matrix} \end{matrix}$$

$$P = \begin{matrix} & \textbf{Coffee} & \textbf{Chocolate} \\ & \begin{bmatrix} \$3.05 & \$2.25 \\ \$3.65 & \$3.05 \\ \$4.15 & \$3.65 \end{bmatrix} & \begin{matrix} \textbf{Small} \\ \textbf{Medium} \\ \textbf{Large} \end{matrix} \end{matrix}$$

a. Compute $P - C$ and interpret its meaning.

b. If the tax rate in a certain city is 7%, use scalar multiplication to find a matrix F that gives the final price to the customer (including sales tax) for both beverages for each size. Round each entry to the nearest cent.

77. A student researches the cost for three cell phone plans. Matrix C contains the cost per text message and the cost per minute over the maximum number of minutes allowed in each plan. Matrix N_1 contains the number of text messages and the number of minutes over the maximum incurred for 1 month. Matrix N_3 represents the number of text messages and number of minutes over the maximum for 3 months.

$$C = \begin{bmatrix} \$0.25 & \$0.40 \\ \$0 & \$0.40 \\ \$0.10 & \$0 \end{bmatrix} \begin{matrix} \text{Plan A} \\ \text{Plan B} \\ \text{Plan C} \end{matrix}$$

$$\begin{matrix} \text{Cost/text} & \text{Cost/min} \end{matrix}$$

$$N_1 = \begin{bmatrix} 24 \\ 100 \end{bmatrix} \begin{matrix} \textbf{Number of texts} \\ \textbf{Minutes over} \end{matrix}$$

$$N_3 = \begin{bmatrix} 24 & 56 & 30 \\ 100 & 24 & 0 \end{bmatrix} \begin{matrix} \textbf{Number of texts} \\ \textbf{Minutes over} \end{matrix}$$

$$\begin{matrix} \text{Month} & \text{Month} & \text{Month} \\ \text{1} & \text{2} & \text{3} \end{matrix}$$

a. Find the product CN_1 and interpret its meaning.

b. Find the product CN_3 and interpret its meaning.

79. Refer to Exercise 77. Suppose that matrix B represents the base cost for each cell phone plan and matrix T represents the tax for each plan.

$$B = \begin{bmatrix} \$39.99 \\ \$49.99 \\ \$59.99 \end{bmatrix} \begin{matrix} \textbf{Plan A} \\ \textbf{Plan B} \\ \textbf{Plan C} \end{matrix}$$

$$T = \begin{bmatrix} \$11.96 \\ \$13.04 \\ \$14.91 \end{bmatrix} \begin{matrix} \textbf{Plan A} \\ \textbf{Plan B} \\ \textbf{Plan C} \end{matrix}$$

a. Compute $B + CN_1 + T$ and interpret its meaning.

b. Which cell phone plan is the least expensive if the student has 60 text messages and talks 20 min more than the maximum?

78. Matrix G represents the gas mileage (in gal/mi) for city and highway driving for four models of Honda cars. (*Source*: U.S. Department of Energy, http://www. fueleconomy.gov/) Matrix N_1 represents the number of city and highway miles driven for one trip. Matrix N_3 represents the number of city and highway miles driven for three trips.

$$G = \begin{bmatrix} \frac{1}{23} & \frac{1}{33} \\ \frac{1}{23} & \frac{1}{34} \\ \frac{1}{26} & \frac{1}{34} \\ \frac{1}{25} & \frac{1}{36} \end{bmatrix} \begin{matrix} \textbf{Accord Manual} \\ \textbf{Accord Automatic} \\ \textbf{Civic Manual} \\ \textbf{Civic Automatic} \end{matrix}$$

$$\begin{matrix} \textbf{City} & \textbf{Highway} \end{matrix}$$

$$N_1 = \begin{bmatrix} 100 \\ 460 \end{bmatrix} \begin{matrix} \textbf{Number of city miles} \\ \textbf{Number of highway miles} \end{matrix}$$

$$N_3 = \begin{bmatrix} 100 & 80 & 24 \\ 460 & 180 & 240 \end{bmatrix} \begin{matrix} \textbf{Number of city miles} \\ \textbf{Number of highway miles} \end{matrix}$$

$$\begin{matrix} \textbf{Trip} & \textbf{Trip} & \textbf{Trip} \\ \textbf{1} & \textbf{2} & \textbf{3} \end{matrix}$$

a. Find the product GN_1 and interpret its meaning. Round each entry to 1 decimal place.

b. Find the product GN_3 and interpret its meaning. Round each entry to 1 decimal place.

80. Refer to Exercise 78.

a. Suppose that gasoline costs \$4.40 per gallon. Compute $4.4(GN_1)$ and interpret its meaning.

b. The costs for the 2011 models of cars from Exercise 78 are given in matrix C. Suppose that a customer plans to keep a car for 10 yr. Further suppose that the customer drives an average of 8000 city miles and 2000 highway miles per year (matrix Y). If the average price of gasoline for the next 10 yr is \$4.90, compute $\frac{1}{10}C + 4.9(GY)$ and interpret its meaning. Round each entry to the nearest dollar.

$$C = \begin{bmatrix} \$21{,}930 \\ \$22{,}730 \\ \$18{,}505 \\ \$19{,}305 \end{bmatrix} \begin{matrix} \textbf{Accord Manual} \\ \textbf{Accord Automatic} \\ \textbf{Civic Manual} \\ \textbf{Civic Automatic} \end{matrix}$$

$$\begin{matrix} \textbf{Cost} \end{matrix}$$

$$Y = \begin{bmatrix} 8000 \\ 2000 \end{bmatrix} \begin{matrix} \textbf{Number of city miles} \\ \textbf{Number of highway miles} \end{matrix}$$

81. a. Write a matrix A that represents the coordinates of the triangle. Place the x-coordinate of each point in the first row of A and the corresponding y-coordinate in the second row of A. **(See Example 9)**

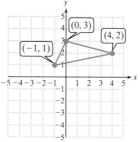

b. Use addition of matrices to shift the triangle 2 units to the right and 4 units downward.

c. Find the product $\begin{bmatrix} -1 & 0 \\ 0 & 1 \end{bmatrix} \cdot A$ and explain the effect on the graph of the triangle.

d. Find the product $\begin{bmatrix} 1 & 0 \\ 0 & -1 \end{bmatrix} \cdot A$ and explain the effect on the graph of the triangle.

e. Find $\begin{bmatrix} 1 & 0 \\ 0 & -1 \end{bmatrix} \cdot A + \begin{bmatrix} -1 & -1 & -1 \\ 2 & 2 & 2 \end{bmatrix}$ and explain the effect on the graph of the triangle.

82. a. Write a matrix A that represents the coordinates of the triangle. Place the x-coordinate of each point in the first row of A and the corresponding y-coordinate in the second row of A.

b. Use addition of matrices to shift the triangle 1 unit to the left and 3 units upward.

c. Find the product $\begin{bmatrix} -1 & 0 \\ 0 & 1 \end{bmatrix} \cdot A$ and explain the effect on the graph of the triangle.

d. Find the product $\begin{bmatrix} 1 & 0 \\ 0 & -1 \end{bmatrix} \cdot A$ and explain the effect on the graph of the triangle.

e. Find $\begin{bmatrix} -1 & 0 \\ 0 & 1 \end{bmatrix} \cdot A + \begin{bmatrix} 2 & 2 & 2 \\ -5 & -5 & -5 \end{bmatrix}$ and explain the effect on the graph of the triangle.

83. a. Write a matrix A that represents the coordinates of the quadrilateral.

b. What operation on A will shift the graph of the quadrilateral 3 units downward?

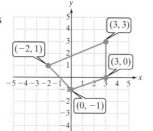

c. What operation on A will shift the graph 4 units to the left?

d. Use matrix multiplication to reflect the graph across the x-axis.

e. Use matrix multiplication to reflect the graph across the y-axis.

84. a. Write a matrix A that represents the coordinates of the quadrilateral.

b. What operation on A will shift the graph of the quadrilateral 6 units upward?

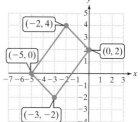

c. What operation on A will shift the graph 2 units to the right?

d. Use matrix multiplication to reflect the graph across the x-axis.

e. Use matrix multiplication to reflect the graph across the y-axis.

85. a. Write a matrix A that represents the coordinates of the triangle.

b. Multiply $\begin{bmatrix} \frac{\sqrt{3}}{2} & -\frac{1}{2} \\ \frac{1}{2} & \frac{\sqrt{3}}{2} \end{bmatrix} \cdot A$ and round each entry to 1 decimal place.

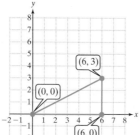

c. Graph the figure represented by the matrix from part (b). What effect does this product have on the graph of the triangle?

86. a. Write a matrix A that represents the coordinates of the triangle.

b. Multiply $\begin{bmatrix} \frac{1}{2} & -\frac{\sqrt{3}}{2} \\ \frac{\sqrt{3}}{2} & \frac{1}{2} \end{bmatrix} \cdot A$ and round each entry to 1 decimal place.

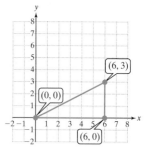

c. Graph the figure represented by the matrix from part (b). What effect does this product have on the graph of the triangle?

For Exercises 87–88, use the following gray scale.

0	1	2	3	4	5	6	7
white	light gray	medium light	gray	medium gray	medium dark	dark gray	black

87. a. Write a 5×3 matrix that represents the letter E in dark gray on a white background. **(See Example 10)**

   b. Use matrix addition to change the pixels so that the letter E is medium dark on a light gray background.

88. a. Write a 5×3 matrix that represents the letter T in medium gray on a medium light background.

   b. Use matrix addition to change the pixels so that the letter T is dark gray on a light gray background.

Mixed Exercises

For Exercises 89–94, use matrices A, B, and C to demonstrate the following properties. Assume that the elements within A, B, and C are real numbers.

$$A = \begin{bmatrix} a_1 & a_2 \\ a_3 & a_4 \end{bmatrix} \quad B = \begin{bmatrix} b_1 & b_2 \\ b_3 & b_4 \end{bmatrix} \quad C = \begin{bmatrix} c_1 & c_2 \\ c_3 & c_4 \end{bmatrix}$$

89. Commutative property of matrix addition

$$A + B = B + A$$

90. Associative property of matrix addition

$$A + (B + C) = (A + B) + C$$

91. Inverse property of matrix addition

$$A + (-A) = 0$$

92. Identity property of matrix addition

$$A + 0 = A$$

93. Associative property of scalar multiplication

$$s(tA) = (st)A$$

94. Distributive property of scalar multiplication

$$t(A + B) = tA + tB$$

95. Given $A = \begin{bmatrix} i & 0 \\ 0 & i \end{bmatrix}$, find A^2, A^3, and A^4.

   $\left(Hint\text{: Recall that } i = \sqrt{-1}.\right)$ Discuss the similarities between A^n and i^n, where n is a positive integer.

96. Given $B = \begin{bmatrix} 0 & -i \\ i & 0 \end{bmatrix}$, find B^2.

97. a. For real numbers a, b, c, and d, find the product.

$$\begin{bmatrix} a & 0 \\ 0 & b \end{bmatrix}\begin{bmatrix} c & 0 \\ 0 & d \end{bmatrix}$$

   b. Based on the form of the product of part (a), compute the following product mentally.

$$\begin{bmatrix} 3 & 0 \\ 0 & 7 \end{bmatrix}\begin{bmatrix} 1 & 0 \\ 0 & 2 \end{bmatrix}$$

98. Find the product.

$$\begin{bmatrix} a & a \\ b & b \end{bmatrix}\begin{bmatrix} 1 & -1 \\ -1 & 1 \end{bmatrix}$$

Write About It

99. Explain why the product of a 3×2 matrix by a 3×2 matrix is undefined.

100. Explain how to add or subtract matrices.

101. Given a matrix, $A = [a_{ij}]$, explain how to find the additive inverse of A.

102. Given two matrices A and B, how can you determine the order of AB, assuming that the product is well defined?

Technology Connections

For Exercises 103–104, use the matrices A and B and perform the indicated operations on a calculator.

$$A = \begin{bmatrix} 1 & 3 \\ 2 & 5 \\ -3 & 10 \end{bmatrix} \quad B = \begin{bmatrix} 6 & 2 \\ -4 & 1 \\ 0 & 8 \end{bmatrix}$$

103. $5A + 2B$

104. $-6A + 11B$

For Exercises 105–106, perform matrix addition and subtraction and scalar multiplication on a spreadsheet. For example, we have entered matrix A and matrix B in the spreadsheet as shown. To find $5A + 2B$, first highlight the six cells into which the resulting matrix will be found (in this case J1 through K3). Then in the formula field labeled f_x, enter $= 5*B1:C3 + 2*F1:G3$. To complete the calculation, simultaneously hold down the shift key and the control key and press ENTER. The resulting matrix should appear in cells J1 through K3.

$$A = \begin{bmatrix} 1 & 3 \\ 2 & 5 \\ -3 & 10 \end{bmatrix}, B = \begin{bmatrix} 6 & 2 \\ -4 & 1 \\ 0 & 8 \end{bmatrix}$$

		J1		▼		f_x	=5*B1:C3+2*F1:G3			
	A	B	C	D	E	F	G	H	I	J	K
1		1	3			6	2			17	19
2	A =	2	5			B =	-4	1		5A+2B =	2	27
3		-3	10				0	8			-15	66

105. Use a spreadsheet to compute $-3A + 7B$.

106. Use a spreadsheet to compute $6A - 2B$.

For Exercises 107–108, use the MMULT function on a spreadsheet for matrix multiplication. For example, we have entered matrix A and matrix B in the spreadsheet as shown. To find AB, first highlight the nine cells into which the resulting matrix will be found (in this case, L1 through N3). Then in the formula field labeled f_x, enter $= MMULT(B1:D3,G1:I3)$. Then simultaneously hold down the shift key and the control key and press ENTER. The resulting matrix should appear in cells L1 through N3.

$$A = \begin{bmatrix} -3 & 4 & 8 \\ 0 & 1 & 6 \\ 7 & -2 & 5 \end{bmatrix} B = \begin{bmatrix} -1 & 2 & 5 \\ 4 & 0 & 1 \\ -3 & 6 & 10 \end{bmatrix} C = \begin{bmatrix} 4 & 2 & 0 \\ 1 & 0 & 6 \\ -3 & 2 & -5 \end{bmatrix}$$

		L1		▼		f_x	=MMULT(B1:D3,G1:I3)				
	A	B	C	D	E	F	G	H	I	J	K	L	M	N
1		-3	4	8			-1	2	5			-5	42	69
2	A =	0	1	6		B =	4	0	1		AB =	-14	36	61
3		7	-2	5			-3	6	10			-30	44	83

107. AC

108. BA

SECTION 6.4 Inverse Matrices and Matrix Equations

OBJECTIVES

1. Identify Identity and Inverse Matrices
2. Determine the Inverse of a Matrix
3. Solve Systems of Linear Equations Using the Inverse of a Matrix

1. Identify Identity and Inverse Matrices

The identity element under the multiplication of real numbers is 1 because $a \cdot 1 = a$ and $1 \cdot a = a$. We now investigate a similar property for the product of square matrices. The **identity matrix** I_n for matrix multiplication is the $n \times n$ square matrix with 1's along the main diagonal and 0's for all other elements. For example:

The identity matrix of order 2

The identity matrix of order 3

$$I_2 = \begin{bmatrix} 1 & 0 \\ 0 & 1 \end{bmatrix} \quad \text{and} \quad I_3 = \begin{bmatrix} 1 & 0 & 0 \\ 0 & 1 & 0 \\ 0 & 0 & 1 \end{bmatrix}$$

For an $n \times n$ square matrix A, we have that

$$AI_n = A \quad \text{and} \quad I_nA = A \quad \text{(Identity property of matrix multiplication)}$$

In Example 1, we illustrate the identity property of matrix multiplication using a 2×2 matrix.

EXAMPLE 1 **Illustrating the Identity Property of Matrix Multiplication**

Given $A = \begin{bmatrix} a & b \\ c & d \end{bmatrix}$ show that

a. $AI_2 = A$ **b.** $I_2A = A$

Solution:

a. $AI_2 = \begin{bmatrix} a & b \\ c & d \end{bmatrix}\begin{bmatrix} 1 & 0 \\ 0 & 1 \end{bmatrix} = \begin{bmatrix} a(1) + b(0) & a(0) + b(1) \\ c(1) + d(0) & c(0) + d(1) \end{bmatrix} = \begin{bmatrix} a & b \\ c & d \end{bmatrix}$ ✓

b. $I_2 A = \begin{bmatrix} 1 & 0 \\ 0 & 1 \end{bmatrix}\begin{bmatrix} a & b \\ c & d \end{bmatrix} = \begin{bmatrix} 1(a) + 0(c) & 1(b) + 0(d) \\ 0(a) + 1(c) & 0(b) + 1(d) \end{bmatrix} = \begin{bmatrix} a & b \\ c & d \end{bmatrix}$ ✓

> **Skill Practice 1**   Given $A = \begin{bmatrix} 3 & -4 \\ -2 & 10 \end{bmatrix}$ show that
>
> **a.** $AI_2 = A$ **b.** $I_2 A = A$

For a nonzero real number a, the multiplicative inverse of a is $\frac{1}{a}$ because $a \cdot \frac{1}{a} = 1$ and $\frac{1}{a} \cdot a = 1$. We define the multiplicative inverse of a square matrix in a similar fashion.

> **Multiplicative Inverse of a Square Matrix**
>
> Let A be an $n \times n$ matrix and let I_n be the identity matrix of order n. If there exists an $n \times n$ matrix A^{-1} such that
>
> $$AA^{-1} = I_n \quad \text{and} \quad A^{-1}A = I_n$$
>
> then A^{-1} (read as "A inverse") is the **multiplicative inverse** of A.

Avoiding Mistakes

Be sure to interpret the notation A^{-1} as the *inverse* of A, rather than the reciprocal of A. That is, $A^{-1} \neq \frac{1}{A}$.

EXAMPLE 2   **Determining Whether Two Matrices are Inverses**

Determine whether $A = \begin{bmatrix} 3 & 2 \\ 7 & 5 \end{bmatrix}$ and $B = \begin{bmatrix} 5 & -2 \\ -7 & 3 \end{bmatrix}$ are inverses.

Solution:

We must show that $AB = I_2$ and $BA = I_2$.

$AB = \begin{bmatrix} 3 & 2 \\ 7 & 5 \end{bmatrix}\begin{bmatrix} 5 & -2 \\ -7 & 3 \end{bmatrix} = \begin{bmatrix} 3(5) + 2(-7) & 3(-2) + 2(3) \\ 7(5) + 5(-7) & 7(-2) + 5(3) \end{bmatrix} = \begin{bmatrix} 1 & 0 \\ 0 & 1 \end{bmatrix}$ ✓

$BA = \begin{bmatrix} 5 & -2 \\ -7 & 3 \end{bmatrix}\begin{bmatrix} 3 & 2 \\ 7 & 5 \end{bmatrix} = \begin{bmatrix} 5(3) + (-2)(7) & 5(2) + (-2)(5) \\ -7(3) + 3(7) & -7(2) + 3(5) \end{bmatrix} = \begin{bmatrix} 1 & 0 \\ 0 & 1 \end{bmatrix}$ ✓

> **Skill Practice 2**
>
> Determine whether $A = \begin{bmatrix} 4 & 3 \\ 13 & 10 \end{bmatrix}$ and $B = \begin{bmatrix} 10 & -3 \\ -13 & 4 \end{bmatrix}$ are inverses.

2. Determine the Inverse of a Matrix

In Example 2, we showed that two given matrices are inverses. Now we look at the task of finding the inverse of a matrix. In Example 3, we will find the inverse of a 2×2 matrix directly from the definition. Then, we develop a general procedure to find the inverse of an $n \times n$ matrix, if the inverse exists.

Answers

1. a.
$\begin{bmatrix} 3 & -4 \\ -2 & 10 \end{bmatrix}\begin{bmatrix} 1 & 0 \\ 0 & 1 \end{bmatrix} = \begin{bmatrix} 3 & -4 \\ -2 & 10 \end{bmatrix}$

b.
$\begin{bmatrix} 1 & 0 \\ 0 & 1 \end{bmatrix}\begin{bmatrix} 3 & -4 \\ -2 & 10 \end{bmatrix} = \begin{bmatrix} 3 & -4 \\ -2 & 10 \end{bmatrix}$

2. Yes; $AB = I_2$ and $BA = I_2$.

EXAMPLE 3 Finding the Inverse of a Matrix

Given $A = \begin{bmatrix} 2 & 9 \\ 1 & 5 \end{bmatrix}$, find A^{-1}.

Solution:

We need to find a matrix $A^{-1} = \begin{bmatrix} x_1 & x_2 \\ x_3 & x_4 \end{bmatrix}$ such that $AA^{-1} = I_2$. That is,

$$\begin{bmatrix} 2 & 9 \\ 1 & 5 \end{bmatrix}\begin{bmatrix} x_1 & x_2 \\ x_3 & x_4 \end{bmatrix} = \begin{bmatrix} 1 & 0 \\ 0 & 1 \end{bmatrix} \longrightarrow \begin{bmatrix} 2x_1 + 9x_3 & 2x_2 + 9x_4 \\ x_1 + 5x_3 & x_2 + 5x_4 \end{bmatrix} = \begin{bmatrix} 1 & 0 \\ 0 & 1 \end{bmatrix}$$

For the matrices to be equal, their corresponding elements must be equal. This results in two systems of equations.

Equating the elements from the 1st column
$\begin{cases} 2x_1 + 9x_3 = 1 \\ x_1 + 5x_3 = 0 \end{cases}$ and $\begin{cases} 2x_2 + 9x_4 = 0 \\ x_2 + 5x_4 = 1 \end{cases}$ Equating the elements from the 2nd column

The corresponding augmented matrices are

$$\begin{bmatrix} 2 & 9 & | & 1 \\ 1 & 5 & | & 0 \end{bmatrix} \quad \text{and} \quad \begin{bmatrix} 2 & 9 & | & 0 \\ 1 & 5 & | & 1 \end{bmatrix}$$

We can solve both systems simultaneously by placing the identity matrix to the right of the array of coefficients.

$$\begin{bmatrix} 2 & 9 & | & 1 & 0 \\ 1 & 5 & | & 0 & 1 \end{bmatrix}$$

$$\begin{bmatrix} 2 & 9 & | & 1 & 0 \\ 1 & 5 & | & 0 & 1 \end{bmatrix} \xrightarrow{R_1 \Leftrightarrow R_2} \begin{bmatrix} 1 & 5 & | & 0 & 1 \\ 2 & 9 & | & 1 & 0 \end{bmatrix} \xrightarrow{-2R_1 + R_2 \to R_2} \begin{bmatrix} 1 & 5 & | & 0 & 1 \\ 0 & -1 & | & 1 & -2 \end{bmatrix}$$

$$\xrightarrow{-1R_2 \to R_2} \begin{bmatrix} 1 & 5 & | & 0 & 1 \\ 0 & 1 & | & -1 & 2 \end{bmatrix} \xrightarrow{-5R_2 + R_1 \to R_1} \begin{bmatrix} 1 & 0 & | & 5 & -9 \\ 0 & 1 & | & -1 & 2 \end{bmatrix}$$

This result represents the following two matrices and their corresponding systems of equations.

$$\begin{matrix} x_1 & x_3 \\ \downarrow & \downarrow \end{matrix}$$
$$\begin{bmatrix} 1 & 0 & | & 5 \\ 0 & 1 & | & -1 \end{bmatrix} \quad \text{and} \quad \begin{bmatrix} 1 & 0 & | & -9 \\ 0 & 1 & | & 2 \end{bmatrix}$$
$$x_1 = 5, x_3 = -1 \qquad\qquad x_2 = -9, x_4 = 2$$

Avoiding Mistakes

The solution to Example 3 can be checked by verifying that $AA^{-1} = I_2$ and $A^{-1}A = I_2$.

Therefore, we have: $A^{-1} = \begin{bmatrix} x_1 & x_2 \\ x_3 & x_4 \end{bmatrix} = \begin{bmatrix} 5 & -9 \\ -1 & 2 \end{bmatrix}$

Skill Practice 3 Given $B = \begin{bmatrix} 9 & 7 \\ 5 & 4 \end{bmatrix}$, find B^{-1}.

In Example 3, we transformed the left side of the augmented matrix into the identity matrix. That is, we performed row operations to make the array on the left of the vertical bar have 1's along the main diagonal, and 0's elsewhere. In the process, we make the following important observation.

- The array of elements to the right of the vertical bar is the inverse of A.

Answer

3. $B^{-1} = \begin{bmatrix} 4 & -7 \\ -5 & 9 \end{bmatrix}$

This observation leads to a general procedure to find the multiplicative inverse of a matrix, provided that the inverse exists.

Finding the Multiplicative Inverse of a Square Matrix

Let A be an $n \times n$ matrix for which A^{-1} exists, and let I_n be the $n \times n$ identity matrix. To find A^{-1},

Step 1   Write a matrix of the form $[A \mid I_n]$.
Step 2   Perform row operations to write the matrix in the form $[I_n \mid B]$.
Step 3   The matrix B is A^{-1}.

It is important to note that not all matrices have a multiplicative inverse. If a matrix A is reducible to a row-equivalent matrix with one or more rows of zeros, then the matrix cannot be written in the form $[I_n \mid B]$. Therefore, the matrix does not have an inverse, and we say that the matrix is **singular.** A matrix that *does* have a multiplicative inverse is said to be **invertible** or **nonsingular.**

In Example 4, we use the general procedure to find the inverse of a 3×3 invertible matrix.

EXAMPLE 4   Finding the Inverse of a Matrix

Given $A = \begin{bmatrix} 1 & 3 & 0 \\ 1 & 1 & -2 \\ -3 & -3 & 5 \end{bmatrix}$, find A^{-1} if possible.

Solution:

$\begin{bmatrix} 1 & 3 & 0 & | & 1 & 0 & 0 \\ 1 & 1 & -2 & | & 0 & 1 & 0 \\ -3 & -3 & 5 & | & 0 & 0 & 1 \end{bmatrix}$

Set up the matrix $[A \mid I_3]$.
Transform the left side of the matrix to the 3×3 identity matrix.

$\xrightarrow[\;3R_1 + R_3 \to R_3\;]{-1R_1 + R_2 \to R_2} \begin{bmatrix} 1 & 3 & 0 & | & 1 & 0 & 0 \\ 0 & -2 & -2 & | & -1 & 1 & 0 \\ 0 & 6 & 5 & | & 3 & 0 & 1 \end{bmatrix} \xrightarrow{-\frac{1}{2}R_2 \to R_2} \begin{bmatrix} 1 & 3 & 0 & | & 1 & 0 & 0 \\ 0 & 1 & 1 & | & \frac{1}{2} & -\frac{1}{2} & 0 \\ 0 & 6 & 5 & | & 3 & 0 & 1 \end{bmatrix}$

$\xrightarrow[\;-6R_2 + R_3 \to R_3\;]{-3R_2 + R_1 \to R_1} \begin{bmatrix} 1 & 0 & -3 & | & -\frac{1}{2} & \frac{3}{2} & 0 \\ 0 & 1 & 1 & | & \frac{1}{2} & -\frac{1}{2} & 0 \\ 0 & 0 & -1 & | & 0 & 3 & 1 \end{bmatrix} \xrightarrow{-1R_3 \to R_3} \begin{bmatrix} 1 & 0 & -3 & | & -\frac{1}{2} & \frac{3}{2} & 0 \\ 0 & 1 & 1 & | & \frac{1}{2} & -\frac{1}{2} & 0 \\ 0 & 0 & 1 & | & 0 & -3 & -1 \end{bmatrix}$

$\xrightarrow[\;-1R_3 + R_2 \to R_2\;]{3R_3 + R_1 \to R_1} \begin{bmatrix} 1 & 0 & 0 & | & -\frac{1}{2} & -\frac{15}{2} & -3 \\ 0 & 1 & 0 & | & \frac{1}{2} & \frac{5}{2} & 1 \\ 0 & 0 & 1 & | & 0 & -3 & -1 \end{bmatrix}$

The left side of the matrix is the 3×3 identity matrix. The right side of the matrix represents the inverse of A.

$A^{-1} = \begin{bmatrix} -\frac{1}{2} & -\frac{15}{2} & -3 \\ \frac{1}{2} & \frac{5}{2} & 1 \\ 0 & -3 & -1 \end{bmatrix}$

Avoiding Mistakes

As a check, verify that $A \cdot A^{-1} = I_3$ and $A^{-1} \cdot A = I_3$.

Answer

4. $A^{-1} = \begin{bmatrix} 4 & -11 & \frac{53}{3} \\ 2 & -5 & 8 \\ 1 & -2 & \frac{10}{3} \end{bmatrix}$

Skill Practice 4   Given $A = \begin{bmatrix} -2 & 4 & 1 \\ 4 & -13 & 10 \\ 3 & -9 & 6 \end{bmatrix}$ find A^{-1} if possible.

TECHNOLOGY CONNECTIONS

Finding the Inverse of a Nonsingular Square Matrix

To find the inverse of a nonsingular matrix [A] using a calculator, first enter the matrix into the calculator using the MATRIX menu. Then place [A] on the home screen and use the x^{-1} key to take the inverse of [A]. It is very important to realize that in this context, the calculator uses the x^{-1} key for the inverse of a matrix, not the reciprocal of a real number.

In Example 5, we identify a singular matrix—that is, a matrix that has no inverse.

EXAMPLE 5   Identifying a Singular Matrix

Show that matrix A is singular. $A = \begin{bmatrix} 1 & 2 & 0 \\ 4 & 5 & 1 \\ 2 & 1 & 1 \end{bmatrix}$

Solution:

$\begin{bmatrix} 1 & 2 & 0 & | & 1 & 0 & 0 \\ 4 & 5 & 1 & | & 0 & 1 & 0 \\ 2 & 1 & 1 & | & 0 & 0 & 1 \end{bmatrix}$ Set up the matrix $[A \,|\, I_3]$.

Transform the left side of the matrix to the 3×3 identity matrix.

$\xrightarrow[\;-2R_1 + R_3 \to R_3\;]{-4R_1 + R_2 \to R_2} \begin{bmatrix} 1 & 2 & 0 & | & 1 & 0 & 0 \\ 0 & -3 & 1 & | & -4 & 1 & 0 \\ 0 & -3 & 1 & | & -2 & 0 & 1 \end{bmatrix}$ On the left of the vertical bar, the elements in rows 2 and 3 are multiples of each other (in fact they are identical). Therefore, $-1R_2 + R_3 \to R_3$ results in zeros in row 3 to the left of the bar.

$\xrightarrow[\;-1R_2 + R_3 \to R_3\;]{} \begin{bmatrix} 1 & 2 & 0 & | & 1 & 0 & 0 \\ 0 & -3 & 1 & | & -4 & 1 & 0 \\ 0 & 0 & 0 & | & 2 & -1 & 1 \end{bmatrix}$ The left side of the matrix cannot be transformed into the 3×3 identity matrix I_3. Therefore, matrix A does not have an inverse.

A is a singular matrix (does not have an inverse).

Skill Practice 5   Show that matrix A is singular. $A = \begin{bmatrix} 1 & -3 & -7 \\ 3 & -7 & -17 \\ 1 & 0 & -1 \end{bmatrix}$

TECHNOLOGY CONNECTIONS

Identifying a Singular Matrix

A calculator will return an error message if we attempt to find the inverse of a singular matrix. Consider matrix A from Example 5. The calculator returns the error message shown.

Answer

5. The matrix $[A \,|\, I_3]$ cannot be written in the form $[I_3 \,|\, B]$ by using row operations. Therefore, A is a singular matrix.

To find the inverse of an invertible 2×2 matrix, we can take a direct approach and apply the following formula.

TIP If A is an invertible matrix then the restriction $ad - bc \neq 0$ is implied.

> **Formula for the Inverse of a 2 × 2 Invertible Matrix**
>
> Let $A = \begin{bmatrix} a & b \\ c & d \end{bmatrix}$ be an invertible matrix. Then the inverse A^{-1} is given by:
>
> $$A^{-1} = \frac{1}{ad - bc} \cdot \begin{bmatrix} d & -b \\ -c & a \end{bmatrix}$$

Avoiding Mistakes

The formula to find the inverse of an invertible 2×2 matrix does not apply to matrices of higher order.

This formula can be verified by applying the general procedure to find the inverse of A. See Exercise 67.

$$\begin{bmatrix} a & b & | & 1 & 0 \\ c & d & | & 0 & 1 \end{bmatrix} \xrightarrow[\text{matrix}]{\text{row-equivalent}} \begin{bmatrix} 1 & 0 & | & \frac{d}{ad-bc} & \frac{-b}{ad-bc} \\ 0 & 1 & | & \frac{-c}{ad-bc} & \frac{a}{ad-bc} \end{bmatrix}$$

$$\xrightarrow{\text{inverse of } A} \frac{1}{ad-bc} \cdot \begin{bmatrix} d & -b \\ -c & a \end{bmatrix}$$

> **EXAMPLE 6**   **Finding the Inverse of a 2 × 2 Matrix**
>
> Given $A = \begin{bmatrix} 2 & 9 \\ 1 & 5 \end{bmatrix}$, find A^{-1} and compare to the result of Example 3.
>
> **Solution:**
>
> $\begin{bmatrix} 2 & 9 \\ 1 & 5 \end{bmatrix}$ $a = 2, b = 9, c = 1, d = 5$
>
> $$A^{-1} = \frac{1}{ad - bc} \cdot \begin{bmatrix} d & -b \\ -c & a \end{bmatrix} = \frac{1}{(2)(5) - (9)(1)} \cdot \begin{bmatrix} 5 & -9 \\ -1 & 2 \end{bmatrix}$$
>
> $$= \frac{1}{1} \cdot \begin{bmatrix} 5 & -9 \\ -1 & 2 \end{bmatrix} = \begin{bmatrix} 5 & -9 \\ -1 & 2 \end{bmatrix}$$ This is the same result as was found in Example 3.

> **Skill Practice 6**   Given $B = \begin{bmatrix} 9 & 7 \\ 5 & 3 \end{bmatrix}$, find B^{-1}.

3. Solve Systems of Linear Equations Using the Inverse of a Matrix

A system of linear equations written in standard form can be represented by using matrix multiplication. For example:

$$\begin{aligned} 3x - 2y + z &= 4 \\ x + 4y - z &= 2 \\ 2x + 5y - 2z &= 1 \end{aligned} \quad \xrightarrow[\text{matrix equation}]{\text{corresponding}} \quad \begin{bmatrix} 3 & -2 & 1 \\ 1 & 4 & -1 \\ 2 & 5 & -2 \end{bmatrix} \begin{bmatrix} x \\ y \\ z \end{bmatrix} = \begin{bmatrix} 4 \\ 2 \\ 1 \end{bmatrix}$$

The matrix on the left is called the **coefficient matrix.** It consists of the coefficients of the variable terms.

coefficient matrix   column matrix of variables   column matrix of constants

Answer

6. $B^{-1} = \begin{bmatrix} -\frac{3}{8} & \frac{7}{8} \\ \frac{5}{8} & -\frac{9}{8} \end{bmatrix}$

If we denote the coefficient matrix by A, the column matrix of variables as X, and the column matrix of constant terms as B, we can write the equation as $AX = B$. If A^{-1} exists, then we can solve the equation for X by multiplying both sides by A^{-1}.

$$AX = B \qquad \text{To solve this equation, the goal is to isolate } X.$$
$$A^{-1}AX = A^{-1}B \qquad \text{Multiply both sides by } A^{-1} \text{ (provided that } A^{-1} \text{ exists).}$$
$$(A^{-1}A)X = A^{-1}B$$
$$I_nX = A^{-1}B \qquad \text{The product of a matrix and its inverse is the identity matrix.}$$
$$X = A^{-1}B$$

This process is summarized as follows.

Solving Systems of Linear Equations Using Inverse Matrices

Suppose that $AX = B$ represents a system of n linear equations in n variables with a unique solution. Then,

$$X = A^{-1}B$$

where A is the coefficient matrix, B is the matrix of constants, and X is the matrix of variables.

EXAMPLE 7 **Solving a System of Equations by Using an Inverse Matrix**

Use the inverse of the coefficient matrix to solve the system.

$$x + 3y \qquad = -10$$
$$x + y - 2z = -4$$
$$-3x - 3y + 5z = 11$$

Solution:

$$
\begin{array}{c}
x + 3y \qquad = -10 \\
x + y - 2z = -4 \\
-3x - 3y + 5z = 11
\end{array}
\longrightarrow
\underset{A}{\begin{bmatrix} 1 & 3 & 0 \\ 1 & 1 & -2 \\ -3 & -3 & 5 \end{bmatrix}}
\cdot
\underset{X}{\begin{bmatrix} x \\ y \\ z \end{bmatrix}}
=
\underset{B}{\begin{bmatrix} -10 \\ -4 \\ 11 \end{bmatrix}}
$$

$X = A^{-1}B$ From Example 4, we have that $A^{-1} = \begin{bmatrix} -\frac{1}{2} & -\frac{15}{2} & -3 \\ \frac{1}{2} & \frac{5}{2} & 1 \\ 0 & -3 & -1 \end{bmatrix}$.

$$
\begin{bmatrix} x \\ y \\ z \end{bmatrix}
=
\begin{bmatrix} -\frac{1}{2} & -\frac{15}{2} & -3 \\ \frac{1}{2} & \frac{5}{2} & 1 \\ 0 & -3 & -1 \end{bmatrix}
\begin{bmatrix} -10 \\ -4 \\ 11 \end{bmatrix}
$$

$$
\begin{bmatrix} x \\ y \\ z \end{bmatrix}
=
\begin{bmatrix} \left(-\frac{1}{2}\right)(-10) + \left(-\frac{15}{2}\right)(-4) + (-3)(11) \\ \left(\frac{1}{2}\right)(-10) + \left(\frac{5}{2}\right)(-4) + (1)(11) \\ (0)(-10) + (-3)(-4) + (-1)(11) \end{bmatrix}
=
\begin{bmatrix} 2 \\ -4 \\ 1 \end{bmatrix}
$$

$$
\begin{bmatrix} x \\ y \\ z \end{bmatrix}
=
\begin{bmatrix} 2 \\ -4 \\ 1 \end{bmatrix}
$$

Therefore, $x = 2$, $y = -4$, and $z = 1$. The solution set is $\{(2, -4, 1)\}$.

Skill Practice 7 Use the inverse of the coefficient matrix found in Skill Practice 4 to solve the system.

$$-2x + 4y + z = 0$$
$$4x - 13y + 10z = 24$$
$$3x - 9y + 6z = 15$$

SECTION 6.4 Practice Exercises

Review Exercises

For Exercises 1–4, a matrix equation of the form $AX = B$ is given.

a. Multiply AX.

b. Write the system of equations represented by $AX = B$ by equating the corresponding elements in the matrices AX and B.

1. $\begin{bmatrix} 2 & -3 \\ 1 & 5 \end{bmatrix} \begin{bmatrix} x \\ y \end{bmatrix} = \begin{bmatrix} 14 \\ -19 \end{bmatrix}$

2. $\begin{bmatrix} 4 & 3 \\ -2 & -1 \end{bmatrix} \begin{bmatrix} x \\ y \end{bmatrix} = \begin{bmatrix} 2 \\ 0 \end{bmatrix}$

3. $\begin{bmatrix} 3 & -4 & 6 \\ 2 & 0 & 4 \\ 9 & 2 & 0 \end{bmatrix} \begin{bmatrix} x \\ y \\ z \end{bmatrix} = \begin{bmatrix} 17 \\ 14 \\ 11 \end{bmatrix}$

4. $\begin{bmatrix} -1 & 4 & 0 \\ 0 & 9 & 1 \\ 2 & 0 & -5 \end{bmatrix} \begin{bmatrix} x \\ y \\ z \end{bmatrix} = \begin{bmatrix} 5 \\ 19 \\ 1 \end{bmatrix}$

Concept Connections

5. The symbol I_n represents the _____ matrix of order n.

6. I_n is an $n \times n$ matrix with _____'s along the main diagonal and _____'s elsewhere.

7. Given an $n \times n$ matrix A, if there exists a matrix A^{-1} such that $A \cdot A^{-1} = I_n$ and $A^{-1} \cdot A = I_n$, then A^{-1} is called the _____ of A.

8. A matrix that does not have an inverse is called a _____ matrix. A matrix that does have an inverse is said to be invertible or _____.

9. Let $A = \begin{bmatrix} a & b \\ c & d \end{bmatrix}$ be an invertible matrix. Then a formula for the inverse A^{-1} is given by _____.

10. Suppose that the matrix equation $AX = B$ represents a system of n linear equations in n variables with a unique solution. Then $X =$ _____.

Objective 1: Identify Identity and Inverse Matrices

For Exercises 11–14, verify that

a. $AI_n = A$

b. $I_nA = A$ (**See Example 1**)

11. $A = \begin{bmatrix} -\frac{7}{8} & \sqrt{5} \\ 5.1 & 8 \end{bmatrix}$

12. $A = \begin{bmatrix} \sqrt{3} & 1 \\ \pi & 4 \end{bmatrix}$

13. $A = \begin{bmatrix} 1 & -3 & 4 \\ 9 & 5 & 3 \\ 11 & -6 & -4 \end{bmatrix}$

14. $A = \begin{bmatrix} -3 & 9 & 1 \\ 0 & 4 & -1 \\ 5 & 0 & 3 \end{bmatrix}$

For Exercises 15–20, determine whether A and B are inverses. (**See Example 2**)

15. $A = \begin{bmatrix} 10 & -3 \\ 4 & -2 \end{bmatrix}$ and $B = \begin{bmatrix} \frac{1}{4} & -\frac{3}{8} \\ \frac{1}{2} & -\frac{5}{4} \end{bmatrix}$

16. $A = \begin{bmatrix} 4 & -1 \\ -8 & 6 \end{bmatrix}$ and $B = \begin{bmatrix} \frac{3}{8} & \frac{1}{16} \\ \frac{1}{2} & \frac{1}{4} \end{bmatrix}$

17. $A = \begin{bmatrix} -2 & -3 & 1 \\ -3 & -3 & 1 \\ -2 & -4 & 1 \end{bmatrix}$ and $B = \begin{bmatrix} 1 & -1 & 0 \\ 1 & 0 & -1 \\ 6 & -2 & -3 \end{bmatrix}$

18. $A = \begin{bmatrix} -1 & 2 & 1 \\ -5 & 8 & 2 \\ 7 & -11 & -3 \end{bmatrix}$ and $B = \begin{bmatrix} 2 & 5 & 4 \\ 1 & 4 & 3 \\ 1 & -3 & -2 \end{bmatrix}$

19. $A = \begin{bmatrix} 2 & 1 \\ 3 & 4 \end{bmatrix}$ and $B = \begin{bmatrix} 4 & -3 \\ -7 & 6 \end{bmatrix}$

20. $A = \begin{bmatrix} 3 & 2 \\ 10 & 7 \end{bmatrix}$ and $B = \begin{bmatrix} -7 & 10 \\ 11 & -15 \end{bmatrix}$

Objective 2: Determine the Inverse of a Matrix

For Exercises 21–36, determine the inverse of the given matrix if possible. Otherwise, state that the matrix is singular. (**See Examples 3–6**)

21. $A = \begin{bmatrix} -4 & -3 \\ 6 & 5 \end{bmatrix}$

22. $A = \begin{bmatrix} 5 & -3 \\ 10 & -7 \end{bmatrix}$

23. $A = \begin{bmatrix} -8 & -2 \\ 10 & 5 \end{bmatrix}$

24. $A = \begin{bmatrix} 0 & 1 \\ 6 & -2 \end{bmatrix}$

25. $A = \begin{bmatrix} 3 & 7 \\ 6 & 14 \end{bmatrix}$

26. $A = \begin{bmatrix} 2 & -5 \\ -6 & 15 \end{bmatrix}$

27. $A = \begin{bmatrix} 2 & -7 & 8 \\ 1 & -3 & 3 \\ 1 & -5 & 6 \end{bmatrix}$

28. $A = \begin{bmatrix} 1 & -1 & 1 \\ 1 & 1 & -2 \\ -1 & 0 & 1 \end{bmatrix}$

29. $A = \begin{bmatrix} 1 & -2 & 2 \\ 2 & -3 & 1 \\ 0 & 1 & -1 \end{bmatrix}$

30. $A = \begin{bmatrix} -2 & 5 & -4 \\ 1 & -2 & 1 \\ 1 & -5 & 9 \end{bmatrix}$

31. $A = \begin{bmatrix} 5 & 7 & -11 \\ 3 & 5 & -9 \\ 1 & 1 & -1 \end{bmatrix}$

32. $A = \begin{bmatrix} 1 & 3 & 9 \\ 2 & 7 & 22 \\ -5 & -17 & -53 \end{bmatrix}$

33. $A = \begin{bmatrix} 0 & 1 & 1 \\ \frac{5}{3} & -1 & -3 \\ -1 & 1 & 2 \end{bmatrix}$

34. $A = \begin{bmatrix} 3 & -1 & -\frac{1}{2} \\ 2 & -1 & \frac{1}{2} \\ -5 & 2 & \frac{1}{2} \end{bmatrix}$

35. $A = \begin{bmatrix} 1 & -2 & 5 & 0 \\ 0 & -1 & 2 & 0 \\ 0 & 1 & -1 & 0 \\ 2 & -1 & 7 & 1 \end{bmatrix}$

36. $A = \begin{bmatrix} 1 & 3 & 0 & -3 \\ 0 & 1 & 0 & -2 \\ -2 & -4 & 1 & 2 \\ 0 & 1 & 1 & 0 \end{bmatrix}$

Objective 3: Solve Systems of Linear Equations Using the Inverse of a Matrix

For Exercises 37–40, write the system of equations as a matrix equation of the form $AX = B$, where A is the coefficient matrix, X is the column matrix of variables, and B is the column matrix of constants.

37. $3x - 4y = -1$
$2x + y = 14$

38. $-6x - y = 1$
$2x + 3y = 13$

39. $9x - 6y + 4z = 27$
$4x - z = 1$
$3y + z = 0$

40. $-3x + 8z = 4$
$6y - z = 7$
$2x - y + 6z = -15$

For Exercises 41–50, solve the system by using the inverse of the coefficient matrix. (See Example 7)

41. $-4x - 3y = -4$
$6x + 5y = 8$
(See Exercise 21 for A^{-1}.)

42. $5x - 3y = -20$
$10x - 7y = -50$
(See Exercise 22 for A^{-1}.)

43. $3x + 7y = -5$
$4x + 9y = -7$

44. $3x - 8y = -1$
$-4x + 11y = 2$

45. $2x - 7y + 8z = 1$
$x - 3y + 3z = 0$
$x - 5y + 6z = 2$
(See Exercise 27 for A^{-1}.)

46. $x - y + z = -4$
$x + y - 2z = 12$
$-x + z = -5$
(See Exercise 28 for A^{-1}.)

47. $x - 2y + 2z = -12$
$2x - 3y + z = -10$
$y - z = 6$
(See Exercise 29 for A^{-1}.)

48. $-2x + 5y - 4z = -20$
$x - 2y + z = 8$
$x - 5y + 9z = 24$
(See Exercise 30 for A^{-1}.)

49. $w - 2x + 5y = 3$
$-x + 2y = 1$
$x - y = -1$
$2w - x + 7y + z = 5$
(See Exercise 35 for A^{-1}.)

50. $w + 3x - 3z = 8$
$x - 2z = 4$
$-2w - 4x + y + 2z = -6$
$x + y = 0$
(See Exercise 36 for A^{-1}.)

Mixed Exercises

For Exercises 51–58, determine whether the statement is true or false.

51. A 3×2 matrix has a multiplicative inverse.

52. A 2×3 matrix has a multiplicative inverse.

53. Every square matrix has an inverse.

54. Every singular matrix has an inverse.

55. Every nonsingular matrix has an inverse.

56. The matrix $\begin{bmatrix} -a & -b \\ a & b \end{bmatrix}$ is invertible.

57. The matrix $\begin{bmatrix} x & y \\ 2x & 2y \end{bmatrix}$ is invertible.

58. The inverse of the matrix I_4 is itself.

59. Find a 2×2 matrix that is its own inverse. Answers will vary.

60. Given an invertible 2×2 matrix A and the nonzero real number k, find the inverse of kA in terms of A^{-1}.

61. Given $A = \begin{bmatrix} 3 & 2 \\ 5 & 6 \end{bmatrix}$,

    a. Find A^{-1}.   **b.** Find $(A^{-1})^{-1}$.

62. Given $B = \begin{bmatrix} -3 & 2 \\ -5 & 4 \end{bmatrix}$,

    a. Find B^{-1}.   **b.** Find $(B^{-1})^{-1}$.

63. Given $A = \begin{bmatrix} a & 0 \\ 0 & b \end{bmatrix}$, where a and b are nonzero real numbers, find A^{-1}.

64. Given $A = \begin{bmatrix} a & 0 & 0 \\ 0 & b & 0 \\ 0 & 0 & c \end{bmatrix}$, where a, b, and c are nonzero real numbers, find A^{-1}.

Write About It

65. Explain how you can determine if two $n \times n$ matrices, A and B, are inverses.

66. Given a matrix $A = \begin{bmatrix} a & b \\ c & d \end{bmatrix}$, for what conditions on a, b, c, and d will the matrix not have an inverse?

Expanding Your Skills

67. Given $A = \begin{bmatrix} a & b \\ c & d \end{bmatrix}$, perform row operations on the matrix $[A \mid I_n]$ to find A^{-1}. This confirms the formula for the inverse of an invertible 2×2 matrix. (See page 635.)

68. Show by counterexample that $(AB)^{-1} \neq A^{-1}B^{-1}$. That is, find two matrices A and B for which $(AB)^{-1} \neq A^{-1}B^{-1}$.

Physicists know that if each edge of a thin conducting plate is kept at a constant temperature, then the temperature at the interior points is the mean (average) of the four surrounding points equidistant from the interior point. Use this principle in Exercise 69 to find the temperature at points x_1, x_2, x_3, and x_4.

69. *Hint*: Set up four linear equations to represent the temperature at points x_1, x_2, x_3, and x_4. Then solve the system. For example, one equation would be:

$$x_1 = \frac{1}{4}(36 + 32 + x_2 + x_3)$$

Technology Connections

For Exercises 70–71, use a graphing utility to find the inverse of the given matrix. Round the elements in the inverse to 2 decimal places.

70. $A = \begin{bmatrix} 0.04 & 0.13 & -0.08 & -0.43 \\ 0.19 & 0.33 & 0.06 & -0.84 \\ 0.01 & 0.08 & -0.11 & 0.46 \\ 0.37 & -1.42 & 0.03 & 0.52 \end{bmatrix}$

71. $A = \begin{bmatrix} 3.5 & 2.1 & 1.6 & 2.4 \\ -4.5 & 3.9 & -9.1 & 3.8 \\ 5.7 & 6.8 & -1.4 & -7.7 \\ 3.3 & 2.8 & 4.6 & -1.0 \end{bmatrix}$

For Exercises 72–73, use a graphing calculator and the inverse of the coefficient matrix to find the solution to the given system. Round to 2 decimal places.

72. $(\log 2)x + (\sqrt{7})y + z = 4.1$

      $(e^2)x - (\sqrt{3})y - \pi z = -3.7$

      $(\ln 10)\, x + y - 2.2z = 7.2$

73. $(\sqrt{11})x + y - (\ln 5)z = 52.3$

      $(\sqrt{7})x - \pi y + (e^3)z = -27.5$

      $-x + (\log 81)\, y - z = 69.8$

SECTION 6.5   Determinants and Cramer's Rule

OBJECTIVES

1. Evaluate the Determinant of a 2 × 2 Matrix
2. Evaluate the Determinant of an $n \times n$ Matrix
3. Apply Cramer's Rule

Avoiding Mistakes

Notice that a determinant is denoted using vertical bars, whereas a matrix is denoted using brackets.

1. Evaluate the Determinant of a 2 × 2 Matrix

In this section, we present yet another method to solve a linear system with one unique solution. This method, called Cramer's rule, enables us to write a formula to solve the system based on the coefficients of the equations in the system.

Before studying Cramer's rule, we need to become familiar with the determinant of a square matrix. Associated with every square matrix is a real number called the determinant of the matrix. A determinant of a square matrix A, denoted $|A|$, is written by enclosing the elements of the matrix within two vertical bars. For example:

$$\text{Given } A = \begin{bmatrix} 3 & -1 \\ 4 & 0 \end{bmatrix}, \text{ then } |A| = \begin{vmatrix} 3 & -1 \\ 4 & 0 \end{vmatrix}$$

Determinants have many applications in mathematics, including solving systems of linear equations, finding the area of a triangle, determining whether three points are collinear, and finding an equation of a line through two points (see Exercises 59–66). The determinant of a 2 × 2 matrix is defined as follows.

Determinant of a 2 × 2 Matrix

The **determinant** of the matrix $A = \begin{bmatrix} a & b \\ c & d \end{bmatrix}$ is $ad - bc$. That is,

$$|A| = \begin{vmatrix} a & b \\ c & d \end{vmatrix} = ad - bc$$

EXAMPLE 1   Evaluating a 2 × 2 Determinant

Evaluate the determinant of each matrix.

a. $A = \begin{bmatrix} 6 & -2 \\ 5 & \frac{1}{3} \end{bmatrix}$ 　　　 **b.** $B = \begin{bmatrix} 2 & -11 \\ 0 & 0 \end{bmatrix}$

Solution:

a. $|A| = \begin{vmatrix} 6 & -2 \\ 5 & \frac{1}{3} \end{vmatrix} = \overset{a\,\cdot\,d}{(6)\left(\tfrac{1}{3}\right)} - \overset{b\,\cdot\,c}{(-2)(5)} = 12$ 　　 $a = 6, b = -2, c = 5, \text{ and } d = \frac{1}{3}$

b. $|B| = \begin{vmatrix} 2 & -11 \\ 0 & 0 \end{vmatrix} = \overset{a\,\cdot\,d}{(2)(0)} - \overset{b\,\cdot\,c}{(-11)(0)} = 0$ 　　 $a = 2, b = -11, c = 0, \text{ and } d = 0$

TIP Example 1(b) illustrates that the determinant of a matrix having a row of all zeros is 0. The same is true for a matrix having a column of all zeros.

Skill Practice 1   Evaluate the determinant.

a. $\begin{vmatrix} 3 & -\frac{1}{2} \\ 10 & 2 \end{vmatrix}$ 　　 **b.** $\begin{vmatrix} 9 & 0 \\ -4 & 0 \end{vmatrix}$

2. Evaluate the Determinant of an $n \times n$ Matrix

We now develop the tools to compute the determinant of a higher-order square matrix. To find the determinant of an $n \times n$ matrix $A = [a_{ij}]$ we first need to define the minor of an element of the matrix. For any element a_{ij}, the **minor** M_{ij} of that

Answers
1. a. 11 　 **b.** 0

element is the determinant of the resulting matrix obtained by deleting the ith row and jth column. For example, consider the matrix

$$A = [a_{ij}] = \begin{bmatrix} 5 & -1 & 6 \\ 0 & -7 & 1 \\ 4 & 2 & 6 \end{bmatrix}$$

The element a_{11} is 5. The minor of this element is found by deleting the first row and first column and then evaluating the determinant of the remaining 2×2 matrix:

$$\begin{bmatrix} 5 & -1 & 6 \\ 0 & -7 & 1 \\ 4 & 2 & 6 \end{bmatrix} \qquad M_{11} = \begin{vmatrix} -7 & 1 \\ 2 & 6 \end{vmatrix} = (-7)(6) - (1)(2) = -44$$

The element a_{32} is 2. The minor of this element is found by deleting the third row and second column and then evaluating the determinant of the remaining 2×2 matrix:

$$\begin{bmatrix} 5 & -1 & 6 \\ 0 & -7 & 1 \\ 4 & 2 & 6 \end{bmatrix} \qquad M_{32} = \begin{vmatrix} 5 & 6 \\ 0 & 1 \end{vmatrix} = (5)(1) - (6)(0) = 5$$

EXAMPLE 2   **Determining the Minor for Elements in a Matrix**

Find the minor for each element in the first column of the matrix.

$$\begin{bmatrix} 3 & 4 & -1 \\ 2 & -4 & 5 \\ 0 & 1 & -6 \end{bmatrix}$$

Solution:

For the element a_{11}:

$$\begin{bmatrix} 3 & 4 & -1 \\ 2 & -4 & 5 \\ 0 & 1 & -6 \end{bmatrix} \qquad M_{11} = \begin{vmatrix} -4 & 5 \\ 1 & -6 \end{vmatrix} = (-4)(-6) - (5)(1) = 19$$

For the element a_{21}:

$$\begin{bmatrix} 3 & 4 & -1 \\ 2 & -4 & 5 \\ 0 & 1 & -6 \end{bmatrix} \qquad M_{21} = \begin{vmatrix} 4 & -1 \\ 1 & -6 \end{vmatrix} = (4)(-6) - (-1)(1) = -23$$

For the element a_{31}:

$$\begin{bmatrix} 3 & 4 & -1 \\ 2 & -4 & 5 \\ 0 & 1 & -6 \end{bmatrix} \qquad M_{31} = \begin{vmatrix} 4 & -1 \\ -4 & 5 \end{vmatrix} = (4)(5) - (-1)(-4) = 16$$

Skill Practice 2   Find the minor for each element in the second row of the matrix from Example 2.

Next, we define the determinant for a 3×3 matrix.

Point of Interest

English mathematician James Sylvester (1814–1897) coined the term *matrix* derived from the Latin "mater" for mother. Sylvester defines "a *matrix* as a rectangular array of terms, out of which different systems of determinants (which today we call minors) may be engendered as from the womb of a common parent."

Answer
2. $M_{21} = -23$; $M_{22} = -18$; $M_{23} = 3$

Determinant of a 3 × 3 Matrix

$$\begin{vmatrix} a_1 & b_1 & c_1 \\ a_2 & b_2 & c_2 \\ a_3 & b_3 & c_3 \end{vmatrix} = a_1 \begin{vmatrix} b_2 & c_2 \\ b_3 & c_3 \end{vmatrix} - a_2 \begin{vmatrix} b_1 & c_1 \\ b_3 & c_3 \end{vmatrix} + a_3 \begin{vmatrix} b_1 & c_1 \\ b_2 & c_2 \end{vmatrix} \text{ or equivalently,}$$

$$= a_1(b_2 c_3 - c_2 b_3) - a_2(b_1 c_3 - c_1 b_3) + a_3(b_1 c_2 - c_1 b_2) \quad \text{or}$$
$$= a_1 b_2 c_3 + b_1 c_2 a_3 + c_1 a_2 b_3 - a_3 b_2 c_1 - b_3 c_2 a_1 - c_3 a_2 b_1$$

From this definition, we see that the determinant of the given 3 × 3 matrix can be written as

$$a_1 \cdot (\text{minor of } a_1) - a_2 \cdot (\text{minor of } a_2) + a_3 \cdot (\text{minor of } a_3)$$

EXAMPLE 3 Evaluating the Determinant of a 3 × 3 Matrix

Evaluate the determinant of the matrix. $A = \begin{bmatrix} 2 & 4 & 2 \\ 1 & -3 & 0 \\ -5 & 5 & -1 \end{bmatrix}$

Solution:

$$|A| = \begin{vmatrix} 2 & 4 & 2 \\ 1 & -3 & 0 \\ -5 & 5 & -1 \end{vmatrix} = 2 \cdot \overbrace{\begin{vmatrix} -3 & 0 \\ 5 & -1 \end{vmatrix}}^{\boxed{\text{minor of } 2}} - (1)\overbrace{\begin{vmatrix} 4 & 2 \\ 5 & -1 \end{vmatrix}}^{\boxed{\text{minor of } 1}} + (-5) \cdot \overbrace{\begin{vmatrix} 4 & 2 \\ -3 & 0 \end{vmatrix}}^{\boxed{\text{minor of } -5}}$$

$$= 2[(-3)(-1) - (0)(5)] - 1[(4)(-1) - (2)(5)] + (-5)[(4)(0) - (2)(-3)]$$
$$= 2(3) - 1(-14) - 5(6)$$
$$= -10$$

Skill Practice 3 Evaluate the determinant. $\begin{vmatrix} -2 & 4 & 9 \\ 5 & -1 & 2 \\ 1 & 1 & 6 \end{vmatrix}$

Although we defined the determinant of a 3 × 3 matrix by expanding the minors of the elements in the first column, *any row or column can be used*. However, we must choose the correct sign to apply to the product of factors of each term. The following array of signs is helpful.

row 1, column 1   row 1, column 2
1 + 1 = 2 (even)   1 + 2 = 3 (odd)

$$\begin{matrix} + & - & + \\ - & + & - \\ + & - & + \end{matrix}$$

Notice that the sign is positive if the sum of the row and column numbers is even. The sign is negative if the sum of the row and column numbers is odd.

To evaluate the determinant of an $n \times n$ matrix, choose any row or column. For each element a_{ij} in the selected row or column, multiply the minor by 1 or -1 depending on whether the sum of the row and column numbers is even or odd. That is, for the element a_{ij}, we have $(-1)^{i+j}M_{ij}$. This product is called the *cofactor* of the element a_{ij}.

Cofactor of an Element of a Matrix

Given a square matrix $A = [a_{ij}]$, the **cofactor** of a_{ij} is $(-1)^{i+j}M_{ij}$, where M_{ij} is the minor of a_{ij}.

Using the definition of the cofactor of an element of an $n \times n$ matrix, we can now present a generic method to find the determinant of the matrix.

Evaluating the Determinant of an $n \times n$ Matrix by Expanding Cofactors

Step 1 Choose any row or column.
Step 2 Multiply each element in the selected row or column by its cofactor.
Step 3 The value of the determinant is the sum of the products from step 2.

EXAMPLE 4   **Evaluating the Determinant of a 3 × 3 Matrix**

Evaluate the determinant of the matrix from Example 3 by expanding cofactors about the elements in the third row.

$$A = \begin{bmatrix} 2 & 4 & 2 \\ 1 & -3 & 0 \\ -5 & 5 & -1 \end{bmatrix}$$

Solution:

$$\begin{vmatrix} 2 & 4 & 2 \\ 1 & -3 & 0 \\ -5 & 5 & -1 \end{vmatrix} = \overbrace{(-5)(-1)^{3+1}\begin{vmatrix} 4 & 2 \\ -3 & 0 \end{vmatrix}}^{\text{cofactor of } -5} + \overbrace{(5)(-1)^{3+2}\begin{vmatrix} 2 & 2 \\ 1 & 0 \end{vmatrix}}^{\text{cofactor of } 5} + \overbrace{(-1)(-1)^{3+3}\begin{vmatrix} 2 & 4 \\ 1 & -3 \end{vmatrix}}^{\text{cofactor of } -1}$$

$$= (-5)(1)[(4)(0) - (2)(-3)] + (5)(-1)[(2)(0) - (2)(1)] + (-1)(1)[(2)(-3) - (4)(1)]$$

$$= -5(6) - 5(-2) - 1(-10)$$

$$= -10$$

This is the same result as in Example 3.

Skill Practice 4   Evaluate the determinant by expanding cofactors about the elements in the third column.

$$\begin{vmatrix} -2 & 4 & 9 \\ 5 & -1 & 2 \\ 1 & 1 & 6 \end{vmatrix}$$

Answer
4. -42

TECHNOLOGY CONNECTIONS

Evaluating a Determinant

To find the determinant of a matrix on a graphing calculator, first enter the matrix in the calculator by using the MATRIX menu and EDIT menu. Select a name for the matrix such as [A]. Then access the determinant function det(under the MATRIX and MATH menus. Enter det([A]) in the home screen and press ENTER.

Alternatively, if the calculator is in "MATHPRINT" mode, enter the matrix by selecting ALPHA F3.

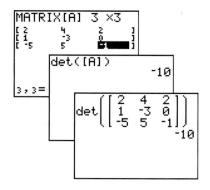

TIP The determinant of a 3 × 3 matrix can also be evaluated by using the "method of diagonals."

Step 1: Recopy columns 1 and 2 to the right of the matrix

Step 2: Multiply the elements on the diagonals labeled d_1 through d_6 (each diagonal has three elements).

Step 3: The value of the determinant is $(d_1 + d_2 + d_3) - (d_4 + d_5 + d_6)$.

The determinant from Example 4 is evaluated as follows:

$$\begin{bmatrix} 2 & 4 & 2 \\ 1 & -3 & 0 \\ -5 & 5 & -1 \end{bmatrix} \begin{matrix} 2 & 4 \\ 1 & -3 \\ -5 & 5 \end{matrix}$$

$$d_4 \quad d_5 \quad d_6 \qquad d_1 \quad d_2 \quad d_3$$

$$= [(2)(-3)(-1) + (4)(0)(-5) + (2)(1)(5)]$$
$$- [(2)(-3)(-5) + (2)(0)(5) + (4)(1)(-1)]$$
$$= -10$$

Some students find the method of diagonals to be a faster technique to find the determinant of a 3 × 3 matrix. However, it is critical to note that the method of diagonals only works for the determinant of a 3 × 3 matrix.

Perhaps one of the most important applications of a determinant of a matrix is to determine whether the matrix has an inverse. In Section 6.4, we found the inverse of a 2 × 2 matrix $A = \begin{bmatrix} a & b \\ c & d \end{bmatrix}$ by applying the formula $A^{-1} = \dfrac{1}{ad - bc}\begin{bmatrix} d & -b \\ -c & a \end{bmatrix}$. This is equivalent to $A^{-1} = \dfrac{1}{|A|}\begin{bmatrix} d & -b \\ -c & a \end{bmatrix}$. Furthermore, the inverse exists if $ad - bc \neq 0$ or equivalently, if $|A| \neq 0$. This is true in general for an $n \times n$ matrix.

Using Determinants to Determine if a Matrix Is Invertible

Let A be an $n \times n$ matrix. Then A is invertible if and only if $|A| \neq 0$.

In Example 5, we will use the determinant of A to determine if A has an inverse.

> **EXAMPLE 5**   **Using a Determinant to Determine if a Matrix Is Invertible**
>
> Use $|A|$ to detrmine if A is invertible. $A = \begin{vmatrix} -2 & 0 & 1 & 2 \\ 6 & 2 & -2 & 5 \\ 5 & 3 & -1 & 1 \\ 0 & 4 & 2 & 1 \end{vmatrix}$
>
> **Solution:**
>
> To evaluate a determinant, we can simplify the arithmetic by expanding around the row or column that contains the greatest number of 0 elements. In this case, we have chosen row 1.

$$\begin{vmatrix} -2 & 0 & 1 & 2 \\ 6 & 2 & -2 & 5 \\ 5 & 3 & -1 & 1 \\ 0 & 4 & 2 & 1 \end{vmatrix} = -2(-1)^{1+1}\begin{vmatrix} 2 & -2 & 5 \\ 3 & -1 & 1 \\ 4 & 2 & 1 \end{vmatrix} + 0(-1)^{1+2}\begin{vmatrix} 6 & -2 & 5 \\ 5 & -1 & 1 \\ 0 & 2 & 1 \end{vmatrix} + 1(-1)^{1+3}\begin{vmatrix} 6 & 2 & 5 \\ 5 & 3 & 1 \\ 0 & 4 & 1 \end{vmatrix} + 2(-1)^{1+4}\begin{vmatrix} 6 & 2 & -2 \\ 5 & 3 & -1 \\ 0 & 4 & 2 \end{vmatrix}$$

> The second term is zero. Evaluating the determinants in the first, third, and fourth terms (shown in red), we have:
>
> $$\begin{vmatrix} -2 & 0 & 1 & 2 \\ 6 & 2 & -2 & 5 \\ 5 & 3 & -1 & 1 \\ 0 & 4 & 2 & 1 \end{vmatrix} = -2(1)(42) + 0 + 1(1)(84) + 2(-1)(0) = 0$$
>
> The determinant of A is zero. Therefore, A is not invertible.

> **Skill Practice 5**   Use $|A|$ to determine if A is invertible. $A = \begin{vmatrix} 3 & 2 & 1 & 0 \\ 4 & 0 & 3 & 1 \\ 2 & 0 & 0 & 5 \\ 3 & -1 & 0 & 9 \end{vmatrix}$

3. Apply Cramer's Rule

We have learned several methods to solve a system of linear equations: the substitution method, the addition method, Gaussian elimination, Gauss-Jordan elimination, and the application of matrix inverses. We now present another method called Cramer's rule.

Cramer's rule involves finding the ratio of several determinants derived from the coefficients of the equations within the system. For example, consider the following system of equations.

$$a_1x + b_1y = c_1$$
$$a_2x + b_2y = c_2$$

Answer

5. $|A| = -9$; Since $|A| \neq 0$, A is invertible.

Using the addition method to solve for x, we have

$$a_1x + b_1y = c_1 \quad \xrightarrow{\text{Multiply by } b_2.}$$
$$a_2x + b_2y = c_2 \quad \xrightarrow{\text{Multiply by } -b_1.}$$

$$a_1b_2x + b_1b_2y = c_1b_2$$
$$-a_2b_1x - b_1b_2y = -c_2b_1$$
$$\overline{(a_1b_2 - a_2b_1)x \qquad\quad = c_1b_2 - c_2b_1}$$

$$x = \frac{c_1b_2 - c_2b_1}{a_1b_2 - a_2b_1} = \frac{\begin{vmatrix} c_1 & b_1 \\ c_2 & b_2 \end{vmatrix}}{\begin{vmatrix} a_1 & b_1 \\ a_2 & b_2 \end{vmatrix}}$$

Using similar logic, we can show that

$$y = \frac{a_1c_2 - a_2c_1}{a_1b_2 - a_2b_1} = \frac{\begin{vmatrix} a_1 & c_1 \\ a_2 & c_2 \end{vmatrix}}{\begin{vmatrix} a_1 & b_1 \\ a_2 & b_2 \end{vmatrix}}$$

These results are summarized as Cramer's rule for a system of linear equations in two variables.

Cramer's Rule for a System of Two Linear Equations in Two Variables

Given the system
$$a_1x + b_1y = c_1$$
$$a_2x + b_2y = c_2$$

let $D = \begin{vmatrix} a_1 & b_1 \\ a_2 & b_2 \end{vmatrix}$, $D_x = \begin{vmatrix} c_1 & b_1 \\ c_2 & b_2 \end{vmatrix}$, and $D_y = \begin{vmatrix} a_1 & c_1 \\ a_2 & c_2 \end{vmatrix}$.

Then if $D \neq 0$, the system has the unique solution: $x = \dfrac{D_x}{D}$ and $y = \dfrac{D_y}{D}$.

TIP Here are some memory tips to remember the patterns presented in Cramer's rule.

$$a_1x + b_1y = c_1$$
$$a_2x + b_2y = c_2$$

Coefficients of
x-terms   y-terms

1. The determinant D is the determinant of the coefficients of x and y.

$$D = \begin{vmatrix} a_1 & b_1 \\ a_2 & b_2 \end{vmatrix}$$

x-coefficients replaced by c_1 and c_2

2. The determinant D_x has the column of x-term coefficients replaced by c_1 and c_2.

$$D_x = \begin{vmatrix} c_1 & b_1 \\ c_2 & b_2 \end{vmatrix}$$

y-coefficients replaced by c_1 and c_2

3. The determinant D_y has the column of y-term coefficients replaced by c_1 and c_2.

$$D_y = \begin{vmatrix} a_1 & c_1 \\ a_2 & c_2 \end{vmatrix}$$

EXAMPLE 6   **Solving a 2 × 2 System by Using Cramer's Rule**

Solve the system by using Cramer's rule. $-11x + 6y = 4$
                                                 $2x - 5y = -3$

Solution:

For this system, $a_1 = -11$, $b_1 = 6$, $c_1 = 4$, $a_2 = 2$, $b_2 = -5$, and $c_2 = -3$.

$$D = \begin{vmatrix} a_1 & b_1 \\ a_2 & b_2 \end{vmatrix} \longrightarrow D = \begin{vmatrix} -11 & 6 \\ 2 & -5 \end{vmatrix} = (-11)(-5) - (6)(2) = 43$$

$$D_x = \begin{vmatrix} c_1 & b_1 \\ c_2 & b_2 \end{vmatrix} \longrightarrow D_x = \begin{vmatrix} 4 & 6 \\ -3 & -5 \end{vmatrix} = (4)(-5) - (6)(-3) = -2$$

$$D_y = \begin{vmatrix} a_1 & c_1 \\ a_2 & c_2 \end{vmatrix} \longrightarrow D_y = \begin{vmatrix} -11 & 4 \\ 2 & -3 \end{vmatrix} = (-11)(-3) - (4)(2) = 25$$

Therefore, $x = \dfrac{D_x}{D} = \dfrac{-2}{43}$ and $y = \dfrac{D_y}{D} = \dfrac{25}{43}$.

The solution set is $\left\{ \left(-\dfrac{2}{43}, \dfrac{25}{43} \right) \right\}$.

Skill Practice 6   Solve the system by using Cramer's rule. $3x - 4y = 9$
                                                                  $-5x + 6y = 2$

The patterns associated with Cramer's rule can be generalized to solve a system of n linear equations in n variables.

Cramer's Rule for a System of n Linear Equations in n Variables

Consider the following system of n linear equations in n variables.

$$a_{11}x_1 + a_{12}x_2 + \cdots + a_{1n}x_n = b_1$$
$$a_{21}x_1 + a_{22}x_2 + \cdots + a_{2n}x_n = b_2$$
$$\vdots$$
$$a_{n1}x_1 + a_{n2}x_2 + \cdots + a_{nn}x_n = b_n$$

If the system has a unique solution, then the solution is $(x_1, x_2, \ldots, x_i, \ldots, x_n)$, where

$$x_1 = \frac{D_1}{D}, x_2 = \frac{D_2}{D}, \ldots, x_i = \frac{D_i}{D}, \ldots, x_n = \frac{D_n}{D}$$

$D \neq 0$ is the determinant of the coefficient matrix, and D_i is the determinant formed by replacing the ith column of the coefficient matrix by the column of constants $b_1, b_2, \ldots, b_n$.

In Example 7, we apply Cramer's rule to a system of equations with three variables.

Answer

6. $\left\{ \left(-31, -\dfrac{51}{2} \right) \right\}$

EXAMPLE 7   Solving a 3 × 3 System by Using Cramer's Rule

Solve the system by using Cramer's rule.

$$2x - 3y + 5z = 11$$
$$-5x + 7y - 2z = -6$$
$$9x - 2y + 3z = 4$$

Solution:

Evaluate the determinants D, D_x, D_y, and D_z.

$$D = \begin{vmatrix} 2 & -3 & 5 \\ -5 & 7 & -2 \\ 9 & -2 & 3 \end{vmatrix} = -222 \qquad D_x = \begin{vmatrix} 11 & -3 & 5 \\ -6 & 7 & -2 \\ 4 & -2 & 3 \end{vmatrix} = 77$$

$$D_y = \begin{vmatrix} 2 & 11 & 5 \\ -5 & -6 & -2 \\ 9 & 4 & 3 \end{vmatrix} = 117 \qquad D_z = \begin{vmatrix} 2 & -3 & 11 \\ -5 & 7 & -6 \\ 9 & -2 & 4 \end{vmatrix} = -449$$

Therefore, $x = \dfrac{D_x}{D} = -\dfrac{77}{222}$, $y = \dfrac{D_y}{D} = -\dfrac{117}{222}$ or $-\dfrac{39}{74}$, and $z = \dfrac{D_z}{D} = \dfrac{449}{222}$.

The solution set is $\left\{ \left(-\dfrac{77}{222}, -\dfrac{39}{74}, \dfrac{449}{222} \right) \right\}$.

Skill Practice 7   Solve the system by using Cramer's rule.

$$5x + 3y - 3z = -14$$
$$3x - 4y + z = 2$$
$$x + 7y + z = 6$$

Although Cramer's rule may seem cumbersome for solving a 3 × 3 system of linear equations, it provides convenient formulas that can be programmed into a computer or calculator to solve the system. However, it is important to remember that Cramer's rule does not apply if $D = 0$. In such a case, the system of equations is either inconsistent (has no solution) or the equations are dependent (the system has infinitely many solutions). For a 2 × 2 system of linear equations with $D = 0$, we offer the following guidelines to determine the nature of the solutions to the system.

Identifying an Inconsistent System or Dependent Equations

Consider a 2 × 2 system of linear equations in which Cramer's rule is used to find the solution.

- If $D = 0$ and at least one of the determinants D_i in the numerator is nonzero, then the system has no solution.
- If $D = 0$ and all determinants D_i in the numerator are zero, then the system has infinitely many solutions.

EXAMPLE 8   Using Cramer's Rule to Determine the Number of Solutions to a System

Solve the system if possible by using Cramer's rule. If the system does not have a unique solution, determine the number of solutions.

$$2x - 3y = 6$$
$$-6x + 9y = -18$$

Answer

7. $\left\{ \left(-\dfrac{13}{34}, \dfrac{5}{17}, \dfrac{147}{34} \right) \right\}$

TIP Cramer's rule does not give the solutions to the system in Example 8. Using another method, we can show that the solution set is $\{(x, y) \mid 2x - 3y = 6\}$.

Solution:

Evaluate the determinants D, D_x, and D_y.

$$D = \begin{vmatrix} 2 & -3 \\ -6 & 9 \end{vmatrix} = 0 \qquad D_x = \begin{vmatrix} 6 & -3 \\ -18 & 9 \end{vmatrix} = 0 \qquad D_y = \begin{vmatrix} 2 & 6 \\ -6 & -18 \end{vmatrix} = 0$$

The determinant D is zero as are both D_x and D_y. Therefore, the equations are dependent and the system has infinitely many solutions.

Skill Practice 8 Solve the system if possible by using Cramer's rule.

$$x - 4y = 6$$
$$-2x + 8y = 4$$

Answer

8. No solution

SECTION 6.5   Practice Exercises

Review Exercises

For Exercises 1–6, solve the system using any method.

1. $2x - 3y = 1$
  $-\frac{1}{3}x = -\frac{1}{6} - \frac{1}{2}y$

2. $-5(x + y) = 2 - 6y$
  $y = 5x + 2$

3. $3x + \qquad z = 4$
  $2y + 5z = 1$
  $9x + 5y \qquad = -1$

4. $-2x + 3y \qquad = -3$
  $4y + 2z = -4$
  $5x \qquad + 2z = 7$

5. $x + y + 4z = 5$
  $-2x - 3y - 14z = -14$
  $-3x - y \qquad = 7$

6. $3x - 7y - 8z = -22$
  $x - 3y - 2z = -10$
  $x \qquad - 5z = -2$

Concept Connections

7. Associated with every square matrix A is a real number denoted by $|A|$ called the _____ of A.

8. For a 2×2 matrix $A = \begin{bmatrix} a & b \\ c & d \end{bmatrix}$, $|A| = \begin{vmatrix} a & b \\ c & d \end{vmatrix} = $ _____.

9. Given $A = [a_{ij}]$, the _____ of the element a_{ij} is the determinant obtained by deleting the ith row and jth column.

10. Given $A = [a_{ij}]$, then the value $(-1)^{i+j} M_{ij}$ is called the _____ of the element a_{ij}.

11. The determinant of a 3×3 matrix
$$A = \begin{bmatrix} a_1 & b_1 & c_1 \\ a_2 & b_2 & c_2 \\ a_3 & b_3 & c_3 \end{bmatrix} \text{ is given by}$$
$$|A| = a_1 \begin{vmatrix} \square & \square \\ \square & \square \end{vmatrix} - a_2 \begin{vmatrix} \square & \square \\ \square & \square \end{vmatrix} + a_3 \begin{vmatrix} \square & \square \\ \square & \square \end{vmatrix}$$

12. Suppose that the given system has one solution.
$$a_1 x + b_1 y = c_1$$
$$a_2 x + b_2 y = c_2$$

Cramer's rule gives the solution as $x = \dfrac{\square}{\square}$ and $y = \dfrac{\square}{\square}$,

where $D = \begin{vmatrix} \square & \square \\ \square & \square \end{vmatrix}$, $D_x = \begin{vmatrix} \square & \square \\ \square & \square \end{vmatrix}$, and

$D_y = \begin{vmatrix} \square & \square \\ \square & \square \end{vmatrix}$.

13. When applying Cramer's rule, if $D = 0$, then the system (does/does not) have a unique solution.

14. When applying Cramer's rule, if $D = 0$, and all other determinants D_i in the numerator are zero, then the system has (no solution/infinitely many solutions).

Objective 1: Evaluate the Determinant of a 2 × 2 Matrix

For Exercises 15–24, evaluate the determinant of the matrix. (See Example 1)

15. $A = \begin{bmatrix} 3 & -2 \\ 6 & 5 \end{bmatrix}$

16. $B = \begin{bmatrix} 7 & 12 \\ -1 & 4 \end{bmatrix}$

17. $C = \begin{bmatrix} \frac{2}{3} & \frac{1}{5} \\ 10 & 12 \end{bmatrix}$

18. $D = \begin{bmatrix} \frac{8}{9} & 4 \\ \frac{5}{2} & 18 \end{bmatrix}$

19. $E = \begin{bmatrix} -3 & 0 \\ 4 & 0 \end{bmatrix}$

20. $F = \begin{bmatrix} 0 & 9 \\ 0 & 4 \end{bmatrix}$

21. $G = \begin{bmatrix} x & 4 \\ 9 & x \end{bmatrix}$

22. $H = \begin{bmatrix} y & 16 \\ 4 & y \end{bmatrix}$

23. $T = \begin{bmatrix} e^x & e^{2x} \\ 4 & -e^x \end{bmatrix}$

24. $V = \begin{bmatrix} \log x & \log x \\ 2 & 5 \end{bmatrix}$

Objective 2: Evaluate the Determinant of an n × n Matrix

For Exercises 25–30, refer to the matrix $A = [a_{ij}] = \begin{bmatrix} -6 & 11 & 8 \\ 4 & -2 & -5 \\ -3 & 7 & 10 \end{bmatrix}$.

a. Find the minor of the given element. (**See Example 2**)

b. Find the cofactor of the given element.

25. a_{12}

26. a_{23}

27. a_{31}

28. a_{13}

29. a_{22}

30. a_{33}

For Exercises 31–40, evaluate the determinant of the matrix and state whether the matrix is invertible. (See Examples 3–5)

31. $A = \begin{bmatrix} 4 & 1 & 3 \\ 0 & -1 & 2 \\ 5 & 8 & 0 \end{bmatrix}$

32. $B = \begin{bmatrix} 9 & 5 & -1 \\ 2 & 0 & 4 \\ 7 & -2 & 0 \end{bmatrix}$

33. $C = \begin{bmatrix} 5 & 1 & 6 \\ 2 & 3 & 4 \\ 8 & -1 & 7 \end{bmatrix}$

34. $D = \begin{bmatrix} -3 & 1 & -2 \\ 10 & 5 & 8 \\ 6 & 7 & -4 \end{bmatrix}$

35. $E = \begin{bmatrix} 2 & 0 & 1 \\ 1 & -1 & 2 \\ 3 & 1 & 0 \end{bmatrix}$

36. $F = \begin{bmatrix} 1 & -3 & 17 \\ 1 & -1 & 7 \\ 2 & -5 & 29 \end{bmatrix}$

37. $G = \begin{bmatrix} 5 & 6 & 4 & 1 \\ 2 & 0 & 3 & 0 \\ 0 & 1 & 4 & 0 \\ -1 & 2 & 0 & 0 \end{bmatrix}$

38. $H = \begin{bmatrix} 8 & 0 & 5 & 1 \\ 0 & 3 & 4 & -2 \\ 2 & 6 & 3 & 0 \\ -1 & 0 & 0 & 0 \end{bmatrix}$

39. $T = \begin{bmatrix} 3 & 8 & 1 & 4 \\ -2 & 4 & 0 & 5 \\ -1 & 1 & 0 & -1 \\ 0 & 5 & 2 & 3 \end{bmatrix}$

40. $W = \begin{bmatrix} 2 & 5 & 2 & 4 \\ 0 & 0 & -3 & 1 \\ 4 & 8 & 0 & 1 \\ -1 & 2 & 0 & 5 \end{bmatrix}$

Objective 3: Apply Cramer's Rule

For Exercises 41–56, solve the system if possible by using Cramer's rule. If the system does not have a unique solution, give the number of solutions. (See Examples 6–8)

41. $2x + 10y = 11$
$3x - 5y = 6$

42. $-5x - 8y = 3$
$4x + 7y = 13$

43. $-10x + 4y = 7$
$6x = 7y + 2$

44. $11x + 6y = 8$
$2x = 9y + 5$

45. $3(x - y) = y + 8$
$y = \frac{3}{4}x - 2$

46. $5(x + y) = 7x + 4$
$4x = 10y - 8$

47. $y = -3x + 7$
$\frac{1}{2}x + \frac{1}{6}y = 1$

48. $x = 4y + 5$
$3(x - 4) = 12y$

49. $11x \qquad - 3z = 1$
$2y + 9z = 6$
$4x + 5y \qquad = -9$

50. $-2x + 6y \qquad = 9$
$5y + 7z = 1$
$4x \qquad - 3z = -8$

51. $2x - 5y + z = 11$
$3x + 7y - 4z = 8$
$x - 9y + 2z = 4$

52. $-5x - 6y + 8z = 1$
$2x + y - 4z = 5$
$3x - 4y - z = -2$

53. $2x - 3y + z = 6$
$-4x + 6y - 2z = -12$
$6x - 9y + 3z = 18$

54. $-x + y - 3z = 4$
$3x - 3y + 9z = -12$
$-2x + 2y - 6z = 8$

55. $x - 2y + 3z = -1$
$5x - 7y + 3z = 1$
$x \qquad - 5z = 2$

56. $x + 3y - 5z = 10$
$-2x - 4y + 8z = -14$
$x + y - 3z = 5$

For Exercises 57–58, use Cramer's rule to solve for the indicated variable.

57. $x_1 + 2x_2 + 3x_3 - 4x_4 = 3$
$\qquad 5x_2 \qquad + x_4 = 9$
$x_1 \qquad + 4x_3 \qquad = -1$
$\qquad 5x_3 - 2x_4 = 8$ Solve for x_2.

58. $-2x_1 - x_2 + x_3 + 3x_4 = 10$
$x_1 \qquad + 5x_3 \qquad = 4$
$\qquad 2x_2 \qquad + x_4 = -1$
$\qquad 4x_3 + 2x_4 = 7$ Solve for x_3.

Mixed Exercises

Determinants can be used to determine whether three points are collinear (lie on the same line). Given the points (x_1, y_1), (x_2, y_2), and (x_3, y_3), the points are collinear if the following determinant equals zero.

$$\begin{vmatrix} x_1 & y_1 & 1 \\ x_2 & y_2 & 1 \\ x_3 & y_3 & 1 \end{vmatrix}$$

For Exercises 59–62, determine if the points are collinear.

59. $(3, 6)$, $(6, 10)$, $(-3, -2)$

60. $(-2, 1)$, $(-4, -4)$, $(4, 16)$

61. $(4, -3)$, $(5, -7)$, $(8, -14)$

62. $(0, 6)$, $(1, 4)$, $(4, -6)$

The following equation represents an equation of the line passing through the distinct points (x_1, y_1) and (x_2, y_2).

$$\begin{vmatrix} x & y & 1 \\ x_1 & y_1 & 1 \\ x_2 & y_2 & 1 \end{vmatrix} = 0$$

For Exercises 63–64,

a. Use the determinant equation to write an equation of the line passing through the given points.

b. Write the equation of the line in slope-intercept form.

63. $(-3, 2)$ and $(-4, 6)$

64. $(-4, 1)$ and $(-5, 4)$

For Exercises 65–66, use the following formula to find the area of the triangle with the given vertices (x_1, y_1), (x_2, y_2), and (x_3, y_3). Choose the $+$ or $-$ sign so that the value of the area is positive.

$$\text{Area} = \pm\frac{1}{2}\begin{vmatrix} x_1 & y_1 & 1 \\ x_2 & y_2 & 1 \\ x_3 & y_3 & 1 \end{vmatrix}$$

65. $(1, 0)$, $(7, -2)$, $(4, -5)$

66. $(-2, 1)$, $(-1, -6)$, $(-8, -5)$

Given a square matrix A, elementary row operations (or column operations) performed on A affect the value of $|A|$ in the following ways:

- Interchanging any two rows (or columns) of A will change the sign of $|A|$.
- Multiplying a row (or column) of A by a constant real number k multiplies $|A|$ by k.
- Adding a multiple of a row (or column) of A to another row (or column) of A does not change the value of $|A|$.

For Exercises 67–72, demonstrate these three properties.

67. Given $A = \begin{bmatrix} 5 & 2 \\ -3 & 6 \end{bmatrix}$ and $B = \begin{bmatrix} -3 & 6 \\ 5 & 2 \end{bmatrix}$,

a. Evaluate $|A|$.

b. Evaluate $|B|$.

c. How are A and B related and how are $|A|$ and $|B|$ related?

68. Given $A = \begin{bmatrix} 2 & -7 \\ 4 & 10 \end{bmatrix}$ and $B = \begin{bmatrix} 4 & 10 \\ 2 & -7 \end{bmatrix}$,

a. Evaluate $|A|$.

b. Evaluate $|B|$.

c. How are A and B related and how are $|A|$ and $|B|$ related?

69. Given $A = \begin{bmatrix} 1 & -3 \\ 4 & 1 \end{bmatrix}$ and $B = \begin{bmatrix} 2 & -6 \\ 4 & 1 \end{bmatrix}$,

  a. Evaluate $|A|$.

  b. Evaluate $|B|$.

  c. How are A and B related and how are $|A|$ and $|B|$ related?

70. Given $A = \begin{bmatrix} 2 & 1 \\ 5 & 7 \end{bmatrix}$ and $B = \begin{bmatrix} -6 & -3 \\ 5 & 7 \end{bmatrix}$,

  a. Evaluate $|A|$.

  b. Evaluate $|B|$.

  c. How are A and B related and how are $|A|$ and $|B|$ related?

71. Given $A = \begin{bmatrix} 1 & 2 \\ 3 & 4 \end{bmatrix}$ and $B = \begin{bmatrix} 1 & 2 \\ 6 & 10 \end{bmatrix}$,

  a. Evaluate $|A|$.

  b. Evaluate $|B|$.

  c. How are A and B related and how are $|A|$ and $|B|$ related?

72. Given $A = \begin{bmatrix} 1 & 1 \\ 5 & 6 \end{bmatrix}$ and $B = \begin{bmatrix} 1 & 1 \\ 3 & 4 \end{bmatrix}$,

  a. Evaluate $|A|$.

  b. Evaluate $|B|$.

  c. How are A and B related and how are $|A|$ and $|B|$ related?

Given a square matrix A, if either of the following conditions are true, then $|A| = 0$.

  • A row (or column) of A consists entirely of zeros.

  • One row (or column) is a constant multiple of another row (or column).

For Exercises 73–76, demonstrate these two properties.

73. Given $A = \begin{bmatrix} 3 & 5 \\ 6 & 10 \end{bmatrix}$, find $|A|$.

74. Given $A = \begin{bmatrix} -2 & 7 \\ -6 & 21 \end{bmatrix}$, find $|A|$.

75. Given $A = \begin{bmatrix} 4 & -5 & 0 \\ 3 & -1 & 0 \\ 0 & 1 & 0 \end{bmatrix}$, find $|A|$.

76. Given $A = \begin{bmatrix} 5 & 3 & 1 \\ -1 & 0 & 3 \\ 0 & 0 & 0 \end{bmatrix}$, find $|A|$.

77. Evaluate $|I_2|$.

78. Evaluate $|I_3|$.

79. Evaluate $\begin{vmatrix} a & 0 & 0 \\ 0 & b & 0 \\ 0 & 0 & c \end{vmatrix}$.

80. Evaluate $\begin{vmatrix} x & 0 \\ 0 & x \end{vmatrix}$.

81. If A and B are square matrices, then the product property of determinants indicates that $|AB| = |A| \cdot |B|$. Use matrix A and matrix B to demonstrate this property.

$$A = \begin{bmatrix} 4 & -2 \\ 3 & 1 \end{bmatrix} \text{ and } B = \begin{bmatrix} -5 & 1 \\ 3 & 2 \end{bmatrix}$$

82. The **transpose** of a square matrix A, denoted as A^T, is a square matrix that results by writing the rows of A as the columns of A^T.

  a. Given $A = \begin{bmatrix} 1 & 2 & 5 \\ 0 & 8 & 4 \\ 3 & 7 & 6 \end{bmatrix}$, find A^T.

  b. Show that $|A| = |A^T|$.

Write About It

83. What is the difference between the minor of an element a_{ij} and the cofactor of the element?

84. Explain the difference between the notation $\begin{bmatrix} a & b \\ c & d \end{bmatrix}$ and $\begin{vmatrix} a & b \\ c & d \end{vmatrix}$.

85. The determinant of a square matrix can be computed by expanding the cofactors of the elements in any row or column. How would you choose which row or column?

86. Consider the system shown here. Describe the pattern associated with constructing the determinants used with Cramer's rule.

$$a_1 x + b_1 y = c_1$$
$$a_2 x + b_2 y = c_2$$

Technology Connections

For Exercises 87–88, use a graphing utility to evaluate the determinant of the matrix. Round to the nearest whole unit.

87. $A = \begin{bmatrix} -0.4 & 1.5 & 9 & 11.3 \\ -3.5 & 0.2 & -1.1 & 3 \\ 8 & 9.4 & -5.4 & 2 \\ -1 & 4.6 & 10.8 & -9.7 \end{bmatrix}$

88. $B = \begin{bmatrix} -2\pi & e^2 & 9.1 & \log 2 \\ \log 50 & -\sqrt{11} & 4.3 & \pi \\ -4.9 & 0 & e^2 & 8.1 \\ \sqrt{7} & \ln 7 & -9.7 & 0 \end{bmatrix}$

PROBLEM RECOGNITION EXERCISES

Using Multiple Methods to Solve Systems of Linear Equations

For Exercises 1–4, solve the system of equations using

a. The substitution method or the addition method (see Sections 5.1 and 5.2).

b. Gaussian elimination (see Section 6.1).

c. Gauss-Jordan elimination (see Section 6.1).

d. The inverse of the coefficient matrix (see Section 6.4).

e. Cramer's rule (see Section 6.5).

1. $x = -3y - 10$
$-3x - 7y = 22$

2. $2x = 2 - 8y$
$3x + 10y = 5$

3. $x + 2y - z = 0$
$2x \quad + z = 4$
$2x - y + 2z = 5$

4. $x + 4y + 2z = 10$
$2y + z = 4$
$x + y \quad = 2$

For Exercises 5–8,

a. Evaluate the determinant of the coefficient matrix.

b. Based on the value of the determinant from part (a), can an inverse matrix or Cramer's rule be used to solve the system?

c. Solve the system using an appropriate method.

5. $1.5x - 2y = 3$
$-3x + 4y = 12$

6. $5x - 2y = 1$
$x - 0.4y = 4$

7. $x - 3y + 7z = 1$
$-2x + 5y - 11z = -3$
$x - 5y + 13z = -1$

8. $x - 2y + 3z = -7$
$-2x + y \quad = -1$
$x \quad - z = 3$

CHAPTER 6   KEY CONCEPTS

SECTION 6.1 Solving Systems of Linear Equations Using Matrices	Reference
A system of linear equations can be represented by an **augmented matrix.**	p. 594
Elementary row operations can be used to write a matrix in row-echelon form or reduced row-echelon form. 1. Interchange two rows. 2. Multiply a row by a nonzero constant. 3. Add a nonzero multiple of one row to another row.	p. 595
The method of **Gaussian elimination** uses elementary row operations to write an augmented matrix in row-echelon form so that the system can be solved by back substitution.	p. 597
With the method of **Gauss-Jordan elimination** the augmented matrix is written in *reduced* row-echelon form.	p. 598

SECTION 6.2 Inconsistent Systems and Dependent Equations	Reference
A system of equations that has no solution is called an **inconsistent system.** An inconsistent system is detected algebraically if a contradiction is reached when solving the system.	p. 604
A system of linear equations may have infinitely many solutions. In such a case, the equations are said to be **dependent.** Dependent equations are detected algebraically if an identity is reached when solving the system.	p. 605

SECTION 6.3 Operations on Matrices	Reference
An $m \times n$ matrix has m rows and n columns.	p. 613
Adding and subtracting matrices: If A and B represent two matrices of the same order, then $A + B$ and $A - B$ are found by adding or subtracting the corresponding elements.	p. 614
Scalar multiplication: Let $A = [a_{ij}]$ be an $m \times n$ matrix and let k be a real number. Then, $kA = [ka_{ij}]$.	p. 616
Matrix multiplication: Let A be an $m \times p$ matrix and let B be a $p \times n$ matrix, then the product AB is an $m \times n$ matrix. For the matrix AB, the element in the ith row and jth column is the sum of the products of the corresponding elements in the ith row of A and the jth column of B. *Note*: If the number of columns in A does not equal the number of rows in B, then the product AB is not defined.	p. 619

SECTION 6.4 Inverse Matrices and Matrix Equations	Reference
The **identity matrix** I_n for the multiplication of matrices is the $n \times n$ square matrix with 1's along the main diagonal and 0's for all other elements.	p. 630
Inverse of a square matrix: Let A be an $n \times n$ matrix. If there exists an $n \times n$ matrix A^{-1} such that $$AA^{-1} = I_n \quad \text{and} \quad A^{-1}A = I_n$$ then A^{-1} is the **multiplicative inverse** of A.	p. 631
A matrix that does not have an inverse is called a **singular matrix.** A matrix that does have an inverse is said to be **invertible** or **nonsingular.**	p. 633
Finding the inverse of a nonsingular matrix: Let A be an $n \times n$ matrix for which A^{-1} exists. To find A^{-1}: **Step 1** Write a matrix of the form $[A \mid I_n]$. **Step 2** Perform row operations to write the matrix in the form $[I_n \mid B]$. **Step 3** The matrix B is A^{-1}.	p. 633
The inverse of a nonsingular 2×2 matrix A can also be found as follows. If $A = \begin{bmatrix} a & b \\ c & d \end{bmatrix}$, then $A^{-1} = \dfrac{1}{ad - bc} \cdot \begin{bmatrix} d & -b \\ -c & a \end{bmatrix}$, or equivalently $A^{-1} = \dfrac{1}{\lvert A \rvert} \begin{bmatrix} d & -b \\ -c & a \end{bmatrix}$.	p. 635
Solving a system using inverse matrices: Suppose that $AX = B$ represents a system of n linear equations in n variables with a unique solution. Then, $$X = A^{-1}B$$ where A is the coefficient matrix, B is the matrix of constants, and X is the matrix of variables.	p. 636

SECTION 6.5 Determinants and Cramer's Rule	Reference
Associated with every square matrix is a real number called the determinant of the matrix.	p. 640
Determinant of a 2 × 2 matrix: Given $A = \begin{bmatrix} a & b \\ c & d \end{bmatrix}$, the determinant of A is denoted by $\lvert A \rvert$ or $\begin{vmatrix} a & b \\ c & d \end{vmatrix}$ and the value is $ad - bc$.	p. 640

The minor and cofactor of an element of a matrix: Given an $n \times n$ matrix $A = [a_{ij}]$, the minor M_{ij} of an element a_{ij} is the determinant of the resulting matrix obtained by deleting the ith row and jth column.	pp. 640–641
The **cofactor** of a_{ij} is $(-1)^{i+j}M_{ij}$ where M_{ij} is the minor of a_{ij}.	p. 643
Determinant of a 3 $\times$ 3 matrix: $$\begin{vmatrix} a_1 & b_1 & c_1 \\ a_2 & b_2 & c_2 \\ a_3 & b_3 & c_3 \end{vmatrix} = a_1 \begin{vmatrix} b_2 & c_2 \\ b_3 & c_3 \end{vmatrix} - a_2 \begin{vmatrix} b_1 & c_1 \\ b_3 & c_3 \end{vmatrix} + a_3 \begin{vmatrix} b_1 & c_1 \\ b_2 & c_2 \end{vmatrix}$$	p. 642
Find the determinant of an $n \times n$ matrix: **Step 1** Choose any row or column. **Step 2** Multiply each element in the selected row or column by its cofactor. **Step 3** The value of the determinant is the sum of the products from step 2.	p. 643
Cramer's rule for a system of two equations and two variables: Given $\begin{array}{l} a_1x + b_1y = c_1 \\ a_2x + b_2y = c_2 \end{array}$ if $D \neq 0$, then $x = \dfrac{D_x}{D}$ and $y = \dfrac{D_y}{D}$, where $D = \begin{vmatrix} a_1 & b_1 \\ a_2 & b_2 \end{vmatrix}$, $D_x = \begin{vmatrix} c_1 & b_1 \\ c_2 & b_2 \end{vmatrix}$, and $D_y = \begin{vmatrix} a_1 & c_1 \\ a_2 & c_2 \end{vmatrix}$.	p. 646
The patterns associated with Cramer's rule can be generalized to solve a system of n linear equations in n variables.	p. 647
When applying Cramer's rule, if $D = 0$, then the system has either no solution or infinitely many solutions.	p. 648

Expanded Chapter Summary available at www.mhhe.com/millerca.

CHAPTER 6   Review Exercises

SECTION 6.1

1. Write a system of linear equations represented by the augmented matrix. Then write the solution set.

$$\begin{bmatrix} 1 & -2 & 3 & | & -1 \\ 0 & 1 & 4 & | & -11 \\ 0 & 0 & 1 & | & -2 \end{bmatrix}$$

For Exercises 2–4, perform the elementary row operations on the matrix. $\begin{bmatrix} 2 & -3 & | & 1 \\ 5 & 6 & | & -4 \end{bmatrix}$

2. $R_1 \Leftrightarrow R_2$

3. $\dfrac{1}{2}R_1 \rightarrow R_1$

4. $-2R_1 + R_2 \rightarrow R_2$

For Exercises 5–8, solve the system by using Gaussian elimination or Gauss-Jordan elimination.

5. $\begin{array}{l} -2x + y = -16 \\ x - 2y = 17 \end{array}$

6. $\begin{array}{l} 2(x - 6y) = 36 \\ 47y = 7x - 141 \end{array}$

7. $\begin{array}{l} 2x - 5y + 18z = 44 \\ x - 3y + 11z = 27 \\ x - 2y + 11z = 29 \end{array}$

8. $\begin{array}{l} w + x \quad\quad - 2z = 3 \\ \quad\quad 2x \quad - 3z = 3 \\ 2w \quad\quad + y + z = 3 \\ \quad\quad 4y - z = 9 \end{array}$

9. Lily borrowed a total of $10,000. She borrowed part of the money from her friend Sly who did not charge her interest. She borrowed part of the money from a credit union at 5% simple interest, and she borrowed the rest of the money from a bank at 7.5% interest. At the end of 1 yr, she owed $500 in interest. If she borrowed $1000 less from her friend than she did from the bank, determine how much she borrowed from each source.

SECTION 6.2

For Exercises 10–13, determine the solution set for the system represented by each augmented matrix.

10. $\begin{bmatrix} 1 & 0 & | & 4 \\ 0 & 1 & | & 0 \end{bmatrix}$

11. $\begin{bmatrix} 1 & -2 & | & 6 \\ 0 & 0 & | & 1 \end{bmatrix}$

12. $\begin{bmatrix} 1 & 4 & | & 0 \\ 0 & 0 & | & 0 \end{bmatrix}$

13. $\begin{bmatrix} 1 & 0 & -3 & | & 0 \\ 0 & 1 & 2 & | & 1 \\ 0 & 0 & 0 & | & 0 \end{bmatrix}$

For Exercises 14–19, solve the system by using Gaussian elimination or Gauss-Jordan elimination.

14. $3x + 6y = -9$
$x + 2y = -3$

15. $-(2x - y) = 8 - y$
$y = x - 6$

16. $x - 2y = 3z - 10$
$x - y = z - 7$
$3x - 7y - 11z = -320$

17. $\quad x \quad - 3z = 5$
$-2x + y + 10z = -7$
$x + y + z = 8$

18. $2x = 3y - z - 4$
$x - 2y = z + 2y - 2$
$x + y = 2z - 2$

19. $5y = x + 2z + 1$
$2(x - 5y) + 4z = -2$
$3(x + 2z) = 15y - 3$

20. The solution set to a system of dependent equations is given. Write three ordered triples that are solutions to the system. Answers may vary.

$\{(2z - 3, z + 2, z) \mid z \text{ is any real number}\}$

21. a. Assume that traffic flows freely around the traffic circle. The flow rates given are measured in vehicles per hour. If the flow rate x_3 is 130 vehicles per hour, determine the flow rates x_1 and x_2.

b. If traffic between intersections B and C flows at a rate of between 100 and 150 vehicles per hour, inclusive, find the range of values for x_1 and x_2.

22. a. Assume that traffic flows freely through intersections A, B, C, and D and that all flow rates are measured in vehicles per hour. If the flow rate x_4 is 220 vehicles per hour, find the flow rates x_1, x_2, and x_3.

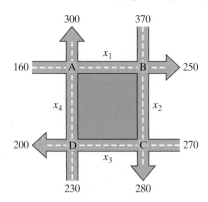

b. If the flow rate x_4 is between 200 and 250 vehicles per hour, inclusive, find the range of values x_1, x_2, and x_3.

SECTION 6.3

For Exercises 23–26,

a. Give the order of the matrix.

b. Classify the matrix as a square matrix, row matrix, column matrix, or none of these.

23. $\begin{bmatrix} 1 & 2 \\ -3 & \pi \\ 4.1 & \sqrt{2} \end{bmatrix}$

24. $\begin{bmatrix} 8 & 4 & 1 & -6 \end{bmatrix}$

25. $\begin{bmatrix} -3.1 \\ 8.7 \end{bmatrix}$

26. $\begin{bmatrix} -3 & 8 \\ 0 & 0 \end{bmatrix}$

For Exercises 27–28, determine the value of the given element of the matrix $A = [a_{ij}]$.

$$A = \begin{bmatrix} -1 & 8 & -3 \\ 4 & 6 & 9 \end{bmatrix}$$

27. a_{21}

28. a_{12}

29. For what value of x, y, and z will $A = B$?

$$A = \begin{bmatrix} 3 & -4 \\ x & z \end{bmatrix} \quad \text{and} \quad B = \begin{bmatrix} y & -4 \\ 6 & 8 \end{bmatrix}$$

30. Given $C = \begin{bmatrix} 2 & -1.1 \\ 6 & 0 \\ -12 & \sqrt{5} \end{bmatrix}$, find the additive inverse.

For Exercises 31–40, perform the indicated operations if possible.

$$A = \begin{bmatrix} -4 & 1 \\ 6 & -2 \\ 1 & 3 \end{bmatrix} \quad B = \begin{bmatrix} 2 & 3 & -7 \\ 1 & 5 & -6 \end{bmatrix} \quad C = \begin{bmatrix} \pi & 4 \\ -3 & 1 \\ 0 & 5 \end{bmatrix}$$

31. $3A$

32. $-2B$

33. $A + B$

34. $B + C$

35. $2A - C$

36. $4A + 3B$

37. AB

38. BC

39. AC

40. CA

For Exercises 41–44, perform the indicated operations if possible.

$$A = \begin{bmatrix} 2 & 6 \\ -1 & 4 \end{bmatrix} \quad B = \begin{bmatrix} 1 \\ -3 \end{bmatrix} \quad C = \begin{bmatrix} 2 & 7 \end{bmatrix}$$

41. A^2 **42.** AB **43.** BC **44.** CB

45. Matrix M gives the manufacturer price for four models of dining room tables. Matrix P gives the retail price to the customer.

$$M = \begin{array}{c} \quad \quad \text{Wood} \quad \text{Metal} \\ \begin{bmatrix} \$1050 & \$940 \\ \$890 & \$800 \end{bmatrix} \begin{array}{l} \text{Large} \\ \text{Small} \end{array} \end{array}$$

$$P = \begin{array}{c} \quad \quad \text{Wood} \quad \text{Metal} \\ \begin{bmatrix} \$1365 & \$1222 \\ \$1157 & \$1040 \end{bmatrix} \begin{array}{l} \text{Large} \\ \text{Small} \end{array} \end{array}$$

a. Compute $P - M$ and interpret its meaning.

b. If the tax rate in a certain city is 6%, use scalar multiplication to find a matrix F that gives the final price (including sales tax) to the customer for each model.

46. Matrix P represents the profit per item for three sizes of popcorn and three sizes of drinks at a movie theater. Matrix N represents the number of items sold. Find the product PN and interpret its meaning.

$$P = \begin{bmatrix} \$1.40 & \$0.90 \\ \$2.10 & \$1.10 \\ \$2.60 & \$1.60 \end{bmatrix} \begin{matrix} \textbf{Small} \\ \textbf{Medium} \\ \textbf{Large} \end{matrix}$$

$$\begin{matrix} \textbf{Popcorn} & \textbf{Drinks} \end{matrix}$$

$$N = \begin{bmatrix} 100 \\ 150 \end{bmatrix} \begin{matrix} \textbf{Number of Popcorns} \\ \textbf{Number of Drinks} \end{matrix}$$

47. a. Write a matrix A that represents the coordinates of the triangle. Place the x-coordinate of each point in the first row of A and the corresponding y-coordinate in the second row of A.

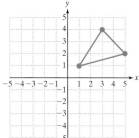

b. Use addition of matrices to shift the triangle 3 units to the left and 1 unit downward.

c. Find the product $\begin{bmatrix} -1 & 0 \\ 0 & 1 \end{bmatrix} \cdot A$ and explain the effect on the graph of the triangle.

d. Find the product $\begin{bmatrix} 1 & 0 \\ 0 & -1 \end{bmatrix} \cdot A$ and explain the effect on the graph of the triangle.

SECTION 6.4

48. Given two $n \times n$ matrices A and B, what are the criteria for the matrices to be inverses?

49. Determine whether A and B are inverses.

$$A = \begin{bmatrix} 4 & 1 \\ 3 & 2 \end{bmatrix} \quad B = \begin{bmatrix} 2 & -3 \\ -1 & 4 \end{bmatrix}$$

50. Determine whether A and B are inverses.

$$A = \begin{bmatrix} 1 & 3 \\ 2 & 1 \end{bmatrix} \quad B = \begin{bmatrix} -\frac{1}{5} & \frac{3}{5} \\ \frac{2}{5} & -\frac{1}{5} \end{bmatrix}$$

For Exercises 51–56, determine the inverse of the given matrix if possible. Otherwise state that the matrix is singular.

51. $A = \begin{bmatrix} 5 & -2 \\ 1 & 2 \end{bmatrix}$ **52.** $A = \begin{bmatrix} \frac{1}{4} & \frac{3}{8} \\ \frac{1}{8} & -\frac{1}{16} \end{bmatrix}$

53. $A = \begin{bmatrix} 2 & 3 \\ 16 & 24 \end{bmatrix}$ **54.** $A = \begin{bmatrix} 1 & 0 & 1 \\ -1 & 5 & -3 \\ 1 & -3 & 2 \end{bmatrix}$

55. $A = \begin{bmatrix} -5 & 4 & 1 \\ 15 & -12 & -4 \\ 4 & -3 & -1 \end{bmatrix}$ **56.** $A = \begin{bmatrix} 1 & -3 & -17 \\ 1 & -2 & -12 \\ 0 & -2 & -10 \end{bmatrix}$

57. Write the system of equations as a matrix equation of the form $AX = B$, where A is the coefficient matrix, X is the column matrix of variables, and B is the column matrix of constants.

$$\begin{aligned} -3x + 7y & = 6 \\ 4x \quad\quad + 2z & = -3 \\ 2x - y + 5z & = -13 \end{aligned}$$

For Exercises 58–61, solve the system using the inverse of the coefficient matrix.

58. $\dfrac{1}{4}x + \dfrac{3}{8}y = 4$ (See Exercise 52 for A^{-1}.)

$\dfrac{1}{8}x - \dfrac{1}{16}y = -2$

59. $5x - 2y = 26$ (See Exercise 51 for A^{-1}.)

$x + 2y = -2$

60. $x \quad\quad + z = 2$ (See Exercise 54 for A^{-1}.)

$-x + 5y - 3z = -6$

$x - 3y + 2z = 3$

61. $-5x + 4y + z = 6$ (See Exercise 55 for A^{-1}.)

$15x - 12y - 4z = -21$

$4x - 3y - z = -5$

SECTION 6.5

For Exercises 62–65, refer to the matrix

$$A = [a_{ij}] = \begin{bmatrix} -5 & 4 & -2 \\ 1 & 0 & 6 \\ 8 & -9 & 0 \end{bmatrix}.$$

a. Find the minor of the given element.

b. Find the cofactor of the given element.

62. a_{13} **63.** a_{31} **64.** a_{32} **65.** a_{23}

For Exercises 66–71, evaluate the determinant of the given matrix.

66. $A = \begin{bmatrix} 9 & -4 \\ 2 & -3 \end{bmatrix}$ **67.** $B = \begin{bmatrix} 3 & x \\ x & 27 \end{bmatrix}$

68. $C = \begin{bmatrix} 9 & -15 \\ -3 & 5 \end{bmatrix}$ **69.** $D = \begin{bmatrix} 4 & -1 & 0 \\ 6 & 8 & -2 \\ 1 & 5 & 3 \end{bmatrix}$

70. $E = \begin{bmatrix} 4 & -9 & 0 \\ -3 & 8 & 0 \\ 6 & 1 & 0 \end{bmatrix}$ **71.** $F = \begin{bmatrix} -2 & 0 & 3 & 1 \\ 1 & 1 & 0 & 5 \\ 4 & 0 & 0 & -2 \\ 0 & -3 & 0 & 6 \end{bmatrix}$

For Exercises 72–76, solve by using Cramer's rule. If the system does not have a unique solution, give the number of solutions.

72. $3x - 7y = 11$ **73.** $9x = 3y + 5$

$4x + 2y = 3$ $-2(x + 3y) = 4$

74. $2x + 5y = 10$
     $10y = -4(x - 5)$

75. $3x - 2y + z = 4$
     $5x + 3y + 6z = 1$
     $-2x \qquad + 5z = 7$

76. $2x + y - z = 5$
     $7x + 7y - 6z = 5$
     $3x + 5y - 4z = -1$

For Exercises 77–78, use Cramer's rule to solve for the indicated variable.

77. $-6x + 7y \qquad = 8$ Solve for y.
     $2x + 5y + z = -3$
     $3x \qquad + 2z = 11$

78. $3x_1 \qquad + 4x_3 \qquad = 6$ Solve for x_4.
     $4x_1 \qquad + 2x_3 + x_4 = -7$
     $x_2 \qquad\qquad - 3x_4 = 2$
     $5x_3 + x_4 = 1$

CHAPTER 6   Test

For Exercises 1–3, perform the elementary row operations on the matrix $A = \begin{bmatrix} 3 & 1 & 4 & -2 \\ 1 & 5 & -3 & 1 \\ 0 & 4 & 2 & 6 \end{bmatrix}$.

1. $R_1 \Leftrightarrow R_2$ **2.** $-3R_2 + R_1 \rightarrow R_1$ **3.** $\frac{1}{4}R_3 \rightarrow R_3$

4. Explain why the matrix is not in reduced row-echelon form.

$$\begin{bmatrix} 1 & 0 & 6 & 4 \\ 0 & 1 & 0 & 2 \\ 0 & 0 & 1 & -3 \end{bmatrix}$$

For Exercises 5–7, write the solution set for the system represented by each augmented matrix.

5. $\begin{bmatrix} 1 & 4 & 2 \\ 0 & 1 & 3 \end{bmatrix}$

6. $\begin{bmatrix} 1 & 0 & 0 & 4 \\ 0 & 1 & 0 & 2 \\ 0 & 0 & 0 & 1 \end{bmatrix}$

7. $\begin{bmatrix} 1 & 0 & -3 & 0 \\ 0 & 1 & 2 & 5 \\ 0 & 0 & 0 & 0 \end{bmatrix}$

For Exercises 8–9, refer to the matrix $A = \begin{bmatrix} -1 & 3 & 0 \\ 2 & 5 & -4 \\ 6 & 9 & -8 \end{bmatrix}$.

a. Find the minor of the given element.

b. Find the cofactor of the given element.

8. a_{12} **9.** a_{31}

For Exercises 10–11, evaluate the determinant of the matrix.

10. $A = \begin{bmatrix} 3 & 7 \\ 4 & -1 \end{bmatrix}$ **11.** $B = \begin{bmatrix} -3 & 4 & 7 \\ 1 & -2 & 3 \\ 6 & 5 & 0 \end{bmatrix}$

12. Use the determinant of A to determine whether A has an inverse.

$$A = \begin{bmatrix} 1 & 2 & 3 \\ 1 & 4 & 11 \\ 2 & 5 & 10 \end{bmatrix}$$

For Exercises 13–16, solve the system by using Gaussian elimination or Gauss-Jordan elimination.

13. $-3(x + y) = 3y - 12$
     $-3x = 4y - 6$

14. $-3x = 11 - 18y$
     $x - 6y = 2$

15. $x - 2y = 5z + 4$
     $6y + 18z = 2x - 8$
     $-3x + 8y + 20z = -18$

16. $2x + 6y + 30z = 2$
     $x + 2y + 11z = 0$
     $-3x - 6y - 33z = 0$

17. Solve the system by using Cramer's rule.

$$3x - 5y = 7$$
$$11x + 2y = 8$$

18. Use Cramer's rule to solve for x.

$$2x = 3y - 4z + 11$$
$$9x + y = z - 1$$
$$3x - 4y = 7$$

19. Given $A = \begin{bmatrix} 2 & 4 & x \\ -7 & y & 6 \end{bmatrix}$ and $B = \begin{bmatrix} 2 & 4 & -9 \\ -7 & 2 & z \end{bmatrix}$, for what values x, y, and z will $A = B$?

For Exercises 20–23, perform the indicated operations if possible.

$$A = \begin{bmatrix} 4 & 1 & -3 \\ 2 & 4 & 6 \end{bmatrix} \quad B = \begin{bmatrix} 1 & 9 \\ 0 & -1 \\ 3 & 5 \end{bmatrix} \quad C = \begin{bmatrix} 0 & 1 & -4 \\ 2 & -1 & 8 \end{bmatrix}$$

20. $2A - 3C$ **21.** $A + B$ **22.** AB **23.** BA

24. Determine whether A and B are inverses.

$$A = \begin{bmatrix} -1 & \frac{2}{3} & -\frac{2}{3} \\ 1 & -\frac{1}{3} & \frac{1}{3} \\ 1 & -\frac{2}{3} & \frac{5}{3} \end{bmatrix} \text{ and } B = \begin{bmatrix} 1 & 2 & 0 \\ 4 & 3 & 1 \\ 1 & 0 & 1 \end{bmatrix}$$

For Exercises 25–27, determine the inverse of the matrix if possible. Otherwise, state that the matrix is singular.

25. $A = \begin{bmatrix} 3 & 2 \\ 5 & 4 \end{bmatrix}$ **26.** $A = \begin{bmatrix} 2 & 5 & 10 \\ 1 & 3 & 7 \\ 1 & 4 & 11 \end{bmatrix}$

27. $A = \begin{bmatrix} 3 & -1 & -1 \\ 2 & -1 & 1 \\ -5 & 2 & 1 \end{bmatrix}$

For Exercises 28–29, solve the system by using the inverse of the coefficient matrix.

28. $3x + 2y = 13$ 　　　(See Exercise 25 for A^{-1}.)
　　$5x + 4y = 25$

29. $3x - y - z = 8$ 　　　(See Exercise 27 for A^{-1}.)
　　$2x + z = y$
　　$-5x + 2y + z = -11$

30. a. Assume that traffic flows freely around the traffic circle. The flow rates given are measured in vehicles per hour. If the flow rate x_3 is 210 vehicles per hour, determine the flow rates x_1 and x_2.

  b. If traffic between intersections B and C flows at a rate of between 200 and 250 vehicles per hour, inclusive, find the range of values for x_1 and x_2.

31. Matrix C represents the number of calories burned per hour of exercise riding a bicycle, running, and walking for individuals of two different weights. Matrix N represents the number of hours spent working out with each type of activity for a given week. Find the product CN and interpret its meaning.

$$C = \begin{bmatrix} 400 & 500 & 320 \\ 550 & 780 & 480 \end{bmatrix} \begin{matrix} \textbf{120-lb person} \\ \textbf{180-lb person} \end{matrix}$$

(with column headers **Bike Run Walk**)

$$N = \begin{bmatrix} 6 \\ 3 \\ 5 \end{bmatrix} \begin{matrix} \textbf{Bike} \\ \textbf{Run} \\ \textbf{Walk} \end{matrix}$$

32. Given three points (x_1, y_1), (x_2, y_2), and (x_3, y_3), the points are collinear if the following determinant is equal to zero.

$$\begin{vmatrix} x_1 & y_1 & 1 \\ x_2 & y_2 & 1 \\ x_3 & y_3 & 1 \end{vmatrix}$$

Determine if the points $(4, -11)$, $(-1, -1)$, and $(-5, 7)$ are collinear.

CHAPTER 6 Cumulative Review Exercises

1. Given $f(x) = x^3$, find the difference quotient
$$\frac{f(x + h) - f(x)}{h}.$$

2. Given $f(x) = -2(x - 4)^2 - 5$,

  a. Determine the vertex of the graph of the parabola.

  b. Determine the intervals over which the graph is increasing.

  c. Determine the intervals over which the graph is decreasing.

  d. Write the domain in interval notation.

  e. Write the range in interval notation.

3. Given $f(x) = \sqrt{2x - 3}$, find the average rate of change on the interval $\left[2, \frac{7}{2}\right]$.

4. Recall that $i = \sqrt{-1}$. Simplify each expression.

  a. i^{57} 　　　　　　　**b.** i^{22}

5. Divide and write the answer in the form $a + bi$. $\dfrac{3 + 4i}{2 - 3i}$

6. Find the distance between the points $(1, -7)$ and $(4, 2)$.

7. Determine the center and radius of the circle defined by $\left(x + \frac{5}{3}\right)^2 + y^2 = 11$.

8. Technetium-99m (abbreviated ^{99m}Tc) is a short-lived gamma-ray emitter that is used in nuclear medicine. Suppose that a patient is given a small amount of ^{99m}Tc

for a diagnostic test. Further suppose that the amount of ^{99m}Tc decays exponentially according to the model $Q(t) = Q_0 e^{-kt}$. The value Q_0 is the initial amount administered, and $Q(t)$ represents the amount of ^{99m}Tc remaining after t hours. The value of k is the decay constant.

  a. If 94% of the technetium has decayed after 24 hr (that is, 6% remains), determine the value of k. Round to 3 decimal places.

  b. If 30 mCi is initially given to a patient for blood pool imaging of the heart, determine the amount remaining after 10 hr. Round to 1 decimal place.

  c. Determine the amount of time required for the amount of ^{99m}Tc to fall below 1% of the original amount given. Round to 1 decimal place.

For Exercises 9–12,

  a. Graph the function.

  b. Write the domain in interval notation.

  c. Write the range in interval notation.

9. $f(x) = e^{x-2} + 1$

10. $g(x) = \ln(x + 4)$

11. $h(x) = \sqrt{-x}$

12. $k(x) = \begin{cases} (x - 1)^2 - 2 & \text{for } x \le 1 \\ x + 1 & \text{for } x > 1 \end{cases}$

For Exercises 13–14, solve the system of equations.

13. $3(x - y) = y - 3$

$-2x + \dfrac{1}{2}y = -11$

14. $2x - y + 5z = -2$

$\quad x \quad\;\; + 4z = 0$

$\quad x + y = 2 - 7z$

15. Determine if the graph of the equation $|x| + y^2 = 9$ is symmetric with respect to the x-axis, y-axis, origin, or none of these.

16. Determine if the function defined by $f(x) = 6x^3 - 4x$ is even, odd, or neither.

For Exercises 17–20, refer to the given matrices and perform the indicated operations.

$$A = \begin{bmatrix} 2 & -3 \\ 1 & 6 \end{bmatrix} \quad B = \begin{bmatrix} 1 & 4 \\ 0 & 7 \end{bmatrix} \quad C = \begin{bmatrix} -1 & 4 & 0 \\ 4 & 2 & 6 \\ 3 & -2 & 0 \end{bmatrix}$$

17. AB **18.** $|C|$ **19.** $4A - B$ **20.** A^{-1}

For Exercises 21–23, find the union or intersection of the given sets. Write the answers in set-builder notation.

$$A = \{x \mid 3 < x\}, B = \{x \mid -2 < x \le 4\}, C = \{x \mid x \ge 5\}$$

21. $A \cup B$ **22.** $A \cap B$ **23.** $A \cap C$

For Exercises 24–27, solve the equation or inequality. Write the solution set to the inequalities in interval notation if possible.

24. $2x - 3 - 5\sqrt{2x - 3} + 4 = 0$

25. $|-x + 4| = |x - 4|$

26. $\dfrac{x + 4}{2x - 1} \ge 1$

27. $\log_2(3x - 4) = \log_2(x + 1) + 1$

28. Find all zeros of $f(x) = 2x^3 - x^2 + 18x - 9$.

29. Find the asymptotes. $r(x) = \dfrac{2x - 1}{x^2 - 9}$

30. Write the expression as a single logarithm.

$$-3 \log x - \dfrac{1}{2} \log y + 5 \log z$$

7

Analytic Geometry

Chapter Outline

Many television viewers today rely on a satellite dish to provide a wide variety of programming options. A satellite dish is a parabolic device that receives microwave signals from broadcast centers via communications satellites. The data are then compressed and rendered into a digital form that can be viewed on an electronic device such as a television, computer, or smartphone.

In this chapter, we study three types of curves called conic sections: the ellipse, the hyperbola, and the parabola. As we work through the chapter, we will learn how the reflective properties of these curves are used in numerous applications. For example, microwaves received by a satellite dish bounce off the parabolic surface to a common point called the focus. It is at this point that the receiver is placed to gather and interpret the signal that ultimately delivers hundreds of channels to our television set.

1. Graph an Ellipse Centered at the Origin

In this chapter, we investigate four types of curves called conic sections. Specifically, these are the circle (covered in detail in Section 2.2), the ellipse, the hyperbola, and the parabola. Conic sections derive their names because each is the intersection of a plane and a double-napped cone (Figure 7-1).

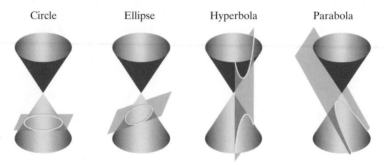

Circle   Ellipse   Hyperbola   Parabola

Figure 7-1

In Section 2.2, we defined a circle and used the standard form of an equation of a circle to identify the center and radius. In this section, we study the ellipse. An ellipse is an oval-shaped curve that appears in applications in many fields including architecture, acoustics, medicine, and astronomy. To determine an equation of an ellipse, we first need to formalize the definition.

Definition of an Ellipse

An **ellipse** is the set of all points (x, y) in a plane such that the sum of the distances between (x, y) and two fixed points is a constant. The fixed points are called the **foci** (plural of **focus**) of the ellipse.

To visualize the definition of an ellipse, consider the following application. Suppose Sonya wants to cut an elliptical rug from a rectangular rug to avoid a stain made by the family dog. She places two tacks along the center horizontal line. Then she ties the ends of a slack piece of rope to each tack. With the rope pulled tight, she traces out a curve. This curve is an ellipse, and the tacks are located at the foci of the ellipse (Figure 7-2).

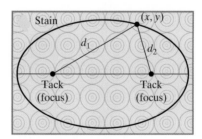

Figure 7-2

An ellipse may be elongated in any direction; however, we will study only those that are elongated horizontally and vertically. Figure 7-3 and Figure 7-4 show ellipses centered at the origin with foci on the x-axis and y-axis, respectively. The line through the foci intersects the ellipse at two points called **vertices.** The line segment with endpoints at the vertices is called the **major axis.** The **center** of the ellipse is the midpoint of the major axis. The line segment perpendicular to the major axis and passing through the center of the ellipse with endpoints on the ellipse is called the **minor axis.**

Figure 7-3   **Figure 7-4**

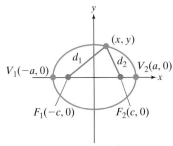

Figure 7-5

We will derive the standard form of an equation of an ellipse centered at the origin with foci on the x-axis. In Figure 7-5, the foci are labeled as $F_1(-c, 0)$ and $F_2(c, 0)$, and the vertices are labeled as $V_1(-a, 0)$ and $V_2(a, 0)$. Let (x, y) be an arbitrary point on the ellipse and let the distances between (x, y) and the two foci be d_1 and d_2.

From Figure 7-5, the distance from F_1 to V_2 is $(a + c)$. The distance from F_2 to V_2 is $(a - c)$. By the definition of an ellipse, the sum of the distances between a point on the ellipse (such as V_2) and the two foci must be constant. Adding $(a + c)$ and $(a - c)$, we see that this constant is $2a$.

$$(a + c) + (a - c) = 2a$$

> The sum of the distances between a point on an ellipse and the two foci is equal to the length of the major axis, $2a$.

The sum of the distances between (x, y) and the two foci is equal to $2a$.

$$\underset{d_1}{\underbrace{}} \quad + \quad \underset{d_2}{\underbrace{}} \quad = 2a$$

$$\sqrt{[x - (-c)]^2 + (y - 0)^2} + \sqrt{(x - c)^2 + (y - 0)^2} = 2a \quad \text{Apply the distance formula.}$$

$$\sqrt{(x + c)^2 + y^2} + \sqrt{(x - c)^2 + y^2} = 2a \quad \text{Simplify within parentheses.}$$

In Exercise 105, we guide you through a series of algebraic steps to eliminate the radicals. Then collecting the variable terms on one side and the constant terms on the other side, the equation becomes

$$(a^2 - c^2)x^2 + a^2y^2 = a^2(a^2 - c^2) \quad (1)$$

From Figure 7-5, we see that the distance between F_1 and F_2 is $2c$. Furthermore, since $d_1 + d_2 = 2a$, we have that $2c < 2a$, which implies that $c < a$ and that $a^2 - c^2 > 0$. Letting $b^2 = a^2 - c^2$, Equation (1) becomes

$$b^2x^2 + a^2y^2 = a^2b^2$$

$$\frac{b^2x^2}{a^2b^2} + \frac{a^2y^2}{a^2b^2} = \frac{a^2b^2}{a^2b^2} \quad \text{Divide both sides by } a^2b^2.$$

$$\frac{x^2}{a^2} + \frac{y^2}{b^2} = 1 \quad \text{Standard form of an equation of an ellipse}$$

This equation represents an ellipse centered at the origin with foci on the x-axis. The length of the major axis is $2a$ and the length of the minor axis is $2b$. The value a is also referred to as the length of the **semimajor axis** (the distance from the center of an ellipse to a vertex). The value b is referred to as the length of the **semiminor axis** (half the length of the minor axis).

In a similar manner, we can develop the standard form of an equation of an ellipse centered at the origin with foci on the y-axis. These two equations are summarized as follows.

Standard Forms of an Equation of an Ellipse Centered at the Origin

The standard forms of an equation of an ellipse centered at the origin are as follows. Assume that

- $a > b > 0$.
- The length of the major axis is $2a$, and the length of the minor axis is $2b$.

	Major Axis: x-axis	Major Axis: y-axis
Equation:	$\dfrac{x^2}{a^2} + \dfrac{y^2}{b^2} = 1$	$\dfrac{x^2}{b^2} + \dfrac{y^2}{a^2} = 1$
Center:	$(0, 0)$	$(0, 0)$
Foci: (*Note:* $c^2 = a^2 - b^2$)	$(c, 0)$ and $(-c, 0)$	$(0, c)$ and $(0, -c)$
Vertices: Endpoints: major axis	$(a, 0)$ and $(-a, 0)$	$(0, a)$ and $(0, -a)$
Endpoints: minor axis	$(0, b)$ and $(0, -b)$	$(b, 0)$ and $(-b, 0)$
Graph:		

Avoiding Mistakes

It is important to note that the foci are not actually on the graph of an elliptical curve. However, the foci are used to define the curve.

For an ellipse centered at the origin, the x- and y-intercepts are the endpoints of the major and minor axes. For example, for an ellipse centered at $(0, 0)$ with foci on the x-axis, we have:

Standard form:

x-intercept: substitute 0 for y.

y-intercept: substitute 0 for x.

$$\frac{x^2}{a^2} + \frac{y^2}{b^2} = 1 \longrightarrow$$

$$\frac{x^2}{a^2} + \frac{(0)^2}{b^2} = 1$$

$$\frac{(0)^2}{a^2} + \frac{y^2}{b^2} = 1$$

$$\frac{x^2}{a^2} = 1$$

$$\frac{y^2}{b^2} = 1$$

$$x^2 = a^2$$

$$y^2 = b^2$$

$$x = \pm a$$

$$y = \pm b$$

In Example 1, we graph an ellipse and identify the key features.

EXAMPLE 1 Graphing an Ellipse Centered at the Origin

Given $\dfrac{x^2}{16} + \dfrac{y^2}{9} = 1$, graph the ellipse, and identify the center, vertices, and foci.

Solution:

$\dfrac{x^2}{16} + \dfrac{y^2}{9} = 1$ The equation is in the standard form of an ellipse. Since $16 > 9$, $a^2 = 16$ and $b^2 = 9$. Since the greater number in the denominator is found in the x^2 term, the ellipse is elongated horizontally and the foci are on the x-axis.

$\dfrac{x^2}{(4)^2} + \dfrac{y^2}{(3)^2} = 1$ $a^2 = 16$, and because $a > 0$, we have that $a = 4$.
$b^2 = 9$, and because $b > 0$, we have that $b = 3$.

$\boxed{a = 4}$ $\boxed{b = 3}$

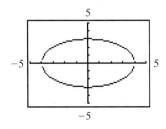

To graph the ellipse, plot the vertices (endpoints of the major axis) and the endpoints of the minor axis, and sketch the ellipse through the points.

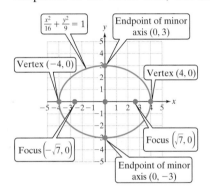

Center: $(0, 0)$

Vertices: $(a, 0)$ and $(-a, 0)$
$(4, 0)$ and $(-4, 0)$

Minor axis endpoints: $(0, b)$ and $(0, -b)$
$(0, 3)$ and $(0, -3)$

To find the foci, use the relationship
$c^2 = a^2 - b^2$
$c^2 = (4)^2 - (3)^2 = 16 - 9 = 7$
$c^2 = 7$ (Recall that $c > 0$.)
$c = \sqrt{7} \approx 2.65$

Foci: $(c, 0)$ and $(-c, 0)$
$(\sqrt{7}, 0)$ and $(-\sqrt{7}, 0)$

It is important to note that the center and foci of the ellipse are not actually part of the curve. For this reason, we graphed the curve in blue and plotted the foci and center in red.

Skill Practice 1 Graph the ellipse, and identify the center, vertices, minor axis endpoints, and foci. $\dfrac{x^2}{9} + \dfrac{y^2}{4} = 1$

Answer
1.

Center: $(0, 0)$
Vertices: $(3, 0)$ and $(-3, 0)$
Minor axis endpoints: $(0, 2)$ and $(0, -2)$
Foci: $(\sqrt{5}, 0)$ and $(-\sqrt{5}, 0)$

TECHNOLOGY CONNECTIONS

Graphing an Ellipse

To graph the ellipse from Example 1 on a graphing utility, first solve the equation for y. We have

$\dfrac{x^2}{16} + \dfrac{y^2}{9} = 1 \longrightarrow y = \pm\sqrt{9 - \dfrac{9x^2}{16}}$

The functions represent the top and bottom semiellipses respectively:

$y = \sqrt{9 - \dfrac{9x^2}{16}}$ top semiellipse

$y = -\sqrt{9 - \dfrac{9x^2}{16}}$ bottom semiellipse

EXAMPLE 2 **Graphing an Ellipse Centered at the Origin**

Given $25x^2 + 9y^2 = 225$, graph the ellipse and identify the center, vertices, minor axis endpoints, and foci.

Solution:

$25x^2 + 9y^2 = 225$ — For the equation to be in the standard form for an ellipse, we require the constant term to be 1.

$\dfrac{25x^2}{225} + \dfrac{9y^2}{225} = \dfrac{225}{225}$ — Divide both sides by 225.

$\dfrac{x^2}{9} + \dfrac{y^2}{25} = 1$ — Since $25 > 9$, $a^2 = 25$ and $b^2 = 9$. Since the greater number in the denominator is found in the y^2 term, the ellipse is elongated vertically and the foci are on the y-axis.

$\dfrac{x^2}{(3)^2} + \dfrac{y^2}{(5)^2} = 1$ — $a^2 = 25$, and because $a > 0$, we have that $a = 5$.
$b^2 = 9$, and because $b > 0$, we have that $b = 3$.

$\boxed{b = 3}$ $\boxed{a = 5}$

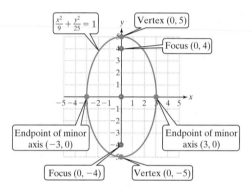

Center: $(0, 0)$

Vertices: $(0, a)$ and $(0, -a)$
$(0, 5)$ and $(0, -5)$

Minor axis endpoints: $(b, 0)$ and $(-b, 0)$
$(3, 0)$ and $(-3, 0)$

To find the foci, use the relationship
$c^2 = a^2 - b^2$
$c^2 = (5)^2 - (3)^2 = 25 - 9 = 16$
$c^2 = 16$
$c = 4$ (Recall that $c > 0$.)

Foci: $(0, c)$ and $(0, -c)$
$(0, 4)$ and $(0, -4)$

Skill Practice 2 Graph the ellipse and identify the center, vertices, minor axis endpoints, and foci. $25x^2 + 9y^2 = 900$

2. Graph an Ellipse Centered at (h, k)

In Section 2.2, we learned that the standard form of an equation of a circle centered at the origin with radius r is given by $x^2 + y^2 = r^2$. For a circle centered at (h, k), we have the equation

$$(x - h)^2 + (y - k)^2 = r^2 \qquad \text{Circle centered at } (h, k) \text{ with radius } r$$

Replacing x by $x - h$ and y by $y - k$ shifts the graph of $x^2 + y^2 = r^2$ a total of h units horizontally and k units vertically. The same is true for an equation of an ellipse.

Answer

2.

Center: $(0, 0)$
Vertices: $(0, 10), (0, -10)$
Minor axis endpoints: $(6, 0), (-6, 0)$
Foci: $(0, 8), (0, -8)$

Standard Forms of an Equation of an Ellipse Centered at (*h*, *k*)

The standard forms of an equation of an ellipse centered at (*h*, *k*) are as follows. Assume that:

- $a > b > 0$.
- The length of the major axis is 2*a*, and the length of the minor axis is 2*b*.

	Major Axis Horizontal	**Major Axis Vertical**
Equation:	$\dfrac{(x-h)^2}{a^2} + \dfrac{(y-k)^2}{b^2} = 1$	$\dfrac{(x-h)^2}{b^2} + \dfrac{(y-k)^2}{a^2} = 1$
Center:	(*h*, *k*)	(*h*, *k*)
Foci: (*Note*: $c^2 = a^2 - b^2$)	$(h + c, k)$ and $(h - c, k)$	$(h, k + c)$ and $(h, k - c)$
Vertices: Endpoints: major axis	$(h + a, k)$ and $(h - a, k)$	$(h, k + a)$ and $(h, k - a)$
Endpoints: minor axis	$(h, k + b)$ and $(h, k - b)$	$(h + b, k)$ and $(h - b, k)$
Graph:		

To graph an ellipse centered at (*h*, *k*), it is helpful to locate the center first as well as to identify the orientation of the ellipse (elongated horizontally or elongated vertically). Then use the values of *a* and *b* to locate the endpoints of the major and minor axes. This is demonstrated in Example 3.

EXAMPLE 3   Graphing an Ellipse Centered at (*h*, *k*)

Graph the ellipse and identify the center, vertices, endpoints of the minor axis, and foci. $\dfrac{(x-3)^2}{16} + \dfrac{(y+2)^2}{25} = 1$

Solution:

$\dfrac{(x-3)^2}{16} + \dfrac{(y+2)^2}{25} = 1$

The standard form of an equation of an ellipse is given. The quantity $(y+2)^2$ is equivalent to $[(y-(-2)]^2$. Therefore, the center of the ellipse is $(3, -2)$.

$\dfrac{(x-3)^2}{(4)^2} + \dfrac{[y-(-2)]^2}{(5)^2} = 1$

$\underbrace{}_{b=4} \qquad \underbrace{}_{a=5}$

Since $25 > 16$, $a^2 = 25$ and $b^2 = 16$. $a = 5$ and $b = 4$.

Since the greater number in the denominator is found in the y^2 term, the ellipse is elongated vertically.

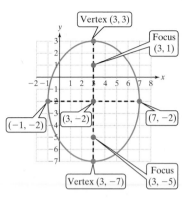

Center: (3, −2)

The vertices are *a* units above and below the center.

Vertices: (3, −2 + 5) and (3, −2 − 5)

      (3, 3) and (3, −7)

The minor axis endpoints are *b* units to the right and left of the center.

Minor axis endpoints: (3 + 4, −2) and (3 − 4, −2)

      (7, −2) and (−1, −2)

To find the foci, use the relationship

$$c^2 = a^2 - b^2$$
$$c^2 = (5)^2 - (4)^2 = 25 - 16 = 9$$
$$c = 3 \qquad \text{(Recall that } c > 0.)$$

The foci are *c* units above and below the center. The foci are (3, 1) and (3, −5).

Skill Practice 3 Graph the ellipse and identify the center, vertices, foci, and endpoints of the minor axis. $\dfrac{(x + 1)^2}{25} + \dfrac{(y - 2)^2}{9} = 1$

The equation of the ellipse from Example 3 can be expanded by expanding the binomials and combining like terms.

$$\frac{(x - 3)^2}{16} + \frac{(y + 2)^2}{25} = 1 \qquad \text{Standard form}$$

$$400\left[\frac{(x - 3)^2}{16} + \frac{(y + 2)^2}{25}\right] = 400(1) \qquad \text{Clear fractions.}$$

$$25(x - 3)^2 + 16(y + 2)^2 = 400$$

$$25(x^2 - 6x + 9) + 16(y^2 + 4y + 4) = 400 \qquad \text{Expand the binomials.}$$

$$25x^2 + 16y^2 - 150x + 64y - 111 = 0 \qquad \text{Expanded form}$$

Given an equation of an ellipse in expanded form, we can reverse this process by completing the square to write the equation in standard form. The benefit of writing an equation in standard form is that we can easily identify the center of the ellipse and the values of *a* and *b*.

EXAMPLE 4 **Writing an Equation of an Ellipse in Standard Form**

Given $3x^2 + 7y^2 + 6x - 28y + 10 = 0$,

  a. Write the equation of the ellipse in standard form.

  b. Identify the center, vertices, foci, and endpoints of the minor axis.

Answer

3.

Center: (−1, 2)
Vertices: (4, 2), (−6, 2)
Minor axis endpoints: (−1, 5), (−1, −1)
Foci: (3, 2), (−5, 2)

Solution:

  a. $3x^2 + 7y^2 + 6x - 28y + 10 = 0$ Group the *x* variable terms and group the *y* variable terms.

$$3x^2 + 6x + 7y^2 - 28y = -10 \qquad$$ Move the constant term to the right side of the equation.

$$3(x^2 + 2x + \underline{\hphantom{00}}) + 7(y^2 - 4y + \underline{\hphantom{00}}) = -10 \qquad$$ Factor out the leading coefficient from the *x* and *y* terms. Leave room to complete the square within parentheses.

3 · 1 is added to   7 · 4 is added to
the left side.   the left side.

Complete the square.

Note that $\left[\frac{1}{2}(2)\right]^2 = 1$ and $\left[\frac{1}{2}(-4)\right]^2 = 4$.

$$3(x^2 + 2x + 1) + 7(y^2 - 4y + 4) = -10 + 3 + 28$$

3 · 1   7 · 4

The values 1 and 4 are added inside parentheses. However, as a result of the factors of 3 and 7 in front of the parentheses, 3 · 1 and 7 · 4 are actually added to the left side of the equation.

$$3(x + 1)^2 + 7(y - 2)^2 = 21$$

To write the equation in standard form, we require that the constant on the right side of the equation be 1.

$$\frac{3(x + 1)^2}{21} + \frac{7(y - 2)^2}{21} = \frac{21}{21}$$

Divide both sides by 21.

$$\frac{(x + 1)^2}{7} + \frac{(y - 2)^2}{3} = 1$$

Standard form

b. $\dfrac{[x - (-1)]^2}{7} + \dfrac{(y - 2)^2}{3} = 1$

The center is $(-1, 2)$.

Since $7 > 3$, $a^2 = 7$ and $b^2 = 3$. The greater number in the denominator is in the x^2 term. Therefore, the ellipse is elongated horizontally.

$$\frac{[x - (-1)]^2}{(\sqrt{7})^2} + \frac{(y - 2)^2}{(\sqrt{3})^2} = 1$$

$\boxed{a = \sqrt{7}}$ $\boxed{b = \sqrt{3}}$

$a^2 = 7$. Because $a > 0$, $a = \sqrt{7}$.
$b^2 = 3$. Because $b > 0$, $b = \sqrt{3}$.
$c^2 = a^2 - b^2 = 7 - 3 = 4$
$c^2 = 4$, and because $c > 0$, we have $c = 2$.

The center is $(-1, 2)$.
The vertices are $\left(-1 + \sqrt{7}, 2\right)$ and $\left(-1 - \sqrt{7}, 2\right)$.
The foci are $(1, 2)$ and $(-3, 2)$.
The endpoints of the minor axis are $\left(-1, 2 + \sqrt{3}\right)$ and $\left(-1, 2 - \sqrt{3}\right)$.

Skill Practice 4   Repeat Example 4 with $2x^2 + 11y^2 - 12x + 44y + 40 = 0$.

Now that we know the standard form of an equation of an ellipse, we can build an equation based on known information about the ellipse. This is demonstrated in Example 5.

EXAMPLE 5   **Finding an Equation of an Ellipse from Given Information**

Determine the standard form of an equation of an ellipse with vertices $(4, 2)$ and $(-4, 2)$ and foci $\left(\sqrt{15}, 2\right)$ and $\left(-\sqrt{15}, 2\right)$.

Solution:

Plotting the given points tells us that the ellipse is elongated horizontally. Therefore, the standard form is

$$\frac{(x - h)^2}{a^2} + \frac{(y - k)^2}{b^2} = 1$$

The center is midway between the vertices. Therefore, the center is $(0, 2)$, indicating that $h = 0$ and $k = 2$.

Answers

4. a. $\dfrac{(x - 3)^2}{11} + \dfrac{(y + 2)^2}{2} = 1$

b. Center: $(3, -2)$; Vertices: $\left(3 + \sqrt{11}, -2\right)$ and $\left(3 - \sqrt{11}, -2\right)$
Foci: $(0, -2)$ and $(6, -2)$; Minor axis endpoints: $\left(3, -2 + \sqrt{2}\right)$ and $\left(3, -2 - \sqrt{2}\right)$

The vertices are located 4 units away from the center. This means that $a = 4$.

The foci are located $\sqrt{15}$ units from the center, indicating that $c = \sqrt{15}$. The only missing piece of information is the value of b. We can find b from the relationship $c^2 = a^2 - b^2$ or equivalently $b^2 = a^2 - c^2$.

$$b^2 = (4)^2 - \left(\sqrt{15}\right)^2$$
$$b^2 = 1$$
$$b = 1 \qquad \text{(Recall that } b > 0.\text{)}$$

$$\frac{(x - 0)^2}{(4)^2} + \frac{(y - 2)^2}{(1)^2} = 1 \qquad \begin{array}{l}\text{Substitute } h = 0, k = 2, a = 4, \text{ and } b = 1 \text{ into the} \\ \text{standard form.}\end{array}$$

$$\frac{x^2}{16} + \frac{(y - 2)^2}{1} = 1 \quad \text{or} \quad \frac{x^2}{16} + (y - 2)^2 = 1 \qquad \text{Standard form}$$

> **Skill Practice 5** Determine the standard form of an equation of an ellipse with vertices $(3, 3)$ and $(-3, 3)$ and foci $\left(2\sqrt{2}, 3\right)$ and $\left(-2\sqrt{2}, 3\right)$.

3. Determine and Apply the Eccentricity of an Ellipse

The degree of elongation of an ellipse is measured by the eccentricity e of the ellipse.

> ### Eccentricity of an Ellipse
>
> For an ellipse defined by $\dfrac{(x - h)^2}{a^2} + \dfrac{(y - k)^2}{b^2} = 1$ or $\dfrac{(x - h)^2}{b^2} + \dfrac{(y - k)^2}{a^2} = 1$,
>
> the **eccentricity** e is given by $e = \dfrac{c}{a}$, where $a > b > 0$, $c > 0$, and
>
> $c^2 = a^2 - b^2$.
>
> *Note*: The eccentricity of an ellipse is a number between 0 and 1; that is, $0 < e < 1$.

With this definition, we see that the eccentricity of an ellipse is the ratio of the distance between a focus and the center to the distance between a vertex and the center; that is, $e = \frac{c}{a}$.

- If the foci are near the vertices (that is, a is only slightly greater than c), then the ellipse is more elongated (Figure 7-6).
- If the foci are near the center, then the ellipse is more circular (Figure 7-7).

Figure 7-6

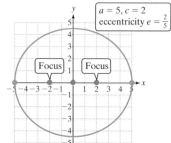

Figure 7-7

The orbits of the planets in our solar system are elliptical with the Sun at one focus. The eccentricities given in Table 7-1 indicate that the orbit of Venus is the most circular and the orbit of Pluto is the most elongated. (*Source*: NASA, www.nasa.gov)

Answer

5. $\dfrac{x^2}{9} + (y - 3)^2 = 1$

Table 7-1

Planet	Eccentricity
Mercury	0.2056
Venus	0.0067 ←
Earth	0.0167
Mars	0.0935
Jupiter	0.0489
Saturn	0.0565
Uranus	0.0457
Neptune	0.0113
Pluto (dwarf planet)	0.2488 ←

The orbit of Venus is the most circular.

The orbit of Pluto is the most elongated.

EXAMPLE 6   **Using Eccentricity in an Application**

The point in a planet's orbit where it is closest to the Sun is called **perihelion** and the point where it is farthest away is called **aphelion** (Figure 7-8). Suppose that Mars is 2.0662×10^8 km from the Sun at perihelion. Use the eccentricity from Table 7-1 to find the distance between Mars and the Sun at aphelion.

Figure 7-8

Solution:

For convenience, we have labeled the center of the ellipse as point C and the focus at which the Sun resides as point S. Aphelion and perihelion are labeled A and P, respectively (Figure 7-9).

We need to find the distance between Mars and the Sun at aphelion. This is given by $a + c$. Since a and c are two unknown values, we need two independent relationships between a and c.

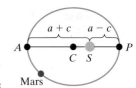

Figure 7-9

The distance at perihelion and the eccentricity give such information.

(1) $a - c = 2.0662 \times 10^8$ (distance at perihelion)   This a nonlinear system of equations.

(2) $\dfrac{c}{a} = 0.0935 \longrightarrow c = 0.0935a$ (eccentricity)   We will use the substitution method.

(1) $a - 0.0935a = 2.0662 \times 10^8$

$\qquad 0.9065a = 2.0662 \times 10^8$ Combine like terms.

$\qquad\qquad a \approx 2.2793 \times 10^8$ Divide by 0.9065.

$\qquad\qquad c = 0.0935(2.2793 \times 10^8)$ Back substitute.

$\qquad\qquad c = 2.1311 \times 10^7$

Thus, $a + c = 2.2793 \times 10^8 + 2.1311 \times 10^7$

$\qquad\qquad = 2.4924 \times 10^8$

The distance between Mars and the Sun at aphelion (the farthest point from the Sun) is approximately 2.4924×10^8 km.

Skill Practice 6   Pluto is 7.376×10^9 km at aphelion (farthest point from the Sun). Use the eccentricity of Pluto's orbit of 0.2488 to find the closest distance between Pluto and the Sun.

Answer
6. 4.437×10^9 km

SECTION 7.1 | Practice Exercises

Review Exercises

For Exercises 1–4, identify the center and radius of the circle.

1. $(x + 4)^2 + y^2 = 49$ **2.** $x^2 + (y - 3)^2 = 9$ **3.** $x^2 + y^2 = 17$ **4.** $x^2 + y^2 = 11$

For Exercises 5–6, an equation of a circle is given in expanded form. Complete the square and write the equation in the standard form.

5. $x^2 + y^2 + 10x - 4y + 22 = 0$ **6.** $x^2 + y^2 - 12x + 14y + 80 = 0$

Concept Connections

7. The circle, the ellipse, the hyperbola, and the parabola are categories of _____ sections.

8. An _____ is a set of points (x, y) in a plane such that the sum of the distances between (x, y) and two fixed points called _____ is a constant.

9. The line through the foci intersects an ellipse at two points called _____.

10. The line segment with endpoints at the vertices of an ellipse is called the _____ axis.

11. The center of an ellipse is the midpoint of the _____ axis.

12. The line segment perpendicular to the major axis, with endpoints on the ellipse, and passing through the center of the ellipse, is called the _____ axis.

13. The standard form of an equation of an ellipse centered at the origin with a horizontal major axis is _____, where $a > b > 0$. If the major axis is vertical, then the equation is _____.

14. The standard form of an equation of an ellipse centered at (h, k) with a horizontal major axis is _____, where $a > b > 0$. If the major axis is vertical, then the equation is _____.

15. Given $\dfrac{x^2}{a^2} + \dfrac{y^2}{b^2} = 1$, where $a > b > 0$, the ordered pairs representing the vertices are _____ and _____. The ordered pairs representing the endpoints of the minor axis are _____ and _____.

16. Given $\dfrac{(x - h)^2}{a^2} + \dfrac{(y - k)^2}{b^2} = 1$, where $a > b > 0$, the ordered pairs representing the endpoints of the vertices are _____ and _____. The ordered pairs representing the endpoints of the minor axis are _____ and _____.

17. Given $\dfrac{(x - h)^2}{b^2} + \dfrac{(y - k)^2}{a^2} = 1$, where $a > b > 0$, the ordered pairs representing the endpoints of the vertices are _____ and _____. The ordered pairs representing the endpoints of the minor axis are _____ and _____.

18. When referring to the standard form of an equation of an ellipse, the _____ e is defined as $e = \dfrac{\square}{\square}$.

Objective 1: Graph an Ellipse Centered at the Origin

For Exercises 19–20,

a. Use the distance formula to find the distances d_1, d_2, d_3, and d_4.   **b.** Find the sum $d_1 + d_2$.

c. Find the sum $d_3 + d_4$.   **d.** How do the sums from parts (b) and (c) compare?

e. How do the sums of the distances from parts (b) and (c) relate to the length of the major axis?

19.

20.

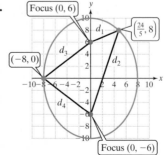

For Exercises 21–22, from the equation of the ellipse, determine if the major axis is horizontal or vertical.

21. a. $\dfrac{x^2}{2} + \dfrac{y^2}{5} = 1$ **b.** $\dfrac{x^2}{5} + \dfrac{y^2}{2} = 1$

22. a. $\dfrac{x^2}{11} + \dfrac{y^2}{10} = 1$ **b.** $\dfrac{x^2}{10} + \dfrac{y^2}{11} = 1$

For Exercises 23–32,

a. Identify the center of the ellipse.
b. Determine the value of a.
c. Determine the value of b.
d. Identify the vertices.
e. Identify the endpoints of the minor axis.
f. Identify the foci.
g. Determine the length of the major axis.
h. Determine the length of the minor axis.
i. Graph the ellipse. **(See Examples 1–2)**

23. $\dfrac{x^2}{100} + \dfrac{y^2}{25} = 1$ **24.** $\dfrac{x^2}{64} + \dfrac{y^2}{49} = 1$ **25.** $\dfrac{x^2}{25} + \dfrac{y^2}{100} = 1$ **26.** $\dfrac{x^2}{49} + \dfrac{y^2}{64} = 1$

27. $4x^2 + 25y^2 = 100$ **28.** $9x^2 + 64y^2 = 576$ **29.** $-36x^2 - 4y^2 = -36$ **30.** $-64x^2 - 16y^2 = -64$

31. $\dfrac{x^2}{12} + \dfrac{y^2}{5} = 1$ **32.** $\dfrac{x^2}{18} + \dfrac{y^2}{7} = 1$

Objective 2: Graph an Ellipse Centered at (h, k)

For Exercises 33–42,

a. Identify the center of the ellipse.
b. Identify the vertices.
c. Identify the endpoints of the minor axis.
d. Identify the foci.
e. Graph the ellipse. **(See Example 3)**

33. $\dfrac{(x-1)^2}{25} + \dfrac{(y+6)^2}{16} = 1$ **34.** $\dfrac{(x-3)^2}{25} + \dfrac{(y+4)^2}{9} = 1$ **35.** $\dfrac{(x+4)^2}{49} + \dfrac{(y-2)^2}{64} = 1$

36. $\dfrac{(x+1)^2}{36} + \dfrac{(y-5)^2}{81} = 1$ **37.** $(x-6)^2 + \dfrac{y^2}{9} = 1$ **38.** $(x-2)^2 + \dfrac{y^2}{4} = 1$

39. $x^2 + 9(y+1)^2 = 81$ **40.** $x^2 + 4(y+4)^2 = 100$ **41.** $\dfrac{4(x-3)^2}{25} + \dfrac{16(y-2)^2}{49} = 1$

42. $\dfrac{4(x-4)^2}{81} + \dfrac{16(y-3)^2}{225} = 1$

For Exercises 43–50,

a. Write the equation of the ellipse in standard form. **(See Example 4)**
b. Identify the center, vertices, endpoints of the minor axis, and foci.

43. $3x^2 + 5y^2 + 12x - 60y + 177 = 0$
44. $7x^2 + 11y^2 + 70x - 66y + 197 = 0$

45. $3x^2 + 2y^2 - 30x - 4y + 59 = 0$
46. $5x^2 + 2y^2 - 40x - 12y + 78 = 0$

47. $4x^2 + y^2 + 14y + 45 = 0$
48. $x^2 + 49y^2 - 6x - 40 = 0$

49. $36x^2 + 100y^2 - 180x + 800y + 925 = 0$
50. $4x^2 + 9y^2 - 12x + 18y - 18 = 0$

For Exercises 51–64, write the standard form of an equation of an ellipse subject to the given conditions. (See Example 5)

51. Vertices: (4, 0) and (−4, 0);
Foci: (3, 0) and (−3, 0)

52. Vertices: (6, 0) and (−6, 0);
Foci: (5, 0) and (−5, 0)

53. Endpoints of minor axis: $\left(\sqrt{17}, 0\right)$ and $\left(-\sqrt{17}, 0\right)$;
Foci: (0, 9) and (0, −9)

54. Endpoints of minor axis: $\left(\sqrt{21}, 0\right)$ and $\left(-\sqrt{21}, 0\right)$;
Foci: (0, 5) and (0, −5)

55. Major axis parallel to the x-axis; Center: (2, 3);
Length of major axis: 14 units;
Length of minor axis: 10 units

56. Major axis parallel to the y-axis; Center: (1, 5);
Length of major axis: 22 units;
Length of minor axis: 14 units

57. Foci: (0, 1) and (8, 1);
Length of minor axis: 6 units

58. Foci: (−3, 3) and (7, 3);
Length of minor axis: 8 units

59. Vertices: $(0, 5)$ and $(0, -5)$;
Passes through $\left(\frac{16}{5}, 3\right)$

60. Vertices: $(0, 13)$ and $(0, -13)$;
Passes through $\left(\frac{25}{13}, 12\right)$

61. Vertices: $(3, 4)$ and $(3, -4)$;
Foci: $\left(3, \sqrt{11}\right)$ and $\left(3, -\sqrt{11}\right)$

62. Vertices: $(4, 5)$ and $(-4, 5)$;
Foci: $\left(\sqrt{6}, 5\right)$ and $\left(-\sqrt{6}, 5\right)$

63. Vertices: $(2, 1)$ and $(-12, 1)$;
Foci: $\left(-5 - \sqrt{33}, 1\right)$ and $\left(-5 + \sqrt{33}, 1\right)$

64. Vertices: $(-8, 4)$ and $(2, 4)$;
Foci: $\left(-3 - \sqrt{21}, 4\right)$ and $\left(-3 + \sqrt{21}, 4\right)$

Objective 3: Determine and Apply the Eccentricity of an Ellipse

65. Choose one: The eccentricity of an ellipse is a number
  a. less than 0.
  b. between 0 and 1.
  c. greater than 1.

66. Choose one: An ellipse with eccentricity close to 0 will appear
  a. more elongated.
  b. more circular.

67. Choose one: An ellipse with eccentricity close to 1 will appear
  a. more elongated.
  b. more circular.

68. Choose one: If the foci of an ellipse are close to the center of the ellipse, then the graph will appear
  a. more elongated.
  b. more circular.

For Exercises 69–74, determine the eccentricity of the ellipse.

69. $\dfrac{x^2}{169} + \dfrac{y^2}{25} = 1$

70. $\dfrac{x^2}{100} + \dfrac{y^2}{64} = 1$

71. $\dfrac{\left(x + \frac{4}{5}\right)^2}{144} + \dfrac{\left(y - \frac{5}{3}\right)^2}{225} = 1$

72. $\dfrac{\left(x - \frac{1}{3}\right)^2}{9} + \dfrac{\left(y + \frac{7}{9}\right)^2}{25} = 1$

73. $\dfrac{x^2}{12} + \dfrac{(y - 3)^2}{6} = 1$

74. $\dfrac{(x + 7)^2}{18} + \dfrac{y^2}{12} = 1$

75. Refer to Exercises 69, 71, and 73.
  a. Which ellipse is the most elongated?
  b. Which ellipse is the most circular?

76. Refer to Exercises 70, 72, and 74.
  a. Which ellipse is the most elongated?
  b. Which ellipse is the most circular?

77. Halley's Comet and the Earth both orbit the Sun in elliptical paths with the Sun at one focus. The eccentricity of the comet's orbit is 0.967 and the eccentricity of the Earth's orbit is 0.0167. The eccentricity for the Earth is close to zero, whereas the eccentricity for Halley's Comet is close to 1. Based on this information, how do the orbits compare?

78. Halley's Comet and the comet Hale-Bopp both orbit the Sun in elliptical paths with the Sun at one focus. The eccentricity of Halley's Comet's orbit is 0.967 and the eccentricity of comet Hale-Bopp's orbit is 0.995. Which comet has a more elongated orbit?

79. The moon's orbit around the Earth is elliptical with the Earth at one focus and with eccentricity 0.0549. If the distance between the moon and Earth at the closest point is 363,300 km, determine the distance at the farthest point. Round to the nearest 100 km.
(**See Example 6**)

80. The planet Saturn orbits the Sun in an elliptical path with the Sun at one focus. The eccentricity of the orbit is 0.0565 and the distance between the Sun and Saturn at perihelion (the closest point) is 1.353×10^9 km. Determine the distance at aphelion (the farthest point). Round to the nearest million kilometers.

For Exercises 81–84, write the standard form of an equation of the ellipse subject to the following conditions.

81. Center: $(0, 0)$; Eccentricity: $\frac{15}{17}$;
Major axis vertical of length 34 units

82. Center: $(0, 0)$; Eccentricity: $\frac{40}{41}$;
Major axis vertical of length 82 units

83. Foci: $(0, -1)$ and $(8, -1)$;
Eccentricity: $\frac{4}{5}$

84. Foci: $(0, -1)$ and $(-6, -1)$;
Eccentricity: $\frac{3}{5}$

Mixed Exercises

85. Charles and Bernice ("Ray") Eames were American designers who made major contributions to modern architecture and furniture design. Suppose that a manufacturer wants to make an Eames elliptical coffee table 90 in. long and 30 in. wide out of an 8 ft by 4 ft piece of birch plywood. If the center of a piece of plywood is positioned at (0, 0), determine the distance from the center at which the foci should be located to draw the ellipse.

86. A window above a door is to be made in the shape of a semiellipse. If the window is 10 ft at the base and 3 ft high at the center, determine the distance from the center at which the foci are located.

The ellipse and its three-dimensional counterpart, the *ellipsoid* (an object in the shape of a blimp) have many useful applications that arise from the reflective property of the ellipse. For example, consider an elliptical-shaped dome. Sound waves and light waves emitted from one focus are reflected off the surface to the other focus. Use this principle for Exercises 87–88.

87. The reflective property of an ellipse is used in lithotripsy. Lithotripsy is a technique for treating kidney stones without surgery. Instead, high-energy shock waves are emitted from one focus of an elliptical shell and reflected painlessly to a patient's kidney stone located at the other focus. The vibration from the shock waves shatter the stone into pieces small enough to pass through the patient's urine.

A vertical cross section of a lithotripter is in the shape of a semiellipse with the dimensions shown. Approximate the distance from the center along the major axis where the patient's kidney stone should be located so that the shock waves will target the stone. Round to 2 decimal places.

88. The reflective property of an ellipse is the principle behind "whispering galleries." These are rooms with elliptically shaped ceilings such that a person standing at one focus can hear even the slightest whisper spoken by another person standing at the other focus. One famous "whispering gallery" is the Statuary Hall in the Capitol Building, the meeting place of the U.S. House of Representatives for nearly 50 years (1807–1857).

The dome in Statuary Hall has a semielliptical ceiling, 96 ft long and 23 ft high. Choose a coordinate system so that the center of the semiellipse is (0, 0) with vertices (−48, 0) and (48, 0) and with the ceiling at the middle of the room (0, 23).

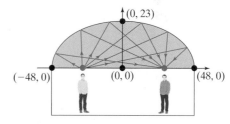

Approximately how far from the center along the major axis should each person be standing to hear the "whispering" effect? Round to 1 decimal place.

89. The graph of $\dfrac{x^2}{9} + \dfrac{y^2}{4} = 1$ represents an ellipse.

Determine the part of the ellipse represented by the given equation.

a. $y = 2\sqrt{1 - \dfrac{x^2}{9}}$ **b.** $y = -2\sqrt{1 - \dfrac{x^2}{9}}$

c. $x = 3\sqrt{1 - \dfrac{y^2}{4}}$ **d.** $x = -3\sqrt{1 - \dfrac{y^2}{4}}$

90. The graph of $\dfrac{x^2}{16} + \dfrac{y^2}{81} = 1$ represents an ellipse.

Determine the part of the ellipse represented by the given equation.

a. $x = -4\sqrt{1 - \dfrac{y^2}{81}}$ **b.** $x = 4\sqrt{1 - \dfrac{y^2}{81}}$

c. $y = 9\sqrt{1 - \dfrac{x^2}{16}}$ **d.** $y = -9\sqrt{1 - \dfrac{x^2}{16}}$

For Exercises 91–94, solve the system of equations.

91. $\dfrac{x^2}{25} + \dfrac{y^2}{9} = 1$

     $3x + 5y = 15$

92. $13y = 12x - 156$

     $\dfrac{x^2}{169} + \dfrac{y^2}{144} = 1$

93. $\dfrac{x^2}{4} + \dfrac{y^2}{16} = 1$

     $y = -x^2 + 4$

94. $\dfrac{x^2}{64} + \dfrac{y^2}{289} = 1$

     $y = \dfrac{13}{64}x^2 - 13$

Given an ellipse with major axis of length 2a and minor axis of length 2b, the area is given by $A = \pi ab$. The perimeter is *approximated* by $P \approx \pi\sqrt{2(a^2 + b^2)}$. **For Exercises 95–96,**

a. Determine the area of the ellipse.   **b.** Approximate the perimeter.

95. $\dfrac{x^2}{8} + \dfrac{(y+3)^2}{4} = 1$

96. $\dfrac{(x-1)^2}{9} + \dfrac{y^2}{11} = 1$

97. A line segment with endpoints on an ellipse, perpendicular to the major axis, and passing through a focus, is called a *latus rectum* of the ellipse. Show that the length of a latus rectum is $\dfrac{2b^2}{a}$ for the ellipse.

$$\frac{x^2}{a^2} + \frac{y^2}{b^2} = 1$$

[*Hint*: Substitute (c, y) into the equation and solve for y. Recall that $c^2 = a^2 - b^2$.]

98. A line segment with endpoints on an ellipse and passing through a focus of the ellipse is called a focal chord. Given the ellipse

$$\frac{x^2}{25} + \frac{y^2}{16} = 1$$

a. Show that one focus of the ellipse lies on the line $y = \frac{4}{3}x + 4$.

b. Determine the points of intersection between the ellipse and the line.

c. Approximate the length of the focal chord that lies on the line $y = \frac{4}{3}x + 4$. Round to 2 decimal places.

Write About It

99. An elliptical pool table is in the shape of an ellipse with one pocket located at one focus of the ellipse. If a ball is located at the other focus, explain why a player can strike the ball in any direction to have the ball land in the pocket.

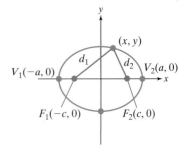

100. Given an equation of an ellipse in standard form, how do you determine whether the major axis is horizontal or vertical?

101. Explain the difference between the graphs of the two equations.

$$\frac{x^2}{9} + \frac{y^2}{4} = 1 \qquad \frac{x^2}{4} + \frac{y^2}{4} = 1$$

102. Explain the difference between the graphs of the two equations.

$$4x^2 + 9y^2 = 36 \qquad 4x + 9y = 36$$

103. Explain what the eccentricity of an ellipse represents.

104. Discuss the solution set of the equation.

$$\frac{(x-4)^2}{9} + \frac{(x+2)^2}{16} = -1$$

Expanding Your Skills

105. This exercise guides you through the steps to find the standard form of an equation of an ellipse centered at the origin with foci on the x-axis.

a. Refer to the figure to verify that the distance from F_1 to V_2 is $(a + c)$ and the distance from F_2 to V_2 is $(a - c)$. Verify that the sum of these distances is $2a$.

b. Write an expression that represents the sum of the distances from F_1 to (x, y) and from F_2 to (x, y). Then set this expression equal to $2a$.

c. Given the equation $\sqrt{(x + c)^2 + y^2} + \sqrt{(x - c)^2 + y^2} = 2a$, isolate the leftmost radical and square both sides of the equation. Show that the equation can be written as $a\sqrt{(x - c)^2 + y^2} = a^2 - xc$.

d. Square both sides of the equation $a\sqrt{(x - c)^2 + y^2} = a^2 - xc$ and show that the equation can be written as $(a^2 - c^2)x^2 + a^2y^2 = a^2(a^2 - c^2)$. (*Hint*: Collect variable terms on the left side of the equation and constant terms on the right side.)

e. Replace $a^2 - c^2$ by b^2. Then divide both sides of the equation by a^2b^2. Verify that the resulting equation is $\dfrac{x^2}{a^2} + \dfrac{y^2}{b^2} = 1$.

106. Find the points on the ellipse that are twice the distance from one focus to the other.

$$\frac{x^2}{25} + \frac{y^2}{9} = 1$$

Technology Connections

For Exercises 107–110, graph the ellipse from the given exercise on a square viewing window.

107. Exercise 25   **108.** Exercise 26   **109.** Exercise 41   **110.** Exercise 42

111. Consider the ellipse defined by $\dfrac{x^2}{16} + \dfrac{y^2}{b^2} = 1$. Graph the upper and lower semiellipses defined by $y = \pm b\sqrt{1 - \dfrac{x^2}{16}}$ for $b = 1$, $b = 2$, $b = 3$, and $b = 4$ on the viewing window $-7.58 \le x \le 7.58$ and $-5 \le y \le 5$. Compare the results. What happens when b reaches 4?

SECTION 7.2   The Hyperbola

OBJECTIVES

1. **Graph a Hyperbola Centered at the Origin**
2. **Graph a Hyperbola Centered at (h, k)**
3. **Determine the Eccentricity of a Hyperbola**
4. **Use Hyperbolas in Applications**

1. Graph a Hyperbola Centered at the Origin

In this section, we will study another type of conic section called the hyperbola (Figure 7-10).

> **Definition of a Hyperbola**
>
> A **hyperbola** is the set of all points (x, y) in a plane such that the difference in distances between (x, y) and two fixed points (foci) is a positive constant.

In Figure 7-11, we present a hyperbola with foci on the x-axis. By definition, the curve is the set of points such that $d_1 - d_2$ is a positive constant.

> **TIP** The definition of a hyperbola differs from the definition of an ellipse in that the curve is the set of points for which the difference (rather than the sum) of d_1 and d_2 is a constant.

Figure 7-10

Figure 7-11

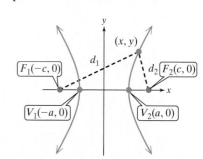

Figure 7-12

Notice that the hyperbola consists of two parts called **branches.** The points where the hyperbola intersects the line through the foci are called the **vertices.** The line segment between the vertices (highlighted in red) is called the **transverse axis.** The midpoint of the transverse axis is the **center** of the hyperbola.

To derive the standard form of an equation of a hyperbola, consider a hyperbola centered at the origin with foci on the x-axis (Figure 7-12). The points $F_1(-c, 0)$ and $F_2(c, 0)$ are the foci and the vertices are $V_1(-a, 0)$ and $V_2(a, 0)$.

The distance between F_1 and V_2 is $c + a$. The distance between F_2 and V_2 is $c - a$. By the definition of a hyperbola, the positive difference between a point on the hyperbola (such as V_2) and the two foci is a positive constant. Subtracting $(c + a)$ and $(c - a)$, we have

$$(c + a) - (c - a) = 2a$$

Therefore, the difference of the distances between (x, y) and the two foci is equal to $2a$.

$$d_1 \quad - \quad d_2 \quad = 2a$$

$$\sqrt{[(x - (-c)]^2 + (y - 0)^2} - \sqrt{(x - c)^2 + (y - 0)^2} = 2a \qquad \text{Apply the distance formula.}$$

$$\sqrt{(x + c)^2 + y^2} - \sqrt{(x - c)^2 + y^2} = 2a \qquad \text{Simplify within parentheses.}$$

In Exercise 88, we guide you through a series of algebraic steps to eliminate the radicals. Then collecting the variable terms on the left side and the constant terms on the right side, the equation becomes

$$(c^2 - a^2)x^2 - a^2 y^2 = a^2(c^2 - a^2) \qquad (1)$$

From Figure 7-12, we see that $d_1 + d_2 = 2a < 2c$. Therefore, $a < c$ and $c^2 - a^2 > 0$. Substituting $b^2 = c^2 - a^2$ in Equation (1) we have

$$b^2 x^2 - a^2 y^2 = a^2 b^2$$

$$\frac{b^2 x^2}{a^2 b^2} - \frac{a^2 y^2}{a^2 b^2} = \frac{a^2 b^2}{a^2 b^2} \qquad \text{Divide both sides by } a^2 b^2.$$

$$\frac{x^2}{a^2} - \frac{y^2}{b^2} = 1 \qquad \text{Standard form}$$

This equation represents a hyperbola centered at the origin with foci on the x-axis. In a similar manner, we can develop the standard equation of a hyperbola centered at the origin with foci on the y-axis. These two equations are summarized as follows.

Standard Forms of an Equation of a Hyperbola Centered at the Origin		
The standard forms of an equation of a hyperbola centered at the origin are as follows. Assume that $a > 0$ and $b > 0$.		
	Transverse Axis: x-axis	**Transverse Axis: y-axis**
Equation:	$\dfrac{x^2}{a^2} - \dfrac{y^2}{b^2} = 1$	$\dfrac{y^2}{a^2} - \dfrac{x^2}{b^2} = 1$
Center:	$(0, 0)$	$(0, 0)$
Foci: ($c^2 = a^2 + b^2$)	$(c, 0)$ and $(-c, 0)$	$(0, c)$ and $(0, -c)$
Vertices:	$(a, 0)$ and $(-a, 0)$	$(0, a)$ and $(0, -a)$
Asymptotes:	$y = \frac{b}{a}x$ and $y = -\frac{b}{a}x$	$y = \frac{a}{b}x$ and $y = -\frac{a}{b}x$
Graph:	Figure 7-13	Figure 7-14

Avoiding Mistakes

Notice that we do not have the restriction that $a > b$ as with the ellipse.

TIP Notice that an equation of a hyperbola shows a *difference* between the square terms, whereas an equation of an ellipse shows a *sum* of the square terms.

From the standard forms of an equation of a hyperbola, notice that the variable term with the positive coefficient always contains a^2 in the denominator. This term also indicates the orientation of the hyperbola.

- If the variable term with the positive coefficient is the x^2 term, then the transverse axis is horizontal and the branches of the hyperbola open horizontally.
- If the variable term with the positive coefficient is the y^2 term, then the transverse axis is vertical and the branches of the hyperbola open vertically.

As x and y increase, the branches of a hyperbola approach a pair of asymptotes. As with the graph of a rational function, the asymptotes are lines of reference that help graph the curve. To identify the asymptotes, first sketch a **reference rectangle** with dimensions $2a$ by $2b$, centered at the center of the hyperbola (Figures 7-13 and 7-14). The asymptotes are the lines through the opposite corners of the rectangle.

The length of the transverse axis is $2a$. The line segment passing through the center of the hyperbola, perpendicular to the transverse axis, and with endpoints on the reference rectangle is called the **conjugate axis.** The length of the conjugate axis is $2b$.

To graph a hyperbola, we suggest the following guidelines.

Graphing a Hyperbola

Step 1   Identify the center and vertices.

Step 2   Draw the reference rectangle centered at the center of the hyperbola, with dimensions $2a$ and $2b$ as shown in Figures 7-13 and 7-14.

Step 3   Draw the asymptotes through the opposite corners of the rectangle.

Step 4   Sketch each branch of the hyperbola starting at the vertices and approaching the asymptotes.

EXAMPLE 1   Graphing a Hyperbola Centered at the Origin

Given $\dfrac{x^2}{4} - \dfrac{y^2}{9} = 1$,

a. Graph the hyperbola.

b. Identify the center, vertices, foci, and equations of the asymptotes.

Solution:

a. $\dfrac{x^2}{4} - \dfrac{y^2}{9} = 1$

Step 1: The equation is in the standard form of a hyperbola centered at $(0, 0)$.

The x^2 term has the positive coefficient, indicating that the transverse axis is horizontal. The denominator of the x^2 term is a^2.

$$\frac{x^2}{(2)^2} - \frac{y^2}{(3)^2} = 1$$

$\boxed{a = 2}$ $\boxed{b = 3}$

$a^2 = 4$, and because $a > 0$, we have that $a = 2$.
$b^2 = 9$, and because $b > 0$, we have that $b = 3$.

Vertices: $(a, 0)$ and $(-a, 0)$
$(2, 0)$ and $(-2, 0)$
Note that $c^2 = a^2 + b^2 = 4 + 9 = 13$.
Since $c > 0$, $c = \sqrt{13}$.
Foci: $(c, 0)$ and $(-c, 0)$
$\left(\sqrt{13}, 0\right)$ and $\left(-\sqrt{13}, 0\right)$

Point of Interest

The James S. McDonnell Planetarium in St. Louis, Missouri, has vertical cross sections in the shape of a hyperbola.

Steps 2–3: Draw the reference rectangle and asymptotes.

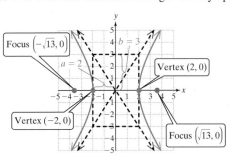

The reference rectangle is centered at the center of the hyperbola, (0, 0).

Draw the rectangle with width $2a$ in the direction of the transverse axis. The height is the length of the conjugate axis $2b$.

Draw the asymptotes through the opposite corners of the reference rectangle.

> **TIP** If you find it difficult to memorize the equations of the asymptotes, the equations can be found by using the point-slope formula and the points defining the opposite corners of the reference rectangle.

Step 4: Sketch each branch of the hyperbola starting at the vertices and approaching the asymptotes.

b. The center is (0, 0).

The vertices are $(-2, 0)$ and $(2, 0)$.

The foci are $\left(-\sqrt{13}, 0\right)$ and $\left(\sqrt{13}, 0\right)$.

The equations of the asymptotes are $y = \frac{b}{a}x$ and $y = -\frac{b}{a}x$.

Therefore, the asymptotes are $y = \frac{3}{2}x$ and $y = -\frac{3}{2}x$.

Skill Practice 1   Repeat Example 1 with the equation: $\dfrac{x^2}{9} - \dfrac{y^2}{4} = 1$

In Example 2, we graph a hyperbola in which the transverse axis is vertical and the conjugate axis is horizontal.

EXAMPLE 2   Graphing a Hyperbola Centered at the Origin

Given $16y^2 - 9x^2 = 144$,

a. Graph the hyperbola.

b. Identify the center, vertices, foci, and equations of the asymptotes.

Solution:

a. $16y^2 - 9x^2 = 144$ For the equation to be in the standard form for a hyperbola, we require the constant term to be 1.

$$\frac{16y^2}{144} - \frac{9x^2}{144} = \frac{144}{144}$$ Divide both sides by 144.

$$\frac{y^2}{9} - \frac{x^2}{16} = 1$$ The y^2 term has the positive coefficient, indicating that the transverse axis is vertical. The denominator of the y^2 term is a^2.

$$\frac{y^2}{(3)^2} - \frac{x^2}{(4)^2} = 1$$ (with $a = 3$ and $b = 4$)

Step 1: The hyperbola is centered at (0, 0).

$a^2 = 9$, and because $a > 0$, we have that $a = 3$.

$b^2 = 16$, and because $b > 0$, we have that $b = 4$.

Vertices: (0, a) and (0, $-a$)

(0, 3) and (0, -3)

Note that $c^2 = a^2 + b^2 = 9 + 16 = 25$ and $c = 5$.

Foci: (c, 0) and ($-c$, 0)

(0, 5) and (0, -5)

Answers

1. a.

b. Center: (0, 0)

Vertices: $(-3, 0)$, $(3, 0)$

Foci: $\left(-\sqrt{13}, 0\right)$, $\left(\sqrt{13}, 0\right)$

Asymptotes: $y = \frac{2}{3}x$ and $y = -\frac{2}{3}x$.

Steps 2–3: Draw the reference rectangle and asymptotes.

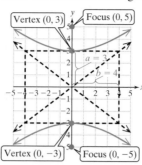

Vertex (0, 3)   Focus (0, 5)

a = 3

b = 4

Vertex (0, −3)   Focus (0, −5)

Draw the rectangle centered at the origin and with height $2a$ and width $2b$.

Draw the asymptotes through the opposite corners of the reference rectangle.

Step 4: Sketch each branch of the hyperbola starting at the vertices and approaching the asymptotes.

b. The center is (0, 0).

  The vertices are (0, 3) and (0, −3).

  The foci are (0, −5) and (0, 5).

  The equations of the asymptotes are $y = \frac{a}{b}x$ and $y = -\frac{a}{b}x$.

  Therefore, the asymptotes are $y = \frac{3}{4}x$ and $y = -\frac{3}{4}x$.

> **Skill Practice 2**   Repeat Example 2 with the equation: $4y^2 - x^2 = 16$

2. Graph a Hyperbola Centered at (h, k)

In the standard form of a hyperbola, if x and y are replaced by $x - h$ and $y - k$, then the graph of the hyperbola is shifted h units horizontally and k units vertically. The hyperbola is then centered at (h, k).

Standard Forms of an Equation of a Hyperbola Centered at (h, k)

The standard forms of an equation of a hyperbola centered at (h, k) are as follows. Assume that $a > 0$ and $b > 0$.

	Transverse Axis Horizontal	**Transverse Axis Vertical**
Equation:	$\dfrac{(x - h)^2}{a^2} - \dfrac{(y - k)^2}{b^2} = 1$	$\dfrac{(y - k)^2}{a^2} - \dfrac{(x - h)^2}{b^2} = 1$
Center:	(h, k)	(h, k)
Foci: (*Note:* $c^2 = a^2 + b^2$)	$(h + c, k)$ and $(h - c, k)$	$(h, k + c)$ and $(h, k - c)$
Vertices:	$(h + a, k)$ and $(h - a, k)$	$(h, k + a)$ and $(h, k - a)$
Asymptotes:	$y - k = \pm\frac{b}{a}(x - h)$	$y - k = \pm\frac{a}{b}(x - h)$
Graph:	*(graph with (h, k), a, b, c labeled)*	*(graph with (h, k), a, b, c labeled)*

Answers

2. a.

b. Center: (0, 0)

  Vertices: (0, 2), (0, −2)

  Foci: $(0, 2\sqrt{5})$, $(0, -2\sqrt{5})$

  Asymptotes: $y = \frac{1}{2}x$ and

  $y = -\frac{1}{2}x$.

To graph a hyperbola centered at (h, k), first locate the center and identify the orientation of the hyperbola (transverse axis horizontal or vertical). Then use the values of a and b to draw the reference rectangle. Draw the asymptotes through the corners of the reference rectangle. Finally, sketch the hyperbola starting at the vertices and approaching the asymptotes.

EXAMPLE 3 **Graphing a Hyperbola Centered at (h, k)**

Given $-\dfrac{(x-2)^2}{9} + (y+3)^2 = 1,$

a. Graph the hyperbola.

b. Identify the center, vertices, foci, and equations of the asymptotes

Solution:

a. $-\dfrac{(x-2)^2}{9} + \dfrac{(y+3)^2}{1} = 1$

$\dfrac{[y-(-3)]^2}{(1)^2} - \dfrac{(x-2)^2}{(3)^2} = 1$

$\boxed{a = 1}$ $\boxed{b = 3}$

Step 1: Center: $(2, -3)$

The y^2 term has a positive coefficient. Therefore, the transverse axis is vertical. We have $a^2 = 1$ and $b^2 = 9$.

Steps 2–3: Draw the reference rectangle and asymptotes.

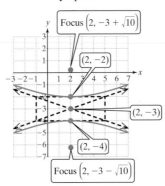

Focus $\left(2, -3 + \sqrt{10}\right)$

$(2, -2)$

$(2, -3)$

$(2, -4)$

Focus $\left(2, -3 - \sqrt{10}\right)$

Draw the rectangle centered at $(2, -3)$ with vertical sides of length $2a$ and horizontal sides of length $2b$.

Draw the asymptotes through the opposite corners of the reference rectangle.

The vertices are a units above and below the center.

Vertices: $(2, -3 + 1)$ and $(2, -3 - 1)$
$(2, -2)$ and $(2, -4)$

Step 4: Sketch the hyperbola.

To find the foci, use the relationship:
$$c^2 = a^2 + b^2$$
$$c^2 = 1 + 9 = 10$$
$$c = \sqrt{10} \quad \text{(Recall that } c > 0.)$$

The foci are c units above and below the center.

The foci are $\left(2, -3 + \sqrt{10}\right)$ and $\left(2, -3 - \sqrt{10}\right)$.

b. The center is $(2, -3)$.

The vertices are $(2, -2)$ and $(2, -4)$.

The foci are $\left(2, -3 + \sqrt{10}\right)$ and $\left(2, -3 - \sqrt{10}\right)$.

The equations of the asymptotes can be found by using the point-slope formula and the points through the opposite vertices of the reference rectangle. Alternatively, the asymptotes can be found by using $y - k = \pm\frac{a}{b}(x - h)$, where h and k are the coordinates of the center.

$y - k = \frac{a}{b}(x - h)$ $\qquad$ $y - k = -\frac{a}{b}(x - h)$

$y - (-3) = \dfrac{1}{3}(x - 2)$ $\qquad$ $y - (-3) = -\dfrac{1}{3}(x - 2)$

$y = \dfrac{1}{3}x - \dfrac{11}{3}$ $\qquad$ $y = -\dfrac{1}{3}x - \dfrac{7}{3}$

Answers

3. a.

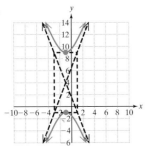

b. Center: $(-1, 4)$
Vertices: $(-1, 9), (-1, -1)$
Foci: $\left(-1, 4 + \sqrt{29}\right)$,
$\left(-1, 4 - \sqrt{29}\right)$
Asymptotes: $y = -\frac{5}{2}x + \frac{3}{2}$,
$y = \frac{5}{2}x + \frac{13}{2}$

Skill Practice 3 Repeat Example 3 with the equation:

$$-\dfrac{(x+1)^2}{4} + \dfrac{(y-4)^2}{25} = 1$$

Graphing a Hyperbola

To graph the hyperbola from Example 3 on a graphing utility, first solve the equation for y. We have

$$-\frac{(x-2)^2}{9} + (y+3)^2 = 1$$

$$y = -3 \pm \sqrt{1 + \frac{(x-2)^2}{9}} \quad \text{(Solve for } y.)$$

The functions represent the top and bottom branches, respectively.

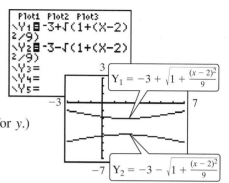

The equation of the hyperbola from Example 3 can be expanded by expanding the binomials and combining like terms.

$$-\frac{(x-2)^2}{9} + (y+3)^2 = 1 \qquad \text{Standard form}$$

$$9 \cdot \left[-\frac{(x-2)^2}{9} + (y+3)^2 \right] = 9 \cdot (1) \qquad \text{Clear fractions.}$$

$$-(x-2)^2 + 9(y+3)^2 = 9$$

$$-x^2 + 4x - 4 + 9y^2 + 54y + 81 = 9 \qquad \text{Expand the binomials.}$$

$$-x^2 + 9y^2 + 4x + 54y + 68 = 0 \qquad \text{Expanded form}$$

Given an equation of a hyperbola in expanded form, we can reverse this process by completing the square to write the equation in standard form. This is shown in Example 4.

EXAMPLE 4   **Writing an Equation of a Hyperbola in Standard Form**

Write the equation of the hyperbola in standard form. $11x^2 - 2y^2 + 66x - 4y + 75 = 0$

Solution:

$11x^2 - 2y^2 + 66x - 4y + 75 = 0$ Group the x variable terms and group the y variable terms.

$11x^2 + 66x - 2y^2 - 4y = -75$ Move the constant term to the right side of the equation.

$11(x^2 + 6x \quad) - 2(y^2 + 2y \quad) = -75$ Factor out the leading coefficient from the x and y terms. Leave room to complete the square within parentheses.

$11 \cdot 9$ is added to the left side. $-2 \cdot 1$ is added to the left side. $11 \cdot 9 \quad -2 \cdot 1$ Complete the square.

$$11(x^2 + 6x + 9) - 2(y^2 + 2y + 1) = -75 + 99 - 2$$

Note that $\left[\frac{1}{2}(6)\right]^2 = 9$ and $\left[\frac{1}{2}(2)\right]^2 = 1$.

The values 9 and 1 were added inside parentheses. However, $11 \cdot 9$ and $-2 \cdot 1$ were actually added to the left side as a result of the factors in front of the parentheses.

$$11(x+3)^2 - 2(y+1)^2 = 22$$

To write the equation in standard form, we require a 1 on the right side of the equation.

$$\frac{11(x+3)^2}{22} - \frac{2(y+1)^2}{22} = \frac{22}{22}$$

Divide both sides by 22.

$$\frac{(x+3)^2}{2} - \frac{(y+1)^2}{11} = 1$$

Standard form

> **Skill Practice 4**   Write the equation of the hyperbola in standard form.
> $3x^2 - 7y^2 + 30x + 56y - 58 = 0$

In Example 5, we determine the standard form of an equation of a hyperbola based on known information about the hyperbola.

EXAMPLE 5   **Finding an Equation of a Hyperbola**

Determine the standard form of an equation of a hyperbola with vertices $(-4, 0)$ and $(8, 0)$ and foci $(-8, 0)$ and $(12, 0)$.

Solution:

Plotting the given points tells us that the foci are aligned horizontally. Therefore, the transverse axis of the hyperbola is horizontal. The standard form is

$$\frac{(x - h)^2}{a^2} - \frac{(y - k)^2}{b^2} = 1$$

The center is midway between the vertices. Therefore, the center is $(2, 0)$, indicating that $h = 2$ and $k = 0$.

The vertices are located 6 units away from the center. This means that $a = 6$.

The foci are located 10 units from the center, indicating that $c = 10$.

The only missing piece of information is the value of b. We can find b from the relationship $c^2 = a^2 + b^2$ or equivalently $b^2 = c^2 - a^2$.

$$b^2 = (10)^2 - (6)^2$$
$$b^2 = 64$$
$$b = 8 \qquad \text{(Recall that } b > 0.)$$

$$\frac{(x - 2)^2}{(6)^2} - \frac{(y - 0)^2}{(8)^2} = 1 \qquad \text{Substitute } h = 2, k = 0, a = 6, \text{ and } b = 8.$$

$$\frac{(x - 2)^2}{36} + \frac{y^2}{64} = 1 \qquad \text{Standard form}$$

> **Skill Practice 5**   Determine the standard form of an equation of a hyperbola with vertices $(-9, 0)$ and $(1, 0)$ and foci $(-17, 0)$ and $(9, 0)$.

3. Determine the Eccentricity of a Hyperbola

The branches of a hyperbola may be wider or narrower depending on the eccentricity of the hyperbola. Like the ellipse, the eccentricity of a hyperbola is given by $e = \frac{c}{a}$.

Answers

4. $\dfrac{(x + 5)^2}{7} - \dfrac{(y - 4)^2}{3} = 1$

5. $\dfrac{(x + 4)^2}{25} - \dfrac{y^2}{144} = 1$

Eccentricity of a Hyperbola

For a hyperbola defined by $\dfrac{(x-h)^2}{a^2} - \dfrac{(y-k)^2}{b^2} = 1$ or

$\dfrac{(y-k)^2}{a^2} - \dfrac{(x-h)^2}{b^2} = 1$, the **eccentricity** e is given by $e = \dfrac{c}{a}$, where $a > 0$, $c > 0$, and $c^2 = a^2 + b^2$.

Note: The eccentricity of a hyperbola is a number greater than 1; that is, $e > 1$.

As the eccentricity of a hyperbola increases, the branches open wider. This is demonstrated in Example 6.

EXAMPLE 6   Finding the Eccentricity of a Hyperbola

Determine the eccentricity of the hyperbola.

a. $\dfrac{x^2}{16} - \dfrac{y^2}{9} = 1$ **b.** $\dfrac{x^2}{9} - \dfrac{y^2}{16} = 1$

Solution:

a. $\dfrac{x^2}{16} - \dfrac{y^2}{9} = 1$ The x^2 term has a positive coefficient. Therefore, $a^2 = 16$.

$\dfrac{x^2}{(4)^2} - \dfrac{y^2}{(3)^2} = 1$

$\boxed{a = 4}$ $\boxed{b = 3}$

$a^2 = 16$, and because $a > 0$, we have that $a = 4$.
$b^2 = 9$, and because $b > 0$, we have that $b = 3$.
$c^2 = a^2 + b^2 = (4)^2 + (3)^2 = 25$
$c = 5$ (Recall that $c > 0$.)

Therefore, $e = \dfrac{c}{a} = \dfrac{5}{4}$.

b. $\dfrac{x^2}{9} - \dfrac{y^2}{16} = 1$ The x^2 term has a positive coefficient. Therefore, $a^2 = 9$.

$\dfrac{x^2}{(3)^2} - \dfrac{y^2}{(4)^2} = 1$

$\boxed{a = 3}$ $\boxed{b = 4}$

$a^2 = 9$, and because $a > 0$, we have that $a = 3$.
$b^2 = 16$, and because $b > 0$, we have that $b = 4$.
$c^2 = a^2 + b^2 = (3)^2 + (4)^2 = 25$
$c = 5$ (Recall that $c > 0$.)

Therefore, $e = \dfrac{c}{a} = \dfrac{5}{3}$.

The graphs of the hyperbolas are shown in Figures 7-15 and 7-16. Compare the graphs, and notice that the hyperbola in Figure 7-16 has a greater eccentricity and that the branches open wider.

Figure 7-15

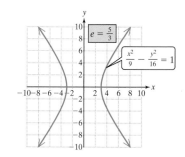

Figure 7-16

Skill Practice 6   Determine the eccentricity of the hyperbola.

a. $\dfrac{y^2}{25} - \dfrac{x^2}{144} = 1$ **b.** $\dfrac{y^2}{144} - \dfrac{x^2}{25} = 1$

Answers

6. a. $e = \dfrac{13}{5}$ **b.** $e = \dfrac{13}{12}$

4. Use Hyperbolas in Applications

Applications of hyperbolas arise in many fields. For example, astronomers know that some comets, such as Halley's comet, follow an elliptical path around the Sun. Other comets have a hyperbolic orbit because they are not captured by the Sun's gravity (Figure 7-17).

Hyperbolas also provide the mathematical basis for LORAN (LOng RAnge Navigation), a technique used for navigation before global positioning systems. A ship using LORAN measures the difference in time between synchronized radio signals from two different transmitters. Using the relationship $d = rt$, the difference in distances between the ship and the two transmitters $(d_1 - d_2)$ can be computed. Thus, the position of the ship is located on the hyperbolic path with the two transmitters at the foci (Figure 7-18).

The same principle used in LORAN can also be used with sound waves to locate the source of sound heard from two different receivers. This is demonstrated in Example 7.

Figure 7-17

Figure 7-18

EXAMPLE 7   **Using a Hyperbola in an Application**

Suppose that two people located 3 mi (15,840 ft) apart at points A and B hear a clap of thunder (Figure 7-19). The time difference between the sound heard at point A and the sound heard at point B is 10 sec. If sound travels 1100 ft/sec, find an equation of the hyperbola (with foci at A and B) on which the point of origination of the sound must lie.

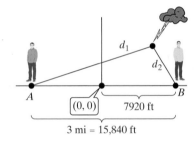

Figure 7-19

Solution:

First, we choose a coordinate system with the origin midway between the two observers. The two observers are at the points (7920, 0) and (−7920, 0). Let d_1 and d_2 represent the distances between each observer and the source of the sound (Figure 7-19).

The difference in distance $d_1 - d_2$ can be computed from the relationship $d = rt$.

$$d_1 - d_2 = (1100 \text{ ft/s})(10 \text{ s}) = 11,000 \text{ ft}$$

By the definition of a hyperbola, the source of the sound must be at a point on the hyperbola for which $d_1 - d_2 = 11,000$. The center of the hyperbola is (0, 0), and the transverse axis is horizontal with foci (7920, 0) and (−7920, 0). The standard form of the equation of the hyperbola is

$$\frac{x^2}{a^2} - \frac{y^2}{b^2} = 1$$

The value $d_1 - d_2 = 2a$
$$11,000 = 2a$$
$$a = 5500 \text{ ft}$$

From the location of the foci, $c = 7920$ ft.
$c^2 = a^2 + b^2$. Taking $b > 0$, we have $b = \sqrt{c^2 - a^2}$.
$$b = \sqrt{(7920)^2 - (5500)^2} \approx 5699 \text{ ft}$$

The source of the sound must be at a point on the curve $\dfrac{x^2}{(5500)^2} - \dfrac{y^2}{(5699)^2} = 1$.

Answer

7. $\dfrac{x^2}{(8800)^2} - \dfrac{y^2}{(5837)^2} = 1$

Skill Practice 7   Repeat Example 7 with two observers 4 mi apart, who hear a clap of thunder 16 sec apart. (*Hint*: 5280 ft = 1 mi.)

SECTION 7.2   Practice Exercises

Review Exercises

For Exercises 1–2, an equation of an ellipse is given. Identify the center, vertices, foci, endpoints of the minor axis, and eccentricity.

1. $\dfrac{(x-3)^2}{169} + \dfrac{(y+10)^2}{144} = 1$

2. $\dfrac{(x+7)^2}{64} + \dfrac{(y-5)^2}{100} = 1$

For Exercises 3–4, write the equation of the ellipse in standard form.

3. $12x^2 + 5y^2 + 240x + 1140 = 0$

4. $3x^2 + 7y^2 - 112y + 427 = 0$

For Exercises 5–6, determine the center and radius of the circle.

5. $(x+8)^2 + \left(y - \frac{3}{2}\right)^2 = 20$

6. $\left(x - \frac{1}{5}\right)^2 + (y-7)^2 = 18$

Concept Connections

7. A _____ is the set of points (x, y) in a plane such that the difference in distances between (x, y) and two fixed points (called _____) is a positive constant.

8. The points where a hyperbola intersects the line through the foci are called the _____.

9. The line segment between the vertices of a hyperbola is called the _____ axis.

10. The midpoint of the transverse axis is the _____ of the hyperbola.

11. The equation $\dfrac{x^2}{a^2} - \dfrac{y^2}{b^2} = 1$ represents a hyperbola with a (horizontal/vertical) transverse axis. The vertices are given by the ordered pairs _____ and _____. The asymptotes are given by the equations _____ and _____.

12. The equation $\dfrac{y^2}{a^2} - \dfrac{x^2}{b^2} = 1$ represents a hyperbola with a (horizontal/vertical) transverse axis. The vertices are given by the ordered pairs _____ and _____. The asymptotes are given by the equations _____ and _____.

13. The line segment perpendicular to the transverse axis passing through the center of a hyperbola, and with endpoints on the reference rectangle is called the _____ axis.

14. When referring to the standard form of an equation of a hyperbola, the _____ e is defined as $e = \dfrac{\square}{\square}$.

15. Given $\dfrac{(y-k)^2}{a^2} - \dfrac{(x-h)^2}{b^2} = 1$, the ordered pairs representing the vertices are _____ and _____.

16. Given $\dfrac{(x-h)^2}{a^2} - \dfrac{(y-k)^2}{b^2} = 1$, the ordered pairs representing the vertices are _____ and _____.

Objective 1: Graph a Hyperbola Centered at the Origin

For Exercises 17–18,

a. Use the distance formula to find the distances d_1, d_2, d_3, and d_4.

b. Find the difference of the distances: $d_1 - d_2$.

c. Find the difference of the distances: $d_3 - d_4$.

d. How do the results from parts (b) and (c) compare?

e. How do the results of part (b) and part (c) compare to the length of the transverse axis?

17.

18.

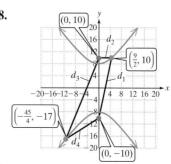

For Exercises 19–22, determine whether the transverse axis and foci of the hyperbola are on the *x*-axis or the *y*-axis.

19. $\dfrac{x^2}{15} - \dfrac{y^2}{20} = 1$

20. $\dfrac{y^2}{12} - \dfrac{x^2}{18} = 1$

21. $-x^2 + \dfrac{y^2}{3} = 1$

22. $-\dfrac{y^2}{16} + x^2 = 1$

For Exercises 23–32,

a. Identify the center.   **b.** Identify the vertices.

c. Identify the foci.   **d.** Write equations for the asymptotes.

e. Graph the hyperbola. (**See Examples 1–2**)

23. $\dfrac{x^2}{16} - \dfrac{y^2}{25} = 1$

24. $\dfrac{x^2}{25} - \dfrac{y^2}{36} = 1$

25. $\dfrac{y^2}{4} - \dfrac{x^2}{36} = 1$

26. $\dfrac{y^2}{9} - \dfrac{x^2}{49} = 1$

27. $25y^2 - 81x^2 = 2025$

28. $49y^2 - 16x^2 = 784$

29. $-5x^2 + 7y^2 = -35$

30. $-7x^2 + 11y^2 = -77$

31. $\dfrac{4x^2}{25} - \dfrac{16y^2}{49} = 1$

32. $\dfrac{4x^2}{81} - \dfrac{16y^2}{225} = 1$

Objective 2: Graph a Hyperbola Centered at (*h*, *k*)

For Exercises 33–42,

a. Identify the center.   **b.** Identify the vertices.

c. Identify the foci.   **d.** Write equations for the asymptotes.

e. Graph the hyperbola. (**See Example 3**)

33. $\dfrac{(x-4)^2}{9} - \dfrac{(y+2)^2}{16} = 1$

34. $\dfrac{(x-3)^2}{36} - \dfrac{(y+1)^2}{64} = 1$

35. $\dfrac{(y-5)^2}{49} - \dfrac{(x+3)^2}{25} = 1$

36. $\dfrac{(y-4)^2}{36} - \dfrac{(x+5)^2}{16} = 1$

37. $100(y-7)^2 - 81(x+4)^2 = -8100$

38. $49(y-3)^2 - 100(x+6)^2 = -4900$

39. $y^2 - \dfrac{(x-3)^2}{12} = 1$

40. $y^2 - \dfrac{(x-2)^2}{18} = 1$

41. $x^2 - \dfrac{(y-4)^2}{8} = 1$

42. $x^2 - \dfrac{(y-6)^2}{24} = 1$

For Exercises 43–50,

a. Write the equation of the hyperbola in standard form. (**See Example 4**)

b. Identify the center, vertices, and foci.

43. $7x^2 - 5y^2 + 42x + 10y + 23 = 0$

44. $5x^2 - 3y^2 + 10x + 24y - 73 = 0$

45. $-5x^2 + 9y^2 + 20x - 72y + 79 = 0$

46. $-7x^2 + 16y^2 - 70x + 96y - 143 = 0$

47. $4x^2 - y^2 - 10y - 29 = 0$

48. $9x^2 - y^2 - 14y - 58 = 0$

49. $-36x^2 + 64y^2 + 108x + 256y - 401 = 0$

50. $-144x^2 + 25y^2 + 720x - 50y - 4475 = 0$

For Exercises 51–60, write the standard form of the equation of the hyperbola subject to the given conditions. (See Example 5)

51. Vertices: $(12, 0)$, $(-12, 0)$; Foci: $(13, 0)$, $(-13, 0)$

52. Vertices: $(40, 0)$, $(-40, 0)$; Foci: $(41, 0)$, $(-41, 0)$

53. Vertices: $(0, 12)$, $(0, -12)$; Asymptotes: $y = \pm\frac{4}{3}x$

54. Vertices: $(0, 15)$, $(0, -15)$; Asymptotes: $y = \pm\frac{15}{8}x$

55. Vertices: $(-3, -3)$, $(7, -3)$;
Slope of the asymptotes: $\pm\frac{7}{5}$

56. Vertices: $(2, 1)$, $(-10, 1)$;
Slope of the asymptotes: $\pm\frac{5}{6}$

57. Vertices: $(-3, 0)$, $(-3, 8)$;
Foci: $\left(-3, 4 + \sqrt{21}\right), \left(-3, 4 - \sqrt{21}\right)$

58. Vertices: $(2, -1)$, $(2, -11)$;
Foci: $\left(2, -6 + \sqrt{31}\right), \left(2, -6 - \sqrt{31}\right)$

59. Corners of the reference rectangle: $(8, 7)$, $(-6, 7)$, $(8, -3)$, $(-6, -3)$; Horizontal transverse axis

60. Corners of the reference rectangle: $(7, 6)$, $(-1, 6)$, $(7, 0)$, $(-1, 0)$; Horizontal transverse axis

Objective 3: Determine the Eccentricity of a Hyperbola

For Exercises 61–62,

a. Determine the eccentricity of each hyperbola. (**See Example 6**)

b. Based on the eccentricity, match the equation with its graph. The scaling is the same for both graphs.

61. Equation 1: $\dfrac{x^2}{144} - \dfrac{y^2}{81} = 1$

   Equation 2: $\dfrac{x^2}{81} - \dfrac{y^2}{144} = 1$

62. Equation 1: $\dfrac{x^2}{225} - \dfrac{y^2}{64} = 1$

   Equation 2: $\dfrac{x^2}{64} - \dfrac{y^2}{225} = 1$

A.   **B.**

A.   **B.**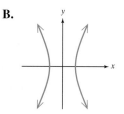

For Exercises 63–64, determine the eccentricity.

63. $\dfrac{\left(y - \frac{2}{3}\right)^2}{1600} - \dfrac{\left(x + \frac{7}{4}\right)^2}{81} = 1$

64. $\dfrac{(y - 3.8)^2}{49} - \dfrac{(x - 2.7)^2}{576} = 1$

65. Determine the eccentricity of a hyperbola with a horizontal transverse axis of length 24 units and asymptotes $y = \pm\frac{3}{4}x$.

66. Determine the eccentricity of a hyperbola with a vertical transverse axis of length 48 units and asymptotes $y = \pm\frac{12}{5}x$.

67. Determine the standard form of an equation of a hyperbola with eccentricity $\frac{5}{4}$ and vertices $(-1, -1)$ and $(7, -1)$.

68. Determine the standard form of an equation of a hyperbola with eccentricity $\frac{13}{12}$ and vertices $(-2, 8)$ and $(-2, -16)$.

Objective 4: Use Hyperbolas in Applications

69. Two radio transmitters are 1000 mi apart at points A and B along a coastline. Using LORAN on the ship, the time difference between the radio signals is 4 milliseconds (0.004 sec). If radio signals travel 186 mi/millisecond, find an equation of the hyperbola with foci at A and B, on which the ship is located. (**See Example 7**)

70. Suppose that two microphones 1500 m apart at points A and B detect the sound of a rifle shot. The time difference between the sound detected at point A and the sound detected at point B is 4 sec. If sound travels at approximately 330 m/sec, find an equation of the hyperbola with foci at A and B defining the points where the shooter may be located.

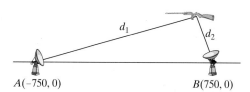

71. In September 2009, Australian astronomer Robert H. McNaught discovered comet C/2009 R₁ (McNaught). The orbit of this comet is hyperbolic with the Sun at one focus. Because the orbit is not elliptical, the comet will not be captured by the Sun's gravitational pull and instead will pass by the Sun only once. The comet reached perihelion on July 2, 2010. (*Source*: Minor Planet Center, http://minorplanetcenter.net/)

The path of the comet can be modeled by the equation

$$\frac{x^2}{(1191.2)^2} - \frac{y^2}{(30.9)^2} = 1$$

where x and y are measured in AU (astronomical units).

a. Determine the distance (in AU) at perihelion. Round to 1 decimal place.

b. If 1 AU ≈ 93,000,000 mi, find the distance in miles.

72. The cross section of a cooling tower of a nuclear power plant is in the shape of a hyperbola, and can be modeled by the equation

$$\frac{x^2}{625} - \frac{(y - 80)^2}{2500} = 1$$

where x and y are measured in meters. The top of the tower is 120 m above the base.

a. Determine the diameter of the tower at the base. Round to the nearest meter.

b. Determine the diameter of the tower at the top. Round to the nearest meter.

Mixed Exercises

For Exercises 73–76, identify the equation as representing an ellipse or a hyperbola, and match the equation with the graph.

73. $\dfrac{(x - 5)^2}{49} + \dfrac{(y + 2)^2}{36} = 1$

74. $\dfrac{(x - 5)^2}{36} + \dfrac{(y + 2)^2}{49} = 1$

75. $\dfrac{(x - 5)^2}{49} - \dfrac{(y + 2)^2}{36} = 1$

76. $-\dfrac{(x - 5)^2}{49} + \dfrac{(y + 2)^2}{36} = 1$

A.

B.

C.

D.

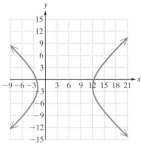

For Exercises 77–80, find the standard form of the equation of the ellipse or hyperbola shown.

77.

78.

79.

80.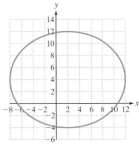

For Exercises 81–82, solve the system of equations.

81. $9x^2 - 4y^2 = 36$
$-13x^2 + 8y^2 = 8$

82. $x^2 + 4y^2 = 36$
$4x^2 - y^2 = 8$

Write About It

83. Given an equation of a hyperbola in standard form, how do you determine whether the transverse axis is horizontal or vertical?

84. Discuss the solution set of the equation.
$$\frac{x^2}{4} - \frac{y^2}{9} = 0$$

Expanding Your Skills

85. What is the eccentricity of a hyperbola if the asymptotes are perpendicular?

86. a. Describe the graph of $y = 4\sqrt{1 + \dfrac{x^2}{9}}$.

  b. Does the equation $y = 4\sqrt{1 + \dfrac{x^2}{9}}$ define y as a function of x?

  c. Sketch $y = 4\sqrt{1 + \dfrac{x^2}{9}}$.

  d. Determine the interval(s) over which the function is increasing.

  e. Determine the interval(s) over which the function is decreasing.

87. A line segment with endpoints on a hyperbola, perpendicular to the transverse axis, and passing through a focus is called a *latus rectum* of the hyperbola (shown in red). Show that the length of a latus rectum is $\dfrac{2b^2}{a}$ for the hyperbola

$$\frac{x^2}{a^2} - \frac{y^2}{b^2} = 1$$

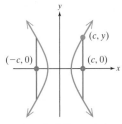

[*Hint*: Substitute (c, y) into the equation and solve for y. Recall that $c^2 = a^2 + b^2$.]

88. This exercise guides you through the steps to find the standard form of an equation of a hyperbola centered at the origin with foci on the x-axis.

  a. Refer to the figure to verify that the distance between F_1 and V_2 is $(c + a)$ and the distance between F_2 and V_2 is $(c - a)$. Verify that the *difference* between these distances is $2a$.

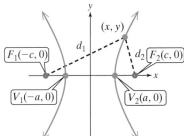

  b. Write an expression that represents the difference of the distances from F_1 to (x, y) and from F_2 to (x, y). Then set this expression equal to $2a$.

  c. Given the equation $\sqrt{(x + c)^2 + y^2} - \sqrt{(x - c)^2 + y^2} = 2a$, isolate the leftmost radical and square both sides of the equation. Show that the equation can be written as $cx - a^2 = a\sqrt{(x - c)^2 + y^2}$.

  d. Square both sides of the equation $cx - a^2 = a\sqrt{(x - c)^2 + y^2}$ and show that the equation can be written as $(c^2 - a^2)x^2 - a^2y^2 = a^2(c^2 - a^2)$. (*Hint*: Collect variable terms on the left side of the equation and constant terms on the right side.)

  e. Replace $c^2 - a^2$ by b^2. Then divide both sides of the equation by a^2b^2. Verify that the resulting equation is $\dfrac{x^2}{a^2} - \dfrac{y^2}{b^2} = 1$.

Technology Connections

For Exercises 89–92, graph the hyperbola from the given exercise.

89. Exercise 25

90. Exercise 26

91. Exercise 37

92. Exercise 38

SECTION 7.3
The Parabola

OBJECTIVES

1. Identify the Focus and Directrix of a Parabola
2. Graph a Parabola with Vertex at the Origin
3. Graph a Parabola with Vertex (h, k)

Figure 7-20

1. Identify the Focus and Directrix of a Parabola

Recall that the graph of the equation $y = ax^2 + bx + c$ $(a \neq 0)$ is a parabola. See Figure 7-20. The parabola opens upward if $a > 0$ and downward if $a < 0$. We now extend our study of parabolas to include those that open to the left and right. To do so, we will define a parabola geometrically.

> **Definition of a Parabola**
>
> A **parabola** is the set of all points in a plane that are equidistant from a fixed line (called the **directrix**) and a fixed point (called the **focus**).

Figure 7-21 shows a parabola opening upward. The line perpendicular to the directrix and passing through the focus is called the **axis of symmetry.** The **vertex** of the parabola is the point of intersection of the parabola and the axis of symmetry.

A point $P(x, y)$ is on the parabola if $d_1 = d_2$ where d_1 is the distance between the focus and P, and d_2 is the perpendicular distance between P and the directrix.

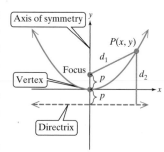

Figure 7-21

To develop an algebraic equation that represents a parabola, we will consider a parabola with vertex at the origin and with a vertical line of symmetry (that is, the parabola opens upward or downward). See Figure 7-22. In the discussion that follows, the same logic may be applied to a parabola with a horizontal line of symmetry (the parabola opens to the left or to the right).

The distance between the vertex and the focus of a parabola is called the **focal length** and is often represented by $|p|$. Suppose that we choose a coordinate system with the vertex at the origin and focus $F(0, p)$. Because the distance between any point on the parabola and the focus must equal the distance between the point and the directrix, the directrix is a horizontal line $|p|$ units from the vertex. The equation of the directrix is $y = -p$.

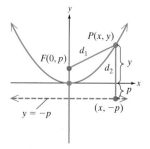

Figure 7-22

TIP The shortest distance between P and the directrix is the *perpendicular distance*. This is the length of the line segment perpendicular to the directrix with one endpoint at P and the other endpoint on the directrix.

Let $P(x, y)$ represent any point on the parabola. Then the distance between $F(0, p)$ and $P(x, y)$ can be found by using the distance formula.

$$d_1 = \sqrt{(x - 0)^2 + (y - p)^2}$$

The distance from $P(x, y)$ to the directrix is the vertical distance between $P(x, y)$ and the point $(x, -p)$ on the directrix.

$$d_2 = y + p$$

Equating d_1 and d_2, we have

$$\sqrt{x^2 + (y - p)^2} = y + p$$
$$x^2 + (y - p)^2 = (y + p)^2 \qquad \text{Square both sides.}$$
$$x^2 + y^2 - 2py + p^2 = y^2 + 2py + p^2 \qquad \text{Expand the binomials.}$$
$$x^2 = 4py$$

Standard form
If $p > 0$, the parabola opens upward.
If $p < 0$, the parabola opens downward.

The equation $x^2 = 4py$ represents a parabola with vertex at the origin and focus on the y-axis. Using similar logic, we can derive the standard form of an equation of a parabola with focus on the x-axis.

Standard Forms of an Equation of a Parabola with Vertex at the Origin		
	Axis of Symmetry: y-axis	**Axis of Symmetry: x-axis**
Equation:	$x^2 = 4py$	$y^2 = 4px$
Vertex:	$(0, 0)$	$(0, 0)$
Focus:	$(0, p)$	$(p, 0)$
Directrix:	$y = -p$	$x = -p$
Axis of symmetry:	$x = 0$	$y = 0$
Graph: ($p > 0$)		
Graph: ($p < 0$)		

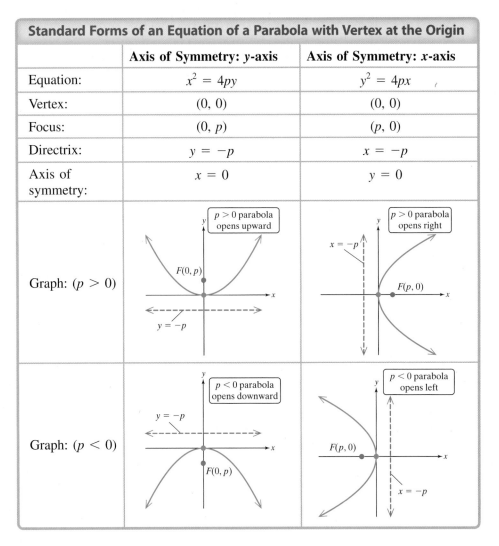

Avoiding Mistakes

Notice that an equation of a parabola has only one variable squared, whereas an equation of an ellipse or hyperbola has both x and y appearing to the second power.

TIP The orientation of a parabola (whether it opens vertically or horizontally) can be determined by noting the linear term in the equation. For the equation $x^2 = 4py$, the y term is linear (to the first power). Therefore, the parabola will open in the y direction (upward or downward). For the equation $y^2 = 4px$, the x term is linear, so the parabola will open to the left or right.

From Section 3.1, we became accustomed to writing an equation of a quadratic function with vertex at the origin in the form $y = ax^2$. The benefit of writing the equation as $x^2 = 4py$ is that we can identify the value of p, which gives us the distance between the vertex and the focus.

Finding the location of the focus is particularly important in applications. For example, a flashlight has a mirror with cross section in the shape of a parabola (Figure 7-23). The bulb is located at the focus. The light emitted from the bulb will reflect off the mirror in lines parallel to the axis of symmetry to form a beam of light. This is a result of the reflective property of a parabola.

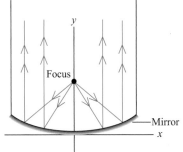

Figure 7-23

> **EXAMPLE 1** **Determining the Focus and Directrix of a Parabola**
>
> An engineer designs a flashlight with a parabolic mirror. A coordinate system is chosen so that the vertex of a cross section through the center of the mirror is located at $(0, 0)$. The equation of the parabola is modeled by $x^2 = 8y$ where x and y are measured in centimeters.
>
> **a.** Where should the bulb be placed to make use of the reflective property of the parabola? That is, find the location of the focus.
>
> **b.** Write an equation of the directrix.
>
> **Solution:**
>
> **a.** $x^2 = 8y$ is in the form $x^2 = 4py$ with $4p = 8$.
>
> $4p = 8$
>
> $p = 2$ Since the equation is in the form $x^2 = 4py$, the focus is on the y-axis. Furthermore, since $p > 0$, the parabola opens upward, and the focus is $|p|$ units above the vertex.
>
>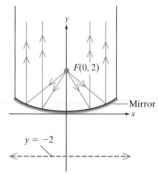
>
>   The focus is $(0, 2)$.
>   The bulb should be placed 2 cm above the vertex.
>
> **b.** The directrix is the horizontal line $|p|$ units below the vertex.
>   The equation of the directrix is $y = -2$.

> **Skill Practice 1**   Given a parabola defined by $x^2 = 4y$, find the focus and an equation of the directrix.

2. Graph a Parabola with Vertex at the Origin

In Examples 2 and 3, we practice graphing parabolas with vertex at the origin. To sketch the graph, we will identify the location of the vertex and the orientation of the parabola (up or down versus left or right). To determine how "wide" to graph the parabola, we will determine the length of the line segment passing through the focus, perpendicular to the axis of symmetry with endpoints on the parabola. This line segment is called the **latus rectum.**

For the parabola defined by $x^2 = 4py$, the endpoints of the latus rectum will have the same y-coordinate as the focus. Therefore, to find the endpoints of the latus rectum, we can substitute p for y in the equation (Figure 7-24).

$$x^2 = 4py$$
$$x^2 = 4p(p) \quad \text{Substitute } p \text{ for } y.$$
$$x^2 = 4p^2$$
$$x = \pm 2|p|$$

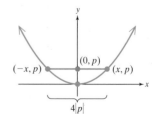

Figure 7-24

Thus, the endpoints of the latus rectum are located $2|p|$ units to the left and right of the focus at $(-2|p|, p)$ and $(2|p|, p)$. The length of the latus rectum is called the **focal diameter** and is equal to $4|p|$.

In Example 2, we graph a parabola by using the vertex, orientation of the parabola, and focal diameter.

Answer
1. Focus: $(0, 1)$; Directrix: $y = -1$

EXAMPLE 2   Graphing a Parabola with Vertex at the Origin

Given $x^2 = -12y$,

a. Identify the vertex, focus, and focal diameter.

b. Identify the endpoints of the latus rectum and graph the parabola.

c. Write equations for the directrix and axis of symmetry.

Solution:

a. $x^2 = -12y$ The equation is in the standard form $x^2 = 4py$. From the standard form, we see that the focus is on the y-axis and that the parabola will open upward or downward. The vertex is $(0, 0)$, with $4p = -12$.

$4p = -12$

$\ \ \ p = -3$ Because $p < 0$, the parabola will open downward.

The vertex is $(0, 0)$.

The focus is $(0, p)$, which is $(0, -3)$.

The focal diameter is $4|p|$, which is $4|(-3)| = 12$.

b. Plot the vertex and locate the focus. Note that the focus is shown in red because it is not actually part of the graph. The focal diameter is 12 units. Therefore, plot points 6 units to the left and right of the focus. These are the endpoints of the latus rectum: $(6, -3)$ and $(-6, -3)$.

c. Equation of the directrix: $y = 3$

Equation of the axis of symmetry: $x = 0$

Skill Practice 2   Repeat Example 2 with the equation: $x^2 = -8y$

In Example 3, we graph a parabola opening horizontally.

EXAMPLE 3   Graphing a Parabola with Vertex at the Origin

Given $2y^2 = 32x$,

a. Identify the vertex, focus, and focal diameter.

b. Identify the endpoints of the latus rectum and graph the parabola.

c. Write equations for the directrix and axis of symmetry.

Solution:

a. $2y^2 = 32x$ Divide both sides by 2 to obtain a coefficient of 1 on the square term.

$\ \ y^2 = 16x$ The equation is in the standard form $y^2 = 4px$. From the standard form, we see that the focus is on the x-axis, and that the parabola will open to the left or right. The vertex is $(0, 0)$ and $4p = 16$.

$4p = 16$

$\ \ p = 4$ Because $p > 0$, the parabola will open to the right.

The vertex is $(0, 0)$.

The focus is $(p, 0)$, which is $(4, 0)$.

The focal diameter is $4|p|$, which is $4|(4)| = 16$.

Answers

2. a. Vertex: $(0, 0)$; Focus: $(0, -2)$; Focal diameter: 8

b. $(-4, -2), (4, -2)$

c. Directrix: $y = 2$; Axis of symmetry: $x = 0$

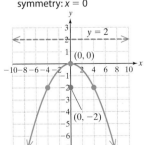

b. Plot the vertex and locate the focus. The focal diameter is 16 units. Therefore, plot points 8 units above and 8 units below the focus. These are the endpoints of the latus rectum, (4, 8) and (4, −8).

c. Equation of the directrix: $x = -4$
Equation of the axis of symmetry: $y = 0$

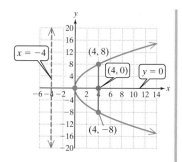

> **Skill Practice 3**   Repeat Example 3 with the equation: $y^2 = -12x$

3. Graph a Parabola with Vertex (*h*, *k*)

In the standard form of a parabola, if x and y are replaced by $x - h$ and $y - k$, then the graph of the parabola is shifted h units horizontally and k units vertically. The vertex is (h, k).

Standard Forms of an Equation of a Parabola with Vertex (*h*, *k*)		
	Vertical Axis of Symmetry	**Horizontal Axis of Symmetry**
Equation:	$(x - h)^2 = 4p(y - k)$	$(y - k)^2 = 4p(x - h)$
Vertex:	(h, k)	(h, k)
Focus:	$(h, k + p)$	$(h + p, k)$
Directrix:	$y = k - p$	$x = h - p$
Axis of symmetry:	$x = h$	$y = k$
Graph:		
Note:	• If $p > 0$, the parabola opens upward as shown. • If $p < 0$, the parabola opens downward.	• If $p > 0$, the parabola opens to the right as shown. • If $p < 0$, the parabola opens to the left.

To graph a parabola with vertex (h, k), first locate the vertex and identify the orientation of the parabola (vertical axis of symmetry or horizontal axis of symmetry). Then identify the focus, directrix, and endpoints of the latus rectum. Finally, sketch the parabola through the vertex and endpoints of the latus rectum.

Answers

3. a. Vertex: (0, 0); Focus: (−3, 0);
Focal diameter: 12
b. (−3, 6), (−3, −6)
c. Directrix: $x = 3$; Axis of symmetry: $y = 0$

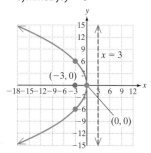

EXAMPLE 4   Graphing a Parabola with Vertex (*h*, *k*)

Given $(y + 3)^2 = -4(x - 2)$,

a. Identify the vertex, focus, and focal diameter.

b. Identify the endpoints of the latus rectum and graph the parabola.

c. Write equations for the directrix and axis of symmetry.

Solution:

a. $(y + 3)^2 = -4(x - 2)$

$$4p = -4$$

$$p = -1$$

The equation is in the form $(y - k)^2 = 4p(x - h)$, where $h = 2$ and $k = -3$. The vertex is $(2, -3)$, and $4p = -4$. This implies that $p = -1$.

The *x* term is linear. Therefore, the parabola will open in the *x* direction (left or right). Furthermore, since $p < 0$, the parabola will open to the left.

The vertex is $(2, -3)$.

The focus is $(1, -3)$.   Since $p = -1$, the focus is 1 unit to the left of the vertex.

The focal diameter is 4.   The focal diameter is $4|p| = 4|(-1)| = 4$.

b. Plot the vertex and locate the focus. The focal diameter is 4 units. Therefore, plot points 2 units above and below the focus. These are the endpoints of the latus rectum: $(1, -1)$ and $(1, -5)$.

Sketch the curve through the vertex and endpoints of the latus rectum.

c. Equation of the directrix: $x = 3$

Equation of the axis of symmetry: $y = -3$

Skill Practice 4   Repeat Example 4 with the equation: $(y - 2)^2 = -8(x - 4)$

Answers

4. a. Vertex: (4, 2); Focus: (2, 2); Focal diameter: 8

b. (2, 6), (2, −2)

c. Directrix: $x = 6$; Axis of symmetry: $y = 2$

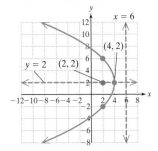

TECHNOLOGY CONNECTIONS

Graphing a Parabola

To graph the parabola from Example 4 on a graphing utility, first solve the equation for *y*.

$$(y + 3)^2 = -4(x - 2)$$

$$y = -3 \pm \sqrt{-4(x - 2)} \qquad \text{Solve for } y.$$

The functions represent the top and bottom branches of the parabola, respectively.

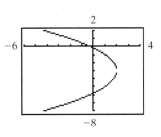

Sometimes an equation of a parabola is given in expanded form. We can complete the square to write the equation in standard form. The process involves completing the square on either the *x* or *y* term, depending on which variable is squared in the equation. This is demonstrated in Example 5.

Writing an Equation of a Parabola in Standard Form

Given the equation of the parabola $4x^2 - 20x - 8y + 57 = 0$,

a. Write the equation in standard form.

b. Identify the vertex, focus, and focal diameter.

c. Graph the parabola.

Solution:

a. $4x^2 - 20x - 8y + 57 = 0$

$4(x^2 - 5x \qquad) = 8y - 57$

> The x term is squared. Therefore, we complete the square on x on the left side. Move the y term and constant term to the right.

$4 \cdot \frac{25}{4}$ is added to the left side.

$4 \cdot \frac{25}{4}$

> Complete the square.
> Note that $\left[\frac{1}{2} \cdot (-5)\right]^2 = \left[-\frac{5}{2}\right]^2 = \frac{25}{4}$.

$4\left(x^2 - 5x + \frac{25}{4}\right) = 8y - 57 + 25$

$4\left(x - \frac{5}{2}\right)^2 = 8y - 32$

> The value $\frac{25}{4}$ was added inside the parentheses. However, $4 \cdot \frac{25}{4}$ was actually added to the left side as a result of the factor 4 in front of the parentheses.

$\dfrac{4\left(x - \frac{5}{2}\right)^2}{4} = \dfrac{8y - 32}{4}$

> To write the equation in standard form, we require the coefficient of the square term to be 1. Divide both sides by 4.

$\left(x - \frac{5}{2}\right)^2 = 2y - 8$

$\left(x - \frac{5}{2}\right)^2 = 2(y - 4)$

> Factor out the leading coefficient on the right side of the equation. The equation is in the form $(x - h)^2 = 4p(y - k)$.

b. $4p = 2$

$p = \frac{1}{2}$

> The y term is linear. Therefore, the parabola will open in the y direction (upward or downward). Furthermore, since $p > 0$, the parabola will open upward.

The vertex is $\left(\frac{5}{2}, 4\right)$.

The focus is $\left(\frac{5}{2}, \frac{9}{2}\right)$

> Since $p = \frac{1}{2}$, the focus is $\frac{1}{2}$ unit above the vertex.

The focal diameter is 2.

> The focal diameter is $4|p| = 4\left|\frac{1}{2}\right| = 2$

c. Plot the vertex and locate the focus. The focal diameter is 2 units. Therefore, plot points 1 unit to the left and right of the focus. These are the points $\left(\frac{3}{2}, \frac{9}{2}\right)$ and $\left(\frac{7}{2}, \frac{9}{2}\right)$.

Sketch the curve.

Answers

5. a. $\left(x - \frac{3}{2}\right)^2 = 3(y - 1)$

b. Vertex: $\left(\frac{3}{2}, 1\right)$; Focus: $\left(\frac{3}{2}, \frac{7}{4}\right)$; Focal diameter: 3

c.

Skill Practice 5 Repeat Example 5 with the equation:

$4x^2 - 12x - 12y + 21 = 0$

In Example 6, we determine the standard form of an equation of a parabola based on known information about the parabola.

EXAMPLE 6   Writing an Equation of a Parabola

Determine the standard form of an equation of the parabola with focus (1, 2) and directrix $x = 7$.

Solution:

The directrix is a vertical line $x = 7$ and the focus is 6 units to the left of the directrix (Figure 7-25). The vertex is halfway between the directrix and focus. Therefore, the vertex is 3 units to the right of the focus at (4, 2). This indicates that $h = 4$ and $k = 2$.

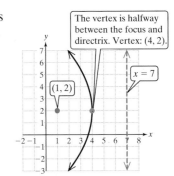

The vertex is halfway between the focus and directrix. Vertex: (4, 2).

Figure 7-25

The parabola must open away from the directrix and toward the focus which in this case is to the left. The standard equation is

$$(y - k)^2 = 4p(x - h)$$

The distance between the focus and vertex is 3. Therefore, $|p| = 3$. Because the parabola opens to the left, $p < 0$, indicating that $p = -3$.

The equation is: $(y - k)^2 = 4p(x - h)$
$(y - 2)^2 = 4(-3)(x - 4)$
$(y - 2)^2 = -12(x - 4)$

Skill Practice 6   Determine the standard form of an equation of a parabola with focus (−2, 3) and directrix $y = 7$.

Answer

6. $(x + 2)^2 = -8(y - 5)$

SECTION 7.3   Practice Exercises

Review Exercises

For Exercises 1–6, identify each equation as representing a circle, an ellipse, or a hyperbola.

- If the equation represents a circle, identify the center and radius.
- If the equation represents an ellipse, identify the center, vertices, endpoints of the minor axis, foci, and eccentricity.
- If the equation represents a hyperbola, identify the center, vertices, foci, equations of the asymptotes, and eccentricity.

1. $\dfrac{x^2}{9} - \dfrac{(y + 7)^2}{16} = 1$

2. $\dfrac{x^2}{9} + \dfrac{(y + 7)^2}{16} = 1$

3. $(x + 3)^2 + (y + 4)^2 = 18$

4. $\dfrac{(x - 8)^2}{144} - \dfrac{y^2}{25} = 1$

5. $\dfrac{(x - 8)^2}{12} + \dfrac{(y - 2)^2}{4} = 1$

6. $4(x - 1)^2 + 4(y - 3)^2 = 16$

Concept Connections

7. A _____ is the set of all points in a plane that are equidistant from a fixed line (called the _____) and a fixed point (called the _____).

8. The line perpendicular to the directrix and passing through the focus is called the axis of _____.

9. The _____ of a parabola is the point of intersection of the parabola and the axis of symmetry.

10. The distance between the vertex and the focus of a parabola is called the _____ length and is often represented by $|p|$.

11. The standard form of an equation of a parabola with vertex (0, 0) and vertical axis of symmetry is _____.

12. Given a parabola defined by $y^2 = 4px$, the directrix is given by $x = -p$ and the focus is given by the ordered pair _____.

13. Given $y^2 = 4px$ with $p < 0$, the parabola opens (upward/downward/left/right).

14. Given $x^2 = 4py$ with $p > 0$, the parabola opens (upward/downward/left/right).

15. The line segment perpendicular to the axis of symmetry, passing through the focus and with endpoints on the parabola is called the _____ _____.

16. The length of the latus rectum is called the _____ diameter.

17. Given $(x - h)^2 = 4p(y - k)$, the ordered pairs representing the vertex and focus are _____ and _____, respectively. The directrix is the line defined by the equation _____.

18. Given $(y - k)^2 = 4p(x - h)$, the ordered pairs representing the vertex and focus are _____ and _____, respectively. The directrix is the line defined by the equation _____.

19. If the directrix is horizontal, then the parabola opens (horizontally/vertically).

20. If the line of symmetry is horizontal, then the parabola opens (horizontally/vertically).

For Exercises 21–22, the graph of a parabola is given.

a. Determine the distances d_1, d_2, d_3, and d_4.

b. Compare d_1 and d_2.

c. Compare d_3 and d_4.

21.

22.

Objective 1: Identify the Focus and Directrix of a Parabola

For Exercises 23–30, a model of the form $x^2 = 4py$ or $y^2 = 4px$ is given.

a. Determine the value of p.

b. Identify the focus.

c. Write an equation for the directrix. (**See Example 1**)

23. $x^2 = 24y$ 24. $x^2 = 12y$ 25. $y^2 = 36x$

26. $y^2 = 48x$ 27. $x^2 = -5y$ 28. $x^2 = -11y$

29. $-x = y^2$ 30. $-3x = y^2$

31. A 20-in. satellite dish for a television has parabolic cross sections. A coordinate system is chosen so that the vertex of a cross section through the center of the dish is located at $(0, 0)$. The equation of the parabola is modeled by $x^2 = 25.2y$, where x and y are measured in inches.

 a. Where should the receiver be placed to maximize signal strength? That is, where is the focus? (**See Example 1**)

 b. Determine the equation of the directrix.

32. A 36-in. solar reflector used for cooking and heating has parabolic cross sections. A coordinate system is chosen with the origin placed at the vertex of a cross section through the center of the mirror. The equation of the parabola is modeled by $x^2 = 82y$, where x and y are measured in inches.

 a. Determine the location of the focus.

 b. Determine the equation of the directrix.

Objective 2: Graph a Parabola with Vertex at the Origin

For Exercises 33–40, an equation of a parabola $x^2 = 4py$ or $y^2 = 4px$ is given.

a. Identify the vertex, value of p, focus, and focal diameter of the parabola.

b. Identify the endpoints of the latus rectum.

c. Graph the parabola.

d. Write equations for the directrix and axis of symmetry. (**See Examples 2–3**)

33. $x^2 = -4y$ **34.** $x^2 = -20y$ **35.** $10y^2 = 80x$ **36.** $3y^2 = 12x$

37. $4x^2 = 40y$ **38.** $2x^2 = 14y$ **39.** $y^2 = -x$ **40.** $y^2 = -2x$

Objective 3: Graph a Parabola with Vertex (h, k)

For Exercises 41–50, an equation of a parabola $(x - h)^2 = 4p(y - k)$ or $(y - k)^2 = 4p(x - h)$ is given.

a. Identify the vertex, value of p, focus, and focal diameter of the parabola.

b. Identify the endpoints of the latus rectum.

c. Graph the parabola.

d. Write equations for the directrix and axis of symmetry. (**See Example 4**)

41. $(y + 1)^2 = -12(x - 4)$ **42.** $(y + 4)^2 = -16(x - 2)$ **43.** $(x - 1)^2 = -4(y + 5)$

44. $(x - 5)^2 = -8(y + 2)$ **45.** $(x + 3)^2 = 2\left(y - \frac{3}{2}\right)$ **46.** $(x + 2)^2 = \left(y - \frac{7}{4}\right)$

47. $-(y - 3)^2 = 7\left(x - \frac{1}{4}\right)$ **48.** $-(y - 6)^2 = 9\left(x - \frac{3}{4}\right)$ **49.** $2(y - 3) = \frac{1}{10}(x + 6)^2$

50. $8(y - 2) = \frac{1}{2}(x + 3)^2$

For Exercises 51–58, an equation of a parabola is given.

a. Write the equation of the parabola in standard form.

b. Identify the vertex, focus, and directrix. (**See Example 5**)

51. $x^2 - 6x - 4y + 5 = 0$ **52.** $x^2 - 4x - 8y - 20 = 0$ **53.** $y^2 + 4y + 8x + 52 = 0$

54. $y^2 + 8y + 4x + 36 = 0$ **55.** $4x^2 - 28x + 24y + 73 = 0$ **56.** $4x^2 + 36x + 40y + 1 = 0$

57. $16y^2 + 24y - 16x + 57 = 0$ **58.** $16y^2 - 56y - 16x + 81 = 0$

For Exercises 59–64, fill in the blanks. Let $|p|$ represent the focal length (distance between the vertex and focus).

59. If the directrix of a parabola is given by $y = 4$ and the focus is $(1, 10)$, then the vertex is given by the ordered pair _____ and the value of p is _____.

60. If the directrix of a parabola is given by $x = 6$ and the focus is $(2, 1)$, then the vertex is given by the ordered pair _____ and the value of p is _____.

61. If the vertex of a parabola is $(-3, 0)$ and the focus is $(-7, 0)$, then the directrix is given by the equation _____, and the value of p is _____.

62. If the vertex of a parabola is $(4, -2)$ and the focus is $(4, -7)$, then the directrix is given by the equation _____, and the value of p is _____.

63. If the focal length of a parabola is 3 units, then the length of the latus rectum is _____ units.

64. If the focal diameter of a parabola is 8 units, then the focal length is _____ units.

65. If the focal length of a parabola is 6 units and the vertex is $(3, 2)$, is it possible to determine whether the parabola opens upward, downward, to the right, or to the left? Explain.

66. If the axis of symmetry of a parabola is given by $x = 4$, is it possible for the directrix to have the equation $x = 3$? Explain.

For Exercises 67–74, determine the standard form of an equation of the parabola subject to the given conditions. (See Example 6)

67. Vertex: $(0, 0)$; Directrix: $x = 4$ **68.** Vertex: $(0, 0)$; Directrix: $y = -2$

69. Focus: $(2, 4)$; Vertex: $(2, 1)$ **70.** Focus: $(5, 3)$: Vertex: $(3, 3)$

71. Focus: $(-6, -2)$; Directrix: $y = 0$ **72.** Focus: $(-4, 5)$; Directrix: $x = 0$

73. Vertex: $(2, 3)$; Parabola passes through $(6, 5)$ **74.** Vertex: $(-4, 2)$; Parabola passes through $(8, 14)$
(*Hint*: There are two possible answers.)   (*Hint*: There are two possible answers.)

Mixed Exercises

75. The Hubble Space Telescope was launched into space in 1990 and now orbits the Earth at 5 mi/sec at a distance of 353 mi above the Earth. From its location in space, the Hubble is free from the distortion of the Earth's atmosphere, enabling it to return magnificent images from distant stars and galaxies. The quality of the Hubble's images result from a large parabolic mirror, 2.4 m (7.9 ft) in diameter, that collects light from space.

Suppose that a coordinate system is chosen so that the vertex of a cross section through the center of the mirror is located at (0, 0). Furthermore, the focal length is 57.6 m.

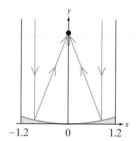

a. Assume that x and y are measured in meters. Write an equation of the parabolic cross section of the mirror for $-1.2 \le x \le 1.2$. See figure.

b. How thick is the mirror at the edge? That is, what is the y value for $x = 1.2$?

76. The James Webb Space Telescope (JWST) is a new space telescope currently under construction. The JWST will orbit the Sun in an orbit roughly 1.5 million km from the earth, in a position with the Earth between the telescope and the Sun. The primary mirror of the JWST will consist of 18 hexagonally shaped segments that when fitted together will be 6.5 m in diameter (over 2.5 times the diameter of the Hubble). With a larger mirror, the JWST will be able to collect more light to "see" deeper into space.

The primary mirror when pieced together will function as a parabolic mirror with a focal length of 131.4 m. Suppose that a coordinate system is chosen with (0, 0) at the center of a cross section of the primary mirror. Write an equation of the parabolic cross section of the mirror for $-3.25 \le x \le 3.25$. Assume that x and y are measured in meters.

For Exercises 77–78, solve the system of nonlinear equations.

77. $(y + 3)^2 = 4(x - 4)$
$2x + y = 9$

78. $(y - 2)^2 = -8(x - 1)$
$2x - y = -8$

Write About It

79. Given an equation of a parabola $(x - h)^2 = 4p(y - k)$ or $(y - k)^2 = 4p(x - h)$, how can you determine whether the parabola opens vertically or horizontally?

80. Give an example of the reflective property of a parabola.

Technology Connections

For Exercises 81–84, graph the parabola from the given exercise.

81. Exercise 35   **82.** Exercise 36   **83.** Exercise 47   **84.** Exercise 48

85. Given the equation $x^2 = 4py$, graph the parabola for the given values of p and comment on the "width" of the parabola.

$$p = 2, p = 1, p = 0.5, p = 0.25, p = -2, p = -1, p = -0.5, p = -0.25$$

PROBLEM RECOGNITION EXERCISES

Comparing Equations of Conic Sections and the General Equation

For Exercises 1–8, identify each equation as representing a circle, an ellipse, a hyperbola, or a parabola.

- If the equation represents a circle, identify the center and radius.
- If the equation represents an ellipse, identify the center, vertices, endpoints of the minor axis, foci, and eccentricity.
- If the equation represents a hyperbola, identify the center, vertices, foci, equations of the asymptotes, and eccentricity.
- If the equation represents a parabola, identify the vertex, focus, equation of the directrix, and equation of the axis of symmetry.

1. $\dfrac{(x-2)^2}{16} - \dfrac{(y+2)^2}{9} = 1$

2. $9x^2 + 25(y-2)^2 = 225$

3. $(y-5)^2 = -(x+2)$

4. $(x-3)^2 + (y+7)^2 = 25$

5. $16(x+1)^2 + y^2 = 16$

6. $(x-1)^2 = 10(y+3)$

7. $-(x+1)^2 - (y+6)^2 = -16$

8. $-\dfrac{(x+4)^2}{25} + \dfrac{(y-1)^2}{144} = 1$

> **TIP** The general form of an equation of a conic section also has a term Bxy which rotates the curve. In this text, we will not address rotated conic sections.

Suppose that the binomials within an equation of a conic section are expanded and all terms are collected on the left side of the equation. The result will be an equation of the conic section written in **general form:**

$$Ax^2 + Cy^2 + Dx + Ey + F = 0, \text{ where } A \text{ and } C \text{ are not both zero.}$$

Furthermore, given an equation of a conic section in general form, we can complete the square to identify the type of conic section that the equation represents. In some cases, however, the graph of an equation in general form is a **degenerate conic section.** Geometrically, a degenerate conic section occurs when a plane intersects a double-napped cone in a point, a line, or a pair of intersecting lines (Figure 7-26).

Figure 7-26

General Equation of a Conic Section

The graph of the equation $Ax^2 + Cy^2 + Dx + Ey + F = 0$, where A and C are not both zero, is a conic section or a degenerate conic. If the graph represents a conic section, then we have the following cases:

1. The graph is a circle if $A = C$.
2. The graph is an ellipse if A and C have the same sign.
3. The graph is a hyperbola if A and C have opposite signs.
4. The graph is a parabola if A or C is zero.

For Exercises 9–16, determine whether the equation represents a circle, an ellipse, a hyperbola, or a parabola. Write the equation in standard form.

9. $9x^2 - 16y^2 - 36x - 64y - 172 = 0$

10. $9x^2 + 25y^2 - 100y - 125 = 0$

11. $y^2 - 10y + x + 27 = 0$

12. $x^2 + y^2 - 6x + 14y + 33 = 0$

13. $16x^2 + y^2 + 32x = 0$

14. $x^2 - 2x - 10y - 29 = 0$

15. $x^2 + y^2 + 2x + 12y + 21 = 0$

16. $-144x^2 + 25y^2 - 1152x - 50y - 5879 = 0$

For Exercises 17–22, an equation of a degenerate conic section is given. Complete the square and describe the graph of each equation.

17. $x^2 + y^2 - 4x + 2y + 5 = 0$

18. $9x^2 + 4y^2 - 24y + 36 = 0$

19. $4x^2 - y^2 - 32x - 4y + 60 = 0$

20. $9x^2 - 4y^2 - 90x - 8y + 221 = 0$

21. $9x^2 + 4y^2 - 16y + 52 = 0$

22. $x^2 + y^2 + 12x + 37 = 0$

CHAPTER 7 KEY CONCEPTS

	Reference
SECTION 7.1 The Ellipse	
An **ellipse** is the set of all points (x, y) in a plane such that the sum of the distances between (x, y) and two fixed points is a constant. The fixed points are called the **foci** of the ellipse.	p. 662
Standard forms of an equation of an ellipse:	p. 667
• Major axis horizontal: Equation: $\dfrac{(x - h)^2}{a^2} + \dfrac{(y - k)^2}{b^2} = 1 \qquad a > b > 0; c^2 = a^2 - b^2 \, (c > 0)$ Center: (h, k) Vertices: $(h + a, k), (h - a, k)$ Foci: $(h + c, k), (h - c, k)$ Minor axis endpoints: $(h, k + b), (h, k - b)$ • Major axis vertical: Equation: $\dfrac{(x - h)^2}{b^2} + \dfrac{(y - k)^2}{a^2} = 1 \qquad a > b > 0; c^2 = a^2 - b^2 \, (c > 0)$ Center: (h, k) Vertices: $(h, k + a), (h, k - a)$ Foci: $(h, k + c), (h, k - c)$ Minor axis endpoints: $(h + b, k), (h - b, k)$	
$2a$ is the length of the major axis. $2b$ is the length of the minor axis.	p. 663
The **eccentricity** $e = \frac{c}{a}$ of an ellipse measures the degree of elongation. Note that for an ellipse, $0 < e < 1$.	p. 670
SECTION 7.2 The Hyperbola	Reference
A **hyperbola** is the set of all points (x, y) in a plane such that the difference in distances between (x, y) and two fixed points (foci) is a positive constant.	p. 677
Standard forms of an equation of a hyperbola:	p. 681
• Transverse axis horizontal: Equation: $\dfrac{(x - h)^2}{a^2} - \dfrac{(y - k)^2}{b^2} = 1 \qquad a > 0, b > 0; c^2 = a^2 + b^2 \, (c > 0)$ Center: (h, k) Vertices: $(h + a, k), (h - a, k)$ Foci: $(h + c, k), (h - c, k)$ Asymptotes: $y - k = \pm\frac{b}{a}(x - h)$ • Transverse axis vertical: Equation: $\dfrac{(y - k)^2}{a^2} - \dfrac{(x - h)^2}{b^2} = 1 \qquad a > 0, b > 0; c^2 = a^2 + b^2 \, (c > 0)$ Center: (h, k) Vertices: $(h, k + a), (h, k - a)$ Foci: $(h, k + c), (h, k - c)$ Asymptotes: $y - k = \pm\frac{a}{b}(x - h)$	
$2a$ is the length of the transverse axis. $2b$ is the length of the conjugate axis.	p. 679
The **eccentricity** of a hyperbola is given by $e = \frac{c}{a}$. Note that for a hyperbola, $e > 1$.	p. 685

SECTION 7.3 The Parabola	Reference
A **parabola** is the set of all points in a plane that are equidistant from a fixed line (called the **directrix**) and a fixed point (called the **focus**).	p. 692

Standard forms of an equation of a parabola:
• Vertical axis of symmetry:
  Equation: $(x - h)^2 = 4p(y - k)$
  Vertex: (h, k)
  Focus: $(h, k + p)$
  Directrix: $y = k - p$
  Axis of symmetry: $x = h$
 	
• Horizontal axis of symmetry:
  Equation: $(y - k)^2 = 4p(x - h)$
  Vertex: (h, k)
  Focus: $(h + p, k)$
  Directrix: $x = h - p$
  Axis of symmetry: $y = k$
	p. 696

The value of $|p|$ is the focal length (distance between the vertex and focus).	p. 693
The **latus rectum** is the line segment perpendicular to the axis of symmetry, through the focus, with endpoints on the parabola.	p. 694
The value of $4|p|$ is the focal diameter (length of the latus rectum).	p. 694

Expanded Chapter Summary available at www.mhhe.com/millerca.

CHAPTER 7   Review Exercises

SECTION 7.1

1. How are the graphs of these ellipses similar and how are they different?

$$\frac{x^2}{100} + \frac{y^2}{225} = 1 \qquad \frac{(x - 1)^2}{100} + \frac{(y + 7)^2}{225} = 1$$

For Exercises 2–5, an equation of an ellipse is given.

a. Identify the center.
b. Identify the vertices.
c. Identify the endpoints of the minor axis.
d. Identify the foci.
e. Determine the eccentricity.
f. Graph the ellipse.

2. $\dfrac{x^2}{289} + \dfrac{y^2}{64} = 1$ 3. $15x^2 + 9y^2 = 135$

4. $\dfrac{(x + 1)^2}{9} + \dfrac{(y - 4)^2}{25} = 1$ 5. $\dfrac{(x - 1)^2}{16} + \dfrac{(y - 2)^2}{9} = 1$

For Exercises 6–7,

a. Write the equation of the ellipse in standard form.
b. Identify the center, vertices, endpoints of the minor axis, and foci.

6. $5x^2 + 8y^2 + 40x - 16y + 48 = 0$
7. $100x^2 + 64y^2 - 100x - 1575 = 0$

For Exercises 8–10, write the standard form of an equation of the ellipse subject to the given conditions.

8. Vertices: $(4, 0)$ and $(-4, 0)$;
   Foci: $\left(\sqrt{11}, 0\right)$ and $\left(-\sqrt{11}, 0\right)$

9. Endpoints of minor axis: $(0, 1)$ and $(6, 1)$;
   Foci: $(3, 5)$ and $(3, -3)$

10. Minor axis parallel to x-axis; Center: $(2, -4)$;
    Length of major axis: 20 units;
    Length of minor axis: 12 units

11. Suppose that one ellipse has an eccentricity of $\frac{4}{7}$ and a second ellipse has an eccentricity of $\frac{5}{7}$. Which ellipse is more elongated?

12. Jupiter orbits the Sun in an elliptical path with the Sun at one focus. At perihelion, Jupiter is closest to the Sun at 7.4052×10^8 km. If the eccentricity of the orbit is 0.0489, determine the distance at aphelion (farthest point between Jupiter and the Sun). Round to the nearest million km.

13. A bridge over a gorge is supported by an arch in the shape of a semiellipse. The length of the bridge is 400 ft and the maximum height is 100 ft. Find the height of the arch 50 ft from the center. Round to the nearest foot.

14. Solve the system of equations.

$$\frac{x^2}{25} + \frac{y^2}{16} = 1$$
$$4x + 5y = 20$$

SECTION 7.2

For Exercises 15–16, an equation of a hyperbola is given. Determine whether the transverse axis is horizontal or vertical.

15. $\dfrac{x^2}{11} - \dfrac{y^2}{16} = 1$ **16.** $-\dfrac{x^2}{11} + \dfrac{y^2}{16} = 1$

For Exercises 17–20, an equation of a hyperbola is given.

a. Identify the center.

b. Identify the vertices.

c. Identify the foci.

d. Write equations for the asymptotes.

e. Graph the hyperbola.

17. $\dfrac{x^2}{9} - \dfrac{y^2}{4} = 1$ **18.** $-3x^2 + 2y^2 = 18$

19. $-\dfrac{(x+3)^2}{16} + \dfrac{(y-2)^2}{9} = 1$

20. $\dfrac{(x-1)^2}{4} - (y+5)^2 = 1$

For Exercises 21–22,

a. Write the equation of the hyperbola in standard form.

b. Identify the center, vertices, and foci.

21. $11x^2 - 7y^2 + 44x - 56y - 145 = 0$

22. $-9x^2 + y^2 + 2y - 8 = 0$

For Exercises 23–25, write the standard form of an equation of a hyperbola subject to the given conditions.

23. Vertices: $(4, 0)$, $(-4, 0)$;
Foci: $(5, 0)$, $(-5, 0)$

24. Vertices $(0, 13)$, $(0, -11)$;
Slope of asymptotes: $\pm\frac{12}{5}$

25. Corners of reference rectangle:
$(19, 15)$, $(19, -1)$, $(-15, -1)$, $(-15, 15)$;
Horizontal transverse axis

26. Suppose that one hyperbola has an eccentricity of $\frac{41}{40}$ and a second hyperbola has an eccentricity of $\frac{41}{9}$. For which hyperbola do the branches open "wider?"

27. Solve the system of equations.

$$6x^2 - 2y^2 = -12$$
$$2x^2 + y^2 = 11$$

28. Suppose that two people standing 2 mi (10,560 ft) apart at points A and B hear a car backfire. The time difference between the sound heard at point A and the sound heard at point B is 8 sec. If sound travels 1100 ft/sec, find an equation of the hyperbola (with foci at A and B) on which the point of origination of the sound must lie.

SECTION 7.3

For Exercises 29–32, an equation of a parabola is given in standard form.

a. Determine the value of p.

b. Identify the vertex.

c. Identify the focus.

d. Determine the focal diameter.

e. Determine the endpoints of the latus rectum.

f. Write an equation of the directrix.

g. Write an equation for the axis of symmetry.

h. Graph the parabola.

29. $x^2 = -2y$ **30.** $\dfrac{1}{10}y^2 = 2x$

31. $(y+2)^2 = -4(x-3)$ **32.** $\left(x - \frac{1}{2}\right)^2 = 6(y - 3)$

For Exercises 33–34, an equation of a parabola is given.

a. Write the equation of the parabola in standard form.

b. Identify the vertex, focus, and directrix.

33. $x^2 - 10x - 4y + 17 = 0$

34. $4y^2 - 12y + 56x + 177 = 0$

For Exercises 35–37, fill in the blank. Let $|p|$ represent the focal length (distance between the vertex and focus).

35. If the directrix of a parabola is given by $y = 3$ and the focus is $(4, 1)$, then the vertex is given by the ordered pair _____, and the value of p is _____.

36. If the vertex of a parabola is $(10, -4)$ and the focus is $(2, -4)$, then the directrix is given by the equation _____, and the value of p is _____.

37. If the focal diameter of a parabola is 12 units, then the focal length is _____ units.

For Exercises 38–40, determine the standard form of the parabola subject to the given conditions.

38. Vertex: (3, 2); Directrix: $x = 5$

39. Vertex: $(-4, 7)$; Focus $(-4, -1)$

40. Focus: $(0, -3)$; Directrix: $y = -6$

41. Solve the system of equations.

$$(y + 2)^2 = 3(x - 5)$$
$$x - y = 7$$

42. The longest span of the Brooklyn Bridge is suspended from cables supported by two towers approximately 1596 ft apart. The top of each cable is approximately 142 ft above the road. Assuming that the cables are parabolic and are at road level halfway between the towers, find the height of the cables above the roadway 200 ft from either end. Round to the nearest foot.

CHAPTER 7   Test

1. How are the graphs of these ellipses similar, and how are they different?

$$\frac{x^2}{36} + \frac{y^2}{144} = 1 \qquad \frac{x^2}{144} + \frac{y^2}{36} = 1$$

2. Write the standard form of an equation of a circle with center (h, k) and radius r.

3. Write the standard form of an equation of an ellipse with center (h, k) and major axis horizontal.

4. Write the standard form of an equation of an ellipse with center (h, k) and major axis vertical.

5. Write the standard form of an equation of a hyperbola with center (h, k) and transverse axis vertical.

6. Write the standard form of an equation of a hyperbola with center (h, k) and transverse axis horizontal.

7. Write the standard form of an equation of a parabola with vertex (h, k) and vertical axis of symmetry.

8. Write the standard form of an equation of a parabola with vertex (h, k) and horizontal axis of symmetry.

For Exercises 9–16,

a. Identify the equation as representing a circle, an ellipse, a hyperbola, or a parabola.

b. Graph the curve.

c. Identify key features of the graph. That is,

- If the equation represents a circle, identify the center and radius.
- If the equation represents an ellipse, identify the center, vertices, endpoints of the minor axis, foci, and eccentricity.
- If the equation represents a hyperbola, identify the center, vertices, foci, equations of the asymptotes, and eccentricity.
- If the equation represents a parabola, identify the vertex, focus, endpoints of the latus rectum, equation of the directrix, and equation of the axis of symmetry.

9. $\dfrac{(x - 2)^2}{9} + \dfrac{y^2}{16} = 1$ **10.** $\dfrac{(x - 2)^2}{9} - \dfrac{y^2}{16} = 1$

11. $\dfrac{(x - 2)^2}{16} + y = 0$

12. $x^2 + y^2 - 4x - 6y + 1 = 0$

13. $-9x^2 + 16y^2 + 64y - 512 = 0$

14. $9x^2 + 25y^2 + 72x - 50y - 731 = 0$

15. $\dfrac{(x + 4)^2}{4} + \dfrac{(y - 1)^2}{4} = 1$ **16.** $y^2 - 8y - 8x + 40 = 0$

17. The entrance to a tunnel is in the shape of a semiellipse over a 24-ft by 8-ft rectangular opening. The height at the center of the opening is 14 ft.

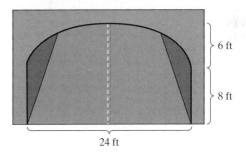

a. Determine the height of the opening at a point 6 ft from the edge of the tunnel. Round to 1 decimal place.

b. Can a 10-ft-high truck pass through the opening if the truck's outer wheel passes at a point 3 ft from the edge of the tunnel?

c. Set up a coordinate system with the origin placed on the ground in the center of the roadway. Write a function that represents the height of the opening $h(x)$ (in ft) as a function of the horizontal distance x (in ft) from the center.

18. Neptune orbits the Sun in an elliptical path with the Sun at one focus. At aphelion, Neptune is farthest from the Sun at 4.546×10^9 km. If the eccentricity of the orbit is 0.0113, determine the distance at perihelion (closest point between Neptune and the Sun). Round to the nearest million km.

19. Suppose that two people standing 1.5 mi (7920 ft) apart at points A and B hear a car accident. The time difference between the sound heard at point A and the sound heard at point B is 6 sec. If sound travels 1100 ft/sec, find an equation of the hyperbola (with foci at A and B) at which the accident occurred.

20. The middle span of the Golden Gate Bridge in San Francisco is supported by cables from two towers 4200 ft apart. The tops of the towers are 500 ft above the roadway. Assuming that the cables are parabolic and are at road level halfway between the towers, find the height of the cables 1000 ft from the center of the bridge. Round to the nearest foot.

21. Write the standard form of an equation of a parabola with focus $(1, 6)$ and directrix $y = -2$.

22. Write the standard form of an equation of an ellipse with vertices $(2, -3)$ and $(6, -3)$ and foci $(3, -3)$ and $(5, -3)$.

23. Write the standard form of an equation of a hyperbola with vertices $(4, -1)$ and $(4, 7)$ and foci $(4, -3)$ and $(4, 9)$.

24. Write the standard form of an equation of a hyperbola with vertices $(-1, -3)$ and $(5, -3)$ and slope of one asymptote $\frac{4}{3}$.

25. If the major axis of an ellipse is 26 units in length and the minor axis is 10 units in length, determine the eccentricity of the ellipse.

26. If the transverse axis of a hyperbola is 20 units and the conjugate axis is 12 units, determine the eccentricity of the hyperbola.

27. If the directrix of a parabola is $x = 2$, and the focus is $(-4, 0)$, determine the focal length and the focal diameter.

28. If the asymptotes of a hyperbola are $y = \frac{3}{5}x + 1$ and $y = -\frac{3}{5}x + 1$, identify the center of the hyperbola.

29. Solve the system of equations.
$$3x^2 - 4y^2 = -13$$
$$5x^2 + 2y^2 = 13$$

30. Describe the graph of the equation.
$$x = -4\sqrt{1 - \frac{y^2}{9}}$$

CHAPTER 7   Cumulative Review Exercises

1. Use long division to divide.
$(3x^4 - 2x^3 - 5x + 1) \div (x^2 + 3)$

2. Is -4 a zero of the polynomial
$f(x) = 3x^4 - 6x^3 + 5x - 12$?

3. Is $(x - 3)$ a factor of $2x^4 - 7x^3 + 8x^2 - 17x + 6$?

For Exercises 4–5, simplify completely.

4. $\dfrac{\sqrt[3]{54x^4}}{\sqrt[3]{2x^5}}$

5. $\left(\dfrac{-2x^2y^{-1}}{z^3}\right)^{-4}\left(\dfrac{4x^{-5}}{y^7}\right)^2$

6. Find the midpoint of the line segment with endpoints $(-362, 147)$ and $(118, 24)$.

7. Given $f(x) = \sqrt[3]{x} - 7$, write an equation defining $f^{-1}(x)$.

8. Write an equation of the line through the points $(1, 8)$ and $(2, -4)$. Write the answer in slope-intercept form.

9. Is function f even, odd, or neither?
$$f(x) = 3|x| + 5x^3$$

For Exercises 10–15, solve the equation or inequality. Write the solution set to the inequalities in interval notation if possible.

10. $e^{3x+2} = 22$

11. $2 - 3\{4 - [x + 2(x - 1) - 3] + 4\} > 0$

12. $21 \le 9 - 2|x + 1|$ 13. $2x^2 - 8x + 3 \ge 0$

14. $\log_3 x + \log_3(x - 6) = 3$ 15. $e^{2x} - 8e^x + 15 = 0$

16. Graph the solution set.
$$x^2 + (y - 1)^2 \le 9$$

17. Graph the solution set. $2x - y < 4$
$$3x + y \le 1$$

18. Find the partial fraction decomposition for
$$\dfrac{8x - 27}{x^2 - 7x + 12}$$

19. Given $f(x) = \dfrac{1}{x - 2}$ and $g(x) = \sqrt{x - 1}$,
    a. Find $(f \circ g)(x)$.
    b. Write the domain of $(f \circ g)(x)$ in interval notation.

20. Given $f(x) = \dfrac{x^2 - 4x}{x + 3}$,

    a. Determine the x-intercept(s) of the graph of f.

    b. Determine the y-intercept.

    c. Find the vertical asymptote(s).

    d. Find the horizontal asymptote.

    e. Find the slant asymptote.

For Exercises 21–24, graph the equations and functions.

21. $\dfrac{x^2}{4} + \dfrac{(y-1)^2}{9} = 1$ **22.** $\dfrac{x^2}{4} - \dfrac{(y-1)^2}{9} = 1$

23. $x^2 = 4(y - 2)$ **24.** $f(x) = \left(\dfrac{1}{2}\right)^x + 2$

For Exercises 25–26, solve the system.

25. $3x - 4y + 2z = 5$
        $5y - 3z = -12$
    $7x \quad\;\; + 2z = 1$

26. $x^2 - 5y^2 = 4$
    $4x^2 + \;\; y^2 = 37$

For Exercises 27–29, refer to the matrices A and B. Simplify each expression.

$$A = \begin{bmatrix} 2 & 4 \\ -1 & 6 \end{bmatrix} \quad B = \begin{bmatrix} -3 & 8 \\ 0 & 4 \end{bmatrix}$$

27. $2AB$ **28.** A^{-1}

29. $|B|$

30. Use Cramer's rule to solve for z.

$$3x - 4y + \;\; z = 3$$
$$2x + 3y \quad\quad = 8$$
$$5y + 8z = 11$$

8

Sequences, Series, Induction, and Probability

Chapter Outline

Have you ever wondered why one individual pays more than another for car insurance? Insurance rates are based on a number of variables including age, gender, Zip code, past driving and claims history, and even grades in school. Insurance companies hire actuaries, special statisticians who analyze data to estimate the probability and cost of accidents for people in various demographic groups. In turn, premiums are established to offset the theoretical cost to cover a customer based on the customer's risk factors.

In this chapter, we study sequences and series, the binomial theorem, and a technique of proof called mathematical induction. We complete the chapter by presenting several methods of counting that will ultimately enable us to calculate simple probabilities. The study of probability is the first step toward unraveling the mystery of car insurance premiums.

SECTION 8.1 **Sequences and Series**

> **TIP** In this text, we address sequences with real-valued terms only.

> **TIP** Lowercase letters such as *a*, *b*, *c*, and so on are often used to represent the terms of a sequence.

1. Write Terms of a Sequence from the *n*th Term

In day-to-day life, we think of a **sequence** as a progression of elements with some order or pattern. For example, suppose that a new college graduate has to choose between two job offers. Job 1 offers $75,000 the first year with a $4000 raise each year thereafter. Job 2 offers $75,000 with a 5% raise each year. The sequences in Table 8-1 represent the salaries for each job as a function of the year number.

Table 8-1

	Year 1	Year 2	Year 3	Year 4	Year 5	Year 6
Job 1	$75,000	$79,000	$83,000	$87,000	$91,000	$95,000
Job 2	$75,000	$78,750	$82,687.50	$86,821.86	$91,162.97	$95,721.12

By studying the two sequences, we see that by year 5, job 2 has a better salary. If we take the *sum* of the first *n* terms of a sequence, we have a **finite series.** The total salary through the first 5 years favors job 1 ($415,000 for job 1 versus $414,422.33 for job 2). However, by the end of year 6, job 2 not only pays more each year, but has a greater total salary for the 6-yr period ($510,143.45 for job 2 versus $510,000 for job 1).

From Table 8-1, we can think of a sequence as a function pairing the year number (a positive integer) with the salary. For this reason, it makes sense to define a sequence mathematically as a function whose domain is the set of positive integers.

Finite and Infinite Sequences

An **infinite sequence** is a function whose domain is the set of positive integers. A **finite sequence** is a function whose domain is the set of the first *n* positive integers.

Although a sequence is defined as a function, we typically do not use function notation to denote the terms of a sequence. Instead, the terms of the sequence are denoted by the letter *a* with a subscript representing the term number. The sequence of salaries for job 1 would be denoted by

term 1
$a_1 = 75{,}000$

term 2
$a_2 = 79{,}000$

term 3
$a_3 = 83{,}000$ and so on.

The notation $a_1 = 75{,}000$ is used in place of function notation $f(1) = 75{,}000$. Likewise $a_2 = 79{,}000$ is used instead of $f(2) = 79{,}000$ and so on. For a positive integer *n*, the value a_n is called the ***n*th term** or **general term** of the sequence. The notation $\{a_n\}$ represents the entire sequence.

$$\{a_n\} = a_1, a_2, a_3, \ldots , a_n, \ldots$$

EXAMPLE 1   **Writing Several Terms of a Sequence**

Write the first four terms of the sequence defined by the nth term.

a. $a_n = 3n^2 - 4$ **b.** $c_n = 9\left(-\frac{1}{3}\right)^n$

Solution:

a. $a_n = 3n^2 - 4$ To find the first four terms, substitute $n = 1, 2, 3,$ and 4.

$a_1 = 3(1)^2 - 4 = -1$
$a_2 = 3(2)^2 - 4 = 8$
$a_3 = 3(3)^2 - 4 = 23$
$a_4 = 3(4)^2 - 4 = 44$ The first four terms are $-1, 8, 23, 44$.

b. $c_n = 9\left(-\frac{1}{3}\right)^n$ To find the first four terms, substitute $n = 1, 2, 3,$ and 4.

$c_1 = 9\left(-\frac{1}{3}\right)^1 = -3$
$c_2 = 9\left(-\frac{1}{3}\right)^2 = 1$
$c_3 = 9\left(-\frac{1}{3}\right)^3 = -\frac{1}{3}$
$c_4 = 9\left(-\frac{1}{3}\right)^4 = \frac{1}{9}$ The first four terms are $-3, 1, -\frac{1}{3}, \frac{1}{9}$.

Skill Practice 1   Write the first four terms of the sequence defined by the nth term.

a. $b_n = 2n + 3$ **b.** $d_n = (-1)^n \cdot n^2$

TECHNOLOGY CONNECTIONS

Displaying Terms of a Sequence

If the nth term of a sequence is known, a seq function on a graphing utility can display a list of terms. Finding the first four terms of the sequence from Example 1(b) is outlined here.

- Select the **MODE** key and highlight SEQ.
- Then access the seq function from the catalog or from the LIST menu and enter the parameters as prompted.
- Paste the seq command on the home screen and select ENTER.

seq(9*(–1/3)^n, n, 1, 4, 1) > Frac

Notice that the terms of the sequence given in Example 1(b) alternate in signs. Such a sequence is called an **alternating sequence**. The alternation in signs can be represented in the nth term by a factor of -1 raised to a variable power that alternates between an even and odd integer. For example:

$a_n = (-1)^n$ odd-numbered terms, negative; even-numbered terms, positive
$b_n = (-1)^{n+1}$ odd-numbered terms, positive; even-numbered terms, negative

Answers
1. a. $5, 7, 9, 11$ **b.** $-1, 4, -9, 16$

Because a sequence is defined only for positive integers, its graph is a discrete set of points (the points are not connected). Compare the graphs of the sequence defined by $a_n = 8\left(\frac{1}{2}\right)^n$ (see Figure 8-1) versus the function defined by $f(x) = 8\left(\frac{1}{2}\right)^x$ (see Figure 8-2).

Figure 8-1

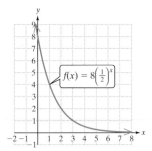

Figure 8-2

The graph of $\{a_n\}$ consists of a discrete set of points that correspond to points on the graph of $f(x) = 8\left(\frac{1}{2}\right)^x$ for positive integers x.

2. Write Terms of a Sequence Defined Recursively

The sequences in Example 1 were defined as a function of the nth term. Now we look at sequences defined *recursively*, using a recursion formula. A **recursion formula** defines the nth term of a sequence as a function of one or more terms preceding it. This is demonstrated in Example 2.

EXAMPLE 2   **Writing Terms of a Sequence Defined Recursively**

Write the first five terms of the sequence defined by $a_1 = 4$ and $a_n = 2a_{n-1} + 1$ for $n > 1$.

Solution:

The first term is given: $a_1 = 4$.

Every term thereafter is defined by $a_n = 2a_{n-1} + 1$

Value of the nth term is   two times the value of the preceding term, plus 1.

$a_1 = 4$

$a_2 = 2a_1 + 1 = 2(4) + 1 = 9$ Substitute $a_1 = 4$.

$a_3 = 2a_2 + 1 = 2(9) + 1 = 19$ Substitute $a_2 = 9$.

$a_4 = 2a_3 + 1 = 2(19) + 1 = 39$ Substitute $a_3 = 19$.

$a_5 = 2a_4 + 1 = 2(39) + 1 = 79$ The first five terms are 4, 9, 19, 39, 79.

Skill Practice 2   Write the first five terms of the sequence defined by:

$c_1 = 5, \; c_n = 3c_{n-1} - 4$

Answer

2. 5, 11, 29, 83, 245

Perhaps the most famous sequence is the Fibonacci sequence, named after the twelfth-century Italian mathematician Leonardo of Pisa (known as Fibonacci). The Fibonacci sequence is defined recursively as

$$a_1 = 1, \quad a_2 = 1, \quad a_n = a_{n-2} + a_{n-1}$$

The first two terms of the Fibonacci sequence are 1, and each term thereafter is the sum of its two predecessors. We have:

Fibonacci sequence: 1, 1, 2, 3, 5, 8, 13, 21, 34, 55, 89, …

Point of Interest

The Fibonacci sequence is of particular interest because it is often observed in nature. For example, male honey bees hatch from eggs that have not been fertilized, so each male honey bee has only 1 parent, a female. A female honey bee hatches from a fertilized egg, so she has two parents: one male and one female. Notice that the number of ancestors for n generations for a male honey bee follows the Fibonacci sequence (Figure 8-3).

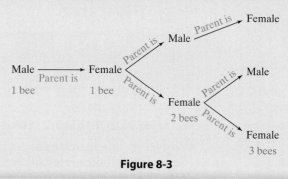

Figure 8-3

3. Use Factorial Notation

We now introduce factorial notation to denote the product of the first n positive integers.

Definition of $n!$

- Let n be a positive integer. The expression $n!$ (read as "n factorial") is defined as $n! = (n)(n-1)(n-2) \cdots (2)(1)$
- For $n = 0$, we define $0! = 1$.

Examples: $0! = 1$ $4! = 4 \cdot 3 \cdot 2 \cdot 1 = 24$
          $1! = 1$ $5! = 5 \cdot 4 \cdot 3 \cdot 2 \cdot 1 = 120$
          $2! = 2 \cdot 1 = 2$ $6! = 6 \cdot 5 \cdot 4 \cdot 3 \cdot 2 \cdot 1 = 720$
          $3! = 3 \cdot 2 \cdot 1 = 6$ $7! = 7 \cdot 6 \cdot 5 \cdot 4 \cdot 3 \cdot 2 \cdot 1 = 5040$

EXAMPLE 3   Evaluating Expressions with Factorial Notation

Evaluate.

a. $\dfrac{8!}{3! \cdot 5!}$ **b.** $\dfrac{n!}{(n+2)!}$

Solution:

a. $\dfrac{8!}{3! \cdot 5!} = \dfrac{8 \cdot 7 \cdot \overset{1}{6} \cdot \overset{1}{5!}}{(\overset{1}{3} \cdot \overset{1}{2} \cdot 1)(5!)} = 56$

b. $\dfrac{n!}{(n+2)!} = \dfrac{\overset{1}{n!}}{(n+2)(n+1)(n!)} = \dfrac{1}{(n+2)(n+1)}$

Skill Practice 3   Evaluate.

a. $\dfrac{9!}{2! \cdot 7!}$ **b.** $\dfrac{(n-1)!}{n!}$

In Example 4, we find a specific term of a sequence in which the expression for the nth term contains factorial notation.

EXAMPLE 4   **Finding a Specific Term of a Sequence**

Given the sequence defined by $b_n = \dfrac{n^2}{(n+1)!}$, find b_6.

Solution:

$$b_n = \dfrac{n^2}{(n+1)!} \xrightarrow[\text{6 for } n.]{\text{Substitute}} b_6 = \dfrac{(6)^2}{(6+1)!} = \dfrac{36}{7!} = \dfrac{36}{7 \cdot 6 \cdot 5 \cdot 4 \cdot 3 \cdot 2 \cdot 1} = \dfrac{1}{140}$$

Skill Practice 4   Given the sequence defined by $c_n = \dfrac{2^n}{(n+1)!}$, find c_4.

4. Use Summation Notation

Consider an infinite sequence $\{a_n\} = a_1, a_2, a_3, \ldots$. The sum S of such a sequence is called an **infinite series** and is represented by $S = a_1 + a_2 + a_3 + \cdots$. The sum of the first n terms of the sequence is called the **nth partial sum** of the sequence and is denoted by S_n. The nth partial sum of a sequence is a **finite series.**

In mathematics, the Greek letter Σ (sigma) is used to represent summations.

Summation Notation

Given a sequence $a_1, a_2, a_3, \ldots$, the nth partial sum S_n is a finite series and is represented by

> n is the upper limit of summation.

$$S_n = \sum_{i=1}^{n} a_i = a_1 + a_2 + a_3 + \cdots + a_n$$

> i is the index of summation.

> 1 is the lower limit of summation.

The sum of *all* terms in the sequence is an infinite series and is given by

$$\sum_{i=1}^{\infty} a_i = a_1 + a_2 + a_3 + \cdots$$

TIP   The summation $\displaystyle\sum_{i=1}^{n} a_i$ is read as the sum of a_i for i equals 1 to n.

Any letter such as i, j, k, and n may be used for the index of summation. However, if i is used for the index of summation, do not confuse it with the imaginary number $i = \sqrt{-1}$.

Answers

3. a. 36   **b.** $\dfrac{1}{n}$ **4.** $\dfrac{2}{15}$

EXAMPLE 5   **Using Summation Notation**

Write the terms for each series and evaluate the sum.

a. $\displaystyle\sum_{i=1}^{5}(2i+3)$ **b.** $\displaystyle\sum_{k=3}^{6}(-1)^k\left(\frac{1}{k}\right)$ **c.** $\displaystyle\sum_{n=1}^{6}3$

Solution:

a.
$$\sum_{i=1}^{5}(2i+3) = \overset{i=1}{[2(1)+3]} + \overset{i=2}{[2(2)+3]} + \overset{i=3}{[2(3)+3]} + \overset{i=4}{[2(4)+3]} + \overset{i=5}{[2(5)+3]}$$
$$= 5 + 7 + 9 + 11 + 13$$
$$= 45$$

b.
$$\sum_{k=3}^{6}(-1)^k\left(\frac{1}{k}\right) = \left[(-1)^3\left(\frac{1}{3}\right)\right] + \left[(-1)^4\left(\frac{1}{4}\right)\right] + \left[(-1)^5\left(\frac{1}{5}\right)\right] + \left[(-1)^6\left(\frac{1}{6}\right)\right]$$
$$= -\frac{1}{3} + \frac{1}{4} - \frac{1}{5} + \frac{1}{6}$$
$$= -\frac{7}{60}$$

c.
$$\sum_{n=1}^{6}3 = \underbrace{3+3+3+3+3+3}_{6 \text{ terms}} = 18$$

Skill Practice 5   Evaluate the sum.

a. $\displaystyle\sum_{i=1}^{5}(3i+1)$ **b.** $\displaystyle\sum_{n=2}^{5}(-1)^{n+1}\frac{1}{2^n}$ **c.** $\displaystyle\sum_{k=1}^{5}4$

TECHNOLOGY CONNECTIONS

Evaluating a Finite Series

A graphing utility can be used to evaluate a finite series if the nth term of the corresponding sequence is known. The Σ symbol can be accessed by selecting ALPHA F2.

- If the calculator is in "Classic" mode, the sum can be evaluated by entering

  Σ (nth term, variable, lower limit, upper limit)

- If the calculator is in "Mathprint" mode, then the user is prompted to enter the nth term, the variable, and limits of summation in text fields.

Answers
5. a. 50   **b.** $-\dfrac{5}{32}$ **c.** 20

Point of Interest

Swiss mathematician and physicist Loenhard Euler (1707–1783) is credited with the use of the modern symbol Σ to represent a sum, i to represent the imaginary unit, and e to represent the base of the natural logarithmic function.

It is important to note that the lower limit of summation need not be 1. In Example 5(b) for instance, the index of summation ranges from 3 to 6. In fact, sometimes we adjust the limits of summation and the expression being summed to write the summation in a more convenient form. For example, the following three series are all equivalent.

$$\sum_{i=1}^{5} 3i = 3(1) + 3(2) + 3(3) + 3(4) + 3(5)$$
$$= 3 + 6 + 9 + 12 + 15 = 45$$

$$\sum_{j=0}^{4} 3(j + 1) = 3(0 + 1) + 3(1 + 1) + 3(2 + 1) + 3(3 + 1) + 3(4 + 1)$$
$$= 3 + 6 + 9 + 12 + 15 = 45$$

$$\sum_{k=2}^{6} 3(k - 1) = 3(2 - 1) + 3(3 - 1) + 3(4 - 1) + 3(5 - 1) + 3(6 - 1)$$
$$= 3 + 6 + 9 + 12 + 15 = 45$$

EXAMPLE 6   Write a Series Using Summation Notation

Write each sum using summation notation.

a. $\dfrac{\sqrt{3}}{1!} + \dfrac{\sqrt{4}}{2!} + \dfrac{\sqrt{5}}{3!} + \cdots + \dfrac{\sqrt{n + 2}}{n!}$ **b.** $\dfrac{2}{1} - \dfrac{3}{4} + \dfrac{4}{9} - \dfrac{5}{16} + \dfrac{6}{25}$

Solution:

a. $\dfrac{\sqrt{3}}{1!} + \dfrac{\sqrt{4}}{2!} + \dfrac{\sqrt{5}}{3!} + \cdots + \dfrac{\sqrt{n + 2}}{n!}$ The series consists of n terms where a formula for the nth term is given.

$$= \sum_{i=1}^{n} \dfrac{\sqrt{i + 2}}{i!}$$

We have used n as the upper limit of summation. Therefore, use a different variable for the index of summation. We have chosen i.

b.

Look for a relationship between the term number and the values in the numerator and denominator. Choose a variable such as i for the index of summation.

Term: 1   2   3   4   5

$$\dfrac{2}{1} - \dfrac{3}{4} + \dfrac{4}{9} - \dfrac{5}{16} + \dfrac{6}{25} \longleftarrow$$ The numerator is 1 more than the term number: $(i + 1)$

$\longleftarrow$ The denominator is the square of the term number: i^2

$$\sum_{i=1}^{5} (-1)^{i+1} \cdot \dfrac{i + 1}{i^2}$$

The odd-numbered terms are positive. This can be generated by the factor $(-1)^{i+1}$.

Skill Practice 6   Write each sum using summation notation.

a. $\dfrac{2!}{7} + \dfrac{3!}{14} + \dfrac{4!}{21} + \cdots + \dfrac{(n + 1)!}{7n}$ **b.** $-\dfrac{1}{5} + \dfrac{8}{25} - \dfrac{27}{125} + \dfrac{64}{625}$

Several important properties of summation are given in Table 8-2.

Table 8-2   Properties of Summation

If $\{a_n\}$ and $\{b_n\}$ are sequences, and c is a real number, then:

1. $\displaystyle\sum_{i=1}^{n} c = cn$ Adding a constant c a total of n times equals cn.

2. $\displaystyle\sum_{i=1}^{n} ca_i = c \sum_{i=1}^{n} a_i$ A constant factor can be factored out of a summation.

3. $\displaystyle\sum_{i=1}^{n} (a_i \pm b_i) = \sum_{i=1}^{n} a_i \pm \sum_{i=1}^{n} b_i$ A single sum or difference can be regrouped as two sums or differences.

Answers

6. a. $\displaystyle\sum_{i=1}^{n} \dfrac{(i + 1)!}{7i}$ **b.** $\displaystyle\sum_{i=1}^{4} (-1)^i \dfrac{i^3}{5^i}$

The proof of Property 2 follows from the distributive property of real numbers.

$$\sum_{i=1}^{n} ca_i = ca_1 + ca_2 + ca_3 + \cdots + ca_n \qquad \text{Expand the terms in the series.}$$

$$= c(a_1 + a_2 + a_3 + \cdots + a_n) \qquad \text{Apply the distributive property.}$$

$$= c\sum_{i=1}^{n} a_i \qquad \text{Write the sum using summation notation.}$$

The proofs of properties 1 and 3 are examined in Exercises 89 and 90.

SECTION 8.1   Practice Exercises

Concept Connections

1. An infinite _____ is a function whose domain is the set of positive integers. A _____ sequence is a function whose domain is the set of the first n positive integers.

2. The expression a_n is called the _____ term or general term of a sequence.

3. An _____ sequence is a sequence in which consecutive terms alternate in sign.

4. A _____ formula defines the nth term of a sequence as a function of one or more terms preceding it.

5. For $n \geq 1$, the expression _____ represents the product of the first n positive integers $n(n-1)(n-2) \cdots (2)(1)$. For $n = 0$, we have $0! = $ _____.

6. Given an infinite sequence $\{a_n\} = a_1, a_2, a_3, \ldots$, the sum of the terms of the sequence is called an infinite _____. The notation S_n is called the nth _____ _____ of the sequence and is called a finite series.

7. Given $\displaystyle\sum_{i=1}^{n} a_i$, the variable i is called the _____ of _____. The value 1 is called the _____ limit of summation. The value n is called the upper _____ of summation.

8. One property of summation indicates that $\displaystyle\sum_{i=1}^{n} c = $ _____.

Objective 1: Write Terms of a Sequence from the nth Term

For Exercises 9–16, the nth term of a sequence is given. Write the first four terms of the sequence. (See Example 1)

9. $a_n = 2n^2 + 3$

10. $b_n = -n^3 + 5$

11. $c_n = 12\left(-\frac{1}{2}\right)^n$

12. $d_n = 64\left(-\frac{1}{4}\right)^n$

13. $a_n = \sqrt{n+3}$

14. $b_n = \sqrt{n-1}$

15. $a_n = e^{3\ln n}$

16. $c_n = \ln e^{2n}$

17. If the nth term of a sequence is $(-1)^n n^2$, which terms are positive and which are negative?

18. If the nth term of a sequence is $(-1)^{n+1}\dfrac{1}{n}$, which terms are positive and which are negative?

For Exercises 19–22, the nth term of a sequence is given. Find the indicated term.

19. $a_n = 2^n - 1$; find a_{10}

20. $b_n = \dfrac{5}{n} - 1$; find b_{20}

21. $c_n = 5n - 4$; find c_{157}

22. $d_n = 6n + 7$; find d_{204}

For Exercises 23–26, match the sequence or function with its graph.

23. $a_n = \sqrt{n}$

24. $f(x) = \sqrt{x}$

25. $f(x) = \dfrac{3}{x}$

26. $a_n = \dfrac{3}{n}$

a.

b.

c.

d.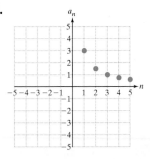

Objective 2: Write Terms of a Sequence Defined Recursively

For Exercises 27–32, write the first five terms of the sequence defined recursively. (See Example 2)

27. $b_1 = -3$; $b_n = 3b_{n-1} + 4$

28. $a_1 = 11$; $a_n = 4a_{n-1} + 3$

29. $c_1 = 4$; $c_n = \frac{1}{2}c_{n-1} + 4$

30. $d_1 = 30$; $d_n = \frac{1}{3}d_{n-1} - 1$

31. $a_1 = 5$; $a_n = \dfrac{1}{a_{n-1}}$

32. $b_1 = 10$; $b_n = -\dfrac{1}{b_{n-1}}$

33. a. Write the first 10 terms of the Fibonacci sequence.

   b. The formula $F_n = \dfrac{1}{\sqrt{5}}\left(\dfrac{1+\sqrt{5}}{2}\right)^n - \dfrac{1}{\sqrt{5}}\left(\dfrac{1-\sqrt{5}}{2}\right)^n$ gives the nth term of the Fibonacci sequence. Use a calculator to verify this statement for $n = 1$, $n = 2$, and $n = 3$.

34. The numbers in the sequence defined by $a_1 = 1$, $a_2 = 3$, and $a_n = a_{n-1} + a_{n-2}$ for $n \geq 3$ are referred to as Lucas numbers in honor of French mathematician Edouard Lucas (1842–1891).

   a. Find the first eight Lucas numbers.

   b. The formula $L_n = \left(\dfrac{1+\sqrt{5}}{2}\right)^n + \left(\dfrac{1-\sqrt{5}}{2}\right)^n$ gives the nth Lucas number. Use a calculator to verify this statement for $n = 1$, $n = 2$, and $n = 3$.

Objective 3: Use Factorial Notation

For Exercises 35–46, evaluate the expression. (See Example 3)

35. $7!$

36. $8!$

37. $0!$

38. $1!$

39. $\dfrac{8!}{6!}$

40. $\dfrac{12!}{9!}$

41. $\dfrac{9!}{5! \cdot 4!}$

42. $\dfrac{10!}{6! \cdot 4!}$

43. $\dfrac{(n-1)!}{(n+1)!}$

44. $\dfrac{(n-2)!}{n!}$

45. $\dfrac{(2n)!}{(2n+1)!}$

46. $\dfrac{(2n-1)!}{(2n)!}$

For Exercises 47–50, the nth term of a sequence is given. Find the indicated term. (See Example 4)

47. $a_n = \dfrac{2^n}{(n+2)!}$; find a_5

48. $b_n = \dfrac{4n}{(n+1)!}$; find b_3

49. $c_n = \dfrac{(3n)!}{5n}$; find c_3

50. $d_n = \dfrac{(n+3)!}{3^n}$; find d_3

Objective 4: Use Summation Notation

For Exercises 51–64, find the sum. (See Example 5)

51. $\displaystyle\sum_{i=1}^{6}(3i-4)$

52. $\displaystyle\sum_{i=1}^{5}(2i+7)$

53. $\displaystyle\sum_{j=1}^{5}(-2j^2)$

54. $\displaystyle\sum_{k=1}^{3}(-3k^3)$

55. $\displaystyle\sum_{j=2}^{5}\left(\dfrac{1}{2}\right)^j$

56. $\displaystyle\sum_{n=2}^{4}\left(\dfrac{1}{3}\right)^n$

57. $\displaystyle\sum_{j=1}^{20}6$

58. $\displaystyle\sum_{i=1}^{50}4$

59. $\displaystyle\sum_{k=3}^{7}(-1)^k(6k)$

60. $\displaystyle\sum_{n=3}^{8}(-1)^{n-1}(2n)$

61. $\displaystyle\sum_{m=1}^{3}\dfrac{m+1}{m}$

62. $\displaystyle\sum_{n=1}^{4}\dfrac{n-1}{n}$

63. $\displaystyle\sum_{k=1}^{3}(k+2)(k+3)$

64. $\displaystyle\sum_{j=1}^{4}(j+1)(j-1)$

65. a. Evaluate $\displaystyle\sum_{i=1}^{n} (-1)^i$ if n is even.

b. Evaluate $\displaystyle\sum_{i=1}^{n} (-1)^i$ if n is odd.

66. a. Evaluate $\displaystyle\sum_{i=1}^{n} (-1)^{i+1}$ if n is even.

b. Evaluate $\displaystyle\sum_{i=1}^{n} (-1)^{i+1}$ if n is odd.

67. Given the sequence defined by $a_n = n^2 - 2n$, find the fifth partial sum.

68. Given the sequence defined by $b_n = n^3 - 3n^2$, find the fourth partial sum.

For Exercises 69–74, write an expression for the apparent nth term a_n for the sequence. For example, given $\frac{4}{5}, \frac{5}{10}, \frac{6}{15}, \frac{7}{20}, \frac{8}{25}, \ldots$, then $a_n = \frac{n+3}{5n}$.

69. 2, 4, 8, 16, 32, ...

70. 3, 9, 27, 81, 243, ...

71. $-\dfrac{2}{3}, -\dfrac{3}{6}, -\dfrac{4}{9}, -\dfrac{5}{12}, -\dfrac{6}{15}, \ldots$

72. $-\dfrac{8}{11}, -\dfrac{9}{22}, -\dfrac{10}{33}, -\dfrac{11}{44}, -\dfrac{12}{55}, \ldots$

73. $-1, 4, -9, 16, -25, \ldots$

74. $1, -8, 27, -64, 125, \ldots$

For Exercises 75–86, write the sum using summation notation. There may be multiple representations. Use i as the index of summation. (See Example 6)

75. $\dfrac{1}{2} + \dfrac{4}{3} + \dfrac{9}{4} + \dfrac{16}{5} + \cdots + \dfrac{n^2}{n+1}$

76. $3 + \dfrac{1}{2} + \dfrac{5}{27} + \dfrac{3}{32} + \cdots + \dfrac{n+2}{n^3}$

77. $1 + 2 + 3 + 4 + 5$

78. $2 + 4 + 6 + 8 + 10 + 12$

79. $8 + 8 + 8 + 8$

80. $11 + 11 + 11 + 11 + 11$

81. $\dfrac{1}{3} - \dfrac{1}{9} + \dfrac{1}{27} - \dfrac{1}{81}$

82. $-\dfrac{1}{2} + \dfrac{1}{4} - \dfrac{1}{8} + \dfrac{1}{16} - \dfrac{1}{32}$

83. $c^3 + c^4 + c^5 + \cdots + c^{20}$

84. $a + ar + ar^2 + \cdots + ar^{12}$

85. $\dfrac{x}{1} + \dfrac{x^2}{2} + \dfrac{x^3}{6} + \dfrac{x^4}{24}$ (*Hint:* Note the pattern produced by $n!$ for $n = 1$, $n = 2$, and so on.)

86. $\dfrac{1}{x+1} + \dfrac{2}{x+2} + \dfrac{6}{x+3} + \dfrac{24}{x+4} + \dfrac{120}{x+5}$

For Exercises 87–88, rewrite each series as an equivalent series with the new index of summation.

87. $\displaystyle\sum_{i=1}^{8} i^2 = \sum_{j=0}^{\square} \square = \sum_{k=2}^{\square} \square$

88. $\displaystyle\sum_{i=1}^{5} (4i) = \sum_{j=0}^{\square} \square = \sum_{k=2}^{\square} \square$

Mixed Exercises

89. Prove that $\displaystyle\sum_{i=1}^{n} c = cn$.

90. Prove that $\displaystyle\sum_{i=1}^{n} (a_i + b_i) = \sum_{i=1}^{n} a_i + \sum_{i=1}^{n} b_i$.

For Exercises 91–94, use the sums $\displaystyle\sum_{i=1}^{50} i^2 = 42{,}925$ and $\displaystyle\sum_{i=1}^{50} i = 1275$ and the properties of summation given on page 718 to evaluate the given expression.

91. $\displaystyle\sum_{i=1}^{50} (i^2 + 3i)$

92. $\displaystyle\sum_{i=1}^{50} (2i^2 - i)$

93. $\displaystyle\sum_{i=1}^{50} (5i + 4)$

94. $\displaystyle\sum_{i=1}^{50} (6i - 7)$

For Exercises 95–98, determine whether the statement is true or false.

95. $\displaystyle\sum_{i=1}^{n} (3i + 7) = 3\sum_{i=1}^{n} i + 7n$

96. $\displaystyle\sum_{i=1}^{n} (i^2 - 4i + 5) = \sum_{i=1}^{n} i^2 - 4\sum_{i=1}^{n} i + 5n$

97. $\displaystyle\sum_{i=1}^{n} a_i b_i = \sum_{i=1}^{n} a_i \sum_{i=1}^{n} b_i$

98. $\displaystyle\sum_{i=1}^{n} \dfrac{a_i}{b_i} = \dfrac{\displaystyle\sum_{i=1}^{n} a_i}{\displaystyle\sum_{i=1}^{n} b_i}$

99. Expenses for a company for year 1 are \$24,000. Every year thereafter, expenses increase by \$1000 plus 3% of the cost of the prior year. Let a_1 represent the original cost for year 1; that is, $a_1 = 24{,}000$. Use a recursion formula to find the cost a_n in terms of a_{n-1} for each subsequent year, $n \geq 2$.

100. A retirement account initially has \$500,000 and grows by 5% per year. Furthermore, the account owner adds \$12,000 to the account each year thereafter. Let a_1 represent the original amount in the account; that is, $a_1 = 500{,}000$. Use a recursion formula to find the amount in the account a_n in terms of a_{n-1} for each subsequent year, $n \geq 2$.

101. In a business meeting, every person at the meeting shakes every other person's hand exactly one time. The total number of handshakes for n people at the meeting is given by $a_n = \frac{1}{2}n(n-1)$. Evaluate a_{12} and interpret its meaning in the context of this problem.

102. Given a polygon of $n \geq 3$ sides, the sum of the interior angles within the polygon is given by $s_n = 180(n-2)$. Evaluate s_{10} and interpret its meaning in the context of this problem.

Given a sequence $a_1, a_2, a_3, \ldots , a_n$, the **arithmetic mean** $\bar{a}$ is given by $\bar{a} = \dfrac{1}{n}\displaystyle\sum_{i=1}^{n} a_i.$

Use the arithmetic mean for Exercises 103–106.

Number of Atlantic Tropical Systems

103. The number of tropical storms and hurricanes in the Atlantic basin is recorded by year in the graph. (*Source:* NOAA, www.noaa.gov)

   a. Write a sequence representing the number of tropical storms and hurricanes in the Atlantic for year n, where $n = 1$ corresponds to the year 2005.

   b. If the terms of the sequence are represented by a_n, evaluate $\dfrac{1}{6}\displaystyle\sum_{n=1}^{6} a_n$ and interpret its meaning in the context of this problem. Round to 1 decimal place.

104. Consider the sequence defined by $\{a_n\} = 18, 32, 44, 20,$ $36, 28, 32, 38$. Evaluate $\displaystyle\sum_{i=1}^{8} (a_i - \bar{a})^2$.

105. Show that $\displaystyle\sum_{i=1}^{n} (a_i - \bar{a}) = 0$.

Write About It

106. Explain the difference between the graph of $a_n = n^2$ and $f(x) = x^2$.

107. What is the difference between a sequence and a series?

108. Given the sequence defined by $a_n = \frac{n}{n-1}$, explain why the domain must be restricted to positive integers $n \geq 2$.

109. The value 1206! is too large to evaluate on most calculators. Explain how you would evaluate $\frac{1206!}{1204!}$ on a calculator.

Expanding Your Skills

110. For $i = \sqrt{-1}$, find the first eight terms of the sequence defined by $a_n = i^n$.

111. The terms of the sequence defined by $a_1 = x$ and $a_n = \dfrac{1}{2}\left(a_{n-1} + \dfrac{x}{a_{n-1}}\right)$ for $n > 1$ give successively better approximations of $\sqrt{x}$ for $x > 1$. Approximate $\sqrt{2}$ by substituting 2 for x and finding the first four terms of the sequence. Round to 4 decimal places if necessary.

112. Find a formula for the nth term of the sequence. $\sqrt{3}, \sqrt{\sqrt{3}}, \sqrt{\sqrt{\sqrt{3}}}, \ldots$

Technology Connections

For Exercises 113–114, use a graphing utility to find the first four terms of the sequence.

113. $a_n = 12\left(-\frac{1}{2}\right)^n$ (Exercise 11)

114. $a_n = 64\left(-\frac{1}{4}\right)^n$ (Exercise 12)

For Exercises 115–116, use a graphing utility to find the sum.

115. $\displaystyle\sum_{k=3}^{7} (-1)^k (6k)$ (Exercise 59)

116. $\displaystyle\sum_{n=3}^{8} (-1)^{n-1}(2n)$ (Exercise 60)

117. Using calculus, we can show that the series $\displaystyle\sum_{k=0}^{n} \dfrac{1}{k!}$ approaches e as n approaches infinity. Investigate this statement by evaluating the sum for $n = 10$ and $n = 50$.

118. Using calculus, we can show that the series $\displaystyle\sum_{k=1}^{n} (-1)^{k-1}\dfrac{(0.5)^k}{k}$ approaches ln 1.5 as n approaches infinity. Investigate this statement by evaluating the sum for $n = 10$ and $n = 50$.

SECTION 8.2

Arithmetic Sequences and Series

OBJECTIVES

1. Identify Specific and General Terms of an Arithmetic Sequence
2. Evaluate a Finite Arithmetic Series
3. Apply Arithmetic Sequences and Series

1. Identify Specific and General Terms of an Arithmetic Sequence

In this section and Section 8.3, we study two special types of sequences. The first is called an arithmetic sequence. For example, consider the salary plan for a job that pays \$75,000 the first year with a \$4000 raise each year thereafter. The sequence of salaries for the first 5 yr is

Year 1	Year 2	Year 3	Year 4	Year 5
\$75,000	\$79,000	\$83,000	\$87,000	\$91,000

Notice that after the first term, each successive term of the sequence differs from its predecessor by a constant value of \$4000. This is the characteristic that makes this sequence arithmetic.

> **Definition of an Arithmetic Sequence**
>
> An **arithmetic sequence** is a sequence $\{a_n\}$ in which each term after the first differs from its predecessor by a fixed constant d, called the **common difference.** The common difference is $d = a_{n+1} - a_n$.

EXAMPLE 1   **Identifying an Arithmetic Sequence and the Common Difference**

Determine whether the sequence is arithmetic. If so, identify the common difference.

a. 35, 25, 15, 5, −5, …   **b.** 1, 5, 10, 16, 23, …

Solution:

a. 35, 25, 15, 5, −5, …

$a_2 - a_1 = 25 - 35 = -10$ The sequence is arithmetic because the difference
$a_3 - a_2 = 15 - 25 = -10$ between each term and its predecessor is the same
constant.

$a_4 - a_3 = 5 - 15 = -10$ The common difference is $d = -10$.
$a_5 - a_4 = -5 - 5 = -10$

b. 1, 5, 10, 16, 23, …   The sequence is *not* arithmetic because the
$a_2 - a_1 = 5 - 1 = 4$ difference between a_2 and a_1 is different than the
$a_3 - a_2 = 10 - 5 = 5$ difference between a_3 and a_2. That is, the difference
between consecutive terms is not the same.

> **Skill Practice 1**   Determine whether the sequence is arithmetic. If so, identify the common difference.
>
> **a.** 12, 5, −2, −9, −16, …   **b.** 1, 4, 9, 16, 25, …

EXAMPLE 2   **Writing Several Terms of an Arithmetic Sequence**

Write the first five terms of an arithmetic sequence with first term −5 and common difference 4.

Answers

1. a. Arithmetic; $d = -7$
   b. Not arithmetic

Solution:

$$-5, \quad -1, \quad 3, \quad 7, \quad 11$$

Because the common difference is 4, each term after the first must be 4 *more than* its predecessor.

$$+4 \quad +4 \quad +4 \quad +4$$

Skill Practice 2   Write the first four terms of the arithmetic sequence with first term 8 and common difference -3.

If the first term of an arithmetic sequence is a_1, then

$$a_1 = a_1$$
$$a_2 = a_1 + d$$
$$a_3 = a_1 + 2d$$
$$a_4 = a_1 + 3d \quad \text{and so on.}$$

Following this pattern, we have the following formula for the *n*th term of an arithmetic sequence.

---

*n*th Term of an Arithmetic Sequence

The *n*th term of an arithmetic sequence is given by

$$a_n = a_1 + (n - 1)d$$

where a_1 is the first term of the sequence and d is the common difference.

EXAMPLE 3   Applying an Arithmetic Sequence

A park ranger in Everglades National Park measures the water level in one region of the park for a 5-day period during a drought.

Day number	1	2	3	4	5
Water level (in.)	54.0	53.2	52.4	51.6	50.8

a. Based on the given data, does the water level follow an arithmetic progression?

b. Write an expression for the *n*th term of the sequence where *n* represents the day number.

c. Predict the water level on day 30 if this trend continues.

Solution:

a.
$$a_2 - a_1 = 53.2 - 54.0 = -0.8$$
$$a_3 - a_2 = 52.4 - 53.2 = -0.8$$
$$a_4 - a_3 = 51.6 - 52.4 = -0.8$$
$$a_5 - a_4 = 50.8 - 51.6 = -0.8$$

The sequence is arithmetic because the difference between each term and its predecessor is the same constant.

The common difference is $d = -0.8$ in.

b.
$$a_n = a_1 + (n - 1)d$$

Formula for the *n*th term of an arithmetic sequence

$$a_n = 54 + (n - 1)(-0.8)$$

Substitute 54 for a_1 and -0.8 for d.

c.
$$a_{30} = 54 + (30 - 1)(-0.8)$$
$$= 30.8$$

To find a_{30}, substitute 30 for *n*.

The water level on day 30 will be 30.8 in. if this trend continues.

Answer

2. $8, 5, 2, -1$

Year	1	2	3	4
Amount ($)	102.60	108.00	113.40	118.80

a. Do the average monthly electric bills follow an arithmetic progression?
b. Write an expression for the nth term of the sequence.
c. Predict the average monthly bill for year 6 if this trend continues.

The nth term of the sequence from Example 3 can be written in several equivalent algebraic forms.

$$a_n = 54 + (n - 1)(-0.8)$$
$$a_n = 54 - 0.8n + 0.8 \qquad \text{Apply the distributive property.}$$
$$a_n = -0.8n + 54.8$$

The expression $a_n = -0.8n + 54.8$ resembles the slope-intercept form of a linear function $f(x) = mx + b$. In fact, an arithmetic sequence is a linear function whose domain is the set of positive integers. The graph of the sequence from Example 3 is shown in Figure 8-4. The value of the common difference is negative ($d = -0.8$), indicating that the progression of points slopes downward.

In Example 4, we find specific terms of an arithmetic sequence given information about the sequence.

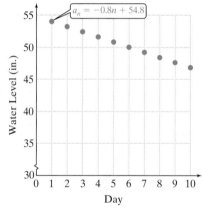

Figure 8-4

EXAMPLE 4   **Finding a Specific Term of an Arithmetic Sequence**

Find the ninth term of the arithmetic sequence in which $a_1 = -4$ and $a_{22} = 164$.

Solution:

To find the value of a_9, we need to determine the common difference d. To find d, substitute $a_1 = -4$, $n = 22$, and $a_{22} = 164$ into the formula for the nth term.

$$a_n = a_1 + (n - 1)d$$
$$164 = -4 + (22 - 1)d$$
$$164 = -4 + 21d$$
$$d = 8$$

Therefore, $a_n = -4 + (n - 1)(8)$.   With the values of a_1 and d known, the nth term is represented by $a_n = -4 + (n - 1)(8)$.

$$a_n = -4 + 8n - 8 \qquad \text{Simplify.}$$
$$a_n = 8n - 12$$
$$a_9 = 8(9) - 12 \qquad \text{To find } a_9 \text{ substitute } n = 9.$$
$$= 60$$

Skill Practice 4   Find the tenth term of the arithmetic sequence in which $a_1 = 12$ and $a_{30} = 128$.

Answers
3. a. Yes
  b. $a_n = 102.6 + (n - 1)(5.4)$
  c. $129.60
4. $a_{10} = 48$

In Example 5, we use the general formula for the nth term of an arithmetic sequence to find the number of terms in an arithmetic sequence.

EXAMPLE 5 **Finding the Number of Terms in an Arithmetic Sequence**

Find the number of terms of the finite arithmetic sequence 7, 3, -1, -5, ... , -113.

Solution:

$a_n = a_1 + (n - 1)d$	The first term of the sequence is 7. The nth term is -113. The common difference is $d = -4$.
$-113 = 7 + (n - 1)(-4)$	To find the number of terms n, substitute $a_1 = 7$,
$-113 = 7 - 4n + 4$	$d = -4$, and $a_n = -113$ into the formula for the
$-113 = 11 - 4n$	nth term.
$4n = 124$	
$n = 31$	There are 31 terms.

Skill Practice 5 Find the number of terms of the finite arithmetic sequence 16, 11, 6, 1, ... , -239.

2. Evaluate a Finite Arithmetic Series

Consider the finite arithmetic sequence 1, 4, 7, 10, 13. The sum of the first n terms of the sequence is called the ***n*th partial sum** and is denoted by S_n. In this case, we have

$$
\begin{aligned}
S_1 &= 1 &&= 1 \\
S_2 &= 1 + 4 &&= 5 \\
S_3 &= 1 + 4 + 7 &&= 12 \\
S_4 &= 1 + 4 + 7 + 10 &&= 22 \\
S_5 &= 1 + 4 + 7 + 10 + 13 &&= 35
\end{aligned}
$$

> **TIP** The sum of the first n terms of an arithmetic sequence is called a **finite arithmetic series.**

For a large number of terms, adding the terms individually would be a cumbersome process, so instead, we observe the following pattern. We write the sum of the first five terms of the sequence in both ascending and descending order.

$$
\begin{aligned}
\text{Ascending order:} \quad S_5 &= \;\;1 + \;\;4 + \;\;7 + 10 + 13 \\
\text{Descending order:} \quad S_5 &= 13 + 10 + \;\;7 + \;\;4 + \;\;1 \\
\hline
2S_5 &= 14 + 14 + 14 + 14 + 14 \quad \text{Now add to get } 2 \cdot S_5. \\
2S_5 &= 5(14) \\
\frac{2S_5}{2} &= \frac{5(14)}{2} = 35 \;\checkmark
\end{aligned}
$$

By adding the terms in ascending and descending order, we double the sum but create a pattern that is easily added. We can use a similar process to find the sum S_n of the first n terms of an arithmetic sequence: $a_1 + a_2 + a_3 + \cdots + a_{n-1} + a_n$.

$$
\begin{aligned}
S_n &= a_1 \quad\;\; + (a_1 + d) + (a_1 + 2d) + \cdots + a_n && \text{Ascending order} \\
S_n &= a_n \quad\;\; + (a_n - d) + (a_n - 2d) + \cdots + a_1 && \text{Descending order} \\
\hline
2S_n &= (a_1 + a_n) + (a_1 + a_n) + (a_1 + a_n) + \cdots + (a_1 + a_n) \\
2S_n &= n(a_1 + a_n) \\
S_n &= \frac{n}{2}(a_1 + a_n)
\end{aligned}
$$

Answer

5. 52 terms

*n*th Partial Sum of an Arithmetic Sequence

The sum S_n of the first n terms of an arithmetic sequence is given by

$$S_n = \frac{n}{2}(a_1 + a_n)$$

where a_1 is the first term of the sequence, and a_n is the nth term of the sequence.

In Example 6, we use the formula for the nth partial sum of an arithmetic sequence to find the sum of the first 50 positive even integers.

EXAMPLE 6   **Finding an *n*th Partial Sum of an Arithmetic Sequence**

Find the sum of the first 50 terms of the sequence. 2, 4, 6, 8, 10, …

Solution:

The sequence is arithmetic because each term is 2 more than its predecessor. The common difference is 2. To find the sum of the first 50 terms, we need to know the values of a_1 and a_{50}. To find a_{50}, we write a formula for the nth term and then evaluate the expression for $n = 50$.

$a_n = a_1 + (n - 1)d$	General expression for the nth term
$a_n = 2 + (n - 1)(2)$	Substitute $a_1 = 2$ and $d = 2$.
$a_n = 2n$	
$a_{50} = 2(50)$	To find a_{50}, substitute 50 for n.
$a_{50} = 100$	
$S_n = \dfrac{n}{2}(a_1 + a_n)$	Now find the sum of the first 50 terms.
$S_{50} = \dfrac{50}{2}(2 + 100)$	Substitute $n = 50$, $a_1 = 2$, and $a_{50} = 100$.
$S_{50} = 2550$	The sum of the first 50 positive even integers is 2550.

Skill Practice 6   Find the sum of the first 50 terms of the sequence. 1, 3, 5, 7, 9, …

Point of Interest

An old story suggests that at the age of 7, Carl Friedrich Gauss (see page 365) amazed his teachers by quickly computing the sum of the first 100 positive integers. Gauss realized that the sum of the integers from 1 to 100, was the same as 50 pairs of numbers each summing to 101. As the story goes, Gauss returned the correct sum of 5050 within minutes by taking the product of 50(101).

Sum of the first 100 positive integers: $1 + 2 + 3 + \cdots + 98 + 99 + 100$

50 pairs, each summing to 101.

In Example 7, we evaluate an arithmetic series written in summation notation.

EXAMPLE 7   Evaluating a Finite Arithmetic Series

Find the sum. $\displaystyle\sum_{i=1}^{60}(3i + 5)$

Solution:

The expression $3i + 5$ is linear in the variable i. This tells us that the terms of the series form an arithmetic progression. To verify, we can write several terms of the sum.

$$\sum_{i=1}^{60}(3i + 5) = [3(1) + 5] + [3(2) + 5] + [3(3) + 5] + \cdots + [3(60) + 5]$$

$$= 8 + 11 + 14 + \cdots + 185$$

The individual terms in the series: 8, 11, 14, ... , 185 form an arithmetic sequence $\{a_n\}$ with a common difference of 3. The first term is $a_1 = 8$, and the 60th term is $a_{60} = 185$. The value of the series is equal to the 60th partial sum of the sequence of terms.

$$S_n = \frac{n}{2}(a_1 + a_n)$$

$$S_{60} = \frac{60}{2}(8 + 185) \qquad \text{Substitute } n = 60, a_1 = 8, \text{ and } a_{60} = 185.$$

$$S_{60} = 5790$$

Skill Practice 7   Find the sum. $\displaystyle\sum_{i=1}^{80}(4i + 3)$

3. Apply Arithmetic Sequences and Series

In Example 8, we use an arithmetic sequence and series in an application.

EXAMPLE 8   Applying an Arithmetic Sequence and Series

Suppose that a job offers a starting salary of $75,000 with a raise of $4000 every year thereafter.

a. Write an expression for the nth term of an arithmetic sequence that represents the salary as a function of the number of years of employment, n.

b. Find the total income for an employee who works at the job for 20 yr.

Solution:

a. $a_n = a_1 + (n - 1)d$

$a_n = 75{,}000 + (n - 1)(4000)$ Substitute $a_1 = 75{,}000$ and $d = 4000$.

$a_n = 75{,}000 + 4000n - 4000$ Simplify.

$a_n = 4000n + 71{,}000$

b. $a_{20} = 75{,}000 + (20 - 1)(4000)$ To find the total income over 20 yr, we need to

$a_{20} = 151{,}000$ know a_1 and a_{20}. Use the nth term to find a_{20}.

$$S_n = \frac{n}{2}(a_1 + a_n)$$

$$S_{20} = \frac{20}{2}(75{,}000 + 151{,}000) \qquad \text{Substitute } n = 20, a_1 = 75{,}000, \text{ and}$$

$$a_{20} = 151{,}000.$$

$$S_{20} = 2{,}260{,}000$$

The total income over 20 yr of employment is $2,260,000.

Answer

7. 13,200

> **Skill Practice 8**   A teaching position has a starting salary of $60,000 with a raise of $3000 every year thereafter.
>
> **a.** Write an expression for the nth term of an arithmetic sequence that represents the salary as a function of the number of years of employment, n.
>
> **b.** Find the total income for an employee who works at the job for 30 yr.

Answers
a. $a_n = 3000n + 57,000$
b. $3,105,000

SECTION 8.2   Practice Exercises

Review Exercises

For Exercises 1–2, a sequence is defined recursively. Find the fourth term.

1. $a_1 = 2;\ a_n = (a_{n-1})^2$

2. $b_1 = 8,\ b_n = \dfrac{1}{b_{n-1}}$

For Exercises 3–4, write a formula for the nth term of the sequence.

3. $\dfrac{5}{3}, \dfrac{10}{9}, \dfrac{15}{27}, \dfrac{20}{81}, \ \cdots$

4. $\dfrac{3}{5}, \dfrac{6}{25}, \dfrac{9}{125}, \dfrac{12}{625}, \ \cdots$

For Exercises 5–6, evaluate the sum.

5. $\displaystyle\sum_{i=1}^{5}(2i^2)$

6. $\displaystyle\sum_{j=1}^{4}\dfrac{6}{j}$

Concept Connections

7. An _____ sequence is a sequence in which each term after the first differs from its predecessor by a fixed constant.

8. The difference between consecutive terms in an arithmetic sequence is called the _____ _____, and is denoted by d.

9. Given an arithmetic sequence with first term a_1 and common difference d, the nth term is represented by the formula $a_n =$ _____.

10. An arithmetic sequence is a linear function whose domain is the set of _____ integers.

11. The sum of the first n terms of a sequence is called the nth _____ sum and is denoted by S_n.

12. Given an arithmetic sequence with first term a_1 and nth term a_n, the nth partial sum is given by the formula $S_n =$ _____.

Objective 1: Identify Specific and General Terms of an Arithmetic Sequence

For Exercises 13–20, determine whether the sequence is arithmetic. If so, find the common difference. (See Example 1)

13. 15, 19, 23, 27, …

14. 256, 268, 280, 292, …

15. 9, −2, −13, −24, …

16. 8, 0, −8, −16, …

17. 18, 22, 27, 33, …

18. 2, 4, 8, 16, …

19. $4, \dfrac{14}{3}, \dfrac{16}{3}, 6, \ \cdots$

20. $3, \dfrac{15}{4}, \dfrac{9}{2}, \dfrac{21}{4}, \ \cdots$

For Exercises 21–24, write the first five terms of an arithmetic sequence $\{a_n\}$, based on the given information about the sequence. (See Example 2)

21. $a_1 = 3,\ d = 10$

22. $a_1 = 6,\ d = 5$

23. $a_1 = 4,\ d = -2$

24. $a_1 = 5,\ d = -3$

For Exercises 25–28,

a. Write an expression for the nth term of the arithmetic sequence $\{a_n\}$ based on the given information. (See Example 3)

b. Find the indicated term.

25. a. $a_1 = -12,\ d = 5$
   b. Find a_{20}.

26. a. $a_1 = -4,\ d = 6$
   b. Find a_{18}.

27. a. $a_1 = \dfrac{1}{2},\ d = \dfrac{1}{3}$
   b. Find a_{10}.

28. a. $a_1 = \dfrac{2}{3},\ d = \dfrac{1}{2}$
   b. Find a_8.

29. Jimmy has 8 unread emails in his inbox before going on vacation. While on vacation, Jimmy does not read email. If he receives an average of 22 emails each day, write the nth term of a sequence defining the number of unread emails in his box at the end of day n of his vacation.

30. Sandy has a personal trainer who encourages her to get plenty of cardiovascular exercise. In her first week of training, Sandy walks for 10 min on a treadmill every day. Each week thereafter, she increases the time on the treadmill by 5 min. Write the nth term of a sequence defining the number of minutes that Sandy spends on the treadmill per day for her nth week at the gym.

31. A new drug and alcohol rehabilitation program performs outreach for members of the community. The number of participants for a 4-week period is given in the table.

Week number	1	2	3	4
Number of participants	34	50	66	82

a. Based on the data given, does the number of participants follow an arithmetic progression?

b. Write an expression for the nth term of the sequence representing the number of participants, where n represents the week number.

c. Predict the number of participants in week 10 if this trend continues.

32. A student studying to be a veterinarian's assistant keeps track of a kitten's weight each week for a 5-week period after birth.

Week number	1	2	3	4	5
Weight (lb)	0.6	0.88	1.16	1.44	1.72

a. Based on the data given, does the weight of the kitten follow an arithmetic progression?

b. Write an expression for the nth term of the sequence representing the kitten's weight, n weeks after birth.

c. If the weight of the kitten continues to increase linearly for 3 months, predit the kitten's weight 12 weeks after birth.

33. Suppose that an object starts with an initial velocity of v_0 (in ft/sec) and moves under a constant acceleration a (in ft/sec^2). Then the velocity v_n (in ft/sec) after n seconds is given by $v_n = v_0 + an$. Show that this sequence is arithmetic. (*Hint*: Show that $v_{n+1} - v_n$ is constant.)

34. Suppose that an object is dropped from rest from an airplane. Assuming negligible air resistance, the vertical acceleration is 32 ft/sec^2. Using the formula for v_n given in Exercise 33,

a. Write the nth term v_n of the sequence representing the velocity in the vertical direction after n seconds.

b. Determine the vertical velocity 1 sec after release and 5 sec after release.

35. The number of people employed in nursing and residential care facilities for the years 2000 and 2010 are given in the graph. (*Source*: Based on data from the U.S. Bureau of Labor Statistics, www.bls.gov)

Number Employed in Nursing and Residential Care Facilities

2583 (2000), 3133 (2010)

Number Employed (1000s) vs. Year

a. Suppose that the number of employees rose linearly from the year 2000 to the year 2010. Let $n = 0$ represent the year 2000 and write a formula for the nth term of an arithmetic sequence representing the number employed as a function of n. In this case, define $\{a_n\}$ with domain $n \geq 0$.

b. Use the sequence in part (a) to estimate the number employed in nursing and residential care facilities in the year 2005.

36. The number of people employed as engineers in the United States for the years 2004 and 2008 are given in the graph. (*Source*: Based on data from the National Science Foundation, www.nsf.gov)

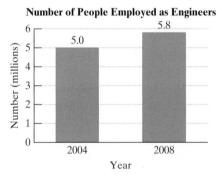

Number of People Employed as Engineers

5.0 (2004), 5.8 (2008)

Number (millions) vs. Year

a. Suppose that the number of engineers rose linearly from the year 2004 to the year 2008. Let $n = 0$ represent the year 2004 and write a formula for the nth term of an arithmetic sequence representing the number of engineers as a function of n. In this case, define $\{a_n\}$ with domain $n \geq 0$.

b. Use the sequence in part (a) to estimate the number of engineers in the year 2006.

37. Find the 8th term of an arithmetic sequence with $a_1 = -2$ and $a_{15} = 68$. (**See Example 4**)

38. Find the 19th term of an arithmetic sequence with $a_1 = -11$ and $a_{30} = 163$.

39. Find the 35th term of an arithmetic sequence with $a_1 = 50$ and $a_{22} = -265$.

40. Find the 46th term of an arithmetic sequence with $a_1 = 210$ and $a_{60} = -262$.

For Exercises 41–44, find the number of terms of the finite arithmetic sequence. (See Example 5)

41. 8, 14, 20, 26, ... , 320

42. 7, 16, 25, 34, ... , 574

43. 11, 10.7, 10.4, 10.1, ... , −3.4

44. 9, 8.4, 7.8, 7.2, ... , −39

45. Given an arithmetic sequence with $a_{14} = 148$ and $a_{35} = 316$, find a_1 and d.

46. Given an arithmetic sequence with $a_{12} = -76$ and $a_{51} = -193$, find a_1 and d.

Objective 2: Evaluate a Finite Arithmetic Series

For Exercises 47–48, find the sum.

47. $4 + 7 + 10 + 13 + 16 + 19 + 22 + 25 + 28 + 31 + 34 + 37$

48. $8 + 12 + 16 + 20 + 24 + 28 + 32 + 36 + 40 + 44$

49. Find the sum of the first 40 terms of the sequence. $\{1, 6, 11, 16, ...\}$ (**See Example 6**)

50. Find the sum of the first 60 terms of the sequence. $\{2, 10, 18, 26, ...\}$

51. Find the sum. $5 + 4.5 + 4 + 3.5 + \cdots + (-30.5)$

52. Find the sum. $8 + 7.2 + 6.4 + 5.6 + \cdots + (-45.6)$

53. If the third and fourth terms of an arithmetic sequence are −6 and −9, what are the first and second terms?

54. If the third and fourth terms of an arithmetic sequence are 12 and 16, what are the first and second terms?

For Exercises 55–64, find the sum. (See Example 7)

55. $\displaystyle\sum_{j=1}^{18} (j + 6)$

56. $\displaystyle\sum_{j=1}^{15} (j - 3)$

57. $\displaystyle\sum_{i=1}^{50} (2i + 6)$

58. $\displaystyle\sum_{i=1}^{40} (3i - 7)$

59. $\displaystyle\sum_{k=1}^{162} \left(3 - \tfrac{1}{2}k\right)$

60. $\displaystyle\sum_{k=1}^{141} \left(4 - \tfrac{1}{4}k\right)$

61. $-1 + 4 + 9 + \cdots + 49$

62. $12 + 16 + 20 + \cdots + 84$

63. $-7 + (-11) + (-15) + \cdots + (-39)$

64. $-18 + (-23) + (-28) + \cdots + (-183)$

Objective 3: Apply Arithmetic Sequences and Series

65. Suzanne must choose between two job offers. The first job offers $64,000 for the first year. Each year thereafter, she would receive a $3200 raise. The second job offers $60,000 in the first year. Each year thereafter, she would receive a $5000 raise. (**See Example 8**)

   a. If she anticipates working for the company for 5 yr, find the total amount she would earn from each job.

   b. If she anticipates working for the company for 10 yr, find the total amount she would earn from each job.

66. José must choose between two job offers. The first job pays $50,000 per year. Each year thereafter, he would receive a raise of $2400. A second job offers $54,000 per year with a raise of $2000 each year thereafter. However, with the second job, José would have to pay $100 per month out of his paycheck for health insurance.

   a. If José anticipates working for the company for 6 yr, find the total amount he would earn from each job.

   b. If he anticipates working for the company for 12 yr, find the total amount he would earn from each job.

67. An object in free fall is dropped from a tall cliff. It falls 16 ft in the 1st second, 48 ft in the 2nd second, 80 ft in the 3rd second, and so on.

   a. Write a formula for the nth term of an arithmetic sequence that represents the distance d_n (in ft) that the object will fall in the nth second.

   b. How far will the object fall in the 8th second?

   c. What is the total distance that the object will fall in 8 sec?

68. A ball rolling down an inclined plane rolls 4 in. in the 1st second, 8 in. in the 2nd second, 12 in. in the 3rd second, and so on.

   a. Write a formula for the nth term of an arithmetic sequence that represents the distance d_n (in inches) that the ball will roll in the nth second.

   b. How far will the ball roll in the 10th second?

   c. What is the total distance that the ball will travel in 10 sec?

69. The students at Prairiewood Elementary plan to make a pyramid out of plastic cups. The bottom row has 15 cups. Moving up the pyramid, the number of cups in each row decreases by 1.

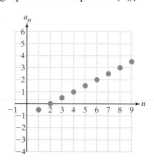

   a. If the students build the pyramid so that there are 15 rows, how many cups will be at the top?

   b. How many total cups will be required?

70. A theater has 32 rows. The first row has 18 seats, and each row that follows has three more seats than the row in front.

   a. Determine the number of seats in row 32.

   b. Determine the total number of seats in the theater.

Mixed Exercises

71. Refer to the graph of the sequence $\{b_n\}$.

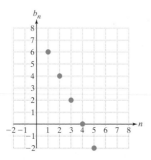

   a. Estimate the first four terms of the sequence.

   b. Write a formula for the nth term of the sequence.

   c. Find the 30th term.

   d. Find the sum of the first 30 terms.

   e. If $b_n = -180$, what is n?

   f. Find the difference between b_{88} and b_{20}.

73. Find the sum of the integers from -20 to 256.

75. Compute the sum of the first 50 positive integers that are exactly divisible by 5.

77. Compute the sum of all integers between 40 and 100 that are exactly divisible by 3.

79. a. Use the formula $S_n = \frac{n}{2}(a_1 + a_n)$ to show that the sum of the first n positive integers is $S_n = \frac{n}{2}(1 + n)$.

   b. Find the sum of the first 100 positive integers.

   c. Find the sum of the first 1000 positive integers.

72. Refer to the graph of the sequence $\{a_n\}$.

   a. Estimate the first four terms of the sequence.

   b. Write a formula for the nth term of the sequence.

   c. Find the 20th term.

   d. Find the sum of the first 20 terms.

   e. If $a_n = 256$, what is n?

   f. Find the difference between a_{50} and a_{32}.

74. Find the sum of the integers from -102 to 57.

76. Compute the sum of the first 60 positive integers that are exactly divisible by 4.

78. Compute the sum of all integers between 60 and 150 that are exactly divisible by 8.

80. a. Use the formula $S_n = \frac{n}{2}(a_1 + a_n)$ to show that the sum 1, 3, 5, ... $(2n - 1) = n^2$.

   b. Find the sum of the first 100 positive odd integers.

The arithmetic mean of two numbers c and d is $\frac{c + d}{2}$. The sequence $c, \frac{c + d}{2}, d$ is an arithmetic sequence. (You can verify this statement by showing that $\frac{c + d}{2} - c = d - \frac{c + d}{2}$.) Generalizing, we can insert k values, $x_1, x_2, x_3, \ldots, x_k$, between two numbers c and d so that the sequence $c, x_1, x_2, x_3, \ldots, x_k, d$ is arithmetic. Use this information for Exercises 81–82.

81. Insert three arithmetic means between 4 and 28. (*Hint*: There will be a total of five terms. Write the nth term of an arithmetic sequence with $a_1 = 4$ and $a_5 = 28$, and then find a_2, a_3, and a_4.)

82. The truss on a roof has a uniform slope. There are five vertical supports that are equidistant apart. If the support at one end is 8 in. high and the support at the other end is 56 in. high, determine the heights of the supports in between.

56 in.

8 in.

Write About It

83. Suppose that $\{a_1, a_2, a_3, ...\}$ is an arithmetic sequence with common difference d. Explain why $\{a_1, a_3, a_5, ...\}$ is also an arithmetic sequence.

84. Suppose you are helping a friend with the homework for this section. Explain how to construct an arithmetic sequence.

Expanding Your Skills

85. Determine the nth term of the arithmetic sequence whose nth partial sum is $n^2 + 2n$. [*Hint*: The nth term of the sequence is the difference between the sum of the first n terms and the first $(n - 1)$ terms.]

86. Determine the nth term of the arithmetic sequence whose nth partial sum is $2n^2$.

Technology Connections

For Exercises 87–88, use a graphing utility to list the first five terms of the sequence.

87. $a_n = 5n - 17$ (Exercises 25)

88. $a_n = 6n - 10$ (Exercises 26)

For Exercises 89–90, use a graphing utility to find the sum.

89. $\sum_{i=1}^{50} (2i + 6)$ (Exercise 57)

90. $\sum_{i=1}^{40} (3i - 7)$ (Exercise 58)

SECTION 8.3   Geometric Sequences and Series

OBJECTIVES

1. Identify Specific and General Terms of a Geometric Sequence
2. Evaluate Finite Geometric Series
3. Evaluate Infinite Geometric Series
4. Find the Value of an Annuity

1. Identify Specific and General Terms of a Geometric Sequence

The sequence 2, 4, 8, 16, 32, … is not an arithmetic sequence because the difference between consecutive terms is not the same constant. However, a different pattern exists. Notice that each term after the first is 2 times the preceding term. This sequence is called a geometric sequence.

> **Definition of an Geometric Sequence**
>
> A **geometric sequence** is a sequence in which each term after the first is the product of the preceding term and a fixed nonzero real number, called the **common ratio.**
>
> If the first term of a geometric sequence is a_1, and the common ratio is r, then the terms of the sequence are $a_1, a_1r, a_1r^2, a_1r^3, \ldots$.
>
> The nth term is given by $a_n = a_1 r^{n-1}$.

A geometric sequence is recognized by dividing any term after the first by its predecessor. In all cases the quotient is the same ratio r.

> **EXAMPLE 1** **Identifying a Geometric Sequence and the Common Ratio**
>
> Determine whether the sequence is geometric. If so, identify the common ratio.
>
> **a.** $18, 6, 2, \dfrac{2}{3}, \ldots$ **b.** $3, 12, 48, 240, \ldots$
>
> **Solution:**
>
> **a.** $18, 6, 2, \dfrac{2}{3}, \ldots$
>
> | | |
> |---|---|
> | $\dfrac{a_2}{a_1} = \dfrac{6}{18} = \dfrac{1}{3},\quad \dfrac{a_3}{a_2} = \dfrac{2}{6} = \dfrac{1}{3},$ | The sequence is geometric because the ratio between each term and its predecessor is the same constant. |
> | $\dfrac{a_4}{a_3} = \dfrac{\frac{2}{3}}{2} = \dfrac{2}{3} \cdot \dfrac{1}{2} = \dfrac{1}{3}$ | The common ratio is $r = \frac{1}{3}$. |
>
> **b.** $3, 12, 48, 240, \ldots$
>
> | | |
> |---|---|
> | $\dfrac{a_2}{a_1} = \dfrac{12}{3} = 4,\quad \dfrac{a_3}{a_2} = \dfrac{48}{12} = 4,$ | The sequence is *not* geometric because the ratio between a_4 and a_3 is different than the ratio of other pairs of consecutive terms. |
> | $\dfrac{a_4}{a_3} = \dfrac{240}{48} = 5$ | |

> **Skill Practice 1** Determine whether the sequence is geometric. If so, identify the common ratio.
>
> **a.** $80, 20, 5, \dfrac{5}{4}, \ldots$ **b.** $1, 8, 64, 640, \ldots$

Example 2 illustrates the fundamental characteristic of a geometric sequence. That is, each term of a geometric sequence is a constant multiple of the preceding term.

> **EXAMPLE 2** **Writing Several Terms of a Geometric Sequence**
>
> Write the first five terms of a geometric sequence with $a_1 = 5$ and $r = -2$.
>
> **Solution:**
>
> By definition a geometric sequence follows the pattern $a_1, a_1r, a_1r^2, a_1r^3, \ldots$ The first five terms are
>
> $a_1 = 5$
> $a_2 = 5(-2) = -10$
> $a_3 = 5(-2)^2 = 20$
> $a_4 = 5(-2)^3 = -40$
> $a_5 = 5(-2)^4 = 80$
>
> **TIP** Alternatively, we can use a recursion formula: $a_1 = 5$ and $a_n = a_{n-1} \cdot r$ for $n \geq 2$.
>
> $a_2 = a_1 \cdot (-2) = 5(-2) = -10$
> $a_3 = a_2 \cdot (-2) = -10(-2) = 20$
> $a_4 = a_3 \cdot (-2) = 20(-2) = -40$
> $a_5 = a_4 \cdot (-2) = -40(-2) = 80$

> **Skill Practice 2** Write the first five terms of the geometric sequence with $a_1 = 2$ and $r = -3$.

Answers

1. a. Geometric; $r = \dfrac{1}{4}$

   b. Not geometric

2. $2, -6, 18, -54, 162$

In Example 3, we write an expression for the nth term of a geometric sequence given the first four terms.

EXAMPLE 3	Writing the *n*th Term of a Geometric Sequence

Write a formula for the *n*th term of the geometric sequence. $2, 3, \dfrac{9}{2}, \dfrac{27}{4}, \ldots$

Solution:

$r = \dfrac{a_2}{a_1} = \dfrac{3}{2}$ Dividing any term by its predecessor, we have a common ratio of $\frac{3}{2}$.

$a_n = a_1 r^{n-1}$ Begin with the formula for the *n*th term of a geometric sequence.

$a_n = 2\left(\dfrac{3}{2}\right)^{n-1}$ Substitute $a_1 = 2$ and $r = \frac{3}{2}$.

Skill Practice 3	Write the *n*th term of the geometric sequence.

$4, 5, \dfrac{25}{4}, \dfrac{125}{16}, \ldots$

A graph of several terms of the geometric sequence from Example 3 is shown in Figure 8-5. The points representing the sequence coincide with points on the graph of the exponential function $f(x) = 2\left(\frac{3}{2}\right)^{x-1}$ for positive integer values of x (Figure 8-6). In fact, a geometric sequence with $r > 0$ and $r \neq 1$ is an exponential function whose domain is restricted to the set of positive integers.

Figure 8-5

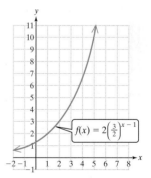

Figure 8-6

EXAMPLE 4	Finding a Specified Term of a Geometric Sequence

Find the fifth term of a geometric sequence $\{a_n\}$ given that $a_1 = 15$ and $a_2 = -9$.

Solution:

$r = \dfrac{a_2}{a_1} = \dfrac{-9}{15} = -\dfrac{3}{5}$ Divide a_2 by a_1 to obtain the common ratio $-\frac{3}{5}$.

$a_n = a_1 r^{n-1}$ Use the formula for the *n*th term of a geometric sequence.

$a_n = 15\left(-\dfrac{3}{5}\right)^{n-1}$ Substitute $a_1 = 15$ and $r = -\frac{3}{5}$ to get the *n*th term for this sequence.

$a_5 = 15\left(-\dfrac{3}{5}\right)^{5-1}$ To find a_5, substitute 5 for *n*.

$a_5 = \dfrac{243}{125}$

Answer

3. $a_n = 4\left(\dfrac{5}{4}\right)^{n-1}$

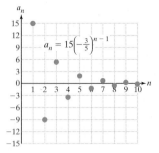

Figure 8-7

> **Skill Practice 4**   Find the sixth term of a geometric sequence $\{a_n\}$ given that $a_1 = 64$ and $a_2 = -16$.

Example 4 illustrates that a geometric sequence with a negative common ratio is an alternating sequence. The graph of the first 10 terms of the sequence is shown in Figure 8-7.

> **EXAMPLE 5**   Writing the nth Term of a Geometric Sequence
>
> Given the terms $a_2 = 80$ and $a_5 = 40.96$ of a geometric sequence, find r, a_1, and a_n.

Solution:

In this example, we need to find two unknown quantities. One strategy is to begin with the formula for the nth term of the geometric sequence and substitute the known values for terms 2 and 5 of the sequence. Then solve the resulting system of nonlinear equations.

$$a_n = a_1 r^{n-1}$$
$$80 = a_1 r^{(2-1)} \longrightarrow 80 = a_1 r \qquad \text{Substitute } a_2 = 80.$$
$$40.96 = a_1 r^{(5-1)} \longrightarrow 40.96 = a_1 r^4 \qquad \text{Substitute } a_5 = 40.96.$$

Substitute $a_1 = \dfrac{80}{r}$ from the first equation into the second equation: $40.96 = a_1 r^4$.

$$40.96 = \frac{80}{r} r^4$$
$$40.96 = 80 r^3$$
$$0.512 = r^3 \qquad \text{Divide by } 80.$$
$$r = 0.8 \qquad \text{Take the cube root of both sides.}$$
$$a_1 = \frac{80}{r} = \frac{80}{0.8} = 100 \qquad \text{To solve for } a_1, \text{ substitute } r = 0.8 \text{ into the equation } a_1 = \frac{80}{r}.$$

The value of r is 0.8, the value of a_1 is 100, and the nth term is $a_n = 100(0.8)^{n-1}$.

> **Skill Practice 5**   Given the terms $a_2 = 54$ and $a_5 = 182.25$ of a geometric sequence, find r, a_1, and a_n.

2. Evaluate Finite Geometric Series

The nth partial sum S_n of the first n terms of a geometric sequence is a **finite geometric series.** Consider the geometric series:

$$S_n = a_1 + a_1 r + a_1 r^2 + a_1 r^3 + \cdots + a_1 r^{n-1}$$

Suppose that we subtract $r S_n$ from S_n.

$$
\begin{array}{llll}
S_n = a_1 & + a_1 r & + a_1 r^2 & + \cdots + a_1 r^{n-1} \\
r S_n = a_1 r & + a_1 r^2 & + a_1 r^3 & + \cdots + a_1 r^n
\end{array}
$$

$$S_n - r S_n = (a_1 - a_1 r) + (a_1 r - a_1 r^2) + (a_1 r^2 - a_1 r^3) + \cdots + (a_1 r^{n-1} - a_1 r^n)$$
$$S_n - r S_n = a_1 - a_1 r^n \qquad \text{The terms in red form a sum of zero.}$$
$$S_n(1 - r) = a_1(1 - r^n) \qquad \text{Factor each side of the equation.}$$
$$S_n = \frac{a_1(1 - r^n)}{1 - r} \qquad \text{Divide by } (1 - r).$$

nth Partial Sum of a Geometric Sequence

The sum S_n of the first n terms of a geometric sequence is given by

$$S_n = \frac{a_1(1 - r^n)}{1 - r}$$

where a_1 is the first term of the sequence and r is the common ratio, $r \neq 1$.

EXAMPLE 6 Evaluating a Finite Geometric Series

Find the sum. $\displaystyle\sum_{i=1}^{6} 4\left(\frac{1}{2}\right)^{i-1}$

Solution:

$$\sum_{i=1}^{6} 4\left(\frac{1}{2}\right)^{i-1} = 4 + 2 + 1 + \frac{1}{2} + \frac{1}{4} + \frac{1}{8}$$

The individual terms in the series form a geometric sequence with $a_1 = 4$ and $r = \frac{1}{2}$. The value of the series is the sixth partial sum of the sequence of terms.

$$S_n = \frac{a_1(1 - r^6)}{1 - r} = \frac{4\left[1 - \left(\frac{1}{2}\right)^6\right]}{1 - \frac{1}{2}} = \frac{4\left(1 - \frac{1}{64}\right)}{\frac{1}{2}} = \frac{63}{8}$$ Apply the formula for the nth partial sum with $n = 6$.

Skill Practice 6 Find the sum. $\displaystyle\sum_{i=1}^{7} 9\left(\frac{1}{3}\right)^{i-1}$

EXAMPLE 7 Evaluating a Finite Geometric Series

Find the sum of the finite geometric series. $5 + 10 + 20 + \cdots + 5120$

Solution:

The common ratio is 2 and $a_1 = 5$. The nth term of the sequence of terms can be written as $a_n = 5(2)^{n-1}$. To find the number of terms n, substitute 5120 for a_n.

$$5120 = 5(2)^{n-1}$$
$$1024 = 2^{n-1}$$ Divide both sides by 5.
$$2^{10} = 2^{n-1}$$ Apply the equivalence property of exponential expressions.
$$10 = n - 1$$
$$n = 11$$ The sequence has 11 terms.

With $a_1 = 5$, $r = 2$, and $n = 11$, we have

$$S_n = \frac{a_1(1 - r^{11})}{1 - r} = \frac{5(1 - 2^{11})}{1 - 2} = 10{,}235$$

Skill Practice 7 Find the sum of the finite geometric series.

$$3 + 6 + 12 + \cdots + 768$$

TIP The equivalence property of exponential expressions indicates that if $b^n = b^m$, then $n = m$. That is, if two exponential expressions with the same base are equal, then their exponents are equal.

Answers

6. $\dfrac{1093}{81}$ **7.** 1533

TIP In Example 7, the equation $1024 = 2^{n-1}$ is an exponential equation (see Section 4.5). If you do not recognize that 1024 is a perfect power of 2, you can solve the equation by using logarithms.

$$1024 = 2^{n-1}$$

$$\ln 1024 = \ln 2^{n-1}$$

$$\ln 1024 = (n-1) \cdot \ln 2 \longrightarrow \frac{\ln 1024}{\ln 2} = n - 1$$

$$\frac{\ln 1024}{\ln 2} + 1 = n$$

$$n = 11$$

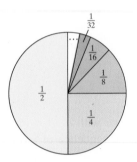

Figure 8-8

3. Evaluate Infinite Geometric Series

Consider the geometric sequence $\frac{1}{2}, \frac{1}{4}, \frac{1}{8}, \frac{1}{16}, \ldots, \left(\frac{1}{2}\right)^n, \ldots$. The sum of all terms in the sequence is an **infinite geometric series**: $\frac{1}{2} + \frac{1}{4} + \frac{1}{8} + \frac{1}{16} + \cdots + \left(\frac{1}{2}\right)^n + \cdots$.

Although it is impossible to add an infinite number of terms on a term-by-term basis, we might ask if the sum approaches a limiting value. For example, if we add $\frac{1}{2}$ of a pie plus $\frac{1}{4}$ of a pie plus $\frac{1}{8}$ of a pie, and so on, will we approach some finite amount of pie? From Figure 8-8, it appears that the sum will be 1 whole unit.

For an infinite geometric sequence with $-1 < r < 1$ (equivalently $|r| < 1$), the value of r^n will become smaller as n gets larger. For example:

$$\approx 0.0009766 \qquad \approx 0.0000305$$

$$\frac{1}{2}, \frac{1}{4}, \frac{1}{8}, \frac{1}{16}, \ldots, \left(\frac{1}{2}\right)^{10}, \ldots, \left(\frac{1}{2}\right)^{15}, \ldots$$

In fact, for $|r| < 1$, as $n \to \infty$, $r^n \to 0$. Therefore, as n approaches infinity

$$S_n = \frac{a_1(1 - r^n)}{1 - r} \text{ approaches } \frac{a_1(1 - 0)}{1 - r} = \frac{a_1}{1 - r}$$

Sum of an Infinite Geometric Series

Given an infinite geometric series $a_1 + a_1r + a_1r^2 + a_1r^3 + \cdots$, with $|r| < 1$, the sum S of all terms in the series is given by

$$S = \frac{a_1}{1 - r}$$

Note: If $|r| \geq 1$, then the sum does not exist.

EXAMPLE 8 **Evaluating an Infinite Geometric Series**

Find the sum if possible. **a.** $\displaystyle\sum_{i=1}^{\infty} 5\left(-\frac{1}{3}\right)^{i-1}$ **b.** $2 + \frac{8}{3} + \frac{32}{9} + \frac{128}{27} + \cdots$

Solution:

a. $\displaystyle\sum_{i=1}^{\infty} 5\left(-\frac{1}{3}\right)^{i-1} = 5 - \frac{5}{3} + \frac{5}{9} - \frac{5}{27} + \frac{5}{81} + \cdots$

The sum is an infinite geometric series with $a_1 = 5$ and $r = -\frac{1}{3}$.

Because $|r| = \left|-\frac{1}{3}\right| < 1$, we have $S = \dfrac{a_1}{1 - r} = \dfrac{5}{1 - \left(-\frac{1}{3}\right)} = \dfrac{15}{4}$.

The sum is $\dfrac{15}{4}$.

b. $2 + \dfrac{8}{3} + \dfrac{32}{9} + \dfrac{128}{27} + \cdots$ is a geometric series with $a_1 = 2$ and $r = \frac{4}{3}$.

Because $|r| = \left|\frac{4}{3}\right| \geq 1$, the sum does not exist.

Skill Practice 8   Find the sum if possible.

a. $\displaystyle\sum_{i=1}^{\infty} 4\left(\frac{3}{4}\right)^{i-1}$ **b.** $2 + \dfrac{5}{2} + \dfrac{25}{8} + \dfrac{125}{32} + \cdots$

In Example 9, we use the formula for the sum of an infinite geometric series to write a repeating decimal as a fraction.

EXAMPLE 9   Writing a Repeating Decimal as a Fraction

Write $0.9\overline{3}$ as a fraction.

Solution:

$0.9\overline{3} = 0.9333\ldots$

$= \dfrac{9}{10} + \left[\dfrac{3}{100} + \dfrac{3}{1000} + \dfrac{3}{10,000} + \cdots\right]$

Infinite geometric series with $a_1 = \frac{3}{100}$ and $r = \frac{1}{10}$ $\longrightarrow$ $S = \dfrac{a_1}{1-r} = \dfrac{\frac{3}{100}}{1 - \frac{1}{10}} = \dfrac{\frac{3}{100}}{\frac{9}{10}} = \dfrac{1}{30}$

$0.9\overline{3} = \dfrac{9}{10} + \dfrac{1}{30} = \dfrac{14}{15}$

Skill Practice 9   Write $0.3\overline{8}$ as a fraction.

When money is infused into the economy, a percentage of the money received by individuals or businesses is often respent over and over again. Economists call this the **multiplier effect.**

EXAMPLE 10   Investigating an Application of an Infinite Geometric Series—The Multiplier Effect

Suppose that \$200 million is spent annually by tourists in a certain state. Further suppose that 75% of the money is respent in the state and then respent over and over again, each time at a rate of 75%. Determine the theoretical total amount spent from the initial \$200 million if the money can be respent an infinite number of times.

Solution:

The total amount spent can be represented by the infinite geometric series where all values are in \$ millions.

75% of 200   75% of 150

$200 + 150 + 112.5 + \cdots$

The value of $a_1 = 200$ and $r = 0.75$. Because $|r| = |0.75| < 1$, we have

$S = \dfrac{a_1}{1-r} = \dfrac{200}{1-0.75} = 800$

Theoretically, the total amount spent is \$800 million.

Answers

8. a. 16

  b. $r = \frac{5}{4} \geq 1$, so the sum does not exist.

9. $\dfrac{7}{18}$

> **Skill Practice 10**   Suppose that after a tax rebate an individual spends
> $210. The money is then respent over and over again, each time at a rate of
> 70%. Determine the total amount spent. Assume that the money can be
> respent an infinite number of times.

4. Find the Value of an Annuity

In Section 4.2, we studied applications of exponential functions involving compound interest. We learned that if P dollars is invested in an account at interest rate r, compounded annually for t years, then the amount A in the account is given by

$$A = P(1 + r)^t$$

However, rather than making a one-time lump sum payment of P dollars, many individuals will invest smaller amounts at regular and more frequent intervals. Such a sequence of fixed payments made (or received) by an individual over a fixed period of time is called an **annuity.**

Suppose that an individual invests P dollars at the *end* of each year for 4 yr at interest rate r. The money deposited at the end of the first year will have 3 yr in which to earn interest. The money invested at the end of the second year will earn interest for 2 yr, and the money invested at the end of the third year will earn interest for 1 yr. However, the money invested at the end of the fourth year will not earn any interest.

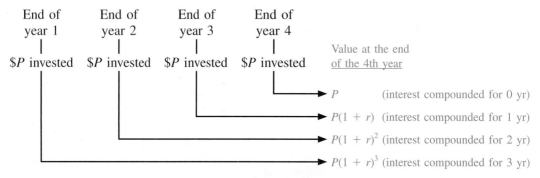

The total amount A, also called the **future value** of the annuity, is given by

$$A = P + P(1 + r) + P(1 + r)^2 + P(1 + r)^3$$

This is a finite geometric series with $a_1 = P$ and common ratio of $(1 + r)$. Using the relationship $S_n = \dfrac{a_1(1 - r^n)}{1 - r}$, the total amount invested for t years is given by

$$A = \frac{P[1 - (1 + r)^t]}{1 - (1 + r)} = \frac{P[1 - (1 + r)^t]}{-r} \quad \text{or simply} \quad A = \frac{P[(1 + r)^t - 1]}{r}$$

If deposits are made n times per year, then the interest rate per compounding period is $\frac{r}{n}$, and the total number of times the money is compounded is nt.

> **TIP** We study **ordinary annuities.** This is an annuity in which money is invested at the *end* of the compounding periods. If the money were invested at the beginning of the compounding periods, such an investment is called an **annuity due** and the future value is computed with a different formula.

> **Future Value of an Ordinary Annuity**
>
> Suppose that P dollars is invested at the end of each compounding period n times per year at interest rate r. Then the value A (in $) of the annuity after t years is given by
>
> $$A = \frac{P\left[\left(1 + \frac{r}{n}\right)^{nt} - 1\right]}{\frac{r}{n}}$$

Answer

10. $700

> ### EXAMPLE 11   Finding the Value of an Annuity
>
> Suppose that an employee working for a state college puts aside $150 at the end of each month in a tax-sheltered annuity. The annuity pays 6% annual interest compounded monthly. Suppose that the employee begins contributing at age 28.
>
> **a.** How much will the annuity be worth by the time the employee reaches age 62?
>
> **b.** How much interest will have been earned?
>
> **Solution:**
>
> **a.** $A = \dfrac{P\left[\left(1 + \frac{r}{n}\right)^{nt} - 1\right]}{\frac{r}{n}}$
>
> $A = \dfrac{150\left[\left(1 + \frac{0.06}{12}\right)^{(12)(34)} - 1\right]}{\frac{0.06}{12}}$
>
> $P = \$150$
> $r = 0.06$
> $n = 12$ (the money is invested monthly)
> $t = 62 - 28 = 34$ yr
>
> $A = 199{,}548.50$
>
> The annuity will be worth \$199,548.50 when the employee reaches age 62.
>
> **b.** \$150 is invested 12 times per year for 34 yr.
> Principal invested: (\$150)(12)(34) = \$61,200
> The amount of interest is \$199,548.50 − \$61,200 = \$138,348.50.

> **Skill Practice 11**   Suppose that an employee contributes \$100 to an annuity at the end of each month for 25 yr. If the annuity earns 7%,
>
> **a.** Determine the value of the annuity at the end of the 25-yr period.
>
> **b.** How much interest will be earned?

Point of Interest

The contributions made to the investment in Example 11 are **tax deferred.** This means that the principal invested each month has not yet been taxed. Because the principal is invested pretax, the individual potentially has more money available to invest. Furthermore, no taxes are paid on either the principal or interest until the money is withdrawn. This type of plan is meant as a long-term investment, and withdrawals are typically taken after age 59½ without penalty.

Answers
11. a. \$81,007.17   **b.** \$51,007.17

SECTION 8.3   Practice Exercises

Review Exercises

For Exercises 1–2, find the indicated term of an arithmetic sequence $\{a_n\}$ based on the given information about the sequence.

1. $a_1 = 5$ and $a_5 = 29$. Find a_{46}.

2. $a_2 = -7$ and $d = 9$. Find a_{63}.

For Exercises 3–6, evaluate the sum.

3. $\displaystyle\sum_{i=1}^{82}(5 - 7i)$

4. $\displaystyle\sum_{j=1}^{61}(6 - 3j)$

5. $28 + 39 + 50 + \cdots + 622$

6. $17 + 26 + 35 + \cdots + 827$

Concept Connections

7. A _____ sequence is a sequence in which each term after the first is the product of the preceding term and a fixed nonzero real number, called the common _____, r.

8. The nth term of a geometric sequence with first term a_1 and common ratio r is given by $a_n = $ _____.

9. The nth partial sum S_n of the first n terms of a geometric sequence is a (finite/infinite) geometric series.

10. The sum S_n of the first n terms of a geometric sequence with first term a_1 and common ratio r is given by the formula $S_n = $ _____.

11. Given a geometric sequence with $|r| < 1$, the value of $r^n \to$ _____ as $n \to \infty$.

12. Given an infinite geometric series with first term a_1 and common ratio r, if $|r| < 1$, then the sum S is given by the formula $S =$ _____. If $|r| \geq 1$, then the sum (does/does not) exist.

13. A sequence of payments made at equal intervals over a fixed period of time is called an _____.

14. If P dollars is invested at the end of each compounding period n times per year at interest rate r, then the value A of the annuity (in \$) after t years is given by the formula $A =$ _____.

Objective 1: Identify Specific and General Terms of a Geometric Sequence

For Exercises 15–24, determine whether the sequence is geometric. If so, find the value of r. (See Example 1)

15. 6, 18, 54, 162, ...

16. 4, 20, 100, 500, ...

17. $-7, \dfrac{7}{2}, -\dfrac{7}{4}, \dfrac{7}{8}, \ldots$

18. $5, -\dfrac{5}{3}, \dfrac{5}{9}, -\dfrac{5}{27}, \ldots$

19. 3, 12, 60, 360, ...

20. 7, 14, 42, 88, ...

21. $\sqrt{5}, 5, 5\sqrt{5}, 25, \ldots$

22. $\sqrt[3]{7}, \sqrt[3]{49}, 7, 7\sqrt[3]{7}, \ldots$

23. $2, \dfrac{4}{t}, \dfrac{8}{t^2}, \dfrac{16}{t^3}, \ldots$

24. $\dfrac{5}{a^2}, \dfrac{15}{a^4}, \dfrac{45}{a^6}, \dfrac{135}{a^8}, \ldots$

For Exercises 25–30, write the first five terms of a geometric sequence $\{a_n\}$ based on the given information about the sequence. (See Example 2)

25. $a_1 = 7$ and $r = 2$

26. $a_1 = 2$ and $r = 3$

27. $a_1 = 24$ and $r = -\frac{2}{3}$

28. $a_1 = 80$ and $r = -\frac{4}{5}$

29. $a_1 = 36$ and $a_n = \frac{1}{2}a_{n-1}$ for $n \geq 2$

30. $a_1 = 27$, $a_n = \frac{1}{3}a_{n-1}$ for $n \geq 2$

For Exercises 31–36, write a formula for the nth term of the geometric sequence. (See Example 3)

31. 5, 10, 20, 40, ...

32. 3, 6, 12, 24, ...

33. $-2, -1, -\dfrac{1}{2}, -\dfrac{1}{4}, \ldots$

34. $-8, -2, -\dfrac{1}{2}, -\dfrac{1}{8}, \ldots$

35. $\dfrac{16}{3}, 4, 3, \dfrac{9}{4}, \ldots$

36. $\dfrac{18}{5}, \dfrac{6}{5}, \dfrac{2}{5}, \dfrac{2}{15}, \ldots$

37. A farmer depreciates a \$100,000 tractor. He estimates that the resale value of the tractor n years after purchase is 85% of its value from the previous year.

   a. Write a formula for the nth term of a sequence that represents the resale value of the tractor n years after purchase.

   b. What will the resale value be in 5 yr? Round to the nearest \$1000.

38. A Coulter Counter is a device used to count the number of microscopic particles in a fluid, most notably, cells in blood. A hospital depreciates a \$9000 Coulter Counter at a rate of 75% per year after purchase.

   a. Write a formula for the nth term of a sequence that represents the resale value of the device n years after purchase.

   b. What will the resale value be in 4 yr? Round to the nearest \$100.

39. Doctors in a certain city report 24 confirmed cases of the flu to the health department. At that time, the health department declares a flu epidemic. If the number of reported cases increases by roughly 30% each week thereafter, find the number of cases 10 weeks after the initial report. Round to the nearest whole unit.

40. After a 5-year slump in the real estate market, housing prices stabilize and even begin to appreciate in value. One homeowner buys a house for \$140,000 and finds that the value of the property increases by 3% per year thereafter. Assuming that the trend continues, find the value of the home 15 yr later. Round to the nearest \$1000.

For Exercises 41–48, find the indicated term of a geometric sequence from the given information. (See Example 4)

41. $a_1 = 12$ and $a_2 = -8$. Find the sixth term.

42. $a_1 = 16$ and $a_2 = -12$. Find the fifth term.

43. $a_1 = 2$ and $a_4 = 16$. Find a_{12}.

44. $a_1 = 4$ and $a_4 = 108$. Find a_{10}.

45. $a_2 = -6$ and $r = \dfrac{1}{2}$. Find a_7.

46. $a_2 = -15$ and $r = \dfrac{1}{3}$. Find a_8.

47. $a_5 = -\dfrac{16}{9}$ and $r = -\dfrac{2}{3}$. Find a_1.

48. $a_6 = \dfrac{5}{16}$ and $r = -\dfrac{1}{2}$. Find a_1.

49. If the second and third terms of a geometric sequence are 15 and 75, what is the first term?

50. If the second and third terms of a geometric sequence are 4 and 1, what is the first term?

For Exercises 51–54, find a_1 and r for a geometric sequence $\{a_n\}$ from the given information. (See Example 5)

51. $a_2 = 18$ and $a_5 = 144$

52. $a_2 = 21$ and $a_7 = 5103$

53. $a_3 = 72$ and $a_6 = -\frac{243}{8}$

54. $a_3 = 45$ and $a_6 = -\frac{243}{25}$

Objectives 2–3: Evaluate Finite and Infinite Geometric Series

For Exercises 55–78, find the sum of the geometric series, if possible. (See Examples 6–8)

55. $\displaystyle\sum_{n=1}^{10} 3(2)^{n-1}$

56. $\displaystyle\sum_{n=1}^{8} 4(3)^{n-1}$

57. $\displaystyle\sum_{k=1}^{7} 6\left(\frac{2}{3}\right)^{k-1}$

58. $\displaystyle\sum_{j=1}^{7} 2\left(\frac{3}{4}\right)^{j-1}$

59. $15 + 5 + \dfrac{5}{3} + \dfrac{5}{9} + \dfrac{5}{27} + \dfrac{5}{81}$

60. $50 + 10 + 2 + \dfrac{2}{5} + \dfrac{2}{25} + \dfrac{2}{125}$

61. $2 + 6 + 18 + \cdots + 13{,}122$

62. $4 + 12 + 36 + \cdots + 78{,}732$

63. $1 + \dfrac{2}{3} + \dfrac{4}{9} + \cdots + \dfrac{32}{243}$

64. $\dfrac{8}{3} + 2 + \dfrac{3}{2} + \cdots + \dfrac{243}{512}$

65. $1 + \dfrac{1}{5} + \dfrac{1}{25} + \dfrac{1}{125} + \cdots$

66. $1 + \dfrac{1}{6} + \dfrac{1}{36} + \dfrac{1}{216} + \cdots$

67. $-2 - \dfrac{1}{2} - \dfrac{1}{8} - \dfrac{1}{32} - \cdots$

68. $-5 - 1 - \dfrac{1}{5} - \dfrac{1}{25} - \cdots$

69. $2 + 8 + 32 + 128 + \cdots$

70. $1 + 6 + 36 + 216 + \cdots$

71. $\displaystyle\sum_{j=1}^{\infty} \left(\frac{2}{3}\right)^{j-1}$

72. $\displaystyle\sum_{i=1}^{\infty} \left(\frac{3}{4}\right)^{i-1}$

73. $\displaystyle\sum_{k=1}^{\infty} \left(\frac{3}{2}\right)^{k-1}$

74. $\displaystyle\sum_{n=1}^{\infty} \left(\frac{4}{3}\right)^{n-1}$

75. $\displaystyle\sum_{i=1}^{12} 4(2)^{i}$ [*Hint*: Rewrite the expression within the summation so that the base of 2 appears to the $(i-1)$ power.]

76. $\displaystyle\sum_{j=1}^{10} 5(2)^{j}$

77. $\displaystyle\sum_{n=3}^{\infty} 4\left(\frac{1}{2}\right)^{n-1}$

78. $\displaystyle\sum_{n=4}^{\infty} 18\left(\frac{1}{3}\right)^{n-1}$

(*Hint*: Evaluate the infinite sum from $n = 1$ to infinity. Then subtract the terms corresponding to $n = 1$ and $n = 2$.)

For Exercises 79–84, write the repeating decimal as a fraction. (See Example 9)

79. $0.\overline{64}$

80. $0.\overline{78}$

81. $0.\overline{81}$

82. $0.\overline{72}$

83. $3.4\overline{25}$

84. $4.1\overline{62}$

85. Bike Week in Daytona Beach brings an estimated 500,000 people to the town. Suppose that each person spends an average of $300.

  a. How much money is infused into the local economy during Bike Week?

  b. If the money is respent in the community over and over again at a rate of 68%, determine the total amount spent. Assume that the money is respent an infinite number of times. (**See Example 10**)

86. An individual with questionable integrity prints and spends $12,000 in counterfeit money. If the "money" is respent over and over again each time at a rate of 76%, determine the total amount spent. Assume that the "money" is respent an infinite number of times without being detected.

87. Rafael received an inheritance of $18,000. He saves $6480 and then spends $11,520 of the money on college tuition, books, and living expenses for school. If the money is respent over and over again in the community an infinite number of times, at a rate of 64%, determine the total amount spent.

88. A tax rebate returns $100 million to individuals in the community. Suppose that $25,000,000 is put into savings, and that $75,000,000 is spent. If the money is spent over and over again an infinite number of times, each time at a rate of 75%, determine the total amount spent.

Objective 4: Find the Value of an Annuity

For Exercises 89–90, find the value of an ordinary annuity in which regular payments of P dollars are made at the end of each compounding period, n times per year, at an interest rate r for t years. (See Example 11)

89. $P = \$200$, $n = 12$, $r = 5\%$, $t = 30$ yr

90. $P = \$100$, $n = 24$, $r = 5.5\%$, $t = 28$ yr

91. a. An employee invests $100 per month in an ordinary annuity. If the interest rate is 6%, find the value of the annuity after 20 yr. (**See Example 11**)

  b. If the employee invests $200 instead of $100 at 6%, find the value of the annuity after 20 yr. Compare the result to part (a).

  c. If the employee invests $100 per month in the annuity at 6% interest, find the value after 40 yr. Compare the result to part (a).

92. a. An employee invests $500 per month in an ordinary annuity. If the interest rate is 5%, find the value of the annuity after 18 yr.

  b. If the employee invests $1000 per month in the annuity instead of $500 at 5% interest, find the value of the annuity after 18 yr. Compare the result to part (a).

  c. If the employee invests $500 per month in the annuity at 5% interest, find the value of the annuity after 36 yr. Compare the result to part (a).

Mixed Exercises

93. a. Given a geometric sequence whose nth term is $a_n = 6(0.4)^n$, are the terms of this sequence increasing or decreasing?

  b. Given a geometric sequence whose nth term is $a_n = 3(1.4)^n$, are the terms of this sequence increasing or decreasing?

94. a. Given a geometric sequence whose nth term is $a_n = -8(0.2)^n$, are the terms of this sequence increasing or decreasing?

  b. Given a geometric sequence whose nth term is $a_n = -5(1.6)^n$, are the terms of this sequence increasing or decreasing?

For Exercises 95–98, match the sequence with its graph.

95. $a_n = 5(0.8)^n$ **96.** $a_n = 2(1.2)^n$ **97.** $a_n = 5(-0.8)^n$ **98.** $a_n = 2(-1.2)^n$

a.   **b.**   **c.**   **d.**

        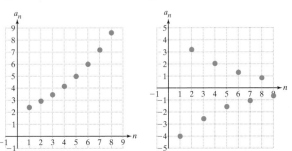

99. The initial swing (one way) of a pendulum makes an arc of 24 in. Each swing (one way) thereafter makes an arc of 98% of the length of the previous swing. What is the total arc length that the pendulum travels?

100. The initial swing (one way) of a pendulum makes an arc of 4 ft. Each swing (one way) thereafter makes an arc of 90% of the length of the previous swing. What is the total arc length that the pendulum travels?

101. A child drops a ball from a height of 4 ft. With each bounce, the ball rebounds to 50% of its original height. After the ball falls from its initial height of 4 ft, the vertical distance traveled for every bounce thereafter is doubled (the ball travels up and down).

The total vertical distance traveled by the ball is given by

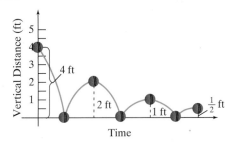

Determine the total vertical distance traveled by the ball.

102. A ball is dropped from a height of 12 ft. With each bounce, the ball rebounds to $\frac{3}{4}$ of its height. Determine the total vertical distance traveled by the ball.

103. Suppose that an individual is paid $0.01 on day 1 and every day thereafter, the payment is doubled.

  a. Write a formula for the nth term of a sequence that gives the payment (in $) on day n.

  b. How much will the individual earn on day 10? day 20? and day 30?

  c. What is the total amount earned in 30 days?

104. The vibration of sound is measured in cycles per second, also called hertz (Hz). The frequency for middle C on a piano is 256 Hz. The C above middle C (one octave above) is 512 Hz. The frequencies of musical notes follow a geometric progression.

  a. Find the frequency for C two octaves above middle C.

  b. Find the frequency for C one octave *below* middle C.

105. The yearly salary for job A is $60,000 initially with an annual raise of $3000 every year thereafter. The yearly salary for job B is $56,000 for year 1 with an annual raise of 6%.

  a. Consider a sequence representing the salary for job A for year n. Is this an arithmetic or geometric sequence? Find the total earnings for job A over 20 yr.

  b. Consider a sequence representing the salary for job B for year n. Is this an arithmetic or geometric sequence? Find the total earnings for job B over 20 yr. Round to the nearest dollar.

  c. What is the difference in total salary between the two jobs over 20 yr?

106. a. Jacob has a job that pays $48,000 the first year. He receives a 4% raise each year thereafter. Find the sum of his yearly salaries over a 20-yr period. Round to the nearest dollar.

  b. Cherise has a job that pays $48,000 the first year. She receives a 4.5% raise each year thereafter. Find the sum of her yearly salaries over a 20-yr period. Round to the nearest dollar.

  c. How much more will Cherise earn than Jacob over the 20-yr period?

107. If a fair coin is flipped n times, the number of head/tail arrangements follows a geometric sequence. In the figure, if the coin is flipped 1 time, there are two possible outcomes, H or T. If the coin is flipped 2 times, then there are four possible outcomes: HH, HT, TH, and TT.

  a. Write a formula for the nth term of a sequence representing the number of outcomes if a fair coin is flipped n times.

  b. How many outcomes are there if a fair coin is flipped 10 times?

108. An ancestor is a person from whom an individual is descended (a parent, a grandparent, a great-grandparent, and so on). Every individual has two biological parents, a mother and a father. The mother and father in turn each have two parents and so on.

1st Generation	2nd Generation	3rd Generation
2 parents	4 grandparents	8 great-grandparents

The terms of the sequence 2, 4, 8, 16, … give the additional number of ancestors for each generation back in time. Determine the total number of ancestors that an individual has going back 12 generations.

Write About It

109. Explain the difference between an arithmetic sequence and a geometric sequence.

110. Explain why a finite number of terms is not sufficient to determine whether an infinite sequence is arithmetic or geometric. For example, explain why 4, 16, … can be arithmetic, geometric, or neither.

111. A geometric sequence $a_1, a_2, a_3, \ldots$ has a common ratio r. Explain why the sequence $a_1, a_3, a_5, \ldots$ is also geometric and determine the common ratio.

Expanding Your Skills

112. Show that $x, x + 2, x + 4, x + 6, \ldots$ is *not* a geometric sequence.

113. If $a_1, a_2, a_3, a_4, \ldots$ is a geometric sequence with common ratio r, show that $\frac{1}{a_1}, \frac{1}{a_2}, \frac{1}{a_3}, \frac{1}{a_4} \ldots$ is also a geometric sequence and determine the value of r.

114. Suppose that $a_1, a_2, a_3, \ldots$ is an arithmetic sequence with common difference d. Show that $10^{a_1}, 10^{a_2}, 10^{a_3}, 10^{a_4}, \ldots$ is a geometric sequence and find the common ratio r.

115. Suppose that $a_1, a_2, a_3, \ldots$ is a geometric sequence with $r > 0$ and $a_1 > 0$. Show that the sequence $\log a_1, \log a_2, \log a_3, \ldots$ is arithmetic and find the common difference d.

116. Given the series $\frac{1}{2} + \frac{1}{4} + \frac{1}{8} + \frac{1}{16} + \cdots$,

  a. Find the sum.

  b. How many terms must be taken so that the nth partial sum is within $\frac{1}{100}$ of the actual sum?

117. Determine whether the sequence $\ln 1, \ln 2, \ln 4, \ln 8, \ldots$ is arithmetic or geometric. If the sequence is arithmetic, find d. If the sequence is geometric, find r.

Technology Connections

For Exercises 118–119, use a graphing utility to list the first four terms of the sequence. If possible, display the terms of the sequence as fractions or integers rather than in decimal form.

118. $a_n = -8\left(\frac{1}{4}\right)^{n-1}$ (Exercises 34)

119. $a_n = -2\left(\frac{1}{2}\right)^{n-1}$ (Exercises 33)

For Exercises 120–121, use a graphing utility to find the sum.

120. $\displaystyle\sum_{n=1}^{8} 4(3)^{n-1}$ (Exercise 56)

121. $\displaystyle\sum_{n=1}^{10} 3(2)^{n-1}$ (Exercise 55)

122. Consider the series $\displaystyle\sum_{i=1}^{\infty} 5\left(\tfrac{1}{2}\right)^{i-1}$. Graph $f(x) = \dfrac{5\left[1 - \left(\frac{1}{2}\right)^{x}\right]}{1 - \frac{1}{2}}$ and interpret the meaning of the horizontal asymptote.

PROBLEM RECOGNITION EXERCISES

Comparing Arithmetic and Geometric Sequences and Series

For Exercises 1–10, determine if the nth term of the sequence defines an arithmetic sequence, a geometric sequence, or neither. If the sequence is arithmetic, find the common difference d. If the sequence is geometric, find the common ratio r.

1. $a_n = \dfrac{2n}{3} + \dfrac{1}{4}$

2. $a_n = -\dfrac{3}{5}n - \dfrac{1}{3}$

3. $a_n = (-1)^{n-1}$

4. $a_n = (-2)^{n}$

5. $a_n = \dfrac{n-1}{n+1}$

6. $a_n = \dfrac{3n-4}{2n+1}$

7. $a_n = 5\left(\sqrt{5}\right)^{n-1}$

8. $a_n = 6\left(\sqrt{2}\right)^{n+1}$

9. $a_n = 5 + \sqrt{2}n$

10. $a_n = \dfrac{\sqrt{3}}{2}n + 4$

For Exercises 11–28, evaluate the sum if possible.

11. $\displaystyle\sum_{i=1}^{1506} 5$

12. $\displaystyle\sum_{i=1}^{417} (-3)$

13. $\displaystyle\sum_{i=1}^{716} (-1)^{i+1}$

14. $\displaystyle\sum_{j=1}^{2651} (-1)^{j}$

15. $\displaystyle\sum_{n=1}^{3} \dfrac{n-2}{n+1}$

16. $\displaystyle\sum_{j=1}^{4} (j^{4} - 2j^{2})$

17. $\displaystyle\sum_{n=1}^{4} -3\left(\dfrac{1}{3}\right)^{n-1}$

18. $\displaystyle\sum_{n=1}^{5} -2\left(\dfrac{3}{4}\right)^{n-1}$

19. $\displaystyle\sum_{n=1}^{\infty} 6\left(\dfrac{5}{3}\right)^{n-1}$

20. $\displaystyle\sum_{i=1}^{\infty} 7\left(\dfrac{4}{3}\right)^{i-1}$

21. $\displaystyle\sum_{i=1}^{27} (-6i - 4)$

22. $\displaystyle\sum_{i=1}^{41} (-5i - 3)$

23. $\displaystyle\sum_{n=1}^{\infty} 8\left(\dfrac{1}{2}\right)^{n}$

24. $\displaystyle\sum_{n=1}^{\infty} 12\left(\dfrac{1}{3}\right)^{n}$

25. $36 + 30 + 25 + \dfrac{125}{6} + \cdots$

26. $54 + 36 + 24 + 16 + \cdots$

27. $3 + 11 + 19 + 27 + \cdots + 363$

28. $36 + 29 + 22 + 15 + \cdots + (-419)$

SECTION 8.4 Mathematical Induction

OBJECTIVES

1. Prove a Statement Using Mathematical Induction

2. Prove a Statement Using the Extended Principle of Mathematical Induction

1. Prove a Statement Using Mathematical Induction

In this section, we present a technique of mathematical proof that enables us to prove the validity of a statement that is true over the set of positive integers. This technique is called mathematical induction.

Consider the following sum:

$$S_n = \frac{1}{1 \cdot 2} + \frac{1}{2 \cdot 3} + \frac{1}{3 \cdot 4} + \frac{1}{4 \cdot 5} + \cdots + \frac{1}{n(n + 1)}$$

The sequence of terms that make up the sum is neither arithmetic nor geometric. Therefore, we have no formula readily available to evaluate the sum of the first n terms.

We might consider evaluating the nth partial sum for several values of n to determine if a pattern exists.

$$S_1 = \frac{1}{1 \cdot 2} = \frac{1}{2}$$

$$S_2 = \frac{1}{1 \cdot 2} + \frac{1}{2 \cdot 3} = \frac{1}{2} + \frac{1}{6} = \frac{2}{3}$$

$$S_3 = \frac{1}{1 \cdot 2} + \frac{1}{2 \cdot 3} + \frac{1}{3 \cdot 4} = \frac{1}{2} + \frac{1}{6} + \frac{1}{12} = \frac{3}{4}$$

$$S_4 = \frac{1}{1 \cdot 2} + \frac{1}{2 \cdot 3} + \frac{1}{3 \cdot 4} + \frac{1}{4 \cdot 5} = \frac{1}{2} + \frac{1}{6} + \frac{1}{12} + \frac{1}{20} = \frac{4}{5}$$

For the first four terms of the nth partial sum, the numerator is the same as the term number n, and the denominator is one more than the term number. From this observation, we make the following hypothesis.

$$S_n = \frac{1}{1 \cdot 2} + \frac{1}{2 \cdot 3} + \frac{1}{3 \cdot 4} + \frac{1}{4 \cdot 5} + \cdots + \frac{1}{n(n + 1)} = \frac{n}{n + 1}$$

We have shown that this statement is true for $n = 1, 2, 3,$ and 4, but what about values of n thereafter? Because there are infinitely many positive integers, there are actually infinitely many statements to prove and we cannot approach them on a case-by-case basis. Instead we use the principle of mathematical induction.

> **TIP** The proof of the statement
>
> $$\frac{1}{1 \cdot 2} + \frac{1}{2 \cdot 3} + \cdots + \frac{1}{n(n + 1)}$$
> $$= \frac{n}{n + 1}$$
>
> is given in Example 2.

Principle of Mathematical Induction

Let S_n be a statement involving the positive integer n, and let k be an arbitrary positive integer. Then S_n is true for all positive integers n if

1. S_1 is true, and
2. The truth of S_k implies the truth of S_{k+1}.

S_n represents the statements, $S_1, S_2, S_3, S_4,$ and so on. Mathematical induction is a two-part process to prove all the statements in the sequence. We first need to show that the statement is true for $n = 1$. That is, prove that S_1 is true. The second part involves proving that if any statement S_k in the sequence is true, then the statement that follows is also true (S_k implies S_{k+1}).

Intuitively, mathematical induction is similar to the sequential effect of falling dominos. Pushing the first domino down is analogous to proving S_1. Then showing that any falling domino in the sequence will cause the next domino to fall is the idea behind part 2 in mathematical induction. That is, if domino 1 falls, and any falling domino makes the next domino in line fall, then all the dominos will fall.

In Examples 1 and 2, we use mathematical induction to prove a statement involving a summation. In such a case, it is helpful to write the sum S_{k+1} as follows:

$$S_{k+1} = S_k + a_{k+1} \qquad \text{The sum of the first } (k + 1) \text{ terms equals the sum of the first } k \text{ terms plus the } (k + 1)\text{th term.}$$

EXAMPLE 1   Using Mathematical Induction

Use mathematical induction to prove that
$S_n = 1 + 3 + 5 + 7 + \cdots + (2n - 1) = n^2$.

Solution:

1. Show that S_n is true for $n = 1$:

$S_1 = 1$, which is the same as $(1)^2 = 1$.

| left side of statement | | right side of statement |

We need to show that S_1 is true. That is, we need to show that the left and right sides of the statement are equal for $n = 1$.

2. Next, assume that S_k is true and show that S_{k+1} is true:

Assume that $S_k = 1 + 3 + 5 + 7 + \cdots + (2k - 1) = k^2$.

The statement that S_k is true is called the **inductive hypothesis.**

We must show that

$$S_{k+1} = 1 + 3 + 5 + \cdots + [2(k + 1) - 1] = (k + 1)^2 \qquad (1)$$

The left side of the statement can be written as

$$S_{k+1} = \overbrace{1 + 3 + 5 + 7 + \cdots + (2k - 1)}^{\text{Sum of first } k \text{ terms}} + \overbrace{[2(k + 1) - 1]}^{(k+1)\text{th term}}$$

$$= k^2 \qquad\qquad + [2(k + 1) - 1]$$

$$= k^2 + [2k + 2 - 1]$$

$$= k^2 + 2k + 1$$

$$= (k + 1)^2 \text{ as desired. This matches Equation (1).}$$

By the inductive hypothesis, we can replace the sum of the first k terms by k^2.

We have shown that S_1 is true, and that if S_k is true, then S_{k+1} is true. By mathematical induction, we conclude that the statement is true for all positive integers.

> **Skill Practice 1**   Use mathematical induction to prove that
> $S_n = 2 + 4 + 6 + 8 + \cdots + 2n = n(n + 1)$.

In Example 2, we prove the statement introduced at the beginning of this section.

EXAMPLE 2   Using Mathematical Induction

Use mathematical induction to prove that

$$S_n = \frac{1}{1 \cdot 2} + \frac{1}{2 \cdot 3} + \frac{1}{3 \cdot 4} + \frac{1}{4 \cdot 5} + \cdots + \frac{1}{n(n + 1)} = \frac{n}{n + 1}.$$

Solution:

1. Show that S_n is true for $n = 1$:

$$S_1 = \frac{1}{1 \cdot 2} = \frac{1}{2} \text{ which is the same as } \frac{n}{n + 1} = \frac{1}{1 + 1} = \frac{1}{2}$$

| left side of statement | | right side of statement |

Avoiding Mistakes

It is important to use parentheses when substituting $(k + 1)$ into the statement for n.

Answer

1. See page SA-45.

2. Next, assume that S_k is true and show that S_{k+1} is true:

Assume that

$$S_k = \frac{1}{1 \cdot 2} + \frac{1}{2 \cdot 3} + \frac{1}{3 \cdot 4} + \frac{1}{4 \cdot 5} + \cdots + \frac{1}{k(k+1)} = \frac{k}{k+1} \qquad \text{Inductive hypothesis.}$$

We must show that $S_{k+1} = \dfrac{k+1}{(k+1)+1}$, or equivalently,

$$S_{k+1} = \frac{k+1}{k+2} \qquad\qquad\qquad (1)$$

The left side of the statement can be written as

$$S_{k+1} = \overbrace{\frac{1}{1 \cdot 2} + \frac{1}{2 \cdot 3} + \frac{1}{3 \cdot 4} + \cdots + \frac{1}{k(k+1)}}^{\text{Sum of first } k \text{ terms}} + \overbrace{\frac{1}{(k+1)[(k+1)+1]}}^{(k+1)\text{th term}}$$

$$= \frac{k}{k+1} + \frac{1}{(k+1)[(k+1)+1]} \qquad \text{By the inductive hypothesis, we can replace the sum of the first } k \text{ terms by } \frac{k}{k+1}.$$

$$= \frac{k}{k+1} + \frac{1}{(k+1)(k+2)} \qquad \text{Simplify.}$$

$$= \frac{k}{(k+1)} \cdot \frac{(k+2)}{(k+2)} + \frac{1}{(k+1)(k+2)} \qquad \text{Common denominator}$$

$$= \frac{k^2 + 2k + 1}{(k+1)(k+2)} \qquad \text{Add the expressions.}$$

$$= \frac{(k+1)^2}{(k+1)(k+2)} \qquad \text{Factor the numerator.}$$

$$= \frac{k+1}{k+2} \quad \text{as desired. This matches Equation (1).}$$

We have shown that S_1 is true, and that if S_k is true, then S_{k+1} is true. By mathematical induction, we conclude that the statement is true for all positive integers.

Skill Practice 2   Use mathematical induction to prove that
$$\frac{1}{1 \cdot 3} + \frac{1}{3 \cdot 5} + \frac{1}{5 \cdot 7} + \cdots + \frac{1}{(2n-1)(2n+1)} = \frac{n}{2n+1}.$$

Mathematical induction can be used to prove the following useful summation formulas involving powers of the first n positive integers (Table 8-3). The proofs of these formulas are addressed in Exercises 21–24.

> **Table 8-3   Sums of Powers**
>
> Let n represent a positive integer. Then,
>
> 1. $\displaystyle\sum_{i=1}^{n} 1 = n$ 　　　　2. $\displaystyle\sum_{i=1}^{n} i = \frac{n(n+1)}{2}$
>
> 3. $\displaystyle\sum_{i=1}^{n} i^2 = \frac{n(n+1)(2n+1)}{6}$ 　　4. $\displaystyle\sum_{i=1}^{n} i^3 = \frac{n^2(n+1)^2}{4}$

Answer
2. See page SA-45.

In Examples 3 and 4, we use mathematical induction to prove statements that do not involve a sum.

EXAMPLE 3   Using Mathematical Induction

Use mathematical induction to prove that 4 is a factor of $9^n - 1$.

Solution:

Let S_n be the statement: 4 is a factor of $9^n - 1$.

To show that 4 is a factor of any expression, we need to write the expression as the product of 4 and some positive integer that we call a.

1. Show that S_n is true for $n = 1$:

    S_1 reads: 4 is a factor of $9^1 - 1 = 8$.

    S_1 is true because $8 = 4 \cdot 2$, indicating that 4 is indeed a factor of 8.

2. Next, assume that S_k is true and show that S_{k+1} is true:

    Assume that 4 is a factor of $9^k - 1$.

    This implies that $9^k - 1 = 4a$ or equivalently $9^k = 4a + 1$.   Inductive hypothesis.

    We must show that 4 is a factor of $9^{k+1} - 1$.

$$9^{k+1} - 1 = 9 \cdot 9^k - 1$$
$$= 9 \cdot (4a + 1) - 1 \qquad \text{From the inductive hypothesis, replace } 9^k \text{ by } 4a + 1.$$
$$= 36a + 9 - 1 \qquad \text{Apply the distributive property.}$$
$$= 36a + 8$$
$$= 4(9a + 2) \qquad \text{Factor. The value 4 is a factor of the expression } 4(9a + 2). \text{ Therefore, 4 is a factor of } 9^{k+1} - 1.$$

We have shown that S_1 is true, and that if S_k is true, then S_{k+1} is true. By mathematical induction, we conclude that the statement is true for all positive integers.

Skill Practice 3   Use mathematical induction to prove that 2 is a factor of $5^n + 1$.

---

2. Prove a Statement Using the Extended Principle of Mathematical Induction

Mathematical induction can be extended to prove statements that might hold true only for integers greater than or equal to some positive integer j. In such a case, we use the extended principle of mathematical induction.

Extended Principle of Mathematical Induction

Let S_n be a statement involving the positive integer n. Then S_n is true for all positive integers $n \geq j$ if

1. S_j is true, and
2. For an integer k, if $k \geq j$, the truth of S_k implies the truth of S_{k+1}.

Answer

3. See page SA-45.

> **EXAMPLE 4** **Using the Extended Principle of Mathematical Induction**

Use mathematical induction to prove that $n! > 2^n$ for positive integers $n \geq 4$.

Solution:

Let S_n be the statement: $n! > 2^n$.

1. First show that S_n is true for $n = 4$:

To prove that S_4 is true, show that $4! > 2^4$.

$4! = 4 \cdot 3 \cdot 2 \cdot 1 = 24$ and $2^4 = 16$. Therefore, $4! > 2^4$, indicating that S_4 is true.

2. Next, assume that S_k is true for $k \geq 4$, and show that S_{k+1} is true:

Assume that $k! > 2^k$ and show that $(k + 1)! > 2^{k+1}$ where $k \geq 4$.

$$(k + 1)! = (k + 1) \cdot k!$$
$$> (k + 1)(2^k) \qquad \text{By the inductive hypothesis, } k! > 2^k. \text{ Therefore, we can replace } k! \text{ by } 2^k \text{ and replace the } = \text{ sign with } >.$$
$$> 2 \cdot 2^k \qquad \text{For } k \geq 4, \text{ the expression } (k + 1) > 2. \text{ Therefore, we can replace } (k + 1) \text{ by } 2 \text{ and maintain the } > \text{ symbol.}$$
$$= 2^{k+1}$$

> **TIP** In part 2 of Example 4, we manipulate the expression $(k + 1)!$ on the left side to show that it is greater than the expression on the right side for $k \geq 4$.

From the string of inequalities we have shown that $(k + 1)! > 2^{k+1}$.

We have shown that S_1 is true, and that if S_k is true, then S_{k+1} is true. By mathematical induction, we conclude that the statement is true for all positive integers.

> **Skill Practice 4** Use mathematical induction to prove that $\left(\dfrac{3}{2}\right)^n > 2n$
>
> for $n \geq 7$.

Point of Interest

Mathematical induction is one type of mathematical proof, but there are many other techniques, including proof by contradiction. This technique uses the premise that a statement's being false would imply a contradiction. This approach was used in the complex proof of Fermat's last theorem.

The equation $x^2 + y^2 = z^2$ has infinitely many positive integer solutions for a, b, and c. Such solutions are called Pythagorean triples, such as $a = 5$, $b = 12$, and $c = 13$. However, French mathematician Pierre de Fermat (1601–1665) posed the statement that the equation $x^n + y^n = z^n$ has *no* such solutions for positive integers $n > 2$. Fermat made this claim, now famously called Fermat's last theorem, while annotating a copy of Diophantus' *Arithmetika*. Fermat included a comment that he had "found a remarkable proof of this fact, but there is not enough space in the margin to write it."

Proof of this theorem eluded mathematicians for over 350 yr until Andrew Wiles of Princeton University announced in June of 1993 that he had solved the problem. Wiles's proof is extremely complex and was revised to correct a slight but critical flaw shortly after publication. The proof involves the use of mathematics that did not exist in Fermat's time, and for this reason mathematicians believe that Fermat did not have a simpler proof.

Answer
4. See page SA-45.

SECTION 8.4   Practice Exercises

Review Exercises

For Exercises 1–4, find the sum.

1. $\displaystyle\sum_{i=1}^{67}(3-8i)$

2. $\displaystyle\sum_{j=1}^{122}(10-2j)$

3. $\displaystyle\sum_{n=1}^{5}5\left(\frac{3}{4}\right)^{n-1}$

4. $\displaystyle\sum_{k=1}^{5}3\left(-\frac{2}{3}\right)^{k-1}$

Concept Connections

5. Let S_n be a statement involving the positive integer n, and let k be an arbitrary positive integer. Proof by mathematical _____ indicates that S_n is true for all positive integers n if (1) _____ is true, and (2) the truth of S_k implies the truth of _____.

6. The statement that S_k is true is called the _____ hypothesis.

Objective 1: Prove a Statement Using Mathematical Induction

For Exercises 7–20, use mathematical induction to prove the given statement for all positive integers n. (See Examples 1–2)

7. $2+6+10+\cdots+(4n-2)=2n^2$

8. $2+8+14+\cdots+(6n-4)=n(3n-1)$

9. $5+8+11+\cdots+(3n+2)=\dfrac{n}{2}(3n+7)$

10. $4+9+14+\cdots+(5n-1)=\dfrac{n}{2}(5n+3)$

11. $8+4+0+\cdots+(-4n+12)=-2n(n-5)$

12. $12+6+0+\cdots+(-6n+18)=-3n(n-5)$

13. $1+2+2^2+2^3+\cdots+2^{n-1}=2^n-1$

14. $1+3+3^2+3^3+\cdots+3^{n-1}=\dfrac{1}{2}(3^n-1)$

15. $\dfrac{3}{4}+\dfrac{3}{16}+\dfrac{3}{64}+\cdots+\dfrac{3}{4^n}=1-\left(\dfrac{1}{4}\right)^n$

16. $\dfrac{1}{2}+\dfrac{1}{4}+\dfrac{1}{8}+\cdots+\dfrac{1}{2^n}=1-\left(\dfrac{1}{2}\right)^n$

17. $1\cdot2+2\cdot3+3\cdot4+\cdots+n(n+1)$
$=\dfrac{n(n+1)(n+2)}{3}$

18. $1\cdot3+2\cdot5+3\cdot7+\cdots+n(2n+1)$
$=\dfrac{n(n+1)(4n+5)}{6}$

19. $\left(1-\dfrac{1}{2}\right)\left(1-\dfrac{1}{3}\right)\left(1-\dfrac{1}{4}\right)\cdots\left(1-\dfrac{1}{n+1}\right)$
$=\dfrac{1}{n+1}$

20. $\left(1-\dfrac{1}{2^2}\right)\left(1-\dfrac{1}{3^2}\right)\left(1-\dfrac{1}{4^2}\right)\cdots\left(1-\dfrac{1}{(n+1)^2}\right)$
$=\dfrac{n+2}{2(n+1)}$

For Exercises 21–24, use mathematical induction to prove the given statement for all natural numbers n.

21. $\displaystyle\sum_{i=1}^{n}1=n$

22. $\displaystyle\sum_{i=1}^{n}i=\dfrac{n(n+1)}{2}$

23. $\displaystyle\sum_{i=1}^{n}i^2=\dfrac{n(n+1)(2n+1)}{6}$

24. $\displaystyle\sum_{i=1}^{n}i^3=\dfrac{n^2(n+1)^2}{4}$

For Exercises 25–28, use mathematical induction to prove the given statement for all natural numbers n. (See Example 3)

25. 2 is a factor of 5^n-3.   **26.** 2 is a factor of 7^n-3.   **27.** 4^n-1 is divisible by 3.   **28.** 5^n-1 is divisible by 4.

Objective 2: Prove a Statement Using the Extended Principle of Mathematical Induction

For Exercises 29–32, use trial-and-error to determine the smallest positive integer n for which the given statement is true.

29. $n!>3^n$ **30.** $(n+1)!>4^n$ **31.** $3n<2^n$ **32.** $5n<3^n$

For Exercises 33–36, use mathematical induction to prove the given statement. (See Example 4)

33. $n!>3^n$ for natural numbers $n\geq7$.

34. $(n+1)!>4^n$ for natural numbers $n\geq6$.

35. $3n<2^n$ for natural numbers $n\geq4$.

36. $5n<3^n$ for natural numbers $n\geq3$.

Mixed Exercises

For Exercises 37–40, use mathematical induction to prove the given statement for all positive integers n and real numbers x and y.

37. $(xy)^n = x^n y^n$ **38.** $\left(\dfrac{x}{y}\right)^n = \dfrac{x^n}{y^n}$ provided that $y \neq 0$.   **39.** If $x > 1$, then $x^n > x^{n-1}$.   **40.** If $0 < x < 1$, then $x^n < x^{n-1}$.

We have used mathematical induction to prove that a statement is true for all natural numbers n. To show that a statement is *not* true, all we need is one case in which the statement is false. This is called a **counterexample**. For Exercises 41–42, find a counterexample to show that the given statement is *not* true.

41. The expression $n^2 - n + 11$ is prime for all natural numbers n.

42. The inequality $5^n > n!$ is true for all natural numbers n.

Write About It

43. Explain the difference between the principle of mathematical induction and the extended principle of mathematical induction.

44. Suppose that a fellow student showed that the expression $n^2 + n + 1$ is prime for $n = 1, 2,$ and 3. Explain why this is not a sufficient proof that the expression is prime for all positive integers n.

Expanding Your Skills

45. Show that $n^2 - n$ is even for all positive integers n.

46. Show that $n^2 - n + 1$ is odd for all positive integers n.

For Exercises 47–48, use the Fibonacci sequence $\{F_n\} = \{1, 1, 2, 3, 5, 8, 13, \ldots\}$. Recall that the Fibonacci sequence can be defined recursively as $F_1 = 1$, $F_2 = 1$, and $F_n = F_{n-1} + F_{n-2}$ for $n \geq 3$.

47. Prove that $F_1 + F_2 + F_3 + \cdots + F_n = F_{n+2} - 1$ for positive integers $n \geq 3$.

48. Prove that $F_1 + F_3 + F_5 + \cdots + F_{2n-1} = F_{2n}$ for all positive integers n.

SECTION 8.5   The Binomial Theorem

OBJECTIVES

1. Determine Binomial Coefficients
2. Apply the Binomial Theorem
3. Find a Specific Term in a Binomial Expansion

1. Determine Binomial Coefficients

In Section R.5 we learned how to square a binomial.

$$(a + b)^2 = a^2 + 2ab + b^2$$

The expression $a^2 + 2ab + b^2$ is called the **binomial expansion** of $(a + b)^2$. To expand $(a + b)^3$, we can find the product $(a + b)(a + b)^2$.

$$(a + b)(a + b)^2 = (a + b)(a^2 + 2ab + b^2)$$

$$= a^3 + 2a^2b + ab^2 + a^2b + 2ab^2 + b^3$$
$$= a^3 + 3a^2b + 3ab^2 + b^3$$

Similarly, to expand $(a + b)^4$, we can multiply $(a + b)$ by $(a + b)^3$. Using this method, we can expand several powers of $(a + b)$.

$(a + b)^0 = 1$

$(a + b)^1 = 1a + 1b$

$(a + b)^2 = 1a^2 + 2ab + 1b^2$

$(a + b)^3 = 1a^3 + 3a^2b + 3ab^2 + 1b^3$

$(a + b)^4 = 1a^4 + 4a^3b + 6a^2b^2 + 4ab^3 + 1b^4$

$(a + b)^5 = 1a^5 + 5a^4b + 10a^3b^2 + 10a^2b^3 + 5ab^4 + 1b^5$

```
            1
          1   1
        1   2   1
      1   3   3   1
    1   4   6   4   1
  1   5  10  10   5   1
```

Figure 8-9

From the expansion of $(a + b)^n$, we note the following patterns.

- The exponent on a decreases from n to 0 on sequential terms from left to right.
- The exponent on b increases from 0 to n on sequential terms from left to right.
- The sum of the exponents on each term (that is, the degree of each term) is n.
- The number of terms in the expansion is $(n + 1)$. For example, the expansion of $(a + b)^4$ has five terms.

The coefficients for the expansion of $(a + b)^n$ follow a triangular array of numbers called **Pascal's triangle** (Figure 8-9), named after the French mathematician Blaise Pascal (1623–1662). Each row begins and ends with a 1, and each entry in between is the sum of the two diagonal entries from the row above. For example, in the last row, we have

$$1, \quad 1 + 4 = 5, \quad 4 + 6 = 10, \quad 6 + 4 = 10, \quad 4 + 1 = 5, \text{ and } 1.$$

EXAMPLE 1   Expanding a Binomial

Expand. $(a + b)^6$

Solution:

The expansion of $(a + b)^6$ will have 7 terms (one more than the exponent of 6). Using the entries of the seventh row of Pascal's triangle as the coefficients, the expansion of $(a + b)^6$ is:

```
            1
          1   1
        1   2   1
      1   3   3   1
    1   4   6   4   1
  1   5  10  10   5   1
1   6  15  20  15   6   1
```

$$(a + b)^6 = 1a^6 + 6a^5b + 15a^4b^2 + 20a^3b^3 + 15a^2b^4 + 6ab^5 + 1b^6$$

Skill Practice 1   Expand. $(a + b)^7$

Determining the coefficients of a binomial expansion using Pascal's triangle would be cumbersome for expansions of higher degree. Instead we can compute the coefficients of a binomial expansion using the following formula.

TIP The expression $\binom{n}{r}$ will also be used in Section 8.6 when we study counting principles. $\binom{n}{r}$ represents the number of ways we can *choose* a group of r items in any order from a group of n items.

Coefficients of a Binomial Expansion

Let n and r be nonnegative integers with $n \geq r$. The expression $\binom{n}{r}$ (read as "n choose r") is called a **binomial coefficient** and is defined by

$$\binom{n}{r} = \frac{n!}{r!(n - r)!}$$

Note: The notation $_nC_r$ is often used in place of $\binom{n}{r}$.

EXAMPLE 2   Computing Binomial Coefficients

Evaluate.

a. $\binom{6}{0}$ **b.** $\binom{6}{1}$ **c.** $\binom{6}{2}$ **d.** $\binom{6}{6}$

Answer

1. $a^7 + 7a^6b + 21a^5b^2 + 35a^4b^3 + 35a^3b^4 + 21a^2b^5 + 7ab^6 + b^7$

Solution:

For parts (a)–(d), apply $\binom{n}{r} = \dfrac{n!}{r!(n-r)!}$

a. $\binom{6}{0} = \dfrac{6!}{0! \cdot (6-0)!} = \dfrac{6!}{0! \cdot 6!} = \dfrac{6!}{1 \cdot 6!} = 1$ $n = 6$ and $r = 0$.
                                                        Recall that $0! = 1$.

b. $\binom{6}{1} = \dfrac{6!}{1! \cdot (6-1)!} = \dfrac{6!}{1! \cdot 5!} = \dfrac{6 \cdot 5!}{1 \cdot 5!} = 6$ $n = 6$ and $r = 1$.

c. $\binom{6}{2} = \dfrac{6!}{2! \cdot (6-2)!} = \dfrac{6!}{2! \cdot 4!} = \dfrac{6 \cdot 5 \cdot 4!}{2 \cdot 1 \cdot 4!} = 15$ $n = 6$ and $r = 2$.

d. $\binom{6}{6} = \dfrac{6!}{6! \cdot (6-6)!} = \dfrac{6!}{6! \cdot 0!} = \dfrac{6!}{6! \cdot 1} = 1$ $n = 6$ and $r = 6$.

Skill Practice 2   Evaluate.

    a. $\binom{5}{0}$ **b.** $\binom{5}{1}$ **c.** $\binom{5}{2}$ **d.** $\binom{5}{5}$

TECHNOLOGY CONNECTIONS

Evaluating Binomial Coefficients

To evaluate binomial coefficients on a graphing utility, use the $_nC_r$ function found in the MATH menu under PRB.

```
MATH NUM CPX PRB
1:rand     6 nCr 0
2:nPr                  1
3:nCr      6 nCr 1
4:!                    6
5:randI    6 nCr 2
6:randN                15
7↓randB
```

---

2. Apply the Binomial Theorem

From Example 2, notice that $\binom{6}{0} = 1$, $\binom{6}{1} = 6$, and $\binom{6}{2} = 15$ are the coefficients for the first three terms of the expansion of $(a + b)^6$. The value $\binom{6}{6} = 1$ is the coefficient of the last term of the expansion. Using the values of $\binom{n}{r}$ for the coefficients, we have a formula for the expansion of the binomial $(a + b)^n$. This is called the **binomial theorem.**

> **TIP** The binomial theorem can be proved by using mathematical induction. See the proof in the online appendix at www.mhhe.com/millerca.

The Binomial Theorem

Let n be a positive integer. The expansion of $(a + b)^n$ is given by

$$(a + b)^n = \binom{n}{0}a^n + \binom{n}{1}a^{n-1}b + \binom{n}{2}a^{n-2}b^2 + \cdots + \binom{n}{n-1}ab^{n-1} + \binom{n}{n}b^n$$

$$= \sum_{r=0}^{n} \binom{n}{r}a^{n-r}b^r$$

Answers

2. a. 1   **b.** 5   **c.** 10   **d.** 1

EXAMPLE 3 **Applying the Binomial Theorem**

Expand by using the binomial theorem. $(2x + 3)^4$

Solution:

The expression $(2x + 3)^4$ is in the form $(a + b)^4$ with $a = 2x$ and $b = 3$.

$$(a + b)^4 = \binom{4}{0}a^4 + \binom{4}{1}a^3b + \binom{4}{2}a^2b^2 + \binom{4}{3}ab^3 + \binom{4}{4}b^4$$

$$(2x + 3)^4 = \binom{4}{0}(2x)^4 + \binom{4}{1}(2x)^3(3) + \binom{4}{2}(2x)^2(3)^2 + \binom{4}{3}(2x)(3)^3 + \binom{4}{4}(3)^4$$

$$= 1(16x^4) + 4(8x^3)(3) + 6(4x^2)(9) + 4(2x)(27) + 1(81)$$

$$= 16x^4 + 96x^3 + 216x^2 + 216x + 81$$

Skill Practice 3 Expand by using the binomial theorem. $(4y + 5)^4$

In Example 4, we expand a difference of terms.

EXAMPLE 4 **Applying the Binomial Theorem**

Expand by using the binomial theorem. $(3x^2 - 5y)^3$

Solution:

The expression $(3x^2 - 5y)^3 = [3x^2 + (-5y)]^3$ is in the form $(a + b)^3$ with $a = 3x^2$ and $b = -5y$.

$$(a + b)^3 = \binom{3}{0}a^3 + \binom{3}{1}a^2b + \binom{3}{2}ab^2 + \binom{3}{3}b^3$$

$$[3x^2 + (-5y)]^3 = \binom{3}{0}(3x^2)^3 + \binom{3}{1}(3x^2)^2(-5y) + \binom{3}{2}(3x^2)(-5y)^2 + \binom{3}{3}(-5y)^3$$

$$= 1(27x^6) + 3(9x^4)(-5y) + 3(3x^2)(25y^2) + 1(-125y^3)$$

$$= 27x^6 - 135x^4y + 225x^2y^2 - 125y^3$$

Skill Practice 4 Expand by using the binomial theorem. $(2t^4 - 3v)^3$

3. Find a Specific Term in a Binomial Expansion

Consider the first four terms of the binomial expansion of $(a + b)^n$.

The exponent on b is one less than the term number.

$$\binom{n}{0}a^nb^0 + \binom{n}{1}a^{n-1}b^1 + \binom{n}{2}a^{n-2}b^2 + \binom{n}{3}a^{n-3}b^3$$

These values match the exponent on b.

From the observed pattern, the kth term has a factor of b raised to the $k - 1$ power. That is, the exponent on b is one less than the term number. Furthermore, the sum of the exponents must equal n. Therefore, the factor a is raised to the $n - (k - 1)$ power. That is, the exponent on a is n minus the exponent on b.

Answers

3. $256y^4 + 1280y^3 + 2400y^2 + 2000y + 625$

4. $8t^{12} - 36t^8v + 54t^4v^2 - 27v^3$

kth Term of a Binomial Expansion

Let n and k be positive integers with $k \le n + 1$. The kth term of $(a + b)^n$ is

$$\binom{n}{k-1} a^{n-(k-1)} b^{k-1}$$

EXAMPLE 5   **Finding a Specific Term of a Binomial Expansion**

Find the eighth term of $(2x + y^4)^{10}$.

Solution:

To find the eighth term of $(a + b)^{10}$, we require the exponent on b to be 7 (one less than the term number). Therefore, the exponent on a must be 3 so that the sum of the exponents is 10.

Therefore, the eighth term of $(a + b)^{10}$ is $\binom{10}{7} a^3 b^7$.

sum of exponents must be 10.

1 less than the term number

same as exponent on b

The eighth term of $(2x + y^4)^{10}$ is $\binom{10}{7}(2x)^3(y^4)^7 = 120(8x^3)(y^{28}) = 960x^3 y^{28}$.

Alternatively, we can apply the formula for the kth term of a binomial expansion with $n = 10$, $k = 8$, $a = 2x$, and $b = y^4$.

$$\binom{n}{k-1} a^{n-(k-1)} b^{k-1} = \binom{10}{8-1}(2x)^{10-(8-1)}(y^4)^{8-1} = \binom{10}{7}(2x)^3(y^4)^7 = 960x^3 y^{28}$$

The eighth term of the expansion is $960x^3 y^{28}$.

Skill Practice 5   Find the seventh term of $(3c + d^5)^9$.

Answer

5. $2268c^3 d^{30}$

SECTION 8.5   Practice Exercises

Review Exercises

For Exercises 1–2, write the sum in expanded form.

1. $\displaystyle\sum_{n=0}^{2}(x + y)^n$

2. $\displaystyle\sum_{n=0}^{2}(a + 4)^n$

For Exercises 3–8, evaluate the sum.

3. $\displaystyle\sum_{i=1}^{52}(3i + 8)$

4. $\displaystyle\sum_{i=1}^{81}(4i - 7)$

5. $\displaystyle\sum_{k=1}^{4} 3\left(\frac{1}{2}\right)^{k-1}$

6. $\displaystyle\sum_{k=1}^{5} 4\left(-\frac{1}{3}\right)^{k-1}$

7. $\displaystyle\sum_{j=1}^{\infty} 3\left(\frac{1}{2}\right)^{j-1}$

8. $\displaystyle\sum_{i=1}^{\infty} 4\left(-\frac{1}{3}\right)^{i-1}$

9. a. Given the series $\displaystyle\sum_{i=1}^{n} x^3(-x)^{i-1}$, expand the sum for $n = 6$ and $x \ne 0$.

    b. Find the sum if $x = 1$ and n is odd.

    c. Find the sum if $x = 1$ and n is even.

10. Given $\displaystyle\sum_{i=1}^{8}(2i + i^2)$, fill in the blanks to write an equivalent series $\displaystyle\sum_{j=0}^{\square} \square$.

Concept Connections

11. The expression $a^3 + 3a^2b + 3ab^2 + b^3$ is called the _____ expansion of $(a + b)^3$.

12. Consider $(a + b)^n$, where n is a whole number. How many terms are in the binomial expansion?

13. Consider $(a + b)^n$, where n is a whole number. What is the degree of each term in the expansion?

14. Consider $(a + b)^n$, where n is a whole number. The coefficients of the terms in the expansion can be found by using _____ triangle or by using $\binom{n}{r}$.

15. For positive integers n and k ($k \leq n + 1$), the kth term of $(a + b)^n$ is given by $\binom{}{}a^{\square}b^{\square}$.

16. Given $(a + b)^{17}$, the 12th term is given by $\binom{}{}a^{\square}b^{\square}$.

Objective 1: Determine Binomial Coefficients

17. a. Write the first five rows of Pascal's triangle.

    b. Write the expansion of $(x - y)^4$. (**See Example 1**)

18. a. Write the first four rows of Pascal's triangle.

    b. Write the expansion of $(c - d)^3$.

For Exercises 19–20, evaluate the given expression. Compare the result to the fifth and sixth rows of Pascal's triangle. (**See Example 2**)

19. a. $\binom{4}{0}$ **b.** $\binom{4}{1}$ **c.** $\binom{4}{2}$

20. a. $\binom{5}{0}$ **b.** $\binom{5}{1}$ **c.** $\binom{5}{2}$

d. $\binom{4}{3}$ **e.** $\binom{4}{4}$

d. $\binom{5}{3}$ **e.** $\binom{5}{4}$ **f.** $\binom{5}{5}$

For Exercises 21–24, evaluate the expression.

21. $\binom{13}{3}$ **22.** $\binom{17}{15}$ **23.** $\binom{11}{5}$ **24.** $\binom{9}{4}$

Objective 2: Apply the Binomial Theorem

For Exercises 25–38, expand the binomial by using the binomial theorem. (**See Examples 3–4**)

25. $(3x + 1)^5$ **26.** $(5x + 3)^5$ **27.** $(7x + 3)^3$ **28.** $(6x + 5)^3$

29. $(2x - 5)^4$ **30.** $(4x - 1)^4$ **31.** $(2x^3 - y)^5$ **32.** $(3y^2 - z)^5$

33. $(p^2 - w^4)^6$ **34.** $(t^3 - v^5)^6$ **35.** $(0.2 + 0.1k)^4$ **36.** $(0.1 + 0.3m)^4$

37. $\left(\dfrac{c}{2} - d\right)^3$ **38.** $\left(\dfrac{x}{3} - n\right)^3$

Objective 3: Find a Specific Term in a Binomial Expansion

For Exercises 39–50, find the indicated term of the binomial expansion. (**See Example 5**)

39. $(m + n)^{10}$; seventh term   **40.** $(p + q)^{11}$; ninth term   **41.** $(c - d)^8$; fourth term

42. $(x - y)^9$; sixth term   **43.** $(u^2 + 2v^4)^{15}$; tenth term   **44.** $(y^3 + 2z^2)^{14}$; tenth term

45. $(\sqrt{3}x^2 + y^3)^9$; fourth term   **46.** $(\sqrt{2}u^3 + v^4)^8$; third term   **47.** $(h^4 - 1)^{12}$; middle term

48. $(k^3 - 1)^{10}$; middle term   **49.** $(p^4 + 3q)^8$; Find the term containing p^{12}.   **50.** $(a^3 + 4b)^6$; Find the term containing a^9.

Mixed Exercises

51. Expand $(e^x - e^{-x})^4$.

52. Expand $(e^x + e^{-x})^3$.

53. Use the binomial theorem to expand $(x + y - z)^3$.

54. Use the binomial theorem to expand $(a + b - 2)^3$.

55. Use the binomial theorem to find $(1.01)^4$. [*Hint*: Write the expression as $(1 + 0.01)^4$.]

56. Use the binomial theorem to find $(1.1)^5$.

57. Simplify. $(x + y)^3 - (x - y)^3$

58. Simplify. $(x + 1)^3 - (x - 1)^3$

For Exercises 59–62, simplify the difference quotient: $\dfrac{f(x+h)-f(x)}{h}$

59. $f(x)=2x^3+4$ **60.** $f(x)=4x^3+3$ **61.** $f(x)=x^4-5x^2+1$ **62.** $f(x)=x^4-6x^2-4$

For Exercises 63–66, use the binomial theorem to find the value of the complex number raised to the given power. Recall that $i=\sqrt{-1}$.

63. $(2+i)^3$ **64.** $(3+i)^3$ **65.** $(5-2i)^4$ **66.** $(6-5i)^4$

67. Show that $\dbinom{n}{r}$ and $\dbinom{n}{n-r}$ are equivalent.   **68.** Show that $\dbinom{n}{0}=1$ and $\dbinom{n}{n}=1$.

69. a. Write the sequence corresponding to the sum of the numbers in each row of Pascal's triangle for the first nine rows.

    b. Let n represent the row number in Pascal's triangle. Write a formula for the nth term of the sequence representing the sum of the numbers in row n.

Write About It

70. Explain why $\dbinom{-13}{3}$ is undefined.   **71.** Explain why $\dbinom{3}{5}$ is undefined.

72. Explain why many graphing utilities give an error message for the expression $\dfrac{120!}{118!}$. How can this expression be evaluated by hand?

Expanding Your Skills

Stirling's formula (named after Scottish mathematician, James Stirling: 1692–1770) is used to approximate large values of $n!$. Stirling's formula is

$$n! \approx \sqrt{2\pi n}\left(\frac{n}{e}\right)^n$$

For Exercises 73–74,

a. Use Stirling's formula to approximate the given expression. Round to the nearest whole unit.

b. Compute the actual value of the expression.

c. Determine the percent difference between the approximate value and the actual value.

73. $8!$ **74.** $12!$

Using techniques from calculus, we can show that $(1+x)^n = 1 + nx + \dfrac{n(n-1)x^2}{2!} + \dfrac{n(n-1)(n-2)}{3!}x^3 + \cdots$, for $|x| < 1$. This formula can be used to evaluate binomial expressions raised to noninteger exponents. For Exercises 75–76, use the first four terms of this infinite series to approximate the given expression. Round to 3 decimal places if necessary.

75. $(1.4)^{3/2}$ [*Hint*: $(1.4)^{3/2} = (1+0.4)^{3/2}$]   **76.** $\sqrt[4]{(1.3)^3}$

SECTION 8.6   Principles of Counting

1. Apply the Fundamental Principle of Counting

Many states have lotteries as a means to raise income. The game "Florida Lotto" for example, pays a grand prize to players who choose six distinct numbers from 1 to 53 (in any order) that match the same group of six numbers in the drawing. The number of such six-number combinations is 22,957,480 (see Example 8). If a player chooses one group of six numbers, then the probability (likelihood) of winning the grand prize is $\frac{1}{22,957,480}$. This value (roughly 1 in 23 million) means that it is highly unlikely to win the grand prize. To put this in perspective, the following events are more likely to happen than winning the grand prize in "Florida Lotto."

- A pedestrian being killed by a motor vehicle: Probability $\approx \frac{1}{1,000,000}$
- Flipping a coin 24 times and getting all heads: Probability $= \frac{1}{16,777,216}$
- Dying from a venomous insect or animal bite: Probability $\approx \frac{1}{100,000}$

In this section and in Section 8.7, we present basic principles of counting and how these principles apply to probability. We begin in Example 1, by using a figure called a tree diagram to organize different outcomes of a sequence of events.

EXAMPLE 1   Counting the Outcomes of a Sequence of Events

Suppose that a frozen custard shop offers 4 flavors of custard, 2 types of syrup, and 2 toppings. If a customer can select 1 item from each group for a sundae, how many different sundaes can be made?

Custard Flavors	Syrups	Toppings
Vanilla (V)	Hot fudge (H)	Nuts (N)
Chocolate (C)	Butterscotch (B)	Granola (G)
Mint chip (M)		
Peanut butter (P)		

Solution:

We can depict the 4 flavors of custard by the left-most branches in Figure 8-10. Then for each branch of custard, there are 2 branches representing the type of syrup. Finally, for each custard-syrup arrangement, there are 2 toppings.

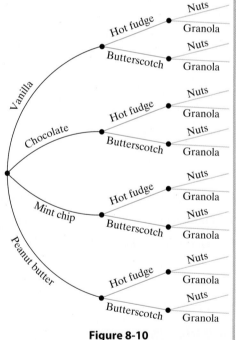

The tree diagram shows 16 different sundaes:

VHN, VHG, VBN, VBG, CHN, CHG, CBN, CBG, MHN, MHG, MBN, MBG, PHN, PHG, PBN, and PBG.

Notice that the number of outcomes is easily found by multiplying the number of choices from each group:

Total outcomes: $(4)(2)(2) = 16$

Figure 8-10

Skill Practice 1   A pizza can be made from either thick or thin crust, and a choice of 6 toppings. How many different types of pizza can be made?

Answer

1. 12

The result from Example 1 suggests that the number of outcomes for the sequence of events is the product of the number of outcomes for each individual event. This is generalized as the fundamental principle of counting.

> **Fundamental Principle of Counting**
>
> If one event can occur in m different ways and a second event can occur in n different ways, then the number of ways that the two events can occur in sequence is $m \cdot n$.

In Example 2, we demonstrate that the fundamental principle of counting can be applied for a sequence of many events.

EXAMPLE 2   Applying the Fundamental Principle of Counting

A computer password must have three letters, followed by two digits. How many passwords can be made if

a. There are no restrictions on the letters or digits?

b. No letter or digit may be used more than once?

Solution:

a. The computer password is a sequence of five characters. The number of arrangements of letters and digits is given by the product of the number of outcomes for each character. There are 26 letters of the alphabet from which to choose. The digits in the password may be selected from 0, 1, 2, 3, 4, 5, 6, 7, 8, 9. Therefore, the total number of passwords is given by

There are 26 choices   There are 10 choices
for each letter.   for each digit.

$$26 \cdot 26 \cdot 26 \cdot 10 \cdot 10 = 1{,}757{,}600$$

b. If no letter may be repeated, then the number of letters from which to choose must be decreased by one when the second letter is selected. Likewise, the number of letters must be decreased by one again when the third letter is selected. The same logic is used when selecting the digits. Once the first digit is selected in the password, there are only nine remaining digits available for the second choice.

The number of letters is   There are 10 choices for the
decreased by one for each   first digit, but only 9
letter in the sequence.   remaining for the second.

$$26 \cdot 25 \cdot 24 \cdot 10 \cdot 9 = 1{,}404{,}000$$

> **Skill Practice 2**   A code for an alarm system is made up of two letters, followed by four digits. How many codes can be made if
>
> **a.** There are no restrictions on the letters or digits?
>
> **b.** No letter or digit may be used more than once?

Answers

2. a. $26 \cdot 26 \cdot 10 \cdot 10 \cdot 10 \cdot 10 = 6{,}760{,}000$
   b. $26 \cdot 25 \cdot 10 \cdot 9 \cdot 8 \cdot 7 = 3{,}276{,}000$

EXAMPLE 3   Applying the Fundamental Principle of Counting

A quiz has five true/false questions and five multiple-choice questions. The multiple-choice questions each have four possible answers of which only one is correct. If a student forgets to study and must guess on each question, in how many ways can the student answer the questions on the test?

Solution:

The quiz questions form a 10-stage event. Each true/false question has two possible choices (true or false). Each multiple-choice question has four possible choices (for example: a, b, c, or d). Therefore, the number of ways that the questions can be answered on the test is given by

$$\underbrace{2 \cdot 2 \cdot 2 \cdot 2 \cdot 2} \cdot \underbrace{4 \cdot 4 \cdot 4 \cdot 4 \cdot 4} = 32{,}768$$

Skill Practice 3   A quiz has four true/false questions and six multiple-choice questions. The multiple-choice questions each have five possible answers of which only one is correct. In how many ways can the questions on the test be answered?

2. Count Permutations

We now look at a situation in which n items are to be arranged in order. Such an arrangement is called a **permutation**. For example, consider the different arrangements of the letters in the word FIVE.

FIVE	FIEV	FVIE	FVEI	FEIV	FEVI	
IFVE	IFEV	IVEF	IVFE	IEVF	IEFV	24 arrangements
VFIE	VFEI	VEIF	VEFI	VIEF	VIFE	
EFIV	EFVI	EIFV	EIVF	EVIF	EVFI	

There are 24 such arrangements. We can arrive at the same conclusion by applying the fundamental principle of counting. There are four letters available for the first choice in the arrangement. That leaves 3 letters remaining for the second choice, followed by 2 letters for the third choice, and only 1 letter for the last choice. Therefore, the number of permutations of 4 distinct letters is given by

$$4 \cdot 3 \cdot 2 \cdot 1 = 24$$

We generalize this as follows.

Number of Permutations of n Distinguishable Elements

The number of permutations of n distinct elements is $n!$.

Note: This means that there are $n!$ ways to arrange n distinguishable items in various orders.

Now suppose that we wanted to arrange the letters in the word NINE. Notice that if we were to switch the first and third letters (both "N's") we would get the same arrangement. This is because the two N's are indistinguishable. This means that when

Answer

3. 250,000

counting the number of permutations we must "divide out" the number of ways that the two N's can be arranged. The two N's can be arranged in 2! different ways. This leads to the following result.

Number of Permutations of *n* Elements, Some Indistinguishable

Consider a set of *n* elements with r_1 duplicates of one kind, r_2 duplicates of a second kind, ... , r_k duplicates of a *k*th kind. Then the number of distinguishable permutations of the *n* elements of the set is

$$\frac{n!}{r_1! \cdot r_2! \cdot \cdots \cdot r_k!}$$

Note: The factors of $r_1!, r_2!, \ldots, r_k!$ in the denominator remove the repetition of arrangements that arise from the indistinguishable elements.

EXAMPLE 4   Counting Permutations

a. Determine the number of ways that 6 people can be arranged in line at a ticket counter.
b. Determine the number of ways that the letters in the word MICROSCOPIC can be arranged.

Solution:

a. No two people can be the same. Therefore, we are arranging 6 different (distinguishable) items in various orders. The number of such permutations is given by

   6! = 720   There are 720 ways in which 6 people can be arranged in line.

b. The word MICROSCOPIC has 11 letters. However, the letter I appears twice, the letter O appears twice, and the letter C appears 3 times. The number of unique arrangements of these letters is

   $$\frac{11!}{2! \cdot 2! \cdot 3!} = 1,663,200$$

Skill Practice 4

a. In how many ways can 7 different books be arranged on a bookshelf?
b. Determine the number of ways that the letters in the word RIFFRAFF can be arranged.

In Example 5, we determine the number of permutations from a group of *n* items in which fewer than *n* items are selected at one time.

EXAMPLE 5   Finding Permutations of *n* Items Taken *r* at a Time

Suppose that 5 students (Alberto, Beth, Carol, Dennis, and Erik) submit applications for scholarships. There are two scholarships available. The first is for $1000 and the second is for $500. In how many ways can 2 students from the 5 be selected to receive the scholarships?

Answers

4. a. 7! = 5040   **b.** $\dfrac{8!}{2! \cdot 4!} = 840$

Solution:

We begin by labeling the students as A, B, C, D, and E. We can construct a list of the possible outcomes.

AB	AC	AD	AE	BC	BD	BE	CD	CE	DE
BA	CA	DA	EA	CB	DB	EB	DC	EC	ED

Each outcome in the second row involves the same 2 people as the outcome directly above in the first row, but in the reverse order. The order of selection is important. For example:

- AB means that Alberto gets $1000 and Beth gets $500, whereas
- BA means that Beth gets $1000 and Alberto gets $500.

There are 20 possible ways to select 2 people from 5 people in which the order of selection is relevant. That is, there are 20 permutations of 5 people taken 2 at a time.

> **Skill Practice 5**   Determine the number of ways that 2 students from a group of 4 students can be selected to hold the positions of president and vice president of student government.

The number of permutations of 5 people taken 2 at a time can also be computed by using the fundamental principle of counting. There are 5 candidates for the $1000 scholarship, which leaves 4 students left over for the $500 scholarship. The product is $5 \cdot 4 = 20$.

This result can also be obtained by using factorial notation:

Number of people in the group (5).

$$\frac{5!}{(5-2)!} = \frac{5!}{3!} = \frac{5 \cdot 4 \cdot (3 \cdot 2 \cdot 1)}{(3 \cdot 2 \cdot 1)} = 20$$

Number of people to be selected (2).

Suppose that n represents the number of distinct elements in a group from which r elements will be chosen in a particular order. We call each arrangement a **permutation** of n elements taken r at a time and denote the number of such permutations as $_nP_r$.

> **Number of Permutations of *n* Elements Taken *r* at a Time**
>
> The number of permutations of n elements taken r at a time is given by
>
> r factors
>
> $$_nP_r = \frac{n!}{(n-r)!}, \text{ or equivalently, } _nP_r = n(n-1)(n-2)\cdots(n-r+1)$$
>
> *Note:* $_nP_r$ counts the number of permutations of n items taken r at a time under the assumption that no item can be selected more than once, and that each of the n items is distinguishable.

> **EXAMPLE 6**   **Counting Permutations in an Application**

If 8 horses enter a race, in how many ways can the horses finish first, second, and third?

Answer
5. 12

Solution:

We must find the number of ways that 3 horses can be selected from 8 horses in a prescribed order (first, second, third). This is given by $_8P_3$.

$$_8P_3 = \frac{8!}{(8-3)!} = \frac{8!}{5!} = \frac{8 \cdot 7 \cdot 6 \cdot \overset{1}{\cancel{5!}}}{\cancel{5!}} = 8 \cdot 7 \cdot 6 = 336$$

Alternatively: $_8P_3 = \underbrace{8 \cdot 7 \cdot 6}_{\text{3 factors}} = 336$ $\boxed{n=8}$

There are 336 possible first-, second-, and third-place arrangements.

> **TIP** The alternative formula for $_nP_r$ indicates that we multiply n times the consecutive integers less than n until a total of r factors is reached.

Skill Practice 6   A judge at the County Fair must give blue, red, and white ribbons for first-, second-, and third-place entries in a poetry contest. If there are 12 contestants, in how many ways can the judge award the ribbons?

TECHNOLOGY CONNECTIONS

Evaluating a Number of Permutations, $_nP_r$

Most graphing utilities can evaluate the number of permutations of n elements taken r at a time. For example, use the $_nP_r$ function found in the MATH menu under PRB.

---

3. Count Combinations

Consider the situation in Example 5 in which 5 students are selected for 2 scholarships. If the scholarships were for *equal* amounts (say for $500 each), then the order in which the 2 students are selected does not matter. This is because the "prizes" are indistinguishable; that is, the outcomes AB and BA are the same because student A and student B would each receive $500.

In this scenario, we want to select a set of 2 people from a set of 5 people without regard to order. In such a case, the outcomes are called *combinations* (rather than permutations). From the list of permutations given in Example 5, we can strike through the redundant cases that arise from the order of the two individuals in the group. As a result, there are 10 combinations of 5 people taken 2 at a time.

AB	AC	AD	AE	BC	BD	BE	CD	CE	DE
~~BA~~	~~CA~~	~~DA~~	~~EA~~	~~CB~~	~~DB~~	~~EB~~	~~DC~~	~~EC~~	~~ED~~

To find the number of combinations, we divide the number of permutations (in this case 20) by 2! because there are 2! ways in which two letters can be arranged in order.

$$\text{Number of combinations} = \frac{_5P_2}{2!} = \frac{20}{2} = 10$$

To generalize, suppose that n represents the number of distinct elements in a group from which r elements will be chosen in *no particular order*. We call each selection a **combination** of n elements taken r at a time and denote the number of such combinations as $_nC_r$.

Answer

6. 1320

TIP The number of combinations $_nC_r$ is equal to the number of permutations $_nP_r$ divided by $r!$. The value $r!$ in the denominator "divides out" the redundant cases involving different arrangements of r elements within the same group.

Number of Combinations of n Elements Taken r at a Time

The number of combinations of n elements taken r at a time is given by

$$_nC_r = \frac{n!}{r! \cdot (n-r)!}, \text{ or equivalently, } _nC_r = \frac{_nP_r}{r!}$$

EXAMPLE 7   Comparing Combinations and Permutations

a. In how many ways can 3 students from a group of 15 students be selected to serve on a committee?

b. In how many ways can 3 students from a group of 15 students be selected to serve on a committee, if the students will hold the offices of president, vice president, and treasurer?

Solution:

a. In this situation, the students will serve indistinguishable roles on the committee. Therefore, the order in which the 3 students are selected is not relevant. The number of such committees is the number of combinations of $n = 15$ students taken $r = 3$ at a time.

$$_{15}C_3 = \frac{15!}{3! \cdot (15-3)!} = \frac{15!}{3! \cdot 12!} = \frac{\overset{5}{\cancel{15}} \cdot \overset{7}{\cancel{14}} \cdot 13 \cdot \cancel{12!}}{\underset{1}{\cancel{3} \cdot 2 \cdot 1} \cdot \cancel{12!}} = 455$$

b. Now the students will be selected to a committee and assigned different roles (president, vice president, and treasurer). In this case, the order in which the students are selected matters. We need to count the number of *permutations* of $n = 15$ students taken $r = 3$ at a time.

$$_{15}P_3 = \frac{15!}{(15-3)!} = \frac{15!}{12!} = \frac{15 \cdot 14 \cdot 13 \cdot \overset{1}{\cancel{12!}}}{\cancel{12!}} = 2730$$

Skill Practice 7   Suppose that 20 people enter a raffle.

a. In how many ways can four different people among the 20 be selected to receive prizes of $50 each?

b. In how many ways can four different people among the 20 be selected to receive prizes of $50, $25, $10, and $5?

In Example 7, notice that there are $3! = 6$ times as many permutations as combinations. The reason is that for each combination of 3 items, such as A, B, and C, there are $3! = 6$ permutations: ABC, ACB, BAC, BCA, CAB, CBA.

EXAMPLE 8   Counting Combinations in an Application

In the game "Florida Lotto," a player must select a group of 6 numbers (without regard to order) from the numbers 1 to 53. If the 6 numbers match the numbers in the drawing, then the player wins the grand prize. How many groups of 6 numbers are possible?

Answers

7. a. 4845   **b.** 116,280

Solution:

In this situation, the order in which the group of 6 numbers is selected does not matter. Therefore, we need to compute the number of combinations of $n = 53$ numbers taken $r = 6$ at a time.

$$_{53}C_6 = \frac{53!}{6! \cdot (53 - 6)!} = \frac{53!}{6! \cdot 47!} = 22,957,480$$

There are 22,957,480 different groups of 6 numbers taken from 53 numbers.

Skill Practice 8   The California lottery game "Fantasy 5" offers a grand prize to a player who selects the correct group of 5 numbers (in any order) from the numbers 1 to 39. How many groups of 5 numbers are possible?

TECHNOLOGY CONNECTIONS

Evaluating a Number of Combinations, $_nC_r$

Most graphing utilities can evaluate the number of combinations of n elements taken r at a time. For example, use the $_nC_r$ function found in the MATH menu under PRB.

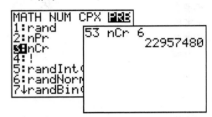

In Example 9 we encounter a situation in which more than one technique of counting must be used.

EXAMPLE 9   Applying Multiple Principles of Counting

Suppose that a committee of 3 women and 2 men must be formed from a group of 8 women and 7 men. In how many ways can such a committee be formed?

Solution:

This situation can be thought of as a sequence of two events in which we apply the fundamental principle of counting.

$$\begin{pmatrix} \text{Total number} \\ \text{of committees} \end{pmatrix} = \begin{pmatrix} \text{Number of ways to select} \\ \text{3 women from 8 women} \\ \text{in any order} \end{pmatrix} \cdot \begin{pmatrix} \text{Number of ways to select} \\ \text{2 men from 7 men} \\ \text{in any order} \end{pmatrix}$$

$$= {_8C_3} \cdot {_7C_2}$$
$$= 56 \cdot 21$$
$$= 1176$$

Skill Practice 9   The coach of a co-ed softball team must select 4 women and 5 men from a group of 7 women and 10 men to play in a game. In how many ways can such a team be formed?

Answers

8. 575,757   **9.** 8820

SECTION 8.6   Practice Exercises

Review Exercises

For Exercises 1–2, determine the value of the binomial coefficients.

1. $\binom{11}{5}$ **2.** $\binom{10}{2}$

For Exercises 3–6, determine whether the sequence defined by a_n is arithmetic, geometric, or neither.

3. $a_n = 4 - 6n$ **4.** $a_n = 5 - 2n$ **5.** $a_n = 4(-6)^n + 1$ **6.** $a_n = 5(-2)^n - 1$

Concept Connections

7. The fundamental _____ of _____ indicates that if one event can occur in m different ways, and a second event can occur in n different ways, then the two events can occur in sequence in _____ different ways.

8. A _____ diagram can be used to illustrate the possible outcomes in a sequence of events.

9. If n items are arranged in order, then each arrangement is called a _____ of n items.

10. The number of ways that n distinguishable items can be arranged in various orders is _____.

11. Consider a set of n elements of which one element is repeated r times. Then the number of permutations of the elements of the set is given by $\frac{\square}{\square}$.

12. Suppose that n represents the number of distinct elements in a group from which r elements will be chosen in a particular order. Then each arrangement is called a _____ of n items taken _____ at a time.

13. The number of permutations of n elements taken r at a time is denoted by $_nP_r$ and is computed by

$$_nP_r = \frac{\square}{\square} \quad \text{or} \quad _nP_r = n(n-1)(n-2)\cdots(n-r+1)$$

14. Suppose that n represents the number of elements in a group from which r elements will be selected in no particular order. Then each group selected is called a _____ of n elements taken _____ at a time.

Objective 1: Apply the Fundamental Principle of Counting

For Exercises 15–20, consider the set of integers from 1 to 20, inclusive. If one number is selected, in how many ways can we obtain

15. an even number?

16. an odd number?

17. a prime number?

18. a number that is a multiple of 5?

19. a number that is a multiple of 10?

20. a number that is divisible by 4?

21. At a hospital, the dinner menu consists of 4 choices of entrée, 3 choices of salad, 6 choices of beverage, and 4 choices of dessert. How many different meals can be formed if a patient chooses one item from each category? (**See Example 1**)

22. Kris travels several times a year for her job. She takes 2 pairs of slacks, 6 blouses, and 4 scarves, all of different colors. Assuming that the items all match together well, how many different outfits does Kris have if she selects one item from each category?

23. A license plate has 3 letters followed by 3 digits.

    a. How many license plates can be made if there are no restrictions on the letters or digits? (**See Example 2**)

    b. How many license plates can be made if no digit or letter may be repeated?

24. A security company requires its employees to have a 7-character computer password that must consist of 5 letters and 2 digits.

    a. How many passwords can be made if there are no restrictions on the letters or digits?

    b. How many passwords can be made if no digit or letter may be repeated?

25. The call letters for a radio station must begin with either K or W.

    a. How many 4-letter arrangements are possible assuming that letters may be repeated?

    b. How many 4-letter arrangements are possible assuming that the letters may not be repeated?

26. An employee identification code for a hospital consists of 2 letters from the set {A, B, C, D} followed by 4 digits.

    a. How many identification codes are possible if both letters and digits may be repeated?

    b. How many identification codes are possible if letters and digits may not be repeated?

27. An online survey is used to monitor customer service. The survey consists of 14 questions. Ten questions have 5 possible responses (strongly agree, agree, neutral, disagree, and strongly disagree). The remaining 4 questions are yes/no questions. In how many different ways can the survey be filled in? (**See Example 3**)

28. A test consists of 3 multiple-choice questions, each with four possible responses, and 7 true/false questions. In how many ways can a student answer the questions on the test?

29. On a computer, 1 *bit* is a single binary digit and has two possible outcomes: either 1 or 0. One *byte* is 8 bits. That is, a byte is a sequence of 8 binary digits. How many arrangements of 1's and 0's can be made with one byte?

30. Older models of garage door remote controls have a sequence of 10 switches that are individually placed in an up or down position. The remote control can "talk to" the overhead door unit if the 10 corresponding switches in the unit are in the same up/down sequence. How many up/down sequences are possible in an arrangement of 10 switches?

Objectives 2–3: Count Permutations and Combinations

31. **a.** In how many ways can the letters in the word FLORIDA be arranged? (**See Example 4**)

   b. In how many ways can the letters in the word MISSISSIPPI be arranged?

32. **a.** In how many ways can the letters in the word ULTRASOUND be arranged?

   b. In how many ways can the letters in the word MAMMOGRAM be arranged?

33. In how many ways can the word WRONG be misspelled?

34. In how many ways can the word EXACTLY be misspelled?

35. A delivery truck must make 4 stops at locations *A*, *B*, *C*, and *D*. Over several weeks, management asks the driver to drive each possible route and record the time required to complete the route. This is to determine the most time-efficient route. How many possible routes are there?

36. In how many ways can 6 people in a family be lined up for a photograph?

For Exercises 37–42, evaluate $_nP_r$.

37. $_6P_4$

38. $_8P_5$

39. $_{12}P_2$

40. $_{11}P_3$

41. $_9P_9$

42. $_5P_5$

43. Evaluate $_{20}P_3$ and interpret its meaning.

44. Evaluate $_{15}P_6$ and interpret its meaning.

For Exercises 45–50, evaluate $_nC_r$.

45. $_6C_4$

46. $_8C_5$

47. $_{12}C_2$

48. $_{11}C_3$

49. $_9C_9$

50. $_5C_5$

51. Evaluate $_{20}C_3$ and interpret its meaning.

52. Evaluate $_{15}C_6$ and interpret its meaning.

53. Given {A, B, C},

   a. List all the permutations of two elements from the set. (**See Example 5**)

   b. List all the combinations of two elements from the set.

54. Given {W, X, Y, Z},

   a. List all the permutations of three elements from the set.

   b. List all the combinations of three elements from the set.

55. Suppose that 9 horses run a race. How many first-, second-, and third-place finishes are possible? (**See Example 6**)

56. In how many ways can a judge award blue, red, and yellow ribbons to 3 films at a film festival if there are 10 films entered?

57. a. In a drama class, 5 students are to be selected from 24 students to perform a synchronized dance. In how many ways can 5 students be selected from the 24? (**See Example 7**)

   b. Determine the number of ways that 5 students can be selected from the class of 24 to play 5 different roles in a short play.

58. a. There are 100 members of the U.S. Senate. Suppose that 4 senators currently serve on a committee. In how many ways can 4 more senators be selected to serve on the committee?

   b. In how many ways can a group of 3 U.S. senators be selected from a group of 7 senators to fill the positions of chair, vice-chair, and secretary for the Ethics Committee?

59. A chess tournament has 16 players. Every player plays every other player exactly once. How many chess matches will be played?

60. Suppose that a tennis tournament has 64 players. In how many ways can the 64 players be paired to play in the first round? Assume that each player can play any other player without regard to seeding.

61. In the Minnesota Lotto game "Gopher 5" a player wins the grand prize by choosing the same group of 5 numbers from 1 through 47 as is chosen by the computer. How many 5-number groups are possible? (**See Example 8**)

62. In the New York state lottery game "Lotto" a player wins the grand prize by choosing the same group of 6 numbers from 1 through 59 as is chosen by the computer. How many 6-number groups are possible?

63. At a ballroom dance lesson, the instructor chooses 3 men and 3 women to demonstrate a new pattern. If there are 9 women and 7 men in the class, in how many ways can the instructor choose 3 men and 3 women? (**See Example 9**)

64. A committee of 4 men and 4 women is to be made from a group of 12 men and 9 women. In how many ways can such a committee be formed?

Mixed Exercises

65. In a "Pick-4" game, a player wins a prize for matching a 4-digit number from 0000 to 9999 with the number randomly selected during the drawing. How many 4-digit numbers can a player choose?

66. In a "Numbers" game, a player wins a prize for matching a 3-digit number from 000 to 999 with the number randomly selected during the drawing. How many 3-digit numbers can a player choose?

67. Pat is a basketball coach and must select 5 players out of 12 players to start a game. In how many ways can she select the 5 players if each player is equally qualified to play each position?

68. Bea has a list of 8 books that she knows she must read for a class in the upcoming fall semester of school. She wants to get a head start by reading several of the books during the summer. If she has time in the summer to read 5 of the 8 books, in how many ways can she select 5 books from 8 books?

69. In how many ways can a manager assign 5 employees at a coffee shop to 5 different tasks? Assume that each employee is assigned to exactly one task.

70. In how many ways can a class of 12 kindergarten children line up at the cafeteria?

71. Twenty batteries have been sitting in a drawer for 2 yr. There are 4 dead batteries among the 20. If three batteries are selected at random, determine the number of ways in which

   a. 3 dead batteries can be selected.

   b. 3 good batteries can be selected.

   c. 2 good batteries and 1 dead battery can be selected.

72. There are 30 seeds in a package. Five seeds are defective (will not germinate). If four seeds are selected at random, determine the number of ways in which

   a. 4 defective seeds can be selected.

   b. 4 good seeds can be selected.

   c. 2 good seeds and 2 defective seeds can be selected.

For Exercises 73–74, consider a set with n elements. **The number of subsets containing exactly r elements is given by $_nC_r$. For example, for $A = \{a, b, c\}$, the subsets of A are:**

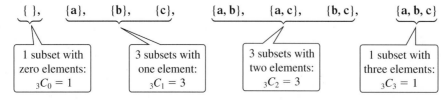

{ },	{a}, {b}, {c},	{a, b}, {a, c}, {b, c},	{a, b, c}
1 subset with zero elements: $_3C_0 = 1$	3 subsets with one element: $_3C_1 = 3$	3 subsets with two elements: $_3C_2 = 3$	1 subset with three elements: $_3C_3 = 1$

73. a. Given $Z = \{a, b, c, d\}$, write all possible subsets of Z.

    b. Evaluate $_4C_0$, $_4C_1$, $_4C_2$, $_4C_3$, and $_4C_4$ and verify that these values correspond to the number of subsets with 0, 1, 2, 3, and 4 elements, respectively.

74. Given a set with 6 elements, how many subsets with 3 elements does the set have?

75. A "combination" lock is opened by correctly "dialing" 3 numbers from 0 to 39, inclusive. The user who knows the code turns the dial to the right to the first number in the code, then to the left to find the second number in the code, and then back to the right for the third number in the code. If someone does not know the code and tries to guess, how many guesses are possible?

76. A palindrome is an arrangement of letters that reads the same way forwards and backwards. For example, one five-letter palindrome is: ABCBA.

    a. How many 5-letter palindromes are possible from a 26-letter alphabet?

    b. How many 4-letter palindromes are possible from a 26-letter alphabet?

A line segment connecting any two nonadjacent vertices of a polygon is called a *diagonal* of the polygon. For Exercises 77–80, determine the number of diagonals for the given polygon.

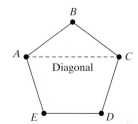

77. quadrilateral (4 sides)

78. pentagon (5 sides)

79. hexagon (6 sides)

80. octagon (8 sides)

For Exercises 81–86, consider the set of numbers $\{0, 1, 2, 3, 4, 5\}$. How many 3-digit codes can be formed with the given restrictions?

81. The code has no restrictions.

82. The code may not contain repeated digits.

83. The code must represent a 3-digit number. (*Hint*: This means that the first digit cannot be zero.)

84. The code must represent a 3-digit number that is a multiple of 5.

85. The code must represent an even 3-digit number.

86. All three digits in the code must be the same.

87. In Exercise 107 from Section 8.3, we learned that if a fair coin is flipped n times, the number of head/tail arrangements follows a geometric sequence.

    a. Determine the number of head/tail arrangements if a fair coin is flipped 3 times, 4 times, and 5 times.

    b. If a couple has 3 children, how many boy/girl sequences are possible for the three births? List the outcomes using "B" for boy and "G" for girl.

    c. If a couple has 4 children, how many boy/girl sequences are possible for the four births?

88. Social Security numbers assigned in the United States are comprised of 9 digits of the form _ _ _-_ _-_ _ _ _. Would there be enough Social Security numbers for the population of China if the Chinese used the same system? (*Hint*: The population of China is approximately 1.5 billion.)

89. Airlines often oversell seats on an airplane. This is done so that the seats for the few passengers that are no-shows will still have been sold. Sometimes, however, all passengers show up and there are more ticketed passengers than seats. Suppose that one flight has 160 passengers and only 156 seats. Determine the number of ways that the airline can select 4 people at random to place on a different flight.

90. In how many ways can a platoon leader select 4 soldiers among 15 soldiers to secure a building?

91. A car can comfortably hold a family of five. If two people among the five can drive, how many different seating arrangements are possible?

92. A television station must play twelve 30-sec commercials during a half-hour show. In how many ways can the commercials be aired?

Write About It

93. Consider a horse race with 8 horses. Explain how the fundamental principle of counting or the permutation rule can be used to determine the number of first-, second-, and third-place arrangements.

94. Explain why the number of combinations of n items taken r at a time can be computed by $\dfrac{_nP_r}{r!}$.

Expanding Your Skills

95. Three biology books, 4 math books, and 2 physics books are to be placed on a book shelf where the books in each discipline are grouped together. In how many ways can the books be arranged on the book shelf?

96. A softball team has 9 players consisting of 3 women and 6 men. In how many ways can the coach arrange the batting order if the men must bat consecutively and the women must bat consecutively?

SECTION 8.7   Introduction to Probability

OBJECTIVES

1. Determine Theoretical Probabilities
2. Determine Empirical Probabilities
3. Find the Probability of the Union of Two Events
4. Find the Probability of Sequential Independent Events

TIP The word "die" is the singular of the word "dice." That is, we roll one die but we roll two dice.

Avoiding Mistakes

The probability $\frac{1}{2}$ does not mean that exactly 1 out of every 2 rolls of a die will result in an even number. Instead, it is a ratio that we expect experimental observations to approach after the experiment is performed a large number of times.

1. Determine Theoretical Probabilities

The Centers for Disease Control publishes National Vital Statistics Reports every year that provide data for birth rates and mortality rates based on gender, race, age, and other factors. The data in Table 8-4 give the 1-yr survival rates for people in the United States for selected ages.

From the table, the probability that a 20-yr-old will live to age 21 is 0.9991. Put another way, this means that approximately 99.91% of 20-yr-olds will live to age 21 (see Example 5).

A **probability** is a value assigned to an event that quantifies the likelihood of the event to occur. To compute the probability of an event, we first need to define several key terms. An **experiment** is a test with an uncertain outcome. The set of all possible outcomes of an experiment is called the **sample space** of the experiment. For example:

Table 8-4

Age (yr)	Probability of 1-yr Survival
10	0.9999
20	0.9991
30	0.9990
40	0.9981
50	0.9959
60	0.9907
70	0.9791
80	0.9434
90	0.8543

Experiment:	**Sample Space:**
Flip a coin	{head, tail}
Roll a single 6-sided die	{1, 2, 3, 4, 5, 6}

An **event** is a subset of the sample space and is often denoted by E or some other capital letter.

Description of Event:	**Set Representing the Event:**
Flip a coin and the outcome is "head"	{head}
Roll a six-sided die and an even number comes up	{2, 4, 6}

The number of elements in an event E is often denoted by $n(E)$. For example, given the event $E = \{2, 4, 6\}$, $n(E) = 3$.

If we assume that all elements in a sample space are equally likely to occur, then we define the theoretical probability of an event as follows.

Theoretical Probability of Event E

Let S represent a sample space with equally likely outcomes, and let E be a subset of S. Then the probability of event E, denoted by $P(E)$, is given by

$$P(E) = \frac{n(E)}{n(S)} \begin{array}{l} \longleftarrow \text{Number of elements in the event} \\ \longleftarrow \text{Number of elements in the sample space} \end{array}$$

The probability of an event is the relative size of the event compared to the sample space. For example, if E is the event of rolling an even number on a die, then $E = \{2, 4, 6\}$ and $S = \{1, 2, 3, 4, 5, 6\}$. Then,

$$P(E) = \frac{n(E)}{n(S)} = \frac{3}{6} = \frac{1}{2}$$

The value of a probability can be written as a fraction, as a decimal, or as a percent. Therefore, $P(E) = \frac{1}{2}$, or 0.5, or 50%.

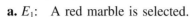 **EXAMPLE 1**   **Finding the Probability of an Event**

Suppose that a box contains two red, three blue, and five green marbles. If one marble is selected at random, find the probability of the event.

   a. E_1:   A red marble is selected.

   b. E_2:   A blue marble is selected.

   c. E_3:   A white marble is selected.

Solution:

Each of the 10 marbles in the box is equally likely to be selected. Denote the sample space as $S = \{R_1, R_2, B_1, B_2, B_3, G_1, G_2, G_3, G_4, G_5\}$.

   a. $E_1 = \{R_1, R_2\}$ The number of red marbles is 2.

      Therefore, $P(E_1) = \dfrac{n(E_1)}{n(S)} = \dfrac{2}{10} = \dfrac{1}{5}$.   The probability of selecting a red marble is $\frac{1}{5}$.

   b. $E_2 = \{B_1, B_2, B_3\}$ The number of blue marbles is 3.

      Therefore, $P(E_2) = \dfrac{n(E_2)}{n(S)} = \dfrac{3}{10}$.   The probability of selecting a blue marble is $\frac{3}{10}$.

   c. $E_3 = \{\ \}$ The number of white marbles is 0.

      Therefore, $P(E_3) = \dfrac{n(E_3)}{n(S)} = \dfrac{0}{10} = 0$.   It is intuitively obvious that a white marble cannot be selected. Mathematically, a probability of 0 means that the event is impossible.

Skill Practice 1   A sock drawer has 6 blue socks, 2 white socks, and 12 black socks. If one sock is selected at random, find the probability of the event.

   a. E_1:   A blue sock is selected.   **b.** E_2:   A black sock is selected.

   c. E_3:   A brown sock is selected.

The number of outcomes in an event must be less than or equal to the number of outcomes in the sample space. Therefore, the value of a probability is a number between 0 and 1, inclusive. That is, $0 \le P(E) \le 1$. Furthermore,

- If $P(E) = 0$, then the event E is called an **impossible event.**
- If $P(E) = 1$, then the event E is called a **certain event.**

In Example 1(c), it is impossible to draw a white marble from the box. However, we would be 100% certain of drawing a red, blue, or green marble from the box and the probability would be 1.

EXAMPLE 2   **Finding the Probability of an Event**

An American roulette wheel has 38 slots, numbered 1 through 36, 0, and 00. Eighteen slots are red, 18 are black, and 2 are green. The dealer spins the wheel in one direction and rolls a small ball in the opposite direction until both come to rest. The ball is equally likely to fall in any one of the 38 slots. On a given spin of an American roulette wheel, find the probability of the event.

   a. E_1:   The ball lands on an odd number.

   b. E_2:   The ball lands on a green slot.

   c. E_3:   The ball does not land on a green slot.

Answers

1. a. $\dfrac{3}{10}$ **b.** $\dfrac{3}{5}$ **c.** 0

Solution:

The sample space has 38 outcomes. That is $n(S) = 38$.

a. There are 18 odd numbers. Therefore, $n(E_1) = 18$ and

$$P(E_1) = \frac{n(E_1)}{n(S)} = \frac{18}{38} = \frac{9}{19} \approx 0.4737.$$

b. There are 2 green slots on the wheel. Therefore, $n(E_2) = 2$ and

$$P(E_2) = \frac{n(E_2)}{n(S)} = \frac{2}{38} = \frac{1}{19} \approx 0.0526.$$

c. There are 36 slots that are not green. Therefore, $n(E_3) = 36$ and

$$P(E_3) = \frac{n(E_3)}{n(S)} = \frac{36}{38} = \frac{18}{19} \approx 0.9474.$$

> **Skill Practice 2** On a given spin of an American roulette wheel, find the probability of the event.
>
> **a.** E_1: The ball lands on the number 7.
> **b.** E_2: The ball lands on a red slot.
> **c.** E_3: The ball does not land on a red slot.

From Example 2(b) and 2(c), notice that event E_3 consists of all elements in the sample space not in event E_2. Therefore, the union of the two events make up the entire sample space, and $P(E_2) + P(E_3) = \dfrac{1}{19} + \dfrac{18}{19} = 1$. In this case, we say that events E_2 and E_3 are *complementary events*.

Definition of Complementary Events

Let E be an event relative to sample space S. The **complement of E,** denoted by $\overline{E}$ (or sometimes by $\sim E$ or E') is the set of outcomes in the sample space but not in event E. It follows that

$$P(E) + P(\overline{E}) = 1$$

EXAMPLE 3 **Finding the Probabilities of Complementary Events**

Suppose that 2 dice are rolled. Determine the probability that

a. The sum of the numbers showing on the dice is 7.

b. The sum of the numbers showing on the dice is *not* 7.

Solution:

Each individual die has 6 equally likely outcomes. Therefore, by the fundamental principle of counting, the number of ways the pair of dice can fall is $6 \cdot 6 = 36$ (Figure 8-11).

First Die

Second Die	1	2	3	4	5	6
1	(1, 1)	(1, 2)	(1, 3)	(1, 4)	(1, 5)	(1, 6)
2	(2, 1)	(2, 2)	(2, 3)	(2, 4)	(2, 5)	(2, 6)
3	(3, 1)	(3, 2)	(3, 3)	(3, 4)	(3, 5)	(3, 6)
4	(4, 1)	(4, 2)	(4, 3)	(4, 4)	(4, 5)	(4, 6)
5	(5, 1)	(5, 2)	(5, 3)	(5, 4)	(5, 5)	(5, 6)
6	(6, 1)	(6, 2)	(6, 3)	(6, 4)	(6, 5)	(6, 6)

Figure 8-11

Answers

2. a. $\dfrac{1}{38}$ **b.** $\dfrac{9}{19}$ **c.** $\dfrac{10}{19}$

a. Let E represent the event that the numbers showing on the dice have a sum of 7. A sum of 7 will occur if the dice land on one of the following 6 outcomes.

$E = \{(1, 6), (2, 5), (3, 4), (4, 3), (5, 2), (6, 1)\}$. Therefore, $n(E) = 6$ and

$$P(E) = \frac{n(E)}{n(S)} = \frac{6}{36} = \frac{1}{6}.$$ The probability of rolling a sum of 7 is $\frac{1}{6}$.

b. The event that the numbers on the dice do not present a sum of 7 is the complement of event E. Therefore, we have the option of using the formula $P(E) + P(\overline{E}) = 1$.

$$P(\overline{E}) = 1 - P(E) = 1 - \frac{1}{6} = \frac{5}{6}$$ The probability of rolling a sum other than 7 is $\frac{5}{6}$.

Skill Practice 3   Suppose that two dice are rolled. Determine the probability that

    a. The sum of the numbers showing on the dice is 8.

    b. The sum of the numbers showing on the dice is *not* 8.

In Example 4, we use the techniques of counting learned in Section 8.6 to determine the probability of an event.

EXAMPLE 4   **Finding the Probability of an Event by Using Counting Techniques**

Suppose that 5 women and 3 men apply for 2 job openings. If the applicants are equally qualified, find the probability that both positions are filled by women.

Solution:

Let E represent the event that two women are chosen. The number of elements in E is the number of possible ways to select 2 women from a group of 5 women without regard to order. That is,

$$n(E) = {}_5C_2 = 10$$

The sample space S consists of all possible ways in which 2 people can be selected from 8 people without regard to order. That is,

$$n(S) = {}_8C_2 = 28$$

The probability that both positions will be filled by women is

$$P(E) = \frac{n(E)}{n(S)} = \frac{{}_5C_2}{{}_8C_2} = \frac{10}{28} = \frac{5}{14} \approx 0.3571$$

Skill Practice 4   Suppose that a committee of three people is to be formed from a group of 8 men and 6 women. Find the probability that the committee will consist of all men.

---

2. Determine Empirical Probabilities

Suppose that the Centers for Disease Control wants to measure the 1-yr survival rates for Americans for specific ages. There is no way that this can be derived theoretically. Instead, the probability can be approximated through observations. A probability computed in this way is called an **empirical probability.**

Answers

3. a. $\dfrac{5}{36}$ **b.** $\dfrac{31}{36}$

4. $\dfrac{2}{13}$

Computing Empirical Probability

The empirical probability of an event E is given by

$$P(E) = \frac{\text{Number of times the event } E \text{ occurs}}{\text{Number of times the experiment is perfomed}}$$

EXAMPLE 5 **Computing an Empirical Probability**

Data from the Centers for Disease Control for a recent year indicate that there were approximately 4,295,000 individuals of age 20 in the United States. One year later 3887 of these individuals had died and 4,291,113 had lived. Determine the probability that a 20-yr-old will survive to age 21. (*Source*: www.cdc.gov)

Solution:

Let E represent the event that a 20-yr-old lives to age 21.

The experiment involves 4,295,000 individuals of age 20. The number of observed outcomes where an individual lives to the age of 21 is 4,291,113. Therefore, the empirical probability is given by

$$P(E) = \frac{4,291,113}{4,295,000} \approx 0.9991$$

Skill Practice 5 Suppose that of approximately 4,224,100 individuals of age 40 in the United States, 8038 die before the age of 41 and 4,216,062 survive. Determine the probability that a 40-yr-old will live to age 41.

3. Find the Probability of the Union of Two Events

We now study the probability of the union of two events. Suppose that one card is drawn from a standard deck of cards. The sample space has the following properties (Figure 8-12).

Figure 8-12

- The deck consists of 52 cards.
- The cards are divided into four suits (or categories) called clubs (♣), spades (♠), hearts (♥), and diamonds (♦).
- Each suit consists of 13 cards labeled Ace, 2, 3, 4, 5, 6, 7, 8, 9, 10, jack, queen, king.
- There are 26 black cards (clubs and spades) and 26 red cards (hearts and diamonds).

Let *A* be the event that an ace is drawn, and let *K* be the event that a king is drawn. Events *A* and *K* have no cards in common (a single card cannot be both an ace and a king). Therefore, we say that events *A* and *K* are **mutually exclusive** (do not overlap). See Figure 8-13.

Now suppose that event *A* is the event that an ace is drawn, and that *R* is the event that a red card is drawn. Events *A* and *R* share common elements. The ace of hearts and the ace of diamonds are elements in both events. Therefore, events *A* and *R* are *not* mutually exclusive, meaning that they overlap. See Figure 8-14.

Figure 8-13

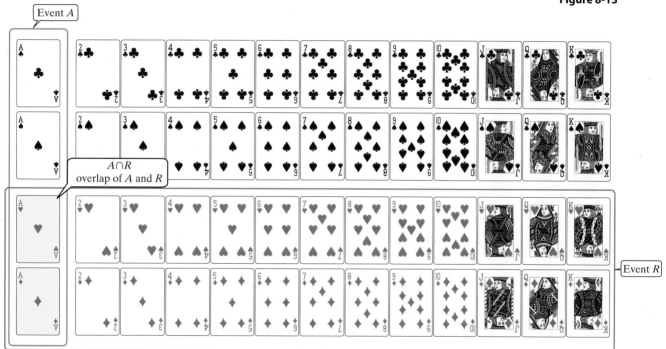

Figure 8-14

Now to generalize, we find the probability of the event (*A* or *B*), denoted *P*(*A* or *B*) by finding the probability of the *union* of *A* and *B*.

Probability of (*A* or *B*)

Given events *A* and *B* in the same sample space, *P*(*A* or *B*) is given by

$$P(A \cup B) = P(A) + P(B) - P(A \cap B)$$

Note: If *A* and *B* are mutually exclusive, then $P(A \cap B) = 0$ and we have $P(A \cup B) = P(A) + P(B)$.

EXAMPLE 6 **Computing the Probability of (A or B)**

Suppose that one card is selected at random from a standard deck of cards. Find the probability that

a. The card is an ace or a king.

b. The card is an ace or a red card.

Solution:

Let A be the event that an ace is drawn.

Let K be the event that a king is drawn.

Let R be the event that a red card is drawn.

a. From Figure 8-13, we see that events A and K are mutually exclusive. Therefore, to find $P(A$ or $K)$, we have

$$P(A \cup K) = P(A) + P(K)$$

$$= \frac{4}{52} + \frac{4}{52} \qquad \text{There are 4 aces in the deck of 52 cards. } P(A) = \frac{4}{52}.$$

$$\text{There are 4 kings in the deck of 52 cards. } P(K) = \frac{4}{52}.$$

$$= \frac{8}{52} \text{ or } \frac{2}{13}$$

> **TIP** In Example 6(a), since A and K are mutually exclusive, then $P(A \cap K) = 0$.

b. From Figure 8-14, we see that events A and R are *not* mutually exclusive. Therefore, to find $P(A$ or $R)$, we have:

$$P(A \cup R) = P(A) + P(R) - P(A \cap R) \qquad \text{There are 4 aces in the deck.}$$

$$= \frac{4}{52} + \frac{26}{52} - \frac{2}{52} \left.\begin{array}{l} \text{ace of hearts and} \\ \text{ace of diamonds} \end{array}\right\} \qquad P(A) = \frac{4}{52}.$$

$$\text{There are 26 red cards in the deck.}$$

$$= \frac{28}{52} \qquad P(R) = \frac{26}{52}.$$

$$\text{There are 2 red aces in the deck.}$$

$$= \frac{7}{13} \qquad \text{Therefore, } P(A \cap R) = \frac{2}{52}.$$

> **TIP** As an alternative to computing $P(A) + P(R) - P(A \cap R)$, count the number of elements in the event $(A \cup R)$, being careful not to count the events common to A and R twice. That is, count 26 red cards plus the 2 black aces for a total of 28 elements in event $(A \cup R)$. Thus, $P(A \cup R) = \frac{28}{52} = \frac{7}{13}$.

Skill Practice 6 Suppose that one card is drawn at random from a standard deck of cards. Find the probability that

a. The card is a 2 or a 10.

b. The card is a 2 or a club.

EXAMPLE 7 **Computing an Empirical Probability of (A or B)**

The safety and security department at a college asked a sample of 265 students to respond to the following question.

"Do you think that the college has adequate lighting on campus at night?"

The table gives the results of the survey based on gender and response.

	Yes	No	No Opinion	Total
Male	92	7	4	103
Female	36	102	24	162
Total	128	109	28	265

If one student is selected at random from the group, find the probability that

a. The student answered "Yes" or had "No Opinion."

b. The student answered "No" or was female.

Answers

6. a. $\frac{2}{13}$ **b.** $\frac{4}{13}$

Solution:

a. Let Y be the event that the student answered "Yes."

Let O be the event that the student had "No Opinion."

Y and O are mutually exclusive events (do not overlap).

	Yes	No	No Opinion	Total
Male	92	7	4	103
Female	36	102	24	162
Total	128	109	28	265

$P(Y \text{ or } O) = P(Y) + P(O)$

$= \dfrac{128}{265} + \dfrac{28}{265}$ $P(Y) = \frac{128}{265}$ and $P(O) = \frac{28}{265}$.

$= \dfrac{156}{265}$

b. Let N be the event that the student answered "No."

Let F be the event that the student is female.

N and F are *not* mutually exclusive (the events overlap).

	Yes	No	No Opinion	Total
Male	92	7	4	103
Female	36	102	24	162
Total	128	109	28	265

$P(N \text{ or } F) = P(N) + P(F) - P(N \cap F)$

$= \dfrac{109}{265} + \dfrac{162}{265} - \dfrac{102}{265}$ $P(N) = \frac{109}{265}$, $P(F) = \frac{162}{265}$, and $P(N \cap F) = \frac{102}{265}$

$= \dfrac{169}{265}$ The 102 females who answered "No" are the elements in the intersection of N and F.

> **TIP** As an alternative to computing $P(N) + P(F) - P(N \cap F)$, count the number of elements in the event $(N \cup F)$, being careful not to count the events common to N and F twice; that is, count 162 females plus the 7 males who answered "No" for a total of 169 elements in event $(N \cup F)$. Thus, $P(N \cup F) = \frac{169}{265}$.

Skill Practice 7   Refer to the data given in Example 7. If one student is selected at random from the group, find the probability that

a. The student answered "Yes" or "No."

b. The student is male or had no opinion.

---

4. Find the Probability of Sequential Independent Events

When a coin is tossed, the probability that it lands heads up is $\frac{1}{2}$. Now suppose that the coin is flipped two times in succession. What is the probability that it lands heads up twice in a row? Our intuition tells us that the probability should be less than $\frac{1}{2}$ because it is more unlikely that the desired outcome will happen twice in a row than one time. We also know that the outcome of the first event (heads up) does not affect the outcome of the second event (also heads up). For this reason, the two events are called **independent events.**

> **Probability of a Sequence of Independent Events**
>
> If events A and B are independent events, then the probability that both A and B will occur is
>
> $$P(A \text{ and } B) = P(A) \cdot P(B)$$

For example,

Let A represent the event that a coin lands heads up on the first toss.

Let B represent the event that a coin lands heads up on the second toss.

Then the probability that the coin will land heads up on both tosses is

$$P(A \text{ and } B) = P(A) \cdot P(B) = \frac{1}{2} \cdot \frac{1}{2} = \frac{1}{4}$$

EXAMPLE 8 **Finding the Probability of Independent Events**

Suppose that a family plans to have three children. Find the probability that all three children will be boys.

Solution:

Each birth is independent of the birth that precedes it. For each birth, the probability that the child is born a boy is $\frac{1}{2}$.

$P(\text{all boys}) = P(\text{boy on 1st}) \cdot P(\text{boy on 2nd}) \cdot P(\text{boy on 3rd})$

$= \frac{1}{2} \cdot \frac{1}{2} \cdot \frac{1}{2} = \frac{1}{8}$

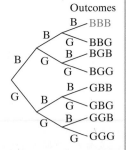

TIP In Example 8 there are 8 elements in the sample space:

BBB, BBG, BGB, BGG,
GBB, GBG, GGB, GGG

The event BBB occurs 1 time. Thus, the probability of all boys is $\frac{1}{8}$.

Skill Practice 8 Suppose that a family plans to have five children. Find the probability that all five children will be girls.

EXAMPLE 9 **Finding the Probability of Independent Events**

In baseball, a player's batting "average" is the quotient of the number of hits to the number of "at bats." It can also be interpreted as the probability that the player will get a hit on a given time at bat. If Albert Pujols had a batting average of 0.279 for a recent season, determine the probability that he would get a hit on four consecutive times at bat.

Solution:

Let H represent the event that Albert Pujols gets a hit on a given time at bat. Furthermore, each time at bat is independent of the time before.

We have that $P(H) = 0.279$. Therefore,

$P(\text{4 consecutive hits}) = (0.279)(0.279)(0.279)(0.279)$
≈ 0.006

If Albert Pujols has four times at bat, there is less than a 1% chance that he will get a hit all four times.

Skill Practice 9 Suppose the probability that a person will catch a winter "cold" is 0.16. What is the probability that four unrelated people will all catch winter "colds"?

Answers

8. $\frac{1}{32}$ **9.** $(0.16)^4 \approx 0.000655$

SECTION 8.7 **Practice Exercises**

Review Exercises

1. In how many ways can a committee of 5 be selected from a group of 30 people?

2. In how many ways can a committee of 4 women be selected from a group of 10 women and 6 men?

For Exercises 3–6, find the union or intersection of the sets as indicated.

$$A = \{1, 2, 3, 4, 5\} \quad B = \{5, 6, 7, 8\} \quad C = \{2, 4\}$$

3. $A \cup B$ **4.** $B \cup C$ **5.** $A \cap B$ **6.** $A \cap C$

Concept Connections

7. An _____ is a test with an uncertain outcome.

8. The _____ _____ of an experiment is the set of all possible outcomes.

9. An _____ is a subset of the sample space of an experiment.

10. The number of elements in event E is often denoted by _____.

11. If S is a sample space with equally likely outcomes and E is an event within the sample space, then $P(E)$ is computed by the formula $P(E) = \dfrac{\square}{\square}$.

12. If $P(E) = 0$, then E is called an _____ event. If $P(E) = 1$, then E is called a _____ event.

13. The notation $\overline{E}$ represents the _____ of event E. Furthermore, $P(E) + P(\overline{E}) = $ _____.

14. Two events in a sample space are _____ _____ if they do not share any common elements. That is, the two events do not overlap.

15. If two events A and B are not mutually exclusive, then $P(A \cup B)$ can be computed by the formula $P(A \cup B) = $ _____.

16. If two events A and B are mutually exclusive, then $P(A \cap B) = $ _____. As a result, $P(A \cup B)$ can be computed from the fomula $P(A \cup B) = $ _____.

17. Two events A and B are _____ if neither event affects the probability of the other.

18. For two independent events A and B, $P(A \text{ and } B) = $ _____.

Objective 1: Determine Theoretical Probabilities

19. Which of the values can represent the probability of an event?

a. 1.84   **b.** $-\frac{3}{7}$ **c.** 0.00   **d.** 1.00
e. 250%   **f.** 6.1   **g.** 0.61   **h.** 6.1%

20. Which of the values can represent the probability of an event?

a. 2.32   **b.** 0.231   **c.** 2.31%   **d.** -1
e. $\frac{3}{8}$ **f.** $-\frac{1}{4}$ **g.** $\sqrt{2}$ **h.** 125%

For Exercises 21–26, match the probability with a statement a, b, c, d, e, or f.

a. Event E is certain to happen.
b. Event E cannot happen.
c. Event E is very likely to happen.
d. Event E is very unlikely to happen.
e. Event E is somewhat likely to happen.
f. Event E is as likely to happen as not to happen.

21. $P(E) = 0.994$ **22.** $P(E) = 1$ **23.** $P(E) = 0.75$

24. $P(E) = 0.003$ **25.** $P(E) = 0.5$ **26.** $P(E) = 0$

For Exercises 27–34, consider an experiment where a single 10-sided die is rolled with the outcomes 1, 2, 3, 4, 5, 6, 7, 8, 9, 10. Determine the probability of each event.

27. A number less than 5 is rolled.

28. A number less than 3 is rolled.

29. A number between 4 and 10, inclusive, is rolled.

30. A number between 2 and 7, inclusive, is rolled.

31. A number greater than 10 is rolled.

32. A number less than 1 is rolled.

33. A number greater than or equal to 1 is rolled.

34. A number less than or equal to 10 is rolled.

35. A course in early civilization has 6 freshmen, 8 sophomores, and 16 juniors. If one student is selected at random, find the probability of the following events. (**See Example 1**)

a. A junior is selected.
b. A freshman is selected.
c. A senior is selected.

36. Suppose that a box contains 4 chocolate chip cookies, 8 molasses cookies, and 12 raisin cookies. If one cookie is selected at random, find the probability of the following events.

a. A chocolate chip cookie is selected.
b. A molasses cookie is selected.
c. A ginger cookie is selected.

For Exercises 37–38, consider an American roulette wheel. (See Example 2) For a given spin of the wheel, find the probability of the following events.

37. a. The ball lands on an even number (do not include 0 and 00).
b. The ball lands on a number that is a multiple of 5 (do not include 0 and 00).
c. The ball does not land on the number 8.

38. a. The ball lands on a black slot.
b. The ball lands on a number that is a multiple of 6 (do not include 0 and 00).
c. The ball does not land on the number 12.

39. If $P(E) = 0.842$, what is the value of $P(\overline{E})$?

40. If $P(A) = 0.431$, what is the value of $P(\overline{A})$?

41. According to the Centers for Disease Control, the probability that a live birth will be of twins in the United States is 0.016. What is the probability that a live birth will *not* be of twins?

42. A baseball player with a batting average of 0.291 has a probability of 0.291 of getting a hit for a given time at bat. What is the probability that the player will *not* get a hit for a given time at bat?

For Exercises 43–46, consider the sample space when two fair dice are rolled. (See Example 3) Determine the probabilities for the following events.

43. a. The sum of the numbers on the dice is 4.

    b. The sum of the numbers on the dice is *not* 4.

44. a. The sum of the numbers on the dice is 12.

    b. The sum of the numbers on the dice is *not* 12.

45. a. The sum of the numbers on the dice is greater than 9.

    b. The sum of the numbers on the dice is less than 4.

46. a. The sum of the numbers on the dice is greater than or equal to 8.

    b. The sum of the numbers on the dice is less than or equal to 5.

47. After a nationally televised trial, a poll of viewers indicated that 68% thought the defendant was guilty, 22% thought the defendant was not guilty, and the rest were undecided. What is the probability that a person selected from the viewing audience was undecided?

48. If a couple plans to have three children, the probability that all three will be boys is 0.125. What is the probability that the couple will have at least one girl?

49. Suppose that a jury pool consists of 18 women and 16 men.

    a. What is the probability that a jury of 9 people taken from the pool will consist only of women? **(See Example 4)**

    b. What is the probability that the jury will consist only of men?

    c. Why do the probabilities from parts (a) and (b) not add up to 1?

50. Suppose that 20 good batteries and 6 defective batteries are in a drawer.

    a. If 4 batteries are drawn at random, what is the probability that all four will be defective?

    b. What is the probability that all four will be good?

    c. Why do the probabilities from parts (a) and (b) not add up to 1?

51. In the Illinois state lottery game "Little Lotto," a player wins the grand prize by choosing the same group of five numbers from 1 through 39 as is chosen by the computer. What is the probability that a player will win the grand prize by playing 1 ticket?

52. In the New York state lottery game "Lotto," a player wins the grand prize by choosing the same group of 6 numbers from 1 through 59 as is chosen by the computer. What is the probability that a player will win the grand prize by playing 5 tickets?

Scientist Gregor Mendel (1822–1884) is often called the "father of modern genetics" and is famous for his work involving the inheritance of certain traits in pea plants. Suppose that the genes controlling the color of peas are Y for yellow and y for green. Each plant has two genes, one from the female (seed) and one from the male (pollen). The Y gene is dominant, and therefore a plant with genes YY will have yellow peas, a plant with genes Yy or yY will have yellow peas, and a plant with genes yy will have green peas.

If a plant with two yellow genes (YY) is crossed with a plant with two green genes (yy), the result is four hybrid offspring with genotypes Yy. The offspring will be yellow, but will carry the recessive green gene.

Parent 2

Parent 1	y	y
Y	Yy	Yy
Y	Yy	Yy

53. Suppose that both parent pea plants are hybrids with genotype Yy.

    a. Make a chart showing the possible genotypes of the offspring.

Parent 2

Parent 1	Y	y
Y		
y		

    b. What is the probability that a given offspring will have green peas?

    c. What is the probability that a given offspring will have yellow peas?

54. Suppose that one parent pea plant has genotype YY and the other has genotype Yy.

    a. Make a chart showing the possible genotypes of the offspring.

Parent 2

Parent 1	Y	y
Y		
Y		

    b. What is the probability that a given offspring will have green peas?

    c. What is the probability that a given offspring will have yellow peas?

Objective 2: Determine Empirical Probabilities

55. At a hospital specializing in treating heart disease, it was found that 222 out of 4624 patients undergoing open heart mitral valve surgery died during surgery or within 30 days after surgery. Determine the probability that a patient will not survive the surgery or 30 days after the surgery. This is called the mortality rate. Round to 3 decimal places. (**See Example 5**)

56. China has the largest population of any country with approximately 1.5 billion people. In a recent year, census results indicated that 199,500,000 Chinese were over the age of 60. If a person is selected at random from the population of China, what is the probability that the person is over 60 years old? Round to 3 decimal places.

57. The data in the pie chart give the method by which a sample of workers in a small college town commute to work. If one worker is selected at random, find the probability that the individual

   a. Commutes by public transportation.

   b. Commutes by driving alone.

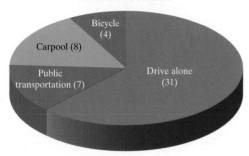

Method of Commute

58. The final exam grades for a sample of students in a physical science class resulted in the following grade distribution.

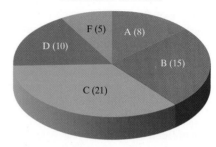

Distribution of Grades

If one student taking physical science is selected at random, find the probability of the following events.

   a. The student earned an "A."

   b. The student earned an "F."

Objective 3: Find the Probability of the Union of Two Events

For Exercises 59–68, consider the sample space for a single card drawn from a standard deck. (See Example 6 and Figure 8-12) Find the probability that the card drawn is

59. A jack or a queen.

60. An ace or a 2.

61. A jack or a diamond.

62. An ace or a spade.

63. A face card (jack, queen, or king).

64. A card numbered between 5 and 10, inclusive.

65. A face card or a red card.

66. A card numbered between 5 and 10, inclusive, or a black card.

67. A heart, club or spade.

68. An ace, 2, or 3.

For Exercises 69–76, use the data in the table categorizing cholesterol levels by the ages of the individuals in a study. If one person is chosen at random, find the probability of the given event. (See Example 7)

	Normal Cholesterol	Elevated Cholesterol	Total
30 and under	14	4	18
31–60	52	28	80
61 or older	22	80	102
Total	88	112	200

69. The person has elevated cholesterol.

70. The person is 61 or older.

71. The person is 60 or under.

72. The person is 31 or older.

73. The person has normal cholesterol or is 61 or older.

74. The person has elevated cholesterol or is 30 or under.

75. The person is between 31 and 60, inclusive, or has elevated cholesterol.

76. The person is 61 or older or has elevated cholesterol.

Objective 4: Find the Probability of Sequential Independent Events

77. Suppose that a die is rolled followed by the flip of a coin. Find the probability that the outcome is a 5 on the die followed by the coin turning up heads. (**See Example 8**)

78. If a code for an alarm is a 4-digit sequence, determine the probability that someone guesses each digit correctly.

79. The 5-yr survival rate for stage I breast cancer is 88%. (*Source*: American Cancer Society, www.cancer.org) If two women with stage I breast cancer are selected at random, what is the probability that they both survive 5 yr? (**See Example 9**)

80. Basketball player Lebron James makes approximately 76% of free throws. If he plays in a game in which he shoots 6 free throws, what is the probability that he will make all 6?

81. In the 2010 Wimbledon Championships, John Isner from the United States and Nicolas Mahut from France played a first-round tennis match that became the longest match in tennis history. (The match stretched over a 3-day period with Isner winning 70-68 in the fifth set.) In 2011, after a random draw, the two men met again in the first round of Wimbledon. This is highly improbable. If there are 128 men in the tournament, estimate the probability that

   a. Isner and Mahut would meet in the first round at Wimbledon in any given year. Assume that any player can play any other player in the first round (that is, disregard the fact that seeded players do not play one another in the first round).

   b. Isner and Mahut would meet in the first round 2 yr in a row.

82. A traffic light at an intersection has a 120-sec cycle. The light is green for 80 sec, yellow for 5 sec, and red for 35 sec.

   a. When a motorist approaches the intersection, find the probability that the light will be red. (Assume that the color of the light is defined as the color when the car's front wheels enter the intersection.)

   b. If a motorist passes through the intersection twice during the day, find the probability that the light will be red both times.

83. A test has 10 questions. Five questions are true/false and five questions are multiple-choice. Each multiple-choice question has 4 possible responses of which exactly one is correct. Find the probability that a student guesses on each question and gets a perfect score.

84. A quiz has 6 multiple-choice questions and each question has 5 possible responses of which exactly one is correct. Find the probability that a student answers each question *incorrectly*.

Mixed Exercises

The blood type of an individual is classified according to the presence of certain antigens, substances that cause the immune system to produce antibodies. These antigens are denoted by A, B, and Rh. If an individual's blood contains either the A or B antigen, these letters are listed in the blood type. If neither A nor B is present, then the letter O is used. If the Rh antigen is present, the blood is said to be Rh positive (Rh^+); otherwise, the blood is Rh negative (Rh^-). Under this system, a person with AB^+ blood has all three antigens, and group O^- is absent all three antigens.

   The distribution of blood types for people living in the United States is given in the table. (*Source*: Stanford School of Medicine, http://bloodcenter.stanford.edu) Refer to the table for Exercises 85–92. Round to 3 decimal places when necessary.

Type	Probability
O^+	0.374
O^-	0.066
A^+	0.357
A^-	0.063
B^+	0.085
B^-	0.015
AB^+	0.034
AB^-	0.006

85. a. If an individual is randomly selected from the population, find the probability that the individual will have the Rh factor.

   b. If three people are selected at random, find the probability that they all have the Rh factor. Round to 3 decimal places.

86. a. If a person is selected at random from the population, find the probability that the individual has the A antigen.

   b. If four people are randomly selected, find the probability that all four have the A antigen. Round to 3 decimal places.

87. a. Which blood type is most common ?

   b. Which blood type is most rare?

88. Across all blood types, is a person more likely to have the Rh factor or less likely to have the Rh factor?

Doctors know that certain restrictions apply when considering the administration of blood to a patient. The antigens of the blood donor and recipient must be compatible. If an antigen is absent from the recipient's blood, then the recipient cannot receive blood from a person who has that antigen. For example, a person with B^+ blood cannot receive AB^+ blood because of the presence of the A antigen from the donor. Use this information for Exercises 89–92.

89. Suppose that a person is randomly selected from the population. What is the probability that this individual's blood can be used for a transfusion for a person with type B^+ blood?

90. Suppose that a person is randomly selected from the population. What is the probability that this individual's blood can be used for a transfusion for a person with type A^+ blood?

91. a. What is the probability that an individual from the population can donate blood to a person with type O^- blood.

   b. Explain why a person with type O^- blood is called a universal donor.

92. a. What is the probability that an individual from the population can donate blood to a person with AB^+ blood?

   b. Explain why a person with AB^+ blood can receive blood from anyone.

93. A slot machine in a casino has three wheels that all spin independently. Each wheel has 11 stops, denoted by 0 through 9, and bar. What is the probability that a given outcome is bar-bar-bar?

94. Airlines often overbook flights because a small percentage of passengers do not show up (perhaps due to missed connections). Past history indicates that for a certain route, the probability that an individual passenger will not show up is 0.04. Suppose that 61 people bought tickets for a flight that has 60 seats. Determine the probability that there will not be enough seats. Round to 3 decimal places.

95. A modified archery target consists of five concentric circles with the given outer diameters and point values.

Color	Outer Diameter (cm)	Points
Gold	12.2	9
Red	24.4	7
Blue	36.6	5
Black	48.4	3
White	61.0	1

On an individual shot, what is the probability that

   a. The player scores a 9 (hits the gold area)? (*Hint*: Compute the ratio of the area of the gold region to the area of the entire target.)

   b. The player scores a 5?

   c. The player gets at least 5 points.

96. South Florida humorist Dave Barry often wrote about his dog, Zippy. Suppose that the Barry home has 3200 ft^2 of living area with tile floor. Further suppose that an expensive 8 ft by 10 ft oriental rug is placed on the floor. If Zippy had an "accident" in the house, what is the probability that it would happen on the expensive rug?

For Exercises 97–98,

a. Shade the area bounded by the given inequalities on a coordinate grid showing $-5 \le x \le 5$ and $-5 \le y \le 5$.

b. Suppose that an enthusiastic mathematics student makes a square dart board out of the portion of the rectangular coordinate system defined by $-5 \le x \le 5$ and $-5 \le y \le 5$. Find the probability that a dart thrown at the target will land in the shaded region.

97. $y \ge |x|$ and $y \le 4$

98. $|y| \le 3$ and $|x| \le 2$

Write About It

99. In a carnival game, players win a prize if they can toss a ring around the neck of a bowling pin. How would you go about estimating the probability of winning the game?

100. Give an example of two events that are mutually exclusive.

101. Give an example of two events that are not mutually exclusive.

102. Explain why a probability of $\frac{5}{4}$ is impossible.

Expanding Your Skills

103. Suppose that a box of DVDs contains 10 action movies and 5 comedies.

 a. If two DVDs are selected from the box with replacement, determine the probability that both are comedies.

 b. It probably seems more reasonable that someone would select two *different* DVDs from the box. That is, the first DVD would not be replaced before the second DVD is selected. In such a case, are the events of selecting comedies on the first and second picks independent events?

 c. If two DVDs are selected from the box *without* replacement, determine the probability that both are comedies.

104. Suppose that 12 students (5 freshmen and 7 sophomores) are being considered for two different scholarships. One scholarship is for $500 and the other is for $250.

 a. Two students are selected at random from the group of 12 to receive the scholarships. If a student may receive both scholarships, determine the probability that both students are freshmen.

 b. Now suppose that an individual student may not receive both scholarships. Determine the probability that both students chosen are freshmen.

105. If five cards are dealt from a standard deck of 52 cards, find the probability that

 a. The cards are all hearts.

 b. The cards are all of the same suit.

106. If five cards are dealt from a standard deck of 52 cards, find the probability that

 a. The cards consist of four aces.

 b. The cards are four of a kind (four cards with the same face value).

Consider an experiment that has two possible outcomes categorized as either a "success" or a "failure." If the experiment is conducted n times, and each trial is independent of all other trials, then we say that the experiment is a binomial experiment. The probability of x successes in n trials of a binomial experiment is given by

$$P(x) = {}_nC_x\, p^x q^{(n-x)}$$

where p is the probability of success on any single trial and q is the probability of failure on any single trial. Use the formula for Exercises 107–108.

107. Suppose that 32% of the households in the United States have a cat. In a group of $n = 10$ households, find the probability that exactly $x = 4$ households have a cat. [*Hint*: The probability of a success (a home with a cat) is $p = 0.32$, and the probability of a failure (a home without a cat) is $q = 0.68$.]

108. Suppose that due to bad weather 40% of flights at JFK Airport are delayed. In a group of 14 flights, find the probability that exactly half are delayed.

109. A trucking company periodically tests its employees for drug use. Observations over the years suggest that the probability that an employee from this population will test positive for drugs is roughly 0.01.

 a. What is the probability that an employee from this population will test negative?

 b. In a group of five employees, what is the probability that all test negative? Round to 3 decimal places.

 c. Because the individual rate for testing positive is so low, the laboratory saves money by pooling small portions of the blood samples taken from five employees and doing a single test on the mixture. If the mixture of blood from five employees tests negative, what do we know about the drug status of these employees?

 d. What is the probability that the mixture of blood from five samples is positive? Round to 3 decimal places. [*Hint*: Refer to part (b).]

 e. If the mixture of blood tests positive, what action does the laboratory need to take?

 f. Why is it advantageous for the laboratory to mix a small portion of the blood from five different samples?

CHAPTER 8   KEY CONCEPTS

SECTION 8.1 Sequences and Series	Reference
An **infinite sequence** is a function whose domain is the set of positive integers. A **finite sequence** is a function whose domain is the set of the first n positive integers.	p. 712
A sequence in which consecutive terms alternate in sign is an **alternating sequence.**	p. 713
A **recursion formula** defines the nth term of a sequence as a function of one or more terms preceding it.	p. 714
For a positive integer n, the quantity $n!$ ("n factorial") is defined as $n! = (n)(n-1)(n-2)\cdots(2)(1)$ For $n = 0$, we have $0! = 1$.	p. 715
The n**th partial sum** of a sequence $\{a_n\}$ is a finite series and is given by $S_n = \displaystyle\sum_{i=1}^{n} a_i = a_1 + a_2 + a_3 + \cdots + a_n$	p. 716
The sum of *all* terms in an infinite sequence is an **infinite series:** $\displaystyle\sum_{i=1}^{\infty} a_i = a_1 + a_2 + a_3 + \cdots$	p. 716
Properties of summation: If $\{a_n\}$ and $\{b_n\}$ are sequences, and c is a real number, then 1. $\displaystyle\sum_{i=1}^{n} c = cn$ 2. $\displaystyle\sum_{i=1}^{n} ca_i = c\sum_{i=1}^{n} a_i$ 3. $\displaystyle\sum_{i=1}^{n} (a_i \pm b_i) = \sum_{i=1}^{n} a_i \pm \sum_{i=1}^{n} b_i$	p. 718

SECTION 8.2 Arithmetic Sequences and Series	Reference
An **arithmetic sequence** is a sequence in which each term after the first differs from its predecessor by a common difference d.	p. 723
The n**th term of an arithmetic sequence:** $$a_n = a_1 + (n-1)d$$ where a_1 is the first term of the sequence and d is the common difference.	p. 724
Sum of the first n terms of an arithmetic sequence: $$S_n = \frac{n}{2}(a_1 + a_n)$$ where a_1 is the first term of the sequence and a_n is the nth term of the sequence.	p. 727

SECTION 8.3 Geometric Sequences and Series	Reference
A **geometric sequence** is a sequence in which each term after the first is the product of the preceding term and a fixed nonzero real number, called the **common ratio.** If the first term of a geometric sequence is a_1, and the common ratio is r, then the nth term of a geometric sequence is given by $a_n = a_1 r^{n-1}$.	p. 733
n**th partial sum of a geometric sequence:** The sum S_n of the first n terms of a geometric sequence is given by $S_n = \dfrac{a_1(1 - r^n)}{1 - r}$ where a_1 is the first term of the sequence and r is the common ratio, $r \neq 1$.	p. 737
Sum of an infinite geometric series: Given an infinite geometric series $a_1 + a_1 r + a_1 r^2 + a_1 r^3 + \cdots$ with $|r| < 1$, the sum S of all terms in the series is given by $$S = \frac{a_1}{1 - r}$$ *Note:* If $|r| \geq 1$, then the sum does not exist.	p. 738

Future value of an ordinary annuity: Suppose that P dollars is invested at the end of each compounding period n times per year at interest rate r. Then the value A (in \$) of the annuity after t years is given by $$A = \frac{P\left[\left(1 + \frac{r}{n}\right)^{nt} - 1\right]}{\frac{r}{n}}$$	p. 740

SECTION 8.4 Mathematical Induction	Reference
Mathematical induction is a technique of mathematical proof that is often used to prove that a statement is true for all positive integers.	p. 746
The principle of mathematical induction: Let S_n be a statement involving the positive integer n, and let k be an arbitrary positive integer. Then S_n is true for all positive integers n if 1. S_1 is true, and 2. The truth of S_k implies the truth of S_{k+1}. The assumption that S_k is true is called the **inductive hypothesis.**	p. 747 p. 748
Extended principle of induction: Mathematical induction can be extended to prove statements that might hold true only for integers greater than or equal to some positive integer j. In such a case, • First prove the statement for $n = j$. • Then show that the truth of the statement for an integer greater than or equal to j implies the truth of the statement for the integer that follows.	p. 750

SECTION 8.5 The Binomial Theorem	Reference
Binomial theorem: Let n be a positive integer. The expansion of $(a + b)^n$ is given by $$(a + b)^n = \binom{n}{0}a^n + \binom{n}{1}a^{n-1}b + \binom{n}{2}a^{n-2}b^2 + \cdots + \binom{n}{n-1}ab^{n-1} + \binom{n}{n}b^n$$ $$= \sum_{r=0}^{n}\binom{n}{r}a^{n-r}b^r$$ The values $\binom{n}{0}, \binom{n}{1}, \binom{n}{2}, \ldots, \binom{n}{n}$ are called the **binomial coefficients** of the expansion of $(a + b)^n$. The binomial coefficients can also be found by using **Pascal's triangle.** $\begin{matrix}&&&&1\\&&&1&&1\\&&1&&2&&1\\&1&&3&&3&&1\\1&&4&&6&&4&&1\\1&\ldots\end{matrix}$	p. 755 p. 753
Finding the kth term of a binomial expansion: Let n and k be positive integers with $k \le n + 1$. The kth term of $(a + b)^n$ is $\binom{n}{k-1}a^{n-(k-1)}b^{k-1}$	p. 757

SECTION 8.6 Principles of Counting	Reference
Fundamental principle of counting: If one event can occur in m different ways and a second event can occur in n different ways, then the number of ways that the two events can occur in sequence is $m \cdot n$.	p. 761

A **permutation** is an ordered arrangement of distinct items.   p. 762

- The number of permutations of n distinct elements is $n!$.

- Consider a set of n elements with r_1 duplicates of one kind, r_2 duplicates of a second kind, ... , r_k p. 763
  duplicates of a kth kind. Then the number of distinguishable permutations of the n elements of the set is:

$$\frac{n!}{r_1! \cdot r_2! \cdot \cdots \cdot r_k!}$$

- The number of permutations of n elements taken r at a time is given by   p. 764

$$_nP_r = \frac{n!}{(n-r)!} \text{ or equivalently, } _nP_r = n(n-1)(n-2)\cdots(n-r+1)$$

A **combination** is a collection of distinct items taken without regard to order.   pp. 765–766

The number of combinations of n elements taken r at a time is given by $_nC_r = \dfrac{n!}{r! \cdot (n-r)!}$

SECTION 8.7 Introduction to Probability	Reference
Theoretical probability of an event: Let S represent a sample space with equally likely outcomes, and let E be a subset of S. Then the probability of event E, denoted by $P(E)$, is given by $$P(E) = \frac{n(E)}{n(S)}$$	p. 772
Let E be an event relative to sample space S. The **complement of E,** denoted by $\overline{E}$, is the set of outcomes in the sample space but not in event E. It follows that $P(E) + P(\overline{E}) = 1$	p. 774
Empirical probability is computed based on observed outcomes of the relative frequency of an event to the number of times an experiment is performed.	p. 776
Two events are **mutually exclusive** if they share no common elements. **The probability of A or B:** Given events A and B in a same sample space, $P(A \text{ or } B)$ is given by $P(A \cup B) = P(A) + P(B) - P(A \cap B)$ If A and B are mutually exclusive, then $P(A \cup B) = P(A) + P(B)$.	p. 777
Probability of a sequence of independent events: Two events are **independent** if the probability of one event does not affect the probability of the second event. If events A and B are independent events, then the probability that both A and B will occur is $$P(A \text{ and } B) = P(A) \cdot P(B).$$	p. 779

Expanded Chapter Summary available at www.mhhe.com/millerca.

CHAPTER 8 Review Exercises

SECTION 8.1

For Exercises 1–2, simplify the expression.

1. $\dfrac{8!}{3! \cdot 5!}$

2. $\dfrac{(2n+1)!}{(2n-3)!}$

For Exercises 3–4, write the first five terms of the sequence.

3. $a_n = \dfrac{(n+1)!}{n!}$

4. $c_1 = 5; c_n = -2c_{n-1} + 1$

5. Given the sequence defined by $b_n = (-1)^{n-1} \cdot n$, which terms will be positive and which will be negative?

6. Given $b_n = \dfrac{n+4}{3n}$, find b_{45}.

7. a. Write the first five terms of the sequence defined by $a_n = 2n + 3$.

    b. Evaluate $\displaystyle\sum_{i=1}^{5}(2i + 3)$.

    c. Use the formula $S_n = \dfrac{n}{2}(a_1 + a_n)$ to verify the fifth partial sum of the arithmetic sequence from part (a).

8. a. Write the sum $4 - \dfrac{4}{3} + \dfrac{4}{5} - \dfrac{4}{7} + \cdots$ using summation notation with n as the index of summation. (Using techniques from calculus, we can show that this sum converges to π.)

   b. Use a calculator to evaluate the 50th and 100th partial sums.

For Exercises 9–11, find the sum.

9. $\displaystyle\sum_{i=3}^{8} 2i$ **10.** $\displaystyle\sum_{i=1}^{34} 10$ **11.** $\displaystyle\sum_{i=1}^{60} (-1)^{i+1}$

12. Write an expression for the apparent nth term a_n for the sequence. $10, -30, 90, -270, \ldots$

For Exercises 13–14, write the sum using summation notation. Use i as the index of summation.

13. $\dfrac{3}{2} + \dfrac{4}{4} + \dfrac{5}{8} + \dfrac{6}{16} + \dfrac{7}{32}$

14. $x^2 + x^2y + x^2y^2 + x^2y^3$

15. Rewrite the series as an equivalent series with the new index of summation.

$$\sum_{i=1}^{10} i^3 = \sum_{j=0}^{\square} \square = \sum_{k=2}^{\square} \square$$

16. Determine if the statement is true or false.

$$\sum_{i=1}^{100} (4i - 2) = -200 + 4\sum_{i=1}^{100} i$$

17. Suppose that a single cell of bacteria divides every 20 min for 4 hr. Write a formula for the sequence $\{a_n\}$ representing the number of cells after the nth cell division.

SECTION 8.2

For Exercises 18–20, determine whether the sequence is arithmetic. If so, identify the common difference d.

18. $11, 10.2, 9.4, 8.6, 7.8, \ldots$

19. $4, \dfrac{21}{4}, \dfrac{13}{2}, \dfrac{31}{4}, \ldots$

20. $9, 12, 16, 21, 27, \ldots$

21. Determine the first five terms of the arithmetic sequence $\{a_n\}$ with $a_1 = 4$, and $d = 8$.

22. a. Write an expression for the nth term of the arithmetic sequence $\{a_n\}$ with $a_1 = -19$, and $d = 5$.

   b. Find a_{36}.

23. Find the 23rd term of an arithmetic sequence with $a_1 = 15$ and $a_{57} = 239$.

24. Given an arithmetic sequence with $a_{15} = 86$ and $a_{37} = 240$, find the 104th term.

25. Find the number of terms of the arithmetic sequence. $11, 14, 17, 20, 23, \ldots, 122$

26. A sales person working for a heating and air-conditioning company earns an annual base salary of $30,000 plus $500 on every new system he sells. Suppose that $\{a_n\}$ is a sequence representing the sales person's total yearly income based on the number of units sold n.

   a. Write a formula for the nth term of a sequence that represents the sales person's total income for n units sold. In this case, define $\{a_n\}$ with domain $n \geq 0$ to allow for the possibility of 0 units sold.

   b. How much will the sales person earn in a year for selling 42 new units?

27. Find the sum of the first 35 terms of the arithmetic sequence $-1, -9, -17, -25, \ldots$.

For Exercises 28–30, find the sum.

28. $3 + 10 + 17 + 24 + \cdots + 437$

29. $\displaystyle\sum_{n=1}^{36} (2 - 5n)$ **30.** $\displaystyle\sum_{i=1}^{68} \left(5 + \tfrac{1}{2}i\right)$

31. How long will it take to pay off a debt of $3960 if $50 is paid off the first month, $60 is paid off the second month, $70 is paid off the third month, and so on?

SECTION 8.3

For Exercises 32–34, determine whether the sequence is geometric. If so, find the value of r.

32. $\dfrac{3}{10}, \dfrac{3}{1000}, \dfrac{3}{100{,}000}, \ldots$ **33.** $3, 9, 36, 180, \ldots$

34. $5p^3, -5p^5, 5p^7, -5p^9, \ldots$

35. Write the first five terms of a geometric sequence with $a_1 = 120$, and $r = \tfrac{2}{3}$.

36. Write a formula for the nth term of the geometric sequence.
$$-40, 20, -10, 5, \ldots$$

For Exercises 37–39, find the indicated term of a geometric sequence from the given information.

37. $a_1 = 4$ and $a_2 = 12$. Find a_6.

38. $a_1 = -15$ and $a_4 = -\dfrac{5}{9}$. Find a_7.

39. $a_7 = \dfrac{1}{64}$ and $r = -\dfrac{1}{4}$. Find a_1.

40. Find a_1 and r for a geometric sequence given that $a_3 = 18$ and $a_6 = 486$.

For Exercises 41–46, find the sum of the geometric series, if possible.

41. $\displaystyle\sum_{n=1}^{7} 5(3)^{n-1}$ **42.** $\displaystyle\sum_{i=1}^{6} 12\left(-\dfrac{2}{3}\right)^{i-1}$

43. $\displaystyle\sum_{k=1}^{\infty} 5\left(\dfrac{5}{6}\right)^{k-1}$ **44.** $\displaystyle\sum_{i=1}^{\infty} \dfrac{2}{3}(4)^{i-1}$

45. $\displaystyle\sum_{n=3}^{\infty} 6\left(\frac{1}{2}\right)^{n-1}$

46. $36 - 12 + 4 - \dfrac{4}{3} + \cdots$

47. Write $0.8\overline{7}$ as a fraction.

48. An estimated 150,000 people attended the Coconut Grove art festival over a 3-day period. Admission to the event is $10 per person. In addition, suppose that each person spends an average of $100 on art, drinks, and food.

    a. How much money is initially infused into the local economy during the festival for admission, art, drinks, and food.

    b. If the money is later respent in the community over and over again at a rate of 70%, determine the total amount spent. Assume that the money is respent an infinite number of times.

For Exercise 49–50, find the value of an ordinary annuity in which regular payments of P dollars are made at the end of each compounding period, n times per year, at an interest rate r for t years.

    49. $P = \$150$, $n = 12$, $r = 4\%$, $t = 16$ yr

    50. $P = \$300$, $n = 12$, $r = 4\%$, $t = 32$ yr

    51. a. At age 28, an employee begins investing $100 each pay period (twice per month) in an ordinary annuity. If the interest rate is 5.5%, find the value of the annuity when the employee retires at age 62.

        b. Determine the value of the annuity if the employee waits to retire at age 65.

52. The initial swing (one way) of a pendulum makes an arc of 2 ft. Each swing (one way) thereafter makes an arc of 85% of the length of the previous swing. What is the total arc length that the pendulum travels?

SECTION 8.4

For Exercises 53–56, use mathematical induction to prove the given statement for all positive integers n.

    53. $3 + 7 + 11 + \cdots + (4n - 1) = n(2n + 1)$

    54. $-5 + 2 + 9 + \cdots + (7n - 12) = \dfrac{n}{2}(7n - 17)$

    55. $1 + 4 + 16 + \cdots + 4^{n-1} = \dfrac{1}{3}(4^n - 1)$

    56. $10^n - 1$ is divisible by 3.

57. Use mathematical induction to show that $4^n < (n + 2)!$ for integers $n \geq 2$.

SECTION 8.5

58. a. Write the first four rows of Pascal's triangle.

    b. Expand $(a + b)^3$.

59. Evaluate the given expression. Compare the results to the result of Exercise 58.

    a. $\dbinom{3}{0}$ **b.** $\dbinom{3}{1}$ **c.** $\dbinom{3}{2}$ **d.** $\dbinom{3}{3}$

For Exercises 60–64, expand the binomial by using the binomial theorem.

    60. $(4y + 3)^4$ **61.** $(2x - 3)^5$ **62.** $(5c^3 - d^2)^4$

    63. $(t^5 + u^3)^6$ **64.** $\left(\dfrac{x}{2} + 2y\right)^3$

For Exercises 65–67, find the indicated term of the binomial expansion.

    65. $(5x + 4y)^6$; fifth term

    66. $(3x^4 - 2)^8$; middle term

    67. $(2c^2 - d^5)^9$; Term containing d^{25}.

68. Given $f(x) = 4x^3 + 2x$, find the difference quotient.

69. Use the binomial theorem to find the value of $(3 + 2i)^4$ where i is the imaginary unit.

SECTION 8.6

70. Gaynelle can travel one of 3 roads from her home to school. From school to work there are 4 different routes. How many different routes are available for Gaynelle to travel from home to school to work?

71. A disc jockey has 7 songs that he must play in a half-hour period. In how many different ways can he arrange the 7 songs?

72. In how many ways can the letters in the word SHUFFLE be arranged?

73. In how many ways can the word SPACE be misspelled?

74. A quiz consists of 6 true/false questions and 4 multiple-choice questions. The multiple-choice questions each have 5 possible responses (a, b, c, d, e) of which only one is correct. In how many different ways can a student fill out the answers to the quiz?

75. A 3-digit code is to be made from the set of digits $\{4, 5, 6, 7, 8\}$.

    a. How many codes can be formed if there are no restrictions?

    b. How many codes can be formed if the corresponding 3-digit number is to be an even number?

    c. How many codes can be formed if the corresponding 3-digit number is to be a multiple of 5 and there can be no repetition of digits?

76. Evaluate $_{21}P_4$ and interpret its meaning.

77. Evaluate $_{21}C_4$ and interpret its meaning.

78. Evaluate $_{10}P_3$ and $_{10}C_3$ and compare the results.

79. In how many ways can a statistician select a sample of 15 people from a population of 90 people?

80. How many triangles can be made if the vertices are from three of the six points on the circle? One such triangle is shown in the figure.

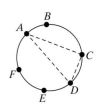

81. The Daytona 500 auto race has 40 cars that initially start the race. How many first-, second-, and third-place finishes can occur?

82. Suppose that a drama class has 22 students.

    a. In how many ways can four students be selected to take part in a survey?

    b. In how many ways can four students be selected to act out a scene from a play involving 4 different parts?

83. To meet the graduation requirements, a student must take 2 English classes out of 10 available, 3 math classes out of 6 available, and 2 history classes out of 7 available. Assuming that the student has met the prerequisites of each course and that there are no scheduling conflicts, determine the number of ways in which the student can select these courses.

SECTION 8.7

84. Which of the following can represent the probability of an event?

    a. 0   **b.** 1   **c.** 1.2   **d.** 0.12

    e. 1.2%   **f.** 120%   **g.** -0.12 **h.** $\frac{4}{5}$

85. If the probability of an event is 0.0042, is the event likely to occur or not likely to occur?

86. If the probability of an event is $\frac{87}{90}$, is the event likely to occur or not likely to occur?

87. If $P(E) = 0.73$, what is the probability of $P(\overline{E})$?

88. Suppose that a box containing music CDs has 4 with country music, 6 with rock music, 3 with jazz music, and 7 with rap music. If one CD is selected at random from the box, determine the probability that

    a. The CD has rap music.

    b. The CD has jazz music.

    c. The CD does not have jazz music.

    d. The CD has classical music.

89. Suppose that two fair dice are rolled. Determine the probability that

    a. The sum of the numbers on the dice is 6.

    b. The sum of the numbers on the dice is greater than 9.

    c. The numbers on the dice form a sum that is a multiple of 5.

90. For a recent season, the batting average for baseball player Starlin Castro was 0.306. (This means that the probability that Castro will get a hit on a given time at bat is 0.306.)

    a. Determine the probability that Castro will not get a hit on a given time at bat.

    b. If Castro is at bat three times in a game, what is the probability that he will get a hit all three times?

    c. If Castro is at bat three times in a game, what is the probability that he will not get a hit on any of the three times at bat?

91. Suppose that 15 lightbulbs are in a cabinet and that 4 are defective. If three bulbs are chosen at random,

    a. What is the probability that all three will be defective?

    b. What is the probability that all three will be good?

    c. Why do the probabilities from parts (a) and (b) not add up to 1?

92. Suppose that a lottery game has the player select 5 distinct numbers from 1 to 30, inclusive. The player wins by choosing numbers that match those randomly selected in a drawing.

    a. What is the probability that a player will win if the numbers do not have to be selected in any particular order?

    b. If the player has to pick the correct 5 numbers in a specific order, what is the probability that the player will win?

93. For a recent year, the Centers for Disease Control reported that the probability that a 50-yr-old will live to age 51 is 0.9959. In a group of ten 50-yr-olds, what is the probability that all ten survive to the age of 51?

For Exercises 94–99, use the data in the table categorizing smokers and nonsmokers according to their blood pressure (BP) levels. If one person is chosen at random, find the probability of the given event.

	Normal BP	Elevated BP	Total
Smokers	42	28	70
Nonsmokers	80	10	90
Total	122	38	160

94. The person has elevated blood pressure.

95. The person is a nonsmoker.

96. The person has elevated blood pressure or is a nonsmoker.

97. The person has normal blood pressure or is a smoker.

98. The person is a smoker or has elevated blood pressure.

99. The person is a nonsmoker or has normal blood pressure.

For Exercises 100–103, refer to the sample space for a card drawn from a standard deck. See page 776.

100. If one card is drawn at random from a standard deck, what is the probability that it is an 8 or a club?

101. If one card is drawn at random from a standard deck, what is the probability that it is a red card or a 5?

102. If *two* cards are drawn at random with replacement from a standard deck, what is the probability that both are hearts?

103. If *two* cards are drawn at random with replacement from a standard deck, what is the probability that both are kings?

CHAPTER 8   Test

1. Write the first six terms of the sequence defined by $a_1 = -2$, $a_2 = 3$, $a_n = a_{n-2} + a_{n-1}$ for $n \geq 3$.

2. Simplify. $\dfrac{(3n + 1)!}{(3n - 1)!}$

For Exercises 3–5,

a. Determine whether the sequence is arithmetic, geometric, or neither.

b. If the sequence is arithmetic, determine d. If the sequence is geometric, determine r.

c. Write an expression a_n for the apparent nth term of the sequence.

3. 0.139, 0.00139, 0.0000139, …

4. 0.52, 0.68, 0.84, 1.00, …

5. $\dfrac{3}{5}, \dfrac{6}{25}, \dfrac{9}{125}, \dfrac{12}{625}, \dots$

6. Write the first four terms of the geometric sequence with $a_1 = 4$ and $r = \frac{3}{2}$.

7. Write the first five terms of the arithmetic sequence with $a_1 = 10$ and $a_{20} = 67$.

8. Find the 78th term of an arithmetic sequence with $a_1 = 64$ and $d = -11$.

9. Find the 6th term of a geometric sequence with $a_1 = -3$ and $r = 2$.

10. Find the number of terms in the arithmetic sequence.
$$-15, -19, -23, -27, \dots, -679$$

11. Find the number of terms in the geometric sequence.
$$16, 8, 4, 2, \dots, \frac{1}{16}$$

12. Given an arithmetic sequence with $a_{12} = -21$ and $a_{50} = -97$, find a_1 and d.

13. Given a geometric sequence with $a_3 = 20$ and $a_8 = 640$, find a_1 and r.

For Exercises 14–18, evaluate the sum if possible.

14. $\dfrac{3}{2} + \dfrac{3}{4} + \dfrac{3}{8} + \dfrac{3}{16} + \cdots$

15. $\displaystyle\sum_{k=1}^{54} (3k + 7)$

16. $\displaystyle\sum_{i=1}^{6} 4\left(\dfrac{3}{2}\right)^{i-1}$

17. $\displaystyle\sum_{k=1}^{4} k!$

18. $\displaystyle\sum_{i=1}^{\infty} \dfrac{1}{2}\left(\dfrac{6}{5}\right)^{i-1}$

19. Suppose that a county fair has an estimated 50,000 people attend over a 2-week period. Admission to the fair is $5.00. In addition, suppose that each person spends an average of $10 on food, drinks, and rides.

a. How much money is initially infused into the local community for admission, food, drinks, and rides?

b. If the money is respent in the local community over and over again at a rate of 65%, determine the total amount spent. Assume that the money is respent an infinite number of times. Round to the nearest dollar.

20. An employee invests $400 per month in an ordinary annuity. If the interest rate is 5.2%, find the value of the annuity after 25 yr.

21. Lakeisha wants to put down new tile in her home. The tile costs $3.50/ft^2 and labor is $4.00/ft^2. Write the nth term of a sequence representing the cost to tile an n by n square foot area where n is an integer and $n \geq 1$ ft.

22. How many days will it take Johan to read a 920-page book if he reads 20 pages the first day, 25 pages the second day, 30 pages the third day, and so on?

For Exercises 23–25, use mathematical induction to prove the given statement for all positive integers n.

23. $6 + 10 + 14 + \cdots + (4n + 2) = n(2n + 4)$

24. $1 + 5 + 25 + \cdots + 5^{n-1} = \frac{1}{4}(5^n - 1)$

25. 2 is a factor of $7^n - 5$.

For Exercises 26–27, expand the binomial by using the binomial theorem.

26. $\left(\dfrac{x}{2} + 3\right)^4$

27. $(4c^2 - t^4)^5$

For Exercises 28–29, find the indicated term of the binomial expansion.

28. $(-2t + v^2)^{10}$; eighth term

29. $(3x + y^2)^7$; Term containing y^6.

30. Evaluate $_{13}P_5$ and $_{13}C_5$.

31. Explain the difference between a permutation and a combination of n items taken r at a time.

32. A musician plans to perform 9 selections. In how many ways can she arrange the musical selections?

33. How many outfits can be made from 4 pairs of slacks, 5 shirts, and 3 ties, if one selection from each category is made? Assume that all items fashionably match.

34. In how many ways can the word HIPPOPOTAMUS be misspelled?

35. Suppose that a jury pool consists of 30 women and 26 men.

   a. In how many ways can a jury of 12 people be selected?

   b. In how many ways can a jury of 6 women and 6 men be selected?

   c. What is the probability of randomly selecting a jury of 6 women and 6 men?

   d. What is the probability of randomly selecting a jury of all men?

36. A review sheet for a history test has 10 essay questions. Suppose that the professor picks 3 questions from the review sheet to put on the test. In how many ways can the professor choose 3 questions from 10 questions?

37. After a service call by a plumber, the company follows up with a survey to rate the service and professionalism of the technician. The survey has 6 yes/no questions and 4 multiple-choice questions each with 3 possible responses. In how many different ways can a customer fill out the survey?

38. Suppose that 50 people buy raffle tickets.

   a. In how many ways can 4 people who bought tickets be selected if each is to receive a $20 gift certificate to a restaurant?

   b. In how many ways can 4 people who bought tickets be selected if the first person wins a $10 gift certificate, the second person wins a $25 gift certificate, the third person wins a $50 gift certificate, and the fourth person wins a $200 camera?

39. For a recent year, approximately 36,000 people were killed in the United States in motor vehicle accidents. If the population had 300,000,000 people at that time, estimate the probability of being killed in a motor vehicle crash.

40. A cable company advertises short wait times for customer service calls. The graph shows the wait times (in seconds) for a sample of customers. Based on the data given, if a customer is selected at random, find the probability that

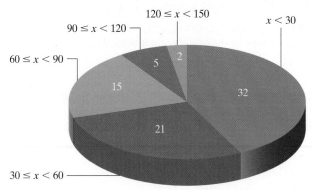

Number of Customers vs. Wait Time, x

   a. The customer will wait less than 30 sec.

   b. The customer will wait at least 30 sec.

   c. The customer will wait at least 90 sec but less than 120 sec.

   d. The customer will wait more than 150 sec.

41. If two fair dice are thrown, find the probability that the sum is between 6 and 8, inclusive.

42. Suppose that two cards are drawn from a standard deck with replacement. What is the probability that an ace is selected, followed by a heart?

43. For a recent year, 31.9% of Americans living below the poverty level were not covered by health insurance. (*Source*: U.S. Census Bureau, www.census.gov) If three people were selected at random from this population, what is the probability that all three would not have coverage?

For Exercises 44–47, use the data in the table categorizing the type of payment used at a grocery store according to the gender of the customer. If one person is chosen at random, find the probability of the given event.

	Cash	Credit Card	Check	Total
Male	19	24	13	56
Female	14	30	20	64
Total	33	54	33	120

44. The customer is female.

45. The customer is male or paid by check.

46. The customer paid by credit card or by cash.

47. The customer paid cash or was female.

CHAPTER 8   Cumulative Review Exercises

For Exercises 1–4, consider sets A and B and determine if the statement is true or false.

$$A = \{x \mid 4 > x\}, B = \{x \mid x \leq 1\}$$

1. $4 \in A$ **2.** $B \subset A$

3. $A \cap B = B$ **4.** $A \cup B = B$

5. a. Write an expression for the distance between t and 5 on the number line.

    b. Simplify the expression from part (a) for $t < 5$.

6. Simplify without using a calculator.

$$\frac{(6.0 \times 10^{13})(9.0 \times 10^{8})}{2.0 \times 10^{-6}}$$

For Exercises 7–10, simplify the expression.

7. $-27^{-4/3}$ **8.** $\left(\sqrt{x} + 5\sqrt{2}\right)\left(3\sqrt{x} - \sqrt{2}\right)$

9. $\dfrac{4 - x^{-2}}{6 - 3x^{-1}}$ **10.** i^{127}

For Exercises 11–18, solve the equation or inequality. Write the solution set to the inequalities in interval notation.

11. $\sqrt{2x^2 - x - 14} + 4 = x$

12. $(x^2 + x)^2 - 14(x^2 + x) + 24 = 0$

13. $|3x - 5| = |2x + 1|$

14. $-5x \leq 20$ and $3 - [2 - (x - 4)] < 2x + 5$

15. $0 \leq |x + 7| - 6$ **16.** $\dfrac{2x + 1}{x + 4} \geq 1$

17. $\log_4(2x + 7) = 2 + \log_4 x$ **18.** $5e^{x+1} - 100 = 0$

19. Given $f(x) = 2x^3 - 5x^2 - 28x + 15$,

    a. Find all the zeros of $f(x)$.

    b. Identify the x-intercepts of the graph of f.

    c. Determine the y-intercept of the graph of f.

    d. Graph $y = f(x)$.

    e. Solve the inequality $2x^3 - 5x^2 - 28x + 15 < 0$.

20. An object is launched straight upward with an initial velocity of 400 ft/sec from a height of 4 ft. The height of the object t seconds after launch can be modeled by $s(t) = -16t^2 + 400t + 4$, where $s(t)$ is the height measured in feet.

    a. Determine the time required for the object to reach its maximum height.

    b. Determine the maximum height of the object.

    c. Determine the time required for the object to hit the ground. Round to 1 decimal place.

21. Given $x^2 + y^2 - 8x - 2y + 1 = 0$,

    a. Write the equation of the circle in standard form.

    b. Identify the center and radius of the circle.

    c. Graph the circle.

For Exercises 22–25, graph the equation.

22. $\dfrac{y^2}{9} - \dfrac{x^2}{16} = 1$

23. $\dfrac{(x + 1)^2}{4} + \dfrac{(y - 2)^2}{9} = 1$

24. $y = \log_2(x + 3)$

25. $y = \begin{cases} |x| + 1 & \text{for } x \leq 1 \\ -x + 1 & \text{for } x > 1 \end{cases}$

26. Explain how the graph of $f(x) = 2\sqrt{x - 1} + 3$ is related to the graph of $y = \sqrt{x}$.

27. Given $f(x) = 4x^3 - 3x$,

    a. Find the difference quotient.

    b. Find the average rate of change on the interval $[1, 3]$.

    c. Determine if the function is even, odd, or neither.

28. Given $g(x) = 5x - 1$,

    a. Is g a one-to-one function?

    b. Write an equation for $g^{-1}(x)$.

29. Given $f(x) = x^3 - x^2 - 7x + 15$,

    a. Is $2 + i$ a zero of $f(x)$?

    b. Is $(x + 3)$ a factor of $f(x)$?

30. Given $r(x) = \dfrac{3x^2 + 2}{x^2 - 5x - 14}$,

    a. Determine the vertical asymptote(s).

    b. Determine the horizontal or slant asymptote if either exist.

31. The population of a city was 320,000 in the year 2000. By 2012, the population reached 360,800.

    a. Write a model of the form $P(t) = P_0 e^{kt}$ to model the population $P(t)$ for a time t years since 2000.

    b. Predict the population in the year 2015 if this trend continues. Round to the nearest 100 people.

    c. Determine the amount of time for the population to reach 400,000 if this trend continues. Round to the nearest tenth of a year.

32. Write the expression in terms of $\log x$, $\log y$, and $\log z$.

$$\log\left(\frac{x^3}{y^5 \sqrt{z}}\right)$$

33. Simplify. $\log_2 \dfrac{1}{16}$

34. Approximate the value of $\log_5 417$ to 4 decimal places.

For Exercises 35–37, solve the system of equations.

35. $2x - 5y = 13$
$-3x + 2y = -3$

36. $4x - 2z = -4$
$6y + 5z = 8$
$7x - 3y = 13$

37. $2x - y = 6$
$x^2 + y = 9$

38. Use Gaussian elimination or Gauss-Jordan elimination to solve the system of equations.

$$-2x - 9y + 16z = -15$$
$$x + y - z = 4$$
$$x - 2y + 5z = 1$$

39. Use Cramer's rule to solve the system.

$$13x - 2y = 11$$
$$5x + 3y = 6$$

40. Graph the solution set.

$x^2 + y^2 \le 16$
$y > -x^2 + 4$

For Exercises 41–46, refer to the matrices given and perform the indicated operations, if possible.

$$A = \begin{bmatrix} 4 & -3 \\ 5 & 9 \end{bmatrix} \qquad B = \begin{bmatrix} -1 & 6 \\ 3 & 7 \end{bmatrix}$$

$$C = \begin{bmatrix} -1 & 4 & 0 \\ 3 & 6 & 1 \\ 2 & -5 & 7 \end{bmatrix} \qquad D = \begin{bmatrix} -5 & 1 & 0 \\ 8 & 4 & 6 \end{bmatrix}$$

41. $-5A + 2B$

42. $3C - A$

43. $|A|$

44. $|C|$

45. CD

46. AD

47. Given $A = \begin{bmatrix} 1 & 2 & -1 \\ 0 & 1 & 3 \\ 1 & 0 & 2 \end{bmatrix}$, find A^{-1}.

48. Use the inverse matrix from Exercise 47 to solve the system of equations.

$$x + 2y - z = -5$$
$$y + 3z = 13$$
$$x + 2z = 5$$

49. Given $(y + 2)^2 = -8(x - 1)$,

a. Determine the vertex of the graph of the parabola.

b. Identify the focus.

c. Write an equation for the directrix.

50. Determine whether the sequence is arithmetic or geometric and find the value of the common difference or the common ratio.

$$-a^2, a^5, -a^8, a^{11}, \ldots$$

51. Find the 500th term of an arithmetic sequence with $a_1 = 6.9$ and $d = 0.3$.

For Exercises 52–53, find the sum.

52. $\displaystyle\sum_{k=1}^{74} (5k + 3)$

53. $\displaystyle\sum_{i=1}^{8} 6(2)^{i-1}$

54. Find the sum if possible. $6 + 2 + \dfrac{2}{3} + \dfrac{2}{9} + \cdots$

55. Use mathematical induction to prove the statement for all positive integers n.

$$8 + 12 + 16 + 20 + \cdots + (4n + 4) = 2n(n + 3)$$

56. Expand the binomial. $(3x - y^2)^5$

57. Simplify. $\dfrac{(3n - 1)!}{2!(3n + 1)!}$

58. In how many ways can 5 children be arranged in a line for a photograph?

59. Suppose that four people are to be randomly selected from a group of 8 women and 5 men. What is the probability of selecting 2 women and 2 men?

60. If one card is selected from a standard deck of cards, what is the probability that the card selected is a diamond or an ace? (*Hint*: Refer to Figure 8-12 from page 776.)

Student Answer Appendix

CHAPTER R

Section R.1 Practice Exercises, pp. 13–16

1. set   **3.** natural   **5.** set, builder   **7.** rational

9. left   **11.** $|a-b|$ or $|b-a|$ **13.** square

15. 3 is an element of the set of natural numbers.

17. -3.1 is not an element of the set of integers.

19. The set of integers is a proper subset of the set of real numbers.

21. a. False   **b.** False   **c.** True   **d.** True

23. a. False   **b.** False   **c.** False   **d.** True

25. True   **27.** False   **29.** True   **31.** False

33. a. True   **b.** False   **35. a.** False   **b.** True

37. a. False   **b.** False

39. a. 6   **b.** 6   **c.** $-12, 6$ **d.** $0.\overline{3}, 0.33, -0.9, -12, \frac{11}{4}, 6$
   e. $\sqrt{5}, \frac{\pi}{6}$ **f.** $\sqrt{5}, 0.\overline{3}, 0.33, -0.9, -12, \frac{11}{4}, 6, \frac{\pi}{6}$

41. $a \ge 5$ **43.** $3c \le 9$ **45.** $m + 4 > 70$ **47.** True

49. True   **51.** False   **53.** False   **55.** $(-7, \infty)$; $\{x \mid x > -7\}$

57. $(-\infty, 4.1]$; $\{x \mid x \le 4.1\}$ **59.** $[-6, 0)$; $\{x \mid -6 \le x < 0\}$

61. $\longrightarrow$; $(-\infty, 6]$

63. $\longleftrightarrow$; $\left(-\frac{7}{6}, \frac{1}{3}\right]$

65. $\longrightarrow$; $(4, \infty)$

67. $\longrightarrow$; $\{x \mid -3 < x \le 7\}$

69. $\longleftarrow$; $\{x \mid x \le 6.7\}$

71. $\longrightarrow$; $\{x \mid x \ge -\frac{3}{5}\}$

73. 6   **75.** 0   **77.** $2 - \sqrt{2}$ **79. a.** $\pi - 3$ **b.** $\pi - 3$

81. a. $x + 2$ **b.** $-x - 2$ **83. a.** 1   **b.** -1

85. $|1 - 6|$ or $|6 - 1|$; 5   **87.** $|3 - (-4)|$ or $|-4 - 3|$; 7

89. $|8 - \sqrt{3}|$ or $|\sqrt{3} - 8|$; $8 - \sqrt{3}$

91. $|6 - 2\pi|$ or $|2\pi - 6|$; $2\pi - 6$

93. a. 16   **b.** 16   **c.** -16 **d.** 2   **e.** -2 **f.** Not a real number

95. a. 2   **b.** -2 **c.** -2 **d.** 10   **e.** Not a real number   **f.** -10

97. $\frac{8}{27}$ **99.** 0.0016   **101.** $\frac{13}{5}$ **103.** -4 **105.** -3

107. 4   **109.** 49   **111.** $-\frac{9}{25}$ **113.** 7   **115.** Undefined

117. 199.5 lb   **119.** 121 cc

121. All terminating decimals can be written as a decimal fraction—that is, a fraction with a denominator that is a power of 10.

123. A parenthesis is used if an endpoint to an interval is *not* included in the set.

125. $\mathbb{Z}$ represents the set of integers. All integers belong to $\mathbb{Q}$ (the set of rational numbers). Therefore, $\mathbb{Z}$ is a subset of $\mathbb{Q}$. However, $\mathbb{Q}$ contains fractions and decimals, such as $\frac{1}{2}$ and 0.2, that are not integers. Therefore, $\mathbb{Q} \not\subset \mathbb{Z}$.

127. 0   **129.** $2n$ **131.** $-n$ **133.** $b > 0$ **135.** $b \ge 0$

137. positive   **139.** negative   **141.** 6744.25   **143.** 0.58

145. Missing parentheses around the denominator. Enter as:
$(-3 + \sqrt{\ }(3^2 - 4(-5)(2)))/(2(-5))$ Correct value: -0.4

Section R.2 Practice Exercises, pp. 23–27

1. $[-5, 2)$; $\{x \mid -5 \le x < 2\}$ **3.** $|\sqrt{2} - 9|$ or $|9 - \sqrt{2}|$; $9 - \sqrt{2}$

5. True   **7.** False   **9.** 11   **11.** dependent   **13.** term

15. commutative   **17.** 1   **19.** $-x$ **21.** reciprocal

23. $(a \cdot b) \cdot c$ **25. a.** 28 mpg   **b.** 31 mpg   **c.** Model breakdown. The value -4 mpg is not possible.

27. a. \$622.25   **b.** \$292.85   **c.** No. Eventually, the model would produce a negative expenditure. This is not possible.

29. $T_n = T_s + 16$ **31.** $P = W + M$

33. a. $J = C - 1$ **b.** $C = J + 1$ **35.** $D \ge 0.25P$

37. $v = \sqrt{2gh}$ **39. a.** $C = 0.12k + 14.89$ **b.** \$158.89

41. a. $C = 640m + 200n + 500$ **b.** \$8780

43. a. $C = 159n + 0.11(159n)$ or $C = 176.49n$ **b.** \$705.96

45. Terms: $12x^2y^5, -xy^4, 9.2xy^3$; coefficients: $12, -1, 9.2$

47. Term: $\frac{5}{m}$; coefficient: 5   **49.** Term: $x \mid y + z \mid$; coefficient: 1

51. $x + 7$ **53.** $w + (-3)$ **55.** $\frac{1}{3}y$ **57.** $t + (3 + 9)$; $t + 12$

59. $\left(\frac{1}{5} \cdot 5\right)w$; w **61. a.** 8   **b.** $-\frac{1}{8}$ **63. a.** $-\frac{5}{4}$ **b.** $\frac{4}{5}$

65. a. 0   **b.** Undefined   **67. a.** -2.1 **b.** $\frac{1}{2.1}$ or $\frac{10}{21}$

69. $-16w^3$ **71.** $9x^3y - 6.9xy^3$ **73.** $-\frac{1}{15}c^7d - \frac{3}{2}cd^7$

75. $12p^3 - 18.3p^2 - 24p + 6.6$ **77.** $-4x + \pi$

79. $-24x^2 - 16x + 8$ **81.** $-4x^2y - 12yz^2 + \frac{4}{3}z^3$

83. $22w$ **85.** $-25u + 16v$ **87.** $88v + 59w - 20$

89. $6y^2$ **91.** -3 **93.** $\sqrt{34}$ **95.** 308   **97.** $W = 2L - 3$

99. $E_{2009} = E_{2008} + 489{,}000$ **101.** 36 gal

103. The commutative property of addition indicates that the order in which two quantities are added does not affect the sum. The associative property of addition indicates that the manner in which quantities are grouped under addition does not affect the sum.

105. 6.01

Section R.3 Practice Exercises, pp. 35–39

1. $-x - \frac{3}{5}y + 1$ **3.** $6 - a$ **5.** $t = w + 1.93$ **7.** 1

9. scientific   **11.** $m + n$ **13. a.** 1   **b.** -1 **c.** 8   **d.** 1

15. a. 1   **b.** $-\frac{1}{3}$ **c.** $-\frac{2}{3}$ **d.** 1

17. a. $\frac{1}{64}$ **b.** $\frac{8}{x^2}$ **c.** $\frac{1}{64x^2}$ **d.** $-\frac{1}{64}$

19. a. q^2 **b.** $\frac{1}{q^2}$ **c.** $\frac{5p^3}{q^2}$ **d.** $\frac{5q^2}{p^3}$ **21.** 2^{12} **23.** x^{11}

25. $-\frac{12d^8}{c^3}$ **27.** y **29.** $\frac{1}{216}$ **31.** $\frac{2p^7}{3k^3}$ **33.** $\frac{n^5}{3m^4}$

35. 4^6 **37.** $\frac{1}{p^{14}}$ **39.** $-8c^3d^3$ **41.** $\frac{49a^2}{b^2}$ **43.** $\frac{16x^4}{y^6}$

45. $\frac{n^4}{49k^2}$ **47.** -1 **49.** $\frac{m^6}{4n^{18}}$ **51.** $\frac{27z^{15}}{x^9y^6}$ **53.** $-\frac{9z^{16}}{2y^7}$

55. 27   **57.** 197   **59.** $\frac{2y^4}{x^7}$ **61.** $\frac{1}{x^{16}}$ **63.** $-\frac{x^{32}}{v^{21}w^{28}}$

65. $(3x + 5)^{12}$ **67.** $(6v - 7)^{90}$ **69.** $\frac{31}{4}$

71. a. 3.5×10^5 **b.** 3.5×10^{-5} **c.** 3.5×10^0

73. a. 8.6×10^{-1} **b.** 8.6×10^0 **c.** 8.6×10^1

75. 2.998×10^{10} cm/sec   **77.** 1.0×10^{-5} cm   **79.** 4.2×10^0 L

81. a. 0.00000261   **b.** 2,610,000   **c.** 2.61

83. a. 0.6718   **b.** 6.718   **c.** 67.18
85. 1,670,000,000,000,000,000,000,000 molecules   **87.** 0.000 007 m
89. 8×10^5 **91.** 4×10^{-4} **93.** 1.86×10^{16} **95.** 7.2×10^{-20}
97. 1.24×10^{11} **99. a.** 3.1536×10^7 sec   **b.** 3.1536×10^{11} gal
101. 2×10^4 songs   **103.** 2.5×10^{13} red blood cells
105. In the expression $6x^0$, the exponent 0 applies to x only. In the expression $(6x)^0$, the exponent 0 applies to a base of $(6x)$. The first expression simplifies to 6, and the second expression simplifies to 1.
107. Yes; $(-4)^2 = 16 > 0$ **109.** No   **111.** 1.55×10^{18} N
113. a. $<$ **b.** $>$ **115. a.** $>$ **b.** $=$ **117.** x^{m+4}
119. x^{2m+7} **121.** x^{m-8} **123.** x^{m+2} **125.** x^{12mn}
127. $x^{3m+4} y^{2n+5}$ **129.** 6,284,000   **131.** 0.000 000 245

Section R.4 Practice Exercises, pp. 49–53

1. a. $\sqrt{36}$ **b.** $\sqrt{36}, \sqrt{0}$ **c.** $\sqrt{36}, -\sqrt{4}, \sqrt{0}$
d. $\sqrt{36}, \sqrt{\frac{9}{49}}, -\sqrt{4}, \sqrt{0}$ **e.** $\sqrt{37}$
f. $\sqrt{37}, \sqrt{36}, \sqrt{\frac{9}{49}}, -\sqrt{4}, \sqrt{0}$
3. $\dfrac{v^2}{w^4}$ **5.** $-6x^2y^3$ **7.** n **9.** $(\sqrt[n]{a})^m$ or $\sqrt[n]{a^m}$ **11.** $|x|$
13. $\sqrt[n]{a \cdot b}$ **15.** 3   **17.** $\dfrac{2}{7}$ **19.** 0.3   **21.** Not a real number
23. -3 **25.** $-\dfrac{1}{2}$ **27. a.** 5   **b.** Undefined   **c.** -5
29. a. 3   **b.** -3 **c.** -3 **31. a.** $\dfrac{11}{13}$ **b.** $\dfrac{13}{11}$
33. a. 8   **b.** $\dfrac{1}{8}$ **c.** -8 **d.** $-\dfrac{1}{8}$ **e.** Undefined   **f.** Undefined
35. a. 16   **b.** $\dfrac{1}{16}$ **c.** -16 **d.** $-\dfrac{1}{16}$ **e.** 16   **f.** $\dfrac{1}{16}$
37. a. $\sqrt[11]{y^4}$ or $(\sqrt[11]{y})^4$ **b.** $6\sqrt[11]{y^4}$ or $6(\sqrt[11]{y})^4$
c. $\sqrt[11]{(6y)^4}$ or $(\sqrt[11]{6y})^4$
39. $a^{3/5}$ **41.** $(6x)^{1/2}$ **43.** $6x^{1/2}$ **45.** $(a^5 + b^5)^{1/5}$
47. a^2 **49.** $\dfrac{3y^{1/3}}{w^{2/3}}$ **51.** $\dfrac{8y^{3/20}}{x^6}$ **53.** $\dfrac{4m^3}{n^7}$ **55.** $\dfrac{(m+n)^{1/2}}{m}$
57. a. $t \geq 0$ **b.** All real numbers   **59.** $|y|$ **61.** y **63.** $|2x - 5|$
65. w^6 **67. a.** $c^3\sqrt{c}$ **b.** $c^2\sqrt[3]{c}$ **c.** $c\sqrt[9]{c^3}$ **d.** $\sqrt[9]{c^7}$
69. a. $2\sqrt{6}$ **b.** $2\sqrt[3]{3}$ **71.** $5y^2z^3\sqrt[3]{2x^2z^2}$ **73.** $2p^3q\sqrt[4]{6p^2q^3}$
75. $2(y-2)\sqrt{21(y-2)}$ **77.** $\dfrac{p^3\sqrt{p}}{6}$ **79.** $2wz\sqrt[3]{z^2}$
81. $\dfrac{x}{5y}$ **83.** $2\sqrt{35}$ **85.** xy **87.** $-15a\sqrt{a}$
89. $-\dfrac{4}{3}ac\sqrt[3]{3ab^2}$ **91.** $\sqrt[20]{x^{17}y^8}$ **93.** $\sqrt[18]{m^5}$ **95.** $\sqrt[8]{x^7}$
97. $-5\sqrt[3]{2y^2}$ **99.** $-\sqrt{2}$ **101.** $-28xy\sqrt[3]{2xy}$
103. $(12 + 5y)\sqrt{2y}$ **105.** $(-z + 3)\sqrt{2z}$ **107.** $2\sqrt{110}$ in.²
109. $6\sqrt{5}$ m   **111.** $16\sqrt{13}$ in. ≈ 58 in.
113. $2\sqrt{29}$ in. ≈ 10.8 in.   **115.** 45π in.²   **117.** 15.9%
119. a. 466.2 Hz, 493.9 Hz, and 523.3 Hz   **b.** 261.6 Hz
121. In each case, add like terms or like radicals by using the distributive property.   **123.** 2.0×10^4 **125.** $2\sqrt{2}$
127. Yes; The model gives a mean surface temperature of approximately 29.1°C.

Section R.5 Practice Exercises, pp. 60–64

1. $7x + 2z - 24$ **3.** 5   **5.** $-\dfrac{81x^{11}y^5}{8}$ **7.** polynomial
9. leading   **11.** binomial, trinomial   **13.** $(a - b)$
15. a. Yes   **b.** Yes   **c.** No   **d.** No
17. $-18x^7 + 7.2x^3 - 4.1$; Leading coefficient -18; Degree 7
19. $-y^2 + \dfrac{1}{3}y$; Leading coefficient -1; Degree 2
21. 11   **23.** $-6p^7 + 2p^4 + p^2 + 2p - 5$
25. $0.08c^3b - 0.06c^2b^2 + 0.01cb^3$ **27.** $-\dfrac{1}{4}x^2 + \dfrac{11}{8}x + 6\sqrt{2}$

29. $-2a^7b^3$ **31.** $14m^6 - 21m^3 + 28m^2$ **33.** $2x^2 + 3x - 20$
35. $8u^4 + 2u^2v^2 - 15v^4$ **37.** $y^3 - 13y^2 - 42y - 24$
39. $a^2 + 2ab + b^2$ **41.** $16x^2 - 25$ **43.** $9w^4 - 49z^2$
45. $\dfrac{1}{25}c^2 - \dfrac{4}{9}d^6$ **47.** $25m^2 - 30m + 9$ **49.** $16t^4 + 24t^2p^3 + 9p^6$
51. $w^3 + 12w^2 + 48w + 64$ **53.** $u^2 + 2uv + v^2 - w^2$
55. $824.74 billion
57. a. $I + P = 56.44x + 651.6$ **b.** The polynomial $I + P$ represents the total amount of health-related expenditures made by individuals with private insurance.   **c.** $990.24 billion; In the year 2006, a total of $990.24 billion was spent on health-related expenses by individuals with private insurance.
59. $10x + 22$ **61.** $25y^2 - 4x^2 - 12x - 9$
63. $x^3 + 14x^2 + 64x + 96$ **65.** $ac + bc$ **67.** $x^2 + 6x - 27$
69. a. $x + 1$ **b.** $x + (x + 1); 2x + 1$ **c.** $x(x + 1); x^2 + x$
d. $x^2 + (x + 1)^2; 2x^2 + 2x + 1$ **71.** $-y^2 + 26y + 31$
73. $x^{2n} - 4x^n - 21$ **75.** $z^{2n} + 2w^m z^n + w^{2m}$ **77.** $a^{2n} - 25$
79. $-60x - 50$ **81.** $20 + 30\sqrt{6} - 20\sqrt{2}$
83. $45\sqrt{2} - 24\sqrt{3} - 18$ **85.** $8y - 2\sqrt{y} - 15$
87. $8\sqrt{15} + 22$ **89.** 5   **91.** $16x^2y - 4xy^2$
93. $36z^2 - 12\sqrt{5}z + 5$ **95.** $25a^4b + 70a^2b^2\sqrt{ab} + 49ab^4$
97. $x - 24$ **99.** $x - 10\sqrt{x + 1} + 26$ **101.** $\sqrt{25 - 4x}$
103. $2x - 2\sqrt{x^2 - y^2}$ **105.** 7 m²
107. A polynomial consists of a finite number of terms in which the coefficient of each term is a real number, and the variable factor x is raised to an exponent that is a whole number.
109. In each case, multiply by using the distributive property.
111. False   **113.** True   **115.** $a^3 + 3a^2b + 3ab^2 + b^3$

Problem Recognition Exercises, p. 64

1. a. 8   **b.** 4   **c.** 16   **d.** $\dfrac{1}{64}$ **e.** -8 **f.** Undefined
g. 16   **h.** $\dfrac{1}{16}$ **2. a.** $25a^2b^6$ **b.** $25a^2 + 10ab^3 + b^6$
c. $\dfrac{1}{25a^2b^6}$ **d.** $\dfrac{1}{25a^2 + 10ab^3 + b^6}$
3. a. $4x^8y^2$ **b.** $4x^8 - 4x^4y + y^2$ **c.** $\dfrac{1}{4x^8y^2}$
d. $\dfrac{1}{4x^8 - 4x^4y + y^2}$ **4. a.** x^8 **b.** x^2 **c.** $\dfrac{1}{x^2}$ **d.** $\dfrac{1}{x^{15}}$
5. a. x^4 **b.** $x^2\sqrt[3]{x^2}$ **c.** $x\sqrt[5]{x^3}$ **d.** $\sqrt[9]{x^8}$
6. a. $a + 5b^2$ **b.** $6a^2 + 5ab^2 - 4b^4$
7. a. $2a^2$ **b.** $a^4 - b^4$ **c.** $-4ab$ **d.** $a^4 - 2a^2b^2 + b^4$
8. a. $b - a$ **b.** $a - b$ **9. a.** $x + 2$ **b.** $-x - 2$
10. a. $x + y$ **b.** $\sqrt{x^2 + y^2}$ **c.** $x + 2\sqrt{xy} + y$ **d.** $x - y$
11. a. $\sqrt[3]{4x^2}$ **b.** $2\sqrt[3]{2x}$ **12. a.** $\sqrt[12]{y^7}$ **b.** $\sqrt[4]{y} + \sqrt[3]{y}$
13. a. $\dfrac{1}{4}$ **b.** 9   **c.** 1   **d.** 1   **14. a.** 10   **b.** 14

Section R.6 Practice Exercises, pp. 74–76

1. a. $4x^8y^4$ **b.** $4x^8 - 4x^4y^2 + y^4$ **3.** $6x^2 + 7xy^2 - 20y^4$
5. $\dfrac{1}{25}c^8 - \dfrac{9}{64}a^2b^2$ **7.** $8x^3 + 27$ **9.** cubes, $(a + b)(a^2 - ab + b^2)$
11. perfect, $(a + b)^2$ **13.** $5c^3(3c^2 - 6c + 1)$
15. $7a^2b(3b^4 - 2ab^3 + 5a^2)$ **17.** $(x - 6y)(5z + 7)$
19. $5k(3k^2 + 7)(2k - 1)$
21. a. $3(-2x^2 + 4x + 3)$ **b.** $-3(2x^2 - 4x - 3)$
23. $-4x^2y(3xy + 2x^2y^2 - 1)$ **25.** $(2a + 5)(4x + 9)$
27. $(3x^2 - 10)(4x - 3)$ **29.** $(c - 2d)(d + 4)$
31. $(p + 9)(p - 7)$ **33.** $2t(t - 4)(t - 10)$ **35.** $(2z + 7)(3z + 2)$
37. $yz(7y + 2z)(y - 6z)$ **39.** $(t - 9)^2$ **41.** $2x(5x + 8y)^2$
43. $(2c^2 - 5d^3)^2$ **45.** $(3w + 8)(3w - 8)$
47. $2(10u^2 + 3v^3)(10u^2 - 3v^3)$ **49.** $(25p^2 + 4)(5p + 2)(5p - 2)$
51. $(y + 4)(y^2 - 4y + 16)$ **53.** $c(c - 3)(c^2 + 3c + 9)$

55. $(2a^2 - 5b^3)(4a^4 + 10a^2b^3 + 25b^6)$
57. $10x(3x + 7)(x + 2)(x - 2)$ **59.** $(a + y - 5)(a - y + 5)$
61. $5xy(3x + 8)(2x + 3)$ **63.** $(x^2 + 2)(x + 3)(x - 3)$
65. $(x^3 + 16)(x + 2)(x^2 - 2x + 4)$ **67.** $(x + y + z)(x + y - z)$
69. $(x + y + z)(x^2 + 2xy + y^2 - xz - yz + z^2)$ **71.** $(3m + 21n + 7)^2$
73. $(3c - 8)(-c + 2)$ or $-(3c - 8)(c - 2)$
75. $(p - 4)(p^2 + 4p + 16)(p^4 + 1)(p^2 + 1)(p + 1)(p - 1)$
77. $(m + 3)(m^2 - 3m + 9)(m - 1)(m^2 + m + 1)$
79. $2z(2x + 3)(4x^2 - 6x + 9)(x - 1)(x^2 + x + 1)$
81. $(x - y)(x + y - 1)$ **83.** $(a - c)(a + 2c + 1)$
85. $x^{-4}(2 - 7x + x^2)$ or $\dfrac{x^2 - 7x + 2}{x^4}$
87. $y^{-4}(y - 4)(y + 3)$ or $\dfrac{(y - 4)(y + 3)}{y^4}$ **89.** $2c^{3/4}(c + 2)$
91. $(3x + 1)^{2/3}(8x + 1)$ **93.** $2(3x + 2)^{-2/3}(2x + 1)$ or $\dfrac{2(2x + 1)}{(3x + 2)^{2/3}}$
95. $A = x^2 - y^2$; $A = (x + y)(x - y)$ **97.** $2\pi r(r + h)$
99. $\dfrac{4}{3}\pi(R - r)(R^2 + Rr + r^2)$ **101.** $(21 + 19)(21 - 19);\ 80$
103. Expand the square of any binomial. For example:
$(2c + 3)^2 = 4c^2 + 12c + 9$
105. In each case, factor out x to the smallest exponent to which it appears in both terms. That is,
$5x^4 + 4x^3 = x^3(5x + 4)$ and $5x^{-4} + 4x^{-3} = x^{-4}(5 + 4x)$
107. $(x + \sqrt{5})(x - \sqrt{5})$ **109.** $(z^2 + 6)(z + \sqrt{6})(z - \sqrt{6})$
111. $(x - \sqrt{5})^2$ **113. a.** $(x - 1)(x^4 + x^3 + x^2 + x + 1)$
    b. $(x - 1)(x^n + x^{n-1} + x^{n-2} + \cdots + 1)$
115. No   **117.** Yes   **119.** No

Section R.7 Practice Exercises, pp. 87–91
1. $5x(3x + 1)(2x - 5)$ **3.** $t(t - 1)(t^2 + t + 1)$
5. $(2x + 3)(x - 4)(x + 4)$ **7.** $(5w^2 - 4u)^2$ **9.** rational
11. $-2, 1$ **13.** complex (or compound)   **15.** $x \neq -7$
17. $a \neq 9, a \neq -9$ **19.** No restricted values   **21.** $a \neq 0, b \neq 0$
23. a and b **25.** $\dfrac{x - 3}{x - 7};\ x \neq -3, x \neq 7$
27. $-\dfrac{4ac}{b^4};\ a \neq 0, b \neq 0$ **29.** $\dfrac{2 - \sqrt{6}}{3}$
31. $-\dfrac{2y}{8 + y};\ y \neq 8, y \neq -8$ **33.** $-\dfrac{4}{x - 2};\ a \neq b; x \neq 2$
35. $\dfrac{a}{2b^3}$ **37.** $\dfrac{2c^3(c - d)}{d(2c - d)}$ **39.** a **41.** $-\dfrac{x - 2}{2x}$
43. $60x^5y^2z^4$ **45.** $t(3t + 4)^3(t - 2)$ **47.** $2x(x + 10)^2$
49. $m + 3$ **51.** $\dfrac{10c^2 + 21}{45c^3}$ **53.** $\dfrac{9y - 22x}{2x^2y^5}$ **55.** $-\dfrac{1}{x(x - y)}$
57. $\dfrac{7y^2 - y - 6}{y^2(y + 1)}$ **59.** 1 **61.** $\dfrac{1}{3}$ **63.** $x + 2$ **65.** $\dfrac{ab}{2b + a}$
67. $-\dfrac{3}{1 + h}$ **69.** $-\dfrac{7}{x(x + h)}$ **71.** $\dfrac{4\sqrt{y}}{y}$ **73.** $\dfrac{4\sqrt[3]{y^2}}{y}$
75. $\dfrac{\sqrt[3]{12w^2}}{2w}$ **77.** $\dfrac{6\sqrt[4]{2w^3x^2}}{wx}$ **79.** $\dfrac{2\sqrt{3x + 3}}{x + 1}$
81. $2(\sqrt{15} + \sqrt{11})$ **83.** $\sqrt{x} - \sqrt{5}$ **85.** $\dfrac{5 + 4\sqrt{2}}{14}$
87. $\dfrac{10\sqrt{3x}}{3x}$ **89.** $-\dfrac{2\sqrt{7}}{7w}$ **91. a.** $S = \dfrac{2r_1 r_2}{r_1 + r_2}$ **b.** 427.9 mph
93. a. At 1 hr: 4.8 ng/mL; At 4 hr: 12.7 ng/mL; At 12 hr: 3.9 ng/mL
    b. The concentration of the drug appears to be approaching 0 ng/mL for large values of t.
95. $\dfrac{13x + 6}{x(x + 1)}$ cm   **97.** $\dfrac{\sqrt{2x}}{x}$ in.^{2} **99.** $\dfrac{x}{5y^4}$ **101.** $\dfrac{3t + 32}{2t + 1}$
103. 1   **105.** $\dfrac{a + 2}{a - 1}$ **107.** $4\sqrt{5} + 2\sqrt{3}$ **109.** $\dfrac{4 - 2\sqrt{3}}{3}$

111. $\dfrac{\sqrt{7x}}{x}$ **113.** $-\dfrac{x + 3}{x - 5}$ **115.** $-\dfrac{8}{t + 2}$
117. If $x = y$, then the denominator $x - y$ will equal zero. Division by zero is undefined.
119. For $\dfrac{1}{\sqrt{x}}$, multiply numerator and denominator by $\sqrt{x}$ to make a perfect square in the radicand in the denominator. For $\dfrac{1}{\sqrt[3]{x}}$, multiply numerator and denominator by $\sqrt[3]{x^2}$ to make a perfect cube in the radicand of the denominator.
121. a. $\dfrac{14}{3} \cdot \dfrac{30}{7} = \dfrac{420}{21} = 20$ **b.** $(5 - \sqrt{5})(5 + \sqrt{5})$
$= (5)^2 - (\sqrt{5})^2$
$= 25 - 5$
$= 20$
123. $\dfrac{w^{2n}}{w + z}$ **125.** $\dfrac{\sqrt{x^2 - y^2}}{x + y}$ **127.** $\dfrac{\sqrt[6]{5^3 2^4}}{2}$
129. $\sqrt[3]{a^2} + \sqrt[3]{ab} + \sqrt[3]{b^2}$ **131.** $\dfrac{1}{\sqrt{4 + h} + 2}$
133. The expression appears to approach 6 as x gets close to 3.

	A	B	C	D	E
1	x	2.9	2.99	2.999	2.9999
2	$\dfrac{x^2 - 9}{x - 3}$	5.9	5.99	5.999	5.9999

	A	B	C	D	E
1	x	3.1	3.01	3.001	3.0001
2	$\dfrac{x^2 - 9}{x - 3}$	6.1	6.01	6.001	6.0001

Chapter R Review Exercises, pp. 94–97
1. a. $\sqrt{9}$ **b.** $0, \sqrt{9}$ **c.** $0, -8, \sqrt{9}$
    d. $0, -8, 1.\overline{45}, \sqrt{9}, -\dfrac{2}{3}$ **e.** $\sqrt{6}, 3\pi$
    f. $\sqrt{6}, 0, -8, 1.\overline{45}, \sqrt{9}, -\dfrac{2}{3}, 3\pi$ **3.** $x \geq 4$

5.

	Graph	Interval Notation	Set-Builder Notation
a.	$\overset{\text{[}}{-3} \qquad \overset{\text{)}}{7}$	$[-3, 7)$	$\{x \mid -3 \leq x < 7\}$
b.	$\overset{(}{2.1}\ \longrightarrow$	$(2.1, \infty)$	$\{x \mid x > 2.1\}$
c.	$\longleftarrow \overset{\text{]}}{4}$	$(-\infty, 4]$	$\{x \mid 4 \geq x\}$

7. a. $|2 - \sqrt{5}|$ or $|\sqrt{5} - 2|$ **b.** $\sqrt{5} - 2$
9. $\dfrac{5}{2}$ **11.** 6   **13. a.** $J = E + 150$ **b.** $E = J - 150$
15. a. $C = 3.6s + 50p + 250n$ **b.** \$8260
17. $23.9c^2d - 16.5cd$ **19.** d   **21.** c   **23.** e   **25.** a
27. b   **29. a.** 1   **b.** -1 **c.** 9   **d.** 1
31. p^3 **33.** $\dfrac{144b^8}{a^6}$ **35.** $\dfrac{2u^{12}}{v^4}$
37. a. 0.98   **b.** 9.8   **c.** 98   **39.** 1.763×10^{12}
41. a. $\sqrt[7]{x^2}$ or $(\sqrt[7]{x})^2$ **b.** $9\sqrt[7]{x^2}$ or $9(\sqrt[7]{x})^2$
    c. $\sqrt[7]{(9x)^2}$ or $(\sqrt[7]{9x})^2$
43. a. -4 **b.** Not a real number
45. a. 1000   **b.** $\dfrac{1}{1000}$ **c.** -1000 **d.** $-\dfrac{1}{1000}$
    e. Undefined   **f.** Undefined
47. $\dfrac{3n^{1/3}}{m^2}$ **49.** $3y^4z^4\sqrt[3]{2xz^2}$ **51.** $\dfrac{p^6\sqrt{p}}{3}$ **53.** $5\sqrt{14}$
55. $\sqrt[12]{c^{11}d^{10}}$ **57.** $-51cd\sqrt[3]{2c^2}$ **59. a.** Yes   **b.** No   **c.** Yes

61. 8   **63.** $-8a^2b^3 + 7.3ab^2 - 2.9b$ **65.** $10w^6 + 7w^3y^2 - 6y^4$
67. $81t^2 - 16$ **69.** $25k^2 - 30k + 9$ **71.** $4v^2 - 4v + 1 - w^2$
73. $30 + 26\sqrt{15}$ **75.** $4c^4d - 20c^2d^2\sqrt{cd} + 25cd^4$
77. $2x^3 + 15x^2 + 37x + 30$ **79.** $16m^2n(5m^2n^7 - 3m^3n^2 - 1)$
81. $(5a + 7b)(3c - 2)$ **83.** $2x(2x - 5y)^2$
85. $3k(k - 3)(k^2 + 3k + 9)$ **87.** $(5n + m + 6)(5n - m - 6)$
89. $-4(3p - 2)(p + 3)$ **91.** $(x^2 + 3y)(x^2 + 3y - 1)$
93. $4x^{5/2}(3x - 1)$ **95. a.** $w \neq 2, w \neq -2$ **b.** No restrictions
97. $\frac{m+4}{m+3}; m \neq 4, m \neq -3$ **99.** $\frac{c}{2}$ **101.** $\frac{21x^3 + 8}{60x^4}$
103. $\frac{x^2 - 2x + 12}{x^2(x + 3)}$ **105.** $\frac{1}{2}$ **107.** $\frac{5\sqrt{k}}{k}$ **109.** $\frac{3\sqrt[4]{2x^2y^3}}{xy}$
111. $\sqrt{x} - 2$

Chapter R Test, pp. 97–98

1. a. 8   **b.** 0, 8   **c.** 0, 8, −3   **d.** 0, 8, $-\frac{5}{7}$, 2.1, $-0.\overline{4}$, −3
e. $\frac{\pi}{6}$ **f.** 0, $\frac{\pi}{6}$, 8, $-\frac{5}{7}$, 2.1, $-0.\overline{4}$, −3
2. a. $M = 2J$ **b.** $J = \frac{1}{2}M$
3. a. $C = 12A + 40L + 30$ **b.** $1070
4. $t - 5$ **5. a.** $|\sqrt{2} - 2|$ or $|2 - \sqrt{2}|$ **b.** $2 - \sqrt{2}$
6. a. $y \neq 11, y \neq -2$ **b.** $\frac{2}{y+2}$ **7.** $-12x - 49$
8. $-\frac{1}{2}a^2b + \frac{7}{2}ab^2$ **9.** $\frac{7}{4}$ **10.** $\frac{a^8}{b^{15}}$ **11.** 32   **12.** $\frac{1}{t^{12}}$
13. $2k^5n^2\sqrt[3]{10m^2n}$ **14.** $\frac{3}{2}pq\sqrt[4]{p}$ **15.** $-b\sqrt{5ab}$ **16.** $x\sqrt[6]{xy^5}$
17. $6n^4 - 36n^3 + 58n^2 + 12n - 20$ **18.** $9a^2 + 6ab + b^2 - c^2$
19. $\frac{1}{16}z - p^4$ **20.** $15x - 7\sqrt{2x} - 4$ **21.** $x - 12z\sqrt{x} + 36z^2$
22. $\frac{3x}{2(x + 7)}$ **23.** $x - 5$ **24.** $\frac{y - 3}{y^2}$ **25.** $x + 3$
26. $\frac{\sqrt[3]{4x^2y}}{xy}$ **27.** $2(\sqrt{13} - \sqrt{10})$ **28.** $\frac{5\sqrt{2}}{2t}$
29. $2x(3x - 1)(5x + 2)$ **30.** $(x + 5a)(y + 2c)$
31. $(x^2 + 9)(x - 3)(x + 3)(x + 2)$ **32.** $(c - 2a - 11)(c + 2a + 11)$
33. $(3u - v^2)(9u^2 + 3uv^2 + v^4)$
34. $w^{-6}(4 + 2w + 7w^2)$ or $\frac{7w^2 + 2w + 4}{w^6}$
35. $(2y - 1)^{-3/4}(3y - 1)$ or $\frac{3y - 1}{(2y - 1)^{3/4}}$ **36.** 100π in.^{3}
37. $x^2 + 11x - 34$ **38.** $4.5 \times 10^{10}; 1.66 \times 10^6$ **39.** $0.000\ 000\ 8$
40. 1.2×10^{14} **41.** $(2.7, \infty)$ **42.** $\{x \mid -3 \leq x < 5\}$

CHAPTER 1

Section 1.1 Practice Exercises, pp. 109–113

1. linear   **3.** solution   **5.** equivalent   **7.** division
9. identity   **11.** rational   **13. a.** Linear; $\{-4\}$ **b.** Nonlinear
c. Linear; $\{-16\}$ **d.** Nonlinear   **e.** Linear; $\{10\}$
15. $\{-4\}$ **17.** $\{0\}$ **19.** $\{2\}$ **21.** $\{-6.2\}$ **23.** $\{5000\}$
25. $\left\{\frac{22}{3}\right\}$ **27.** $\{14\}$ **29.** $\left\{-\frac{33}{2}\right\}$ **31.** $\{-54\}$ **33.** $\{41\}$
35. a. 5560 m^3 **b.** 81,000 m^3 **37. a.** $119.4 billion   **b.** 2009
39. a. 204.68°F   **b.** 10,400 ft   **41.** 2009   **43.** Contradiction; { }
45. Identity; $\mathbb{R}$ **47.** Conditional equation; $\{-8\}$
49. $x \neq 5, x \neq -4$ **51.** $x \neq \frac{3}{2}, x \neq 5, x \neq -5$ **53.** $\{17\}$
55. $\{-23\}$ **57.** { }; The value 3 does not check.   **59.** $\{2\}$
61. $\{-4\}$ **63.** $\{16\}$ **65.** { }; The value −4 does not check.
67. $\left\{-\frac{5}{13}\right\}$ **69.** $l = \frac{A}{w}$ **71.** $c = P - a - b$

73. $s_1 = s_2 - \Delta s$ **75.** $y = -\frac{7}{2}x + 4$ **77.** $y = \frac{5}{4}x - \frac{1}{2}$
79. $y = -\frac{3}{2}x + 3$ **81.** $d = \frac{2S}{n} - a$ or $d = \frac{2S - an}{n}$
83. $h = \frac{3V}{\pi r^2}$ **85.** $x = \frac{6}{4 + t}$ **87.** $x = \frac{5 - ay}{6 - b}$ or $x = \frac{ay - 5}{b - 6}$
89. $P = \frac{A}{1 + rt}$ **91.** $\left\{\frac{18}{19}\right\}$ **93.** $\{0\}$ **95.** $\{-3\}$ **97.** $\{9\}$
99. $\mathbb{R}$ **101.** $\{1\}$ **103.** { }   **105.** 16 yr   **107.** 33 mi
109. The value 5 is not defined within the expressions in the equation. Substituting 5 into the equation would result in division by 0.
111. The equation cannot be written in the form $ax + b = 0$. The term $\frac{3}{x} = 3x^{-1}$. Therefore, the term $\frac{3}{x}$ is not first degree and the equation is not a first-degree equation.
113. The equation is a contradiction. There is no real number x to which we add 1 that will equal the same real number x to which we add 2.
115. $a = 6$ **117.** $a = 3$ **119.** $\frac{511}{990}$ **121.** $\frac{534}{999}$

Section 1.2 Practice Exercises, pp. 120–124

1. $5x - 2$ **3.** $0.06x$ **5.** $40 - x$ **7.** $x + 1$
9. $P = 2l + 2w$ **11.** $90 - x$ **13.** $900
15. $\frac{d}{r}$ **17.** The width of the easement is 8 ft.
19. a. The kitchen is 14 ft by 10 ft.   **b.** 154 ft^2 **c.** $1958.88
21. $90 - x$ **23.** $180 - (131 + x)$ or $49 - x$
25. The angle between the ladder and the ground is 56° and the angle that the ladder makes with the wall is 34°.
27. Rocco borrowed $1500 at 3% and $3500 at 2.5%.
29. Fernando invested $4500 in the 3-yr CD and $2500 in the 18-month CD.
31. 1250 gal of E5   **33.** 96 ft^3 of sand
35. The plane to Los Angeles travels 400 mph and the plane to New York City travels 460 mph.   **37.** The distance is 24 mi.
39. a. $S_1 = 45,000 + 2250x$ **b.** $S_2 = 48,000 + 2000x$ **c.** 12 yr
41. a. $C = 7x$ **b.** The motorist will save money beginning on the 16th working day.
43. $\frac{220}{7}$ sec or approximately 31.4 sec   **45.** 15 hr
47. 62.5 lb of cement and 225 lb of gravel
49. LDL is 144 mg/dL and the total cholesterol is 204 mg/dL.
51. 480 deer   **53.** 300 km   **55.** $336
57. a. $C = 110 + 60x$ **b.** 4 hr   **59.** 555 ft
61. The pole is 7.2 ft long, and the snow is 4.8 ft deep.
63. 10 L should be drained and replaced by water.
65. The angles measure 153° and 27°.
67. Aliyah invested $2760 in the stock returning 11% and $3000 in the stock returning 5%.
69. The lengths of the sides are 6 ft, 7 ft, and 11 ft.
71. $x = 11.2$ ft and $y = 7.5$ cm
73. No. If x represents the measure of the smallest angle, then the equation $x + (x + 2) + (x + 4) = 180$ does not result in an odd integer value for x. Instead the measures of the angles would be even integers.
75. No. If x represents the number of each type of bill, then the solution to the equation $20x + 10x + 5x = 100$ is not a whole number.
77. The numbers are 7 and 23.   **79.** The original number is 68.
81. $x_2 = 1.8$ m   **83.** 4 kg

Section 1.3 Practice Exercises, pp. 132–134

1. $-2x + 1$ **3.** $15a^2 - 14a - 8$ **5.** $\frac{1}{36}m^2 - \frac{4}{25}n^2$
7. $z^2 + 4z + 4$ **9.** -1 **11.** real, imaginary   **13.** pure
15. complex   **17.** $11i$ **19.** $7i\sqrt{2}$ **21.** $i\sqrt{19}$ **23.** $-4i$
25. -6 **27.** $-5\sqrt{2}$ **29.** $-2\sqrt{21}$ **31.** 7   **33.** $3i$

35. Real part: 3; Imaginary part: -7 **37.** Real part: 0; Imaginary part: 19   **39.** Real part: $-\frac{1}{4}$; Imaginary part: 0

41. a. True   **b.** False   **43. a.** True   **b.** True

45. $5 + 0i$ **47.** $0 + 8i$ **49.** $2 + 2\sqrt{3}i$ or $2 + 2i\sqrt{3}$

51. $\frac{4}{7} + \frac{3}{14}i$ **53.** $-\frac{9}{2} + \sqrt{3}i$ or $-\frac{9}{2} + i\sqrt{3}$

55. a. 1   **b.** i **c.** -1 **d.** $-i$

57. a. i **b.** $-i$ **c.** -1 **d.** -1

59. $10 - 10i$ **61.** $-3 + 61i$ **63.** $-\frac{1}{3} + \frac{7}{12}i$ **65.** $-1.2 + 0i$

67. $-2 - 3i$ **69.** $-2 + 10i$ **71.** $\sqrt{21} + i\sqrt{33}$

73. $36 - 57i$ **75.** $-40 - 42i$ **77.** $17 - i\sqrt{5}$

79. $-11 - 7i$ **81.** 6   **83. a.** $3 + 6i$ **b.** 45

85. a. $0 - 8i$ **b.** 64   **87.** 116   **89.** 49   **91.** 5

93. $\frac{8}{5} + \frac{6}{5}i$ **95.** $\frac{94}{173} - \frac{81}{173}i$ **97.** $\frac{6}{41} - \frac{\sqrt{5}}{41}i$ **99.** $0 - \frac{5}{13}i$

101. $0 + \frac{\sqrt{3}}{3}i$ **103.** $4i\sqrt{2}$ **105.** $2i$

107. a. $(5i)^2 + 25 = 0$ ✓   **b.** $(-5i)^2 + 25 = 0$ ✓

109. a. $(2 + i\sqrt{3})^2 - 4(2 + i\sqrt{3}) + 7 = 0$ ✓
   b. $(2 - i\sqrt{3})^2 - 4(2 - i\sqrt{3}) + 7 = 0$ ✓

111. $(a + bi)(c + di)$
$$= ac + adi + bci + bdi^2$$
$$= ac + (ad + bc)i + bd(-1)$$
$$= (ac - bd) + (ad + bc)i$$

113. The second step does not follow because the multiplication property of radicals can be applied only if the individual radicals are real numbers. Because $\sqrt{-9}$ and $\sqrt{-4}$ are imaginary numbers, the correct logic for simplification would be
$$\sqrt{-9} \cdot \sqrt{-4} = i\sqrt{9} \cdot i\sqrt{4} = i^2\sqrt{36} = -1 \cdot 6 = -6$$

115. Any real number. For example: 5.   **117.** $a^2 + b^2$

119. a. $(x + 3)(x - 3)$ **b.** $(x + 3i)(x - 3i)$

121. a. $(x + 8)(x - 8)$ **b.** $(x + 8i)(x - 8i)$

123. a. $(x + \sqrt{3})(x - \sqrt{3})$ **b.** $(x + i\sqrt{3})(x - i\sqrt{3})$

125.
```
√(-16)
              4i
(4-5i)-(2+3i)
              2-8i
(12-15i)(-2+9i)
        111+138i
```

127.
```
(4-9i)²
          -65-72i
7/(2i)►Frac
            -7/2i
(14+8i)/(3-i)►Fr
ac
        17/5+19/5i
```

Section 1.4 Practice Exercises, pp. 145–148

1. $(5t - 3)(t + 2)$ **3.** $(x + 7)^2$ **5.** $2 + \frac{\sqrt{11}}{2}i$ **7.** quadratic

9. $a; b$ **11.** $\pm\sqrt{k}$ **13.** $x = \frac{-b \pm \sqrt{b^2 - 4ac}}{2a}$

15. $\{-8, 3\}$ **17.** $\left\{-\frac{5}{2}, -\frac{1}{4}\right\}$ **19.** $\left\{\frac{3}{2}, -\frac{3}{2}\right\}$ **21.** $\{0, 4\}$

23. $\{9, -9\}$ **25.** $\{\sqrt{7}, -\sqrt{7}\}$ **27.** $\{4i, -4i\}$

29. $\{-2 \pm 2\sqrt{7}\}$ **31.** $\{8, 2\}$ **33.** $\left\{\frac{1}{2} \pm \frac{\sqrt{17}}{2}i\right\}$

35. $n = 49; (x + 7)^2$ **37.** $n = 169; (p - 13)^2$

39. $n = \frac{9}{4}; \left(w - \frac{3}{2}\right)^2$ **41.** $n = \frac{1}{81}; \left(m + \frac{1}{9}\right)^2$

43. $\{-11 \pm 5\sqrt{5}\}$ **45.** $\{4 \pm 2i\sqrt{2}\}$ **47.** $\{-3 \pm i\sqrt{31}\}$

49. $\left\{4, -\frac{1}{2}\right\}$ **51.** $\left\{-\frac{3}{2} \pm \frac{\sqrt{14}}{2}\right\}$ **53.** False   **55.** True

57. $\left\{\frac{3 \pm \sqrt{37}}{2}\right\}$ **59.** $\{-2 \pm i\sqrt{2}\}$ **61.** $\{3 \pm i\}$

63. $\left\{\frac{7 \pm i\sqrt{11}}{10}\right\}$ **65.** $\left\{\frac{1}{2}, -\frac{3}{10}\right\}$ **67.** $\left\{\pm\frac{7}{3}i\right\}$

69. $\left\{\frac{5 \pm \sqrt{137}}{14}\right\}$ **71.** $\left\{\frac{5}{2}\right\}$ **73.** Linear; $\{-2\}$

75. Quadratic; $\{0, -2\}$ **77.** Linear; $\{1\}$ **79.** Neither

81. $\left\{\frac{4}{3}\right\}$ **83.** $\{-2 \pm \sqrt{2}\}$ **85.** $\{7 \pm \sqrt{55}\}$ **87.** $\mathbb{R}$

89. $\left\{1, -\frac{5}{6}\right\}$ **91.** $\{\ \}$ **93.** $\{-2\}$ **95.** $\left\{\pm\frac{\sqrt{35}}{7}i\right\}$

97. $\{\pm\sqrt[4]{5}\}$ **99. a.** -56 **b.** 2 imaginary solutions

101. a. 40   **b.** 2 real solutions (irrational numbers)

103. a. 121   **b.** 2 real solutions (rational numbers)

105. a. 0   **b.** 1 real solution

107. $r = \sqrt{\frac{A}{\pi}}$ or $r = \frac{\sqrt{A\pi}}{\pi}$ **109.** $t = \sqrt{\frac{2s}{g}}$ or $t = \frac{\sqrt{2sg}}{g}$

111. $a = \sqrt{c^2 - b^2}$ **113.** $I = \frac{1}{c}\sqrt{\frac{L}{Rt}}$ or $I = \frac{\sqrt{LRt}}{cRt}$

115. $w = \frac{c \pm \sqrt{c^2 + 4kr}}{2k}$ **117.** $t = \frac{-v_0 \pm \sqrt{v_0^2 + 2as}}{a}$

119. $I = \frac{-CR \pm \sqrt{C^2R^2 - 4CL}}{2CL}$

121. The right side of the equation is not equal to zero.

123. If the discriminant is negative, then the equation has two solutions that are imaginary numbers.

125. $x = 2y$ or $x = -y$ **127.** $x^2 - 2x - 8 = 0$

129. $12x^2 - 11x + 2 = 0$ **131.** $x^2 - 5 = 0$ **133.** $x^2 + 4 = 0$

135. $x^2 - 2x + 5 = 0$

137. $x_1 + x_2 = \dfrac{-b + \sqrt{b^2 - 4ac}}{2a} + \dfrac{-b - \sqrt{b^2 - 4ac}}{2a}$
$$= \frac{-b + \sqrt{b^2 - 4ac} + (-b) - \sqrt{b^2 - 4ac}}{2a}$$
$$= \frac{-2b}{2a}$$
$$= -\frac{b}{a}$$

139. $x_1 + x_2 = 2 + (-5) = -3$, which is $-\frac{3}{1}$.

$x_1 x_2 = (2)(-5) = -10$, which is $\frac{-10}{1}$.

141. $x = \dfrac{5 + \sqrt{277}}{18} \approx 1.2024$ and $x = \dfrac{5 - \sqrt{277}}{18} \approx -0.6469$

143. Yes;
```
(7+√(37))/6→X
        2.180460422
3X²
        14.26322295
7X-1
        14.26322295
```

Problem Recognition Exercises, p. 148

1. a. Expression; $6x^2 - 13x - 5$ **b.** Equation; $\left\{\frac{5}{2}, -\frac{1}{3}\right\}$

2. a. Expression; $\dfrac{4x + 36}{(x - 3)(x + 7)}$ **b.** Equation; $\{-9\}$

3. a. Equation; $\left\{\dfrac{3 \pm 2\sqrt{2}}{2}\right\}$ **b.** Expression; $4x^2 - 12x + 1$

4. a. Equation; $\{3\}$ **b.** Expression; $15y - 38$

5. a. Equation; $\{7, 4\}$ **b.** Equation; $\left\{\dfrac{11 \pm \sqrt{233}}{2}\right\}$

6. a. Equation; $\left\{\dfrac{2}{3}, -10\right\}$ **b.** Equation; $\left\{-\dfrac{7}{4}\right\}$

7. a. Equation; $\{-7, -5\}$ **b.** Expression; $\dfrac{35 + 12x + x^2}{x}$

8. a. Equation; $\{\ \}$; The value 2 does not check.

   b. Expression; $\dfrac{5}{3}$; for $x \neq 2$

Section 1.5 Practice Exercises, pp. 154–157

1. $A = \dfrac{1}{2}bh$ **3.** $V = lwh$ **5.** $629 = (2x + 3)(x)$

7. $88\pi = \pi(x)^2$ **9.** $50 = \dfrac{1}{2}x(x - 8)$ **11.** $640 = x(8)\left(\dfrac{1}{5}x\right)$

13. $(x)^2 + (x + 2)^2 = (2x - 2)^2$ **15.** $x + 2$

17. a. $x(x + 2) = 120$ **b.** The integers are 10 and 12 or -10 and -12.

19. a. $x^2 + (x + 1)^2 = 113$ **b.** The integers are 7 and 8 or -7 and -8.

21. The dimensions of the cargo space are 6 ft by 7 ft by 12 ft.

23. The radius is approximately 25 yd.

25. The base is 9 ft and the height is 12 ft.

27. The distance is $90\sqrt{2}$ ft or approximately 127.3 ft.

29. a. The lengths of the sides of the lower triangle are 6 ft, 8 ft, and 10 ft.
   b. The total area is 44 ft^2.

31. a. The length is approximately 2.91 in. and the width is
approximately 1.94 in.   **b.** Using the rounded values from part
(a), the screen is approximately 949 pixels by 632 pixels.

33. There were 8 players.   **35.** There were 600,000 organisms
approximately 9 hr and 39 hr after the culture was started.

37. a. 235 ft   **b.** 62 mph   **39. a.** $s = -16t^2 + 16t$ **b.** It would
take Michael Jordan 0.5 sec to reach his maximum height of 4 ft.

41. a. $s = -16t^2 + 75t + 4$ **b.** The ball will be at an 80-ft height
1.5 sec and 3.2 sec after being kicked.

43. a. $L = \dfrac{1 + \sqrt{5}}{2} \approx 1.62$ **b.** 14.6 ft

45. a. $y = \dfrac{160 - 4x}{6}$ or $y = \dfrac{80 - 2x}{3}$ **b.** $A = x\left(\dfrac{80 - 2x}{3}\right)$

   c. Each pen can be 25 yd by 10 yd, or it can be 15 yd by $\dfrac{50}{3}$ yd.

Section 1.6 Practice Exercises, pp. 166–168

1. $(x + 3)(x^2 - 3x + 9)$ **3.** $x \neq \dfrac{5}{2}, x \neq -\dfrac{5}{2}$ **5.** 9

7. radical   **9.** quadratic; $m^{1/3}$ **11.** $\left\{\pm\dfrac{1}{5}, -\dfrac{4}{3}\right\}$

13. $\{\pm 2i, \pm 2\}$ **15.** $\{0, -4, 2 \pm 2i\sqrt{3}\}$ **17.** $\left\{\pm\dfrac{2\sqrt{3}}{3}, \pm i\sqrt{5}\right\}$

19. $\{5\}$; The value -2 does not check.   **21.** $\left\{\dfrac{6 \pm \sqrt{51}}{3}\right\}$

23. $\left\{\dfrac{5}{2}, -1\right\}$ **25.** { }; The value 3 does not check.

27. Jesse travels 6 km/hr in still water.

29. Jean runs 8 mph and rides 16 mph.   **31.** $\{20\}$

33. $\{7\}$; The value -2 does not check.   **35.** $\{2\}$

37. $\left\{\dfrac{4}{3}\right\}$ **39.** $\{-1\}$; The value 4 does not check.   **41.** $\{-2, 1\}$

43. a. $\{5^{4/3}\}$ **b.** $\{\pm 5^{3/2}\}$ **45.** $\{7^{6/5} - 2\}$ **47.** $\left\{\pm\dfrac{1}{32}\right\}$

49. $\{-10\}$ **51. a.** 55%   **b.** 9.3 hr

53. a. 14 m/sec   **b.** 36.6 m   **55.** $\{\pm 3i, \pm 2\}$

57. $\left\{\dfrac{3}{2}, -\dfrac{3}{5}\right\}$ **59.** $\left\{\dfrac{1}{3125}, 32\right\}$ **61.** $\left\{\pm\sqrt{\dfrac{-5 \pm \sqrt{53}}{2}}\right\}$

63. $\left\{\dfrac{3}{2}, 10\right\}$ **65.** $\{9\}$ **67.** $p = \dfrac{fq}{q - f}$ **69.** $T = \sqrt[4]{\dfrac{E}{k}}$

71. $m = \dfrac{kF}{a}$ **73.** $x = \pm\sqrt{(z - 16)^2 + y^2}$ **75.** $T_1 = \dfrac{P_1V_1T_2}{P_2V_2}$

77. $g = \dfrac{4\pi^2 L}{T^2}$

79. An equation is in quadratic form if after a suitable substitution, the
equation can be written in the form $au^2 + bu + c = 0$, where u
is a variable expression.

81. When solving a radical equation, if both sides of the equation are
raised to an even power, then the potential solutions must be

checked. This is because some or all of the solutions may be
extraneous solutions.

83. It would take Joan approximately 5.5 hr working alone, and it would
take Henry approximately 6.5 hr.

85. Pam can row to a point $166\dfrac{2}{3}$ ft down the beach or to a point 300 ft
down the beach to be home in 5 min.

Section 1.7 Practice Exercises, pp. 175–179

1. $(-\infty, -5)$ **3.** $[4, \infty)$ **5.** $\left\{x \middle| -\dfrac{5}{6} < x \le 4\right\}$

7. union, $A \cup B$ **9.** intersection, $A \cap B$ **11.** $a < x < b$

13. $\{x \mid x < -11\}; (-\infty, -11)$

-11

15. $\{w \mid w \le 3\}; (-\infty, 3]$

3

17. $\{a \mid a \le 8.5\}; (-\infty, 8.5]$

8.5

19. $\{c \mid c < 2\}; (-\infty, 2)$

2

21. $\{x \mid x < -\tfrac{13}{2}\}; \left(-\infty, -\tfrac{13}{2}\right)$

$-\dfrac{13}{2}$

23. $\{x \mid x \le \tfrac{17}{6}\}; \left(-\infty, \tfrac{17}{6}\right]$

$\dfrac{17}{6}$

25. { }

27. $\{x \mid x \ge -\tfrac{5}{6}\}; \left[-\tfrac{5}{6}, \infty\right)$

$-\dfrac{5}{6}$

29. $\mathbb{R}; (-\infty, \infty)$

31. a. $\{0, 3, 4, 6, 8, 9, 12\}$ **b.** $\{0, 12\}$ **c.** $\{-2, 0, 4, 8, 12\}$
   d. $\{4, 8\}$ **e.** $\{-2, 0, 3, 4, 6, 8, 9, 12\}$ **f.** { }

33. a. $\mathbb{R}$ **b.** $\{x \mid -1 \le x < 9\}$ **c.** $\{x \mid x < 9\}$ **d.** $\{x \mid x < -8\}$
   e. $\{x \mid x < -8 \text{ or } x \ge -1\}$ **f.** { }

35. $\{-1, 0, 1, 2, 3, 4, 5\}$ **37.** $\{1\}$

39. a. $[-2, 4)$

-2 4

   b. $(-\infty, \infty)$

41. a. $(-\infty, 5]$

5

   b. $(-\infty, -6)$

-6

43. a. $(-\infty, 3.2]$

3.2

   b. $(-\infty, 18)$

18

45. a. $(-\infty, -2] \cup \left(-\dfrac{1}{3}, \infty\right)$

-2 $-\dfrac{1}{3}$ **b.** { }

47. $-2.8 < y$ and $y \le 15$

49. $[-4, 2)$

-4 2

51. $\left[\dfrac{6}{5}, 2\right)$

53. $\left[-\dfrac{5}{2}, \dfrac{13}{2}\right]$

55. $12.0 \le x \le 15.2$ g/dL   **57.** $90 \le d \le 110$ ft

59. Marilee needs to score at least 96 on the final exam.

61. It will take more than 1.6 hr or 1 hr 36 min.

63. The length must be 300 ft or less.

65. An average score in league play between 140 and 220, inclusive, would produce a handicap of 72 or less.

67. At least 5 yr is required.

69. Hypothermia would set in for a core body temperature below 95°F.

71. a. Donovan would need to sell more than $250,000 in merchandise.
b. Job A   **73.** Water will boil at temperatures less than 200°F at altitudes of 6600 ft or more.

75. a. $\{x \mid x \ge 2\}$ **b.** $\{x \mid x \le 2\}$ **77. a.** $\{x \mid x \ge -4\}$ **b.** $\mathbb{R}$

79. a. $\{x \mid x \ge \frac{9}{2}\}$ **b.** $\{x \mid x \ge \frac{9}{2}\}$ **81.** False   **83.** True

85. $[1, 2)$ **87.** $[-5, -2)$ **89.** $(-\infty, -2) \cup (0, \infty)$

91. $\left[\dfrac{1}{3}, 1\right]$ **93.** $(-3, -2)$ **95.** $(-\infty, -4)$ **97.** $(2, 10]$

99. The steps are the same with the following exception. If both sides of an inequality are multiplied or divided by a negative real number, then the direction of the inequality sign must be reversed.

101. The statement $-3 > w > -1$ is equivalent to $w < -3$ and $w > -1$. No real number is less than -3 and simultaneously greater than -1.

Section 1.8 Practice Exercises, pp. 184–187

1. $|x - 4|$ or $|4 - x|$ **3.** $\{x \mid 3 < x < 7\}$; $(3, 7)$

5. $\{m \mid m \le -4 \text{ or } m \ge 4\}$; $(-\infty, -4] \cup [4, \infty)$

7. absolute, $\{k, -k\}$ **9.** $-k, k$ **11.** $\mathbb{R}$

13. a. $\{6, -6\}$ **b.** $\{0\}$ **c.** $\{\,\}$

15. a. $\{7, -1\}$ **b.** $\{3\}$ **c.** $\{\,\}$

17. $\left\{\dfrac{5}{3}, 1\right\}$ **19.** $\{11, 3\}$ **21.** $\{\,\}$ **23.** $\left\{\dfrac{19}{3}, \dfrac{29}{3}\right\}$

25. $\left\{-2, -\dfrac{3}{2}\right\}$ **27.** $\{0\}$ **29.** $\left\{\dfrac{3}{2}\right\}$ **31.** $\mathbb{R}$

33. a. $\{7, -7\}$ **b.** $(-7, 7)$ **c.** $(-\infty, -7) \cup (7, \infty)$

35. a. $\{-13, -5\}$ **b.** $[-13, -5]$ **c.** $(-\infty, -13] \cup [-5, \infty)$

37. $(-2, 10)$ **39.** $(-\infty, -8] \cup [2, \infty)$ **41.** $[-10, 6]$

43. $\left(-\infty, -\dfrac{12}{5}\right) \cup \left(\dfrac{4}{5}, \infty\right)$ **45.** $(-15, 9)$

47. $(-\infty, 11.98] \cup [12.02, \infty)$

49. a. $\{\,\}$ **b.** $\{\,\}$ **c.** $\mathbb{R}$; $(-\infty, \infty)$

51. a. $\{\,\}$ **b.** $\{\,\}$ **c.** $\mathbb{R}$; $(-\infty, \infty)$

53. a. $\{0\}$ **b.** $\{\,\}$ **c.** $\{0\}$ **d.** $(-\infty, 0) \cup (0, \infty)$
e. $\mathbb{R}$; $(-\infty, \infty)$ **55. a.** $\{-4\}$ **b.** $\{\,\}$ **c.** $\{-4\}$
d. $(-\infty, -4) \cup (-4, \infty)$ **e.** $\mathbb{R}$; $(-\infty, \infty)$

57. a. $|x - 4| = 6$ or equivalently $|4 - x| = 6$ **b.** $\{-2, 10\}$

59. a. $|v - 16| < 0.01$ or equivalently $|16 - v| < 0.01$ **b.** $(15.99, 16.01)$

61. a. $|x - 4| > 1$ or equivalently $|4 - x| > 1$ **b.** $(-\infty, 3) \cup (5, \infty)$

63. $0 < |x - c| < \delta$ or equivalently $0 < |c - x| < \delta$

65. a. $|t - 36.5| \le 1.5$ or equivalently $|36.5 - t| \le 1.5$ **b.** $[35, 38]$; If the refrigerator is set to 36.5°F, the actual temperature would be between 35°F and 38°F, inclusive.

67. a. $|x - 0.51| \le 0.03$ or equivalently $|0.51 - x| \le 0.03$
b. $[0.48, 0.54]$; The candidate is expected to receive between 48% of the vote and 54% of the vote, inclusive.

69. a. $[470, 530]$; In a group of 1000 jurors selected at random, it would be reasonable to have between 470 and 530 women, inclusive.
b. Yes, because 560 is above the "reasonable" range.

71. $|3x - 1| > 7$ **73.** $|2z| \le 4$ **75.** $|x - 2| \le 5$ **77.** $|x - 7| > 3$

79. The absolute value of any nonzero real number is greater than or equal to zero. Therefore, no real number x has an absolute value of -5.

81. The inequality $|x - 3| \le 0$ will be true only for values of x for which $x - 3 = 0$ (the absolute value will never be less than 0). The solution set is $\{3\}$. The inequality $|x - 3| > 0$ is true for all values of x *excluding* 3. The solution set is $\{x \mid x < 3 \text{ or } x > 3\}$.

83. $\left(-\infty, \dfrac{11}{2}\right)$ **85.** $(-9, -1) \cup (1, 9)$ **87.** $[-4, -3] \cup [2, 3]$

89. $\hat{p} - z\sqrt{\dfrac{\hat{p}\hat{q}}{n}} < p < \hat{p} + z\sqrt{\dfrac{\hat{p}\hat{q}}{n}}$

Problem Recognition Exercises, p. 187

1. a. Equation in quadratic form and a polynomial equation
b. $\{\pm 3, \pm\sqrt{6}\}$

2. a. Absolute value inequality   **b.** $\left(-\infty, -\dfrac{7}{3}\right] \cup [3, \infty)$

3. a. Radical equation   **b.** $\{16\}$

4. a. Absolute value equation   **b.** $\{\,\}$

5. a. Rational equation   **b.** $\left\{\dfrac{9 \pm \sqrt{41}}{2}\right\}$

6. a. Polynomial equation   **b.** $\left\{-\dfrac{5}{3}, \pm\dfrac{1}{4}\right\}$

7. a. Compound inequality   **b.** $(-9, 3]$

8. a. Compound inequality   **b.** $(-\infty, 12)$

9. a. Quadratic equation   **b.** $\left\{\dfrac{5}{2}, -7\right\}$

10. a. Linear equation   **b.** $\{2\}$

11. a. Linear inequality   **b.** $[-18, \infty)$

12. a. Quadratic equation   **b.** $\left\{\pm\dfrac{\sqrt{21}}{3}i\right\}$

13. a. Compound inequality   **b.** $[1, 41]$

14. a. Radical equation   **b.** $\{2\}$; The value 142 does not check.

15. a. Absolute value equation   **b.** $\{1, 3\}$

16. a. Rational equation   **b.** $\{-1\}$; The value $\frac{1}{2}$ does not check.

17. a. Absolute value inequality   **b.** $(-9, 1)$

18. a. Radical equation and an equation in quadratic form   **b.** $\{36\}$

19. a. Radical equation   **b.** $\{\pm 64\}$

20. a. Absolute value inequality   **b.** $(-\infty, \infty)$

Chapter 1 Review Exercises, pp. 190–193

1. $x \ne 2, x \ne -2, x \ne \dfrac{7}{2}$ **3.** $\left\{-\dfrac{40}{3}\right\}$ **5.** $\{\,\}$ **7.** $\left\{\dfrac{1}{2}\right\}$

9. $\{\,\}$; The value 1 does not check.   **11.** $t_2 = 2t_a - t_1$ **13.** 123 mi

15. Cassandra invested $8000 in the Treasury note and $12,000 in the bond.

17. $166\dfrac{2}{3}$ ft^3 **19.** The northbound boat travels 8 mph and the southbound boat travels 14 mph.

21. a. $C = 5x$ **b.** The dancer will save money on the 17th dance during a 3-month period.

23. $\dfrac{55}{3}$ hr $= 18.\overline{3}$ hr

25. There are approximately 144 turtles in the pond.   **27.** $2i\sqrt{3}$

29. a. Real part: 3; Imaginary part: -7 **b.** Real part: 0; Imaginary part: 2

31. $\dfrac{1}{2} + \dfrac{1}{5}i$ **33.** $-\sqrt{15} + i\sqrt{55}$ **35.** $-20 - 48i$ **37.** 73

39. $\dfrac{6}{41} + \dfrac{\sqrt{5}}{41}i$ **41.** $\left\{\dfrac{4}{3}, -2\right\}$ **43.** $\{\pm 11i\}$ **45.** $\left\{-\dfrac{3}{2}\right\}$

47. 81; $(x + 9)^2$ **49.** $\{1, 9\}$ **51.** False   **53. a.** 0
b. 1 real solution   **55. a.** -219 **b.** 2 imaginary solutions

57. $y = k \pm \sqrt{r^2 - (x - h)^2}$ **59.** The rug is 9 ft by 12 ft.

61. The width is 26.5 in. and the length is 42.4 in.   **63.** $n = 91$

65. a. $s = -16t^2 + 200t + 2$ **b.** 0.4 sec

67. $\left\{\pm\sqrt{5}, \dfrac{3}{2}\right\}$ **69.** $\{2\}$; The value -6 does not check.

71. $\left\{-\dfrac{1}{2}, -11\right\}$ **73.** $\{\ \}$ **75.** $\{\pm7^{3/2}\}$ **77.** $\{5 + 11^{4/5}\}$

79. $\left\{-\dfrac{1}{27}, \dfrac{27}{8}\right\}$ **81.** $\{1, -4\}$

83. $a = \sqrt{2m^2 + c^2 - b^2}$ **85.** $v_2 = \dfrac{a_2 t_2 v_1}{a_1 t_1}$

87. $\{x \mid x > 2\}$; $(2, \infty)$

89. $\{t \mid t \geq -3\}$; $[-3, \infty)$

91. a. $\mathbb{R}$ **b.** $\{x \mid -2 \leq x < 7\}$
   c. $\{x \mid x < 7\}$ **d.** $\{x \mid x < -3\}$
   e. $\{x \mid x < -3 \text{ or } x \geq -2\}$ **f.** $\{\ \}$

93. a. $(-\infty, -6] \cup (1, \infty)$ **b.** $\{\ \}$

95. $(3, 11)$

97. More than 8.36 in. is needed.

99. a. $\{x \mid x \geq 12\}$ **b.** $\{x \mid x \leq 12\}$

101. a. $\{-7, 3\}$ **b.** $(-7, 3)$ **c.** $(-\infty, -7] \cup [3, \infty)$

103. a. $\{-5\}$ **b.** $\{\ \}$ **c.** $\{-5\}$ **d.** $(-\infty, -5) \cup (-5, \infty)$
   e. $(-\infty, \infty)$ **105.** $\left\{0, -\dfrac{2}{5}\right\}$ **107.** $\{0\}$ **109.** $(15.98, 16.02)$

111. a. $|x - 3| \leq 0.5$ or $|3 - x| \leq 0.5$ **b.** $[2.5, 3.5]$

Chapter 1 Test, pp. 193–194

1. -10 **2. a.** i **b.** -1 **c.** $-i$ **d.** 1 **e.** i

3. $38 - 34i$ **4.** $-16 - 30i$ **5.** $-\dfrac{7}{29} + \dfrac{26}{29}i$

6. a. -40 **b.** 2 imaginary solutions
7. a. 0 **b.** 1 real solution
8. a. 76 **b.** 2 real solutions (irrational numbers)

9. $\left\{\dfrac{83}{2}\right\}$ **10.** $\{25\}$ **11.** $\mathbb{R}$

12. $\{\ \}$; The value -3 does not check.

13. $\left\{\dfrac{4 \pm \sqrt{13}}{3}\right\}$ **14.** $\{-5 \pm \sqrt{29}\}$ **15.** $\left\{\dfrac{1}{3}, -\dfrac{5}{4}\right\}$

16. $\left\{\dfrac{2 \pm i\sqrt{2}}{3}\right\}$ **17.** $\left\{\pm\dfrac{1}{2}, -2\right\}$ **18.** $\{-4\}$

19. $\{\ \}$; The values 2 and 18 do not check.
20. $\{4\}$; The value -6 does not check.   **21.** $\{\pm11^{5/4}\}$

22. $\left\{\dfrac{1}{4}, -\dfrac{1}{2}\right\}$ **23.** $\{-1, 7\}$ **24.** $\{-1\}$

25. $P = \dfrac{6}{a - t}$ or $P = -\dfrac{6}{t - a}$ **26.** $b = \sqrt{a^2 - c^2}$

27. $t = \dfrac{-v_0 \pm \sqrt{v_0^2 + 128}}{-32}$ or $t = \dfrac{v_0 \pm \sqrt{v_0^2 + 128}}{32}$

28. a. $\mathbb{R}$ **b.** $\{x \mid 0 \leq x < 2\}$ **c.** $\{x \mid x < 2\}$
   d. $\{x \mid x < -1\}$ **e.** $\{x \mid x < -1 \text{ or } x \geq 0\}$ **f.** $\{\ \}$
29. $[-14, 10]$ **30.** $[10, \infty)$ **31.** $(6, \infty)$
32. $(-\infty, 0) \cup (\tfrac{3}{2}, \infty)$ **33.** $[2, 14]$ **34. a.** $\{\ \}$ **b.** $\{\ \}$ **c.** $\mathbb{R}$
35. a. $\{13\}$ **b.** $\{\ \}$ **c.** $\{13\}$ **d.** $(-\infty, 13) \cup (13, \infty)$
   e. $(-\infty, \infty)$ **36.** 1 gal of 80% antifreeze should be used.
37. The plane flying to Seattle flies 440 mph, and the plane flying to New York flies 500 mph.
38. The second hose can fill the pool in 2 hr.
39. The LDL level is 196 mg/dL and the total cholesterol is 266 mg/dL.
40. The base of the triangular portions is 5 ft and the height is 12 ft.
41. a. $s = -16t^2 + 60t + 2$ **b.** The ball will be at a height of 52 ft at times 1.25 sec and 2.5 sec after being kicked.
42. The golfer would need to score less than 84.

Chapter 1 Cumulative Review Exercises, p. 194

1. $3600x^2$ **2.** 40 **3.** $\dfrac{3(x + 3)}{2}$ **4.** $\dfrac{2x - 22}{(x + 2)(x - 2)}$

5. $\dfrac{1 - 3x}{10 + x}$ **6.** $\dfrac{\sqrt{7} - \sqrt{3}}{2}$ **7.** $3yw^4\sqrt[3]{3y^2z^2}$

8. a. $|4\pi - 11|$ or $|11 - 4\pi|$ **b.** $4\pi - 11$
9. $4(x - 2y^2)(x^2 + 2xy^2 + 4y^4)$ **10.** $-1 - i$
11. Stephan borrowed $6000 at 5% and $2000 at 4%.

12. $\left\{\dfrac{1 \pm \sqrt{3}}{4}\right\}$ **13.** $\left\{\dfrac{5 \pm \sqrt{35}}{2}\right\}$ **14.** $\left\{\dfrac{3}{2}, -15\right\}$

15. $\{0\}$; The value -3 does not check.   **16.** $\{3, 7\}$ **17.** $\{0, 17\}$
18. a. $A \cup B = \mathbb{R}$ **b.** $A \cap B = \{x \mid 4 \leq x < 11\}$
   c. $A \cup C = \{x \mid x < 11\}$ **d.** $A \cap C = \{x \mid x < 2\}$
   e. $B \cup C = \{x \mid x < 2 \text{ or } x \geq 4\}$ **f.** $B \cap C = \{\ \}$
19. $[0, 11]$ **20.** $(-25, \infty)$

CHAPTER 2

Section 2.1 Practice Exercises, pp. 203–208

1. origin   **3.** $d = \sqrt{(x_2 - x_1)^2 + (y_2 - y_1)^2}$ **5.** solution   **7.** 0
9.

11. a. $2\sqrt{5}$ **b.** $(-3, 9)$ **13. a.** $9\sqrt{2}$ **b.** $\left(-\dfrac{5}{2}, \dfrac{1}{2}\right)$

15. a. 5 **b.** $(3.7, -4.4)$ **17. a.** $\sqrt{117}$ **b.** $\left(\dfrac{5\sqrt{5}}{2}, -4\sqrt{2}\right)$

19. Yes   **21.** No   **23. a.** Yes   **b.** No   **c.** Yes
25. $\{x \mid x \neq 3\}$ **27.** $\{x \mid x \geq 10\}$ **29.** $\{x \mid x \leq 1.5\}$
31.   **33.**

35.   **37.**

39.   **41.**

43.

45. x-intercepts: $(-1, 0)$, $(9, 0)$; y-intercepts: $(0, -3)$, $(0, 3)$
47. x-intercept: $(-2, 0)$; y-intercept: none   **49.** x-intercept: $(0, 0)$;
   y-intercept $(0, 0)$ **51.** x-intercept: none; y-intercept: none
53. x-intercept: $(1, 0)$; y-intercept: $(0, -2)$ **55.** x-intercept: $(-6, 0)$;
   y-intercept: $(0, 3)$ **57.** x-intercepts: $(-3, 0)$, $(3, 0)$; y-intercept: $(0, 9)$

59. x-intercepts: $(3, 0)$, $(7, 0)$; y-intercept: $(0, 3)$ **61.** x-intercept: $(-1, 0)$; y-intercepts: $(0, -1)$, $(0, 1)$ **63.** x-intercept: $(0, 0)$; y-intercept: $(0, 0)$ **65.** x-intercept: none; y-intercept: none

67. Observation tower B is closer.   **69. a.** Length: $3\sqrt{2}$ ft; Width: $2\sqrt{2}$ ft   **b.** Perimeter: $10\sqrt{2}$ ft; Area: 12 ft^2

71. Center: $(1, 2)$; Radius: $\sqrt{10}$ **73.** Area: 25 m^2 **75.** b   **77.** c

79. d   **81.** 70.65 yr   **83.** Collinear   **85.** Not collinear

87. The points (x_1, y_1) and (x_2, y_2) define the endpoints of the hypotenuse d of a right triangle. The lengths of the legs of the triangle are $|x_2 - x_1|$ and $|y_2 - y_1|$. Applying the Pythagorean theorem produces $d^2 = |x_2 - x_1|^2 + |y_2 - y_1|^2$, or equivalently $d = \sqrt{(x_2 - x_1)^2 + (y_2 - y_1)^2}$ for $d \geq 0$.

89. To find the x-intercept(s), substitute 0 for y and solve for x. To find the y-intercept(s), substitute 0 for x and solve for y.

91. $\sqrt{91}$ **93.** $9\sqrt{2}$

95.
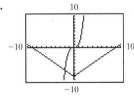

97. 5   **99.** $\sqrt{53}$

101. The viewing window is part of the Cartesian plane shown in the display screen of a calculator. The boundaries of the window are often denoted by [Xmin, Xmax, Xscl] by [Ymin, Ymax, Yscl].

103.

105.

107.

109. x-intercepts: $(-1, 0)$, $(1, 0)$, $(3, 0)$; y-intercept: $(0, 3)$

Section 2.2 Practice Exercises, pp. 212–214

1. a. $\sqrt{146}$ **b.** $\left(\frac{1}{2}, \frac{9}{2}\right)$

3. x-intercepts: $(-4, 0)$, $(4, 0)$; y-intercepts: $(0, -4)$, $(0, 4)$ **5.** 5 ft

7. circle; center   **9.** $(x - h)^2 + (y - k)^2 = r^2$ **11.** No   **13.** Yes

15. Center: $(4, -2)$; Radius: 9   **17.** Center: $(0, 2.5)$; Radius: 2.5

19. Center: $(0, 0)$; Radius: $2\sqrt{5}$ **21.** Center: $\left(\frac{3}{2}, -\frac{3}{4}\right)$; Radius: $\frac{9}{7}$

23. a. $(x + 2)^2 + (y - 5)^2 = 1$ **25. a.** $(x + 4)^2 + (y + 3)^2 = 11$
b.

b.

27. a. $x^2 + y^2 = 6.76$ **29. a.** $(x - 2)^2 + (y - 1)^2 = 25$
b.

b.

31. a. $(x + 2)^2 + (y + 1)^2 = 100$ **33. a.** $(x - 4)^2 + (y - 6)^2 = 16$
b.

b.

35. a. $(x - 5)^2 + (y + 5)^2 = 25$
b.

37. $(x - 8)^2 + (y + 11)^2 = 25$ **39.** $\{(-1, 5)\}$ **41.** $\{\ \}$

43. $(x + 3)^2 + (y - 1)^2 = 4$; Center: $(-3, 1)$; Radius: 2

45. $x^2 + (y - 10)^2 = 104$; Center: $(0, 10)$; Radius: $2\sqrt{26}$

47. $(x - 4)^2 + (y + 10)^2 = 24$; Center: $(4, -10)$; Radius: $2\sqrt{6}$

49. $(x - 2)^2 + (y - 9)^2 = -4$; Degenerate case: $\{\ \}$

51. $x^2 + \left(y - \frac{5}{2}\right)^2 = 0$; Degenerate case (single point): $\left\{\left(0, \frac{5}{2}\right)\right\}$

53. $\left(x - \frac{1}{2}\right)^2 + \left(y - \frac{3}{4}\right)^2 = \frac{25}{16}$; Center: $\left(\frac{1}{2}, \frac{3}{4}\right)$; Radius: $\frac{5}{4}$

55. $(x - 4)^2 + (y - 6)^2 = 2.25$

57.

59. $y = -2$ and $y = 14$

61. $(3 + \sqrt{17}, 3 + \sqrt{17})$ and $(3 - \sqrt{17}, 3 - \sqrt{17})$

63. a.

b.

c.

d.

65. a.

b.

c.
d.

67. A circle is the set of all points in a plane that are equidistant from a fixed point called the center.

69. The calculator does not connect the pixels at the ends of the semicircle with the x-axis because of limited resolution.

71. $[-15.1, 15.1, 1]$ by $[-10, 10, 1]$

73. $[-14, 39, 5]$ by $[-30, 5, 5]$

Section 2.3 Practice Exercises, pp. 222–227

1.

3. Center: $\left(\dfrac{1}{2}, 5\right)$; Radius: $\dfrac{5}{2}$

5. x-intercepts: $(2, 0), (-2, 0), (-5, 0)$; y-intercept: $(0, -20)$

7. relation, domain, y **9.** does not   **11.** y **13.** -5

15. a. $\{$(Tom Hanks, 5), (Jack Nicholson, 12), (Sean Penn, 5), (Dustin Hoffman, 7)$\}$ **b.** $\{$Tom Hanks, Jack Nicholson, Sean Penn, Dustin Hoffman$\}$ **c.** $\{5, 12, 7\}$ **d.** Yes

17. a. $\{(-4, 3), (-2, -3), (1, 4), (3, -2), (3, 1)\}$ **b.** $\{-4, -2, 1, 3\}$ **c.** $\{3, -3, 4, -2, 1\}$ **d.** No

19. False   **21.** Yes   **23.** No   **25.** Yes   **27.** Yes   **29.** No

31. Yes   **33.** No   **35.** Yes   **37. a.** Yes   **b.** No   **39.** $(4, 1)$

41. a. -2 **b.** -2 **c.** 0 **d.** 4 **e.** 10

43. a. 5 **b.** 5 **c.** 5 **d.** 5 **e.** 5 **45.** $\dfrac{1}{3}$ **47.** 3

49. Undefined   **51.** 3 **53.** $\dfrac{1}{t}$ **55.** $\sqrt{a + b + 1}$

57. $a^2 + 11a + 28$ **59.** Undefined   **61.** 7 **63.** 4 **65.** -1

67. 2 **69. a.** $d(2) = 36$; Joe rides 36 mi in 2 hr.   **b.** 12 mi

71. $C(225) = 279$; If the cost of the food is $225, then the total bill including tax and tip is $279.

73. x-intercept: $(2, 0)$; y-intercept: $(0, -4)$ **75.** x-intercepts: $(8, 0)$, $(-8, 0)$; y-intercept: $(0, -8)$ **77.** x-intercepts: $(2\sqrt{3}, 0)$, $(-2\sqrt{3}, 0)$; y-intercept: $(0, 12)$ **79.** x-intercept: $(8, 0)$; y-intercept: $(0, 8)$ **81.** x-intercept: $(4, 0)$; y-intercept: $(0, -2)$

83. $(0, 35.7)$; The y-intercept means that for $x = 0$ (the year 2006), the average amount spent on video games per person in the United States was $35.70.

85. Domain: $\{-3, -2, -1, 2, 3\}$; Range: $\{-4, -3, 3, 4, 5\}$

87. Domain: $(-3, \infty)$; Range: $[1, \infty)$ **89.** Domain: $(-\infty, \infty)$; Range: $(-\infty, \infty)$ **91.** Domain: $(-\infty, \infty)$; Range: $[-3, \infty)$

93. Domain: $(-5, 1]$; Range: $\{-1, 1, 3\}$

95. $(-\infty, 4) \cup (4, \infty)$ **97.** $\left(-\infty, -\dfrac{7}{2}\right) \cup \left(-\dfrac{7}{2}, \infty\right)$

99. $(-\infty, \infty)$ **101.** $[-15, \infty)$ **103.** $(-\infty, 3]$ **105.** $(-\infty, 3)$

107. $(-\infty, \infty)$ **109. a.** -4 **b.** 2 **c.** $x = -3, x = -1, x = 1$ **d.** $x = -2, x = 2$ **e.** $(0, 0)$ and $\left(-\dfrac{10}{3}, 0\right)$ **f.** $(0, 0)$ **g.** $(-\infty, \infty)$ **h.** $[-4, \infty)$

111. a. 0 **b.** 5 **c.** $x = -3, x = -1, x = 1$ **d.** $x = -4, x = 0$ **e.** $(-2, 0)$ and $\left(\dfrac{4}{3}, 0\right)$ **f.** $(0, -4)$ **g.** $[-4, \infty)$ **h.** $[-4, 5]$

113. $r(x) = 400 - x$ **115.** $P(x) = 3x$ **117.** $C(x) = 90 - x$

119. $f(x) = 3x^2 - 2$ **121.** If two points in a set of ordered pairs are aligned vertically in a graph, then they have the same x-coordinate but different y-coordinates. This contradicts the definition of a function. Therefore, the points do not define y as a function of x.

123. a. $P(s) = 4s$ **b.** $A(s) = s^2$ **c.** $A(P) = \left(\dfrac{P}{4}\right)^2$ or $A(P) = \dfrac{P^2}{16}$ **d.** $P(A) = 4\sqrt{A}$ **e.** $d(s) = \sqrt{2}s$ **f.** $s(d) = \dfrac{d}{\sqrt{2}}$ or $s(d) = \dfrac{d\sqrt{2}}{2}$ **g.** $P(d) = 2\sqrt{2}d$ **h.** $A(d) = \dfrac{d^2}{2}$

Section 2.4 Practice Exercises, pp. 238–244

1. a. Yes   **b.** $(-\infty, \infty)$ **c.** $(-\infty, \infty)$ **d.** $(-2, 0)$ **e.** $(0, 3)$

3. a. No   **b.** $\{3\}$ **c.** $(-\infty, \infty)$ **d.** $(3, 0)$ **e.** None

5. a. $\left(2\sqrt{2}, -\dfrac{3\sqrt{5}}{2}\right)$ **b.** $\sqrt{133}$

7. scatter   **9.** vertical   **11.** True   **13.** zero

15. slope, intercept   **17.** $m = \dfrac{f(x_2) - f(x_1)}{x_2 - x_1}$

19. x-intercept: $(-4, 0)$; y-intercept: $(0, 3)$

21. x-intercept: $\left(\tfrac{2}{5}, 0\right)$; y-intercept: $(0, 1)$

23. x-intercept: $(-6, 0)$; y-intercept: None

25. x-intercept: None; y-intercept: $(0, 2)$

27. x-intercept: $(5, 0)$; y-intercept: $(0, 2)$

29. x-intercept: $(0, 0)$; y-intercept: $(0, 0)$

31. $m = \dfrac{3}{10}$ **33.** $m = \dfrac{1}{40}$ **35.** $m = -3$ **37.** $m = -\dfrac{1}{4}$

39. $m = -\dfrac{26}{23}$ **41.** $m = -\dfrac{20}{7}$ **43.** $m = \dfrac{\sqrt{30}}{12}$ **45.** $m = 3$

47. $m = -\dfrac{1}{3}$ **49.** $m = 0$ **51.** Undefined   **53.** 0

55. 41.6 ft   **57.** Change in population over change in time

59. a. $y = \frac{1}{2}x - 2$; $m = \frac{1}{2}$; y-intercept: $(0, -2)$
b.

61. a. $y = \frac{3}{2}x + 2$; $m = \frac{3}{2}$; y-intercept: $(0, 2)$
b.

63. a. $y = \frac{3}{4}x$; $m = \frac{3}{4}$; y-intercept: $(0, 0)$
b.

65. a. $y = 7$; $m = 0$; y-intercept: $(0, 7)$
b.

67. a. $y = -\frac{1}{3}x + 1$; $m = -\frac{1}{3}$; y-intercept: $(0, 1)$
b.

69. a. $y = -\frac{7}{4}x + 7$; $m = -\frac{7}{4}$; y-intercept: $(0, 7)$
b.

71. a. Linear **b.** Linear **c.** Neither **d.** Constant
73. a. $y = \frac{1}{2}x + 9$ **b.** $f(x) = \frac{1}{2}x + 9$ **75. a.** $y = -3x - 3$
b. $f(x) = -3x - 3$ **77. a.** $y = \frac{2}{3}x + \frac{1}{3}$ **b.** $f(x) = \frac{2}{3}x + \frac{1}{3}$
79. a. $y = 5$ **b.** $f(x) = 5$ **81. a.** $y = 1.2x + 0.78$
b. $f(x) = 1.2x + 0.78$ **83. a.** $y = 2x - 6$ **b.** $f(x) = 2x - 6$
85. a. $y = -\frac{4}{3}x + \frac{19}{3}$ **b.** $f(x) = -\frac{4}{3}x + \frac{19}{3}$
87. $m = \frac{3}{2}$ **89. a.** $364.80/yr **b.** $772.20/yr **c.** Increasing
91. a. 2.2 million/yr **b.** 2.9 million/yr **c.** Increasing
93. a. 1 **b.** 4 **c.** -2 **95. a.** 1 **b.** 1 **c.** 7
97. a. 1 **b.** $\frac{1}{3}$ **c.** $\frac{1}{5}$ **99. a.** $\{-1\}$ **b.** $(-\infty, -1)$
c. $[-1, \infty)$ **101. a.** $\{2\}$ **b.** $(-\infty, 2)$ **c.** $[2, \infty)$
103. a. $\{-5\}$ **b.** $[-5, \infty)$ **c.** $(-\infty, -5]$
105. a. $\{14\}$ **b.** $(14, \infty)$ **c.** $(-\infty, 14)$
107. a. $\{8\}$; The number of men and women in college was approximately the same in 1978. **b.** $[0, 8)$; The number of women in college was less than the number of men in college from 1970 to 1978.
c. $(8, 40]$; The number of women in college exceeded the number of men in college from 1978 to 2010.
109. The line will be slanted if both A and B are nonzero. If A is zero and B is not zero, then the equation can be written in the form $y = k$ and the graph is a horizontal line. If B is zero and A is not zero, then the equation can be written in the form $x = k$, and the graph is a vertical line. **111.** The slope and y-intercept are easily determined by inspection of the equation.
113. 4 units^2 **115.** 10 units^2 **117. a.** $y = -\frac{A}{B}x + \frac{C}{B}$
b. $m = -\frac{A}{B}$ **c.** $\left(0, \frac{C}{B}\right)$
119. a. $\{-1.5\}$
b. $(-\infty, -1.5)$
c. $(-1.5, \infty)$

121. a. $\{-4, 7.8\}$ **b.** $(-\infty, -4] \cup [7.8, \infty)$ **c.** $[-4, 7.8]$

123. a. $\{13\}$
b. $(13, \infty)$
c. $\left[\frac{3}{4}, 13\right)$

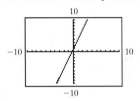

125. The lines are not exactly the same. The slopes are different.

Section 2.5 Practice Exercises, pp. 254–261

1. $y = \frac{3}{2}x + 8$ **3.** $m = 3$; y-intercept: $\left(0, \frac{3}{2}\right)$
5. a. Vertical **b.** Slope is undefined. **c.** No y-intercept
7. $y - y_1 = m(x - x_1)$ **9.** -1 **11.** $y = -2x - 1$
13. $y = \frac{2}{3}x + \frac{2}{3}$ **15.** $y = 1.2x - 1.48$ **17.** $y = \frac{1}{9}x + \frac{4}{3}$
19. $y = -\frac{8}{5}x + 8$ **21.** $y = 3.5x - 2.95$ **23.** $y = -4$
25. $x = \frac{2}{3}$ **27.** Undefined **29. a.** $m = \frac{3}{11}$ **b.** $m = -\frac{11}{3}$
31. a. $m = -6$ **b.** $m = \frac{1}{6}$ **33. a.** $m = 1$ **b.** $m = -1$
35. Perpendicular **37.** Parallel **39.** Perpendicular
41. Neither **43.** $y = -2x + 9$; $2x + y = 9$
45. $y = -5x + 26$; $5x + y = 26$ **47.** $y = \frac{3}{7}x + \frac{38}{7}$; $3x - 7y = -38$
49. $y = 0.5x + 5.3$; $5x - 10y = -53$ **51.** $y = 6$
53. $y = -\frac{3}{4}$ **55.** $x = -61.5$
57. a. $S(x) = 0.12x + 400$ for $x \geq 0$ **b.** $S(8000) = 1360$ means that the sales person will make $1360 if $8000 in merchandise is sold for the week.
59. a. $W(t) = 120,000 - 2400(2.7)t$ for $0 < t \leq 4.5$
b. $W(2.5) = 103,800$ means that 2.5 hr into the flight, the mass is 103,800 kg.
61. a. $T(x) = 0.019x + 172$ for $x > 0$ **b.** $T(80,000) = 1692$ means that the property tax is $1692 for a home with a taxable value of $80,000.
63. a. $C(x) = 34.5x + 2275$ **b.** $R(x) = 80x$ **c.** $P(x) = 45.5x - 2275$
d. 50 items **65. a.** $\{730\}$ **b.** $[0, 730)$ **c.** $(730, \infty)$
67. a. $C(x) = 2.88x + 790$ **b.** $R(x) = 6x$ **c.** $P(x) = 3.12x - 790$
d. The business will make a profit if it produces and sells 254 dozen or more cookies. **e.** The business will lose $322.
69. a. $y = -0.5x + 51.3$ **b.** $m = -0.5$; The slope means that alcohol usage among high school students 1 month prior to the CDC survey has dropped by an average rate of 0.5% per yr.
c. The y-intercept is $(0, 51.3)$ and means that in the year 1990, approximately 51.3% of high school students used alcohol within 1 month prior to the date that the survey was taken.

d. Approximately 41.3%   **e.** No. There is no guarantee that the linear trend will continue well beyond the last observed data point.

71. a. $y = 0.18x + 10.48$ **b.** $m = 0.18$ means that enrollment in public colleges increased at an average rate of 0.18 million per yr (180,000 per yr).   **c.** The y-intercept is (0, 10.48) and means that in the year 1990, there were approximately 10,480,000 students enrolled in public colleges.   **d.** Approximately 14.98 million

73. a.

Amount of Cholesterol vs. Number of Calories for Selected Hamburgers

b. $c(x) = 0.125x$
c. $m = 0.125$ means that the amount of cholesterol increases at an average rate of 0.125 mg per calorie of hamburger.
d. 81.25 mg

75. Yes   **77.** No

79. a. $y = -0.5x + 52.3$ **b.**

c. Approximately 42.3%

81. a. $y = 0.175x + 10.46$ **b.**

c. Approximately 14.8 million

83. a. $y = 0.136x - 4.27$ **b.**

c. Approximately 84 mg

85. $\left(\dfrac{8}{5}, 0\right)$ **87.** $f(x) = \dfrac{7}{3}x + 4$ **89.** $h(x) = x + 5$

91. If the slopes of the two lines are the same and the y-intercepts are different, then the lines are parallel. If the slope of one line is the opposite of the reciprocal of the slope of the other line, then the lines are perpendicular.   **93.** Profit is equal to revenue minus cost.

95. $y = -x + 4$ **97.** $y = 12x + 17$

99. $y = -\dfrac{5}{2}x + \dfrac{21}{2}$ for $1 \leq x \leq 5$

Problem Recognition Exercises, p. 261

1.

2.

3.

4.

5.

6.

7.

8.

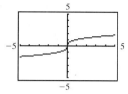

9. The graphs have the shape of $y = x^2$ with a vertical shift.

10. The graphs have the shape of $y = |x|$ with a vertical shift.

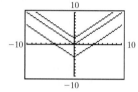

11. The graphs have the shape of $y = \sqrt{x}$ with a horizontal shift.

12. The graphs have the shape of $y = x^2$ with a horizontal shift.

13. The graph of $g(x) = -|x|$ has the shape of the graph of $y = |x|$ but is reflected across the x-axis.

14. The graph of $g(x) = -\sqrt{x}$ has the shape of the graph of $y = \sqrt{x}$ but is reflected across the x-axis.

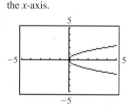

15. The graphs have the shape of $y = x^2$ but show a vertical shrink or stretch.

16. The graphs have the shape of $y = |x|$ but show a vertical shrink or stretch.

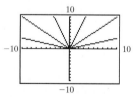

17. The graph of $g(x) = \sqrt{-x}$ has the shape of the graph of $y = \sqrt{x}$ but is reflected across the y-axis.

18. The graph of $g(x) = \sqrt[3]{-x}$ has the shape of the graph of $y = \sqrt[3]{x}$ but is reflected across the y-axis.

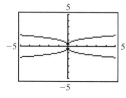

Section 2.6 Practice Exercises, pp. 270–274

1. a. $m = -\frac{3}{2}$ **b.** $(0, 1)$ **c.**

3.

The y-intercepts are different. The graphs differ by a vertical shift. Or we can interpret the difference as a horizontal shift.

5. linear   **7.** left   **9.** down   **11.** horizontal shrink
13. vertical shrink   **15.** e   **17.** b   **19.** a

21.

23.

25.

27.

29.

31.

33.

35.

37.

39.

41.

43.

45.

47.

49.

51.

53.

55.

57.

59.

61.

63.

65.

67.

69.

71.

73.

75.

77.

79.

81. c   **83.** b
85. As written, $h(x) = \sqrt{\frac{1}{2}x}$ is in the form $h(x) = f(ax)$ with $0 < a < 1$. This indicates a horizontal stretch. However, $h(x)$ can also be written as $h(x) = \sqrt{\frac{1}{2}} \cdot \sqrt{x}$. This is written in the form $h(x) = af(x)$ with $0 < a < 1$. This represents a vertical shrink.

87. $f(x) = (x - 2)^2 - 3$ **89.** $f(x) = \dfrac{1}{x + 3}$

91. $f(x) = -x^3 + 1$

93. a.   **b.**

c. The general shape of $y = x^n$ is similar to the graph of $y = x^2$ for even values of n greater than 1.

d. The general shape of $y = x^n$ is similar to the graph of $y = x^3$ for odd values of n greater than 1.

Section 2.7 Practice Exercises, pp. 287–294

1.   **3.**

5. $f(-x) = -3x^2 + 5x + 1$ **7.** y **9.** origin   **11.** origin

13. y-axis   **15.** x-axis   **17.** x-axis, y-axis, and origin

19. None of these   **21.** x-axis, y-axis, and origin   **23.** None of these

25. y-axis symmetry   **27.** Odd   **29.** Even

31. Neither even nor odd   **33. a.** $f(-x) = 4x^2 - 3|x|$

b. Yes   **c.** Even   **35. a.** $h(-x) = -4x^3 + 2x$

b. $-h(x) = -4x^3 + 2x$ **c.** Yes   **d.** Odd

37. a. $m(-x) = 4x^2 - 2x - 3$ **b.** $-m(x) = -4x^2 - 2x + 3$

c. No   **d.** No   **e.** Neither   **39.** Even   **41.** Odd

43. Neither   **45.** Even   **47.** Odd   **49. a.** 12   **b.** 13

c. 4   **d.** 5   **e.** 5   **51. a.** 1   **b.** 2   **c.** −1   **d.** 1

e. −1   **53.** c   **55.** d

57. a.   **b.**   **c.**

59. a.   **b.**   **c.**

61.   **63.**

65.   **67.**

69.   **71. a.**   **b.** $y = |x|$

73. −5   **75.** −1   **77.** 0   **79.** −9

81.   **83.**

85. a. $C(x) = \begin{cases} 0.44 & \text{for } 0 < x \le 1 \\ 0.61 & \text{for } 1 < x \le 2 \\ 0.78 & \text{for } 2 < x \le 3 \\ 0.95 & \text{for } 3 < x \le 3.5 \end{cases}$

b.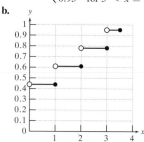

87. $S(x) = \begin{cases} 2000 & \text{for } 0 \le x < 40{,}000 \\ 2000 + 0.05(x - 40{,}000) & \text{for } x \ge 40{,}000 \end{cases}$

89. a. $(2, \infty)$ **b.** $(-3, -2)$ **c.** $(-2, 2)$

91. a. $(-\infty, \infty)$ **b.** Never decreasing   **c.** Never constant

93. a. $(1, \infty)$ **b.** $(-\infty, 1)$ **c.** Never constant

95. a. $(-\infty, -2) \cup (2, \infty)$ **b.** Never decreasing   **c.** $(-2, 2)$

97. At $x = 1$, the function has a relative minimum of −3.

99. At $x = -2$, the function has a relative minimum of 0. At $x = 0$, the function has a relative maximum of 2. At $x = 2$, the function has a relative minimum of 0.

101. At $x = -2$, the function has a relative minimum of −4.
At $x = 0$, the function has a relative maximum of 0.
At $x = 2$, the function has a relative minimum of −4.

103. a. $(0, 3)$ and $(7, 9)$; These intervals correspond to the years 2000 to 2003 and 2007 to 2009.   **b.** $(3, 7)$; This interval corresponds to the years 2003 to 2007.   **c.** Relative maximum approximately 6%; Relative minimum approximately 4.5%.

105. $f(x) = \begin{cases} -2 & \text{for } x < 1 \\ 3 & \text{for } x \ge 1 \end{cases}$ **107.** $f(x) = \begin{cases} -|x| & \text{for } x < 2 \\ -2 & \text{for } x \ge 2 \end{cases}$

109. $f(x) = \begin{cases} \dfrac{1}{x} & \text{for } x < 0 \\ x & \text{for } x > 0 \end{cases}$

111. 15 ft/sec; 30 ft/sec; 2.7 ft/sec; and 1.4 ft/sec

113. Graph b   **115. a.** 2   **b.** −4   **c.** 4   **d.** 3   **e.** −3   **f.** 4

117. If replacing y by $-y$ in the equation results in an equivalent equation, then the graph is symmetric to the x-axis. If replacing x by $-x$ in the equation results in an equivalent equation, then the graph is symmetric to the y-axis. If replacing both x by $-x$ and y by $-y$ results in an equivalent equation, then the graph is symmetric to the origin.

119. At $x = 1$, there are two different y values. The relation contains the ordered pairs $(1, 2)$ and $(1, 3)$.

121. A relative maximum of a function is the greatest function value relative to other points on the function nearby.

123. Relative minimum   **125. a.** Concave down   **b.** Decreasing

127. a. Concave up   **b.** Decreasing

129.

131. The graph does *not* have a gap at $x = 2$, however, the limited resolution on the calculator gives the appearance of a gap.

133.

135. Relative maximum 4.667

Section 2.8 Practice Exercises, pp. 303–308

1. $\left(-\infty, \dfrac{5}{2}\right]$ **3.** $(-\infty, -9) \cup (-9, 9) \cup (9, \infty)$

5. $3t^2 + 17t + 21$ **7.** $f(x); g(x)$ **9.** $\dfrac{f(x + h) - f(x)}{h}$

11. $(f + g)(x) = |x| + 3$; Graph d

13. $(f + g)(x) = x^2 - 4$; Graph a **15.** -13 **17.** 6 **19.** $\dfrac{11}{3}$

21. $-\dfrac{4}{3}$ **23.** Undefined **25.** $(r - p)(x) = -x^2 - 6x; (-\infty, \infty)$

27. $(p \cdot q)(x) = (x^2 + 3x)\sqrt{1 - x}; (-\infty, 1]$

29. $\left(\dfrac{q}{p}\right)(x) = \dfrac{\sqrt{1 - x}}{x^2 + 3x}; (-\infty, -3) \cup (-3, 0) \cup (0, 1]$

31. $\left(\dfrac{p}{q}\right)(x) = \dfrac{x^2 + 3x}{\sqrt{1 - x}}; (-\infty, 1)$

33. $(r + q)(x) = -3x + \sqrt{1 - x}; (-\infty, 1]$

35. $\left(\dfrac{p}{r}\right)(x) = \dfrac{x + 3}{-3}; (-\infty, 0) \cup (0, \infty)$

37. a. $5x + 5h + 9$ **b.** 5 **39. a.** $x^2 + 2xh + h^2 + 4x + 4h$

  b. $2x + h + 4$ **41.** -2 **43.** $-10x - 5h - 4$

45. $3x^2 + 3xh + h^2$ **47.** $-\dfrac{1}{x(x + h)}$ **49. a.** $\dfrac{4\sqrt{x + h} - 4\sqrt{x}}{h}$

  b. $1.6569; 1.9524; 1.9950; 1.9995$ **c.** 2

51. 48 **53.** -3 **55.** 192 **57.** $\sqrt{210}$ **59.** -27

61. Undefined **63. a.** $(f \circ g)(x) = 2x^2 + 4$

  b. $(g \circ f)(x) = 4x^2 + 16x + 16$ **c.** No

65. $(n \circ p)(x) = x^2 - 9x - 5; (-\infty, \infty)$

67. $(m \circ n)(x) = \sqrt{x + 3}; [-3, \infty)$

69. $(q \circ n)(x) = \dfrac{1}{x - 15}; (-\infty, 15) \cup (15, \infty)$

71. $(q \circ r)(x) = \dfrac{1}{|2x + 3| - 10}; \left(-\infty, -\dfrac{13}{2}\right) \cup \left(-\dfrac{13}{2}, \dfrac{7}{2}\right) \cup \left(\dfrac{7}{2}, \infty\right)$

73. $(n \circ r)(x) = |2x + 3| - 5; (-\infty, \infty)$

75. $(n \circ n)(x) = x - 10; (-\infty, \infty)$ **77. a.** $C(x) = 21.95x$

  b. $T(a) = 1.06a + 10.99$ **c.** $(T \circ C)(x) = 23.267x + 10.99$

  d. $(T \circ C)(4) = 104.058$; The total cost to purchase 4 boxes of stationery is $104.06.

79. a. $r(t) = 80t$ **b.** $d(r) = 7.2r$ **c.** $(d \circ r)(t) = 576t$ represents the distance traveled (in ft) in t minutes.

  d. $(d \circ r)(30) = 17{,}280$ means that the bicycle will travel 17,280 ft (approximately 3.27 mi) in 30 min.

81. $f(x) = x^2$ and $g(x) = x + 7$ **83.** $f(x) = \sqrt[3]{x}$ and $g(x) = 2x + 1$

85. $f(x) = |x|$ and $g(x) = 2x^2 - 3$ **87.** $f(x) = \dfrac{5}{x}$ and $g(x) = x + 4$

89. a. 1 **b.** -1 **c.** -6 **d.** $-\dfrac{1}{2}$ **e.** 1 **f.** 1 **g.** -2

91. a. -1 **b.** 0 **c.** Undefined **d.** -3

  e. -3 **f.** 0 **g.** 2 **93.** 1 **95.** 3 **97.** 6

99. Undefined **101.** 8 **103.** 6 **105.** 6

107. $T(x) = (M + W)(x) = 0.11x + 6.5$ represents the total number of adults (in millions) on probation, on parole, or incarcerated x years after the year 2000.

109. a. $C(x) = 2.8x + 5000$ **b.** $R(x) = 40x$

  c. $(R - C)(x) = 37.2x - 5000$ represents the profit for selling x CDs.

  d. $84,280

111. $\left(\dfrac{H + L}{2}\right)(x)$ represents the average of the high and low temperatures for day x. **113. a.** $S_1(x) = x^2 + 4x$ **b.** $S_2(x) = \dfrac{1}{8}\pi x^2$

  c. $(S_1 - S_2)(x) = x^2 + 4x - \dfrac{1}{8}\pi x^2$ and represents the area of the region outside the semicircle, but inside the rectangle.

115. The domain of $(f \circ g)(x)$ is the set of real numbers x in the domain of g such that $g(x)$ is in the domain of f.

117. a. $\dfrac{\sqrt{x + h + 3} - \sqrt{x + 3}}{h}$ **b.** $\dfrac{1}{\sqrt{x + h + 3} + \sqrt{x + 3}}$

  c. $\dfrac{1}{2\sqrt{x + 3}}$ **119. a.** $-9.68t - 4.84h + 88$

  b. 78.32 ft/sec **c.** 58.96 ft/sec **d.** 39.6 ft/sec **e.** 20.24 ft/sec

121. a. $-0.56x - 0.28h + 20.8$ **b.** 12.4; The difference quotient of 12.4 means that cigarette production increased at an average rate of 12.4 billion per yr between the years 1950 and 1960.

  c. -10; The difference quotient of -10 means that cigarette production decreased at an average rate of 10 billion per yr between the years 1990 and 2000.

123. $(f \circ f)(x) = \dfrac{1}{\dfrac{1}{x - 2} - 2} = \dfrac{x - 2}{-2x + 5}; (-\infty, 2) \cup \left(2, \dfrac{5}{2}\right) \cup \left(\dfrac{5}{2}, \infty\right)$

125. $(g \circ g)(x) = \sqrt{\sqrt{x - 3} - 3}; [12, \infty)$

127. $(f \circ g \circ h)(x) = 2(\sqrt[3]{x})^2 + 1$ **129.** $(h \circ g \circ f)(x) = \sqrt[3]{(2x + 1)^2}$

131. $m(x) = \sqrt[3]{x}, n(x) = x + 1, h(x) = 4x, k(x) = x^2$

Chapter 2 Review Exercises, pp. 310–315

1. a. $5\sqrt{5}$ **b.** $\left(\dfrac{3}{2}, 3\right)$ **3. a.** Yes **b.** No

5. x-intercept: $(4, 0)$; y-intercepts: $(0, -4), (0, -10)$

7.

9. Center: $(4, -3)$; Radius: 2

11. a. $(x + 3)^2 + (y - 1)^2 = 11$ **13. a.** $(x - 4)^2 + (y - 1)^2 = 25$
b.

b.

15. a. $(x + 5)^2 + (y - 1)^2 = 9$ **b.** Center: $(-5, 1)$; Radius: 3
17. $\{(-3, 5)\}$ **19. a.** {(Dara Torres, 12), (Carl Lewis, 10), (Bonnie Blair, 6), (Michael Phelps, 16)}   **b.** {Dara Torres, Carl Lewis, Bonnie Blair, Michael Phelps}
c. {12, 10, 6, 16}   **d.** Yes
21. No   **23.** Yes   **25. a.** 5   **b.** 4   **c.** 3
27. x-intercepts: (4, 0), (2, 0); y-intercept: (0, 2)
29. Domain: $\{-4, -2, 0, 2, 3, 5\}$; Range: $\{-3, 0, 2, 1\}$
31. $(-\infty, 5) \cup (5, \infty)$ **33.** $(-\infty, \infty)$
35. a. -2 **b.** -1 **c.** $x = -1, x = 3$ **d.** $x = -4$
e. (0, 0), (2, 0)   **f.** (0, 0)   **g.** $(-\infty, \infty)$ **h.** $(-\infty, 1]$
37. x-intercept: $(-4, 0)$;   **39.** x-intercept: None;
y-intercept: (0, 2) y-intercept: (0, 2)

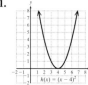

41. $m = \dfrac{1}{8}$ **43.** $m = \dfrac{f(b) - f(a)}{b - a}$ **45.** Undefined

47. $\dfrac{\Delta C}{\Delta t}$ represents the change in cost per change in time.

49. $y = -\dfrac{2}{3}x - \dfrac{13}{3}$; $f(x) = -\dfrac{2}{3}x - \dfrac{13}{3}$ **51.** $m = \dfrac{3}{7}$

53. a. -4 **b.** -28 **55. a.** $\dfrac{2}{3}$ **b.** $-\dfrac{3}{2}$

57. $y = 3x - 1$ **59.** $y = -0.9x + 6.29$ **61.** $y = 2x - 10$
63. $y = 7$ **65. a.** $C(x) = 1500 + 35x$ **b.** $R(x) = 60x$

c. $P(x) = 25x - 1500$ **d.** The studio needs more than 60 private lessons per month to make a profit.   **e.** \$550
67. a. $y = 369.6x + 22{,}111$ **b.**
c. 27,655 students

69.

71.

73.

75.

77.

79.

81.

83.

85. y-axis   **87.** None of these   **89.** Odd   **91.** Even
93. Neither   **95. a.** 18   **b.** 1   **c.** 5   **d.** 4
97.

99. a. -3 **b.** -3 **c.** -1 **d.** 5
101. a. $(2, \infty)$ **b.** $(-\infty, 2)$ **c.** Never constant
103. At $x = -2$, the function has a relative maximum of 4.
105. $-\dfrac{19}{3}$ **107.** -28 **109.** 17
111. $(n - m)(x) = x^2$; Domain: $(-\infty, \infty)$
113. $\left(\dfrac{n}{p}\right)(x) = \dfrac{x^2 - 4x}{\sqrt{x - 2}}$; Domain: $(2, \infty)$
115. $(q \circ n)(x) = \dfrac{1}{x^2 - 4x - 5}$; Domain: $(-\infty, -1) \cup (-1, 5) \cup (5, \infty)$
117. -6 **119.** $f(x) = x^2$ and $g(x) = x - 4$
121. a. $d(t) = 60t$ **b.** $n(d) = \dfrac{d}{28}$ **c.** $(n \circ d)(t) = \dfrac{60t}{28}$ represents the number of gallons of gasoline used in t hours.
d. $(n \circ d)(7) = 15$ means that 15 gal of gasoline is used in 7 hr.

Chapter 2 Test, pp. 315–316

1. a. $(3, -1)$ **b.** $\sqrt{41}$ **c.** $(x - 3)^2 + (y + 1)^2 = 41$
2. a. x-intercept: $(-4, 0)$; y-intercepts: (0, 4), (0, −4)   **b.** No
3. a. $(x + 7)^2 + (y - 5)^2 = 4$ **b.** Center: $(-7, 5)$; Radius: 2
4. Yes   **5.** No   **6. a.** -12
b. $-2x^2 - 4xh - 2h^2 + 7x + 7h - 3$ **c.** $-4x - 2h + 7$
d. $\left(\frac{1}{2}, 0\right)$ and (3, 0)   **e.** (0, −3)   **f.** -1
7. a. -2 **b.** 0   **c.** $x = -2$ and $x = 2$
d. $(-\infty, -2) \cup (0, 2)$ **e.** $(-2, 0) \cup (2, \infty)$
f. $f(0) = -2$ is a relative minimum.
g. $f(-2) = 2$ and $f(2) = 2$ are relative maxima.
h. $(-\infty, \infty)$ **i.** $(-\infty, 2]$ **j.** Even
8. $\left(-\infty, -\dfrac{7}{3}\right) \cup \left(-\dfrac{7}{3}, \infty\right)$ **9.** $(-\infty, 4]$

10. a. $m = -\dfrac{3}{4}$ **b.** (0, 2)   **c.**

d. $\dfrac{4}{3}$ **e.** $-\dfrac{3}{4}$

11. $y = 3x + 12$ **12. a.** $\{-2\}$ **b.** $\{x \mid x < -2\}$ **c.** $\{x \mid x \geq -2\}$

13.

14.

15.

16.

17. Symmetric to the *y*-axis, *x*-axis, and origin.

18. Odd   **19.** Neither   **20. a.** 4   **b.** −5   **21.** 1   **22.** 0

23. Undefined   **24.** $(f \cdot g)(x) = \dfrac{x - 4}{x - 3}$; Domain: $(-\infty, 3) \cup (3, \infty)$

25. $\left(\dfrac{g}{f}\right)(x) = \dfrac{1}{(x - 3)(x - 4)}$; Domain: $(-\infty, 3) \cup (3, 4) \cup (4, \infty)$

26. $(g \circ h)(x) = \dfrac{1}{\sqrt{x - 5} - 3}$; Domain: $[5, 14) \cup (14, \infty)$

27. $f(x) = \sqrt[3]{x}$ and $g(x) = x - 7$ **28. a.** −1   **b.** −1

   c. −2   **d.** Undefined   **e.** $(-3, 0)$ **f.** $(-\infty, 2)$

29. a. $E(x) = 98x + 1833$ **b.** \$3303 million

30. a. $y = 92.3x + 1912$ **b.** \$3297 million

Chapter 2 Cumulative Review Exercises, p. 317

1. a. −1   **b.** $x = 0$ and $x = 3$ **c.** $(-4, \infty)$ **d.** $[-2, \infty)$

   e. $(1, \infty)$ **f.** $(-1, 1)$ **g.** $(-4, -1)$ **h.** −1

2. a. $(x + 6)^2 + (y - 2)^2 = 9$ **b.** Center: $(-6, 2)$; Radius: 3

3. $(g \circ f)(x) = \dfrac{1}{-x^2 + 3x}$; Domain: $(-\infty, 0) \cup (0, 3) \cup (3, \infty)$

4. $(g \cdot h)(x) = \dfrac{\sqrt{x + 2}}{x}$; Domain: $[-2, 0) \cup (0, \infty)$

5. $-2x - h + 3$ **6.** 0

7. *x*-intercepts: $(0, 0)$ and $(3, 0)$; *y*-intercept: $(0, 0)$

8.

9.

10. $y = -\dfrac{2}{5}x + \dfrac{1}{5}$ **11.** $|x - 7|$ or $|7 - x|$

12. $2(x - 4)(x^2 + 4x + 16)$ **13.** $\left\{ \dfrac{1}{6} \pm \dfrac{\sqrt{71}}{6}i \right\}$

14. $\{0, 1\}$ **15.** $\{1, 32\}$ **16.** $\left[-4, \dfrac{10}{3} \right]$ **17.** $(-3, -1]$

18. $\dfrac{3\sqrt{15} - 3\sqrt{11}}{2}$ **19.** $9c^2d\sqrt{2d}$ **20.** $\dfrac{uw}{2w + u}$

CHAPTER 3

Section 3.1 Practice Exercises, pp. 328–333

1. quadratic   **3.** vertex   **5.** downward   **7.** *k*

9. a. Downward   **b.** $(4, 1)$ **c.** $(3, 0)$ and $(5, 0)$ **d.** $(0, -15)$

   e.

   f. $x = 4$ **g.** Maximum: 1

   h. Domain: $(-\infty, \infty)$; Range: $(-\infty, 1]$

11. a. Upward   **b.** $(-1, -8)$ **c.** $(-3, 0)$ and $(1, 0)$ **d.** $(0, -6)$

   e.

   f. $x = -1$ **g.** Minimum: −8

   h. Domain: $(-\infty, \infty)$; Range: $[-8, \infty)$

13. a. Upward   **b.** $(1, 0)$ **c.** $(1, 0)$ **d.** $(0, 3)$

   e.

   f. $x = 1$ **g.** Minimum: 0

   h. Domain: $(-\infty, \infty)$; Range: $[0, \infty)$

15. a. Downward   **b.** $(-4, 1)$ **c.** $\left(-4 + \sqrt{5}, 0\right)$ and $\left(-4 - \sqrt{5}, 0\right)$

   d. $\left(0, -\dfrac{11}{5}\right)$

   e.

   f. $x = -4$ **g.** Maximum: 1

   h. Domain: $(-\infty, \infty)$; Range: $(-\infty, 1]$

17. a. $f(x) = (x + 3)^2 - 4$ **b.** $(-3, -4)$ **c.** $(-1, 0)$ and $(-5, 0)$

   d. $(0, 5)$

   e.

   f. $x = -3$ **g.** Minimum: −4

   h. Domain: $(-\infty, \infty)$; Range: $[-4, \infty)$

19. a. $p(x) = 3(x - 2)^2 - 19$ **b.** $(2, -19)$

   c. $\left(\dfrac{6 + \sqrt{57}}{3}, 0\right)$ and $\left(\dfrac{6 - \sqrt{57}}{3}, 0\right)$ **d.** $(0, -7)$

   e.

   f. $x = 2$ **g.** Minimum: −19

   h. Domain: $(-\infty, \infty)$; Range: $[-19, \infty)$

21. a. $c(x) = -2\left(x + \dfrac{5}{2}\right)^2 + \dfrac{33}{2}$ **b.** $\left(-\dfrac{5}{2}, \dfrac{33}{2}\right)$

   c. $\left(\dfrac{-5 + \sqrt{33}}{2}, 0\right)$ and $\left(\dfrac{-5 - \sqrt{33}}{2}, 0\right)$ **d.** $(0, 4)$

   e.
   f. $x = -\dfrac{5}{2}$ **g.** Maximum: $\dfrac{33}{2}$

   h. Domain: $(-\infty, \infty)$;

   Range: $\left(-\infty, \dfrac{33}{2}\right]$

23. $(7, -238)$ **25.** $(9, 28)$

27. a. Downward   **b.** (1, –3)   **c.** None   **d.** (0, –4)
e.

f. $x = 1$ **g.** Maximum: –3
h. Domain: $(-\infty, \infty)$; Range: $(-\infty, -3]$

29. a. Upward   **b.** $\left(\dfrac{3}{2}, -\dfrac{33}{4}\right)$

c. $\left(\dfrac{15 + \sqrt{165}}{10}, 0\right)$ and $\left(\dfrac{15 - \sqrt{165}}{10}, 0\right)$ **d.** (0, 3)

e.

f. $x = \dfrac{3}{2}$ **g.** Minimum: $-\dfrac{33}{4}$

h. Domain: $(-\infty, \infty)$;

Range: $\left[-\dfrac{33}{4}, \infty\right)$

31. a. 24 hr   **b.** 988,000   **33. a.** 0.55 sec   **b.** 4.5 m
35. a. 11.1 m   **b.** 6.2 m   **c.** 14 m   **37.** The numbers are 12 and 12.
39. The numbers are 5 and −5.   **41. a.** 40 ft by 80 ft   **b.** 3200 ft^2
43. a. $V(x) = -40x^2 + 240x$ **b.** $x = 3$; The sheet of aluminum should be folded 3 in. from each end.   **c.** 360 in.^{3}
45. a.

$y(t) = -0.000838t^2 + 0.0812t + 0.040$
b. 48 hr

c. 2 g

47. a. 15.3 sec   **b.** 16.7 sec
c. $v(x) = -0.1436x^2 - 0.4413x + 195.7$

d. 188.9 cm/sec
49. False   **51.** True   **53.** Discriminant is 0; one x-intercept
55. Discriminant is 57; two x-intercepts   **57.** Discriminant is −96; no x-intercepts   **59.** Graph g   **61.** Graph h   **63.** Graph f
65. Graph c   **67.** For a parabola opening upward, such as the graph of $f(x) = x^2$, the minimum value is the y-coordinate of the vertex. There is no maximum value because the y values of the function become arbitrarily large for large values of $|x|$.
69. No function defined by $y = f(x)$ can have two y-intercepts because the graph would fail the vertical line test.
71. Because a parabola is symmetric with respect to the vertical line through the vertex, the x-coordinate of the vertex must be equidistant from the x-intercepts. Therefore, given $y = f(x)$, the x-coordinate of the vertex is 4 because 4 is midway between 2 and 6. The y-coordinate of the vertex is $f(4)$.
73. $f(x) = 2(x - 2)^2 - 3$ **75.** $f(x) = -\dfrac{1}{3}(x - 4)^2 + 6$

77. $c = 9$ **79.** $b = 4$ or $b = -4$

Section 3.2 Practice Exercises, pp. 344–347

1. $\left(\dfrac{3}{2}, \dfrac{13}{2}\right)$ **3.** 5 and $-\dfrac{1}{2}$ **5.** $-x^4(x - 3)(4x - 3)(4x + 3)$
7. polynomial   **9.** is not   **11.** 1   **13.** False
15. up; down   **17.** 3; 4   **19.** 5   **21.** cross
23. f has at least one zero on the interval $[a, b]$.
25. origin   **27.** $-600x^9$ **29.** Down left and down right
31. Down left and up right   **33.** Up left and down right
35. Up left and up right   **37.** $-2, 5, -5$; each of multiplicity 1
39. $0, -4, \dfrac{5}{2}$; each of multiplicity 1   **41.** 0 (multiplicity 3), 5 (multiplicity 2)   **43.** 0 (multiplicity 1), −2 (multiplicity 3), −4 (multiplicity 1)   **45.** $0, \dfrac{5}{3}, -\dfrac{9}{2}, \pm\sqrt{3}$; each of multiplicity 1
47. $3 \pm \sqrt{5}$; each of multiplicity 1   **49. a.** Yes   **b.** No
c. No   **d.** Yes   **51. a.** Yes   **b.** Yes
c. No   **d.** No   **53. a.** Yes   **b.** $-\dfrac{5}{2}$
55. Not a polynomial function. The graph is not smooth.
57. Polynomial function **a.** Minimum degree 3   **b.** Leading coefficient positive; degree odd   **c.** −4 (odd multiplicity), 1 (odd multiplicity), 3 (odd multiplicity)
59. Polynomial function **a.** Minimum degree 6   **b.** Leading coefficient negative; degree even   **c.** −4 (odd multiplicity), −3 (odd multiplicity), −1 (even multiplicity), 2 (odd multiplicity), $\dfrac{7}{2}$ (odd multiplicity)
61. Not a polynomial function. The graph is not continuous.
63.

65.

67.

69.

71.

73.

75. False   **77.** False   **79.** True   **81.** False   **83.** False
85. True   **87. a.** $(0, 12) \cup (68, 184)$ **b.** $(12, 68) \cup (184, 200)$
c. 3   **d.** Degree 4; leading coefficient negative
e. 184 sec after launch   **f.** 2.85 G-forces
89. The x-intercepts are the real solutions to the equation $f(x) = 0$.
91. A function is continuous if its graph can be drawn without lifting the pencil from the paper.
93. b   **95.** a   **97. a.** $f(3) = 2; f(4) = 6$ **b.** By the intermediate value theorem, because $f(3) = 2$ and $f(4) = 6$, then f must take on every value between 2 and 6 on the interval $[3, 4]$.
c. $x = \dfrac{3 + \sqrt{17}}{2} \approx 3.56$

99. $V(t) = -0.0406t^3 + 0.154t^2 + 0.173t - 0.0024$

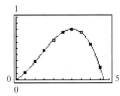

101. The end behavior is down to the left and up to the right.

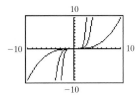

103. Window b is better.   **105.**

    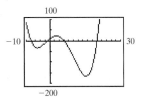

Section 3.3 Practice Exercises, pp. 357–360

1. a. Upward   **b.** $(5, -4)$ **c.** $x = 5$ **d.** Minimum value: -4
e. $(3, 0)$ and $(7, 0)$ **f.** $(0, 21)$

g.

3. $595\dfrac{29}{42}$; Check: $42(595) + 29 = 25{,}019$ ✓   **5.** $-2x^4$

7. Quotient: $(x + 3)$; Remainder: 0

9. Dividend: $f(x)$; Divisor: $d(x)$; Quotient: $q(x)$; Remainder: $r(x)$

11. $f(c)$ **13.** True   **15.** True

17. a. $3x + 12 + \dfrac{65}{2x - 5}$ **b.** Dividend: $6x^2 + 9x + 5$;

  Divisor: $2x - 5$; Quotient: $3x + 12$; Remainder: 65

  c. $(2x - 5)(3x + 12) + 65 = 6x^2 + 9x + 5$ ✓

19. $3x^2 + x + 4 + \dfrac{6}{x - 4}$ **21.** $4x^3 - 20x^2 + 13x + 4$

23. $3x^3 - 6x^2 + 2x - 4$ **25.** $x^3 + 4x^2 - 5x - 2 + \dfrac{5x}{x^2 + 5}$

27. $3x^2 + 1 + \dfrac{5x - 2}{2x^2 + x - 3}$ **29.** $x^2 + 3x + 9$

31. a. $2x^4 - 5x^3 - 5x^2 - 4x + 29$ **b.** $x - 3$
  c. $2x^3 + x^2 - 2x - 10$ **d.** -1 **33. a.** $x^3 - 2x^2 - 25x - 4$
  b. $x + 4$ **c.** $x^2 - 6x - 1$ **d.** 0   **35.** $4x - 9 + \dfrac{55}{x + 6}$

37. $5x + 3$ **39.** $-5x^3 + 10x^2 - 23x + 38 + \dfrac{-72}{x + 2}$

41. $4x^4 - 13x^3 - 97x^2 - 59x + 21$ **43.** $x^4 - 2x^3 + 4x^2 - 8x + 16$
45. a. 201   **b.** 201   **47. a.** -112 **b.** 0   **c.** 123   **d.** 0
49. a. -2 **b.** 0   **c.** 0   **d.** 18   **51. a.** No   **b.** Yes
53. a. No   **b.** Yes   **55. a.** Yes   **b.** Yes   **57. a.** Yes
  b. Yes   **59. a.** Yes   **b.** No   **61. a.** No   **b.** Yes
63. a. Yes   **b.** Yes   **c.** $\{2 \pm 5i\}$ **d.** $2 \pm 5i$

65. $f(x) = (x + 1)(2x - 9)(x + 4)$ **b.** $\left\{-1, \dfrac{9}{2}, -4\right\}$

67. a. $f(x) = 4\left(x - \frac{1}{4}\right)(5x + 1)(x + 2)$ or $f(x) = (4x - 1)(5x + 1)(x + 2)$
  b. $\left\{\dfrac{1}{4}, -\dfrac{1}{5}, -2\right\}$ **69. a.** $f(x) = (x - 3)(3x - 1)^2$
  b. $\left\{3, \dfrac{1}{3}\right\}$ **71.** $f(x) = x^3 - x^2 - 14x + 24$

73. $f(x) = x^4 - \dfrac{5}{2}x^3 + \dfrac{3}{2}x^2$ or $f(x) = 2x^4 - 5x^3 + 3x^2$

75. $f(x) = x^2 - 44$ **77.** $f(x) = x^3 + 2x^2 + 9x + 18$
79. $f(x) = 6x^3 - 23x^2 - 6x + 8$ **81.** $f(x) = x^2 - 14x + 113$
83. Direct substitution; -2 **85. a.** Yes   **b.** Yes   **c.** Yes
  d. No   **e.** Yes   **f.** No   **87.** False   **89.** $m = 28$
91. $m = -5$ **93.** $r = 0$ **95. a.** $V(x) = 2x^3 + 3x^2 - x$ **b.** 534 cm^3
97. The divisor must be of the form $(x - c)$, where c is a constant.
99. Compute $f(c)$ either by direct substitution or by using the remainder
  theorem. The remainder theorem states that $f(c)$ is equal to the
  remainder obtained after dividing $f(x)$ by $(x - c)$.
101. a. $f(x) = (x - 5)(x - i)(x + i)$
  b. $\{5, i, -i\}$ **103. a.** $f(x) = (x + 1)^2(x - \sqrt{3})(x + \sqrt{3})$
  b. $\{-1, \sqrt{3}, -\sqrt{3}\}$ **105. a.** 3   **b.** 3 is a solution.
  c. $\left\{3, -4, -\dfrac{2}{5}\right\}$

Section 3.4 Practice Exercises, pp. 373–377

1. a. $-4, \dfrac{2}{5}$ **b.** $\sqrt{10}, 4 - \sqrt{2}$ **c.** $-4, \dfrac{2}{5}, \sqrt{10}, 4 - \sqrt{2}$

  d. $6i, 3 + 8i$ **e.** $-4, \dfrac{2}{5}, \sqrt{10}, 6i, 3 + 8i, 4 - \sqrt{2}$

3. 0 (multiplicity 4); 2 (multiplicity 3); $\frac{7}{4}$ (multiplicity 2)
5. a. -4 **b.** -4 **7.** zeros   **9.** n **11.** Descartes'; $f(-x)$
13. greater than   **15.** $\pm 1, \pm 2, \pm 4$

17. $\pm 1, \pm 2, \pm 3, \pm 6, \pm\dfrac{1}{2}, \pm\dfrac{3}{2}, \pm\dfrac{1}{4}, \pm\dfrac{3}{4}$

19. $\pm 1, \pm 2, \pm 4, \pm 8, \pm\dfrac{1}{2}, \pm\dfrac{1}{3}, \pm\dfrac{2}{3}, \pm\dfrac{4}{3}, \pm\dfrac{8}{3}, \pm\dfrac{1}{4}, \pm\dfrac{1}{6}, \pm\dfrac{1}{12}$

21. 7 and $\dfrac{5}{3}$ **23.** $-\dfrac{1}{2}, 1$ **25.** $5, 1 \pm \sqrt{5}$ **27.** $\dfrac{1}{5}, \pm\sqrt{7}$

29. 2 (multiplicity 2), $\dfrac{1}{3}, -4$ **31.** $-2, 3 \pm i$ **33.** $\pm\sqrt{10}, \pm 3i$

35. one   **37.** 7   **39. a.** $2 \pm 5i, \pm\sqrt{7}$
  b. $[x - (2 + 5i)][x - (2 - 5i)](x - \sqrt{7})(x + \sqrt{7})$

  c. $\{2 \pm 5i, \pm\sqrt{7}\}$ **41. a.** $4 \pm i, \dfrac{4}{3}$

  b. $[x - (4 + i)][x - (4 - i)](3x - 4)$ **c.** $\left\{4 \pm i, \dfrac{4}{3}\right\}$

43. a. $-3 \pm 2i, -\dfrac{1}{4}, 1, -4$

  b. $[x - (-3 + 2i)][x - (-3 - 2i)](4x + 1)(x - 1)(x + 4)$

  c. $\left\{-3 \pm 2i, -\dfrac{1}{4}, 1, -4\right\}$ **45.** $f(x) = 5x^3 - 4x^2 + 180x - 144$

47. $f(x) = -5x^4 + 10x^3 + 60x^2 - 200x + 160$
49. $f(x) = 18x^3 + 39x^2 + 8x - 16$ **51.** $f(x) = x^6 - 14x^5 + 65x^4$
53. Positive: 3 or 1; Negative: 3 or 1
55. Positive: 6, 4, 2, or 0; Negative: 1
57. Positive: 0; Negative: 4, 2, or 0   **59.** Positive: 0; Negative: 0
61. 4 real zeros; $f(x)$ has 1 positive real zero, no negative real zeros, and
  the number 0 is a zero of multiplicity 3.
63. a. Yes   **b.** No   **65. a.** Yes   **b.** Yes   **67. a.** Yes   **b.** Yes

69. True   **71.** False   **73.** $\dfrac{7}{4}, -\dfrac{1}{2}$, and 4 (each with multiplicity 1)

75. $\pm\sqrt{5}, \dfrac{1}{2}, -2$, and -4 (each with multiplicity 1)

77. -3 (multiplicity 2) and $\frac{1}{2}$ (multiplicity 2)
79. 0 (multiplicity 2), -1 (multiplicity 2), and $\pm i\sqrt{10}$ (each multiplicity 1)
81. 0 (multiplicity 3) and $5 \pm 3i$ (each multiplicity 1)
83. -1 and $2 \pm 3i$ (each multiplicity 1)   **85.** False   **87.** False
89. True   **91.** All statements are true.

93. a. $f(2) = -2$ and $f(3) = 1$. Since $f(2)$ and $f(3)$ have opposite signs, the intermediate value theorem guarantees that f has at least one real zero between 2 and 3.

b. $\dfrac{7 \pm \sqrt{17}}{4}$; Furthermore, $\dfrac{7 + \sqrt{17}}{4} \approx 2.78$ is on the interval $[2, 3]$.

95. If a polynomial has real coefficients, then all imaginary zeros must come in conjugate pairs. This means that if the polynomial has imaginary zeros, there would be an even number of them. A third-degree polynomial has 3 zeros (including multiplicities). Therefore, it would have either 2 or 0 imaginary zeros, leaving room for either 1 or 3 real zeros.

97. $f(x)$ has no variation in sign, nor does $f(-x)$. By Descartes' rule of signs, there are no positive or negative real zeros. Furthermore, 0 itself is not a zero of $f(x)$ because x is not a factor of $f(x)$. Therefore, there are no real zeros of $f(x)$.

99. $n - 2$ possible imaginary zeros   **101.** The triangular front has a base of 6 ft and a height of 4 ft. The length is 9 ft.

103. Each dimension was decreased by 1 in.   **105.** The dimensions are either 2 cm by 3 cm or $-1 + \sqrt{13}$ cm by $\dfrac{1 + \sqrt{13}}{2}$ cm.

107. a. $(x + 3)(x - 1)(x^2 + 4)$ **b.** $(x + 3)(x - 1)(x + 2i)(x - 2i)$

109. a. $\left(x - \sqrt{5}\right)\left(x + \sqrt{5}\right)(x^2 + 7)$
b. $\left(x - \sqrt{5}\right)\left(x + \sqrt{5}\right)\left(x + \sqrt{7}i\right)\left(x - \sqrt{7}i\right)$

111. The fourth roots of 1 are $1, -1, i,$ and $-i$.

113. The number $\sqrt{5}$ is a real solution to the equation $x^2 - 5 = 0$ and a zero of the polynomial $f(x) = x^2 - 5$. However, by the rational zeros theorem, the only possible rational zeros of $f(x)$ are ± 1 and ± 5. This means that $\sqrt{5}$ is irrational.   **115.** -2

Section 3.5 Practice Exercises, pp. 392–398

1. $\dfrac{3}{2}, -\dfrac{3}{2}, 2, -2$ **3.** $h(1) = -6$; $h(1.9) = -60$; $h(1.99) = -600$

5. rational   **7.** x approaches infinity   **9.** vertical; c

11. c   **13.** left; down   **15.** denominator   **17.** $(-\infty, 5) \cup (5, \infty)$

19. $(-\infty, -1) \cup \left(-1, \dfrac{1}{4}\right) \cup \left(\dfrac{1}{4}, \infty\right)$ **21.** $(-\infty, \infty)$

23. a. 2   **b.** $-\infty$ **c.** ∞ **d.** 2   **e.** Never increasing
f. $(-\infty, 4) \cup (4, \infty)$ **g.** $(-\infty, 4) \cup (4, \infty)$
h. $(-\infty, 2) \cup (2, \infty)$ **i.** $x = 4$ **j.** $y = 2$

25. a. -1 **b.** ∞ **c.** ∞ **d.** -1 **e.** $(-\infty, -3)$
f. $(-3, \infty)$ **g.** $(-\infty, -3) \cup (-3, \infty)$ **h.** $(-1, \infty)$

i. $x = -3$ **j.** $y = -1$ **27.** $x = 4$ **29.** $x = 5$ and $x = -\dfrac{1}{2}$

31. None   **33.** $t = \dfrac{-2 + \sqrt{10}}{2}$ and $t = \dfrac{-2 - \sqrt{10}}{2}$

35. a. $y = 0$ **b.** Graph does not cross $y = 0$.   **37. a.** $y = 3$
b. $\left(\dfrac{7}{4}, 3\right)$ **39. a.** No horizontal asymptote   **b.** Not applicable

41. a. $y = 0$ **b.** $(-2, 0)$ **43. a.** $\dfrac{1 + \dfrac{3}{x} + \dfrac{1}{x^2}}{2 + \dfrac{5}{x^2}}$ **b.** 0   **c.** $y = \dfrac{1}{2}$

45. Vertical asymptote: $x = 0$; Slant asymptote: $y = 2x$
47. Vertical asymptote: $x = -6$; Slant asymptote: $y = -3x + 22$
49. Vertical asymptotes: $x = \sqrt{5}$ and $x = -\sqrt{5}$;
Slant asymptote: $y = x + 5$
51. Vertical asymptotes: $x = 2, x = -2,$ and $x = -1$;
Horizontal asymptote: $y = 0$
53. Slant asymptote: $y = 2x - 5$

55.

57.

59.   **61.**

63. a. $(-3, 0)$ and $\left(\dfrac{7}{2}, 0\right)$ **b.** $x = -2$ and $x = -\dfrac{1}{4}$
c. Horizontal asymptote: $y = \dfrac{1}{2}$ **d.** $\left(0, -\dfrac{21}{2}\right)$

65. a. $\left(\dfrac{9}{4}, 0\right)$ **b.** $x = 3$ and $x = -3$
c. Horizontal asymptote: $y = 0$ **d.** $(0, 1)$

67. a. $\left(\dfrac{1}{5}, 0\right)$ and $(-3, 0)$ **b.** $x = -2$
c. Slant asymptote: $y = 5x + 4$ **d.** $\left(0, -\dfrac{3}{2}\right)$

69.   **71.**

73.   **75.**

77.   **79.**

81.   **83.**

85.   **87.**

89.   **91.**

93. a. $C(x) = 109.94 + 20x$ **b.** $\overline{C}(x) = \dfrac{109.94 + 20x}{x}$
c. $\overline{C}(5) = 41.99$; $\overline{C}(30) = 23.67$; $\overline{C}(120) = 20.92$
d. The average cost would approach $20 per session. This is the same as the fee paid to the gym in the absence of fixed costs.

95. a. $\overline{C}_1(252) = 0.24$; $\overline{C}_1(366) = 0.16$; $\overline{C}_1(400) = 0.15$
b. $\overline{C}_1(436) = 0.17$; $\overline{C}_1(582) = 0.24$; $\overline{C}_1(700) = 0.28$
c. $\overline{C}_2(x) = \dfrac{79.95}{x}$
d. $\overline{C}_2(252) = 0.32$; $\overline{C}_2(400) = 0.20$; $\overline{C}_2(700) = 0.11$
97. a. \$200,000   **b.** \$600,000; \$1,800,000; \$5,400,000   **c.** 70%
99. a. $N(t) = -0.091t^3 + 3.48t^2 + 38.4t + 494$; $N(t)$ represents the total number of adults incarcerated in both prisons and jails, t years since 1980.
b. $R(t) = \dfrac{23.0t + 159}{-0.091t^3 + 3.48t^2 + 38.4t + 494}$; $R(t)$ represents the percentage of incarcerated adults who are in jail, t years since 1980.
c. $R(25) = 0.333$ means that in the year 2005, 33.3% of incarcerated adults were in jail.
101. a. $f(x) = \dfrac{1}{(x + 1)^2} + 3$
b. Domain: $(-\infty, -1) \cup (-1, \infty)$; Range: $(3, \infty)$
103. a. $f(x) = 2 + \dfrac{1}{x + 3}$ **b.**

105. The numerator and denominator share a common factor of $x + 2$. The value -2 is not in the domain of f. The graph will have a "hole" at $x = -2$ rather than a vertical asymptote.
107. $f(x) = \dfrac{x^2 + 4x + 3}{x^2 - 4x + 4}$ **109.** $f(x) = \dfrac{20x - 30}{x^2 - 3x - 10}$
111. a.

b.

c. Vertical asymptotes: $x = -2$ and $x = \dfrac{3}{5}$; Horizontal asymptote: $y = \dfrac{4}{5}$ **113. a.** No vertical asymptotes
b. On the window $[-9.4, 9.4, 1]$ by $[-6.2, 6.2, 1]$, the calculator shows a discontinuity or "hole" at $(4, 3)$. The graph on the standard viewing window does not show the discontinuity.

Problem Recognition Exercises, pp. 398–399
1. 2, -1, and -4 **2.** -2, 1, and 3 **3.** $(-2, 0)$, $(1, 0)$, and $(3, 0)$
4. $(2, 0)$, $(-1, 0)$, and $(-4, 0)$ **5.** $(2, 0)$, $(-1, 0)$, and $(-4, 0)$
6. $x = -2$, $x = 1$, and $x = 3$ **7.** Horizontal asymptote: $y = 1$
8. $\left(\dfrac{1 + \sqrt{281}}{10}, 1\right) \approx (1.78, 1)$ and $\left(\dfrac{1 - \sqrt{281}}{10}, 1\right) \approx (-1.58, 1)$
9. 4, $\sqrt{2}$, and $-\sqrt{2}$ **10.** 1, -2 (multiplicity 2)
11. $(1, 0)$ and $(-2, 0)$ **12.** $(4, 0)$, $\left(\sqrt{2}, 0\right)$, and $\left(-\sqrt{2}, 0\right)$
13. $(4, 0)$, $\left(\sqrt{2}, 0\right)$, and $\left(-\sqrt{2}, 0\right)$ **14.** $x = 1$ and $x = -2$
15. Horizontal asymptote: $y = 1$
16. $\left(\dfrac{-1 + \sqrt{85}}{7}, 1\right) \approx (1.17, 1)$ and $\left(\dfrac{-1 - \sqrt{85}}{7}, 1\right) \approx (-1.46, 1)$

17. Graph b   **18.** Graph a   **19. a.** $q(x) = 2x - 4$
b. $r(x) = 12x - 32$ **20.** $y = 2x - 4$ **21.** $\left(\dfrac{8}{3}, \dfrac{4}{3}\right)$
22. $\left\{\dfrac{8}{3}\right\}$; The solution to $r(x) = 0$ gives the x-coordinate of the point where the graph of f crosses its slant asymptote.

Section 3.6 Practice Exercises, pp. 407–412
1. $\left\{0, \dfrac{3}{2}, -4\right\}$ **3.** $\left\{-\dfrac{1}{2}\right\}$ **5.** $x = 5$ **7.** polynomial; 2
9. negative   **11. a.** $(-4, -1)$ **b.** $[-4, -1]$
c. $(-\infty, -4) \cup (-1, \infty)$ **d.** $(-\infty, -4] \cup [-1, \infty)$
13. a. $(-\infty, -3) \cup (-3, \infty)$ **b.** $(-\infty, \infty)$ **c.** $\{\ \}$ **d.** $\{-3\}$
15. a. $(-\infty, -2) \cup (0, 3)$ **b.** $(-\infty, -2] \cup [0, 3]$
c. $(-2, 0) \cup (3, \infty)$ **d.** $[-2, 0] \cup [3, \infty)$
17. a. $(0, 3) \cup (3, \infty)$ **b.** $[0, \infty)$ **c.** $(-\infty, 0)$ **d.** $(-\infty, 0] \cup \{3\}$
19. a. $(-\infty, \infty)$ **b.** $(-\infty, \infty)$ **c.** $\{\ \}$ **d.** $\{\ \}$
21. a. $\left\{\dfrac{3}{5}, 5\right\}$ **b.** $\left(\dfrac{3}{5}, 5\right)$ **c.** $\left[\dfrac{3}{5}, 5\right]$ **d.** $\left(-\infty, \dfrac{3}{5}\right) \cup (5, \infty)$
e. $\left(-\infty, \dfrac{3}{5}\right] \cup [5, \infty)$ **23. a.** $\{-3, 4\}$ **b.** $(-\infty, -3) \cup (4, \infty)$
c. $(-\infty, -3] \cup [4, \infty)$ **d.** $(-3, 4)$ **e.** $[-3, 4]$
25. a. $\{-6\}$ **b.** $\{\ \}$ **c.** $\{-6\}$ **d.** $(-\infty, -6) \cup (-6, \infty)$
e. $(-\infty, \infty)$ **27.** $\left(-1, \dfrac{4}{3}\right)$ **29.** $(-\infty, 0] \cup [3, \infty)$
31. $\left(\dfrac{-3 - \sqrt{59}}{5}, \dfrac{-3 + \sqrt{59}}{5}\right)$ **33.** $[-4, 1] \cup [3, \infty)$
35. $(-\infty, -2) \cup (-2, 0) \cup (4, \infty)$ **37.** $[-3, -1] \cup [1, 3]$
39. $\left(-\infty, -\dfrac{5}{2}\right) \cup (-2, 2)$ **41.** $[-1, 0] \cup \{3\}$
43. $\left(-\infty, \dfrac{3}{5}\right] \cup [5, \infty)$ **45.** $\left(-\infty, -\dfrac{1}{3}\right) \cup \left(0, \dfrac{5}{2}\right) \cup \left(\dfrac{5}{2}, 4\right)$
47. $(-\infty, \infty)$ **49.** $\{\ \}$ **51.** $\left(-\infty, \dfrac{3}{4}\right) \cup \left(\dfrac{3}{4}, \infty\right)$
53. $\{-2\}$ **55. a.** $(2, 3)$ **b.** $[2, 3)$ **c.** $(-\infty, 2) \cup (3, \infty)$
d. $(-\infty, 2] \cup (3, \infty)$ **57. a.** $(-\infty, 2) \cup (2, \infty)$
b. $(-\infty, 2) \cup (2, \infty)$ **c.** $\{\ \}$ **d.** $\{\ \}$ **59. a.** $[-2, 3)$
b. $(-2, 3)$ **c.** $(-\infty, -2] \cup (3, \infty)$ **d.** $(-\infty, -2) \cup (3, \infty)$
61. a. $\{0\}$ **b.** $\{\ \}$ **c.** $(-\infty, \infty)$ **d.** $(-\infty, 0) \cup (0, \infty)$
63. $(-1, 5]$ **65.** $[2, \infty)$ **67.** $(-3, -1] \cup [2, \infty)$
69. $\left(\dfrac{7}{2}, 6\right)$ **71.** $(-\infty, 2)$ **73.** $(-5, -2]$ **75.** $(-\infty, 2]$
77. $(-2, \infty)$ **79.** $(-3, -1) \cup (0, \infty)$ **81.** $(-\infty, 1) \cup (4, 7]$
83. $[2, 4) \cup (4, \infty)$ **85. a.** $s(t) = -16t^2 + 216t$
b. The shell will explode 6.75 sec after launch.   **c.** The spectators can see the shell between 1 sec and 6.75 sec after launch.
87. The car will stop within 250 ft if the car is traveling less than 50 mph.
89. a. The horizontal asymptote is $y = 0$ and means that the temperature will approach 0°C as time increases without bound.   **b.** More than 6 hr is required for the temperature to fall below 5°C.
91. The width should be between $2\sqrt{15}$ ft and $4\sqrt{5}$ ft. This is between approximately 7.7 ft and 8.9 ft.
93. $[-3, 3]$ **95.** $\left(-\infty, -\sqrt{5}\right] \cup \left[\sqrt{5}, \infty\right)$
97. $(-\infty, -6] \cup \left[\dfrac{3}{2}, \infty\right)$ **99.** $(-\infty, -6) \cup \left(\dfrac{3}{2}, \infty\right)$
101. $(-\infty, -2) \cup [0, \infty)$
103. a.

Sign of $(x - a)^2$:	$+$	$+$	$+$	$+$
Sign of $(b - x)$:	$+$	$+$	$-$	$-$
Sign of $(x - c)^3$:	$-$	$-$	$-$	$+$
Sign of $(x - a)^2(b - x)(x - c)^3$:	$-$	$-$	$+$	$-$
		a	b	c

b. (b, c) **c.** $(-\infty, a) \cup (a, b) \cup (c, \infty)$

105. The solution set to the inequality $f(x) < 0$ corresponds to the values of x for which the graph of $y = f(x)$ is below the x-axis.

107. Both the numerator and denominator of the rational expression are positive for all real numbers x. Therefore, the expression cannot be negative for any real number.

109. $[3, 5)$ **111.** $(-\infty, -32]$ **113.** $[2, 18)$ **115.** $[0, 2) \cup (4, 6]$

117. $(-3, 3)$ **119.** $(-\infty, -2\sqrt{5}) \cup (-4, 4) \cup (2\sqrt{5}, \infty)$

121. a. $0.552x^3 + 4.13x^2 - 1.84x - 10.2 < 0$

b.

c. The real zeros are approximately -7.6, -1.5, and 1.6.

d. $(-\infty, -7.6) \cup (-1.5, 1.6)$

123. a.

b.

c. The radius should be no more than 1.9 in. to keep the amount of aluminum to at most 90 in.^{2}.

Problem Recognition Exercises, p. 412

1. $(-28, -18]$ **2.** $\left\{ \dfrac{3 \pm \sqrt{19}}{2} \right\}$ **3.** $\left\{ \pm\dfrac{1}{5}, \dfrac{1}{2} \right\}$

4. $(-\infty, -2) \cup [0, \infty)$ **5.** $\{77\}$ **6.** $(-5, -1]$ **7.** $\left\{ -\dfrac{1}{5}, \dfrac{9}{5} \right\}$

8. $\left\{ \dfrac{133}{66} \right\}$ **9.** $\left\{ \dfrac{10}{7} \right\}$ **10.** $\{5\}$; The value -2 does not check.

11. $[4, 10]$ **12.** $(4, 10)$ **13.** $\{0.05\}$ **14.** $[1, 37]$ **15.** $\{9\}$

16. $\{-2\} \cup [0, 3] \cup [5, \infty)$ **17.** $\{ \}$

18. $\{5\}$; The value -4 does not check. **19.** $\{\pm 4, \pm\sqrt{7}\}$

20. $\left\{ \dfrac{3}{2}, -5 \right\}$ **21.** $\{ \}$ **22.** $\{17\}$ **23.** $(-\infty, -2) \cup (1, 4)$

24. $(-5, -1]$ **25.** $(-\infty, \infty)$ **26.** $\left(-\infty, -\dfrac{7}{5} \right) \cup \left(-\dfrac{7}{5}, \infty \right)$

27. $(-\infty, -8) \cup (14, \infty)$ **28.** $(-\infty, -4) \cup (1, \infty)$

29. $\left(-\infty, \dfrac{14}{5} \right)$ **30.** $[-3, 2]$

Section 3.7 Practice Exercises, pp. 417–421

1. $\{24\}$ **3.** $\{49\}$ **5.** directly **7.** constant; variation

9. a. 2; 4; 6; 8; 10 **b.** y is also doubled. **c.** y is also tripled.

d. increases **e.** decreases

11. $C = kr$ **13.** $\overline{C} = \dfrac{k}{n}$ **15.** $V = khr^2$ **17.** $E = \dfrac{ks}{\sqrt{n}}$

19. $c = \dfrac{kmn}{t^3}$ **21.** $k = \dfrac{5}{2}$ **23.** $k = 972$ **25.** $k = 5$

27. a. 2 **b.** 8 **29. a.** 225 mg **b.** 270 mg **c.** 315 mg

d. 30 lb **31. a.** \$0.40 per mile **b.** \$0.27 per mile

c. \$0.20 per mile **d.** 500 mi **33.** 638 ft

35. a. 333.2 ft **b.** 60 mph **37. a.** 6.4 days **b.** 12 people

39. 32 A **41.** \$1440 **43.** 27.37 **45.** 7.75 mph **47.** \$11,145.60

49. $y = 3.2x$ **51.** $y = \dfrac{12}{x}$ **53.** $y = \dfrac{3}{x}$ **55.** a and c

57. The variable P varies directly as the square of v and inversely as t.

59. a. 1600π m^2 **b.** The surface area is 4 times as great. Doubling the radius results in $(2)^2$ times the surface area of the sphere.

c. The intensity at 20 m should be $\frac{1}{4}$ the intensity at 10 m. This is because the energy from the light is distributed across an area 4 times are great. **d.** 50 lux

61. The intensity is $\frac{1}{100}$ as great. **63.** y will be $\frac{1}{4}$ its original value.

65. y will be 9 times its original value.

Chapter 3 Review Exercises, pp. 424–427

1. $(-5, 2)$

3. a. $f(x) = -2(x - 1)^2 + 8$ **f.**

b. Downward

c. $(1, 8)$

d. $(-1, 0)$ and $(3, 0)$

e. $(0, 6)$

g. $x = 1$

h. Maximum value: 8

i. Domain: $(-\infty, \infty)$; Range: $(-\infty, 8]$

5. a. 45 yd by 90 yd **b.** 4050 yd^2

7. a.

$E(a) = -0.476a^2 + 37.0a - 44.6$

b. 39 yr **c.** \$674

9. a. Up to the left and up to the right **f.**

b. Zeros: 3, -3, 1, -1 (each with multiplicity 1)

c. $(3, 0), (-3, 0), (1, 0), (-1, 0)$

d. $(0, 9)$ **e.** Even function

11. a. Down to the left and up to the right **f.**

b. Zeros: 0 (with multiplicity 3) and $4 \pm \sqrt{3}$ (each with multiplicity 1)

c. $(0, 0), (4 + \sqrt{3}, 0), (4 - \sqrt{3}, 0)$

d. $(0, 0)$ **e.** Neither even nor odd

13. False **15.** False

17. a. $-2x^2 + 3x - 9 + \dfrac{22x - 28}{x^2 + x - 3}$

b. Dividend: $-2x^4 + x^3 + 4x - 1$; Divisor: $x^2 + x - 3$; Quotient: $-2x^2 + 3x - 9$; Remainder: $22x - 28$

19. $2x^4 - 4x^3 + 8x^2 - 15x + 25 + \dfrac{-49}{x + 2}$ **21.** 65

23. a. No **b.** Yes **25. a.** Yes **b.** Yes

27. $f(x) = (3x - 2)(5x + 1)(x - 4)$ **29.** $f(x) = 8x^3 - 22x^2 - 7x + 3$

31. a. 4 **b.** $\pm 1, \pm 2, \pm 4, \pm 8$ **c.** -2 (multiplicity 2)

d. -2 (multiplicity 2), $\pm\sqrt{2}$ **33. a.** $3 \pm i, \pm\sqrt{5}$

b. $[x - (3 - i)][x - (3 + i)](x - \sqrt{5})(x + \sqrt{5})$

c. $\{3 \pm i, \pm\sqrt{5}\}$ **35.** $f(x) = 3x^3 - 5x^2 + 12x - 20$

37. Positive: 0; Negative: 2 or 0 **39. a.** Yes **b.** Yes

41. $x = \dfrac{5}{2}, x = -3$ **43. a.** $y = 0$ **b.** Graph does not cross $y = 0$.

45. a. No horizontal asymptote **b.** Not applicable

47. Vertical asymptotes: $x = -\dfrac{1}{3}, x = 5$; Horizontal asymptote: $y = -\dfrac{4}{3}$

49. **51.**

53. a. $(-\infty, -4)$ **b.** $(-\infty, -4] \cup \{1\}$ **c.** $(-4, 1) \cup (1, \infty)$

d. $[-4, \infty)$ **55. a.** $\{-5, -2\}$ **b.** $(-5, -2)$

c. $[-5, -2]$ **d.** $(-\infty, -5) \cup (-2, \infty)$

e. $(-\infty, -5] \cup [-2, \infty)$ **57.** $(-\infty, -3] \cup [6, \infty)$

59. $\{1\}$ **61.** $(-3, 2) \cup (4, \infty)$ **63.** $(-\infty, 0) \cup (0, 3]$

65. $(-\infty, 0) \cup \left(\dfrac{4}{5}, 2\right)$ **67. a.** $\overline{C}(x) = \dfrac{120 + 15x}{x}$

b. The trainer must have more than 120 sessions with his clients for his average cost to drop below \$16 per session.

69. $m = kw$ **71.** $y = \dfrac{kx\sqrt{z}}{t^3}$ **73.** $k = 2.4$ **75.** 5 lb

77. The force will be 16 times as great.

Chapter 3 Test, pp. 427–428

1. a. $f(x) = 2(x - 3)^2 - 2$ **b.** Upward   **f.**
c. $(3, -2)$ **d.** $(2, 0), (4, 0)$
e. $(0, 16)$ **g.** $x = 3$
h. Minimum value: -2
i. Domain: $(-\infty, \infty)$; Range: $[-2, \infty)$

2. a. Up to the left and up to the right

b. $\pm 1, \pm 3, \pm 7, \pm 21, \pm\dfrac{1}{2}, \pm\dfrac{3}{2}, \pm\dfrac{7}{2}, \pm\dfrac{21}{2}$

c. $\dfrac{7}{2}, -3$ (each multiplicity 1), and 1 (multiplicity 2)

d. $\left(\dfrac{7}{2}, 0\right), (-3, 0), (1, 0)$ **e.** $(0, -21)$ **f.** Neither even nor odd

g.

3. a. $-0.25x^9$ **b.** Up to the left and down to the right
c. 0 (multiplicity 3), 2 (multiplicity 2), -1 (multiplicity 4)

4. a. 4   **b.** $2, -2, 3i, -3i$ **c.** $(2, 0)$ and $(-2, 0)$ **d.** Even

5. a. No   **b.** Yes   **c.** No   **d.** Yes

6. a. $2x^2 + 2x + 4 + \dfrac{11x - 9}{x^2 - 3x + 1}$ **b.** Dividend: $2x^4 - 4x^3 + x - 5$;
Divisor: $x^2 - 3x + 1$; Quotient: $2x^2 + 2x + 4$; Remainder: $11x - 9$

7. a. Yes   **b.** No   **c.** No   **d.** Yes   **e.** 117

8. a. $\pm 2i, 4 \pm i$ **b.** $(x - 2i)(x + 2i)[x - (4 + i)][x - (4 - i)]$
c. $\{\pm 2i, 4 \pm i\}$ **9. a.** 4

b. $\pm 1, \pm 2, \pm 3, \pm 4, \pm 6, \pm 12, \pm\dfrac{1}{3}, \pm\dfrac{2}{3}, \pm\dfrac{4}{3}$ **c.** Yes   **d.** Yes

e. $\pm 1, \pm\dfrac{1}{3}, \pm\dfrac{2}{3}, \pm\dfrac{4}{3}, -2, -3$; From part (c), the value 2 itself
is not a zero of $f(x)$. Likewise, from part (d), the value -4 itself is not a zero. Therefore, 2 and -4 are also eliminated from the list of possible rational zeros.

f. $\dfrac{2}{3}$ and -3 **g.** $\dfrac{2}{3}, -3, \sqrt{2}, -\sqrt{2}$

h.

10. $f(x) = 15x^3 - 53x^2 - 30x + 8$
11. Positive: 3 or 1; Negative: 2 or 0
12. Vertical asymptote: $x = 7$; Slant asymptote: $y = 2x + 11$
13. Vertical asymptotes: $x = \dfrac{1}{2}, x = -\dfrac{1}{2}$; Horizontal asymptote: $y = 0$
14. Horizontal asymptote: $y = \dfrac{5}{3}$

15.

16.

17.

18. $(-4, 5)$ **19.** $(-4, 1) \cup (3, \infty)$ **20.** $(-\infty, -1] \cup [0, \infty)$

21. $\left(-\infty, -\dfrac{7}{3}\right) \cup \left(-\dfrac{7}{3}, \infty\right)$ **22.** $(-\infty, -3] \cup (2, \infty)$

23. $(-3, 3)$ **24.** $(-\infty, 0) \cup \left(\dfrac{3}{7}, 1\right)$ **25.** $E = kv^2$

26. $k = 4.2$ **27.** 294 ft^2 **28.** 178 lb
29. The pressure is 9 times as great.   **30. a.** 1000 rabbits after 1 yr,
1667 rabbits after 5 yr, and 1818 after 10 yr.   **b.** The rabbit
population will approach 2000 as t increases.
31. a. $y(20) = 140.3$ means that with 20,000 plants per acre, the yield
will be 140.3 bushels per acre; $y(30) = 172$ means that with 30,000
plants per acre, the yield will be 172 bushels per acre; $y(60) = 143.5$
means that with 60,000 plants per acre, the yield will be 143.5
bushels per acre.   **b.** 40,400   **c.** 183 bushels
32. a. $s(t) = -4.9t^2 + 98t$ **b.** 10 sec after launch
c. 490 m   **d.** $2.3 < t < 17.7$ sec

33. a.

$n(a) = 0.0011a^2 - 0.027a + 2.46$

b. 12 yr   **c.** 2.3 visits per year

Chapter 3 Cumulative Review Exercises, p. 429

1. a. $x = 4, x = -4$ **b.** Horizontal asymptote: $y = 2$
2. $f(x) = x^3 - 8x^2 + 25x - 26$
3. a. Down to the left and up to the right   **b.** $\dfrac{5}{2}$ (multiplicity 1) and -1
(multiplicity 2)   **c.** $\left(\dfrac{5}{2}, 0\right)$ and $(-1, 0)$ **d.** $(0, -5)$

e.

4. $\dfrac{10}{17} + \dfrac{11}{17}i$ **5.** Center: $(-4, 7)$; Radius: 3   **6.** $y = -\dfrac{5}{2}x + 2$
7. x-intercept: $(-9, 0)$; y-intercepts: $(0, 3), (0, -3)$
8.

9. $m = (v_0 t)^2 + t$ **10. a.** $\left(\dfrac{3 + \sqrt{7}}{2}, 0\right), \left(\dfrac{3 - \sqrt{7}}{2}, 0\right)$

b. $(0, 1)$ **c.** $\left(\dfrac{3}{2}, -\dfrac{7}{2}\right)$ **11.** $(5x^2 - y^3)(25x^4 + 5x^2y^3 + y^6)$

12. $\dfrac{y^{12}}{32x^3z^6}$ **13.** $5zy^7\sqrt[3]{2z^2x}$ **14.** $\dfrac{1}{x + 3}$ **15.** $(10, 32]$

16. $[-3, 9]$ **17.** $\{-5, 1\}$ **18.** $\left(\dfrac{9}{8}, \infty\right)$ **19.** $(0, \infty)$ **20.** $\{5\}$

CHAPTER 4

Section 4.1 Practice Exercises, pp. 440–444

1. $\{(2, 1), (3, 2), (4, 3)\}$ **3.** $y = x$ **5.** is   **7.** $x; x$

9. (b, a) **11.** Yes   **13.** No   **15.** Yes   **17.** No   **19.** No

21. Yes   **23.** No   **25.** No   **27.** No

29. Yes; If $f(a) = f(b)$, then $4a - 7 = 4b - 7$, which implies that $a = b$.

31. Yes; If $g(a) = g(b)$, then $a^3 + 8 = b^3 + 8$, which implies that $a = b$.

33. No; For example the points $(1, -3)$ and $(-1, -3)$ have the same y value but different x values. That is, $m(a) = m(b) = -3$, but $a \neq b$.

35. No; For example, the points $(2, 3)$ and $(-4, 3)$ have the same y value but different x values. That is, $p(a) = p(b) = 3$, but $a \neq b$.

37. Yes   **39.** No   **41.** Yes

43. a. Yes   **b.** The value $g(x)$ represents the number of years since the year 2010 based on the number of applicants to the freshman class, x.

45. a. If $f(a) = f(b)$, then $2a - 3 = 2b - 3$, which implies that $a = b$. The function is one-to-one.

b. $f^{-1}(x) = \dfrac{x + 3}{2}$

c.

47. $f^{-1}(x) = 4 - 9x$

49. $h^{-1}(x) = x^3 + 5$

51. $m^{-1}(x) = \sqrt[3]{\dfrac{x - 2}{4}}$

53. $c^{-1}(x) = \dfrac{5 - 2x}{x}$

55. $t^{-1}(x) = -\dfrac{2x + 4}{x - 1}$

57. $f^{-1}(x) = \sqrt[n]{b(x + c)} + a$

59. a.

b. Yes   **c.** $(-\infty, 0]$

d. $[-3, \infty)$

e. $f^{-1}(x) = -\sqrt{x + 3}$

f.

g. $[-3, \infty)$ **h.** $(-\infty, 0]$

61. a.

b. Yes   **c.** $[-1, \infty)$

d. $[0, \infty)$

e. $f^{-1}(x) = x^2 - 1; x \geq 0$

f. The range of f is $[0, \infty)$. Therefore, the domain of f^{-1} must be $[0, \infty)$.

g.

h. $[0, \infty)$ **i.** $[-1, \infty)$

63. Domain: $[0, 4)$; Range: $[0, \infty)$ **65.** $f^{-1}(x) = 3 - x; x \geq 3$

67. subtracts; $x - 6$ **69.** $f^{-1}(x) = \dfrac{x + 4}{7}$ **71.** $f^{-1}(x) = \sqrt[3]{x - 20}$

73. $f^{-1}(x) = \dfrac{x - 1}{8}$ **75.** $q^{-1}(x) = (x - 1)^5 + 4$

77.

79.

81. a. 12   **b.** 0.5   **c.** 10   **83.** True   **85.** False

87. a. $T(x) = 6.33x$ **b.** $T^{-1}(x) = \dfrac{x}{6.33}$

c. $T^{-1}(x)$ represents the mass of a mammal based on the amount of air inhaled per breath, x.

d. $T^{-1}(170) = 27$ means that a mammal that inhales 170 mL of air per breath during normal respiration is approximately 27 kg (this is approximately 60 lb—the size of a Labrador retriever).

89. a. $T(x) = 24x + 108$ **b.** $T^{-1}(x) = \dfrac{x - 108}{24}$

c. $T^{-1}(x)$ represents the taxable value of a home (in \$1000) based on x dollars of property tax paid on the home.

d. $T^{-1}(2988) = 120$ means that if a homeowner is charged \$2998 in property taxes, then the taxable value of the home is \$120,000.

91. $r(V) = \sqrt[3]{\dfrac{3V}{4\pi}}$ represents the radius of a sphere as a function of its volume.

93. The domain and range of a function and its inverse are reversed.

95. If a horizontal line intersects the graph of a function in more than one point, then the function has at least two ordered pairs with the same y-coordinate but different x-coordinates. This conflicts with the definition of a one-to-one function.

97. a. $f(8) = 3$ **b.** $f(32) = 5$ **c.** $f(2) = 1$ **d.** $f\left(\frac{1}{8}\right) = -3$

99. Let f be an increasing function. Then for every value a and b in the domain of f such that $a < b$ we have $f(a) < f(b)$. Now if $u \neq v$, then either $u < v$ or $v < u$. Then either $f(u) < f(v)$ or $f(v) < f(u)$. In either case, $f(u) \neq f(v)$, and f is one-to-one.

101. a. The graphs of f and g appear to be symmetric with respect to the line $y = x$. This suggests that f and g are inverses.

b.

c. The expressions $Y_1(Y_2)$ and $Y_2(Y_1)$ represent the composition of functions $(f \circ g)(x)$ and $(g \circ f)(x)$. In each case, $Y_1(Y_2)$ and $Y_2(Y_1)$ equal the value of x. This suggests that f and g are inverses.

Section 4.2 Practice Exercises, pp. 453–458

1. Yes   **3.** $f^{-1}(x) = \dfrac{6 - 2x}{x}$

5.

7. b^x **9.** increasing   **11.** $(-\infty, \infty)$

13. $(0, 1)$ **15.** is not

17. e; natural

19. a. 0.2   **b.** 2264.9364   **c.** 9.7385

d. 156.9925

21. a. 64   **b.** 0.1436   **c.** 0.0906

d. 0.1520   **23.** a, d

25. Domain: $(-\infty, \infty)$;
Range: $(0, \infty)$

27. Domain: $(-\infty, \infty)$;
Range: $(0, \infty)$

29. Domain: $(-\infty, \infty)$;
Range: $(0, \infty)$

31. Domain: $(-\infty, \infty)$;
Range: $(0, \infty)$

33. Domain: $(-\infty, \infty)$;
Range: $(2, \infty)$

35. Domain: $(-\infty, \infty)$;
Range: $(0, \infty)$

37. Domain: $(-\infty, \infty)$;
Range: $(-1, \infty)$

39. Domain: $(-\infty, \infty)$;
Range: $(-\infty, 0)$

41. Domain: $(-\infty, \infty)$;
Range: $(0, \infty)$

43. Domain: $(-\infty, \infty)$;
Range: $(-3, \infty)$

45. Domain: $(-\infty, \infty)$;
Range: $(-\infty, 2)$

47. a. 54.5982   **b.** 0.0408
   c. 36.8020   **d.** 23.1407

49. Domain: $(-\infty, \infty)$;
Range: $(0, \infty)$

51. Domain: $(-\infty, \infty)$;
Range: $(2, \infty)$

53. Domain: $(-\infty, \infty)$;
Range: $(-\infty, -3)$

55.

Compounding Option		n Value	Result
a.	Annually	1	$12,166.53
b.	Quarterly	4	$12,201.90
c.	Monthly	12	$12,209.97
d.	Daily	365	$12,213.89
e.	Continuously	n/a	$12,214.03

57. a. $26,997.18   **b.** $29,836.49   **c.** $34,665.06
59. a. $2200   **b.** $2214.03
   c. 5.5% simple interest results in less interest.
61. 3.8% compounded continuously for 30 yr results in more interest.
63. a. $A(28.9) = 5$ means that after 28.9 yr, the amount of ^{90}Sr
   remaining is 5 μg. After one half-life, the amount of substance
   has been halved.

b. $A(57.8) = 2.5$ means that after 57.8 yr, the amount of ^{90}Sr
   remaining is 2.5 μg. After two half-lives, the amount of substance
   has been halved, twice.
c. $A(100) = 0.909$ means that after 100 yr, the amount of ^{90}Sr
   remaining is approximately 0.909 μg.
65. a. Increasing
   b. $P(0) = 310$ means that in the year 2010, the U.S. population was
   approximately 310 million. This is the initial population in 2010.
   c. $P(10) = 341$ means that in the year 2020, the U.S. population will
   be approximately 341 million if this trend continues.
   d. $P(20) = 376$; $P(30) = 414$
   e. $P(200) = 2137$; In the year 2210 the U.S population will be
   approximately 2.137 billion. The model cannot continue
   indefinitely because the population will become too large to be
   sustained from the available resources.
67. a. 760 mmHg   **b.** 241 mmHg
69. a. $T(t) = 78 + 272e^{-0.046t}$ **b.** 250°F
   c. Yes; after 60 min, the cake will be approximately 95.2°F.
71. a. $39,000   **b.** It costs the farmer $84,800 to run the tractor for
   800 hr during the first year.

73. a. $P(2) = \dfrac{1}{16} = 0.0625$; $P(3) = \dfrac{1}{64} = 0.015625$;

   $P(4) = \dfrac{1}{256} \approx 0.003906$; $P(5) = \dfrac{1}{1024} \approx 0.000977$

   b. Decrease   **c.** Unlikely

75. a. $\{2\}$ **b.** $\{3\}$ **c.** $\{4\}$ **d.** x is between 2 and 3.
   e. x is between 3 and 4.
77. a. and **d.**
   b. Yes
   c. Domain: $(-\infty, \infty)$; Range: $(0, \infty)$
   e. Domain: $(0, \infty)$; Range: $(-\infty, \infty)$
   f. $f^{-1}(1) = 0$; $f^{-1}(2) = 1$; $f^{-1}(4) = 2$

79. a. ∞ **b.** 0   **c.** ∞ **d.** $-\infty$
81. The range of an exponential function is the set of positive real
   numbers; that is, 2^x is nonnegative for all values of x in the domain.
83. a. 0.375   **b.** 1.5   **c.** 6   **d.** 24
85. a. -1.5 **b.** -0.375 **c.** -0.0938 **d.** -0.0234

87. $\{0, 2\}$ **89. a.** e^{x+h} **b.** e^{2x} **c.** e^{x-h} **d.** 1   **e.** $\dfrac{1}{e^{2x}}$

91. $e^{2x} + 2 + e^{-2x}$ or $\dfrac{e^{4x} + 2e^{2x} + 1}{e^{2x}}$

93. $\left(\dfrac{e^x + e^{-x}}{2}\right)^2 - \left(\dfrac{e^x - e^{-x}}{2}\right)^2$

   $= \dfrac{1}{4}[(e^{2x} + 2 + e^{-2x}) - (e^{2x} - 2 + e^{-2x})] = \dfrac{1}{4}(4) = 1$

95. $\dfrac{e^x(e^h - 1)}{h}$

97. The graphs of Y_2 and Y_3 are close
   approximations of $Y_1 = e^x$
   near $x = 0$.

Section 4.3 Practice Exercises, pp. 468–472
1. $f^{-1}(x) = x^3 + 4$ **3.** 4   **5.** -2 **7.** logarithmic
9. exponential   **11.** common; natural   **13.** 0; 0   **15.** x; x

17. $x = 0$; vertical   **19.** $8^2 = 64$ **21.** $10^{-4} = \dfrac{1}{10,000}$

23. $4^0 = 1$ **25.** $a^c = b$ **27.** $\log_5 125 = 3$ **29.** $\log_{1/5} 125 = -3$
31. $\log 1,000,000,000 = 9$ **33.** $\log_a b = 7$ **35.** 2   **37.** 1

39. 8   **41.** −4   **43.** −1   **45.** 6   **47.** −3   **49.** −2

51. 5   **53.** −5   **55. a.** Between 4 and 5; 4.6705   **b.** Between 6 and 7; 6.0960   **c.** Between −1 and 0; −0.6198   **d.** Between −6 and −5; −5.4949   **e.** Between 5 and 6; 5.7482   **f.** Between −3 and −2; −2.2924

57. a. 4.5433   **b.** −1.7037   **c.** 2.5217   **d.** 2.5310   **e.** 22.0842   **f.** −7.2502   **59.** 11   **61.** 1   **63.** $x + y$

65. $a + b$ **67.** 0

69.

71.

73.

75. a.

b. Domain: $(-2, \infty)$; Range: $(-\infty, \infty)$ **c.** $x = -2$

77. a.

b. Domain: $(0, \infty)$; Range: $(-\infty, \infty)$ **c.** $x = 0$

79. a.

b. Domain: $(1, \infty)$; Range: $(-\infty, \infty)$ **c.** $x = 1$

81. a.

b. Domain: $(0, \infty)$; Range: $(-\infty, \infty)$ **c.** $x = 0$

83. $(-\infty, 8)$ **85.** $\left(-\dfrac{7}{6}, \infty\right)$ **87.** $(-\infty, \infty)$

89. $(-\infty, -3) \cup (4, \infty)$ **91.** $(-\infty, 4) \cup (4, \infty)$

93. a. 6.9   **b.** 3.2   **c.** Approximately 5012 times more intense

95. a. 150 dB   **b.** 90 dB   **c.** 1,000,000 times more intense

97. a. 2.3   **b.** 2   **c.** Lemon juice is more acidic.

99.

Sediment Class	Diameter d (in mm)	$\varphi(d)$
Cobble	128	−7
Gravel	8	−3
Fine gravel	4	−2
Course sand	1	0
Medium sand	0.5	1

101. a. $3^4 = x + 1$ **b.** $\{80\}$ **c.** The solution checks.

103. a. $4^3 = 7x - 6$ **b.** $\{10\}$ **c.** The solution checks.

105. 1   **107.** $-\dfrac{1}{2}$ **109. a.** 3   **b.** 3   **c.** They are the same.

111. a. 2   **b.** 2   **c.** They are the same.

113. a. 5   **b.** 5   **c.** They are the same.

115. a. 19.8 yr   **b.** $t(0.04) = 17.3$; $t(0.06) = 11.6$; $t(0.08) = 8.7$

117. a. 23.7797   **b.** −33.1787   **c.** Given a number $a \times 10^n$, then log $(a \times 10^n)$ is between n and $n + 1$, inclusive.

119. a. 0.6020   **b.** 0.1111   **c.** 0.0301   **d.** 0.0176

121. $(-\infty, 1) \cup (3, \infty)$ **123.** $(-4, \infty)$ **125.** $(6, \infty)$

127. a. The graphs match closely on the interval $(0, 2)$.   **129.** The graphs are the same.

b. $\ln 1.5 \approx 0.4010$

Problem Recognition Exercises, p. 473

1. a. $(-\infty, \infty)$ **b.** $\{3\}$ **c.** No x-intercept   **d.** $(0, 3)$ **e.** No asymptotes   **f.** Never increasing   **g.** Never deceasing   **h.** Graph E

2. a. $(-\infty, \infty)$ **b.** $(-\infty, \infty)$ **c.** $\left(\dfrac{3}{2}, 0\right)$ **d.** $(0, -3)$ **e.** No asymptotes   **f.** $(-\infty, \infty)$ **g.** Never deceasing   **h.** Graph G

3. a. $(-\infty, \infty)$ **b.** $[-4, \infty)$ **c.** $(1, 0)$ and $(5, 0)$ **d.** $(0, 5)$ **e.** No asymptotes   **f.** $(3, \infty)$ **g.** $(-\infty, 3)$ **h.** Graph N

4. a. $(-\infty, \infty)$ **b.** $(-\infty, \infty)$ **c.** $(2, 0)$ **d.** $\left(0, -\sqrt[3]{2}\right)$ **e.** No asymptotes   **f.** $(-\infty, \infty)$ **g.** Never decreasing   **h.** Graph B

5. a. $(-\infty, 1) \cup (1, \infty)$ **b.** $(-\infty, 0) \cup (0, \infty)$ **c.** None   **d.** $(0, -2)$ **e.** Vertical asymptote: $x = 1$; Horizontal asymptote: $y = 0$ **f.** Never increasing   **g.** $(-\infty, 1) \cup (1, \infty)$ **h.** Graph L

6. a. $(-\infty, -2) \cup (-2, \infty)$ **b.** $(-\infty, 3) \cup (3, \infty)$ **c.** $(0, 0)$ **d.** $(0, 0)$ **e.** Vertical asymptote: $x = -2$; Horizontal asymptote: $y = 3$ **f.** $(-\infty, -2) \cup (-2, \infty)$ **g.** Never decreasing   **h.** Graph A

7. a. $(-\infty, \infty)$ **b.** $(0, \infty)$ **c.** No x-intercept   **d.** $(0, 1)$ **e.** Horizontal asymptote: $y = 0$ **f.** $(-\infty, \infty)$ **g.** Never deceasing   **h.** Graph M

8. a. $(-\infty, \infty)$ **b.** $(-\infty, 0]$ **c.** $(-3, 0)$ **d.** $(0, -9)$ **e.** No asymptotes   **f.** $(-\infty, -3)$ **g.** $(-3, \infty)$ **h.** Graph C

9. a. $(-\infty, \infty)$ **b.** $[-1, \infty)$ **c.** $(3, 0)$ and $(5, 0)$ **d.** $(0, 3)$ **e.** No asymptotes   **f.** $(4, \infty)$ **g.** $(-\infty, 4)$ **h.** Graph I

10. a. $(-\infty, \infty)$ **b.** $(-\infty, 3]$ **c.** $(-3, 0)$ and $(3, 0)$ **d.** $(0, 3)$ **e.** No asymptotes   **f.** $(-\infty, 0)$ **g.** $(0, \infty)$ **h.** Graph D

11. a. $(-\infty, 3]$ **b.** $[0, \infty)$ **c.** $(3, 0)$ **d.** $(0, \sqrt{3})$ **e.** No asymptotes   **f.** Never increasing   **g.** $(-\infty, 3)$ **h.** Graph F

12. a. $[3, \infty)$ **b.** $[0, \infty)$ **c.** $(3, 0)$ **d.** No y-intercept   **e.** No asymptotes   **f.** $(3, \infty)$ **g.** Never decreasing   **h.** Graph K

13. a. $(-\infty, \infty)$ **b.** $(2, \infty)$ **c.** No x-intercept   **d.** $(0, 3)$ **e.** Horizontal asymptote: $y = 2$ **f.** $(-\infty, \infty)$ **g.** Never deceasing   **h.** Graph H

14. a. $(-2, \infty)$ **b.** $(-\infty, \infty)$ **c.** $(-1, 0)$ **d.** $(0, \ln 2)$ **e.** Vertical asymptote: $x = -2$ **f.** $(-2, \infty)$ **g.** Never deceasing   **h.** Graph J

Section 4.4 Practice Exercises, pp. 480–483

1. a. 5   **b.** 5   **3. a.** 2   **b.** 2   **5. a.** 4   **b.** 4

7. 1   **9.** x **11.** $\log_b x + \log_b y$ **13.** $p \log_b x$ **15.** $10; e$

17. $3 + \log_5 z$ **19.** $\log 8 + \log c + \log d$ **21.** $\log_2(x + y) + \log_2 z$

23. $\log_{12} p - \log_{12} q$ **25.** $1 - \ln 5$ **27.** $\log(m^2 + n) - 2$

29. $4 \log(2x - 3)$ **31.** $\dfrac{3}{7}\log_6 x$ **33.** $kt \ln 2$

35. $-1 + \log_7 m + 2\log_7 n$ **37.** $5\log_6 p - \log_6 q - 3\log_6 t$

39. $1 - \dfrac{1}{2}\log(a^2 + b^2)$ **41.** $\dfrac{1}{3}\ln x + \dfrac{1}{3}\ln y - \ln w - 2\ln z$

43. $\dfrac{1}{4}\ln(a^2 + 4) - \dfrac{3}{4}$

45. $\log 2 + \log x + 8 \log(x^2 + 3) - \dfrac{1}{2}\log(4 - 3x)$

47. $\dfrac{1}{3}\log_5 x + \dfrac{1}{6}$ **49.** 1 **51.** 2 **53.** 1 **55.** $\log_2(x^2 t)$

57. $\log_8\left(\dfrac{m^4}{n^3 p^2}\right)$ **59.** $\ln\sqrt{\dfrac{x + 1}{x - 1}}$ **61.** $\log\left(\dfrac{x^6}{\sqrt[3]{yz^2}}\right)$

63. $\log_4\left[\sqrt[3]{p}(q + 4)\right]$ **65.** $\ln\left[\dfrac{(x + 2)^3}{\sqrt{x}}\right]$ **67.** $\log(8y - 7)$

69. 1.392 **71.** 2.26 **73.** 2.01 **75.** 1.036 **77.** 2.366

79. a. Between 3 and 4 **b.** 3.9069 **c.** $2^{3.9069} \approx 15$

81. a. Between 0 and 1 **b.** 0.6826 **c.** $5^{0.6826} \approx 3$

83. a. Between -2 and -1 **b.** -1.7370 **c.** $2^{-1.7370} \approx 0.3$

85. 25.4800; $2^{25.4800} \approx 46{,}800{,}000$

87. -8.7128; $4^{-8.7128} \approx 5.68 \times 10^{-6}$ **89.** True **91.** False;

$\log_5\left(\dfrac{1}{125}\right) \neq \dfrac{1}{\log_5 125}$ (The left side is -3 and the right side is $\frac{1}{3}$.)

93. True **95.** False; $\log(10 \cdot 10) \neq (\log 10)(\log 10)$ (The left side is 2 and the right side is 1.) **97.** True

99. The given statement $\log_5(-5) + \log_5(-25)$ is not defined because the arguments to the logarithmic expressions are not positive real numbers.

101. a. $\dfrac{\ln(x + h) - \ln x}{h}$ **b.** $\dfrac{1}{h}[\ln(x + h) - \ln x] = \dfrac{1}{h}\ln\left(\dfrac{x + h}{x}\right)$

$= \ln\left(\dfrac{x + h}{x}\right)^{1/h}$

103. $\log\left(\dfrac{-b + \sqrt{b^2 - 4ac}}{2a}\right) + \log\left(\dfrac{-b - \sqrt{b^2 - 4ac}}{2a}\right)$

$= \log\left(\dfrac{-b + \sqrt{b^2 - 4ac}}{2a} \cdot \dfrac{-b - \sqrt{b^2 - 4ac}}{2a}\right)$

$= \log\left(\dfrac{b^2 - (b^2 - 4ac)}{4a^2}\right) = \log\left(\dfrac{4ac}{4a^2}\right)$

$= \log\left(\dfrac{c}{a}\right) = \log c - \log a$

105. $\log_2 9$

107. Let $M = \log_b x$ and $N = \log_b y$, which implies that $b^M = x$ and $b^N = y$. Then $\dfrac{x}{y} = \dfrac{b^M}{b^N} = b^{M-N}$. Writing the expression $\dfrac{x}{y} = b^{M-N}$ in logarithmic form, we have $\log_b\left(\dfrac{x}{y}\right) = M - N$, or equivalently, $\log_b\left(\dfrac{x}{y}\right) = \log_b x - \log_b y$ as desired.

109.

111.
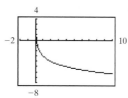

113. a. The graphs are the same.

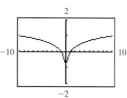

b. $\dfrac{1}{2}\log x^2 = \log(x^2)^{1/2}$

$= \log\sqrt{x^2}$

$= \log|x|$

Section 4.5 Practice Exercises, pp. 492–496

1. $\ln 400 = -0.2t$ **3.** $10^{4w+6} = 11{,}000$ **5.** $\left\{\dfrac{2\ln 3 + 7\ln 2}{14\ln 7}\right\}$

7. exponential **9.** x; y **11.** $\{4\}$ **13.** $\left\{\dfrac{1}{3}\right\}$ **15.** $\{-1\}$

17. $\{1\}$ **19.** $\{-15\}$ **21.** $\left\{\dfrac{19}{9}\right\}$

23. $\left\{\dfrac{\ln 87}{\ln 6}\right\}$; $t \approx 2.4925$ **25.** $\left\{\dfrac{\ln 1020}{\ln 19}\right\}$; $x \approx 2.3528$

27. $\left\{\dfrac{\log 128{,}100 - 3}{4}\right\}$; $x \approx 0.5269$ **29.** $\left\{\dfrac{\ln 3}{0.2}\right\}$ or $\{5\ln 3\}$;

$t \approx 5.4931$ **31.** $\left\{\dfrac{5\ln 3}{2\ln 5 - 6\ln 3}\right\}$; $x \approx -1.6286$

33. $\left\{\dfrac{\ln 2 - 4\ln 7}{3\ln 7 + 6\ln 2}\right\}$; $x \approx -0.7093$ **35.** $\{\ln 11\}$; $x \approx 2.3979$

37. $\{\ \}$ **39. a.** No **b.** Yes **c.** No

41. $\{-2\}$ **43.** $\{-9, 2\}$ **45.** $\{32\}$ **47.** $\{23\}$

49. $\{10^{4.1} - 17\}$; $p \approx 12{,}572.2541$ **51.** $\left\{\dfrac{4 - e^3}{3}\right\}$; $t \approx -5.3618$

53. $\{2\}$; The value -4 does not check. **55.** $\{32\}$ **57.** $\{25\}$; The value -5 does not check. **59.** $\{5\}$; The value 2 does not check.

61. $\{\ \}$; The values 5 and 3 do not check. **63.** 20 yr

65. 10 yr 2 months **67. a.** 72 mCi **b.** 5.3 days

69. Ocean: 14.1 m; Tahoe: 8.7 m; Erie: 3.5 m

71. Ocean: 93.8 m **73.** 69 min (1 hr 9 min)

75. a. 3.4×10^{-8} W/m^2 corresponds to 45.3 dB which indicates a moderate hearing impairment. **b.** 10^{-9} W/m^2

77. a. 12.8 **b.** 21 in. **79. a.** 3.16×10^{-9} mol/L

b. 5.01×10^{-3} mol/L **81.** 4 months **83.** 4 min $\leq t \leq$ 376 min

85. $f^{-1}(x) = \log_2(x + 7)$ **87.** $f^{-1}(x) = e^x - 5$

89. $f^{-1}(x) = \log(x - 1) + 3$ **91.** $f^{-1}(x) = 10^{x+9} - 7$

93. $\{-3, 3\}$ **95.** $\{900\}$ **97.** $\{2, -2\}$ **99.** $\{-10, 2\}$

101. $\{3, -3\}$ **103.** $\{3\}$ **105.** $\left\{e^4, \dfrac{1}{e^4}\right\}$; $x \approx 54.5982$, $x \approx 0.0183$

107. $\{\ \}$; The value -4 does not check.

109. $\left\{\ln\left(\dfrac{1}{2}\right), \ln 4\right\}$; $x \approx -0.6931$, $x \approx 1.3863$ **111.** If two exponential expressions of the same base are equal, then their exponents must be equal.

113. Take a logarithm of any base b on each side of the equation. Then apply the power property of logarithms to write the product of x and the $\log_b 4$. Finally divide both sides by $\log_b 4$.

115. $\{\log 13\}$; $x \approx 1.1139$ **117.** $\{e, e^4\}$; $x \approx 2.7183$, $x \approx 54.5982$

119. $\{100, 1\}$ **121.** $\{10{,}000\}$

123. $\{\ln(4 \pm \sqrt{10})\}$; $x \approx 1.9688$, $x \approx -0.1771$

125. $\left\{\dfrac{5}{3}\right\}$; The value $-\dfrac{5}{2}$ does not check.

127. $\{-1.4408, 2.8584\}$ **129.** $\{2.0960\}$

Section 4.6 Practice Exercises, pp. 506–512

1. a and e only **3.** $\log 80{,}600 = 2x - 4$ **5.** $f^{-1}(x) = 2 + \ln x$

7. $\left(-\infty, \dfrac{5}{3}\right)$ **9.** growth; decay **11.** logistic **13.** $k = -\dfrac{\ln\left(\dfrac{Q}{Q_0}\right)}{t}$

15. $D = 10^{(M-8.8)/5.1}$ **17.** $H^+ = 10^{-pH}$ **19.** $t = \dfrac{\ln\left(\dfrac{A}{P}\right)}{\ln(1 + r)}$

21. $k = Ae^{-E/(RT)}$ **23. a.** 4.4% **b.** 11.6 yr **25. a.** \$8000 **b.** 7 yr

27. a.

Country	Population in 2000 (millions)	Population in 2010 (millions)	$P(t) = P_0 e^{kt}$
Australia	19.0	22.6	$P(t) = 19e^{0.01735t}$
Taiwan	22.9	23.7	$P(t) = 22.9e^{0.00343t}$

b. Australia: 26.9 million; Taiwan: 24.5 million **c.** The population growth rate for Australia is greater. **d.** Australia: 2026; Taiwan: 2078

29. a.

Country	$P(t) = ab^t$	$P(t) = P_0e^{kt}$	Population in 2000
Costa Rica	$P(t) = 4.3(1.0135)^t$	$P(t) = 4.3e^{0.01341t}$	4.3 million
Norway	$P(t) = 4.6(1.0062)^t$	$P(t) = 4.6e^{0.00618t}$	4.6 million

b. Costa Rica: 2011; Norway: 2013   **c.** The population growth rate for Costa Rica is greater.   **31.** 2053 yr

33. a. $Q(t) = 2e^{-0.0079t}$ **b.** 28 yr

35. a. $Q(t) = 300e^{-0.0063t}$ **b.** 110 min

37. a. $P(t) = 2,000,000e^{-0.1155t}$ **b.** $P(0) = 2,000,000$; $P(6) = 1,000,000$; $P(12) = 500,000$; $P(60) = 1953$

39. a. $P(0) = 78$ means that on January 1, 1900, the U.S. population was approximately 78 million.   **b.** 338 million   **c.** 427 million   **d.** 2076   **e.** 0   **f.** 725 million   **41. a.** 150,000   **b.** 2,000,000   **c.** 3.3 months   **d.** 2,400,000   **43.** exponential   **45.** logarithmic

47. a. exponential

b. $y = 2.3(1.12)^x$

49. a. linear

b. $y = 2.28x - 4.08$

51. a. logarithmic

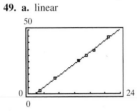

b. $y = 20.7 + 9.72 \ln x$

53. a. logistic

b. $y = \dfrac{18}{1 + 496e^{-1.1x}}$

55. a. $y = 1.4663(1.096)^t$ **b.** $y = 1.4663e^{0.09167t}$
c. Approximately 29 billion; This is unreasonable because this exceeds the total world population. A logistic model would probably fit the long-term trend better.
d. $y = \dfrac{889}{1 + 576e^{-0.0986t}}$ **e.** 877 million

57. a. $H(t) = 4.86 + 6.35 \ln t$ **b.** 24 yr   **c.** No, the tree will eventually die.

59. a. $y = -2920t + 29,200$ **b.** $y = 29,200(0.8)^t$ **c.** $14,600 and $0   **d.** $9568 and $3135

61. A visual representation of the data can be helpful in determining the type of equation or function that best models the data.

63. An exponential growth model has unbounded growth, whereas a logistic growth model imposes a limiting value on the dependent variable. That is, a logistic growth model has an upper bound restricting the amount of growth.

65. a. $t = -\dfrac{\ln\left(1 - \dfrac{Ar}{12P}\right)}{12 \ln\left(1 + \dfrac{r}{12}\right)}$ **b.** This represents the amount of time (in yr) required to completely pay off a loan of A dollars at interest rate r, by paying P dollars per month.

67. a. 0.23791   **b.** 0.35214   **c.** 0.42374   **d.** 0.39940   **e.** 0.29850   **f.** 0.18680   **g.** The value 0.23791 means that the number of additional computers infected with the virus between month 1 and month 2 increased at a rate of 237,910 per month.

h. The rate of change increases up through approximately month 4 and then begins to decrease. This can be visualized in the graph of the function.

Chapter 4 Review Exercises, pp. 515–517

1. No   **3.** Yes; If $f(a) = f(b)$, then $a^3 - 1 = b^3 - 1$, which implies that $a = b$.   **5.** Yes, because $(f \circ g)(x) = (g \circ f)(x) = x$

7. $f^{-1}(x) = \sqrt[3]{\dfrac{x + 5}{2}}$

9. a.

f.

b. Yes   **c.** $(-\infty, 0]$ **g.** $[-3, \infty)$
d. $[-3, \infty)$ **h.** $(-\infty, 0]$
e. $f^{-1}(x) = -\sqrt{x + 3}$

11. a. $f^{-1}(x) = \dfrac{x}{5280}$

b. f^{-1} represents the conversion from x feet to $f^{-1}(x)$ miles.   **c.** 4.2 mi

13. a.

15. a.

b. $(-\infty, \infty)$ **c.** $(0, \infty)$ **b.** $(-\infty, \infty)$ **c.** $(-\infty, 1)$
d. $y = 0$ **d.** $y = 1$

17. Increasing   **19. a.** $3456   **b.** $3563.16   **c.** 7.2% simple interest results in less interest.   **21.** $b^4 = x^2 + y^2$

23. $\log 1,000,000 = 6$ **25.** 4   **27.** -6 **29.** 0   **31.** 7

33. $(4, \infty)$ **35.** $(-\infty, \infty)$ **37.** $(-\infty, 4) \cup (4, \infty)$

39. a.

b. $(0, \infty)$ **c.** $(-\infty, \infty)$
d. $x = 0$

41. pH ≈ 4.5; acidic   **43.** 1   **45.** x **47.** $\log_b x - \log_b y$

49. $2 - \dfrac{1}{2}\log(c^2 + 10)$ **51.** $\dfrac{1}{3}\ln a + \dfrac{2}{3}\ln b - \ln c - 5\ln d$

53. $\log_5\left(\dfrac{y^4\sqrt{z}}{x^3}\right)$ **55.** $\ln\sqrt[4]{x + 3}$ **57.** 1.587

59. 3.2839; $7^{3.2839} \approx 596$ **61.** $\{5\}$

63. $\left\{\dfrac{\ln 51}{\ln 7}\right\}$; $x \approx 2.0206$ **65.** $\left\{\dfrac{\ln 3}{3\ln 4 - 2\ln 3}\right\}$; $x \approx 0.5600$

67. $\left\{\dfrac{\ln\left(\frac{2.989}{400}\right)}{-2}\right\}$; $t \approx 2.4483$ **69.** $\{\ln 8\}$; $x \approx 2.0794$

71. $\{-1\}$ **73.** $\{-4\}$ **75.** $\{e^{2.1} + 8\}$; $n \approx 16.1662$
77. $\{\ \}$; The value $-\dfrac{22}{3}$ does not check.   **79.** $\{32\}$

81. $f^{-1}(x) = \log_4 x$ **83. a.** 1.39 m; murky   **b.** 9.2 m

85. $t = -\dfrac{1}{k}\ln\left(\dfrac{T - T_f}{T_0}\right)$ **87. a.** Decreasing   **b.** 32 yr   **89.** 2800 yr

91. a. $Y_1 = 2.38(1.5)^x$ **b.**

Chapter 4 Test, pp. 518–519

1. a. $f^{-1}(x) = \sqrt[3]{\dfrac{x+1}{4}}$

b. $(f \circ f^{-1})(x) = 4\left(\sqrt[3]{\dfrac{x+1}{4}}\right)^3 - 1 = 4\left(\dfrac{x+1}{4}\right) - 1 = x + 1 - 1 = x$

$(f^{-1} \circ f)(x) = \sqrt[3]{\dfrac{4x^3 - 1 + 1}{4}} = \sqrt[3]{\dfrac{4x^3}{4}} = \sqrt[3]{x^3} = x$

2. a. Yes   **b.**   **3.** $f^{-1}(x) = \dfrac{4x+3}{x-1}$

4. a. Domain: $(-\infty, 0]$; Range: $(-\infty, 1]$ **b.** $f^{-1}(x) = -\sqrt{1-x}$
c. Domain: $(-\infty, 1]$; Range: $(-\infty, 0]$

5. a. Domain: $(0, \infty)$; Range: $(-\infty, \infty)$ **b.** $f^{-1}(x) = 10^x$
c. Domain: $(-\infty, \infty)$; Range: $(0, \infty)$

6. a. Domain: $(-\infty, \infty)$; Range: $(1, \infty)$ **b.** $f^{-1}(x) = \log_3(x-1)$
c. Domain: $(1, \infty)$; Range: $(-\infty, \infty)$

7. a.   **8. a.**

b. $(-\infty, \infty)$ **c.** $(2, \infty)$ **b.** $(-\infty, \infty)$ **c.** $(0, \infty)$
d. $y = 2$ **d.** $y = 0$

9. a.   **10. a.**

b. $(0, \infty)$ **c.** $(-\infty, \infty)$ **b.** $(-1, \infty)$ **c.** $(-\infty, \infty)$
d. $x = 0$ **d.** $x = -1$

11. $e^a = x + y$ **12.** $\log y = 4x + 3$ **13.** -2 **14.** 3
15. 8   **16.** -4 **17.** $a^2 + b^2$ **18.** 0   **19.** $\left(-\infty, \dfrac{7}{2}\right)$
20. $(-\infty, -5) \cup (5, \infty)$ **21.** $5 \ln x + 2 \ln y - \ln w - \dfrac{1}{3}\ln z$
22. $\dfrac{1}{2}\log(a^2 + b^2) - 4$ **23.** $\log_2\left(\dfrac{a^6 \sqrt[3]{c^2}}{b^4}\right)$ **24.** $\ln\sqrt{x+3}$
25. 1.783   **26.** -2.013 **27.** $\left\{-\dfrac{7}{3}\right\}$
28. $\left\{\dfrac{\ln 53}{\ln 5} - 3\right\}$; $x \approx -0.5331$
29. $\left\{\dfrac{7 \ln 2 - 3 \ln 3}{2 \ln 3 - \ln 2}\right\}$; $c \approx 1.0346$ **30.** $\left\{\dfrac{\ln 2}{4}\right\}$; $x \approx 0.1733$
31. $\{0\}$ **32.** $\{1\}$ **33.** $\{e^3 - 2\}$; $x \approx 18.0855$
34. $\{4\}$; The value -3 does not check.
35. $\{2\}$; The value -32 does not check.   **36.** $\{4\}$
37. $t = e^{(92-S)/k} - 1$ **38.** $t = \dfrac{\ln\left(\frac{A}{P}\right)}{n \ln\left(1 + \frac{r}{n}\right)}$
39. a. 6.1%   **b.** 26.4 yr
40. a. $P(t) = 10{,}000e^{0.1386t}$ **b.** Approximately 45 hr
41. a. 400 deer were present when the park service began tracking the
herd.   **b.** 536 deer   **c.** 680 deer   **d.** 15 yr   **e.** 0   **f.** 1200 deer
42. a. $y = 88.6 - 7.475 \ln x$ **b.** 70

Chapter 4 Cumulative Review Exercises, pp. 519–520

1. -3 **2.** $\dfrac{5\sqrt[3]{4x}}{2x}$ **3.** $(a - b)(a^2 + ab + b^2 - 1)$
4. 2.0×10^{10} **5.** $\left(-\infty, \dfrac{5}{2}\right] \cup \left[\dfrac{9}{2}, \infty\right)$ **6.** $\left\{\dfrac{2 \pm \sqrt{22}}{3}\right\}$
7. $\{6\}$; The value 1 does not check.   **8.** $\{9\}$
9. $(-5, -2) \cup (2, \infty)$ **10.** $\left\{\dfrac{4}{9}, -2\right\}$
11. $\{\pm 4, \pm 2\}$ **12.** $\{ \ \}$; The value $-\dfrac{9}{5}$ does not check.
13. $(-2, 4]$ **14.** $-1, -9, \pm i$
15. a. Upward   **b.** $(8, -9)$ **c.** Minimum point: $(8, -9)$
d. Minimum value: -9 **e.** $(5, 0)$ and $(11, 0)$ **f.** $(0, 55)$
g.   **h.** $x = 8$ **i.** $(-\infty, \infty)$
j. $[-9, \infty)$

16.   **17. a.** $x = 2$ **c.**
b. Horizontal
asymptote:
$y = 3$

18. a.   **b.** $y = -3$ **c.** $(-\infty, \infty)$
d. $(-3, \infty)$

19. 3   **20.** $f^{-1}(x) = (x - 1)^3 + 4$

CHAPTER 5

Section 5.1 Practice Exercises, pp. 530–535

1. system   **3.** substitution; addition   **5.** inconsistent
7. a. Yes   **b.** No   **9. a.** Yes   **b.** Yes   **11.** One solution
13. Infinitely many solutions; The equations are dependent.
15. $\{(-4, 3)\}$ **17.** $\{(-10, 3)\}$ **19.** $\left\{\left(-\dfrac{1}{2}, 1\right)\right\}$ **21.** $\{(-2, -1)\}$
23. $\{(1, -4)\}$ **25.** $\left\{\left(\dfrac{1}{2}, 1\right)\right\}$ **27.** $\left\{\left(\dfrac{79}{45}, \dfrac{2}{45}\right)\right\}$ **29.** $\{ \ \}$; The
system is inconsistent.   **31.** $\{(x, y) \mid 3x + y = 6\}$; The equations
are dependent.   **33.** $\{(0, 0)\}$ **35.** $\{(300, -100)\}$
37. $\left\{\left(-\dfrac{4}{41}, -\dfrac{71}{41}\right)\right\}$ **39.** $\{(6, 3)\}$ **41.** $\{ \ \}$
43. $\{(x, y) \mid 4x - y = 2\}$ **45.** $\{(1.6, 2.3)\}$ **47.** $\{(18, -17)\}$
49. 25 L of 36% solution and 15 L of 20% solution should be mixed.
51. 3.5 L should be replaced.
53. Cherry has 13 g of fat and Mint Chocolate Chunk has 17 g of fat.
55. She borrowed $3500 at 4.6% and $1500 at 6.2%.
57. One makes $1200 and the other makes $1500.
59. The sidewalk moves at 1 ft/sec and Josie walks 4 ft/sec on nonmoving
ground.   **61.** The speeds are 8 m/sec and 5 m/sec.
63. a. $C(x) = 1.25x + 54.3$ **b.** $B(x) = -0.32x + 64.5$
c. $\{(6.5, 62.4)\}$; The solution indicates that midyear in 2006, the per
capita consumption of beef and chicken was approximately equal at
62.4 lb each.
65. a. $C(x) = 52x + 480$ **b.** $R(x) = 100x$ **c.** 10 offices
d. The company will make money.

67. a.

b. 20 square units

69. a. $y = \frac{4}{5}x + \frac{7}{5}$ **b.** $y = -x + 5$ **c.** $(2, 3)$

71. The angles are $32°$ and $58°$.   **73.** $x = 60°, y = 88°$

75. For example: $x + y = 2; 2x + y = -1$ **77.** $C = 2$ and $D = 3$

79. $m = \frac{1}{3}$ and $b = -4$ **81.** $\{(\frac{1}{3}, -1)\}$

83. Marta bicycles 18 mph and runs 6 mph.   **85.** The truck was driven 144 mi in the city and 110 mi on the highway.

87. a. $\{(1600, 40)\}$ **b.** \$40   **c.** 1600 tickets

89. If the system represents two intersecting lines, then the lines intersect in exactly one point. The solution set consists of the ordered pair representing that point. If the lines in the system are parallel, then the lines do not intersect and the system has no solution. If the equations in a system of linear equations represent the same line, then the solution set is the set of points on the line.

91. If the system of equations reduces to a contradiction such as $0 = 1$, then the system has no solution and is said to be inconsistent.

93. $(9, 12, 15)$ and $(9, 40, 41)$ **95.** $|F_1| = 50(\sqrt{3} - 1)$ lb ≈ 36.6 lb and $|F_2| = 25\sqrt{2}(3 - \sqrt{3})$ lb ≈ 44.8 lb

97. $\{(2.017, -0.015)\}$ **99.** $\{(1.028, 15.772)\}$

Section 5.2 Practice Exercises, pp. 543–546

1. $\{(2, -2)\}$ **3.** $\{(x, y) \mid y = -\frac{3}{4}x + 1\}$ **5.** linear

7. plane   **9.** For example: $(0, 0, -2)$, $(0, 3, 0)$, and $(6, 0, 0)$

11. a. Yes   **b.** No   **13. a.** Yes   **b.** Yes

15. $\{(1, 4, -2)\}$ **17.** $\{(-2, 1, 3)\}$ **19.** $\{(1, 3, 0)\}$

21. No solution   **23.** $\{(\frac{1}{2}, \frac{1}{3}, -\frac{1}{6})\}$ **25.** Infinitely many solutions

27. $\{(0, 0, 0)\}$ **29.** $\{(1, -2, 3)\}$ **31.** $\{(6, -8, 2)\}$

33. $\{(1, 12, 17)\}$ **35.** No solution   **37.** He invested \$4000 in the large cap fund, \$2000 in the real estate fund, and \$2000 in the bond fund.   **39.** He made eight free-throws, six 2-point shots, and two 3-point shots.   **41.** b   **43.** The sides are 15 in., 18 in., and 22 in.

45. The angles are $16°$, $24°$, and $140°$.

47. a. The slopes are 5 and -1.   **c.**

b. $y = 2x^2 - 3x + 1$

49. $y = -x^2 - 4x + 6$ **51. a.** $y = \frac{1}{60}x^2 + \frac{11}{60}x + 6$ **b.** 10.6%

53. $a = 4, v_0 = 18$, and $s_0 = 10$ **55. a.** $y = 7x_1 + 10x_2 + 24$

b. \$168,000   **57.** The set of all ordered pairs that are solutions to a linear equation in three variables forms a plane in space.

59. Pair up two equations in the system and eliminate a variable. Choose a different pair of two equations from the system and eliminate the same variable. The result should be a system of two linear equations in two variables. Solve this system using either the substitution or addition method. Then back substitute to find the third variable.

61. $\{(2, -1, 0, 4)\}$ **63.** $\{(-13, 11, 10)\}$

65. a. $x^2 + y^2 - 4x + 6y - 12 = 0$ **b.** Center: $(2, -3)$; Radius: 5

67. $2x + 3y - 4z = 1$ **69.** $A = 5, B = 3, C = -1$

Section 5.3 Practice Exercises, pp. 554–556

1. a. $y = \frac{3}{2}x - 3; y = \frac{3}{2}x - 3$ **b.** Infinitely many solutions

c. $\{(x, y) \mid y = \frac{3}{2}x - 3\}$ **3.** $\{(0, 4, 1)\}$

5. $3x - 4 + \dfrac{4x - 1}{x^2 + 2x + 1}$ **7.** fraction decomposition

9. linear; $Ax + B$ **11.** $\dfrac{A}{x + 4} + \dfrac{B}{2x - 3}$ **13.** $\dfrac{A}{x} + \dfrac{B}{x - 2}$

15. $\dfrac{A}{w - 2} + \dfrac{B}{w + 3}$ **17.** $\dfrac{A}{x} + \dfrac{B}{x + 5} + \dfrac{C}{(x + 5)^2}$

19. $\dfrac{A}{2x} + \dfrac{Bx + C}{x^2 + 9}$ **21.** $\dfrac{Ax + B}{x^2 + 5} + \dfrac{Cx + D}{(x^2 + 5)^2}$

23. $\dfrac{A}{x - 4} + \dfrac{Bx + C}{x^2 + x + 4}$

25. $\dfrac{A}{x} + \dfrac{B}{x + 2} + \dfrac{C}{(x + 2)^2} + \dfrac{D}{(x + 2)^3} + \dfrac{Ex + F}{x^2 + 2x + 7} + \dfrac{Gx + H}{(x^2 + 2x + 7)^2}$

27. $\dfrac{3}{x + 4} + \dfrac{-7}{2x - 3}$ **29.** $\dfrac{5}{x} + \dfrac{3}{x - 2}$ **31.** $\dfrac{1}{w - 2} + \dfrac{5}{w + 3}$

33. $\dfrac{4}{x} + \dfrac{-3}{x + 5} + \dfrac{1}{(x + 5)^2}$ **35.** $\dfrac{5}{2x} + \dfrac{4x + 1}{x^2 + 9}$

37. $x - 3 + \dfrac{4}{x} + \dfrac{2x - 7}{x^2 + 7}$ **39.** $\dfrac{2x - 1}{x^2 + 5} + \dfrac{3x}{(x^2 + 5)^2}$

41. $\dfrac{3}{x - 4} + \dfrac{2x + 1}{x^2 + x + 4}$ **43.** $\dfrac{3x + 1}{x^2 + 2} + \dfrac{x - 5}{x^2 + 3}$

45. $2x - 5 + \dfrac{4}{x + 2} - \dfrac{-3}{x - 5}$ **47.** $3x - 4 + \dfrac{4}{x + 1} + \dfrac{-5}{(x + 1)^2}$

49. a. $(x - 3)^2 (x + 5)$ **b.** $\dfrac{2}{x - 3} + \dfrac{1}{(x - 3)^2} + \dfrac{-5}{x + 5}$

51. a. $(x + 2)^3$ **b.** $\dfrac{3}{x + 2} + \dfrac{-4}{(x + 2)^2} + \dfrac{1}{(x + 2)^3}$

53. Partial fraction decomposition is a procedure in which a rational expression is written as a sum of two or more simpler rational expressions.   **55.** A proper rational expression is a rational expression in which the degree of the numerator is less than the degree of the denominator.

57. a. $\dfrac{1}{n} - \dfrac{1}{n + 2}$

b. $\left(\dfrac{1}{1} - \dfrac{1}{3}\right) + \left(\dfrac{1}{2} - \dfrac{1}{4}\right) + \left(\dfrac{1}{3} - \dfrac{1}{5}\right) + \left(\dfrac{1}{4} - \dfrac{1}{6}\right) + \left(\dfrac{1}{5} - \dfrac{1}{7}\right) + \cdots$

c. 0   **d.** $\dfrac{3}{2}$ **59.** $\dfrac{1}{ax} - \dfrac{b}{a(a + bx)}$ **61.** $\dfrac{2}{e^x + 1} + \dfrac{3}{e^x + 2}$

Section 5.4 Practice Exercises, pp. 562–565

1.

3.

5. $(3, -1)$ **7.** nonlinear

9. a.

11. a.

b. $\{(2, 2), (0, -2)\}$ **b.** $\{(-3, 4), (4, -3)\}$

13. a.

15. a.

b. $\{(4, 2)\}$ **b.** $\{ \}$

17. a.

b. $\{(-1, -1), (0, 0), (1, 1)\}$

19.

21.

19. $\{(2, 1), (2, -1), (-2, 1), (-2, -1)\}$

21. $\{(4, -1), (-4, 1)\}$

23. $\left\{\left(1, \sqrt{2}\right), \left(1, -\sqrt{2}\right), \left(-1, \sqrt{2}\right), \left(-1, -\sqrt{2}\right)\right\}$

25. $\{\ \}$ **27.** $\left\{(3, 1), \left(\frac{7}{3}, \frac{5}{3}\right)\right\}$ **29.** $\{(0, 5)\}$ **31.** $\{(1, 1)\}$

33. $\{(0, 9), (-3, 0), (3, 0)\}$ **35.** $\left\{\left(1, \frac{1}{3}\right), \left(-1, \frac{1}{3}\right), \left(1, -\frac{1}{3}\right), \left(-1, -\frac{1}{3}\right)\right\}$

37. The numbers are 5 and 7. **39.** The numbers are 5 and 2.

41. The numbers are 12 and 10. **43.** The numbers are 9 and 12 or -9 and -12. **45.** The rectangle is 10 m by 8 m.

47. The floor is 20 ft by 12 ft. **49.** The truck is 6 ft by 6 ft by 8 ft.

51. The aquarium is 24 in. by 12 in. by 16 in. **53.** The legs are 4 ft and 7 ft. **55.** The ball will hit the ground at the point $\left(128\sqrt{3}, -128\right)$ or approximately $(221.7, -128)$.

57. A system of linear equations contains only linear equations, whereas a nonlinear system has one or more equations that are nonlinear.

59. a. $0.69 = A_0 e^{-3k}$ **b.** $0.655 = A_0 e^{-4k}$ **c.** $k \approx 0.052$
d. $A_0 \approx 0.81 \ \mu\text{g/dL}$ **e.** $0.43 \ \mu\text{g/dL}$

61. a. $k \approx 0.058$ **b.** The original population is 40,000.
c. The population will reach 300,000 approximately 35 hr after the culture is started. **63.** Infinitely many solutions

65. $\{(10, 100)\}$ **67.** $\{(2, 1)\}$ **69.** $\left\{(2, 1), \left(\frac{7}{5}, \frac{6}{5}\right)\right\}$

71. $\{(1, 3, 1), (-1, -3, -1)\}$ **73. a.** $(0, -5)$ and $(4, 3)$
b. $y = 2x - 5$ for $0 \le x \le 4$

75. $\{(2.359, 5.584)\}$ **77.** $\{(1.538, 6.135), (-1.538, 6.135), (3.693, -5.135), (-3.693, -5.135)\}$

79. $\{\ \}$

Section 5.5 Practice Exercises, pp. 573–576

1.

3.

5. $\{(-2, 2)\}$ **7.** linear **9.** above; horizontal **11.** II

13. a. Yes **b.** No **c.** No **15. a.** No **b.** Yes **c.** Yes

17. a.

b. The bounding line would be drawn as a dashed line.
c. The bounding line would be dashed and the graph would be shaded strictly below the line.

23.

25.

27.

29.

31. a.

b. The region outside the circle would be shaded.
c. The shaded region would contain points on the circle (solid curve) and points outside the circle.

33.

35.

37.

39.

41.

43. a. Yes **b.** No **c.** No

45. a. Yes **b.** No **c.** Yes **d.** No

47.

49.

51.

53. The solution set is $\{\ \}$.

55.

57.

d.

e.

59.

61.

2. a.

b.

c. { }

63. The solution set is { }.   **65.** $x \le 6$ **67.** $y \ge -2$

69. $x + y \le 18$

71. a. $x + y \le 9$

   b. $x \ge 3$

   c. $y \le 4$

   d. $x \ge 0$

   e. $y \ge 0$

f.

d.

e. { }

3. a. $\{(0, 0)\}$

b.

73. a. $x + y \le 60{,}000$

   b. $y \ge 2x$

   c. $x \ge 0$

   d. $y \ge 0$

e.

c.

75. $x^2 + y^2 < 9$
    $x > 0$
    $y > 0$

77. $y > x - 1$
    $y > -4x - 16$
    $y < -\frac{1}{4}x + \frac{11}{4}$

79. a. $(x + 12)^2 + (y + 9)^2 \le 256$ **b.** Yes; The center of Hawthorne is 15 km from the earthquake.   **81.** If the inequality is strict—that is, posed with $<$ or $>$— then the bounding line or curve should be dashed.

83. Find the solution set to each individual inequality in the system. Then to find the solution set for the system of inequalities, take the intersection of the solution sets to the individual inequalities.

85.

87.

4. a. $\{(2, 1), (5, 4)\}$

b.

c.

Problem Recognition Exercises, p. 576

1. a.

b.

c. $\{(1, 2)\}$

Section 5.6 Practice Exercises, pp. 582–586

1. $x + y \le 70$ **3.** $3x + 4y \ge 60$ **5.** $y \le 3x$

7. $60 < x \le 80$ **9.** linear   **11.** feasible

13. $z = 0.80x + 1.10y$ **15.** $z = 0.62x + 0.50y$

17. a. $x = 7, y = 5$ **b.** Maximum value: 31

19. a. $x = 10, y = 30$ **b.** Minimum value: 37,000

21. a. Vertices: $(0, 0)$, $(20, 40)$, $(60, 0)$

b. $x = 60$, $y = 0$
c. Maximum: 15,000

23. a. Vertices: $(0, 50)$, $(10, 20)$, $(20, 0)$

b. $x = 20$, $y = 0$
c. Minimum: 60

25. a. Vertices: $(0, 0)$, $(0, 40)$, $(8, 40)$, $(36, 12)$, $(36, 0)$

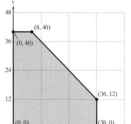

b. $x = 36$, $y = 12$
c. Maximum: 6480

27. a. 1520 at $(8, 6)$ **b.** 1660 at $(4, 9)$

29. a. Profit: $z = 160x + 240y$ **c.**
b. $x \geq 0$
$y \geq 0$
$x \leq 120$
$y \leq 90$
$240x + 320y \leq 48,000$

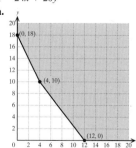

d. $(0, 0)$, $(0, 90)$, $(80, 90)$, $(120, 60)$, $(120, 0)$
e. Profit at $(0, 0)$: $z = 0$
Profit at $(0, 90)$: $z = 21,600$
Profit at $(80, 90)$: $z = 34,400$
Profit at $(120, 60)$: $z = 33,600$
Profit at $(120, 0)$: $z = 19,200$
f. The greatest profit is realized when 80 kitchen tables and 90 dining room tables are produced.   **g.** The maximum profit is $34,400.

31. a. 280 large trees and 120 small trees would maximize profit.
b. The maximum profit is $13,400.
c. In this case, the nursery should have 360 large trees and no small trees.

33. a. The company should make 8 trips with the small truck and 6 trips with the large truck.
b. The minimum cost is $1860.

35. a. The manufacturer should produce 600 grill A units and 500 grill B units to maximize profit.
b. The maximum profit is $114,000.
c. In this case, the manufacturer should produce 1200 grill A units and 0 grill B units.

37. a. The farmer should plant 900 acres of corn and 300 acres of soybeans.
b. The maximum profit is $138,000.
c. In this case, 500 acres of corn and 700 acres of soybeans should be planted.

39. Linear programming is a technique that enables us to maximize or minimize a function under specific constraints.

41. The feasible region for a linear programming application is found by first identifying the constraints on the relevant variables. Then the regions defined by the individual constraints are graphed. The intersection of the constraints define the feasible region.

Chapter 5 Review Exercises, pp. 588–590

1. a. Yes   **b.** No   **3.** One solution   **5.** $\{(2, -3)\}$ **7.** $\{\ \}$
9. Milk has 300 mg per cup and spinach has 240 mg per cup.
11. The speed of the plane in still air is 420 mph and the speed of the wind is 60 mph.
13. $\{(-1, 2, -3)\}$ **15.** Infinitely many solutions
17. There are 1000 seats in Section A, 5000 in Section B, and 6000 in Section C.
19. $y = -x^2 + 5x + 2$
21. $\dfrac{A}{x + 2} + \dfrac{B}{x - 1}$ **23.** $\dfrac{A}{x} + \dfrac{B}{x^2} + \dfrac{C}{2x + 3}$
25. $\dfrac{Ax + B}{x^2 + 1} + \dfrac{Cx + D}{x^2 + 4}$
27. Use long division to divide the numerator by the denominator. Then perform partial fraction decomposition on the expression (remainder/divisor).
29. $\dfrac{5}{x + 4} + \dfrac{2}{(x + 4)^2}$ **31.** $\dfrac{-2}{x} + \dfrac{4x + 1}{x^2 + 5}$
33. a.   **b.** $\{(-1, 2), (2, 5)\}$

35. $\{(2, 4), (2, -4), (-2, 4), (-2, -4)\}$ **37.** $\{(4, 2)\}$
39. The numbers are 8 and 6 or -8 and -6.
41. The billboard is 12 ft by 24 ft.
43. a.   **b.**

45.   **47.**

49. a. No   **b.** Yes

51.   **53.** $\{\ \}$

55. $z = 24x + 20y$

57. a.

b. $x = 4$, $y = 10$ **c.** 620

Chapter 5 Test, pp. 590–591

1. a. Yes **b.** No **2. a.** No **b.** Yes
3. a. Yes **b.** No **4.** {(1, 1)} **5.** {(5, 10)}
6. {(x, y) | 10x − 4y = 3} **7.** { } **8.** {(1, −4, 3)}
9. {(−2, 5, 3)} **10.** { } **11.** {(0, −3), (7, 4)}
12. {(1, 3), (1, −3), (−1, 3), (−1, −3)}
13. {(5, −2), (−5, 2)} **14.** $\left\{ \left(-2, \dfrac{5}{4} \right) \right\}$

15. The manager should mix 4 lb of peanuts with 16 lb of the 45% mixture.
16. One runner runs 6 m/sec and the other runs 4 m/sec.
17. Dylan invested $3000 in the risky stock, $7000 in the second stock, and $5000 in the third stock.
18. The numbers are 7 and 4. **19.** The screen is 44 in. by 33 in.

20. $y = 2x^2 - 4x + 1$ **21.** $\dfrac{A}{x + 1} + \dfrac{B}{3x - 2}$

22. $\dfrac{A}{x} + \dfrac{B}{x^2} + \dfrac{C}{x^3} + \dfrac{D}{x - 3} + \dfrac{Ex + F}{x^2 + 5x + 1} + \dfrac{Gx + H}{(x^2 + 5x + 1)^2}$

23. $\dfrac{-7}{x + 3} + \dfrac{2}{2x + 5}$ **24.** $\dfrac{6}{x + 2} - \dfrac{4}{(x + 2)^2}$

25. $x - 2 - \dfrac{3}{x} + \dfrac{8}{x^2} - \dfrac{1}{x - 4}$ **26.** $\dfrac{-3}{x} + \dfrac{4x - 2}{x^2 + 7}$

27. $\dfrac{7x + 1}{x^2 + 2} + \dfrac{3}{x^2 + 9}$

28.   **29.**

30.   **31.**

32.   **33.** $z = 2.4x + 0.55y$

34. a. $x = 2, y = 8$ **b.** Minimum value: 48

35. a.

b. $x = 12, y = 36$ **c.** Maximum value: 37,800
36. a. 30 scoops of each type of protein powder should be mixed to maximize protein content. **b.** The maximum protein content is 1140 g. **c.** In this case, 24 scoops of whey protein should be mixed with 36 scoops of soy protein.

Chapter 5 Cumulative Review Exercises, pp. 591–592

1. $\left\{ \dfrac{1 \pm \sqrt{57}}{4} \right\}$ **2.** {−2, −4} **3.** {±4, ±i}

4. { }; The value $-\dfrac{12}{7}$ does not check. **5.** $\left\{ \dfrac{-1 + \ln 40}{2} \right\}$ **6.** $(-\infty, 2)$

7. $(-\infty, -5) \cup (1, \infty)$ **8.** $\dfrac{-5}{x - 3} + \dfrac{2}{(x - 3)^2}$

9. a. $(f \circ g)(x) = 50x^2 + 5x - 1$
  b. $(g \circ f)(x) = 10x^2 - 15x + 1$

10. $f^{-1}(x) = x^3 + 2$ **11.** 3.4454 **12.** $\dfrac{19}{2}$ **13.** $y = 3x - 7$

14. $3i$ (multiplicity 1); $-3i$ (multiplicity 1); 1 (multiplicity 2)

15. a.   **16. a.**

b. $(-\infty, \infty)$ **c.** $[-3, \infty)$ **b.** $(3, \infty)$ **c.** $(-\infty, \infty)$

17. a.

b. $(-\infty, \infty)$ **c.** $(-\infty, \infty)$
18. { } **19.** {(1, 2, 3)} **20.** {(1, 2), (1, −2), (−1, 2), (−1, −2)}
21.   **22.** $-2x - h + 5$

23. $\dfrac{6\sqrt{5x}}{x}$ **24. a.** $A(t) = 8000e^{0.062t}$ **b.** 11.2 yr
25. $y = 76.8$

CHAPTER 6

Section 6.1 Practice Exercises, pp. 600–603

1. {(1, −4)} **3.** {(4, 3, 2)} **5.** matrix **7.** Elementary
9. Interchange rows 2 and 3. **11.** Multiply row 1 by 3 and replace the original row 1 with the result. **13.** Add 3 times row 1 to row 2 and replace the original row 2 with the result.

15. $\begin{bmatrix} -3 & 2 & -1 & | & 4 \\ 8 & 0 & 4 & | & 12 \\ 0 & 2 & -5 & | & 1 \end{bmatrix}$ **17.** $\begin{bmatrix} 4 & -14 & | & 2 \\ 3 & -5 & | & 7 \end{bmatrix}$

19. $\begin{bmatrix} 1 & 0 & 0 & | & 2 \\ 0 & 1 & 0 & | & \frac{6}{7} \\ 0 & 0 & 1 & | & 12 \end{bmatrix}$ **21.** $\begin{aligned} -4x + 6y &= 11 \\ -3x + 9y &= 1 \end{aligned}$

23. $\begin{aligned} x + 4y + 3z &= 8 \\ y + 2z &= 12 \\ z &= 6 \end{aligned}$ **25.** $\begin{aligned} x &= 8 \\ y &= -9 \\ z &= \tfrac{3}{2} \end{aligned}$

27. $\begin{bmatrix} -3 & 6 & | & 6 \\ 1 & 4 & | & 2 \end{bmatrix}$ **29.** $\begin{bmatrix} 3 & 12 & | & 6 \\ -3 & 6 & | & 6 \end{bmatrix}$ **31.** $\begin{bmatrix} 0 & 6 & | & 4 \\ -3 & 6 & | & 6 \end{bmatrix}$

33. $\begin{bmatrix} 1 & 5 & 6 & | & 2 \\ 4 & -2 & -3 & | & 10 \\ 2 & 1 & 5 & | & 1 \end{bmatrix}$ **35.** $\begin{bmatrix} 1 & 5 & 6 & | & 2 \\ 2 & 1 & 5 & | & 1 \\ 1 & -\frac{1}{2} & -\frac{3}{4} & | & \frac{5}{2} \end{bmatrix}$

37. $\begin{bmatrix} 1 & 5 & 6 & | & 2 \\ 0 & -9 & -7 & | & -3 \\ 4 & -2 & -3 & | & 10 \end{bmatrix}$ **39.** No; The element on the main diagonal in the second row is not 1.

41. Yes **43.** No; The elements on the main diagonal are not 1 with zeros above and below. **45.** Yes **47.** $\{(-2, -3)\}$

49. $\{(4, 7)\}$ **51.** $\{(5, -8)\}$ **53.** $\{(1, 2, 3)\}$ **55.** $\{(0, 1, 3)\}$

57. $\{(7, -2, 1)\}$ **59.** $\{(0, 2, -4)\}$ **61.** $\{(-6, -4, 3)\}$

63. $\{(1, 2, 3, 4)\}$ **65.** $\{(-10, 1, 0, 1)\}$ **67.** He borrowed $10,000 from his parents, $8000 from the credit union, and $2000 from the bank. **69.** She spent 4 nights in Washington, 2 nights in Atlanta, and 8 nights in Dallas.

71. $\dfrac{2}{x + 3} + \dfrac{3}{x - 2} - \dfrac{1}{(x - 2)^2}$

73. Interchanging two rows in an augmented matrix represents interchanging two equations in a system of equations. This operation does not affect the solution set of the system.

75. Reduced row-echelon form is the same format as row-echelon form with the added condition that all elements above the leading 1's must be 0's.

77. $\{(9.32, -17.48, 12.93)\}$

79. a. $2400a + 800b + c = 36,000$
$2000a + 500b + c = 30,000$
$3000a + 1000b + c = 44,000$
b. [rref([A]) screen]
c. $y = 12x_1 + 4x_2 + 4000$
d. $36,000

81. a. $9a - 3b + c = -7.28$
$a - b + c = 3.68$
$100a + 10b + c = 18.2$
b. [rref([A]) screen]
c. $f(x) = -0.32x^2 + 4.2x + 8.2$

Section 6.2 Practice Exercises, pp. 609–612

1. Yes **3.** $\{(x, y) \mid 3x - 5y = 10\}$ **5.** $\{\ \}$ **7.** True

9. False **11.** inconsistent **13.** No solution **15.** Infinitely many solutions **17.** One solution **19.** Infinitely many solutions

21. a. $\{(5, 0)\}$ **b.** $\{(x, y) \mid x + 2y = 5\}$ **c.** $\{\ \}$

23. a. $\{(3, 5, 0)\}$ **b.** $\{\ \}$ **c.** $\{(-6z + 3, -4z + 5, z) \mid z$ is any real number$\}$ **25.** $\{\ \}$ **27.** $\{(x, y) \mid 2x + 7y = 10\}$

29. $\{\ \}$ **31.** $\{(-2z + 16, 3z - 5, z) \mid z$ is any real number$\}$

33. $\{(4, 0, 2)\}$ **35.** $\{(5z + 3, -2z + 6, z) \mid z$ is any real number$\}$

37. $\{(x, y, z) \mid 2x + 3y + 4z = 12\}$ **39.** $\{(-3z + 5, z + 4, z) \mid z$ is any real number$\}$ **41.** $\{(-4z + 7, 2, z) \mid z$ is any real number$\}$

43. $\{\ \}$ **45. a.** $(3, -3, 1)$ **b.** $(9, 0, 4)$ **c.** $(-3, -6, -2)$

47. For example: $(0, 6, 0), (4, 5, 1), (8, 4, 2)$

49. For example: $(0, 0, 1), (0, 2, 0), (3, 0, 0)$

51. a. $180 + 190 = x_1 + x_3$ **b.** $x_1 + x_2 = 180 + 220$
c. $x_3 + 120 = x_2 + 90$
d. $x_1 \quad + x_3 = 370$
$x_1 + x_2 \quad = 400$
$x_2 - x_3 = 30$
e. $\begin{bmatrix} 1 & 0 & 1 & | & 370 \\ 0 & 1 & -1 & | & 30 \\ 0 & 0 & 0 & | & 0 \end{bmatrix}$
f. $x_1 = 250$ vehicles per hour; $x_2 = 150$ vehicles per hour
g. $220 \le x_1 \le 270$ vehicles per hour; $130 \le x_2 \le 180$ vehicles per hour

53. a. $x_1 = 60$ vehicles per hour; $x_2 = 210$ vehicles per hour; $x_3 = 170$ vehicles per hour
b. $40 \le x_1 \le 90$ vehicles per hour; $190 \le x_2 \le 240$ vehicles per hour; $150 \le x_3 \le 200$ vehicles per hour

55. a. $80x + 400y + 480z = 9280$
$50x + 350y + 400z = 7800$
$75x + 525y + 600z = 10,500$

b. $\{\ \}$ **c.** The system of equations reduces to a contradiction. There are no values for x, y, and z that can simultaneously meet the conditions of this problem.

57. $5(-2z + 16) + 7(3z - 5) - 11z = 45$ ✓
$3(-2z + 16) + 5(3z - 5) - 9z = 23$ ✓
$(-2z + 16) + (3z - 5) - z = 11$

59. $(0, 0, 0)$ is the only solution.

61. Infinitely many solutions; $\{(2z, 3z, z) \mid z$ is any real number$\}$

63. If a row of the reduced row-echelon form results in a contradiction (that is, zeros to the left of the vertical bar and a nonzero element to the right), then the system is inconsistent.

65. The equations are equivalent, meaning that they all have the same solution set. The points in the solution set represent a common plane in space.

67. $\{\ \}$ **69.** $\{(-2z + 16, 3z - 5, z) \mid z$ is any real number$\}$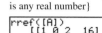

71. $\{(x, y, z) \mid x + \frac{3}{2}y + 2z = 6\}$ or $\{(x, y, z) \mid 2x + 3y + 4z = 12\}$

Section 6.3 Practice Exercises, pp. 624–630

1. $-a; -a$ **3.** $\frac{2}{3}$ **5.** $(5, 2)$ **7.** order; rows; columns

9. square **11.** The order of the matrices must be the same, and the corresponding elements must be equal. **13.** $[-a_{ij}]$

15. columns; rows **17.** False **19. a.** 2×3 **b.** None of these

21. a. 3×1 **b.** Column matrix **23. a.** 2×2 **b.** Square matrix **25.** $\sqrt{5}$ **27.** $\frac{1}{3}$ **29.** 2

31. $x = 4, y = 2, z = 10$ **33.** $\begin{bmatrix} 4 & -6 & -9 \\ -\frac{3}{5} & -1 & -7 \end{bmatrix}$

35. $\begin{bmatrix} -3 & 1 \\ 13.2 & \frac{5}{2} \\ \frac{7}{3} & 3\sqrt{2} \end{bmatrix}$ **37.** $\begin{bmatrix} -4 & 7 \\ 0.2 & \frac{7}{6} \\ -\frac{2}{3} & 6 + \sqrt{2} \end{bmatrix}$ **39.** Not possible

41. $\begin{bmatrix} 6 & 12 & -27 \\ 3 & 3\sqrt{3} & \frac{3}{2} \end{bmatrix}$ **43.** $\begin{bmatrix} 3 & -8 & -10 \\ -16 & -2\sqrt{3} - 63 & -\frac{17}{3} \end{bmatrix}$

45. $\begin{bmatrix} -4 & -16 & 20 \\ -12 & -4\sqrt{3} - 36 & -\frac{14}{3} \end{bmatrix}$ **47.** $\begin{bmatrix} 9 & 8 & -38 \\ -8 & 2\sqrt{3} - 45 & -\frac{7}{3} \end{bmatrix}$

49. $X = \begin{bmatrix} \frac{3}{2} & 1 \\ 5 & \frac{7}{2} \end{bmatrix}$ **51.** $X = \begin{bmatrix} \frac{1}{5} & -2 \\ \frac{2}{5} & \frac{11}{5} \end{bmatrix}$ **53.** $X = \begin{bmatrix} 0 & \frac{8}{5} \\ \frac{1}{5} & -\frac{13}{10} \end{bmatrix}$

55. a. Yes; 4×1 **b.** No **57. a.** Yes; 5×5 **b.** Yes; 1×1

59. a. $\begin{bmatrix} -1 & 17 \\ -2 & 41 \end{bmatrix}$ **b.** $\begin{bmatrix} 22 & 31 \\ 13 & 18 \end{bmatrix}$ **c.** $\begin{bmatrix} 19 & 27 \\ 45 & 64 \end{bmatrix}$

61. a. $\begin{bmatrix} -6 & 8 & 38 \\ -12 & -24 & 36 \\ -13 & 4 & 69 \end{bmatrix}$ **b.** $\begin{bmatrix} -23 & 9 \\ 6 & 62 \end{bmatrix}$ **c.** Not possible

63. a. $\begin{bmatrix} 19 \\ 26 \\ 5 \end{bmatrix}$ **b.** Not possible **c.** $\begin{bmatrix} 79 & -5 & 2 \\ 4 & 27 & 45 \\ -1 & 12 & 53 \end{bmatrix}$

65. a. $[\frac{2}{3}]$ **b.** $\begin{bmatrix} -\frac{1}{3} & -\frac{1}{6} \\ 2 & 1 \end{bmatrix}$ **c.** Not possible

67. a. $\begin{bmatrix} 4 & 8 & 20 & 24 \\ -6 & -12 & -30 & -36 \end{bmatrix}$ **b.** Not possible **c.** Not possible **69. a.** $[-25]$ **b.** $[-25]$ **c.** $[25]$

71. $\begin{bmatrix} 3.1 & -2.3 \\ 1.1 & 6.5 \end{bmatrix}$ **73.** $\begin{bmatrix} \frac{9}{5} & -3 & \sqrt{6} \\ 5 & \frac{1}{2} & 2 \\ 3 & 0 & 1 \end{bmatrix}$

75. a. $M - D = \begin{bmatrix} \$1967 & \$1396 \\ \$2044 & \$1462 \end{bmatrix}$; This represents the profit that the
dealer clears for each model of car.

b. $F = 1.06D = \begin{bmatrix} \$21,161 & \$18,136 \\ \$21,927 & \$18,914 \end{bmatrix}$

77. a. $CN_1 = \begin{bmatrix} \$46 \\ \$40 \\ \$2.40 \end{bmatrix}$; The matrix CN_1 represents the additional cost for
24 text messages and 100 extra minutes for each of the cell phone plans.

b. $CN_3 = \begin{bmatrix} \$46 & \$23.60 & \$7.50 \\ \$40 & \$9.60 & \$0 \\ \$2.40 & \$5.60 & \$3 \end{bmatrix}$; The matrix CN_3 represents the
additional cost per month for each plan. For example, row 1 represents
the cost for plan A for months 1, 2, and 3, respectively.

79. a. $B + CN_1 + T = \begin{bmatrix} \$97.95 \\ \$103.03 \\ \$77.30 \end{bmatrix}$; This matrix represents the total
cost (including the base cost and tax) for each plan for 24 text
messages and 100 additional minutes.   **b.** Plan B

81. a. $A = \begin{bmatrix} -1 & 0 & 4 \\ 1 & 3 & 2 \end{bmatrix}$ **b.** $\begin{bmatrix} -1 & 0 & 4 \\ 1 & 3 & 2 \end{bmatrix} + \begin{bmatrix} 2 & 2 & 2 \\ -4 & -4 & -4 \end{bmatrix}$
$= \begin{bmatrix} 1 & 2 & 6 \\ -3 & -1 & -2 \end{bmatrix}$

c. $\begin{bmatrix} 1 & 0 & -4 \\ 1 & 3 & 2 \end{bmatrix}$; This matrix represents the reflection of the
triangle across the y-axis.   **d.** $\begin{bmatrix} -1 & 0 & 4 \\ -1 & -3 & -2 \end{bmatrix}$; This matrix
represents the reflection of the triangle across the x-axis.

e. $\begin{bmatrix} -2 & -1 & 3 \\ 1 & -1 & 0 \end{bmatrix}$; This matrix represents the reflection of the
triangle across the x-axis, followed by a shift to the left 1 unit and
a shift upward 2 units.

83. a. $A = \begin{bmatrix} -2 & 3 & 3 & 0 \\ 1 & 3 & 0 & -1 \end{bmatrix}$ **b.** $A + \begin{bmatrix} 0 & 0 & 0 & 0 \\ -3 & -3 & -3 & -3 \end{bmatrix}$

c. $A + \begin{bmatrix} -4 & -4 & -4 & -4 \\ 0 & 0 & 0 & 0 \end{bmatrix}$

d. $\begin{bmatrix} 1 & 0 \\ 0 & -1 \end{bmatrix} \cdot A = \begin{bmatrix} -2 & 3 & 3 & 0 \\ -1 & -3 & 0 & 1 \end{bmatrix}$

e. $\begin{bmatrix} -1 & 0 \\ 0 & 1 \end{bmatrix} \cdot A = \begin{bmatrix} 2 & -3 & -3 & 0 \\ 1 & 3 & 0 & -1 \end{bmatrix}$

85. a. $\begin{bmatrix} 0 & 6 & 6 \\ 0 & 3 & 0 \end{bmatrix}$ **b.** $\begin{bmatrix} 0 & 3.7 & 5.2 \\ 0 & 5.6 & 3 \end{bmatrix}$

c. It appears that the triangle was rotated
approximately 30° counterclockwise.

87. a. $\begin{bmatrix} 6 & 6 & 6 \\ 6 & 0 & 0 \\ 6 & 6 & 6 \\ 6 & 0 & 0 \\ 6 & 6 & 6 \end{bmatrix}$

b. $\begin{bmatrix} 6 & 6 & 6 \\ 6 & 0 & 0 \\ 6 & 6 & 6 \\ 6 & 0 & 0 \\ 6 & 6 & 6 \end{bmatrix} + \begin{bmatrix} -1 & -1 & -1 \\ -1 & 1 & 1 \\ -1 & -1 & -1 \\ -1 & 1 & 1 \\ -1 & -1 & -1 \end{bmatrix} = \begin{bmatrix} 5 & 5 & 5 \\ 5 & 1 & 1 \\ 5 & 5 & 5 \\ 5 & 1 & 1 \\ 5 & 5 & 5 \end{bmatrix}$

89. $A + B = \begin{bmatrix} a_1 & a_2 \\ a_3 & a_4 \end{bmatrix} + \begin{bmatrix} b_1 & b_2 \\ b_3 & b_4 \end{bmatrix}$
$= \begin{bmatrix} a_1 + b_1 & a_2 + b_2 \\ a_3 + b_3 & a_4 + b_4 \end{bmatrix} = \begin{bmatrix} b_1 + a_1 & b_2 + a_2 \\ b_3 + a_3 & b_4 + a_4 \end{bmatrix}$
$= B + A$

91. $A + (-A) = \begin{bmatrix} a_1 & a_2 \\ a_3 & a_4 \end{bmatrix} + \begin{bmatrix} -a_1 & -a_2 \\ -a_3 & -a_4 \end{bmatrix}$
$= \begin{bmatrix} a_1 + (-a_1) & a_2 + (-a_2) \\ a_3 + (-a_3) & a_4 + (-a_4) \end{bmatrix} = \begin{bmatrix} 0 & 0 \\ 0 & 0 \end{bmatrix} = 0$

93. $s(tA) = s \cdot \left(t \begin{bmatrix} a_1 & a_2 \\ a_3 & a_4 \end{bmatrix} \right) = s \cdot \begin{bmatrix} ta_1 & ta_2 \\ ta_3 & ta_4 \end{bmatrix}$
$= \begin{bmatrix} sta_1 & sta_2 \\ sta_3 & sta_4 \end{bmatrix} = (st) \begin{bmatrix} a_1 & a_2 \\ a_3 & a_4 \end{bmatrix} = (st)A$

95. $A^2 = \begin{bmatrix} -1 & 0 \\ 0 & -1 \end{bmatrix}$, $A^3 = \begin{bmatrix} -i & 0 \\ 0 & -i \end{bmatrix}$, $A^4 = \begin{bmatrix} 1 & 0 \\ 0 & 1 \end{bmatrix}$; The entries
along the main diagonal in matrix A^n are the same as the value of i^n.

97. a. $\begin{bmatrix} ac & 0 \\ 0 & bd \end{bmatrix}$ **b.** $\begin{bmatrix} 3 & 0 \\ 0 & 14 \end{bmatrix}$ **99.** The number of columns in
the first matrix is not equal to the number of rows in the second
matrix.   **101.** To find $-A$, take the additive inverse of each
individual element of A. That is, $-A = [-a_{ij}]$.

103.
```
5[A]+2[B]
     [[17  19]
      [2   27]
      [-15 66]]
```

105.

	A	B	C	D	E	F	G	H	I	J	K
1		1	3			6	2			39	5
2	A =	2	5		B =	-4	1	-3A + 7B =		-34	-8
3		-3	10			0	8			9	26

107.

L1 ▾ ⨀ f_x =MMULT(B1:D3,G1:I3)

	A	B	C	D	E	F	G	H	I	J	K	L	M	N
1		-3	4	8			4	2	0			-32	10	-16
2	A =	0	1	6		C =	1	0	6	AC =		-17	12	-24
3		7	-2	5			-3	2	-5			11	24	-37

Section 6.4 Practice Exercises, pp. 637–639

1. a. $\begin{bmatrix} 2x - 3y \\ x + 5y \end{bmatrix}$ **b.** $\begin{aligned} 2x - 3y &= 14 \\ x + 5y &= -19 \end{aligned}$

3. a. $\begin{bmatrix} 3x - 4y + 6z \\ 2x + 4z \\ 9x + 2y \end{bmatrix}$ **b.** $\begin{aligned} 3x - 4y + 6z &= 17 \\ 2x + 4z &= 14 \\ 9x + 2y &= 11 \end{aligned}$

5. identity   **7.** inverse   **9.** $\dfrac{1}{ad - bc} \begin{bmatrix} d & -b \\ -c & a \end{bmatrix}$

11. a. $AI_n = \begin{bmatrix} -\frac{7}{8} & \sqrt{5} \\ 5.1 & 8 \end{bmatrix} \begin{bmatrix} 1 & 0 \\ 0 & 1 \end{bmatrix} = \begin{bmatrix} -\frac{7}{8} & \sqrt{5} \\ 5.1 & 8 \end{bmatrix}$ ✓

b. $I_nA = \begin{bmatrix} 1 & 0 \\ 0 & 1 \end{bmatrix} \begin{bmatrix} -\frac{7}{8} & \sqrt{5} \\ 5.1 & 8 \end{bmatrix} = \begin{bmatrix} -\frac{7}{8} & \sqrt{5} \\ 5.1 & 8 \end{bmatrix}$ ✓

13. a. $AI_n = \begin{bmatrix} 1 & -3 & 4 \\ 9 & 5 & 3 \\ 11 & -6 & -4 \end{bmatrix} \begin{bmatrix} 1 & 0 & 0 \\ 0 & 1 & 0 \\ 0 & 0 & 1 \end{bmatrix} = \begin{bmatrix} 1 & -3 & 4 \\ 9 & 5 & 3 \\ 11 & -6 & -4 \end{bmatrix}$ ✓

b. $I_nA = \begin{bmatrix} 1 & 0 & 0 \\ 0 & 1 & 0 \\ 0 & 0 & 1 \end{bmatrix} \begin{bmatrix} 1 & -3 & 4 \\ 9 & 5 & 3 \\ 11 & -6 & -4 \end{bmatrix} = \begin{bmatrix} 1 & -3 & 4 \\ 9 & 5 & 3 \\ 11 & -6 & -4 \end{bmatrix}$ ✓

15. Yes **17.** Yes **19.** No **21.** $A^{-1} = \begin{bmatrix} -\frac{5}{2} & -\frac{3}{2} \\ 3 & 2 \end{bmatrix}$

23. $A^{-1} = \begin{bmatrix} -\frac{1}{4} & -\frac{1}{10} \\ \frac{1}{2} & \frac{2}{5} \end{bmatrix}$ **25.** Singular matrix

27. $A^{-1} = \begin{bmatrix} 3 & -2 & -3 \\ 3 & -4 & -2 \\ 2 & -3 & -1 \end{bmatrix}$ **29.** $A^{-1} = \begin{bmatrix} 1 & 0 & 2 \\ 1 & -\frac{1}{2} & \frac{3}{2} \\ 1 & -\frac{1}{2} & \frac{1}{2} \end{bmatrix}$

31. Singular matrix

33. $A^{-1} = \begin{bmatrix} 3 & -3 & -6 \\ -1 & 3 & 5 \\ 2 & -3 & -5 \end{bmatrix}$ **35.** $A^{-1} = \begin{bmatrix} 1 & -3 & -1 & 0 \\ 0 & 1 & 2 & 0 \\ 0 & 1 & 1 & 0 \\ -2 & 0 & -3 & 1 \end{bmatrix}$

37. $\begin{bmatrix} 3 & -4 \\ 2 & 1 \end{bmatrix}\begin{bmatrix} x \\ y \end{bmatrix} = \begin{bmatrix} -1 \\ 14 \end{bmatrix}$ **39.** $\begin{bmatrix} 9 & -6 & 4 \\ 4 & 0 & -1 \\ 0 & 3 & 1 \end{bmatrix}\begin{bmatrix} x \\ y \\ z \end{bmatrix} = \begin{bmatrix} 27 \\ 1 \\ 0 \end{bmatrix}$

41. $\{(-2, 4)\}$ **43.** $\{(-4, 1)\}$ **45.** $\{(-3, -1, 0)\}$
47. $\{(0, 2, -4)\}$ **49.** $\{(1, -1, 0, 2)\}$ **51.** False

53. False **55.** True **57.** False **59.** For example: $\begin{bmatrix} 0 & 1 \\ 1 & 0 \end{bmatrix}$

61. a. $A^{-1} = \begin{bmatrix} \frac{3}{4} & -\frac{1}{4} \\ -\frac{5}{8} & \frac{3}{8} \end{bmatrix}$ **b.** $(A^{-1})^{-1} = A = \begin{bmatrix} 3 & 2 \\ 5 & 6 \end{bmatrix}$

63. $A^{-1} = \begin{bmatrix} \frac{1}{a} & 0 \\ 0 & \frac{1}{b} \end{bmatrix}$

65. If $AB = I_n$ and $BA = I_n$, then the matrices are inverses.

67. $\begin{bmatrix} a & b & | & 1 & 0 \\ c & d & | & 0 & 1 \end{bmatrix} \overset{\frac{1}{a}R_1 \to R_1}{=} \begin{bmatrix} 1 & \frac{b}{a} & | & \frac{1}{a} & 0 \\ c & d & | & 0 & 1 \end{bmatrix}$

$\overset{-c \cdot R_1 + R_2 \to R_2}{=} \begin{bmatrix} 1 & \frac{b}{a} & | & \frac{1}{a} & 0 \\ 0 & d - \frac{cb}{a} & | & -\frac{c}{a} & 1 \end{bmatrix}$

$= \begin{bmatrix} 1 & \frac{b}{a} & | & \frac{1}{a} & 0 \\ 0 & \frac{ad - bc}{a} & | & -\frac{c}{a} & 1 \end{bmatrix}$

$\overset{\frac{a}{ad-bc} \cdot R_2 \to R_2}{=} \begin{bmatrix} 1 & \frac{b}{a} & | & \frac{1}{a} & 0 \\ 0 & 1 & | & -\frac{c}{ad-bc} & \frac{a}{ad-bc} \end{bmatrix}$

$\overset{-\frac{b}{a} \cdot R_2 + R_1 \to R_1}{=} \begin{bmatrix} 1 & 0 & | & \frac{d}{ad-bc} & -\frac{b}{ad-bc} \\ 0 & 1 & | & -\frac{c}{ad-bc} & \frac{a}{ad-bc} \end{bmatrix}$

Therefore, $A^{-1} = \dfrac{1}{ad - bc}\begin{bmatrix} d & -b \\ -c & a \end{bmatrix}$, provided $ad - bc \neq 0$.

69. $x_1 = 36.5°F$, $x_2 = 37.5°F$, $x_3 = 40.5°F$, $x_4 = 41.5°F$

71.
```
[A]⁻¹
[ .29  -.10  .08
 -.09   .12  -.00
 -.12   .00  -.07
  .15   .03  -.06 ]
```

$A^{-1} = \begin{bmatrix} 0.29 & -0.10 & 0.08 & -0.27 \\ -0.09 & 0.12 & 0.00 & 0.27 \\ -0.12 & 0.00 & -0.07 & 0.25 \\ 0.15 & 0.03 & -0.06 & -0.01 \end{bmatrix}$

73. $\{(5.35, 41.71, 4.45)\}$

Section 6.5 Practice Exercises, pp. 649–652

1. $\{(x, y) \mid 2x - 3y = 1\}$ **3.** $\{(1, -2, 1)\}$ **5.** $\{\ \}$

7. determinant **9.** minor **11.** $\begin{vmatrix} b_2 & c_2 \\ b_3 & c_3 \end{vmatrix}$; $\begin{vmatrix} b_1 & c_1 \\ b_3 & c_3 \end{vmatrix}$; $\begin{vmatrix} b_1 & c_1 \\ b_2 & c_2 \end{vmatrix}$

13. does not **15.** 27 **17.** 6 **19.** 0 **21.** $x^2 - 36$
23. $-5e^{2x}$ **25. a.** 25 **b.** -25 **27. a.** -39 **b.** -39
29. a. -36 **b.** -36 **31.** -39; Yes **33.** -13; Yes
35. 0; No **37.** 13; Yes **39.** 121; Yes **41.** $\left\{\left(\frac{23}{8}, \frac{21}{40}\right)\right\}$

43. $\left\{\left(-\frac{57}{46}, -\frac{31}{23}\right)\right\}$ **45.** Infinitely many solutions

47. No solution **49.** $\left\{\left(\frac{63}{157}, -\frac{333}{157}, \frac{536}{471}\right)\right\}$ **51.** $\left\{\left(\frac{13}{2}, \frac{3}{2}, \frac{11}{2}\right)\right\}$

53. Infinitely many solutions **55.** No solution

57. $x_2 = \dfrac{113}{60}$ **59.** Yes

61. No **63. a.** $\begin{vmatrix} x & y & 1 \\ -3 & 2 & 1 \\ -4 & 6 & 1 \end{vmatrix} = 0$ **b.** $y = -4x - 10$

65. 12 **67. a.** 36 **b.** -36 **c.** Rows 1 and 2 are interchanged between matrix A and matrix B. The determinants are opposite in sign.
69. a. 13 **b.** 26 **c.** Row 1 of matrix B is 2 times row 1 of matrix A. The value $|B| = 2|A|$. **71. a.** -2 **b.** -2 **c.** Row 2 of matrix B is the same as the sum of 3 times row 1 of A and row 2 of A. The value of $|A|$ equals $|B|$. **73.** 0 **75.** 0 **77.** 1
79. abc **81.** $|AB| = -130$; $|A| = 10$ and $|B| = -13$. So, $|A| \cdot |B| = (10)(-13) = -130$ and, therefore, $|A| \cdot |B| = |AB|$.
83. The minor is the determinant of the matrix obtained by deleting the ith row and jth column of the original matrix. The cofactor is the product of the minor and the factor $(-1)^{i+j}$.
85. Choose the row or column with the greatest number of zero elements.
87. 10,112

Problem Recognition Exercises, p. 653

1. $\{(2, -4)\}$ **2.** $\{(5, -1)\}$ **3.** $\{(2, -1, 0)\}$ **4.** $\{(2, 0, 4)\}$
5. a. $\begin{vmatrix} 1.5 & -2 \\ -3 & 4 \end{vmatrix} = 0$ **b.** No **c.** $\{\ \}$ **6. a.** $\begin{vmatrix} 5 & -2 \\ 1 & -0.4 \end{vmatrix} = 0$
b. No **c.** $\{\ \}$ **7. a.** $\begin{vmatrix} 1 & -3 & 7 \\ -2 & 5 & -11 \\ 1 & -5 & 13 \end{vmatrix} = 0$
b. No **c.** $\{(2z + 4, 3z + 1, z) \mid z$ is any real number$\}$
8. a. $\begin{vmatrix} 1 & -2 & 3 \\ -2 & 1 & 0 \\ 1 & 0 & -1 \end{vmatrix} = 0$ **b.** No
c. $\{(z + 3, 2z + 5, z) \mid z$ is any real number$\}$

Chapter 6 Review Exercises, pp. 655–658

1. $x - 2y + 3z = -1$
$\quad\quad y + 4z = -11$
$\quad\quad\quad\quad z = -2$;
Solution set: $\{(-1, -3, -2)\}$

3. $\begin{bmatrix} 1 & -\frac{3}{2} & | & \frac{1}{2} \\ 5 & 6 & | & -4 \end{bmatrix}$

5. $\{(5, -6)\}$ **7.** $\{(0, 2, 3)\}$ **9.** Lily borrowed \$1000 from her friend, \$7000 from the credit union, and \$2000 from the bank.
11. $\{\ \}$ **13.** $\{(3z, -2z + 1, z) \mid z$ is any real number$\}$
15. $\{\ \}$ **17.** $\{(3z + 5, -4z + 3, z) \mid z$ is any real number$\}$
19. $\{(x, y, z) \mid x - 5y + 2z = -1\}$ **21. a.** $x_1 = 76$ vehicles per hour; $x_2 = 97$ vehicles per hour **b.** $46 \leq x_1 \leq 96$ vehicles per hour; $67 \leq x_2 \leq 117$ vehicles per hour **23. a.** 3×2
b. None of these **25. a.** 2×1 **b.** Column matrix

27. 4 **29.** $x = 6, y = 3, z = 8$ **31.** $3A = \begin{bmatrix} -12 & 3 \\ 18 & -6 \\ 3 & 9 \end{bmatrix}$

33. Not possible **35.** $2A - C = \begin{bmatrix} -8 - \pi & -2 \\ 15 & -5 \\ 2 & 1 \end{bmatrix}$

37. $AB = \begin{bmatrix} -7 & -7 & 22 \\ 10 & 8 & -30 \\ 5 & 18 & -25 \end{bmatrix}$ **39.** Not possible

41. $A^2 = \begin{bmatrix} -2 & 36 \\ -6 & 10 \end{bmatrix}$ **43.** $BC = \begin{bmatrix} 2 & 7 \\ -6 & -21 \end{bmatrix}$

45. a. $P - M = \begin{bmatrix} \$315 & \$282 \\ \$267 & \$240 \end{bmatrix}$; This represents the profit that the store

clears for each model.   **b.** $F = 1.06P = \begin{bmatrix} \$1446.90 & \$1295.32 \\ \$1226.42 & \$1102.40 \end{bmatrix}$

47. a. $A = \begin{bmatrix} 1 & 3 & 5 \\ 1 & 4 & 2 \end{bmatrix}$ **b.** $\begin{bmatrix} 1 & 3 & 5 \\ 1 & 4 & 2 \end{bmatrix} + \begin{bmatrix} -3 & -3 & -3 \\ -1 & -1 & -1 \end{bmatrix}$

$= \begin{bmatrix} -2 & 0 & 2 \\ 0 & 3 & 1 \end{bmatrix}$

c. $\begin{bmatrix} -1 & -3 & -5 \\ 1 & 4 & 2 \end{bmatrix}$; This matrix represents the reflection of the

triangle across the y-axis.   **d.** $\begin{bmatrix} 1 & 3 & 5 \\ -1 & -4 & -2 \end{bmatrix}$; This matrix

represents the reflection of the triangle across the x-axis.   **49.** No

51. $A^{-1} = \begin{bmatrix} \frac{1}{6} & \frac{1}{6} \\ -\frac{1}{12} & \frac{5}{12} \end{bmatrix}$ **53.** Singular matrix

55. $A^{-1} = \begin{bmatrix} 0 & -1 & 4 \\ 1 & -1 & 5 \\ -3 & -1 & 0 \end{bmatrix}$ **57.** $\begin{bmatrix} -3 & 7 & 0 \\ 4 & 0 & 2 \\ 2 & -1 & 5 \end{bmatrix} \begin{bmatrix} x \\ y \\ z \end{bmatrix} = \begin{bmatrix} 6 \\ -3 \\ -13 \end{bmatrix}$

59. $\{(4, -3)\}$ **61.** $\{(1, 2, 3)\}$ **63. a.** 24   **b.** 24

65. a. 13   **b.** -13 **67.** $81 - x^2$ **69.** 156   **71.** -270

73. $\left\{\left(\frac{3}{10}, -\frac{23}{30}\right)\right\}$ **75.** $\left\{\left(-\frac{7}{25}, -\frac{222}{125}, \frac{161}{125}\right)\right\}$ **77.** $y = -\frac{94}{67}$

Chapter 6 Test, pp. 658–659

1. $\begin{bmatrix} 1 & 5 & -3 & | & 1 \\ 3 & 1 & 4 & | & -2 \\ 0 & 4 & 2 & | & 6 \end{bmatrix}$ **2.** $\begin{bmatrix} 0 & -14 & 13 & | & -5 \\ 1 & 5 & -3 & | & 1 \\ 0 & 4 & 2 & | & 6 \end{bmatrix}$

3. $\begin{bmatrix} 3 & 1 & 4 & | & -2 \\ 1 & 5 & -3 & | & 1 \\ 0 & 1 & \frac{1}{2} & | & \frac{3}{2} \end{bmatrix}$

4. The elements above the leading 1 in the third column are not all zero. Specifically, the element in row 1, column 3 should be 0.

5. $\{(-10, 3)\}$ **6.** $\{\ \}$ **7.** $\{(3z, -2z + 5, z) \mid z$ is any real number$\}$

8. a. 8   **b.** -8 **9. a.** -12 **b.** -12 **10.** -31

11. 236   **12.** $|A| = 0$. Therefore, A is singular (does not have an inverse).

13. $\{(-2, 3)\}$ **14.** $\{\ \}$ **15.** $\{(-2, -8, 2)\}$

16. $\{(-3z - 2, -4z + 1, z) \mid z$ is any real number$\}$

17. $\left\{\left(\frac{54}{61}, -\frac{53}{61}\right)\right\}$ **18.** $x = \frac{7}{31}$ **19.** $x = -9, y = 2$, and $z = 6$

20. $2A - 3C = \begin{bmatrix} 8 & -1 & 6 \\ -2 & 11 & -12 \end{bmatrix}$

21. Not possible   **22.** $AB = \begin{bmatrix} -5 & 20 \\ 20 & 44 \end{bmatrix}$

23. $BA = \begin{bmatrix} 22 & 37 & 51 \\ -2 & -4 & -6 \\ 22 & 23 & 21 \end{bmatrix}$ **24.** Yes   **25.** $A^{-1} = \begin{bmatrix} 2 & -1 \\ -\frac{5}{2} & \frac{3}{2} \end{bmatrix}$

26. Singular matrix   **27.** $A^{-1} = \begin{bmatrix} 3 & 1 & 2 \\ 7 & 2 & 5 \\ 1 & 1 & 1 \end{bmatrix}$ **28.** $\{(1, 5)\}$

29. $\{(2, 1, -3)\}$ **30. a.** $x_1 = 128$ vehicles per hour; $x_2 = 173$ vehicles per hour   **b.** $118 \le x_1 \le 168$ vehicles per hour; $163 \le x_2 \le 213$ vehicles per hour

31. $CN = \begin{bmatrix} 5500 \\ 8040 \end{bmatrix}$; This represents the total number of calories burned

by two individuals with different weights after biking 6 hr, running 3 hr, and walking 5 hr. For example, the element 5500 in the first row tells us that 5500 cal would be burned by a 120-lb individual who biked 6 hr, ran 3 hr, and walked 5 hr in a given week.   **32.** Yes

Chapter 6 Cumulative Review Exercises, pp. 659–660

1. $3x^2 + 3xh + h^2$ **2. a.** $(4, -5)$ **b.** $(-\infty, 4)$ **c.** $(4, \infty)$

d. $(-\infty, \infty)$ **e.** $(-\infty, -5]$ **3.** $\frac{2}{3}$ **4. a.** i **b.** -1

5. $-\frac{6}{13} + \frac{17}{13}i$ **6.** $3\sqrt{10}$ **7.** Center: $\left(-\frac{5}{3}, 0\right)$; Radius: $\sqrt{11}$

8. a. $k = 0.117$ **b.** 9.3 mCi   **c.** More than 39.4 hr

9. a.   **10. a.**

b. $(-\infty, \infty)$ **c.** $(1, \infty)$ **b.** $(-4, \infty)$ **c.** $(-\infty, \infty)$

11. a.   **12. a.**

b. $(-\infty, 0]$ **c.** $[0, \infty)$ **b.** $(-\infty, \infty)$ **c.** $[-2, \infty)$

13. $\{(7, 6)\}$ **14.** $\{(-4z, -3z + 2, z) \mid z$ is any real number$\}$

15. x-axis, y-axis, and origin   **16.** odd

17. $AB = \begin{bmatrix} 2 & -13 \\ 1 & 46 \end{bmatrix}$ **18.** 60   **19.** $4A - B = \begin{bmatrix} 7 & -16 \\ 4 & 17 \end{bmatrix}$

20. $A^{-1} = \begin{bmatrix} \frac{2}{5} & \frac{1}{5} \\ -\frac{1}{15} & \frac{2}{15} \end{bmatrix}$ **21.** $\{x \mid x > -2\}$ **22.** $\{x \mid 3 < x \le 4\}$

23. $\{x \mid x \ge 5\}$ **24.** $\left\{\frac{19}{2}, 2\right\}$ **25.** $\mathbb{R}$ **26.** $\left(\frac{1}{2}, 5\right]$

27. $\{6\}$ **28.** The zeros are $\frac{1}{2}, 3i$, and $-3i$.

29. Vertical asymptotes: $x = 3, x = -3$; Horizontal asymptote: $y = 0$

30. $\log\left(\frac{z^5}{x^3\sqrt{y}}\right)$

CHAPTER 7

Section 7.1 Practice Exercises, pp. 672–677

1. Center: $(-4, 0)$; Radius: 7   **3.** Center: $(0, 0)$; Radius: $\sqrt{17}$

5. $(x + 5)^2 + (y - 2)^2 = 7$ **7.** conic   **9.** vertices   **11.** major

13. $\frac{x^2}{a^2} + \frac{y^2}{b^2} = 1; \frac{x^2}{b^2} + \frac{y^2}{a^2} = 1$ **15.** $(a, 0); (-a, 0); (0, b); (0, -b)$

17. $(h, k + a); (h, k - a); (h + b, k); (h - b, k)$

19. a. $d_1 = \frac{37}{5}, d_2 = \frac{13}{5}, d_3 = 5, d_4 = 5$ **b.** 10   **c.** 10

d. They are the same.   **e.** The sums equal the length of the major axis.   **21. a.** Vertical   **b.** Horizontal

23. a. Center: $(0, 0)$ **25. a.** Center: $(0, 0)$
b. $a = 10$ **c.** $b = 5$ **b.** $a = 10$ **c.** $b = 5$
d. Vertices: $(10, 0), (-10, 0)$ **d.** Vertices: $(0, 10), (0, -10)$
e. Endpoints of minor axis: **e.** Endpoints of minor axis:
$(0, 5), (0, -5)$ $(5, 0), (-5, 0)$
f. Foci: $(5\sqrt{3}, 0), (-5\sqrt{3}, 0)$ **f.** Foci: $(0, 5\sqrt{3}), (0, -5\sqrt{3})$
g. 20   **h.** 10   **g.** 20   **h.** 10
i.   **i.**

27. a. Center: $(0, 0)$
 b. $a = 5$ **c.** $b = 2$
 d. Vertices: $(5, 0), (-5, 0)$
 e. Endpoints of minor axis:
   $(0, 2), (0, -2)$
 f. Foci: $\left(\sqrt{21}, 0\right), \left(-\sqrt{21}, 0\right)$
 g. 10   **h.** 4
 i.

29. a. Center: $(0, 0)$
 b. $a = 3$ **c.** $b = 1$
 d. Vertices: $(0, 3), (0, -3)$
 e. Endpoints of minor axis
   $(1, 0), (-1, 0)$
 f. Foci: $\left(0, 2\sqrt{2}\right), \left(0, -2\sqrt{2}\right)$
 g. 6   **h.** 2
 i.

31. a. Center: $(0, 0)$
 b. $a = 2\sqrt{3}$ **c.** $b = \sqrt{5}$
 d. Vertices: $\left(2\sqrt{3}, 0\right), \left(-2\sqrt{3}, 0\right)$
 e. Endpoints of minor axis:
   $\left(0, \sqrt{5}\right), \left(0, -\sqrt{5}\right)$
 f. Foci: $\left(\sqrt{7}, 0\right), \left(-\sqrt{7}, 0\right)$
 g. $4\sqrt{3}$ **h.** $2\sqrt{5}$
 i.

33. a. Center: $(1, -6)$
 b. Vertices: $(6, -6), (-4, -6)$
 c. Endpoints of minor axis:
   $(1, -2), (1, -10)$
 d. Foci: $(4, -6), (-2, -6)$
 e.

35. a. Center: $(-4, 2)$
 b. Vertices: $(-4, 10), (-4, -6)$
 c. Endpoints of minor axis:
   $(-11, 2), (3, 2)$
 d. Foci: $\left(-4, 2 + \sqrt{15}\right),$
   $\left(-4, 2 - \sqrt{15}\right)$
 e.

37. a. Center: $(6, 0)$
 b. Vertices: $(6, 3), (6, -3)$
 c. Endpoints of minor axis:
   $(5, 0), (7, 0)$
 d. Foci: $\left(6, 2\sqrt{2}\right), \left(6, -2\sqrt{2}\right)$
 e.

39. a. Center: $(0, -1)$
 b. Vertices: $(9, -1), (-9, -1)$
 c. Endpoints of minor axis:
   $(0, 2), (0, -4)$
 d. Foci: $\left(6\sqrt{2}, -1\right),$
   $\left(-6\sqrt{2}, -1\right)$
 e.

41. a. Center: $(3, 2)$
 b. Vertices: $\left(\frac{1}{2}, 2\right), \left(\frac{11}{2}, 2\right)$
 c. Endpoints of minor axis:
   $\left(3, \frac{1}{4}\right), \left(3, \frac{15}{4}\right)$
 d. Foci: $\left(3 + \frac{\sqrt{51}}{4}, 2\right),$
   $\left(3 - \frac{\sqrt{51}}{4}, 2\right)$
 e.

43. a. $\dfrac{(x + 2)^2}{5} + \dfrac{(y - 6)^2}{3} = 1$
 b. Center: $(-2, 6)$
   Vertices: $\left(-2 - \sqrt{5}, 6\right), \left(-2 + \sqrt{5}, 6\right)$
   Endpoints of minor axis: $\left(-2, 6 + \sqrt{3}\right), \left(-2, 6 - \sqrt{3}\right)$
   Foci: $\left(-2 - \sqrt{2}, 6\right), \left(-2 + \sqrt{2}, 6\right)$

45. a. $\dfrac{(x - 5)^2}{6} + \dfrac{(y - 1)^2}{9} = 1$
 b. Center: $(5, 1)$
   Vertices: $(5, 4), (5, -2)$
   Endpoints of minor axis: $\left(5 + \sqrt{6}, 1\right), \left(5 - \sqrt{6}, 1\right)$
   Foci: $\left(5, 1 + \sqrt{3}\right), \left(5, 1 - \sqrt{3}\right)$

47. a. $x^2 + \dfrac{(y + 7)^2}{4} = 1$
 b. Center: $(0, -7)$
   Vertices: $(0, -5), (0, -9)$
   Endpoints of minor axis: $(-1, -7), (1, -7)$
   Foci: $\left(0, -7 + \sqrt{3}\right), \left(0, -7 - \sqrt{3}\right)$

49. a. $\dfrac{\left(x - \frac{5}{2}\right)^2}{25} + \dfrac{(y + 4)^2}{9} = 1$
 b. Center: $\left(\frac{5}{2}, -4\right)$
   Vertices: $\left(\frac{15}{2}, -4\right), \left(-\frac{5}{2}, -4\right)$
   Endpoints of minor axis: $\left(\frac{5}{2}, -1\right), \left(\frac{5}{2}, -7\right)$
   Foci: $\left(\frac{13}{2}, -4\right), \left(-\frac{3}{2}, -4\right)$

51. $\dfrac{x^2}{16} + \dfrac{y^2}{7} = 1$ **53.** $\dfrac{x^2}{17} + \dfrac{y^2}{98} = 1$

55. $\dfrac{(x - 2)^2}{49} + \dfrac{(y - 3)^2}{25} = 1$ **57.** $\dfrac{(x - 4)^2}{25} + \dfrac{(y - 1)^2}{9} = 1$

59. $\dfrac{x^2}{16} + \dfrac{y^2}{25} = 1$ **61.** $\dfrac{(x - 3)^2}{5} + \dfrac{y^2}{16} = 1$

63. $\dfrac{(x + 5)^2}{49} + \dfrac{(y - 1)^2}{16} = 1$ **65.** b   **67.** a

69. $e = \dfrac{12}{13}$ **71.** $e = \dfrac{3}{5}$ **73.** $e = \dfrac{\sqrt{2}}{2}$

75. a. The ellipse from Exercise 69   **b.** The ellipse from Exercise 71

77. The Earth's orbit is more circular, and the orbit for Halley's Comet is very elongated.   **79.** 405,500 km

81. $\dfrac{x^2}{64} + \dfrac{y^2}{289} = 1$ **83.** $\dfrac{(x - 4)^2}{25} + \dfrac{(y + 1)^2}{9} = 1$

85. The foci should be located $\pm 30\sqrt{2}$ in. (approximately 42.4 in.) from the center along the major axis.   **87.** 16.94 cm

89. a. Top semiellipse   **b.** Bottom semiellipse
 c. Right semiellipse   **d.** Left semiellipse

91. $\{(0, 3), (5, 0)\}$ **93.** $\{(0, 4), (-2, 0), (2, 0)\}$

95. a. $A = 4\pi\sqrt{2}$ square units   **b.** $P \approx 2\pi\sqrt{6}$ units

97. $\dfrac{x^2}{a^2} + \dfrac{y^2}{b^2} = 1$

$\dfrac{c^2}{a^2} + \dfrac{y^2}{b^2} = 1$

$y = b\sqrt{1 - \dfrac{c^2}{a^2}}$

$y = b\sqrt{\dfrac{a^2 - c^2}{a^2}}$

$y = \dfrac{b}{a}\sqrt{a^2 - c^2}$

Recall that $c^2 = a^2 - b^2$, or equivalently $b^2 = a^2 - c^2$ and $b > 0$.

Therefore, $y = \dfrac{b}{a}\sqrt{b^2}$ or $y = \dfrac{b^2}{a}$. The length of a latus rectum is $2y = \dfrac{2b^2}{a}$.

99. By the reflective property of an ellipse, any shot passing through one focus is reflected through the other focus.

101. The first equation represents an ellipse centered at the origin, whereas the second equation represents a circle with radius 2.

103. The eccentricity of an ellipse is a measure of elongation. It is computed by finding the ratio of c and a; that is, eccentricity is the ratio of the distance between a focus and the center to the distance between a vertex and the center.

105. a. $(a + c) + (a - c) = 2a$
 b. $\sqrt{(x + c)^2 + y^2} + \sqrt{(x - c)^2 + y^2} = 2a$

c. $\sqrt{(x + c)^2 + y^2} = 2a - \sqrt{(x - c)^2 + y^2}$

$(x + c)^2 + y^2 = 4a^2 - 4a\sqrt{(x - c)^2 + y^2} + (x - c)^2 + y^2$

$4a\sqrt{(x - c)^2 + y^2} = 4a^2 + (x - c)^2 - (x + c)^2$

$4a\sqrt{(x - c)^2 + y^2} = 4a^2 - 4xc$

$a\sqrt{(x - c)^2 + y^2} = a^2 - xc$

d. $\left(a\sqrt{(x - c)^2 + y^2}\right)^2 = (a^2 - xc)^2$

$a^2[(x - c)^2 + y^2] = a^4 - 2a^2xc + c^2x^2$

$a^2[x^2 - 2xc + c^2 + y^2] = a^4 - 2a^2xc + c^2x^2$

$a^2x^2 - 2a^2xc + a^2c^2 + a^2y^2 = a^4 - 2a^2xc + c^2x^2$

$a^2x^2 - c^2x^2 + a^2y^2 = a^4 - a^2c^2$

$(a^2 - c^2)x^2 + a^2y^2 = a^2(a^2 - c^2)$

e. $b^2x^2 + a^2y^2 = a^2b^2$

$\dfrac{b^2x^2}{a^2b^2} + \dfrac{a^2y^2}{a^2b^2} = \dfrac{a^2b^2}{a^2b^2}$

$\dfrac{x^2}{a^2} + \dfrac{y^2}{b^2} = 1$

107.

109.

111. The eccentricity varies for different values of b. For values of b closer to 4, the ellipse appears more circular. For values of b closer to 0, the ellipse is more elongated. When $b = 4$, the curve is a circle rather than an ellipse.

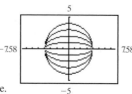

Section 7.2 Practice Exercises, pp. 687–691

1. Center: $(3, -10)$; Vertices: $(16, -10)$, $(-10, -10)$; Foci: $(8, -10)$, $(-2, -10)$; Endpoints of minor axis: $(3, 2)$, $(3, -22)$; Eccentricity: $\frac{5}{13}$

3. $\dfrac{(x + 10)^2}{5} + \dfrac{y^2}{12} = 1$ **5.** Center: $\left(-8, \frac{3}{2}\right)$; Radius: $2\sqrt{5}$

7. hyperbola; foci   **9.** transverse   **11.** horizontal; $(a, 0)$; $(-a, 0)$; $y = \frac{b}{a}x$; $y = -\frac{b}{a}x$ **13.** conjugate   **15.** $(h, k + a)$; $(h, k - a)$

17. a. $d_1 = \dfrac{101}{12}$, $d_2 = \dfrac{29}{12}$, $d_3 = \dfrac{37}{4}$, $d_4 = \dfrac{13}{4}$ **b.** 6   **c.** 6

d. They are the same.   **e.** The difference in distances equals the length of the transverse axis.   **19.** x-axis   **21.** y-axis

23. a. Center: $(0, 0)$ **e.**

b. Vertices: $(4, 0)$, $(-4, 0)$

c. Foci: $\left(\sqrt{41}, 0\right)$, $\left(-\sqrt{41}, 0\right)$

d. $y = \frac{5}{4}x$ and $y = -\frac{5}{4}x$

25. a. Center: $(0, 0)$ **e.**

b. Vertices: $(0, 2)$, $(0, -2)$

c. Foci: $\left(0, 2\sqrt{10}\right)$, $\left(0, -2\sqrt{10}\right)$

d. $y = \frac{1}{3}x$ and $y = -\frac{1}{3}x$

27. a. Center: $(0, 0)$ **e.**

b. Vertices: $(0, 9)$, $(0, -9)$

c. Foci: $\left(0, \sqrt{106}\right)$, $\left(0, -\sqrt{106}\right)$

d. $y = \frac{9}{5}x$ and $y = -\frac{9}{5}x$

29. a. Center: $(0, 0)$ **e.**

b. Vertices: $\left(\sqrt{7}, 0\right)$, $\left(-\sqrt{7}, 0\right)$

c. Foci: $\left(2\sqrt{3}, 0\right)$, $\left(-2\sqrt{3}, 0\right)$

d. $y = \frac{\sqrt{35}}{7}x$ and $y = -\frac{\sqrt{35}}{7}x$

31. a. Center: $(0, 0)$ **e.**

b. Vertices: $\left(\frac{5}{2}, 0\right)$, $\left(-\frac{5}{2}, 0\right)$

c. Foci: $\left(\frac{\sqrt{149}}{4}, 0\right)$, $\left(-\frac{\sqrt{149}}{4}, 0\right)$

d. $y = \frac{7}{10}x$ and $y = -\frac{7}{10}x$

33. a. Center: $(4, -2)$ **e.**

b. Vertices: $(1, -2)$, $(7, -2)$

c. Foci: $(-1, -2)$, $(9, -2)$

d. $y = \frac{4}{3}x - \frac{22}{3}$ and $y = -\frac{4}{3}x + \frac{10}{3}$

35. a. Center: $(-3, 5)$ **e.**

b. Vertices: $(-3, -2)$, $(-3, 12)$

c. Foci: $\left(-3, 5 + \sqrt{74}\right)$, $\left(-3, 5 - \sqrt{74}\right)$

d. $y = \frac{7}{5}x + \frac{46}{5}$ and $y = -\frac{7}{5}x + \frac{4}{5}$

37. a. Center: $(-4, 7)$

b. Vertices: $(6, 7)$, $(-14, 7)$

c. Foci: $\left(-4 + \sqrt{181}, 7\right)$, $\left(-4 - \sqrt{181}, 7\right)$

d. $y = \frac{9}{10}x + \frac{53}{5}$ and $y = -\frac{9}{10}x + \frac{17}{5}$

e.

39. a. Center: $(3, 0)$ **e.**

b. Vertices: $(3, 1)$, $(3, -1)$

c. Foci: $\left(3, \sqrt{13}\right)$, $\left(3, -\sqrt{13}\right)$

d. $y = \frac{\sqrt{3}}{6}x - \frac{\sqrt{3}}{2}$ and $y = -\frac{\sqrt{3}}{6}x + \frac{\sqrt{3}}{2}$

41. a. Center: $(0, 4)$ **e.**

b. Vertices: $(1, 4)$, $(-1, 4)$

c. Foci: $(3, 4)$, $(-3, 4)$

d. $y = 2\sqrt{2}x + 4$ and $y = -2\sqrt{2}x + 4$

43. a. $\dfrac{(x + 3)^2}{5} - \dfrac{(y - 1)^2}{7} = 1$ **b.** Center: $(-3, 1)$;

Vertices: $\left(-3 + \sqrt{5}, 1\right)$, $\left(-3 - \sqrt{5}, 1\right)$;

Foci: $\left(-3 + 2\sqrt{3}, 1\right)$, $\left(-3 - 2\sqrt{3}, 1\right)$

45. a. $\dfrac{(y - 4)^2}{5} - \dfrac{(x - 2)^2}{9} = 1$ **b.** Center: $(2, 4)$;

Vertices: $\left(2, 4 + \sqrt{5}\right)$, $\left(2, 4 - \sqrt{5}\right)$;

Foci: $\left(2, 4 + \sqrt{14}\right)$, $\left(2, 4 - \sqrt{14}\right)$

47. a. $x^2 - \dfrac{(y+5)^2}{4} = 1$ **b.** Center: $(0, -5)$;

Vertices: $(1, -5), (-1, -5)$; Foci: $\left(\sqrt{5}, -5\right), \left(-\sqrt{5}, -5\right)$

49. a. $\dfrac{(y+2)^2}{9} - \dfrac{\left(x - \frac{3}{2}\right)^2}{16} = 1$ **b.** Center: $\left(\frac{3}{2}, -2\right)$;

Vertices: $\left(\frac{3}{2}, 1\right), \left(\frac{3}{2}, -5\right)$; Foci: $\left(\frac{3}{2}, 3\right), \left(\frac{3}{2}, -7\right)$

51. $\dfrac{x^2}{144} - \dfrac{y^2}{25} = 1$ **53.** $\dfrac{y^2}{144} - \dfrac{x^2}{81} = 1$

55. $\dfrac{(x-2)^2}{25} - \dfrac{(y+3)^2}{49} = 1$ **57.** $\dfrac{(y-4)^2}{16} - \dfrac{(x+3)^2}{5} = 1$

59. $\dfrac{(x-1)^2}{49} - \dfrac{(y-2)^2}{25} = 1$

61. a. Equation 1: $e = \frac{5}{4}$, Equation 2: $e = \frac{5}{3}$

b. Graph B represents Equation 1. Graph A represents Equation 2.

63. $e = \dfrac{41}{40}$ **65.** $e = \dfrac{5}{4}$ **67.** $\dfrac{(x-3)^2}{16} - \dfrac{(y+1)^2}{9} = 1$

69. $\dfrac{x^2}{(372)^2} - \dfrac{y^2}{(334)^2} = 1$ **71. a.** 0.4 AU   **b.** 37,200,000 mi

73. Ellipse; B   **75.** Hyperbola; D   **77.** $\dfrac{(x+1)^2}{16} + \dfrac{y^2}{25} = 1$

79. $\dfrac{(y+3)^2}{9} - \dfrac{(x-2)^2}{16} = 1$

81. $\left\{\left(4, 3\sqrt{3}\right), \left(4, -3\sqrt{3}\right), \left(-4, 3\sqrt{3}\right), \left(-4, -3\sqrt{3}\right)\right\}$

83. The transverse axis is horizontal if the coefficient of the x^2 term is positive. The transverse axis is vertical if the coefficient of the y^2 term is positive.   **85.** $\sqrt{2}$

87. $\dfrac{x^2}{a^2} - \dfrac{y^2}{b^2} = 1$

$\dfrac{c^2}{a^2} - \dfrac{y^2}{b^2} = 1$

$y = b\sqrt{\dfrac{c^2}{a^2} - 1}$

$y = b\sqrt{\dfrac{c^2 - a^2}{a^2}}$

$y = \dfrac{b}{a}\sqrt{c^2 - a^2}$

Recall that $c^2 = a^2 + b^2$ or equivalently $b^2 = c^2 - a^2$ and $b > 0$.

Therefore, $y = \dfrac{b}{a}\sqrt{b^2}$ or $y = \dfrac{b^2}{a}$.

The length of a latus rectum is $2y = \dfrac{2b^2}{a}$.

89.   **91.**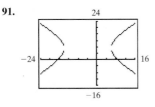

Section 7.3 Practice Exercises, pp. 699–702

1. Hyperbola; Center: $(0, -7)$; Vertices: $(3, -7), (-3, -7)$;
Foci: $(5, -7), (-5, -7)$; Asymptotes: $y = \frac{4}{3}x - 7$ and $y = -\frac{4}{3}x - 7$;
Eccentricity: $\frac{5}{3}$ **3.** Circle; Center: $(-3, -4)$; Radius: $3\sqrt{2}$

5. Ellipse; Center: $(8, 2)$; Vertices: $\left(8 + 2\sqrt{3}, 2\right), \left(8 - 2\sqrt{3}, 2\right)$;
Endpoints of minor axis: $(8, 4), (8, 0)$;
Foci: $\left(8 + 2\sqrt{2}, 2\right), \left(8 - 2\sqrt{2}, 2\right)$; Eccentricity: $\frac{\sqrt{6}}{3}$

7. parabola; directrix; focus   **9.** vertex   **11.** $x^2 = 4py$

13. left   **15.** latus rectum   **17.** (h, k); $(h, k + p)$; $y = k - p$

19. vertically   **21. a.** $d_1 = 2, d_2 = 2, d_3 = 5, d_4 = 5$

b. They are the same.   **c.** They are the same.

23. a. $p = 6$ **b.** $(0, 6)$ **c.** $y = -6$ **25. a.** $p = 9$ **b.** $(9, 0)$

c. $x = -9$ **27. a.** $p = -\frac{5}{4}$ **b.** $\left(0, -\frac{5}{4}\right)$ **c.** $y = \frac{5}{4}$

29. a. $p = -\frac{1}{4}$ **b.** $\left(-\frac{1}{4}, 0\right)$ **c.** $x = \frac{1}{4}$

31. a. Focus: $(0, 6.3)$; Place the receiver 6.3 in. above the center of the dish.   **b.** $y = -6.3$

33. a. Vertex: $(0, 0)$; $p = -1$;
Focus: $(0, -1)$; Focal diameter: 4
b. $(2, -1), (-2, -1)$
d. Directrix: $y = 1$;
Axis of symmetry: $x = 0$
c.

35. a. Vertex: $(0, 0)$; $p = 2$;
Focus: $(2, 0)$; Focal diameter: 8
b. $(2, 4), (2, -4)$
d. Directrix: $x = -2$;
Axis of symmetry: $y = 0$
c.

37. a. Vertex: $(0, 0)$; $p = \frac{5}{2}$;
Focus: $\left(0, \frac{5}{2}\right)$; Focal diameter: 10
b. $\left(5, \frac{5}{2}\right), \left(-5, \frac{5}{2}\right)$
d. Directrix: $y = -\frac{5}{2}$;
Axis of symmetry: $x = 0$
c.

39. a. Vertex: $(0, 0)$; $p = -\frac{1}{4}$;
Focus: $\left(-\frac{1}{4}, 0\right)$; Focal diameter: 1
b. $\left(-\frac{1}{4}, \frac{1}{2}\right), \left(-\frac{1}{4}, -\frac{1}{2}\right)$
d. Directrix: $x = \frac{1}{4}$;
Axis of symmetry: $y = 0$
c.

41. a. Vertex: $(4, -1)$; $p = -3$;
Focus: $(1, -1)$; Focal diameter: 12
b. $(1, 5), (1, -7)$
d. Directrix: $x = 7$;
Axis of symmetry: $y = -1$
c.

43. a. Vertex: $(1, -5)$; $p = -1$;
Focus: $(1, -6)$; Focal diameter: 4
b. $(3, -6), (-1, -6)$
d. Directrix: $y = -4$;
Axis of symmetry: $x = 1$
c.

45. a. Vertex: $\left(-3, \frac{3}{2}\right)$; $p = \frac{1}{2}$;
Focus: $(-3, 2)$; Focal diameter: 2
b. $(-4, 2), (-2, 2)$
d. Directrix: $y = 1$;
Axis of symmetry: $x = -3$
c.

47. a. Vertex: $\left(\frac{1}{4}, 3\right)$; $p = -\frac{7}{4}$;
Focus: $\left(-\frac{3}{2}, 3\right)$;
Focal diameter: 7
b. $\left(-\frac{3}{2}, \frac{13}{2}\right), \left(-\frac{3}{2}, -\frac{1}{2}\right)$
d. Directrix: $x = 2$;
Axis of symmetry: $y = 3$
c.

49. a. Vertex: $(-6, 3)$; $p = 5$;
Focus: $(-6, 8)$; Focal diameter: 20
b. $(4, 8), (-16, 8)$
d. Directrix: $y = -2$;
Axis of symmetry: $x = -6$
c.

51. a. $(x - 3)^2 = 4(y + 1)$ **b.** Vertex: $(3, -1)$; Focus: $(3, 0)$;
Directrix: $y = -2$ **53. a.** $(y + 2)^2 = -8(x + 6)$
b. Vertex: $(-6, -2)$; Focus: $(-8, -2)$; Directrix: $x = -4$
55. a. $\left(x - \frac{7}{2}\right)^2 = -6(y + 1)$ **b.** Vertex: $\left(\frac{7}{2}, -1\right)$; Focus: $\left(\frac{7}{2}, -\frac{5}{2}\right)$;
Directrix: $y = \frac{1}{2}$ **57. a.** $\left(y + \frac{3}{4}\right)^2 = (x - 3)$
b. Vertex: $\left(3, -\frac{3}{4}\right)$; Focus: $\left(\frac{13}{4}, -\frac{3}{4}\right)$; Directrix: $x = \frac{11}{4}$
59. $(1, 7)$; 3 **61.** $x = 1$; -4 **63.** 12
65. No; Focal length is a distance and gives no information regarding
the orientation of a parabola.   **67.** $y^2 = -16x$
69. $(x - 2)^2 = 12(y - 1)$ **71.** $(x + 6)^2 = -4(y + 1)$
73. $(x - 2)^2 = 8(y - 3)$ or $(y - 3)^2 = (x - 2)$
75. a. $x^2 = 230.4y$ for $-1.2 \le x \le 1.2$ **b.** 0.00625 m or 6.25 mm
77. $\{(5, -1), (8, -7)\}$ **79.** If the y term is linear, then the parabola
opens vertically. If the x term is linear, then the parabola opens
horizontally.

81.   **83.**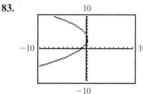

85. The greater the value of $|p|$ (the focal length), the wider the parabola.

Problem Recognition Exercises, pp. 702–703

1. Hyperbola; Center: $(2, -2)$; Vertices: $(6, -2)$, $(-2, -2)$;
Foci: $(7, -2)$, $(-3, -2)$; Asymptotes: $y = \frac{3}{4}x - \frac{7}{2}$ and $y = -\frac{3}{4}x - \frac{1}{2}$;
Eccentricity: $\frac{5}{4}$ **2.** Ellipse: Center: $(0, 2)$; Vertices: $(5, 2)$, $(-5, 2)$;
Endpoints of minor axis: $(0, 5)$, $(0, -1)$; Foci: $(4, 2)$, $(-4, 2)$;
Eccentricity: $\frac{4}{5}$ **3.** Parabola; Vertex: $(-2, 5)$; Focus: $\left(-\frac{9}{4}, 5\right)$;
Directrix: $x = -\frac{7}{4}$; Axis of symmetry: $y = 5$
4. Circle; Center: $(3, -7)$; Radius: 5 **5.** Ellipse; Center: $(-1, 0)$;
Vertices: $(-1, 4)$, $(-1, -4)$; Endpoints of minor axis: $(-2, 0)$, $(0, 0)$;
Foci: $\left(-1, \sqrt{15}\right)$, $\left(-1, -\sqrt{15}\right)$; Eccentricity: $\frac{\sqrt{15}}{4}$
6. Parabola; Vertex: $(1, -3)$; Focus: $\left(1, -\frac{1}{2}\right)$;
Directrix: $y = -\frac{11}{2}$; Axis of symmetry: $x = 1$
7. Circle; Center: $(-1, -6)$; Radius: 4
8. Hyperbola; Center: $(-4, 1)$; Vertices: $(-4, 13)$, $(-4, -11)$;
Foci: $(-4, 14)$, $(-4, -12)$; Asymptotes: $y = \frac{12}{5}x + \frac{53}{5}$ and
$y = -\frac{12}{5}x - \frac{43}{5}$; Eccentricity: $\frac{13}{12}$
9. Hyperbola; $\dfrac{(x - 2)^2}{16} - \dfrac{(y + 2)^2}{9} = 1$
10. Ellipse; $\dfrac{x^2}{25} + \dfrac{(y - 2)^2}{9} = 1$ **11.** Parabola; $(y - 5)^2 = -(x + 2)$
12. Circle; $(x - 3)^2 + (y + 7)^2 = 25$ **13.** Ellipse; $(x + 1)^2 + \dfrac{y^2}{16} = 1$
14. Parabola; $(x - 1)^2 = 10(y + 3)$ **15.** Circle; $(x + 1)^2 + (y + 6)^2 = 16$
16. Hyperbola; $\dfrac{(y - 1)^2}{144} - \dfrac{(x + 4)^2}{25} = 1$
17. $(x - 2)^2 + (y + 1)^2 = 0$; The graph is a single point: $(2, -1)$.
18. $\dfrac{x^2}{4} + \dfrac{(y - 3)^2}{9} = 0$; The graph is a single point: $(0, 3)$.
19. $(x - 4)^2 - \dfrac{(y + 2)^2}{4} = 0$; The graph is a pair of intersecting lines:
$y = -2x + 6$ and $y = 2x - 10$.
20. $\dfrac{(x - 5)^2}{4} - \dfrac{(y + 1)^2}{9} = 0$; The graph is a pair of intersecting lines:
$y = \frac{3}{2}x - \frac{17}{2}$ and $y = -\frac{3}{2}x + \frac{13}{2}$.

21. $\dfrac{x^2}{4} + \dfrac{(y - 2)^2}{9} = -1$; No solution. There are no real numbers x and
y that would make the sum of two squares equal to -1.
22. $(x + 6)^2 + y^2 = -1$; No solution. There are no real numbers x and y
that would make the sum of two squares equal to -1.

Chapter 7 Review Exercises, pp. 705–707

1. Each equation represents an ellipse with a vertical major axis of
length 30 units and horizontal minor axis of length 20 units. However,
the first equation represents an ellipse centered at $(0, 0)$, whereas the
second equation represents an ellipse centered at $(1, -7)$.
3. a. $(0, 0)$ **b.** $\left(0, -\sqrt{15}\right)$, $\left(0, \sqrt{15}\right)$ **f.**
c. $(3, 0)$, $(-3, 0)$
d. $\left(0, -\sqrt{6}\right)$, $\left(0, \sqrt{6}\right)$
e. $\dfrac{\sqrt{10}}{5}$

5. a. $(1, 2)$ **b.** $(-3, 2)$, $(5, 2)$ **f.**
c. $(1, -1)$, $(1, 5)$
d. $\left(1 - \sqrt{7}, 2\right)$, $\left(1 + \sqrt{7}, 2\right)$
e. $\dfrac{\sqrt{7}}{4}$

7. a. $\dfrac{\left(x - \frac{1}{2}\right)^2}{16} + \dfrac{y^2}{25} = 1$ **b.** Center: $\left(\frac{1}{2}, 0\right)$; Vertices: $\left(\frac{1}{2}, 5\right)$, $\left(\frac{1}{2}, -5\right)$;
Endpoints of minor axis: $\left(-\frac{7}{2}, 0\right)$, $\left(\frac{9}{2}, 0\right)$; Foci: $\left(\frac{1}{2}, 3\right)$, $\left(\frac{1}{2}, -3\right)$
9. $\dfrac{(x - 3)^2}{9} + \dfrac{(y - 1)^2}{25} = 1$
11. The second ellipse with eccentricity $\frac{5}{7}$ is more elongated.
13. The height 50 ft from the center is approximately 97 ft.
15. Horizontal
17. a. $(0, 0)$ **b.** $(3, 0)$, $(-3, 0)$ **e.**
c. $\left(\sqrt{13}, 0\right)$, $\left(-\sqrt{13}, 0\right)$
d. $y = \frac{2}{3}x$ and $y = -\frac{2}{3}x$

19. a. $(-3, 2)$ **b.** $(-3, 5)$, $(-3, -1)$ **e.**
c. $(-3, 7)$, $(-3, -3)$
d. $y = \frac{3}{4}x + \frac{17}{4}$ and $y = -\frac{3}{4}x - \frac{1}{4}$

21. a. $\dfrac{(x + 2)^2}{7} - \dfrac{(y + 4)^2}{11} = 1$
b. Center: $(-2, -4)$;
Vertices: $\left(-2 + \sqrt{7}, -4\right)$, $\left(-2 - \sqrt{7}, -4\right)$
Foci: $\left(-2 + 3\sqrt{2}, -4\right)$, $\left(-2 - 3\sqrt{2}, -4\right)$
23. $\dfrac{x^2}{16} - \dfrac{y^2}{9} = 1$ **25.** $\dfrac{(x - 2)^2}{289} - \dfrac{(y - 7)^2}{64} = 1$
27. $\{(1, 3), (1, -3), (-1, 3), (-1, -3)\}$
29. a. $p = -\frac{1}{2}$ **b.** $(0, 0)$ **31. a.** $p = -1$ **b.** $(3, -2)$
c. $\left(0, -\frac{1}{2}\right)$ **d.** 2 **c.** $(2, -2)$ **d.** 4
e. $\left(-1, -\frac{1}{2}\right)$, $\left(1, -\frac{1}{2}\right)$ **e.** $(2, 0)$, $(2, -4)$
f. $y = \frac{1}{2}$ **g.** $x = 0$ **f.** $x = 4$ **g.** $y = -2$
h.   **h.**

33. a. $(x - 5)^2 = 4(y + 2)$
  b. Vertex: $(5, -2)$; Focus: $(5, -1)$; Directrix: $y = -3$
35. $(4, 2)$; -1 **37.** 3 **39.** $(x + 4)^2 = -32(y - 7)$
41. $\{(8, 1), (5, -2)\}$

Chapter 7 Test, pp. 707–708

1. Each equation represents an ellipse centered at the origin with a major axis of length 24 units and minor axis of length 12 units. However, the ellipse represented by the first equation has foci on the y-axis, whereas the second equation represents an ellipse with foci on the x-axis.

2. $(x - h)^2 + (y - k)^2 = r^2$ **3.** $\dfrac{(x - h)^2}{a^2} + \dfrac{(y - k)^2}{b^2} = 1$

4. $\dfrac{(x - h)^2}{b^2} + \dfrac{(y - k)^2}{a^2} = 1$ **5.** $\dfrac{(y - k)^2}{a^2} - \dfrac{(x - h)^2}{b^2} = 1$

6. $\dfrac{(x - h)^2}{a^2} - \dfrac{(y - k)^2}{b^2} = 1$ **7.** $(x - h)^2 = 4p(y - k)$

8. $(y - k)^2 = 4p(x - h)$

9. a. Ellipse   **b.**
  c. Center: $(2, 0)$; Vertices: $(2, 4), (2, -4)$;
    Endpoints of minor axis: $(-1, 0), (5, 0)$;
    Foci: $\left(2, \sqrt{7}\right), \left(2, -\sqrt{7}\right)$;
    Eccentricity: $\dfrac{\sqrt{7}}{4}$

10. a. Hyperbola   **b.**
  c. Center: $(2, 0)$; Vertices: $(-1, 0), (5, 0)$;
    Foci: $(-3, 0), (7, 0)$;
    Asymptotes:
    $y = \frac{4}{3}x - \frac{8}{3}$ and $y = -\frac{4}{3}x + \frac{8}{3}$;
    Eccentricity: $\frac{5}{3}$

11. a. Parabola   **b.**
  c. Vertex: $(2, 0)$; Focus: $(2, -4)$;
    Endpoints of latus rectum:
    $(10, -4), (-6, -4)$
    Directrix: $y = 4$; Axis of symmetry: $x = 2$

12. a. Circle   **b.**
  c. Center: $(2, 3)$; Radius: $2\sqrt{3}$

13. a. Hyperbola   **b.**
  c. Center: $(0, -2)$; Vertices: $(0, 4), (0, -8)$;
    Foci: $(0, 8), (0, -12)$;
    Asymptotes:
    $y = \frac{3}{4}x - 2$ and $y = -\frac{3}{4}x - 2$;
    Eccentricity: $\frac{5}{3}$

14. a. Ellipse   **b.**
  c. Center: $(-4, 1)$;
    Vertices: $(-14, 1), (6, 1)$;
    Endpoints of minor axis:
    $(-4, 7), (-4, -5)$;
    Foci: $(-12, 1), (4, 1)$; Eccentricity: $\frac{4}{5}$

15. a. Circle   **b.**
  c. Center: $(-4, 1)$; Radius: 2

16. a. Parabola   **b.**
  c. Vertex: $(3, 4)$; Focus: $(5, 4)$;
    Endpoints of latus rectum: $(5, 0), (5, 8)$
    Directrix: $x = 1$;
    Axis of symmetry: $y = 4$

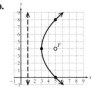

17. a. 13.2 ft   **b.** Yes; The height of the opening is approximately 12 ft at a point 3 ft from the edge.
  c. $h(x) = 6\sqrt{1 - \dfrac{x^2}{144}} + 8$ **18.** 4.444×10^9 km

19. $\dfrac{x^2}{(3300)^2} - \dfrac{y^2}{(2189)^2} = 1$ **20.** 113 ft   **21.** $(x - 1)^2 = 16(y - 2)$

22. $\dfrac{(x - 4)^2}{4} + \dfrac{(y + 3)^2}{3} = 1$ **23.** $\dfrac{(y - 3)^2}{16} - \dfrac{(x - 4)^2}{20} = 1$

24. $\dfrac{(x - 2)^2}{9} - \dfrac{(y + 3)^2}{16} = 1$ **25.** $\dfrac{12}{13}$ **26.** $\dfrac{\sqrt{34}}{5}$

27. Focal length: 3; Focal diameter: 12   **28.** Center: $(0, 1)$
29. $\{(1, 2), (1, -2), (-1, 2), (-1, -2)\}$
30. The graph is a left semiellipse with center at the origin and major axis of length 8 units and minor axis of length 6 units.

Chapter 7 Cumulative Review Exercises , pp. 708–709

1. $3x^2 - 2x - 9 + \dfrac{x + 28}{x^2 + 3}$ **2.** No   **3.** Yes   **4.** $\dfrac{3\sqrt[3]{x^2}}{x}$

5. $\dfrac{z^{12}}{x^{18}y^{10}}$ **6.** $\left(-122, \dfrac{171}{2}\right)$ **7.** $f^{-1}(x) = x^3 + 7$

8. $y = -12x + 20$ **9.** Neither   **10.** $\left\{\dfrac{-2 + \ln 22}{3}\right\}$

11. $\left(\dfrac{37}{9}, \infty\right)$ **12.** $\{\ \}$ **13.** $\left(-\infty, \dfrac{4 - \sqrt{10}}{2}\right] \cup \left[\dfrac{4 + \sqrt{10}}{2}, \infty\right)$
14. $\{9\}$; The value -3 does not check.   **15.** $\{\ln 5, \ln 3\}$
16.   **17.**

18. $\dfrac{3}{x - 3} + \dfrac{5}{x - 4}$ **19. a.** $(f \circ g)(x) = \dfrac{1}{\sqrt{x - 1} - 2}$
  b. $[1, 5) \cup (5, \infty)$ **20. a.** $(0, 0), (4, 0)$ **b.** $(0, 0)$
  c. $x = -3$ **d.** None   **e.** $y = x - 7$

21.   **22.**

23.   **24.**

25. $\{(-1, 0, 4)\}$ **26.** $\{(3, 1), (3, -1), (-3, 1), (-3, -1)\}$
27. $\begin{bmatrix} -12 & 64 \\ 6 & 32 \end{bmatrix}$ **28.** $\begin{bmatrix} \frac{3}{8} & -\frac{1}{4} \\ \frac{1}{16} & \frac{1}{8} \end{bmatrix}$ **29.** -12

30. $z = \dfrac{97}{146}$

CHAPTER 8

Section 8.1 Practice Exercises, pp. 719–722

1. sequence; finite   **3.** alternating   **5.** $n!; 1$
7. index; summation; lower; limit   **9.** 5, 11, 21, 35
11. $-6, 3, -\frac{3}{2}, \frac{3}{4}$ **13.** $2, \sqrt{5}, \sqrt{6}, \sqrt{7}$ **15.** 1, 8, 27, 64
17. The odd-numbered terms are negative, and the even-numbered terms are positive.   **19.** 1023   **21.** 781   **23.** c   **25.** a
27. $-3, -5, -11, -29, -83$ **29.** $4, 6, 7, \frac{15}{2}, \frac{31}{4}$ **31.** $5, \frac{1}{5}, 5, \frac{1}{5}, 5$
33. a. 1, 1, 2, 3, 5, 8, 13, 21, 34, 55   **b.** $F_1 = 1, F_2 = 1, F_3 = 2$
35. 5040   **37.** 1   **39.** 56   **41.** 126
43. $\dfrac{1}{n(n+1)}$ **45.** $\dfrac{1}{2n+1}$ **47.** $a_5 = \dfrac{2}{315}$ **49.** $c_3 = 24{,}192$
51. 39   **53.** -110 **55.** $\dfrac{15}{32}$ **57.** 120   **59.** -30 **61.** $\dfrac{29}{6}$
63. 62   **65. a.** 0   **b.** -1 **67.** 25   **69.** $a_n = 2^n$
71. $a_n = -\dfrac{n+1}{3n}$ **73.** $a_n = (-1)^n(n^2)$ **75.** $\displaystyle\sum_{i=1}^{n} \dfrac{i^2}{i+1}$
77. $\displaystyle\sum_{i=1}^{5} i$ **79.** $\displaystyle\sum_{i=1}^{4} 8$ **81.** $\displaystyle\sum_{i=1}^{4} (-1)^{i+1}\dfrac{1}{3^i}$ **83.** $\displaystyle\sum_{i=1}^{18} c^{i+2}$
85. $\displaystyle\sum_{i=1}^{4} \dfrac{x^i}{i!}$ **87.** $\displaystyle\sum_{i=1}^{8} i^2 = \sum_{j=0}^{7} (j+1)^2 = \sum_{k=2}^{9} (k-1)^2$
89. Expanding the series, there are n terms and each term is c. Therefore, the sum is cn.
$$\sum_{i=1}^{n} c = c + c + c + \cdots + c = cn$$
91. 46,750   **93.** 6575   **95.** True   **97.** False
99. $a_n = 1.03a_{n-1} + 1000; n \geq 2$ **101.** 66; If 12 people are present at the meeting, then there will be 66 handshakes.
103. a. {31, 10, 17, 17, 11, 21}   **b.** 17.8; The mean (average) number of tropical storms and hurricanes in the Atlantic was 17.8 during this period.
105.
$$\sum_{i=1}^{n} (a_i - \bar{a}) = \sum_{i=1}^{n} a_i - \sum_{i=1}^{n} \bar{a} = \sum_{i=1}^{n} a_i - n\bar{a} = \sum_{i=1}^{n} a_i - n \cdot \frac{1}{n}\sum_{i=1}^{n} a_i = 0$$
107. A sequence is an ordered list of terms. A series is the sum of the terms of a sequence.   **109.** Write 1206! as (1206)(1205)(1204!) and then simplify the fraction before multiplying. The result is the product $(1206)(1205) = 1{,}453{,}230$.   **111.** 2, 1.5, 1.4167, 1.4142
113.

115.

117.

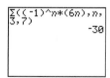

Section 8.2 Practice Exercises, pp. 729–733

1. $a_4 = 256$ **3.** $a_n = \dfrac{5n}{3^n}$ **5.** 110   **7.** arithmetic
9. $a_1 + (n-1)d$ **11.** partial   **13.** Yes; $d = 4$

15. Yes; $d = -11$ **17.** No   **19.** Yes; $d = \dfrac{2}{3}$
21. 3, 13, 23, 33, 43   **23.** 4, 2, 0, -2, -4 **25. a.** $a_n = 5n - 17$
b. $a_{20} = 83$ **27. a.** $a_n = \dfrac{1}{3}n + \dfrac{1}{6}$ **b.** $a_{10} = \dfrac{7}{2}$
29. $a_n = 22n + 8$ **31. a.** Yes   **b.** $a_n = 16n + 18$ **c.** 178
33. $v_{n+1} - v_n = [v_0 + a(n+1)] - (v_0 + an)$
$\quad\quad\quad\quad = v_0 + an + a - v_0 - an$
$\quad\quad\quad\quad = a$
The difference between two consecutive terms is the constant a. Therefore, the sequence is arithmetic.
35. a. $a_n = 55n + 2583$ where a_n is represented in 1000s, and $n \geq 0$.
b. Approximately 2,858,000 people were employed in nursing and residential care facilities in the year 2005.   **37.** $a_8 = 33$
39. $a_{35} = -460$ **41.** $n = 53$ **43.** $n = 49$ **45.** $a_1 = 44; d = 8$
47. 246   **49.** 3940   **51.** -918 **53.** $a_1 = 0, a_2 = -3$
55. 279   **57.** 2850   **59.** -6115.5 **61.** 264   **63.** -207
65. a. Job 1 for 5 yr: $352,000; Job 2 for 5 yr: $350,000
b. Job 1 for 10 yr: $784,000; Job 2 for 10 yr: $825,000
67. a. $d_n = 32n - 16$ **b.** 240 ft   **c.** 1024 ft   **69. a.** 1 cup
b. 120 cups   **71. a.** 6, 4, 2, 0   **b.** $b_n = -2n + 8$
c. $b_{30} = -52$ **d.** -690 **e.** $n = 94$ **f.** -136
73. 32,686   **75.** 6375   **77.** 1410
79. a. Substitute $a_1 = 1$ and $a_n = n$. $S_n = \frac{n}{2}(a_1 + a_n) = \frac{n}{2}(1 + n)$
b. 5050   **c.** 500,500   **81.** The three arithmetic means between 4 and 28 are 10, 16, and 22.   **83.** The terms in the given sequence $a_1, a_2, a_3, \ldots$ differ by d units. Therefore, every other term would differ by $2d$ units. Thus, $a_1, a_3, a_5, \ldots$ is an arithmetic sequence with common difference $2d$.
85. $a_n = 2n + 1$; The sequence is $\{3, 5, 7, \ldots, (2n+1), \ldots\}$.
87.

89.

Section 8.3 Practice Exercises, pp. 741–746

1. $a_{46} = 275$ **3.** $-23{,}411$ **5.** 17,875   **7.** geometric; ratio
9. finite   **11.** 0   **13.** annuity   **15.** Yes; $r = 3$
17. Yes; $r = -\dfrac{1}{2}$ **19.** No   **21.** Yes; $r = \sqrt{5}$ **23.** Yes; $r = \dfrac{2}{t}$
25. 7, 14, 28, 56, 112   **27.** 24, -16, $\dfrac{32}{3}$, $-\dfrac{64}{9}$, $\dfrac{128}{27}$ **29.** 36, 18, 9, $\dfrac{9}{2}$, $\dfrac{9}{4}$
31. $a_n = 5(2)^{n-1}$ **33.** $a_n = -2\left(\dfrac{1}{2}\right)^{n-1}$ **35.** $a_n = \dfrac{16}{3}\left(\dfrac{3}{4}\right)^{n-1}$
37. a. $a_n = 100{,}000(0.85)^n$ **b.** $44,000   **39.** 331 cases
41. $a_6 = -\dfrac{128}{81}$ **43.** $a_{12} = 4096$ **45.** $a_7 = -\dfrac{3}{16}$
47. $a_1 = -9$ **49.** $a_1 = 3$ **51.** $a_1 = 9; r = 2$
53. $a_1 = 128; r = -\dfrac{3}{4}$ **55.** 3069   **57.** $\dfrac{4118}{243}$ **59.** $\dfrac{1820}{81}$
61. 19,682   **63.** $\dfrac{665}{243}$ **65.** $\dfrac{5}{4}$ **67.** $-\dfrac{8}{3}$
69. Sum does not exist   **71.** 3   **73.** Sum does not exist
75. 32,760   **77.** 2   **79.** $\dfrac{29}{45}$ **81.** $\dfrac{9}{11}$ **83.** $\dfrac{3391}{990}$
85. a. $150,000,000   **b.** $468,750,000   **87.** $32,000

89. \$166,451.73　**91. a.** \$46,204.09　**b.** \$92,408.18; The value of the annuity doubles.　**c.** \$199,149.07; The value of the annuity more than doubles.　**93. a.** Decreasing　**b.** Increasing
95. Graph b　**97.** Graph d　**99.** 1200 in. or 100 ft.　**101.** 12 ft
103. a. $a_n = 0.01(2)^{n-1}$ (dollars)　**b.** Day 10: \$5.12; Day 20: \$5242.88; Day 30: \$5,368,709.12　**c.** \$10,737,418.23
105. a. Arithmetic; \$1,770,000　**b.** Geometric; \$2,059,993　**c.** \$289,993　**107. a.** $a_n = 2^n$　**b.** 1024
109. In an arithmetic sequence, the difference between a term and its predecessor is a fixed constant. In a geometric sequence, the ratio between a term and its predecessor is a fixed constant.
111. Each term of the sequence $a_1, a_2, a_3, \ldots$ after the first term is obtained by multiplying the preceding term by r. Therefore, every other term is obtained by multiplying by r^2. Therefore, the sequence $a_1, a_3, a_5, \ldots$ is geometric with common ratio r^2.
113. The sequence $\frac{1}{a_1}, \frac{1}{a_2}, \frac{1}{a_3}, \frac{1}{a_4}, \ldots$ can be written as $\frac{1}{a_1}, \frac{1}{a_1 r}, \frac{1}{a_1 r^2}, \frac{1}{a_1 r^3}, \ldots$ or equivalently as $\frac{1}{a_1}, \frac{1}{a_1}(\frac{1}{r}), \frac{1}{a_1}(\frac{1}{r})^2, \frac{1}{a_1}(\frac{1}{r})^3, \ldots$. Therefore, the sequence is geometric with common ratio $\frac{1}{r}$.
115. Each term of the geometric sequence $a_1, a_2, a_3, \ldots$ can be written in the form $a_1 r^{n-1}$. Therefore, $\log a_1, \log a_2, \log a_3, \ldots = \log a_1, \log a_1 r, \log a_1 r^2, \ldots, \log a_1 r^{n-1}, \log a_1 r^n, \ldots$.
$$a_{n+1} - a_n = \log a_1 r^n - \log a_1 r^{n-1}$$
$$= (\log a_1 + \log r^n) - (\log a_1 + \log r^{n-1})$$
$$= (\log a_1 + n \log r) - [\log a_1 + (n-1) \log r]$$
$$= \log r$$
The common difference is $\log r$.
117. Arithmetic; $d = \ln 2$
119.

121.

Problem Recognition Exercises, p. 746

1. Arithmetic; $d = \dfrac{2}{3}$　**2.** Arithmetic; $d = -\dfrac{3}{5}$
3. Geometric; $r = -1$　**4.** Geometric; $r = -2$　**5.** Neither
6. Neither　**7.** Geometric; $r = \sqrt{5}$　**8.** Geometric; $r = \sqrt{2}$
9. Arithmetic; $d = \sqrt{2}$　**10.** Arithmetic; $d = \dfrac{\sqrt{3}}{2}$　**11.** 7530
12. -1251　**13.** 0　**14.** -1　**15.** $-\dfrac{1}{4}$　**16.** 294
17. $-\dfrac{40}{9}$　**18.** $-\dfrac{781}{128}$　**19.** The sum does not exist.
20. The sum does not exist.　**21.** -2376　**22.** -4428　**23.** 8
24. 6　**25.** 216　**26.** 162　**27.** 8418　**28.** $-12,639$

Section 8.4 Skill Practice

Answers 1

1. $S_1 = 2$, which equals $1(1 + 1)$.
2. Assume that $S_k = k(k + 1)$. Show that $S_{k+1} = (k + 1)[(k + 1) + 1]$, or equivalently, that $S_{k+1} = (k + 1)(k + 2)$. We have $S_{k+1} = [2 + 4 + \cdots + 2k] + 2(k + 1)$.
Replacing $[2 + 4 + \cdots + 2k]$ by $k(k + 1)$, we have $S_{k+1} = k(k + 1) + 2(k + 1) = k^2 + 3k + 2 = (k + 1)(k + 2)$ as desired.

Answers 2

1. $S_1 = \frac{1}{3}$, which equals $\frac{1}{2(1) + 1} = \frac{1}{3}$.
2. Assume that $S_k = \frac{k}{2k + 1}$. Show that $S_{k+1} = \frac{k + 1}{2(k + 1) + 1}$, or equivalently, $S_{k+1} = \frac{k + 1}{2k + 3}$.
We have
$$S_{k+1} = \frac{1}{1 \cdot 3} + \frac{1}{3 \cdot 5} + \cdots + \frac{1}{(2k - 1)(2k + 1)} + \frac{1}{[2(k + 1) - 1][2(k + 1) + 1]}.$$
Replacing $\frac{1}{1 \cdot 3} + \frac{1}{3 \cdot 5} + \cdots + \frac{1}{(2k - 1)(2k + 1)}$ by $\frac{k}{2k + 1}$, we have
$$S_{k+1} = \frac{k}{2k + 1} + \frac{1}{(2k + 1)(2k + 3)} = \frac{2k^2 + 3k + 1}{(2k + 1)(2k + 3)} = \frac{(2k + 1)(k + 1)}{(2k + 1)(2k + 3)} = \frac{k + 1}{2k + 3}$$
as desired.

Answers 3

1. S_1 is true because 2 is a factor of $5^1 + 1 = 6$.
2. Assume that 2 is a factor of $5^k + 1$. Then $5^k + 1 = 2a$ for some positive integer a. Equivalently, $5^k = 2a - 1$. Show that 2 is a factor of $5^{k+1} + 1$.
We have $5^{k+1} + 1 = 5 \cdot 5^k + 1 = 5(2a - 1) + 1 = 10a - 4 = 2(5a - 2)$. The value 2 is a factor of $2(5a - 2)$, and therefore a factor of $5^{k+1} + 1$ as desired.

Answers 4

1. Show that S_7 is true. That is, show that $(\frac{3}{2})^7 > 2(7)$. We have $(\frac{3}{2})^7 = \frac{2187}{128} = 17\frac{11}{128}$, which is greater than $2(7) = 14$. Therefore, $(\frac{3}{2})^7 > 2(7)$.
2. Assume that $(\frac{3}{2})^k > 2k$ for $k \geq 7$. Show that $(\frac{3}{2})^{k+1} > 2(k + 1)$.
We have $(\frac{3}{2})^{k+1} = \frac{3}{2}(\frac{3}{2})^k > \frac{3}{2}(2k) = 3k$ for $k \geq 7$. Furthermore, $3k = 2k + k > 2k + 2$ for $k \geq 7$. Therefore, $(\frac{3}{2})^{k+1} > 2(k + 1)$ as desired.

Section 8.4 Practice Exercises, pp. 752–753

1. $-18,023$　**3.** $\frac{3905}{256}$　**5.** induction; S_1; S_{k+1}
7. 1. S_1 is true because $2 = 2(1)^2$.
　2. Assume that $S_k = 2k^2$. Show that $S_{k+1} = 2(k + 1)^2$.
$$S_{k+1} = [2 + 6 + \cdots + (4k - 2)] + [4(k + 1) - 2]$$
$$= 2k^2 + (4k + 2) \quad \text{Inductive hypothesis}$$
$$= 2(k^2 + 2k + 1)$$
$$= 2(k + 1)^2 \text{ as desired.}$$
9. 1. S_1 is true because $5 = \frac{1}{2}[3(1) + 7]$.
　2. Assume that $S_k = \frac{k}{2}(3k + 7)$. Show that
$$S_{k+1} = \frac{k + 1}{2}[3(k + 1) + 7] = \frac{(k + 1)(3k + 10)}{2}.$$
$$S_{k+1} = [5 + 8 + \cdots + (3k + 2)] + [3(k + 1) + 2]$$
$$= \frac{k}{2}(3k + 7) + (3k + 5) \quad \text{Inductive hypothesis}$$
$$= \frac{3k^2 + 13k + 10}{2}$$
$$= \frac{(k + 1)(3k + 10)}{2} \text{ as desired.}$$
11. 1. S_1 is true because $8 = -2(1)(1 - 5)$.
　2. Assume that $S_k = -2k(k - 5)$. Show that
$$S_{k+1} = -2(k + 1)[(k + 1) - 5] = -2k^2 + 6k + 8.$$
$$S_{k+1} = [8 + 4 + \cdots + (-4k + 12)] + [-4(k + 1) + 12]$$
$$= -2k(k - 5) + (-4k + 8) \quad \text{Inductive hypothesis}$$
$$= -2k^2 + 6k + 8 \text{ as desired.}$$
13. 1. S_1 is true because $1 = 2^1 - 1$.
　2. Assume that $S_k = 2^k - 1$. Show that
$$S_{k+1} = 2^{k+1} - 1.$$
$$S_{k+1} = [1 + 2 + 2^2 + \cdots + 2^{k-1}] + 2^{(k+1) - 1}$$
$$= (2^k - 1) + 2^k \quad \text{Inductive hypothesis}$$
$$= 2 \cdot 2^k - 1$$
$$= 2^{k+1} - 1 \text{ as desired.}$$

15. 1. S_1 is true because $\frac{3}{4} = 1 - \left(\frac{1}{4}\right)^1$.

2. Assume that $S_k = 1 - \left(\frac{1}{4}\right)^k$. Show that $S_{k+1} = 1 - \left(\frac{1}{4}\right)^{k+1}$.

$$S_{k+1} = \left[\frac{3}{4} + \frac{3}{16} + \cdots + \frac{3}{4^k}\right] + \frac{3}{4^{k+1}}$$

$$= 1 - \left(\frac{1}{4}\right)^k + \frac{3}{4^{k+1}} \quad \text{Inductive hypothesis}$$

$$= 1 - \left(\frac{1}{4}\right)^k + \frac{3}{4}\left(\frac{1}{4}\right)^k$$

$$= 1 - \left(\frac{1}{4}\right)^k\left(1 - \frac{3}{4}\right) = 1 - \left(\frac{1}{4}\right)^k\left(\frac{1}{4}\right)$$

$$= 1 - \left(\frac{1}{4}\right)^{k+1} \text{ as desired.}$$

17. 1. S_1 is true because $1 \cdot 2 = \frac{(1)(1 + 1)(1 + 2)}{3}$.

2. Assume that $S_k = \frac{k(k + 1)(k + 2)}{3}$. Show that

$$S_{k+1} = \frac{(k + 1)[(k + 1) + 1][(k + 1) + 2]}{3} = \frac{k^3 + 6k^2 + 11k + 6}{3}.$$

$$S_{k+1} = 1 \cdot 2 + 2 \cdot 3 + \cdots + k(k + 1) + (k + 1)[(k + 1) + 1]$$

$$= \frac{k(k + 1)(k + 2)}{3} + (k + 1)(k + 2) \quad \text{Inductive hypothesis}$$

$$= \frac{k^3 + 3k^2 + 2k}{3} + k^2 + 3k + 2$$

$$= \frac{k^3 + 6k^2 + 11k + 6}{3} \text{ as desired.}$$

19. 1. S_1 is true because $\left(1 - \frac{1}{2}\right) = \frac{1}{1 + 1}$.

2. Assume that $S_k = \frac{1}{k + 1}$. Show that

$$S_{k+1} = \frac{1}{(k + 1) + 1} = \frac{1}{k + 2}.$$

$$S_{k+1} = \left(1 - \frac{1}{2}\right)\left(1 - \frac{1}{3}\right)\cdots\left(1 - \frac{1}{k + 1}\right)\left[1 - \frac{1}{(k + 1) + 1}\right]$$

$$= \frac{1}{k + 1}\left(1 - \frac{1}{k + 2}\right) \quad \text{Inductive hypothesis}$$

$$= \frac{1}{k + 1} \cdot \left(\frac{k + 1}{k + 2}\right)$$

$$= \frac{1}{k + 2} \text{ as desired.}$$

21. 1. S_1 is true because $\sum_{i=1}^{1} 1 = 1$.

2. Assume that S_k is true; that is, $\sum_{i=1}^{k} 1 = k$.

Show that S_{k+1} is true: $\sum_{i=1}^{k+1} 1 = (k + 1)$.

$$\sum_{i=1}^{k+1} 1 = \left(\sum_{i=1}^{k} 1\right) + 1 = k + 1 \text{ as desired.}$$

23. 1. S_1 is true because $\sum_{i=1}^{1} i^2 = (1)^2 = \frac{1(1 + 1)[2(1) + 1]}{6}$.

2. Assume that S_k is true; that is, $S_k = \sum_{i=1}^{k} i^2 = \frac{k(k + 1)(2k + 1)}{6}$.

Show that S_{k+1} is true:

$$\sum_{i=1}^{k+1} i^2 = \frac{(k + 1)[(k + 1) + 1][2(k + 1) + 1]}{6}, \text{ or equivalently,}$$

$$\sum_{i=1}^{k+1} i^2 = \frac{2k^3 + 9k^2 + 13k + 6}{6}.$$

$$\sum_{i=1}^{k+1} i^2 = \left(\sum_{i=1}^{k} i^2\right) + (k + 1)^2 = \frac{k(k + 1)(2k + 1)}{6} + (k + 1)^2$$

$$= \frac{2k^3 + 9k^2 + 13k + 6}{6} \text{ as desired.}$$

25. Let S_n be the statement 2 is a factor of $5^n - 3$.

1. S_1 is true because 2 is a factor of $(5)^1 - 3 = 2$.

2. Assume that S_k is true; that is, assume that 2 is a factor of $5^k - 3$. This implies that $5^k - 3 = 2a$ and that $5^k = 2a + 3$ for some positive integer a.

Show that S_{k+1} is true; that is, show that 2 is a factor of $5^{k+1} - 3$.

$$5^{k+1} - 3 = 5 \cdot 5^k - 3$$

$$= 5(2a + 3) - 3 \quad \text{Replace } 5^k \text{ by } 2a + 3.$$

$$= 10a + 12$$

$$= 2(5a + 6)$$

Therefore, 2 is a factor of $5^{k+1} - 3$.

27. Let S_n be the statement $4^n - 1$ is divisible by 3. This is equivalent to saying that 3 is a factor of $4^n - 1$.

1. S_1 is true because 3 is a factor of $(4)^1 - 1 = 3$.

2. Assume that S_k is true; that is, assume that 3 is a factor of $4^k - 1$. This implies that $4^k - 1 = 3a$ and that $4^k = 3a + 1$ for some positive integer a.

Show that S_{k+1} is true; that is, show that 3 is a factor of $4^{k+1} - 1$.

$$4^{k+1} - 1 = 4 \cdot 4^k - 1$$

$$= 4 \cdot (3a + 1) - 1 \quad \text{Replace } 4^k \text{ by } 3a + 1.$$

$$= 12a + 3$$

$$= 3(4a + 1)$$

Therefore, 3 is a factor of $4^{k+1} - 1$ as desired.

29. $n = 7$ **31.** $n = 4$

33. Let S_n be the statement $n! > 3^n$ for $n \geq 7$.

1. S_7 is true because $7! = 5040$ and $3^7 = 2187$. Therefore, $7! > 3^7$.

2. Assume that $k! > 3^k$ for a natural number $k \geq 7$. Show that $(k + 1)! > 3^{k+1}$.

$$(k + 1)! = (k + 1) \cdot k!$$

$$> (k + 1)(3^k) \quad \text{Inductive hypothesis}$$

$$> 3(3^k) \quad\quad \text{Since } k \geq 7, \text{ then } (k + 1) > 3.$$

$$= 3^{k+1}$$

Therefore, $(k + 1)! > 3^{k+1}$ as desired.

35. Let S_n be the statement $3n < 2^n$ for $n \geq 4$.

1. S_4 is true because $3(4) = 12$ and $2^4 = 16$. Therefore, $3(4) < 2^{(4)}$.

2. Assume that $3k < 2^k$ for a natural number $k \geq 4$. Show that $3(k + 1) < 2^{k+1}$.

$$3(k + 1) = 3k + 3. \quad \text{Furthermore, since } k \geq 4, 3k > 3.$$

$$< 3k + 3k$$

$$< 2^k + 2^k \quad \text{Inductive hypothesis}$$

$$= 2(2^k)$$

$$= 2^{k+1}$$

Therefore, $3(k + 1) < 2^{k+1}$ as desired.

37. 1. S_1 is true because $(xy)^1 = xy = x^1y^1$.

2. Assume that S_k is true: $(xy)^k = x^ky^k$.

Show that S_{k+1} is true. Show that $(xy)^{k+1} = x^{k+1}y^{k+1}$.

S_{k+1} follows by multiplying S_k by (xy).

$(xy)^k(xy) = x^ky^k(xy) = x^{k+1}y^{k+1}$ as desired.

39. 1. S_1 is true because $x^1 > 1$ for $x > 1$ and since $x^0 = 1$, we have $x^1 > x^0$ for $x > 1$.

2. Assume that S_k is true: $x^k > x^{k-1}$ for $x > 1$.

Show that S_{k+1} is true: $x^{k+1} > x^{(k+1)-1}$, or equivalently, $x^{k+1} > x^k$.

$$x^{k+1} = x^k \cdot x$$

$$> x^{k-1} \cdot x \quad \text{by the inductive hypothesis.}$$

$$= x^k x^{-1} \cdot x$$

$$= x^k \text{ as desired.}$$

41. The statement is false for $n = 11$.

43. The principle of mathematical induction has us test the truth of a statement for $n = 1$. The extended principle of mathematical induction has us test the truth of a statement for the first allowable value of n. In each case, the proof is concluded by showing that the truth of a statement for any other positive integer after the first allowable value of n follows directly from its predecessor.

45. Let S_n be the statement that $n^2 - n$ is even.

1. S_1 is true because $(1)^2 - (1) = 0$, which is even.

2. Assume that S_k is true; that is, assume that $k^2 - k$ is even. This implies that $k^2 - k = 2a$ for some natural number a, and that $k = k^2 - 2a$.

Show that S_{k+1} is true; that is, show that $(k + 1)^2 - (k + 1)$ is even.

$$(k + 1)^2 - (k + 1)$$

$$= k^2 + k$$

$$= k^2 + (k^2 - 2a) \quad \text{Inductive hypothesis}$$

$$= 2k^2 - 2a$$

$$= 2(k^2 - a), \text{ which is an even integer.}$$

47. 1. S_3 is true because $F_1 + F_2 + F_3 = 1 + 1 + 2 = 4$ and
$F_{3+2} - 1 = F_5 - 1 = 5 - 1 = 4$.

2. Assume that S_k is true; that is, assume that
$F_1 + F_2 + \cdots + F_k = F_{k+2} - 1$.

Show that S_{k+1} is true; that is, show that
$F_1 + F_2 + \cdots + F_k + F_{k+1} = F_{[(k+1)+2]} - 1 = F_{k+3} - 1$.
$F_1 + F_2 + \cdots + F_k + F_{k+1} = (F_1 + F_2 + \cdots + F_k) + F_{k+1}$
$= (F_{k+2} - 1) + F_{k+1}$ Inductive hypothesis
$= (F_{k+1} + F_{k+2}) - 1$ Replace $F_{k+1} + F_{k+2}$ by F_{k+3}.
$= F_{k+3} - 1$ as desired.

Section 8.5 Practice Exercises, pp. 757–759

1. $1 + x + y + x^2 + 2xy + y^2$ **3.** 4550 **5.** $\frac{45}{8}$ **7.** 6

9. a. $x^3 - x^4 + x^5 - x^6 + x^7 - x^8$ **b.** 1 **c.** 0

11. binomial **13.** n **15.** $\binom{n}{k-1}a^{n-(k-1)}b^{k-1}$

17. a. See Figure 8-9 on page 753. **b.** $x^4 - 4x^3y + 6x^2y^2 - 4xy^3 + y^4$

19. a. 1 **b.** 4 **c.** 6 **d.** 4 **e.** 1 **21.** 286 **23.** 462

25. $243x^5 + 405x^4 + 270x^3 + 90x^2 + 15x + 1$

27. $343x^3 + 441x^2 + 189x + 27$

29. $16x^4 - 160x^3 + 600x^2 - 1000x + 625$

31. $32x^{15} - 80x^{12}y + 80x^9y^2 - 40x^6y^3 + 10x^3y^4 - y^5$

33. $p^{12} - 6p^{10}w^4 + 15p^8w^8 - 20p^6w^{12} + 15p^4w^{16} - 6p^2w^{20} + w^{24}$

35. $0.0016 + 0.0032k + 0.0024k^2 + 0.0008k^3 + 0.0001k^4$

37. $\frac{1}{8}c^3 - \frac{3}{4}c^2d + \frac{3}{2}cd^2 - d^3$ **39.** $210\,m^4n^6$ **41.** $-56c^5d^3$

43. $2{,}562{,}560u^{12}v^{36}$ **45.** $2268x^{12}y^9$ **47.** $924h^{24}$

49. $13{,}608\,p^{12}q^5$ **51.** $e^{4x} - 4e^{2x} + 6 - \dfrac{4}{e^{2x}} + \dfrac{1}{e^{4x}}$

53. $x^3 + 3x^2y + 3xy^2 + y^3 - 3x^2z - 6xyz - 3y^2z + 3xz^2 + 3yz^2 - z^3$

55. 1.04060401 **57.** $6x^2y + 2y^3$ **59.** $6x^2 + 6xh + 2h^2$

61. $4x^3 + 6x^2h + 4xh^2 + h^3 - 10x - 5h$ **63.** $2 + 11i$

65. $41 - 840i$

67. $\binom{n}{r} = \dfrac{n!}{r! \cdot (n-r)!}$ and
$\binom{n}{n-r} = \dfrac{n!}{(n-r)! \cdot [n-(n-r)]!} = \dfrac{n!}{(n-r)! \cdot r!}$.

By the commutative property of multiplication,
$\dfrac{n!}{r! \cdot (n-r)!} = \dfrac{n!}{(n-r)! \cdot r!}$.

69. a. 1, 2, 4, 8, 16, 32, 64, 128, 256 **b.** $a_n = 2^{n-1}$

71. In this expression $n = 3$ and $r = 5$. The value $(n - r)!$ is
$(3 - 5)! = (-2)!$, which is undefined.

73. a. 39,902 **b.** 40,320 **c.** 1.0% error **75.** 1.656

Section 8.6 Practice Exercises, pp. 768–771

1. 462 **3.** Arithmetic **5.** Neither

7. principle; counting; $m \cdot n$ **9.** permutation **11.** $\dfrac{n!}{r}$

13. $\dfrac{n!}{(n-r)!}$ **15.** 10 **17.** 8 **19.** 2 **21.** $4 \cdot 3 \cdot 6 \cdot 4 = 288$

23. a. $26^3 \cdot 10^3 = 17{,}576{,}000$
b. $26 \cdot 25 \cdot 24 \cdot 10 \cdot 9 \cdot 8 = 11{,}232{,}000$

25. a. $2 \cdot 26 \cdot 26 \cdot 26 = 35{,}152$ **b.** $2 \cdot 25 \cdot 24 \cdot 23 = 27{,}600$

27. $5^{10} \cdot 2^4 = 156{,}250{,}000$

29. $2^8 = 256$

31. a. $7! = 5040$ **b.** $\dfrac{11!}{4! \cdot 4! \cdot 2!} = 34{,}650$

33. $5! - 1 = 119$ **35.** $4! = 24$ **37.** 360 **39.** 132

41. 362,880 **43.** 6840; There are 6840 ways to select 3 distinct items
in a specific order from a group of 20 items.

45. 15 **47.** 66 **49.** 1 **51.** 1140; There are 1140 ways to select
3 distinct items in *no specific order* from a group of 20 items.

53. a. AB, BA, AC, CA, BC, CB **b.** AB, AC, BC (*Note:* The order
within the individual combinations does not matter. That is, AB or
BA represents the same group of two elements.)

55. $_9P_3 = 9 \cdot 8 \cdot 7 = 504$

57. a. $_{24}C_5 = 42{,}504$ **b.** $_{24}P_5 = 5{,}100{,}480$

59. $_{16}C_2 = 120$ **61.** $_{47}C_5 = 1{,}533{,}939$ **63.** $(_9C_3) \cdot (_7C_3) = 2940$

65. $10^4 = 10{,}000$ **67.** $_{12}C_5 = 792$ **69.** $_5P_5 = 5! = 120$

71. a. $_4C_3 = 4$ **b.** $_{16}C_3 = 560$ **c.** $(_{16}C_2) \cdot (_4C_1) = 480$

73. a. { }, {a}, {b}, {c}, {d}, {a, b}, {a, c}, {a, d}, {b, c}, {b, d},
{c, d}, {a, b, c}, {a, b, d}, {a, c, d}, {b, c, d}, {a, b, c, d}
b. $_4C_0 = 1$, $_4C_1 = 4$, $_4C_2 = 6$, $_4C_3 = 4$, and $_4C_4 = 1$

75. $40^3 = 64{,}000$ **77.** 2 **79.** 9 **81.** $6^3 = 216$

83. $5 \cdot 6 \cdot 6 = 180$ **85.** $5 \cdot 6 \cdot 3 = 90$

87. a. 8; 16; 32 **b.** 8; BBB, BBG, BGB, BGG, GBB, GBG, GGB,
GGG **c.** 16

89. $_{160}C_4 = 26{,}294{,}360$ **91.** $2 \cdot 4 \cdot 3 \cdot 2 \cdot 1 = 48$

93. Using the fundamental principle of counting, we have $8 \cdot 7 \cdot 6 = 336$.
There are 8 horses that can cross the finish line first. Once the first
horse finishes, there are 7 horses remaining that can come in second.
Then there are 6 horses that are available for third place.
Alternatively, the number of first-, second-, and third place ordered
arrangements can be found by taking the number of permutations of
8 horses taken 3 at a time, $_8P_3$.

95. $[(_3P_3) \cdot (_4P_4) \cdot (_2P_2)] \cdot (_3P_3) = 1728$

Section 8.7 Practice Exercises, pp. 780–786

1. $_{30}C_5 = 142{,}506$ **3.** {1, 2, 3, 4, 5, 6, 7, 8} **5.** {5}

7. experiment **9.** event **11.** $\dfrac{n(E)}{n(S)}$ **13.** complement; 1

15. $P(A) + P(B) - P(A \cap B)$ **17.** independent

19. c, d, g, h **21.** c **23.** e **25.** f **27.** $\dfrac{4}{10} = \dfrac{2}{5}$ **29.** $\dfrac{7}{10}$

31. 0 **33.** 1 **35. a.** $\dfrac{16}{30} = \dfrac{8}{15}$ **b.** $\dfrac{6}{30} = \dfrac{1}{5}$ **c.** 0

37. a. $\dfrac{18}{38} = \dfrac{9}{19}$ **b.** $\dfrac{7}{38}$ **c.** $\dfrac{37}{38}$ **39.** 0.158 **41.** 0.984

43. a. $\dfrac{3}{36} = \dfrac{1}{12}$ **b.** $\dfrac{33}{36} = \dfrac{11}{12}$

45. a. $\dfrac{6}{36} = \dfrac{1}{6}$ **b.** $\dfrac{3}{36} = \dfrac{1}{12}$ **47.** 0.10

49. a. $\dfrac{_{18}C_9}{_{34}C_9} = \dfrac{48{,}620}{52{,}451{,}256} \approx 0.00093$

b. $\dfrac{_{16}C_9}{_{34}C_9} = \dfrac{11{,}440}{52{,}451{,}256} \approx 0.00022$

c. The events from parts (a) and (b) are not complementary events.
There are many other cases to consider regarding the number of
male and female jurors: for example, 4 male, 5 female, etc.

51. $\dfrac{1}{_{39}C_5} = \dfrac{1}{575{,}757}$

53. a.

	Parent 2	
	Y	y
Y	YY	Yy
y	yY	yy

(Parent 1)

b. $\dfrac{1}{4}$ **c.** $\dfrac{3}{4}$ **55.** 0.048 **57. a.** $\dfrac{7}{50}$ or 0.14 **b.** $\dfrac{31}{50}$ or 0.62

59. $\dfrac{8}{52} = \dfrac{2}{13}$ **61.** $\dfrac{16}{52} = \dfrac{4}{13}$ **63.** $\dfrac{12}{52} = \dfrac{3}{13}$ **65.** $\dfrac{32}{52} = \dfrac{8}{13}$

67. $\dfrac{39}{52} = \dfrac{3}{4}$ **69.** $\dfrac{112}{200} = \dfrac{14}{25}$ **71.** $\dfrac{98}{200} = \dfrac{49}{100}$ **73.** $\dfrac{168}{200} = \dfrac{21}{25}$

75. $\dfrac{164}{200} = \dfrac{41}{50}$ **77.** $\dfrac{1}{6} \cdot \dfrac{1}{2} = \dfrac{1}{12}$ **79.** $(0.88)(0.88) = 0.7744$

81. a. $\dfrac{1}{127} \approx 0.007874$ **b.** $\dfrac{1}{127} \cdot \dfrac{1}{127} \approx 0.000062$

83. $\left(\dfrac{1}{2}\right)^5 \cdot \left(\dfrac{1}{4}\right)^5 = \dfrac{1}{32,768} \approx 0.0000305$

85. a. 0.85 **b.** $(0.85)^3 \approx 0.614$ **87. a.** O^+ **b.** AB^-

89. 0.54 **91. a.** 0.066 **b.** O^- blood is absent all three antigens and will not introduce a new antigen to the recipient's blood.

93. $\left(\dfrac{1}{11}\right)^3 = \dfrac{1}{1331}$ **95. a.** 0.04 **b.** 0.20 **c.** 0.36

97. a.

b. 0.16

99. Observe the game being played by other players. Approximate the probability by dividing the number of times a player wins to the number of games played.

101. Answers will vary.

103. a. $\dfrac{5}{15} \cdot \dfrac{5}{15} = \dfrac{1}{9}$ **b.** No   **c.** $\dfrac{5}{15} \cdot \dfrac{4}{14} = \dfrac{2}{21}$

105. a. $\dfrac{_{13}C_5}{_{52}C_5} = \dfrac{1287}{2,598,960} \approx 0.000495$

b. $(4)\dfrac{_{13}C_5}{_{52}C_5} = (4)\dfrac{1287}{2,598,960} \approx 0.001981$

107. $P(4) = {_{10}C_4}(0.32)^4(0.68)^6 \approx 0.2177$

109. a. 0.99 **b.** $(0.99)^5 \approx 0.951$ **c.** All five employees test negative.   **d.** $1 - 0.951 = 0.049$ **e.** The lab must test the individual blood samples separately to determine which individual (or individuals) is positive.   **f.** Roughly 95% of the time, the mixture will test negative, and the lab determines the results for five employees for the cost of doing one test. On the other hand, only 5% of the time does the mixture test positive making it necessary to test the individual samples. In such a case, the lab tests five samples for the cost of running six samples. But again, this occurs infrequently.

Chapter 8 Review Exercises, pp. 789–793

1. 56   **3.** 2, 3, 4, 5, 6

5. The odd-numbered terms will be positive, and the even-numbered terms will be negative.

7. a. 5, 7, 9, 11, 13   **b.** 45   **c.** $S_5 = 45$ **9.** 66   **11.** 0

13. $\displaystyle\sum_{i=1}^{5} \dfrac{i+2}{2^i}$ **15.** $\displaystyle\sum_{i=1}^{10} i^3 = \sum_{j=0}^{9} (j+1)^3 = \sum_{k=2}^{11} (k-1)^3$

17. $a_n = 2^n; 1 \le n \le 12$ **19.** Yes; $d = \dfrac{5}{4}$

21. 4, 12, 20, 28, 36   **23.** $a_{23} = 103$ **25.** $n = 38$ **27.** -4795

29. -3258 **31.** 24 months   **33.** No

35. $120, 80, \dfrac{160}{3}, \dfrac{320}{9}, \dfrac{640}{27}$ **37.** $a_6 = 972$ **39.** $a_1 = 64$

41. 5465   **43.** 30   **45.** 3   **47.** $\dfrac{79}{90}$ **49.** $40,250.86

51. a. $238,884.21   **b.** $289,503.57

53. 1. S_1 is true because $3 = 1[2(1) + 1]$.
2. Assume that $S_k = k(2k + 1)$.
Show that $S_{k+1} = (k + 1)[2(k+1) + 1] = (k + 1)(2k + 3)$.
$S_{k+1} = 3 + 7 + 11 + \cdots + (4k - 1) + [4(k + 1) - 1]$
$= k(2k + 1) + [4(k + 1) - 1]$ Inductive hypothesis
$= 2k^2 + k + 4k + 3$
$= 2k^2 + 5k + 3$
$= (k + 1)(2k + 3)$ as desired.

55. 1. S_1 is true because $1 = \frac{1}{3}(4^1 - 1)$.
2. Assume that $S_k = \frac{1}{3}(4^k - 1)$.
Show that $S_{k+1} = \frac{1}{3}(4^{k+1} - 1)$.
$S_{k+1} = 1 + 4 + 16 + \cdots + 4^{k-1} + 4^{(k+1)-1}$
$= \frac{1}{3}(4^k - 1) + 4^k$ Inductive hypothesis
$= \frac{1}{3}4^k - \frac{1}{3} + 4^k$
$= \frac{4}{3}4^k - \frac{1}{3}$
$= \frac{1}{3}(4 \cdot 4^k - 1)$
$= \frac{1}{3}(4^{k+1} - 1)$ as desired.

57. Let S_n be the statement $4^n < (n + 2)!$ for $n \ge 2$.
1. S_2 is true because $4^2 = 16$ and $(2 + 2)! = 24$. Therefore, $4^2 < (2 + 2)!$.
2. Assume that $4^k < (k + 2)!$ for a natural number $k \ge 2$. Show that $4^{k+1} < [(k + 1) + 2]!$, or equivalently, that $4^{k+1} < (k + 3)!$.
$4^{k+1} = 4 \cdot 4^k < 4 \cdot (k + 2)!$ Inductive hypothesis
If $k \ge 2$, then $(k + 3) > 4$. Therefore,
$4^{k+1} < 4(k + 2)! < (k + 3)(k + 2)! = (k + 3)!$ as desired.

59. a. 1   **b.** 3   **c.** 3   **d.** 1

The values of $\dbinom{3}{0}, \dbinom{3}{1}, \dbinom{3}{2},$ and $\dbinom{3}{3}$ match the entries in the fourth row of Pascal's triangle.

61. $32x^5 - 240x^4 + 720x^3 - 1080x^2 + 810x - 243$

63. $t^{30} + 6t^{25}u^3 + 15t^{20}u^6 + 20t^{15}u^9 + 15t^{10}u^{12} + 6t^5u^{15} + u^{18}$

65. $96,000x^2y^4$ **67.** $-2016c^8d^{25}$ **69.** $-119 + 120i$

71. $7! = 5040$ **73.** $5! - 1 = 119$

75. a. $5^3 = 125$ **b.** $5 \cdot 5 \cdot 3 = 75$ **c.** $4 \cdot 3 \cdot 1 = 12$

77. 5985; There are 5985 ways to select 4 distinct items in no specific order from a group of 21 items.

79. $_{90}C_{15} \approx 4.58 \times 10^{16}$ **81.** $_{40}P_3$ or $40 \cdot 39 \cdot 38 = 59,280$

83. $(_{10}C_2) \cdot (_6C_3) \cdot (_7C_2) = 18,900$ **85.** Not likely   **87.** 0.27

89. a. $\dfrac{5}{36}$ **b.** $\dfrac{6}{36} = \dfrac{1}{6}$ **c.** $\dfrac{7}{36}$

91. a. $\dfrac{_4C_3}{_{15}C_3} = \dfrac{4}{455} \approx 0.00879$ **b.** $\dfrac{_{11}C_3}{_{15}C_3} = \dfrac{165}{455} \approx 0.36264$

c. The events from parts (a) and (b) are not complementary events. There are many other cases to consider regarding the number of defective and good lightbulbs: for example, 2 good, 1 defective, etc.

93. $(0.9959)^{10} \approx 0.9597$ **95.** $\dfrac{90}{160} = \dfrac{9}{16}$ **97.** $\dfrac{150}{160} = \dfrac{15}{16}$

99. $\dfrac{132}{160} = \dfrac{33}{40}$ **101.** $\dfrac{28}{52} = \dfrac{7}{13}$ **103.** $\dfrac{4}{52} \cdot \dfrac{4}{52} = \dfrac{1}{169}$

Chapter 8 Test, pp. 793–794

1. $-2, 3, 1, 4, 5, 9$ **2.** $(3n + 1)(3n)$ **3. a.** Geometric
b. $r = 0.01$ **c.** $a_n = 0.139(0.01)^{n-1}$ **4. a.** Arithmetic
b. $d = 0.16$ **c.** $a_n = 0.16n + 0.36$

5. a. Neither   **b.** Not applicable   **c.** $a_n = \dfrac{3n}{5^n}$ **6.** $4, 6, 9, \dfrac{27}{2}$

7. 10, 13, 16, 19, 22   **8.** $a_{78} = -783$ **9.** $a_6 = -96$ **10.** 167

11. 9   **12.** $a_1 = 1, d = -2$ **13.** $a_1 = 5, r = 2$ **14.** 3

15. 4833   **16.** $\dfrac{665}{8}$ **17.** 33   **18.** The sum is undefined.

19. a. $750,000   **b.** $2,142,857   **20.** $245,446.68

21. $a_n = 7.50n^2$ **22.** 16 days

23. 1. S_1 is true because $6 = 1[2(1) + 4]$.
2. Assume that $S_k = k(2k + 4)$.
Show that $S_{k+1} = (k + 1)[2(k + 1) + 4] = (k + 1)(2k + 6)$.
$S_{k+1} = 6 + 10 + 14 + \cdots + (4k + 2) + [4(k + 1) + 2]$
$= k(2k + 4) + [4(k + 1) + 2]$ Inductive hypothesis
$= 2k^2 + 4k + 4k + 6$
$= 2k^2 + 8k + 6$
$= (k + 1)(2k + 6)$ as desired.

24. **1.** S_1 is true because $1 = \frac{1}{4}(5^1 - 1)$.

    2. Assume that $S_k = \frac{1}{4}(5^k - 1)$.

      Show that $S_{k+1} = \frac{1}{4}(5^{k+1} - 1)$.

$$S_{k+1} = 1 + 5 + 25 + \cdots + 5^{k-1} + 5^{(k+1)-1}$$
$$= \frac{1}{4}(5^k - 1) + 5^k \quad \text{Inductive hypothesis}$$
$$= \frac{1}{4}5^k - \frac{1}{4} + 5^k$$
$$= \frac{5}{4}5^k - \frac{1}{4}$$
$$= \frac{1}{4}(5 \cdot 5^k - 1)$$
$$= \frac{1}{4}(5^{k+1} - 1) \text{ as desired.}$$

25. Let S_n be the statement that 2 is a factor of $7^n - 5$.

    1. S_1 is true because 2 is a factor of $(7)^1 - 5 = 2$.

    2. Assume that S_k is true; that is, assume that 2 is a factor of $7^k - 5$. This implies that $7^k - 5 = 2a$ and that $7^k = 2a + 5$ for some positive integer a.

      Show that S_{k+1} is true; that is, show that 2 is a factor of $7^{k+1} - 5$.

$$7^{k+1} - 5 = 7 \cdot 7^k - 5$$
$$= 7 \cdot (2a + 5) - 5 \quad \text{Replace } 7^k \text{ by } 2a + 5.$$
$$= 14a + 30$$
$$= 2(7a + 15)$$

      Therefore, 2 is a factor of $7^{k+1} - 5$ as desired.

26. $\dfrac{x^4}{16} + \dfrac{3}{2}x^3 + \dfrac{27}{2}x^2 + 54x + 81$

27. $1024c^{10} - 1280c^8 t^4 + 640c^6 t^8 - 160c^4 t^{12} + 20c^2 t^{16} - t^{20}$

28. $-960r^3 v^{14}$ **29.** $2835x^4 y^6$ **30.** The value $_{13}P_5 = 154{,}440$ and $_{13}C_5 = 1287$.   **31.** A permutation of n items taken r at a time is an arrangement of r items taken from a group of n items in a specific order. A combination of n items taken r at a time is a group of r items taken from a group of n items in no particular order.

32. $9! = 362{,}880$ **33.** $4 \cdot 5 \cdot 3 = 60$

34. $\dfrac{12!}{3! \cdot 2!} - 1 = 39{,}916{,}799$ **35. a.** $_{56}C_{12} \approx 5.584 \times 10^{11}$

  b. $(_{30}C_6) \cdot (_{26}C_6) \approx 1.367 \times 10^{11}$ **c.** $\dfrac{(_{30}C_6) \cdot (_{26}C_6)}{_{56}C_{12}} \approx 0.245$

  d. $\dfrac{_{26}C_{12}}{_{56}C_{12}} \approx 0.0000173$ **36.** $_{10}C_3 = 120$ **37.** $2^6 \cdot 3^4 = 5184$

38. a. $_{50}C_4 = 230{,}300$ **b.** $_{50}P_4 = 5{,}527{,}200$

39. $\dfrac{36{,}000}{300{,}000{,}000} = 0.00012$ **40. a.** $\dfrac{32}{75}$ **b.** $\dfrac{43}{75}$ **c.** $\dfrac{5}{75} = \dfrac{1}{15}$

  d. 0 **41.** $\dfrac{16}{36} = \dfrac{4}{9}$ **42.** $\dfrac{4}{52} \cdot \dfrac{13}{52} = \dfrac{1}{52}$

43. $(0.319)^3 \approx 0.0325$ **44.** $\dfrac{64}{120} = \dfrac{8}{15}$ **45.** $\dfrac{76}{120} = \dfrac{19}{30}$

46. $\dfrac{87}{120} = \dfrac{29}{40}$ **47.** $\dfrac{83}{120}$

Chapter 8 Cumulative Review Exercises, pp. 795–796

1. False   **2.** True   **3.** True   **4.** False

5. a. $|t - 5|\text{ or }|5 - t|$ **b.** $5 - t$ **6.** 2.7×10^{28} **7.** $-\dfrac{1}{81}$

8. $3x + 14\sqrt{2x} - 10$ **9.** $\dfrac{2x + 1}{3x}$ **10.** $-i$

11. $\{\ \}$; The values 3 and -10 do not check.   **12.** $\{-4, 3, -2, 1\}$

13. $\left\{6, \dfrac{4}{5}\right\}$ **14.** $[-4, \infty)$ **15.** $(-\infty, -13] \cup [-1, \infty)$

16. $(-\infty, -4) \cup [3, \infty)$ **17.** $\left\{\dfrac{1}{2}\right\}$ **18.** $\{-1 + \ln 20\}$

19. a. $-3, 5, \frac{1}{2}$ **b.** $(-3, 0), (5, 0), \left(\frac{1}{2}, 0\right)$ **c.** $(0, 15)$

  d.   **e.** $(-\infty, -3) \cup \left(\frac{1}{2}, 5\right)$

20. a. 12.5 sec   **b.** 2504 ft   **c.** 25 sec

21. a. $(x - 4)^2 + (y - 1)^2 = 16$ **b.** Center: $(4, 1)$; Radius: 4

  c.

22.   **23.**

24.   **25.**

26. The graph of f is the graph of $y = \sqrt{x}$ shifted to the right 1 unit, stretched vertically by a factor of 2, and shifted upwards 3 units.

27. a. $12x^2 + 12xh + 4h^2 - 3$ **b.** 49   **c.** Odd

28. a. Yes   **b.** $g^{-1}(x) = \dfrac{x + 1}{5}$ **29. a.** Yes   **b.** Yes

30. a. $x = 7, x = -2$ **b.** Horizontal asymptote: $y = 3$

31. a. $P(t) = 320{,}000e^{0.01t}$ **b.** 371,800   **c.** 22.3 yr

32. $3 \log x - 5 \log y - \frac{1}{2}\log z$ **33.** -4 **34.** 3.7486

35. $\{(-1, -3)\}$ **36.** $\{(1, -2, 4)\}$ **37.** $\{(-5, -16), (3, 0)\}$

38. $\{(-z + 3, 2z + 1, z)\,|\,z \text{ is a real number}\}$ **39.** $\left\{\left(\dfrac{45}{49}, \dfrac{23}{49}\right)\right\}$

40.

41. $\begin{bmatrix} -22 & 27 \\ -19 & -31 \end{bmatrix}$ **42.** Not possible   **43.** 51   **44.** -123

45. Not possible   **46.** $\begin{bmatrix} -44 & -8 & -18 \\ 47 & 41 & 54 \end{bmatrix}$

47. $A^{-1} = \begin{bmatrix} \frac{2}{9} & -\frac{4}{9} & \frac{7}{9} \\ \frac{1}{3} & \frac{1}{3} & -\frac{1}{3} \\ -\frac{1}{9} & \frac{2}{9} & \frac{1}{9} \end{bmatrix}$ **48.** $\{(-3, 1, 4)\}$

49. a. $(1, -2)$ **b.** $(-1, -2)$ **c.** $x = 3$

50. Geometric; $r = -a^3$ **51.** $a_{500} = 156.6$ **52.** 14,097

53. 1530   **54.** 9

55. **1.** S_1 is true because $8 = 2(1)(1 + 3)$.

  2. Assume that $S_k = 2k(k + 3)$. Show that

$$S_{k+1} = 2(k + 1)[(k + 1) + 3] = 2(k + 1)(k + 4).$$
$$S_{k+1} = [8 + 12 + \cdots + (4k + 4)] + [4(k + 1) + 4]$$
$$= 2k(k + 3) + (4k + 8) \quad \text{Inductive hypothesis}$$
$$= 2k^2 + 10k + 8$$
$$= 2(k^2 + 5k + 4)$$
$$= 2(k + 1)(k + 4) \text{ as desired.}$$

56. $243x^5 - 405x^4 y^2 + 270x^3 y^4 - 90x^2 y^6 + 15xy^8 - y^{10}$

57. $\dfrac{1}{2(3n + 1)(3n)}$ **58.** $5! = 120$ **59.** $\dfrac{_8C_2 \cdot _5C_2}{_{13}C_4} \approx 0.3916$

60. $\dfrac{16}{52} = \dfrac{4}{13}$

● Photo Credits

Page 1: © Tetra Images/SuperStock RF; p.15: © Pixtal/Superstock RF; p.24: © Andersen Ross/Blend RF; p. 27: © Brand X Pictures RF; p. 34: NASA, ESA, and the Hubble Heritage (STScI/AURA)-ESA/Hubble Collaboration; p. 39: © StockTrek/Getty RF; p. 52: © Ingram Publishing RF; p. 53: © Frederic Charpentier/Alamy RF; p. 62: © Indeed/Digital Vision/Getty RF; p. 99: © Stockbyte/Getty RF; p. 100: © Echo/Getty RF; p. 112: © Design Pics/Raven Regan RF; p. 113: © Julie Miller; p. 121: © BananaStock/Jupiter Images RF; p. 123: © David Wasserman/Getty RF; p. 156: © Gaja Snover/Alamy Images RF; p. 164: © Jose Luis Pelaez Inc/Blend Images RF; p. 166: © Julie Miller; p. 173: © JGI/Jamie Grill/Getty RF; p. 178: © Ingram Publishing RF; p. 179: © Ryan McVay/Photodisc/Getty RF; p. 186: © Ingram Publishing RF; p. 194: © Tetra Images/Getty RF;

p. 195: © Image Source/Getty RF; p. 196: © Keith Eng 2007; p. 214 © Erik Isakson/Getty RF; p. 275(left): © Jeremy Woodhouse/Getty RF; p. 275(middle): © Julie Miller; p. 275(right): © The McGraw-Hill Companies; p. 319: NASA; p. 320: Courtesy of Rick Iossi; p. 333: © Julie Miller; p. 340: NASA; p. 395: © Denkou Images/Getty RF; p. 417: Courtesy of NOAA; p.418: © Ingram Publishing RF; p. 426: © Chris Ryan/Getty RF; p.431: © Jupiterimages/Imagesource RF; p. 443(left): © Malcolm Schuyl/Alamy RF; p. 443(right): © Julie Miller; p. 452: © Corbis; p. 456: © Brand X Pictures/Superstock RF; p. 470: © Design Pics/Don Hammond RF; p. 471(left): © Julie Miller; p. 471(right): © Julie Miller; p. 483: © Comstock Images/Jupiter Images RF; p. 495: © Julie Miller; p. 507: © Adam Gault/Getty RF; p. 517: © Peter Adams/Getty RF; p. 521: © Michael Hitoshi/Getty RF;

p. 536: © Digital Vision/Punchstock RF; p. 556: © Jupiterimages/Imagesource RF; p. 565: © Image Source/Getty RF; p. 583: © Julie Miller; p. 588: © Royalty-Free/Corbis; p. 593: © Image Source/Getty RF; p. 613(computer): © Jeffrey Coolidge/Photodisc/Getty RF; p. 613(screen): © Royalty-Free/Corbis; p. 661: © Nick M Do/PhotoDisc/Getty RF; p. 665: © Best View Stock/Alamy RF; p. 674: NASA/JPL/Space Science Institute; p. 679: © Visions of America, LLC/Alamy RF; p. 702: NASA/GSFC; p. 711: © Image Source/Getty RF; p. 712: © David Lees/Getty RF; p. 724: © Julie Miller; p. 747: © Image Source/Getty RF; P. 751: Copyright C.J. Mozzochi, Princeton, NJ; p.769: © Royalty-Free/Corbis; p. 770: © Blend Images/SuperStock RF; p. 772: © Ingram Publishing RF; p. 773: © Brand X Pictures RF; p. 792: © U.S. Air Force photo by Master Sgt. Michael A. Kaplan.

Subject Index

Tests for Symmetry	Even and Odd Functions
Consider the graph of an equation in x and y. The graph of the equation is • Symmetric to the **y-axis** if substituting $-x$ for x results in an equivalent equation. • Symmetric to the **x-axis** if substituting $-y$ for y results in an equivalent equation. • Symmetric to the **origin** if substituting $-x$ for x and $-y$ for y results in an equivalent equation.	• f is an **even function** if $f(-x) = f(x)$ for all x in the domain of f. • f is an **odd function** if $f(-x) = -f(x)$ for all x in the domain of f.

Properties of Logarithms	Variation
$\log_b 1 = 0$ $\log_b(xy) = \log_b x + \log_b y$ $\log_b b = 1$ $\log_b\left(\dfrac{x}{y}\right) = \log_b x - \log_b y$ $\log_b b^x = x$ $\log_b x^p = p \log_b x$ $b^{\log_b x} = x$ Change-of-base formula: $\log_b x = \dfrac{\log_a x}{\log_a b}$ $b^x = b^y$ implies that $x = y$. $\log_b x = \log_b y$ implies that $x = y$.	$\left.\begin{array}{l}y \text{ varies } \textbf{directly} \text{ as } x.\\ y \text{ is } \textbf{directly} \text{ proportional to } x.\end{array}\right\} y = kx$ $\left.\begin{array}{l}y \text{ varies } \textbf{inversely} \text{ as } x.\\ y \text{ is } \textbf{inversely} \text{ proportional to } x.\end{array}\right\} y = \dfrac{k}{x}$ $\left.\begin{array}{l}y \text{ varies } \textbf{jointly} \text{ as } w \text{ and } x.\\ y \text{ is } \textbf{jointly} \text{ proportional to }\\ w \text{ and } x.\end{array}\right\} y = kwx$

Arithmetic Sequences and Series	Geometric Sequences and Series
nth term: $a_n = a_1 + (n-1)d$ Sum of a finite arithmetic series: $$S_n = \frac{n}{2}(a_1 + a_n)$$	nth term: $a_n = a_1 r^{n-1}$ Finite geometric series: $\displaystyle\sum_{i=1}^{n} a_1 r^{i-1} = \frac{a_1(1 - r^n)}{1 - r}$ Infinite geometric series: $$\sum_{i=1}^{\infty} a_1 r^{i-1} = \frac{a_1}{1 - r} \text{ provided that } |r| < 1$$

Binomial Theorem

Factorial notation: $n! = n(n-1)(n-2)...(2)(1)$ and $0! = 1$

Binomial coefficients: $\dbinom{n}{r} = {}_nC_r = \dfrac{n!}{r! \cdot (n-r)!}$

Binomial theorem: $(a+b)^n = \dbinom{n}{0}a^n + \dbinom{n}{1}a^{n-1}b + \dbinom{n}{2}a^{n-2}b^2 + \cdots + \dbinom{n}{n-1}ab^{n-1} + \dbinom{n}{n}b^n = \displaystyle\sum_{r=0}^{n}\dbinom{n}{r}a^{n-r}b^r$

Perimeter and Circumference

Rectangle
$P = 2l + 2w$

Square
$P = 4s$

Triangle
$P = a + b + c$

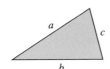

Circle
Circumference: $C = 2\pi r$

Area

Rectangle
$A = lw$

Square
$A = s^2$

Parallelogram
$A = bh$

Triangle
$A = \frac{1}{2}bh$

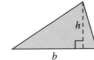

Trapezoid
$A = \frac{1}{2}(b_1 + b_2)h$

Circle
$A = \pi r^2$

Volume

Rectangular Solid
$V = lwh$

Right Circular Cylinder
$V = \pi r^2 h$

Right Circular Cone
$V = \frac{1}{3}\pi r^2 h$

Sphere
$V = \frac{4}{3}\pi r^3$

Angles

- Two angles are complementary if the sum of their measures is 90°.

$x + y = 90°$

- Two angles are supplementary if the sum of their measures is 180°.

$x + y = 180°$

Triangles

- The sum of the measures of the angles of a triangle is 180°.

$x + y + z = 180°$

- Given a right triangle with legs of length a and b, and hypotenuse of length c, the Pythagorean theorem indicates that

$a^2 + b^2 = c^2$

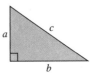